the green book of calculus

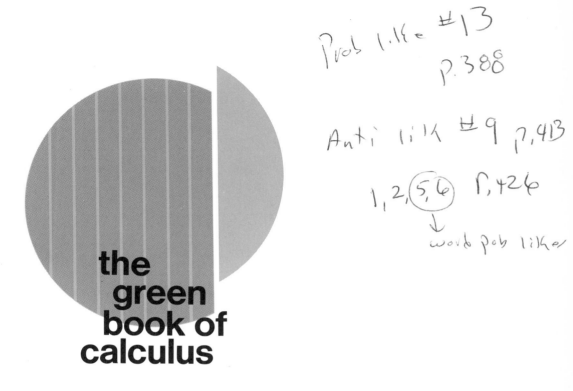

the green book of calculus

Joshua Chover · University of Wisconsin

W. A. Benjamin, Inc.
Menlo Park, California

Prob like #13
p.388

Anti lik #9 p.413

1,2,(5,6) p.426
↓
word prob like

Fred Brauer and John A. Nohel
Consulting Editors

to the memory of
William Feller

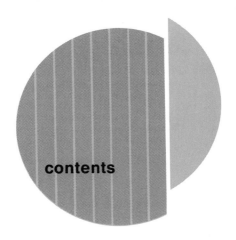

contents

CHAPTER 12   MAXIMA OF CONTINUOUS FUNCTIONS

CHAPTER 13   MORE FEATURES OF CONTINUITY

CHAPTER 14   PROPERTIES OF DERIVATIVES

CHAPTER 15   THE MEAN VALUE THEOREM AND APPLICATIONS

CHAPTER 16   DIFFERENTIAL EQUATIONS AND TRIG FUNCTIONS

CHAPTER 17   AREA

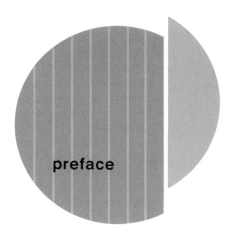

preface

HOW TO READ THIS BOOK

The sections in black type present a "main road" through the material, along which you can go at a varying pace, as you choose — slowly at some points, quickly at others, skipping over still others. The sections in green type form "byways." Some lead to applications away from the main road. Some present short notes. Some go deeper into the primary material and then rejoin the main path. Thus you can follow a number of different routes, depending on your interest. I have outlined two of them in some detail later in the preface, corresponding to two types of beginning college course.

The several sections prefixed by "*" are somewhat more involved than their neighbors. If you wish, you can leave them to later reading.

Problems for the reader appear in separate sections. The most routine are marked with a "°" sign; the most challenging with an "*." The others fall somewhere in between.

At the end of each chapter is a summary of the main definitions and results.

The usual topics of high school algebra, geometry, perhaps a little trigonometry, and the notion of sets, are all that a reader need have met in order to begin this book. For those whose memories of these subjects are dim, I have included a brief review in Appendixes A and B.

ASPECTS OF THE BOOK

Tone. A common practice has been to hand material down to the reader "from on high." What I have tried to do here instead is to engage the reader in *exploratory discussions*, insofar as the "one-way" nature of a book will allow. Hopefully the reader will view the book as a *guide* through territory which *he himself* might have pioneered had he just been at the right place at the right time, and with the right background.

One of the fascinations of mathematics is the interplay between idealized concepts and practical applications. I think that a beginning reader can benefit best by seeing a mixture of both—whether he seeks merely a brief acquaintance with mathematics, or is interested in one particular kind of application, or intends to go on studying the "pure" aspects of the subject.

Applications. What can one learn of the power of mathematics if he sees mainly artificial examples, and if "real" cases appear only as a promise for the future? In this book, I have selected a number of actual applications from widely separated fields—such as economics, biology, and physics—and have discussed them in depth starting from first principles.

Probability. One of the areas in which many people have some ready intuition for appreciating simple mathematical models is that of probability. At the same time probability provides examples—with a special flavor—of key concepts in calculus. In this text, I have interwoven a continuing sequence of probabilistic discussions. A reader can omit them, however, if he is pressed for time. Or he can take them up in midsequence.

Concepts. These are inventions—or, if you like, discoveries—works of the minds of men. I have urged the reader to explore them, to see what makes them tick. In some examples, I have noted unexpected consequences. in other places I have discussed why we might have confidence in applying the conceptual tools to new tasks. The phrase, "It can be shown (in higher texts) that . . . ," is a discouraging one. It implies that there are matters which must remain beyond the reader's grasp for he knows not how long—perhaps forever; and that he should be satisfied with such a situation. In this book, I've addressed the question "Why?" to almost all results which appear —sometimes in the main text, sometimes in problems, often in supplementary (green) sections. A reader needn't go far into such discussions and "proofs." But he should know that it is all accessible to him, if only he has enough time and inclination.

Many a teacher of mathematics has not the chance to take extensive courses in the subject. Nevertheless, such a person might hope to guide his students through the "main road" material in this book, on the basis of a deeper understanding which he himself might acquire from studying the supplementary applications and explanations.

Pictures. Much understanding in mathematics comes from seeing the right pictures with one's inner eye. For this reason I have presented a large number of figures, corresponding to the blackboard work of a course. Most of them are not merely illustrations, but integral parts of the discussion.

The order of the topics. Many texts assume that the concept of passage to a limit is an intuitively easy one for beginners, and that the important goal is to get as quickly as possible to the novel computations of "calculus" — derivatives and integrals, and their applications. They view basic discussions of limit and continuity properties as refinements which can be considered later. Often this approach is dictated by the needs of concurrent physics and chemistry courses. I have provided for such a schedule in this book too: After the basic definition of "function" in Chapter 2, one can pick up elements of the analytic geometry of lines in Chapter 4, and of operating with functions in Chapter 5, and then go on to Chapter 7 for a preview of the uses of derivatives and antiderivatives. From Chapters 8–13 the reader need select only the main properties of limits and continuity, and then begin a heavier study of differentiation in Chapters 14–16 and integration in Chapters 17–19. (See also the right-hand column on pages xviii and xix.

However, I suggest an alternate approach, where possible. The contact after high school is a crucial time. Most students emerge from secondary school with a feeling that mathematics is dry, inflexible, and "no fun." I think that such people — as well as the more dedicated — can benefit from a period of exploring examples, drawing pictures, asking questions, hearing about unusual concepts. If possible, the buildup to the formal calculus should be gradual. What is important is creating interest and confidence. It is true that even rote ability to differentiate and integrate creates confidence. But I believe that the confidence can be greater still if underpinned by some understanding of basic properties. For this reason, I have included the material of Chapters 1, 3–4, 6, and 8–13, to be read at whatever level the student finds comfortable.

I have introduced the notion of limits via sequences, because I think that it is more easily visualized that way for beginners. (The "ϵ-δ" version appears in various problems.) In Chapter 8 there is a fork in the road: Those who wish can merely accept the pictured properties of null sequences as axiomatic and go on to later chapters. Those who wish an introduction to the formal "ϵ" reasoning of calculus can begin with a definition of a null sequence. (There are few "proofs" as such prior to Chapter 8.)

Although approximation of areas may be intuitively clear, the definite integral itself is a sophisticated notion — especially in other applications. I think that, if possible, it is best introduced after the student is comfortable with all sorts of differentiation. Thus it appears in Chapters 17–19.

The reader will come upon several recurrent themes, which illustrate at each appearance the use of some new concept — themes such as the ideas of optimizing a special quantity, of treating a function by treating its simpler parts, of "rate," of "average"; also models of growing populations and of random occurrences.

Madison, Wisconsin
October 1971

J.C.

schedule of study

Here are two possible patterns for studying the material. The shading in the frames indicates level of treatment. For the corresponding section numbers, parentheses denote "light treatment."

Chapter		A two-semester course for students in Liberal Arts, Social Sciences, Biology, or Business — Sections		For the first two semesters of a "standard" course — Sections
1. Examples		(1.1–1.4)		
2. Functions		2.1–2.4		2.1–2.4
3. Probability		3.1–3.2, (3.3), 3.4, (3.5–3.6), 3.7		(3.1–3.3)
4. Anal. geometry, Lines and Slopes. Geometry. Probability. Axioms		4.1–4.4, (4.5) (4.6–4.8) (4.9–4.12)		4.1–4.4 (4.5) 4.6–4.8 (4.9–4.10)
5. Combining Functions		5.1–5.7, (5.8)		5.1–5.7 (5.8)
6. Induction, Counting		6.1, (6.2), 6.3–6.5, (6.6), 6.7, (6.8–6.9)		(6.1), 6.3–6.5, (6.6), 6.7, (6.8–6.9)
7. Intuitive Derivatives		7.1–7.7		7.1–7.7
8. Properties of Null Sequences. Definition		8.1–8.3 (8.4–8.10 or omit)		8.1–8.3
9. Limits of Sequences		9.1–9.6, (9.7–9.8), 9.9, (9.10–9.11)		9.1–9.3 9.5–9.6 9.9, 9.11
10. Lub Axiom Series		10.1 (10.2–10.3) 10.5, 10.6–10.7		(10.1–10.3) (10.5–10.7)
11. Limits of Functions, Continuity, Derivatives		11.1–11.7, (11.8) 11.9–11.11		11.1–11.7 11.9–11.11
12. Maxima of Continuous Functions		12.1, (12.2–12.5) 12.6–12.8		12.1 (12.2–12.5) 12.6–12.8
13. Intermed. Values of Contin. Functions. Exponentials, Logs		13.1 13.3 13.5–13.7 (13.8 or omit)		(13.1) 13.3 13.5–13.7
14. Properties of Derivatives		14.1–14.7 14.9–14.10 14.15		14.1–14.7 14.9–14.10 14.15

Chapter	A two-semester course for students in Liberal Arts, Social Sciences, Biology, or Business Sections	For the first two semesters of a "standard" course Sections
15. Mean Value Theorem and Applications	15.1–15.3 15.5–15.11	(15.1–15.3) 15.5–15.8 (15.9) 15.10–15.11
16. Differential Equations, Trigonometric functions	(16.1) 16.2–16.5 (16.6–16.7) 16.8–16.11	(16.1) 16.2–16.5 (16.6–16.7) 16.8–16.11
17. Area	17.1–17.6 (17.7) 17.8	(17.1–17.2) 17.3–17.4 (17.5) 17.6, 17.8
18. Definite Integral and Applications Change of Variables	18.1–18.3 (18.4–18.6) 18.8 (18.9) 18.10	18.1–18.3 (18.5) 18.6, 18.8–18.10
19. Integration Techniques. Taylor's Expansion		19.1–19.14 (19.15) 19.16
20. More Probability: "Variables" and Averages. Conditional Probability.	(20.1–20.2) (20.3 or omit) (20.4) (20.5–20.7) (20.8–20.14 or omit)	
21. Functions of Two Variables	(21.1–21.7)	(21.1–21.7)

Code: □ = omit,
⊞ = note main results and go lightly,
▨ = detailed study

Then return to omitted sections in Chapters 8 through 13 and 18, or in Chapters 3, 18 and 20 (probability), or proceed with several variables.

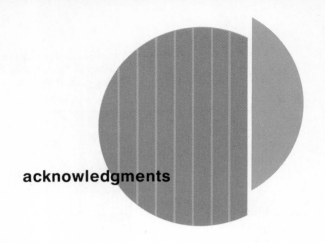

acknowledgments

In preparing this book I received valuable help from many people. Principal among them was Evelyn R. McMillan, who supplied material and steadfast detailed criticism. Also assisting in this way were Joyce Olson Hughes, Michael Olinick, and Harvey Salgo. Gordon Prichett and Carol Carter Shilepsky helped with an earlier version. Critical reviews and suggestions came from Fred Brauer, Flo Chover, Melvin Hausner, Schlomo Liebeskerd, Norman Locksley, Peter Ney, John Nohel, Dan Shea, Wolfgang Wasow, and numerous colleagues and students. Margaret Blumberg and Phyllis J. Rickli labored faithfully to get the manuscript typed in its several versions. The staff of W. A. Benjamin, Inc. worked patiently to get the project into print. To all these people, my thanks. The book owes its faults to me.

J.C.

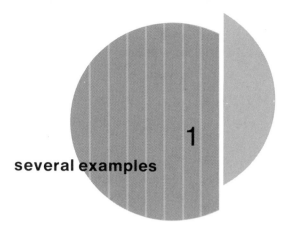

several examples

1

To start off—try your hand at answering the following questions.

1. Can you enclose more area by one big circle or by two smaller ones, using the same total length of string?

2. Which of the following clinical reports would provide better evidence in favor of a new treatment for a disease?

(a) Of three independent treated victims, all survive (100%); or:

(b) Of seven independent treated victims, six survive (86%). In the past, *un*treated victims, considered independently, had 50–50 chances for survival.

3. Among the "real numbers," the "rational numbers" are those which can be expressed as ratios of integers m/n. Think of the real numbers as corresponding to points on a horizontal line, and think of the "rationals" among them as being very sensitive to sunlight coming down vertically—as in Fig. 1-1. We could protect those rationals between 0 and 1 from sunlight by laying a unit length of string above the interval, as in Fig. 1-2. Two shorter segments of string of total length less than 1, as in Fig. 1-3, would not do, for there would be a gap—say, with end points x and y. And between x and y must be some unshielded rationals (r). (The rationals are very closely packed.) *Question*: Is it nevertheless possible to shield *all* the rationals between 0 and 1 with less than one unit of string, by cutting the string into *many* segments (possibly infinitely many) and placing these segments cleverly enough? (Overlaps are allowed.) See Fig. 1-4. If so, what is the *least* length of string necessary to do the job?

FIGURE 1-1

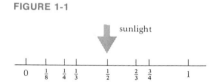

FIGURE 1-2

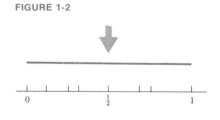

FIGURE 1-3

FIGURE 1-4

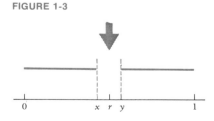

1.1 AN ANSWER TO THE PROBLEM ON AREAS

One big circle encloses more area than two smaller ones. In fact, if two smaller ones have equal radii, they contribute together only $\frac{1}{2}$ the area of the one large circle.

Here's how we can reason if we accept the validity of the statements that the circumference c of a circle is proportional to its diameter d or to its radius r ($c = \pi d = 2\pi r$) and that the area A of a circle is proportional to the square of its radius ($A = \pi r^2$). We can use a given length of string c_0 as the circumference of one large circle $c_0 = \pi d_0 = 2\pi r_0$, or we can cut it into two parts

$$c_0 = c_1 + c_2 \tag{1}$$

to form the circumferences of two circles ($c_1 = \pi d_1 = 2\pi r_1$ and $c_2 = \pi d_2 = 2\pi r_2$). We can rewrite (1) as

$$\pi d_0 = \pi d_1 + \pi d_2 \quad \text{and} \quad 2\pi r_0 = 2\pi r_1 + 2\pi r_2. \tag{2}$$

Finally, let's cancel π's and 2π's in (2) to get the relationships

$$d_0 = d_1 + d_2 \tag{3}$$

and

$$r_0 = r_1 + r_2. \tag{4}$$

Equation (3) suggests that we can even draw the two smaller circles inside the larger one, as in Fig. 1-5, to get a pictorial answer.

FIGURE 1-5

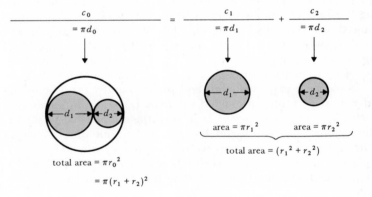

Algebraically we can compare areas by writing

$$\pi r_0^2 = \pi (r_1 + r_2)^2 = \pi (r_1^2 + 2r_1 r_2 + r_2^2)$$
$$= \underbrace{\pi r_1^2 + \pi r_2^2}_{\substack{\text{total area for} \\ \text{two circles}}} + \underbrace{2\pi r_1 r_2}_{\substack{\text{excess area in} \\ \text{one large circle}}} \tag{5}$$

As long as $r_1 > 0$ and $r_2 > 0$, the "excess" term in (5) will be positive. If $r_1 = r_2$, then the excess term in (5) equals the total two-circle area — in which case the large circle area will be twice that amount.

Some applications. Several farmers who can afford only 1500 sq ft of siding material could store approximately twice as much grain in one flat-topped cylindrical silo of diameter 16 ft and height 30 ft as they could in two similar silos of the same height but 8 ft in diameter each. Why? Because the volumes of cylinders of the same height are proportional to their respective base areas.

Two shepherds can provide each of their sheep with twice the grazing area if they agree to share in guarding the circumference of one large circle, as against what each can provide by grazing his flock in a separate circle.

For a similar reason, merchant ships in World War II were sent in large convoys rather than in staggered smaller ones.

So far the moral has been: for a fixed perimeter, one can *maximize* interior area by using one large circle. Can't one turn this lesson around and say that for a *fixed area*, one can *minimize* external perimeter by using one large circle? And shouldn't such conclusions extend to three-dimensional regions: for a given volume won't one mimimize external surface area by using one large sphere rather than several smaller ones? If so, we have an explanation for why droplets of oil in water tend to coalesce to reduce total surface tension.

1.2   AN ANSWER TO THE PROBLEM ON CLINICAL EVIDENCE

Report II (6 survive and one dies) *provides roughly* $2\frac{1}{3}$ *times as much evidence in favor of the treatment as does Report I* (all 3 survive) *despite the lower survival rate* (86%) — if you accept the following reasoning.

Each report announces a certain result. Let's try to find the probabilities that such results will occur in the case of *untreated* groups of victims. The less probable a result is for an untreated group, the more evidence we have — when that result occurs in a *treated* group — that the treatment *is* effective in changing matters.

To calculate probabilities, let's first ask what we can infer from the information that any one untreated victim, independently of others, has a 50–50 chance for survival. Suppose that X and Y are two independent victims (in different towns, say). The outcome that X survives and Y dies (50% survival between the two) should *not* be more likely than the outcome that both survive — since Y's germs don't know what X's are doing. To the contrary, both outcomes should be *equally likely*; even if it is published in the newspapers that X has survived, the chances for Y's survival or death should still be the same. Isn't that what independence of X and Y should mean?

Similarly with three independent victims X, Y, Z, the outcome that X and Y survive and Z dies should be just as likely as the outcome that X survives and Y and Z die, since the survival or death of Y should not depend whatsoever on what happens to X and Z. If you believe this reasoning, then you might follow it a few steps further to the conclusion that all of the following 8 ($= 2^3$) possible patterns of survival (s) and death (d) are equally likely. In Fig. 1-6, only one of the outcomes (that colored green) leads to the statement "3 out

FIGURE 1-6

		X	Y	Z		X	Y	Z
odds: $\frac{1}{8}$	←	s	s	s		s	d	d
		s	s	d		d	s	d
		s	d	s		d	d	s
		d	s	s		d	d	d

of 3 survive." So the odds for this result in the case of 3 untreated independent victims are 1 in 8, or $\frac{1}{8}$.

In Fig. 1-7, I've indicated a list of the 128 ($= 2^7$) possible outcomes for 7 untreated independent victims $X_1, X_2, \ldots, X_7$. Should not these patterns all be equally likely, by the same reasoning as before? Suppose so.

FIGURE 1-7

	X_1	X_2	X_3	X_4	X_5	X_6	X_7		X_1	X_2	X_3	X_4	X_5	X_6	X_7
	s	s	s	s	s	s	s		s	s	s	s	s	d	d
odds: $\frac{7}{128}$ ←	s	s	s	s	s	s	d		s	s	s	s	d	s	d
	s	s	s	s	s	d	s		s	s	s	d	s	s	d
	s	s	s	s	d	s	s		s	s	d	s	s	s	d
	s	s	s	d	s	s	s		s	d	s	s	s	s	d
	s	s	d	s	s	s	s		d	s	s	s	s	s	d
	s	d	s	s	s	s	s		s	s	s	s	d	d	s
	d	s	s	s	s	s	s		and so on to						
									d	d	d	d	d	d	d

There are exactly 7 outcomes, those colored green, which lead to the statement "6 survive and 1 dies." So the odds for this result in the case of 7 untreated independent victims are 7 in 128, or $7/128$ — which is about $2\frac{1}{3}$ times smaller than $\frac{1}{8}$. Conclusion: Report II — announced for treated victims — argues much more strongly than Report I would that the treatment causes a significant change.

1.3 AN ANSWER TO THE PROBLEM ABOUT "SHIELDING" THE RATIONALS

I claim that I can shield all of the rationals between 0 *and* 1 *with as little an amount of string as* **you** *please!* This is one of the most amazing answers in mathematics! *Reasoning*: We play a little game. I permit you the first move: Choose an amount of string, say A. Choose it as small as you like so as to make my task harder, but it must be a fixed number greater than zero. The next move is mine: I take your amount A and show a scheme for covering all of the rationals with this total amount of string.

To do this I write out all the rationals between 0 and 1 in groups according to increasing denominator (and within each group, according to increasing numerator). I put in parentheses any fraction that is equivalent to another fraction on its left. See the first row of Fig. 1-8. Then I pair off (by the symbol $\updownarrow$) the rationals not in parentheses with the integers 1, 2, 3, . . . as in the second row of Fig. 1-8. Finally I pair off these integers with lengths of string, as in the third row of Fig. 1-8. The scheme is that the rational paired with

rationals: $0;\ \frac{1}{1};\ \frac{1}{2},\ (\frac{2}{2});\ \frac{1}{3},\ \frac{2}{3},\ (\frac{3}{3});\ \frac{1}{4},\ (\frac{2}{4}),\ \frac{3}{4},\ (\frac{4}{4});\ \frac{1}{5},\ \frac{2}{5},\ \frac{3}{5},\ \frac{4}{5},\ \ldots$ **FIGURE 1-8**

integers: 1   2   3   4   5   6   7   8   9   10   11 $\ldots$

lengths of string: $\dfrac{A}{2^1}$ $\dfrac{A}{2^2}$ $\dfrac{A}{2^3}$ $\dfrac{A}{2^4}$ $\dfrac{A}{2^5}$ $\dfrac{A}{2^6}$ $\dfrac{A}{2^7}$ $\ldots$

the integer k is to be shielded by a length of string $A/2^k$. All rationals are shielded in this way!

How much string do I use to cover the first n of these? Exactly the sum

$$S_n = \frac{A}{2^1} + \frac{A}{2^2} + \frac{A}{2^3} + \cdots + \frac{A}{2^n}. \tag{1}$$

How large is S_n? To get a simpler formula for S_n, multiply the equation (1) through by $\frac{1}{2}$. This gives

$$\frac{1}{2} S_n = \frac{A}{2^2} + \frac{A}{2^3} + \cdots + \frac{A}{2^n} + \frac{A}{2^{n+1}}. \tag{2}$$

Now subtract (2) from (1): many terms cancel between the right-hand sides, and we get

$$S_n - \frac{1}{2} S_n = \frac{A}{2} - \frac{A}{2^{n+1}}. \tag{3}$$

Multiply (3) by 2 to get

$$S_n = A - \frac{A}{2^n}. \tag{4}$$

All the numbers S_n are $< A$. Moreover, as n gets larger and larger, the term $A/2^n$ approaches zero, so that the S_n "tend" to A. I assert therefore that A units of string are sufficient to "shield" *all* of the rationals in between 0 and 1.

1.4 THE GOAL OF MATHEMATICS

In each of the above examples, what was the goal? It was to *discover* something: which configuration has the most area? which experiment provides the most evidence? how much space do the rationals occupy? It is time to dispel a popular misconception. The goal of mathematics is *discovery*, not "proof." "Proofs" are just tools that help us be sure that our reasoning is correct.

The present-day research mathematician works in a laboratory. Of course there are no test tubes, merely pencil and paper as physical apparatus. But the experiments are there, consisting of many examples and partial results to be studied. Among these the mathematician searches for relationships. Only after he has found explanations that seem to tie together the examples and previous results does he sometimes "dress them up" in terms of axioms and formal proofs.

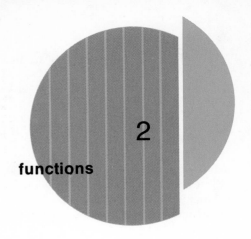

functions

2

A common situation occurs many times in the examples of Chapter 1, namely: *there is a collection of objects and each of these objects gets a number assigned to it.*

In the example about circles, the formula $A = \pi r^2$ assigns to each possible choice of radius r (object) a number πr^2, the area of a circle of that radius. On a higher level, to each *pair* of numbers c_1 and c_2 — representing a scheme for dividing a given length c_0 of string — the formula $\pi(r_1^2 + r_2^2)$ assigns a number, the total area encompassed by two circles with circumferences c_1 and c_2.

In the example about clinical reports, I argued that it might be reasonable to assign to the green pattern *sss* (object) in Fig. 1-6 a "probability" number $\frac{1}{8}$, and to assign to the set of green patterns in Fig. 1-7 (taken together as one object) the "probability" number 7/128.

In the example about shielding the rationals, I assigned an integer k to each object in the collection of rationals between 0 and 1 (the top row in Fig. 1-8). Then I went on to consider the integers themselves as objects in a collection (the middle row in Fig. 1-8), and to each integer k I assigned a particular number, $A/2^k$.

It's hard to find a mathematical example or an instance of quantitative description of the "real world" where one does *not* meet assignments such as I have been noting.

Here are just a few more, from scattered fields:

Objects		Numbers
persons' ages	→	IQ scores
psychological states	→	pulse rates
family income levels	→	high school drop out rates
years	→	gross national product values
temperatures	→	molecular collision rates
insulin levels	→	cancer cell concentrations

2.1 FUNCTIONS

Since the notion of assignment arises so often and seems to be so basic in analyzing problems, people have given it a name "function," and have tried to define it precisely.

Definition. A *function* (more precisely, a *real valued function*) consists of two items:

(i) a set, called the *domain* of the function, consisting of objects each of which is called an *input value*; and

(ii) a precise rule which assigns, to each input value, exactly one real number called an *output value*.

The set of all numbers assigned as output values is called the *range* of the function.

One way to picture a function is in terms of a machine, enclosed in a box, as in Fig. 2-1. The *domain* is the collection of inputs which the box will accept. When any one input enters the box on the left, there comes out on the right a *unique* number (output) determined by the input according to the rule of the function. The *range* of the function is the collection of all possible output numbers.

Here are a few more examples of functions.

EXAMPLE 1: *Squaring.* Domain: all real numbers. Rule: to any real number x, assign its square, x^2. (See Fig. 2-2.) What is the *range* of this function; that is, what is the collection of all possible outputs? Answer: the set of all nonnegative numbers $y \geqslant 0$. Why? First of all, any number which is a square, x^2, must be $\geqslant 0$. But moreover, you should expect to see any given nonnegative number y come out of the box in Fig. 2-2 when you feed in as input its square root $x = \sqrt{y}$, since $y = (\sqrt{y})^2$.

NOTE: Two different inputs ($x = 3$ and $x = -3$ in Fig. 2-2) can lead to the same output; but no one input should ever have two or more outputs — by the very definition of "function."

EXAMPLE 2: *Counting survivors.* Domain: the eight patterns of s's and d's in Fig. 1-6. Rule: to any pattern assign the *number* of s's in that pattern. For example, look at Fig. 2-3. The range of this "s-counting" function consists of the integers 0, 1, 2, and 3, since each is a possible number of s's for a pattern in Fig. 1-6.

EXAMPLE 3: *Tagging rationals.* Domain: all real numbers x between 0 and 1. Rule: let the output be 1 if the input x is a rational number and let the output be 0 if the input x is an irrational number (Fig. 2-4, for example).

NOTE: There is no reason why a rule has to be given only by a formula. Any combination of formulas or any other precise description will do.

SYMBOLS: One of the great advances in mathematics long ago was the introduction of symbols — often letters — to serve as shorthand for various notions. Thus in algebra, a letter such as c or x can be

FIGURE 2-1

FIGURE 2-2

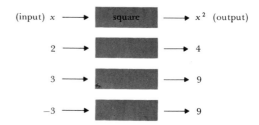

FIGURE 2-3

FIGURE 2-4

FIGURE 2-5

FIGURE 2-6

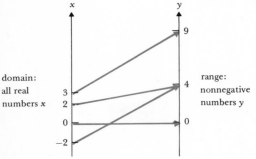

FIGURE 2-7

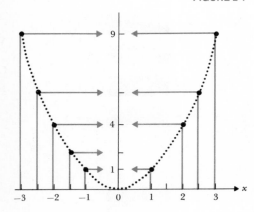

used to stand for a number whose specific value is not important to the discussion or whose value is unknown. In studying functions, we can similarly use letters such as f, g, h; F, G, H, etc., to stand for rules whose precise statements we may not care to specify or to keep repeating. The common notation is as follows: If c denotes an input object and f denotes a rule, then the symbol $f(c)$ should be understood as standing for the *output* assigned to c by the rule f. Thus the "squaring" rule in Example 1 can be described as $f(x) = x^2$. In particular, $f(3) = 9$, $f(-3) = 9$. For a picture, see Fig. 2-5. The "tagging" function in Example 3 can be described as

$$f(x) = \begin{cases} 1 \text{ if } x \text{ is rational} & (0 \leq x \leq 1) \\ 0 \text{ if } x \text{ is irrational} & (0 \leq x \leq 1). \end{cases}$$

In particular, $f(1/2) = 1$, $f(1/\pi) = 0$ (because $1/\pi$ is irrational).

Another way to picture the action of a function is to draw arrows from inputs to their corresponding outputs, as for the squaring function in Fig. 2-6.

When inputs are *numbers* (or can be represented by numbers), we can get a more orderly picture by indicating the domain of a function on a horizontal number line and the range of the function on a vertical number line. (See Fig. 2-7.) The heights of the elbows in the arrows correspond to output values.

With the understanding that the range of the function is a subset of the vertical axis, we can often omit the arrows and show only the collection of elbow points, as in Fig. 2-8. Or, for emphasis, we can retain the vertical parts of the arrows, as in Fig. 2-9.

Figures 2-8 and 2-9 show examples of "graphs." The precise concept of a "graph" involves subsets of the plane. I'll discuss such matters in Chapter 5, and you can also find more about "subsets" in Appendix B and Chapters 3 and 4.

But first, try your hand at some problems involving the basic concept of "function" — the key notion of the rest of the book.

FIGURE 2-8

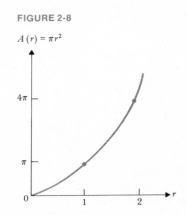

FIGURE 2-9

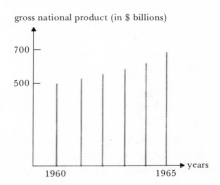

2.2 PROBLEMS ABOUT FUNCTIONS

°1. Which of the following diagrams represent functions? For those which do not, explain why. (In each diagram the points on the left are the objects in the domain, the inputs; the points on the right, the outputs.)

(a) *Sample:*

domain   range

This does not represent a function since one object in the domain does not have an output assigned to it.

(b) *Sample:*

domain   range

This does represent a function since each input has exactly one output assigned to it.

(c)    (d) 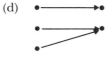   (e)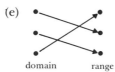

    domain   range   domain   range   domain   range

(f) 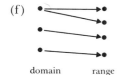   (g)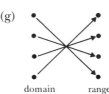

    domain   range   domain   range

°2. If a function f has the rule $f(x) = x^2 - 2x + 3$ and domain all real numbers, calculate:

(a) *Sample:* $f(0) = 0^2 - 2 \cdot 0 + 3 = 3$ (b) $f(2)$

(c) $f(1)$ (d) $f(-1)$

(e) $f(1+t)$ (f) $f(1-t)$

(g) $f(t) + f(1)$ (h) $f(t) \cdot f(1)$

(i) $f(t^2)$

(j) $\dfrac{f(t) - f(1)}{t - 1}$

°3. If $g(x) = 1/(x-1)$ with domain all real numbers except 1, calculate:

(a) *Sample:* $g(2) = \dfrac{1}{2-1} = 1$ (b) $g(0)$

(c) $g(-1)$ (d) $g(10)$

(e) *Sample:*

$$g(a+b) = \frac{1}{(a+b)-1} = \frac{1}{a+b-1}$$

(f) $g(a) + g(b)$ (g) $g(1-a)$

(h) $g(1+a)$ (i) $g\left(\dfrac{1}{a}\right)$

°4. Let f and g be the functions defined in Problems 2 and 3. Calculate:

(a) $f(3) \cdot g(3)$

(b) $f(3) + 2 \cdot g(3)$

(c) *Sample:* $f\left(g\left(\dfrac{5}{4}\right)\right) = 11$:

$$g\left(\frac{5}{4}\right) = \frac{1}{(5/4)-1} = 4 \quad \text{and} \quad f(4) = 4^2 - 2 \cdot 4 + 3 = 11$$

(d) $f(g(\tfrac{1}{2}))$

(e) $g(f(\tfrac{1}{2}))$

5. Which of the following pictures represent functions? For those which do not, explain why. (In each picture the domain is a subset of the horizontal number line and the range is a subset of the vertical line.) Give a possible rule for each function and specify its domain and range.

(a) *Sample:*   (b)

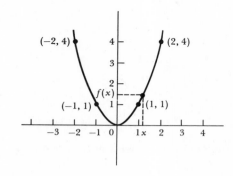
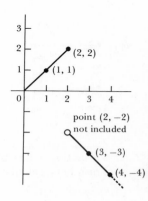

Domain: $-2 \leqslant x \leqslant 2$.

Range: $0 \leqslant f(x) \leqslant 4$.

Rule: $f(x) = x^2$.

This represents a function since to each input there corresponds exactly one output.

(c)

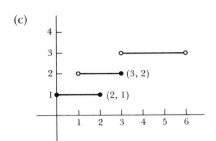

(d)

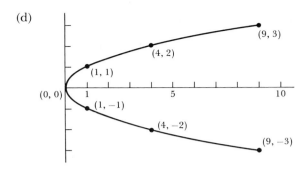

(e)

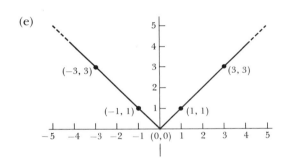

(f)

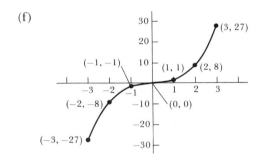

6. (a) *Sample:* Suppose that a rectangle has a perimeter of 8 units. Find a rule for the area of the rectangle (output) in terms of the length of one of the sides (the input). What is the domain of this function?

Answer: $A(w) = 4w - w^2$ for all $0 \leqslant w \leqslant 4$. Since the perimeter equals 8 units, the length (l) plus the width (w) must equal 4 units ($= \frac{1}{2}(8)$). Hence

$$A(w) = \text{width} \times \text{length} = w(4 - w) = 4w - w^2.$$

Since w can be no greater than half the perimeter, the domain of A is $0 \leqslant w \leqslant 4$.

(b) Express the radius of a circle as a function of its area; that is, find a function whose input is the area of a circle and whose output is the radius of the circle with that area.

7. (The famous fence and river problem) A farmer has 100 feet of fence with which he wishes to enclose three sides of a rectangular region bounded on the fourth side by a river. Express the area of the enclosure as a function of the length of one of the sides.

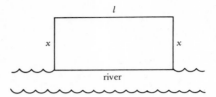

8. From each corner of a square of paper, 12 inches on a side, remove a small square of side x inches and turn up the edges to form an open box. What are the dimensions of the box? Express the volume, V cubic inches, as a function of x. What is the domain of V?

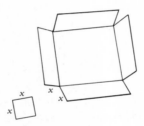

9. Suppose that you want to dig a (right circular cylindrical) swimming hole in the ground which will have a fixed vertical side area $A = 100$ square feet—so that you can shore up the sides with that given amount of material. You can choose any base radius $r > 0$, and the height h will then be determined by A and r. Express the volume V of the hole as a function of the single input r.

volume = base area × height = $\pi r^2 h$

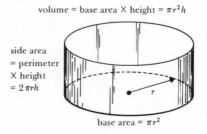

side area
= perimeter
× height
= $2\pi rh$

base area = πr^2

10. (Queen Dido's Problem) In founding Carthage in North Africa, Queen Dido was promised as much land as would lie inside the

bounds of an ox-hide. Being a wily person, she cut the hide into narrow strips, joined the strips together, and laid them out to obtain a large territory for herself. This deed led mathematicians to the following general problem: Given a fixed perimeter (such as the strips of ox-hide), what geometric plane figure encloses the largest area? If you were in Queen Dido's place, which of the following four figures would you choose: (i) circle, (ii) square, (iii) equilateral triangle, (iv) rectangle with length = 2 × width?

(a) Express the area A of each of the four figures as a function of the perimeter p.

(b) Suppose $p = 100$ yards. Which of the four figures has the largest area? What is that area?

11. Suppose that a bacterial population doubles every day. What is the population size after two days if the original population was 10,000? After ten days? After n days?

12. The human population on earth is said to be growing at such a rate as to double itself every 40 years. There are approximately 3.5 billion people alive now. If the growth rate remains unchanged, then what will be the population 80 years from now? After $40n$ years ($n = 1, 2, 3, \ldots$)?

13. Consider the following two properties of functions:

(i) $f(a+b) = f(a) + f(b)$ for all a and b in the domain.

(ii) $f(a \cdot b) = f(a) \cdot f(b)$ for all a and b in the domain.

For each function defined below, determine whether it has either of these properties.

(a) *Sample:* $f(x) = 2x + 3$ for all real x.

$\left. \begin{array}{l} \text{(i)} f(a+b) = 2(a+b) + 3 = 2a + 2b + 3 \\[4pt] f(a) + f(b) = (2a+3) + (2b+3) = 2a + 2b + 6 \end{array} \right\}$ not equal

$\left. \begin{array}{l} \text{(ii)} f(ab) = 2ab + 3 \\ f(a)f(b) = (2a+3)(2b+3) \\ \qquad = 4ab + 6b + 6a + 9 \end{array} \right\}$ not equal for all a, b in the domain

For example, let $a = b = 1$ $f(1 \cdot 1) = 5$ $f(1)f(1) = 25$

(b) $f(x) = 0$ for all real x

(c) $f(x) = 1$ for all real x

(d) $f(x) = -4x$ for all real x

(e) $f(x) = x$ for all real x

(f) $f(x) = \sqrt{x}$ for $x \geq 0$

(g) $f(x) = x^2$ for all real x

*(h) $f(x) = \log_{10} x$ for $x > 0$

14. For each of the following function rules, find the largest set of real numbers which when used as inputs gives real numbers as outputs.

(a) *Sample:* $f(x) = 1/x$.

Answer: Domain consists of all real numbers except zero.

(b) $f(x) = 2x$

(c) $g(x) = \sqrt{x}$

(d) $h(x) = \dfrac{1}{x^2 - 1}$

(e) $j(x) = \sqrt{1-x^2}$

(f) *Sample:* $K(x) = \dfrac{\sqrt{x-2}}{x-7}.$

   Answer: Domain consists of numbers $x \geq 2$ *and* $x \neq 7$.

(g) $l(x) = \dfrac{1}{x-1} + \dfrac{1}{x-2}$

(h) $m(x) = \dfrac{1}{\sqrt{-x}}$

(i) $n(x) = \sqrt{\dfrac{1-x}{x+2}}$

15. Find the range of each of the following functions whose domain and rule are specified.

(a) *Sample:* Domain: All x with $0 \leq x < 1$. Rule: $f(x) = 1/(1-x)$.
   Answer: Range is the set of all y with $y \geq 1$. Note that $f(0) = 1$ and $f(x) > 1$, for any input different from 0. To see that every real number $y > 1$ occurs as an output, solve $y = 1/(1-x)$ for x: $x = 1 - (1/y)$. Since $y \geq 1$, $0 \leq 1 - (1/y) < 1$, and this x can be used as an input yielding y as its output.

(b) All real numbers $\qquad\qquad f(x) = 1$

(c) The set of numbers $0 \leq x \leq 1 \quad f(x) = 2x - 3$

(d) The set of four numbers $\qquad f(x) = |x|$
   $-2, -1, 0, 2$

(e) The set of positive integers $\qquad f(x) = \dfrac{1}{x}$

(f) The set of numbers $0, \frac{1}{2}, \frac{2}{3}, \frac{3}{4}, 1 \quad f(x) = 2(x+1)$

(g) All negative numbers $\qquad f(x) = x^2$

(h) All positive numbers $\qquad f(x) = \dfrac{1}{\sqrt{x}}$

*(i) All real numbers $\qquad\qquad f(x) = \sqrt{x^2 - |x|}$

*(j) All real numbers $\qquad\qquad f(x) = \dfrac{1}{x^2 + 1}$

16. Describe functions by formula or by "mapping diagram" (as in Problem 1 above) whose domains and ranges are as given below:

(a) *Sample:* Domain: the set of three numbers 1, 2, 3; and Range: $-2, -4, -6$.
   Answer: $f(x) = -2x$ for $x = 1, 2, 3$. Note, however, that this is not the only possibility. Another answer, equally correct, is

   domain   range

(b) All real numbers   The single number 3
(c) All positive numbers   All negative numbers
(d) All positive integers   The two numbers 0, 1

(e) All positive integers   The single number 0
(f) The set 1, 2, 3, 4   The set 1, 4, 9, 16
(g) The set 1, 2, 3, 4   The set 0, 3, 5, 7
(h) The set 1, 2, 3, 4   The set 0, 1, 4, 9
(i) All real numbers   All nonnegative real numbers

*17. Let's call a function "one-to-one" if distinct inputs $a \neq b$ always produce distinct outputs $f(a) \neq f(b)$.

(a) *Sample:* Consider the function represented by the diagram in Problem 1(b). This is *not* a one-to-one function since two inputs (the first and the last) have the same output assigned to them.

(b) Which of the diagrams in Problem 1 represent one-to-one functions?

(c) *Sample:* The function $g(x) = 1/(x-1)$ for all real numbers $x \neq 1$ is one-to-one. To show this, suppose a and b are inputs with $g(a) = g(b)$. Then $1/(a-1) = 1/(b-1)$, and hence $a-1 = b-1$ or $a = b$. Thus if inputs a and b are different, then outputs $g(a)$ and $g(b)$ must be different.

(d) Is the function f given by the rule $f(x) = x^2 - 2x + 3$, for all real numbers, one-to-one? *Hint*: Look back at some of the outputs you computed for this function in Problem 2.

(e) Are there functions in Problem 5 which are one-to-one? Which ones?

(f) Which of the pictures in Problem 6 represent one-to-one functions?

*18. Find one-to-one functions with the following domains and ranges:

Domain	Range
(a) All odd positive integers	All even positive integers
(b) All odd positive integers except 1	All even positive integers
(c) All even positive integers except 0, 2, 4, ..., 20	All odd positive integers
(d) All positive integers	All even positive integers

**Having found such "one-to-one pairings" what is your feeling about the relative sizes of the two sets of integers which form the domain and range of the one-to-one function?

*19. Are there as many positive integers as there are positive rational numbers? Yes, if we can make a one-to-one pairing between the set $\{1, 2, 3, \ldots\}$ and the set of positive rationals. One way to do so is to display the positive rationals in an orderly table, with repetitions shaded out.

Describe a meandering path starting at the upper left corner of the table, along which you can visit each new (nonshaded) rational once and "pair" it with a new positive integer.

	1	2	3	4	5	6	...
1	1/1	2/1	3/1	4/1	5/1	6/1	...
2	1/2	2/2	3/2	4/2	5/2	6/2	...
3	1/3	2/3	3/3	4/3	5/3	6/3	...
4	1/4	2/4	3/4	4/4	5/4	6/4	...
5	1/5	2/5	3/5	4/5	5/5	6/5	...
:	:	:	:	:	:	:	

20. Consider the following functions with domain of all real numbers:

$$f(x) = x^2 \text{ and } g(x) = \begin{cases} 1 \text{ if } x \text{ is rational} \\ \\ 0 \text{ if } x \text{ is irrational.} \end{cases}$$

(a) *Sample:* For which x is $g(x) \leq x$?
   Answer: $g(x) \leq x$ if x is a positive irrational number or if x is a rational number ≥ 1.
(b) For which x is $g(x) \leq f(x)$?
(c) Write an explicit rule for $f(g(x)) - g(x)$.
(d) For which x is $f(x) \leq x$?
(e) For which x is $f(f(x)) = f(x)$?

2.3 MAXIMA AND MINIMA

There is a second theme common to the examples of Chapter 1: *maximization* or *minimization*. In each case we faced a set of objects, each with an assigned number, and the problem was to pick out that object for which the assigned number was the largest, or the smallest.

In the "area" example, the scheme that allots all of a fixed length of string to make one circle (rather than two) yields the *largest* amount of enclosed area.

In the "treatment" example, that situation (Report II) which would have the *least* associated probability for occurring if the treatment were ineffective argues best in favor of the treatment's effectiveness.

In the example on "shielding the rationals," I argued a negative conclusion: that there is *no* shielding scheme which requires a *least* amount of material — for I can always do the job with a lesser amount.

The goal of maximization or minimization is basic to many of the applications of mathematics in the 20th century. So when examining functions, I'll often make it a point to ask, *how can one find a maximum or a minimum output in a simple way?*

Here is a precise definition for future use:

Definition. Let's call a number M the (absolute) *maximum* of a function f with a given domain if

$$f(x) \leq M \quad \text{for all inputs } x \text{ in the domain of } f \tag{1}$$

and if M is itself an output number, $M = f(c)$ for some input c in the domain of f. Let's call a number m the (absolute) *minimum* of a function f with a given domain if

$$f(x) \geq m \quad \text{for all inputs } x \text{ in the domain of } f \tag{2}$$

and if m is itself an output number, $m = f(d)$ for some input d in the domain of f.

EXAMPLE. $f(x) = x^2$, with domain all x such that $-2 \leq x \leq 2$. The (absolute) maximum of f is $4 = 2^2 = f(2) = (-2)^2 = f(-2)$: because for any x with $0 \leqslant x \leqslant 2$ we must have $x^2 \leqslant 4$, that is, $f(x) \leqslant 4$; and for any x with $-2 \leqslant x \leqslant 0$ we must similarly have $4 = (-2)^2 \geqslant x^2 = f(x)$. The (absolute) minimum of f is $0 = 0^2 = f(0)$, since $x^2 \geqslant 0$ for any x.

NOTE: Two different inputs can provide the same maximum (or minimum) output value (e.g., 2 and -2 in the above example). Also, the value of an absolute maximum (or minimum) depends on the domain of a function as well as on its rule. If the domain above had been all x with $-3 \leqslant x \leqslant 3$, then the maximum would have been 9.

Try your hand at finding maxima and minima in the problems that follow.

2.4 MAXIMIZATION PROBLEMS

1. Find the maximum and minimum values (if they exist) for each of the following functions. Specify all inputs for which the output is equal to this maximum or minimum value.
   (a) *Sample:* $f(x) = 1/x$ for $0 < x \leqslant 1$.
   Answer: No maximum exists since as x gets very small, $1/x$ becomes arbitrarily large. To see this, let N be any number >1. Then $1/N$ is in the domain of f and

   $$f\left(\frac{1}{N}\right) = \frac{1}{1/N} = N.$$

   The minimum value is 1 and it occurs for $x = 1$. Note that if $a > b$, $(1/a) < (1/b)$ so that the minimum will occur at the largest input (in this case $x = 1$).
   °(b) $f(x) = 1$ for all real x
   °(c) $f(x) = 2x$ for $0 \leqslant x \leqslant 2$
   °(d) $f(x) = 0$ for all real x
   (e) $f(x) = x$ for $x < 0$
   *(f) $f(x) = \dfrac{1}{x-1}$ for all real $x \neq +1$
   *(g) $f(x) = \begin{cases} x & \text{for } x < -1 \\ x^2 & \text{for } -1 \leqslant x \leqslant 1 \\ 1 & \text{for } 1 < x \leqslant 2 \end{cases}$
   (h) *Sample:* $f(x) = x^3$ for $-4 \leqslant x < 3$.
   Answer: Check to see that $a^3 > b^3$ if and only if $a > b$. With this information the minimum will occur at the smallest input and the maximum at the largest (if they exist). -4 is the smallest input so $f(-4) = -64$ is the minimum. However, there is *no* largest output since 3 is not in the domain so there is *no* maximum value.
   (i) $f(x) = x^2$ for $-4 \leqslant x < 3$
   (j) $f(x) = |x|$ for all real x
   *(k) $f(x) = |x|/x$ for all $x \neq 0$
   (l) *Sample:* $f(x) = 1 - |x|$ for $-1 \leqslant x \leqslant 1$.

Answer: Minimum value is 0 at $x = \pm 1$. Maximum value is 1 at $x = 0$.

NOTE: $|x|$ is always positive or zero so the maximum of $1 - |x|$ will occur when the smallest value of $|x|$ is subtracted, and minimum, when the largest value of $|x|$ is subtracted, for x in the domain.
(m) $f(x) = 1 - |x|$ for $-1 < x < 1$
(n) $f(x) = (x - 1)^2$ $\frac{1}{2} \leqslant x \leqslant 2$
(o) $f(x) = (x - 1)^2$ $\frac{1}{2} < x < 2$

2. Does there exist an input radius r for which the swimming pool volume V in Problem 9 (Sec. 2.2) is a maximum? Why or why not?

°3. *Sample:* Let $f(x) = -x^2 + 4x + 10$, with domain the set of all real numbers. Determine the maximum and minimum of f if they exist.

Solution: A BASIC ALGEBRAIC TECHNIQUE for studying *quadratic* functions ($f(x) = ax^2 + bx + c$) is "completing the square." (See Appendix A.)

Write: $f(x) = -(x^2 - 4x) + 10$
$$= -(x^2 - 4x + 4 - 4) + 10$$
$$= -(x - 2)^2 + 14$$

The largest output occurs when $x = 2$, since for all other inputs $f(x) = 14$ *minus* the positive number $(x - 2)^2$. Thus 14 is the maximum of f.

The function f has *no* minimum: For any negative number $-k$ the inputs $\sqrt{k + 14} + 2$ and $-\sqrt{k + 14} + 2$ both yield $-k$ as an output; and if $x > \sqrt{k + 14} + 2$ or if $x < -\sqrt{k + 14} + 2$, then $-(x - 2)^2 + 14 < -k$, that is, $f(x) < -k$.

4. For the "famous fence and river problem" (Prob. 7, Sec. 2.2), what dimensions will give the farmer the maximum enclosed area?

5. What rectangular region with perimeter two feet will have the largest area?

6. Find maximum and minimum values (if they exist) for each of the following functions. List the inputs at which they occur.
   (a) $f(x) = 3x^2 - 6x$ for all x
   (b) $f(x) = 6x - 3x^2$ for all $x \geqslant 0$
   (c) $f(x) = 2x^2 + 3x - 5$ for all x
   *(d) $f(x) = ax^2 + bx + c$ for all x; $a \neq 0$

7. Suppose that the finance minister of a certain nation wants to attract more outside currency, say dollars, by devaluating the local unit, call it a "franc." The idea is that if a franc costs less in terms of a dollar, then more tourists will come to the country to spend their dollars (because each dollar will then buy more local goods and services than before). The minister must be careful, however, because even if the demand becomes greater for francs, each franc will bring in less currency, and he may end up with fewer dollars than ever.

For correctness, suppose we can represent the demand for francs as it is influenced by the exchange rate by the following function:

$$x = -2000r + 1000,$$

where r is the exchange rate, that is, the cost of a franc in terms of dollars, and x is the (estimated) total number of francs tourists will want at a rate r.

(a) What is the total dollar income of that country when it sells x francs to tourists at rate r?

(b) What is the most advantageous rate r for that country?

8. Suppose that a movie theater which charges $2 for admission averages 100 customers per showing. And suppose that for every five cents decrease in the admission price, the average number of customers will increase by 10. What price ticket will maximize cash receipts?

9. A Task: to construct a vertical cylindrical water tank which will hold 1600 cubic feet. Because of building zone requirements, the radius must not be smaller than four feet nor larger than ten feet. Find the dimensions (i.e., radius and height) which will minimize the amount of material needed for the sides of the cylinder.

10. Suppose that a calf weighs 300 lbs and gains weight at the rate of one pound per day. How many days hence should the calf be sold in order to maximize its selling price if calves are currently selling for 35 cents per pound but the price is falling at a rate of 1/30 of one cent per day?

2.5 SUMMARY OF CHAPTER 2

Here are the main concepts of this chapter:

Definitions. A FUNCTION consists of (i) a set of objects (inputs) — called the *domain* of the function — together with (ii) a *rule* which assigns a *unique* number (output) to each input. The set of all outputs of the function is its *range*.
(Sec. 2.1)

The (absolute) MAXIMUM of a function f with given domain: a number M such that

$$f(x) \leq M \text{ for all inputs } x \text{ in the domain of } f, \text{ and such that}$$
$$M = f(c) \text{ for some input } c \text{ in the domain of } f.$$

The (absolute) MINIMUM of a function f with given domain: a number m such that

$$f(x) \geq m \text{ for all inputs } x \text{ in the domain of } f, \text{ and such that}$$
$$m = f(d) \text{ for some input } d \text{ in the domain of } f.$$

(Sec. 2.3)

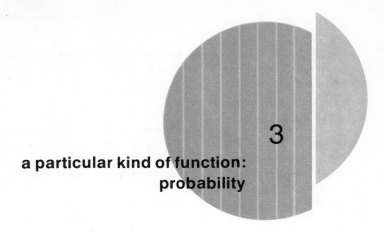

3

a particular kind of function:
probability

When does something appear to be a "matter of chance"? It appears so when we can think of several possible outcomes but don't know which will take place—because we don't know enough about the inner details of the situation. Despite such ignorance we may, however, have feelings about the relative "likelihoods" of various outcomes—feelings which we might capture quantitatively by assigning numbers ("probabilities") of different magnitudes to these outcomes.

Such assignments constitute *functions*. In this chapter I'll explore several examples of such functions and try to point out the special properties which they have in common.

3.1 TO BET OR NOT TO BET: AN OLD QUESTION

Suppose that someone gives you a die   which he claims is "true," and proposes a bet. You are told to toss the die once. If it reads 1 or 6, you'll win \$4; if it reads 2, 3, 4, or 5 you'll lose \$3. Should you accept the bet?

You have to consider

$$\left.\begin{array}{l}\text{\$4 with chances}\\ \text{2 out of 6}\end{array}\right\} \text{ vs. } \left\{\begin{array}{l}-3\text{\$ with chances}\\ \text{4 out of 6.}\end{array}\right. \tag{1}$$

Many people judge a single-toss bet in terms of what they might win "on the average" (per toss) if they played the game many times. From such a point of view, if you tossed the die many times—say n—you might expect to see each face on top approximately $\frac{1}{6}$ of the time ($\frac{1}{6}n$). Hence you might expect to read "1 or 6" approximately $\frac{2}{6}$ of the time ($\frac{2}{6}n$), and to read "2, 3, 4, or 5" approximately $\frac{4}{6}$ of the time ($\frac{4}{6}n$). So in n tosses you might expect a net payoff of

$$(\$4) \times (\tfrac{2}{6}n) + (-\$3) \times (\tfrac{4}{6}n). \tag{2}$$

Divide this payoff by n to get an "average payoff per toss" of

$$(\$4) \times (\tfrac{2}{6}) + (-\$3) \times (\tfrac{4}{6}) = -\$\tfrac{4}{6}. \tag{3}$$

Perhaps you shouldn't accept the bet even for a single toss.

Now let's check back for functions—partly veiled—which may have guided the above reasoning. How could I have assigned chances of

2-out-of-6 to the result "1 or 6" and of 4-out-of-6 to the result "2, 3, 4, or 5" without first quietly having assigned *equal* weights to the six possible outcomes for a single toss? Such an assignment captures the "trueness" of the die. I've displayed it quantitatively as the function p in Fig. 3-1. Let's call the weights "elementary probabilities." In Fig. 3-1, I choose $\frac{1}{6}$ as the common value for the elementary probabilities for two reasons: (i) so that the total "probability" will be 1—a handy standardization; and (ii) so as to correspond approximately to the proportion of appearances which each face might make during many tosses of the die.

FIGURE 3-1

FIGURE 3-2

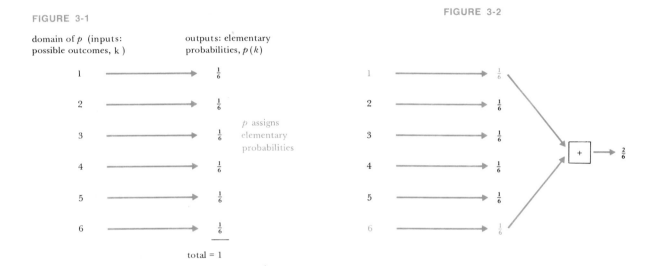

domain of p (inputs: possible outcomes, k)

outputs: elementary probabilities, $p(k)$

p assigns elementary probabilities

total = 1

From Fig. 3-1 it was a short step to assign a probability number to the compound result "1 or 6." See Fig. 3-2, where I've represented this compound result as a green colored subset of the total list of possible outcomes. Here you can see a second function operating— call it P—whose rule is as follows:

to a subset S of possible outcomes, assign the *probability*

$$P(S) = \begin{cases} \text{the sum of the elementary} \\ \text{probabilities of outcomes in } S. \end{cases} \qquad (4)$$

Let's call this the "compound probabilities rule." The subsets represent compound results.

Does the above rule give an intuitively reasonable assignment of relative weights (probabilities) to different subsets? Note that it does assign to the subset $\{1, 6\}$ a number $(\frac{2}{6})$ which approximates the proportion of times that we might expect to see the result "1 or 6" during many tosses of a true die. Similarly for

$$P(2, 3, 4, 5) = \tfrac{1}{6} + \tfrac{1}{6} + \tfrac{1}{6} + \tfrac{1}{6} = \tfrac{4}{6}.$$

Note also that the "compound probabilities rule" implies that

$$P(\text{some outcome}) = P(1, 2, 3, 4, 5, 6) = 1 \tag{5}$$

and

$$P(\text{no outcome}) = P(\text{empty set}) = 0. \tag{6}$$

In fact, for any list of n *equally likely* outcomes — each with elementary probability $1/n$ — and for any subset S containing k of these outcomes $(0 \leqslant k \leqslant n)$, the "compound probabilities rule" will assign probability

$$P(S) = \underbrace{\frac{1}{n} + \frac{1}{n} + \cdots + \frac{1}{n}}_{k \text{ terms}} = \frac{k}{n}$$

$$= \frac{\text{size of } S}{\text{size of entire list}}. \tag{7}$$

And whether we start with equal elementary probabilities or not, the numbers $P(S)$ assigned by the "compound probabilities rule" behave very much like weights (or areas or volumes) of physical objects. They have the following general properties:

For any subset S,

$$P(S) \geqslant 0. \tag{8}$$

If the subset S is contained in the subset T, then

$$P(S) \leqslant P(T). \tag{9}$$

And finally, if S and T are *mutually exclusive* (i.e., if S and T have no outcome in common), then the union of $S \cup T$ — the set of all outcomes lying either in S or in T or in both — will have probability

$$P(S \cup T) = P(S) + P(T). \tag{10}$$

(I invite you to check (9) and (10) in doing Problem 20 of Sec. 3.4. Also, to review subsets and their operations, turn to Appendix B.)

For all these reasons, people have been willing to go along with the "compound probabilities rule" as a basis for assigning probabilities in ordinary situations. I shall explore the use of that rule with further examples in the following sections.

Meanwhile, as regards tossing a "true" die n times, you might think about these questions: Let N_n denote the number of times the die reads "1" in n tosses. In what sense will the ratio

$$a_n = \frac{N_n}{n} \tag{11}$$

"approach" the number $\frac{1}{6}$ "in the limit" if we choose larger and larger values for n? Is the approach a matter of empirical verification, or of bald supposition, or of definition, or of proof from some other principle? And what, if anything, can such a "limit" notion *really* say about a single toss of a die?

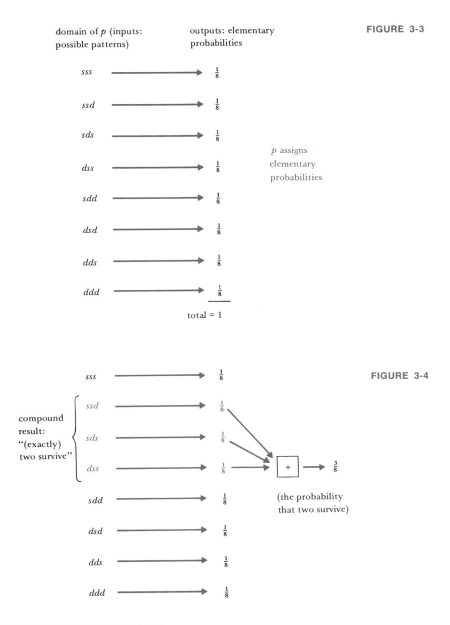

domain of p (inputs: outputs: elementary   **FIGURE 3-3**
possible patterns)   probabilities

sss $\longrightarrow$ $\frac{1}{8}$

ssd $\longrightarrow$ $\frac{1}{8}$

sds $\longrightarrow$ $\frac{1}{8}$
                                          p assigns
dss $\longrightarrow$ $\frac{1}{8}$ elementary
                                          probabilities
sdd $\longrightarrow$ $\frac{1}{8}$

dsd $\longrightarrow$ $\frac{1}{8}$

dds $\longrightarrow$ $\frac{1}{8}$

ddd $\longrightarrow$ $\frac{1}{8}$

total = 1

sss $\longrightarrow$ $\frac{1}{8}$ **FIGURE 3-4**

ssd $\longrightarrow$ $\frac{1}{8}$
compound
result: sds $\longrightarrow$ $\frac{1}{8}$
"(exactly) $+$ $\longrightarrow$ $\frac{3}{8}$
two survive" dss $\longrightarrow$ $\frac{1}{8}$

sdd $\longrightarrow$ $\frac{1}{8}$ (the probability
                                                 that two survive)
dsd $\longrightarrow$ $\frac{1}{8}$

dds $\longrightarrow$ $\frac{1}{8}$

ddd $\longrightarrow$ $\frac{1}{8}$

3.2 SURVIVAL VS. DEATH, AGAIN

EXAMPLE 1: *A disease with 50–50 chances of survival for an untreated victim.* In Sec. 1.2 I argued that all possible patterns of survival vs. death for three independent victims were "equally likely." Here, in Figs. 3-3, 3-4, and 3-5, is how we can picture the corresponding probability functions. First, elementary probabilities are shown in Fig. 3-3. Next, an example of adding elementary probabilities for a compound result (represented as a green subset in Fig. 3-4). Finally, a table showing the further operation of a function (P) assigning probabilities to compound results by addition of elementary probabilities (see Fig. 3-5).

FIGURE 3-5

(interpretation of subsets)	domain of p (inputs: *subsets* of patterns)					outputs (probabilities)
"three survive"	sss sdd	ssd dsd	sds dds	dss ddd	→	$\frac{1}{8}$
"(exactly) two survive"	sss sdd	ssd dsd	sds dds	dss ddd	→	$\frac{3}{8}$
"(exactly) one survives"	sss sdd	ssd dsd	sds dds	dss ddd	→	$\frac{3}{8}$
"none survive"	sss sdd	ssd dsd	sds dds	dss ddd	→	$\frac{1}{8}$
"at least one survives"	sss sdd	ssd dsd	sds dds	dss ddd	→	$\frac{7}{8}$
"at most one survives"	sss sdd	ssd dsd	sds dds	dss ddd	→	$\frac{4}{8}$
"the first victim survives"	sss sdd	ssd dsd	sds dds	dss ddd	→	$\frac{4}{8}$
etc.		etc.				etc.

EXAMPLE 2: *A disease with 2-to-1 chances of survival for an untreated victim.* In this case it seems reasonable to assign twice as much elementary probability to a pattern such as *dsd* as to the pattern *ddd*— since the middle victim's chances are independent of the fates of the other two. Similarly, let's assign twice as much elementary probability to *ssd* as to *dsd*, and twice as much to *sss* as to *ssd*. Let's denote the elementary probability of *ddd* by w. In terms of w, I've listed all resulting elementary probabilities in the second column of Fig. 3-6. I let $w = 1/27$ in the third column of Fig. 3-6 to preserve the standardization that the total probability be one.

For this disease, the probability of the result "(exactly) two survive" is 12/27, as you can see from Fig. 3-7. (Compare with Fig. 3-4.) In similar manner, we can assign a probability for any compound result concerning the three victims' fates.

Note in particular that the assignment procedure of Figs. 3-6 and 3-7 reserves to each individual victim the probabilities for survival or death with which we started. For example, we can represent the result "the first victim survives" as the green colored subset in Fig. 3-8 consisting of all patterns beginning with *s*. Our procedure assigns probabilities 18/27 = 2/3, as it should. Similarly, we can represent the result "the second victim dies" as in Fig. 3-9. The procedure assigns probability 9/27 = 1/3, as it should.

In the next section I'll describe the probability assignments which figured in Mendel's formulation of his "laws of heredity." You may

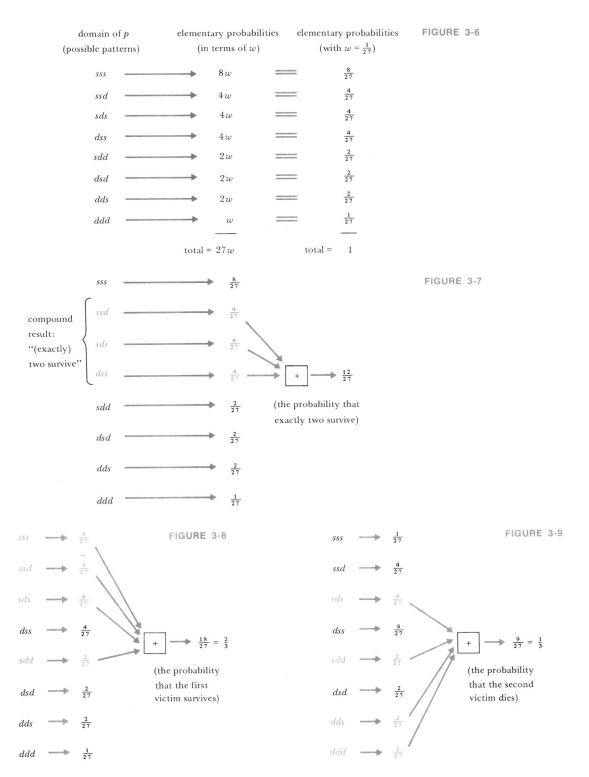

FIGURE 3-6

domain of p (possible patterns)		elementary probabilities (in terms of w)		elementary probabilities (with $w = \frac{1}{27}$)
sss	$\longrightarrow$	$8w$	$=$	$\frac{8}{27}$
ssd	$\longrightarrow$	$4w$	$=$	$\frac{4}{27}$
sds	$\longrightarrow$	$4w$	$=$	$\frac{4}{27}$
dss	$\longrightarrow$	$4w$	$=$	$\frac{4}{27}$
sdd	$\longrightarrow$	$2w$	$=$	$\frac{2}{27}$
dsd	$\longrightarrow$	$2w$	$=$	$\frac{2}{27}$
dds	$\longrightarrow$	$2w$	$=$	$\frac{2}{27}$
ddd	$\longrightarrow$	w	$=$	$\frac{1}{27}$

total = $27w$ total = 1

FIGURE 3-7

compound result: "(exactly) two survive"

$sss \longrightarrow \frac{8}{27}$

$ssd \longrightarrow \frac{4}{27}$
$sds \longrightarrow \frac{4}{27}$
$dss \longrightarrow \frac{4}{27}$

$+ \longrightarrow \frac{12}{27}$

$sdd \longrightarrow \frac{2}{27}$

(the probability that exactly two survive)

$dsd \longrightarrow \frac{2}{27}$

$dds \longrightarrow \frac{2}{27}$

$ddd \longrightarrow \frac{1}{27}$

FIGURE 3-8

$sss \longrightarrow \frac{8}{27}$
$ssd \longrightarrow \frac{4}{27}$
$sds \longrightarrow \frac{4}{27}$
$dss \longrightarrow \frac{4}{27}$
$sdd \longrightarrow \frac{2}{27}$
$dsd \longrightarrow \frac{2}{27}$
$dds \longrightarrow \frac{2}{27}$
$ddd \longrightarrow \frac{1}{27}$

$+ \longrightarrow \frac{18}{27} = \frac{2}{3}$

(the probability that the first victim survives)

FIGURE 3-9

$sss \longrightarrow \frac{1}{27}$
$ssd \longrightarrow \frac{4}{27}$
$sds \longrightarrow \frac{4}{27}$
$dss \longrightarrow \frac{4}{27}$
$sdd \longrightarrow \frac{2}{27}$
$dsd \longrightarrow \frac{2}{27}$
$dds \longrightarrow \frac{2}{27}$
$ddd \longrightarrow \frac{1}{27}$

$+ \longrightarrow \frac{9}{27} = \frac{1}{3}$

(the probability that the second victim dies)

or may not wish to postpone that section to a later reading. In any event, try your own hand at setting up probability assignments in doing the problems of Sec. 3-4.

*3.3   MENDEL'S LAW OF INHERITANCE

In the 1860's, G. Mendel, a monk, performed experiments in his garden. The following is an account of one of these.

(Part A) He crossed a 6-ft tall variety of garden peas with a 1-ft short variety. (Part B) Then he allowed the hybrids from each cross to be self-pollinated and observed the subsequent generation. He found 787 tall and 277 short plants, roughly 3 to 1. (Part C) He permitted that generation to self-pollinate, and found that short plants had only short offspring. On the other hand, the tall plants were of two types. About $\frac{1}{3}$ of them produced only tall offspring, the remaining $\frac{2}{3}$ produced both tall and short plants in the proportions of roughly 3 to 1. See Fig. 3-10.

FIGURE 3-10

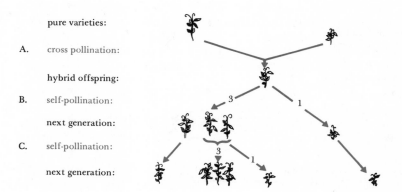

pure varieties:

A.   cross pollination:

hybrid offspring:

B.   self-pollination:

next generation:

C.   self-pollination:

next generation:

Now, we are seldom privileged to see the real workings of nature! Progress in understanding most often consists of somebody's concocting a *model* to explain observations, and this model is kept on until a better one is found. To explain the ratios he observed in the above experiment, Mendel proposed an amazing model—which has stood the test of time. Mendel conceived of unseen entities which he called "genes." These he supposed to be inside cells, and to be the causative agents of tallness and shortness. (Nowadays "genes" are identified with certain patterns of molecular structure in cells. They still can't be seen.) For the tallness-vs.-shortness attribute, genes come in two versions, say, t (causing tallness) and s (causing shortness).

Mendel's basic assumption is that each individual plant (or animal) has a characteristic pattern, either tt, st, or ss (he considered ts to be the same as st); and that every cell in the plant has *two* genes reflecting that pattern—except for *reproductive cells*, each of which has only one gene, one or the other of the pattern. For example, if the pattern is st, then each nonreproductive cell has one s gene and one t gene;

FIGURE 3-11

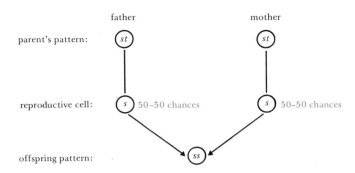

a reproductive cell has either one *s* gene or one *t* gene. In such a case, Mendel assumed that *s* and *t* could occur *with 50–50 chances*. If the pattern is *tt*, then each nonreproductive cell has two *t* genes and each reproductive cell has one *t* gene.

Reproduction involves the joining of two reproductive cells to make a new cell which now has *two* genes (one from each reproductive cell); and these two genes set a new pattern for the offspring. A final assumption of the model is that *t dominates s*; namely, that both *tt* and *st* patterns cause tall individuals and only *ss* causes short ones.

See Fig. 3-11 for a sample diagram, which incidentally shows how two tall parents can have a short child.

Now how does this complicated model explain Mendel's experimental results? Via Part A of his experiment he got a generation of hybrid plants each with *st* patterns. In Part B he got together two reproductive cells each of which could (with *equal likelihood*) contain an *s* or a *t* gene—one, say, from the "father" and one from the "mother." What possible combinations could there be? In Fig. 3-12 I've written the father's contribution on the left and the mother's on the right to get a list of four possible gene pairs, *all equally likely*. The last column in Fig. 3-12 shows a ratio of 3 to 1 in favor of tallness for the offspring in Part B of Mendel's experiment—which is what Mendel observed.

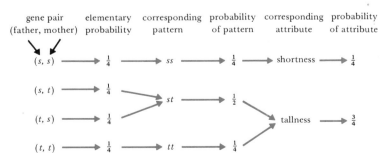

FIGURE 3-12

In part C of the experiment, short parents must have *ss* patterns and hence can produce only short (*ss*) offspring by *self*-pollination. Tall parents are of two kinds: pure (*tt*) or mixed (*st*). The pure pattern can produce only tall (*tt*) offspring by *self*-pollination; and the others produce 3-to-1 results just as in Part B. All is explained!

3.4 PROBLEMS

Before beginning these problems, you might find it helpful to read the summary at the end of the chapter.

°1. Imagine an experiment of tossing a penny and a nickel.

(a) Make a list Ω of all possible outcomes of this experiment.

Sample answer: Writing penny result on left and nickel result on right:

$$\Omega = \left\{ HH, HT, TH, TT \right\} \quad \text{Pictorially} \quad \left(\begin{array}{cc} HH & TH \\ HT & TT \end{array}\right) \Omega$$

(b) Describe a subset A representing the result, "the penny falls heads," and a subset B representing the result, "the nickel falls heads."

Sample answer:

$$A = \left\{ HH, HT \right\},$$

$$\left(\begin{array}{c} HH \\ HT \end{array}\right) \begin{array}{c} TH \\ TT \end{array}$$
$$A$$

(c) In terms of A, B, and the set of operations of union $\cup$, intersection $\cap$, and complementation $'$ (see Appendix B for definitions), describe the following results:

(i) Either the penny falls heads *or* the nickel falls heads (or both) — that is, there is at least one head.

Sample answer:

$$A \cup B = \{HH, HT\} \cup \{HH, TH\} = \{HH, HT, TH\}$$

$$A \cup B$$

(ii) The penny falls heads *and* the nickel falls heads.
(iii) The penny does *not* fall heads.

Sample answer:

$$A' = \Omega - A = \left\{ TH, TT \right\}. \qquad \left(\begin{array}{c} HH \\ HT \end{array}\right) \left(\begin{array}{c} TH \\ TT \end{array}\right)$$
$$\qquad\qquad\qquad\qquad\qquad\qquad A \qquad A'$$

(iv) The nickel does not fall heads.

(v) No heads. Equivalently: *not* "at least one head." Equivalently: not a penny head *and* not a nickel head.

Sample answer:

$$(A \cup B)' = \Omega - (A \cup B) = \Omega - \{HH, HT, TH\} = \{TT\},$$

$(A \cup B)$

$(A \cup B)'$

or equivalently,

$$A' \cap B' = \{TH, TT\} \cap \{HT, TT\} = \{TT\}.$$

$A' \cap B'$

(vi) At most one head. Equivalently: *not* both heads. Equivalently: not a penny head *or* not a nickel head, or neither head.

(vii) exactly one head. Equivalently: penny head and not nickel head *or* nickel head and not penny head.

°2. Set up a *probability model* for the experiment in Problem 1 under the assumption that both coins are "true."

(a) Assign reasonable "elementary probabilities" to each of the outcomes in Ω.

$HH \rightarrow$?
$HT \rightarrow$?
$TH \rightarrow$?
$TT \rightarrow$?

(b) Assign a "compound probability" for each of the results (i)–(vii) in Problem 1(c).

Sample:

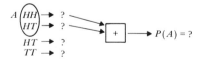

(c) How are the compound probability outputs $P(A)$ and $P(A')$ related? $P(B)$ and $P(B')$? $P(A \cap B')$, $P(B \cap A')$, and $P((A \cap B') \cup (B \cap A'))$? $P(A)$, $P(B)$ and $P(A \cup B)$? $P(A)$, $P(B)$, and $P(A \cap B)$?

°3. Consider tossing a "true" penny and a loaded nickel which favors "heads" 2 to 1 — so that, for example, the result "both heads" (*HH*) is twice as probable as the result "penny heads, nickel tails" (*HT*). In a list of possible outcomes, let the subset A represent "the penny falls heads" and the subset B represent "the nickel falls heads" (as in Problems 1 and 2). Assign compound probabilities. How are the probabilities $P(A)$ and $P(A')$ related? $P(B)$ and $P(B')$? $P(A)$, $P(B)$, $P(A \cap B)$, and $P(A \cup B)$?

°4. Imagine an experiment of simultaneously tossing three coins, a penny, a nickel, and a dime.

(a) Make a list Ω of all possible outcomes of the experiment.

(b) Describe subsets representing the following results:

A: the penny reads heads

B: the nickel reads heads

C: the dime reads heads.

(c) In terms of A, B, C and $\cap$, $\cup$, and ' describe the following results:

(i) There is at least one head.

(ii) All coins fall heads.

(iii) The penny does not show heads.

(iv) The nickel shows tails.

(v) Only the penny shows heads.

(vi) Between the nickel and the dime, at least one shows tails.

(vii) Between the nickel and the dime, exactly one shows tails.

(viii) At least one coin shows tails.

(ix) There is at most one tail.

(x) There are exactly two heads.

(xi) There is exactly one head.

(xii) No heads.

°5. Set up a probability model for the experiment in Problem 4 under the assumption that all three coins are "true," and assign appropriate "elementary probabilities."

6. (a) With the list Ω of Problem 4 as a domain, set up a "head counting" function f, and describe its range.

Sample outputs: $f(HHH) = 3$, $f(HHT) = 2$

(b) For $k = 0, 1, 2, 3$, record the set A_k of all those inputs ω whose corresponding output $f(\omega) = k$.

(c) Find the probabilities $P(A_k)$ for $k = 0, 1, 2, 3$.

(d) If I were to give you \$1 for each head appearing, what "average payoff" might you expect from one performance of the experiment?

(Does the sum

$$(\$0) \times P(A_0) + (\$1) \times P(A_1) + (\$2) \times P(A_2) + (\$3) \times P(A_3)$$

seem reasonable in this situation?)

In each of the following problems, as a first step, make a list of all possible outcomes, assign elementary probabilities, and identify the result in question as a subset of the list. Then determine its compound probability.

7. *Sample:* Suppose someone is about to toss a green die and a red die. What is the probability that a "double" will turn up, that is, that the numbers on the top faces will be the same? Answer: 6/36. Reasoning: Represent a possible outcome by an ordered pair (g, r) where g and $r = 1, 2, 3, 4, 5,$ or 6 are the numbers on

the green and red die, respectively. There are 36 such ordered pairs. Assuming the dice are true, assign weights 1/36 to each of those outcomes. The set $D = \{(1, 1), (2, 2), (3, 3), (4, 4), (5, 5), (6, 6)\}$ represents the result "a double turns up." Since D contains 6 elements, the probability of D is 6/36.

8. (a) If two honest dice were tossed, and the sum of the numbers showing on the faces were recorded, what is the probability that this sum would be even? odd? 7 or 11?

   (b) Suppose someone proposes a bet with this pair of dice. He will pay you $10 if the sum is 7 or 11, and you will pay him $2 if not. What might you expect to win "on the average" in this game?

9. Here are two versions of a game. Are they really different? Both versions involve a deck of four cards: a red ace, a red king, a black ace and a black king. Your friend mixes the deck and (simultaneously) extracts two cards from it, which he keeps hidden.

   Version I: Your friend says: "One of my cards is an ace. What are the chances that I have two aces?"

   Version II: Your friend says: "One of my cards is a red ace. What are the chances that I have two aces?"

   The second version differs from the first only in that your friend communicates information about color. Can such information change the chances?

   To answer, write two lists, Ω_I and Ω_{II}, each describing the possible hands your friend might have in light of the information he gave you in the respective version. (In describing your friend's "hand," remember that his two cards are in no particular order.) In each list, identify the result "two aces." Finally, assign appropriate elementary probabilities to each list. Compare the respective probabilities, in each list, for the result "two aces."

10. Suppose that on a quiz you are asked to match three given dates with three given historical events; and not having studied, you propose to match the dates with the events randomly.
    (a) What is the probability that you will match all dates correctly?
    (b) What is the probability that you will match no dates correctly?

11. Suppose that you are about to take a quiz consisting of three true-false questions; and that you have not studied, and propose to answer each question randomly.
    (a) What is the probability that you will answer all questions correctly?
    (b) Suppose that, after taking the quiz, you learn that the man who composed the test never writes questions all requiring a "true" answer or all requiring a "false" answer. How does this new information change the probability that you answered all questions correctly?

12. Suppose that a die is loaded in such a way that getting a 1 is just as probable as not getting a 1 on a given toss, and that all other

numbers are equally likely. What is the probability that a toss will yield an odd number? (How about assigning equal weights w to each of the outcomes $2, 3, 4, 5, 6$? Then we should assign $5w$ to the outcome "1." The total elementary probability then equals $10w$.)

13. Suppose that a die has its faces weighted so that the probabilities are in the same ratio as the numbers on the faces. (That is, a 6 is six times as likely as a 1 and twice as likely as a 3, etc.) For a single toss of the die, what is the probability that an odd number will show? An even number?

14. Suppose that a player rolls a die and receives a number of dollars corresponding to the number of dots on the face which turns up. What should the player pay as an entrance fee for playing this game in order that it be fair between him and "the house"?

Definition. A game between two players is called "fair" if the winnings of the two are equal to zero "on the average."

15. Look again at the "clinical evidence" problem in Sect. 1.2, regarding the effectiveness of a treatment in fighting a disease for which victims have 50–50 chances of survival. In each of the following pairs of reports, which provides better evidence in favor of the treatment?
    (a) (i) *one* out of 3 victims dies, vs. (ii) *two* out of 7 die.
    (b) (i) *one* out of 3 victims dies, vs. (ii) *three* out of 7 die.

Problems 16–18 refer to the (*) Section 3.3 on Mendel's genetic model.

*16. If Mendel had crossed hybrid garden peas (*st*) with the short variety (*ss*), what proportion of the resulting plants should he expect to be short?

*17. If Mendel finds a tall pea plant in his garden, crosses it with a short plant, and a short plant results, what can you conclude about the genetic pattern of the tall plant he found?

*18. In the study of genetics, the eye color blue is considered a recessive gene, that is, for a child to have blue eyes it must have received a blue-eye gene from both of its parents.
    (a) What is the probability for a child to have blue eyes if his mother has blue eyes and his father has hybrid blue-brown eyes?
    (b) What if both parents have blue eyes?
    (c) What if both parents have pure brown eyes?
    (d) What if both parents have hybrid blue-brown eyes?

19. You may have noticed in Problem 2(c) that for subsets $A = \{HH, HT\}$, $B = \{HH, TH\}$, and $A \cup B = \{HH, HT, TH\}$, there was an inequality

$$P(A \cup B) < P(A) + P(B).$$

By how much is the right-hand side too large?

20. Show that the "compound probabilities rule" assigns numbers $P(S)$ to subsets S of all possible outcomes in such a way that the the following properties hold:

   (a) If the subset S is contained in the subset T, then

$$P(S) < P(T).$$

   Sample "proof": $P(S)$ is the sum of elementary probabilities of outcomes in S. Since elementary probabilities are nonnegative and T contains all the outcomes in S with, perhaps, some additional outcomes, $P(T)$ must be at least as large as $P(S)$.

   (b) If the subsets S and T are *mutually exclusive*, that is, $S \cap T$ is empty, then

$$P(S \cup T) = P(S) + P(T).$$

   (c) For any subset S and its complement S' in the list of all possible outcomes,

$$P(S') = 1 - P(S).$$

   (d) For any two subsets S and T

$$P(S \cup T) = P(S) + P(T) - P(S \cap T).$$

   (e) For any three subsets S, T, and W which are *pairwise* mutually exclusive, that is, $S \cap T = \emptyset$, $T \cap W = \emptyset$, and $S \cap W = \emptyset$,

$$P(S \cup T \cup W) = P(S) + P(T) + P(W).$$

**Trouble with sets.

21. In Fig. 3–5 of Sec. 3.2, I pictured part of a probability function: a set containing many elements, each one a *set in its own right*. And there seemed to be no *logical flaw* hidden in considering such a *set* of *sets*.

   It was Bertrand Russell who carried the notion of a set of sets to its logical extreme, and asked, "Can a set be an element of itself?" To follow this question up, let's call a set a "Russell set" if it does contain itself as an element; and let's call a set an "ordinary set" if it does *not* contain itself as an element. From these definitions and the way our minds work, it would seem that any set you may care to consider must be *either* a "Russell set" *or* an "ordinary set." But consider now the set A consisting of all "ordinary sets" and no others. Is A a "Russell set" or an "ordinary set"? If it is a "Russell set," then it must contain itself, in which case it contains a "Russell set" (namely itself): but this contradicts its definition — it contains *only* "ordinary sets"! On the other hand, if it is an "ordinary set" then it does not contain itself, in which case it doesn't contain at least one "ordinary set" (namely itself): but this contradicts its definition — it contains *all* "ordinary sets"!

   What can you do with a paradox like that? The reaction of logicians has been to declare it "out of bounds"; that is, to demand that a set must be described in a "reasonable way"—where "reasonable" excludes letting the set contain itself as an element.

Since we use sets as tools, it is important to study them with an eye open for pitfalls. You may or may not be comforted to know that there are no *known* pitfalls attaching to any of the sets I'll be using in the rest of this book.

*3.5 INDEPENDENCE

How can we capture, mathematically, the intuitive notion of two results being "independent" of each other? You may recall that I used the intuitive notion in deciding upon elementary probabilities for the survival vs. death patterns in Sec. 1.2 and 3.2. But once probabilities are assigned, is there any distinctive way in which we can recognize two subsets—via their probabilities—as representing "independent" results?

To help answer this question, here is an intuitive criterion for "independence" between two results: *knowledge that one of them has taken place should not change our feelings about the chances for the other to take place* Let's see how we can apply this criterion in an example.

EXAMPLE 1: *A coin and a die.* Think of tossing a "true coin" and independently a "true" die. A result such as

"the coin reads 'heads'"

should certainly be independent of a result such as

"the die reads 2, 3, 4, or 5."

In order to look at these results *jointly*, I've represented them in Fig. 3-13 as two subsets A and B, of the list—call it Ω—of 12 possible outcomes for the experiment. (H stands for "heads" on the coin, and T for "tails.")

Since all the outcomes in Ω seem *equally likely*, we can calculate the probability of A (without regard to B) simply as the ratio

$$P(A) = \frac{\text{size of } A}{\text{size of } \Omega}. \tag{1}$$

(Such was the conclusion (7) of Sec. 3.1.)

Now suppose someone tosses the coin and the die for us and reports only the information that "the die reads 2, 3, 4, or 5" (we don't know which). How should this information affect our calculation of the probability that "the coin reads 'heads'"? The information tells us that we must now restrict our attention to outcomes in the subset B. In other words, B constitutes a *new list* for recalculating probabilities. See the right-hand side of Fig. 3-13. In this new list, the result "the coin reads 'heads'" is represented by the subset $A \cap B$. Since the outcomes in B are still equally likely among themselves, the probability of $A \cap B$—in the new list B—should be the ratio

$$\frac{\text{size of } A \cap B}{\text{size of } B} \tag{2}$$

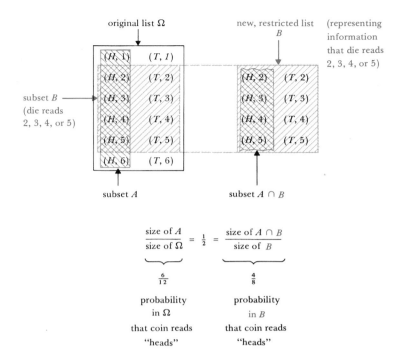

FIGURE 3-13

$$\underbrace{\frac{\text{size of } A}{\text{size of } \Omega}}_{\frac{6}{12}} = \tfrac{1}{2} = \underbrace{\frac{\text{size of } A \cap B}{\text{size of } B}}_{\frac{4}{8}}$$

probability   probability
in Ω in B
that coin reads   that coin reads
"heads"   "heads"

Now, how can we decide whether A and B are "independent" according to the above intuitive criterion? By that criterion, we must have the probability of A as calculated in (1) *without* regard to B equal to the probability as calculated in (2) *with* regard to B. That is, we must have

$$\frac{\text{size of } A}{\text{size of } \Omega} = \frac{\text{size of } A \cap B}{\text{size of } B}. \tag{3}$$

Check Fig. 3-13 to see that we do.

Note that by multiplying equation (3) through by the ratio (size of B)/(size of A) and canceling on the right we can get an equivalent expression

$$\frac{\text{size of } B}{\text{size of } \Omega} = \frac{\text{size of } A \cap B}{\text{size of } A} \tag{4}$$

which says that, vice versa, the probability of B remains unchanged by information about A. Hence *equation (3)—or (4)—gives a complete quantitative version of the intuitive criterion for independence of A and B.*

For still another equivalent—and more symmetric—version of (3) and (4), multiply (3) through by the ratio (size of B)/(size of Ω) and cancel, to get

$$\frac{\text{size of } A \cap B}{\text{size of } \Omega} = \frac{\text{size of } A}{\text{size of } \Omega} \cdot \frac{\text{size of } B}{\text{size of } \Omega}. \tag{5}$$

In the present example, where all outcomes are equally likely, we can rewrite this equation — and thus the intuitive criterion for independence — in terms of *probabilities* as

$$P(A \cap B) = P(A) \cdot P(B). \tag{6}$$

By such reasoning, people have arrived at a quantitative definition for independence:

Definition: Once probabilities $P(S)$ have been assigned to subsets S of a list Ω, call two subsets S and T *independent* if

$$P(S \cap T) = P(S)P(T). \tag{7}$$

If you think that this definition captures the idea of independence well — at least in situations where outcomes are equally likely — here's how to shortcut many calculations:

EXAMPLE 2. What's the probability of getting a 1 or 6 on each of two tosses of a "true" die?   *Answer:* $(\frac{1}{3})^2$.

In a suitable list, let subset A represent "1 or 6 on the first toss" and subset B represent "1 or 6 on the second toss." These should be independent subsets, each with probability $\frac{1}{3}$, as we calculated in Sec. 3.1. Hence $P(A \cap B) = P(A)P(B) = (\frac{1}{3})^2$.

EXAMPLE 3. What's the probability that three independent victims will all recover from a disease with 50–50 chances of survival for individual patients?   *Answer:* $(\frac{1}{2})^3$.

In a suitable list, let subsets A, B and C represent the survival of the respective victims. Since $A \cap B \cap C = (A \cap B) \cap C$, and since C should be independent of the *joint* survival $A \cap B$ of the first two victims as well as of their individual survivals, we should have $P(A \cap B \cap C) = P(A \cap B)P(C) = P(A)P(B)P(C) = (\frac{1}{2})^3$ — just as in Sec. 1.2.

EXAMPLE 4. What's the probability that a family with 3 children will have at least one boy?   *Answer:* $\frac{7}{8}$.

For a simplified model we might suppose the sexes of successive offspring to be independent and equally weighted between male and female — although birth records show such assumptions to be a bit off. Reasoning as in Example 3 above, we can conclude that the probability of three successive female offspring should be

$$P(A \cap B \cap C) = (\frac{1}{2})^3.$$

Since

$$P(\text{at least one boy}) + P(\text{all girls}) = 1$$

we can get

$$P(\text{at least one boy}) = 1 - (\frac{1}{2})^3 = \frac{7}{8}.$$

So far, we've considered only problems with equally likely outcomes. Can we expect relationship $P(S \cap T) = P(S)P(T)$ to capture the intuitive criterion for independence in other cases too? If you have doubts, I invite you to read the following discussion of an old example—which, though specific, points to the general situation.

EXAMPLE 5. The disease with 2-to-1 chances for survival. In Fig. 3-6 of Sec. 3.1, I assigned elementary probabilities to survival-vs.-death patterns for three disease victims—using a scheme based on an intuitive assumption of "independence" between victims. Then I summed these elementary probabilities to get probabilities for such compound results as

"the first victim survives"

—represented by a subset (call it A) in Fig. 3-8, and

"the second victim dies"

—represented by a subset (call it B) in Fig. 3-9. Since the subsets A and B refer to separate victims, their probabilities should satisfy the intuitive criterion for independence.

Let's check. In Fig. 3-8, I calculated

$$P(A) = \frac{8}{27} + \frac{4}{27} + \frac{4}{27} + \frac{2}{27} = \frac{18}{27} = \frac{2}{3}$$ (8)

without regard to B. Now suppose someone tells us that the second victim has died. To recalculate the probability that the first victim will survive, given this new information, we must restrict ourselves to a *new list* of patterns all having a symbol "*d*" in second position —namely the subset B, which I've recorded again (in green) in Fig. 3-14a. In that new list the result "the 1st victim survives" is represented by the subset $A \cap B$ ("the 1st victim survives *and* the 2nd victim dies").

To calculate the probability for the subset $A \cap B$ *relative to the new list B* we must also assign *new elementary probabilities* for outcomes in B—which should add to 1. How can we do so while still preserving

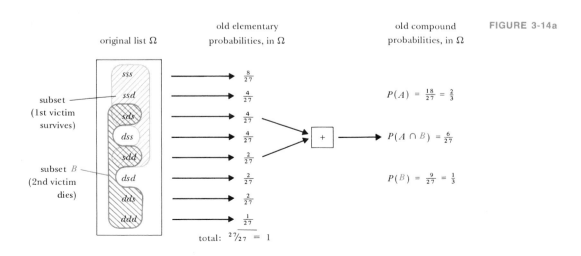

FIGURE 3-14a

original list Ω — old elementary probabilities, in Ω — old compound probabilities, in Ω

subset (1st victim survives)

subset B (2nd victim dies)

sss $\frac{8}{27}$

ssd $\frac{4}{27}$

sds $\frac{4}{27}$

dss $\frac{4}{27}$

sdd $\frac{2}{27}$

dsd $\frac{2}{27}$

dds $\frac{2}{27}$

ddd $\frac{1}{27}$

total: $\frac{27}{27} = 1$

$P(A) = \frac{18}{27} = \frac{2}{3}$

$P(A \cap B) = \frac{6}{27}$

$P(B) = \frac{9}{27} = \frac{1}{3}$

the relative weights of outcomes as represented by the old elementary probabilities? Just form ratios with denominator $P(B) = 9/27$, as in Fig. 3-14b. The ratios will add to $P(B)/P(B) = 1$. Finally, the new compound probability for $A \cap B$ should be the sum of the new elementary probabilities for the outcomes in $A \cap B$, namely

$$\frac{4/27}{P(B)} + \frac{2/27}{P(B)} = \frac{4/27 + 2/27}{P(B)} = \frac{P(A \cap B)}{P(B)} = \frac{6/27}{9/27} = \frac{2}{3}. \tag{9}$$

Behold: the same value as for $P(A)$ in (8), calculated there without regard to B. That is, (8) and (9) together say that

$$P(A) = \frac{P(A \cap B)}{P(B)}.$$

or equivalently,

$$P(A \cap B) = P(A)P(B).$$

The quantitative ("product") criterion for independence holds again!

FIGURE 3-14b

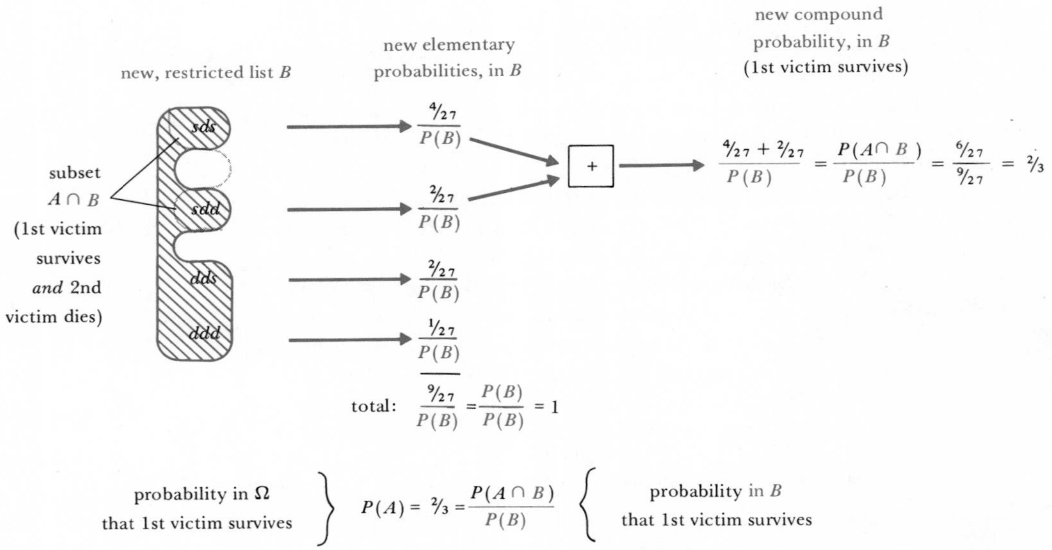

subset
$A \cap B$
(1st victim
survives
and 2nd
victim dies)

new, restricted list B

new elementary
probabilities, in B

new compound
probability, in B
(1st victim survives)

$\dfrac{4/27}{P(B)}$

$\dfrac{2/27}{P(B)}$

$\dfrac{2/27}{P(B)}$

$\dfrac{1/27}{P(B)}$

$+$

$\dfrac{4/27 + 2/27}{P(B)} = \dfrac{P(A \cap B)}{P(B)} = \dfrac{6/27}{9/27} = 2/3$

total: $\dfrac{9/27}{P(B)} = \dfrac{P(B)}{P(B)} = 1$

probability in Ω
that 1st victim survives $\Big\}$ $P(A) = 2/3 = \dfrac{P(A \cap B)}{P(B)}$ $\Big\{$ probability in B
that 1st victim survives

*3.6 PROBLEMS INVOLVING INDEPENDENCE

1. Here are the possible sibling sex patterns for a family with two children:

   $\begin{matrix} bb & bg \\ gb & gg \end{matrix}$ (b = boy, g = girl, first born on the left).

   For a simple model suppose all the patterns are equally likely.
   (a) *Sample:* What's the probability that one child is a girl if it's *known* that (at least) one is a boy?

Answer: $\frac{2}{3}$. The given information excludes gg, leaving a restricted list of three equally likely patterns, two having girls.

(b) What's the probability that the second born is a boy?

(c) What's the probability that the second born is a boy if it's *known* that the first born is a boy?

(d) Are the results "first born is a boy" and "second born is a boy" *independent* according to the intuitive criterion of Sec. 3.5?

2. If male births were twice as likely as female births—so that a pattern such as bg were twice as likely as gg—how would this affect independence between the sexes of first born and second born siblings (part (d) of Problem 1)?

3. Indicate the possible sibling sex patterns for a family with three children, and suppose that they are all equally likely. Let A, B, and C denote subsets representing, respectively, the results "first born is a boy," "second born is a boy," and "third born is a boy."

(a) Are A and C independent? A' and C?

(b) Are $A \cup B$ and C independent? $A \cap B$ and C?

(c) How is the probability $P(A \cap B \cap C)$ related to $P(A)$, $P(B)$, and $P(C)$?

4. Can two mutually exclusive subsets S and T, with $P(S) > 0$ and $P(T) > 0$, ever be independent?

*5. If subsets S and T are independent in some model—that is, $P(S \cap T) = P(S)P(T)$—must it follow that S' and T are independent? (Note that $P(T) = P(S \cap T) + P(S' \cap T)$, since $S \cap T$ and $S' \cap T$ are mutually exclusive and have T as their union.)

6. An *intuitive criterion* for the "mutual independence" of three results: *any one of the results should be independent of any logical combination of the other two*. In terms of subsets A, B, and C: C should be independent not only of A and of B but also of A', B', $A \cup B$, $A \cap B$, $A' \cup B$, and so on.

(a) Show that in quantitative terms the criterion implies that

$$P(A \cap B \cap C) = P(A)P(B)P(C).$$

*(b) Show that the criterion implies even more: namely, that

$$P(\tilde{A} \cap \tilde{B} \cap \tilde{C}) = P(\tilde{A})P(\tilde{B})P(\tilde{C})$$

for any choice of $\tilde{A} = A$ or A', $\tilde{B} = B$ or B', and $\tilde{C} = C$ or C'.

*(c) Conversely: given three subsets A, B, and C for which all $2 \times 2 \times 2 = 8$ equalities in (b) are known to hold, would you say that A, B, and C are "mutually independent" according to the above intuitive criteria?

7. Suppose that a test consists of five true-false questions.

(a) What is the probability of answering all questions correctly by flipping a "true" coin to decide each answer independently?

(b) What is the probability of answering at least 4 correctly?

8. *Sample:* Suppose that at a carnival booth, a child is given three tries to win a prize. Each try consists of his blindfoldedly drawing a ball from a box containing five balls — four green and one red. Red wins. Balls are replaced between tries.
   (a) What are the chances that the child will fail in any one try? *Answer:* $\frac{4}{5}$.
   (b) What are the chances that a child will go away completely frustrated? *Answer:* Complete frustration means (i) failure on the first try *and* (ii) failure on the second try (independently of the first), *and* (iii) failure on the third try independently of the first and the second. So $P(A \cap B \cap C) = P(A)P(B)P(C) = (\frac{4}{5})^3$.

9. A bag contains 4 black marbles, 3 red marbles, and 7 white marbles. If three marbles are drawn in succession, each marble being replaced before the next one is drawn, what is the probability that the first marble is black, the second one red, and the third white?

10. Suppose that with a given amount of money for development, a country could either build one spaceship which will have probability 0.8 of getting to a given planet and back, or could build two spaceships each with probability 0.5 for round-trip success — the second to be used as a rescue ship in case the first fails. Which plan is safer? (Compare probabilities for total failure.)

11. If you send three independent messages for help with respective probabilities of 0.2, 0.4, and 0.7 for getting through, what is the probability
   (a) that none get through?
   (b) that at least one gets through?
   (c) that at least two get through?

12. Suppose that we have a loaded coin which falls heads 2 times out of 3, and a loaded die which favors all faces equally except for the one with 6 points — which it favors twice as much as any one of the others. Describe a list of outcomes for the joint experiment of tossing the coin once and the die once. Assign appropriate elementary probabilities by reasoning about the relative likelihood of the outcomes as was done for the disease with 2-to-1 chances of survival in Sec. 3.2.
   (a) Find the probability of the following subsets:
      A: the coin reads heads,
      B: the die reads "5,"
      C: the die reads at least 3 points,
      $A \cap C$: the coin reads heads *and* the die reads at least 3 points.
   (b) Are A and C independent?
   *(c) Do the elementary probabilities which you assigned for the joint experiment happen to be the products of numbers which you might assign for separate experiments with the

coin and the die individually? For example:

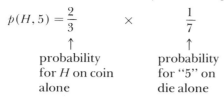

$$p(H, 5) = \frac{2}{3} \qquad \times \qquad \frac{1}{7}$$

probability   probability
for H on coin   for "5" on
alone   die alone

   If so, why?

*13. Which is safer, a two motor or a four motor plane? Set up a model for each kind of plane assuming:

(a) Motors are independent, and each has the same probability x for failure.

(b) A two-motor plane can fly on one motor.

(c) A four-motor plane can fly on any two or more motors, but not on less.

   Find how each model depends on the probability x of failure for a single motor.

14. Imagine throwing two dice, one red and one green; and consider the following three possible results:

(i) The red die shows an odd number.

(ii) The green die shows an odd number.

(iii) The sum of the numbers on the two dice is odd.

(a) Are these results independent two-by-two?

(b) Are these results "mutually independent" of each other according to the intuitive criterion of Problem 6?

Problems 15 and 16 refer to Sec. 3.3 on Mendel's laws.

*15. Assume eye-color of successive offspring in a family to be independent. If one parent has blue eyes and one hybrid blue-brown eyes, what is the probability of two brown-eyed children? Of two blue-eyed children? Of one brown-eyed and one blue-eyed child?

**16. Suppose that a child has brown eyes, both of its parents have brown eyes, and both of its grandmothers have blue eyes. What is the probability that the child carries a blue-eyed gene?

3.7 SUMMARY OF CHAPTER 3

At least two functions are basic to analyzing a situation involving chance and a finite number of outcomes: one assigns "elementary probabilities" (p), the other assigns "compound probabilities" (P). They arise through the following steps (see Sec. 3.1):

1. Write a list—call it Ω— of all *possible outcomes*.

2. To each possible outcome ω in Ω assign an *elementary probability* $p(\omega)$. Choose the $p(\omega)$'s so that the following standardizations hold:

(i) $p(\omega) \geqslant 0$ for all ω in Ω,

(ii) the sum of the $p(\omega)$'s for all ω's in Ω equals 1.

3. Consider *subsets* S of Ω as representing "compound results."

4. To each subset S in Ω assign a *probability* P(S) by the *rule*

$$P(S) = \text{the sum of the } p(\omega)\text{'s for all } \omega\text{'s in } S. \tag{1}$$

PROPERTIES FOLLOWING FROM (1):

(i) $P(\Omega) = 1$, $P(\text{empty set}) = 0$.

(ii) $0 \leq P(S) \leq 1$ for any subset S of Ω.

(iii) $P(S) \leq P(T)$ if S is contained in T.

(iv) *If* S and T are *mutually exclusive* subsets of Ω, that is, if $S \cap T$ is empty, then

$$P(S \cup T) = P(S) + P(T). \tag{2}$$

(v) $P(S') = 1 - P(S)$ for any subset S and its complement S' (Problem 20 of Sec. 3.4).

REMARK. If Ω has n possible outcomes ω and $p(\omega) = 1/n$ for each ω, and if a subset S of Ω contains k outcomes ($0 \leq k \leq n$), then

$$P(S) = \frac{k}{n} \tag{3}$$

(Sec. 3.1).

DEFINITION. (Sec. 3.5). Call two subsets S and T of Ω *independent* if

$$P(S \cap T) = P(S) \cdot P(T). \tag{4}$$

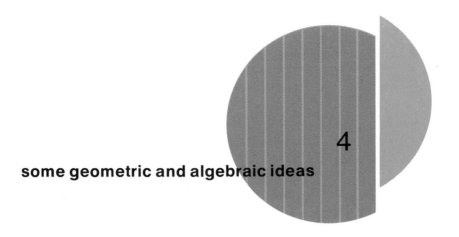

4

some geometric and algebraic ideas

For newcomers, and for those who would like a review, I'll discuss "coordinates" and an algebraic description of lines and slopes — topics helpful for analyzing functions. Also, other applications: how to calculate probabilities of random encounter, and how 20-dimensional space enters the public schools. Finally, a few words about axioms.

4.1 ANALYTIC GEOMETRY

The separate studies of geometry and algebra can be brought together to their mutual advantage. For example, look at Fig. 4-1 for a hybrid geometric-algebraic proof of the "Pythagorean theorem" by addition of areas.

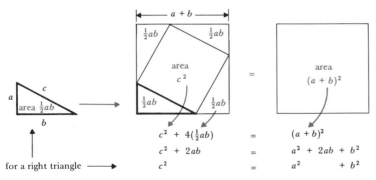

FIGURE 4-1

$$c^2 + 4(\tfrac{1}{2}ab) = (a + b)^2$$
$$c^2 + 2ab = a^2 + 2ab + b^2$$
$$c^2 = a^2 + b^2$$

For a systematic connection between points and numbers, an old scheme is to choose two points on a line, and label one "0" and the other "1". Then with compass and straight edge lay off equal lengths to get new points deserving the labels (or "coordinates") 2, 3, −1, and so on, as in Fig. 4-2. Divide the segments of unit length into equal parts to determine points deserving rational numbers as labels, $\tfrac{1}{2}$, $\tfrac{1}{3}$, etc. Next, pick an irrational number; for example, $\sqrt[3]{\pi}$. Which point deserves $\sqrt[3]{\pi}$ as its label? Descartes and other originators of this scheme thought that — in principle — one can always determine such a point by making suitable approximations.

FIGURE 4-2

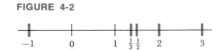

They had no doubts that the scheme leads to a *one-to-one* correspondence between the set of *all* real numbers and the set of *all* points on the line.

Do you share their confidence? I'll return to this question in later sections; meanwhile, let's see what we can do *assuming* we can get such a correspondence.

By its very construction, the correspondence will give us an algebraic hold on the notion of distance: if a point P corresponds to a real number x, then the *distance* between the origin and P should be

$$|OP| = \left\{ \begin{array}{ll} x \text{ units} & \text{if } x \geqslant 0 \\ -x \text{ units} & \text{if } x < 0 \end{array} \right\} = \sqrt{x^2} \text{ units} \tag{1}$$

You may recall the number in (1) as the *absolute value* $|x|$ of x, for any real number x. (See Appendix A for a review of absolute values.)

More generally, if points P and Q correspond to numbers a and b, then the number of units between P and Q should be the same as the number of units between the two values $0 = a - a$ and $x = b - a$, got from the original numbers by a simultaneous "shift" of a units. See Fig. 4-3.

FIGURE 4-3

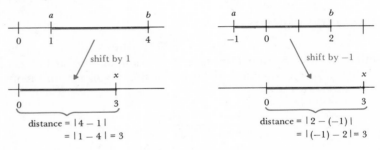

shift by 1

distance = $|4 - 1|$
= $|1 - 4| = 3$

shift by -1

distance = $|2 - (-1)|$
= $|(-1) - 2| = 3$

So let's take the *distance between P and Q* to be the same as that between 0 and x; namely $|x| = |b - a|$:

$$|PQ| = |b - a| \tag{2}$$

(P will be to the left of Q if, and only if, $a < b$. But in any case, the absolute value $|b - a| = |a - b|$ should measure distance properly.)

For future use, let's note here that we can interpret an inequality of the form

$$|x| \leqslant d \tag{3}$$

FIGURE 4-4

as saying that the point P with label x must lie within d units from the origin. In other words, P must lie somewhere in a symmetric *interval* of radius d about the origin—the segment colored green in Fig. 4-4. Algebraically, the inequality $|x| \leqslant d$ is equivalent to two simultaneous inequalities on x:

$$-d \leqslant x \quad \text{and} \quad x \leqslant d, \tag{4}$$

which are commonly written together as

$$-d \leqslant x \leqslant d. \tag{5}$$

Similarly, we can interpret an inequality of the form

$$|x-a| \leq d \tag{6}$$

as saying that the point P with label x must lie somewhere in a symmetric interval of radius d about the point with label a—the segment colored green in Fig. 4-5. And algebraically the inequality $|x-a| \leq d$ is equivalent to two simultaneous inequalities

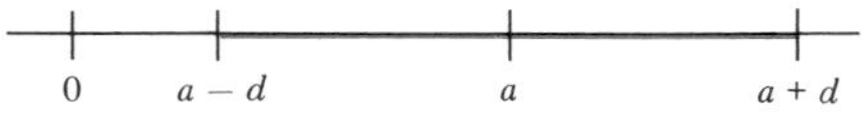

$$-d \leq x-a \quad \text{and} \quad x-a \leq d. \tag{7}$$

In turn, adding a to all sides, we can write these as

$$a-d \leq x \quad \text{and} \quad x \leq a+d, \tag{8}$$

or together as

$$a-d \leq x \leq a+d. \tag{9}$$

NOTATION. For $a < b$, let's call the set of all numbers x satisfying the inequality $a \leq x \leq b$ a *closed interval*—"closed" because it contains its end points a and b. Let's denote it by the symbol $[a, b]$. We can call the set of all x satisfying $a < x < b$ an *open interval*, and denote it by $\langle a, b \rangle$.

Now, on to

4.2 TWO DIMENSIONS, THE HOME OF GRAPHS AND LINES

Here is the simplest of many ways to label points in the plane: Draw two perpendicular lines—an "x axis" and a "y axis"—and label the points of each by real numbers, as in Fig. 4-6. From any given point P in the plane, drop arrows perpendicular to the axes, and record the real numbers where they hit, x_0 and y_0. To avoid confusion, let's always write the x-axis label on the left and the y-axis label on the right in a symbol (x_0, y_0)—commonly called an *ordered pair*. The idea is to use such "ordered pairs" as handy algebraic labels for points in the plane. (Let's write "$P = (x_0, y_0)$".) Starting with a given ordered pair (x_0, y_0) one can always follow arrows backwards, as in Fig. 4-6, to arrive at a unique point P deserving the label (x_0, y_0). So there is a *one-to-one correspondence* between the set

FIGURE 4-5

FIGURE 4-6

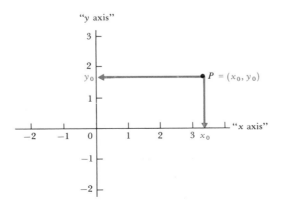

FIGURE 4-7

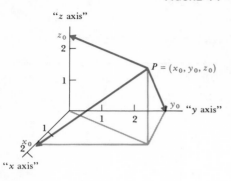

of all possible ordered pairs (x, y) of real numbers and the set of all points in the plane.

Similarly, we could describe points in 3-dimensional space by "ordered triples" (x_0, y_0, z_0) of real numbers, as in Fig. 4-7.

Distance in two dimensions. Can we get an algebraic hold on the distance between two points $P_1 = (x_1, y_1)$ and $P_2 = (x_2, y_2)$ purely in terms of their coordinates? For a special case, see Fig. 4-8. The green construction lines there enclose a (shaded) right triangle with vertex Q; and the problem is to find the length of its hypotenuse $|P_1 P_2|$. The Pythagorean theorem serves nicely here:

$$|P_1 P_2|^2 = |P_1 Q|^2 + |Q P_2|^2$$
$$= (x_2 - x_1)^2 + (y_2 - y_1)^2, \tag{1}$$

or

FIGURE 4-8

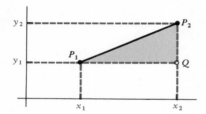

$$|P_1 P_2| = \sqrt{(x_2 - x_1)^2 + (y_2 - y_1)^2}. \tag{2}$$

Behold: a purely algebraic formula for a most basic geometric notion! Check to see that it works well regardless of the signs of the coordinates — as in Fig. 4-9, for example.

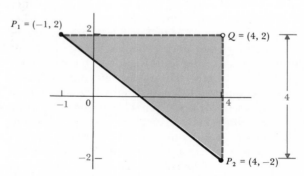

FIGURE 4-9 $|P_1 P_2| = \sqrt{[4 - (-1)]^2 + [(-2) - 2]^2} = \sqrt{5^2 + 4^2} = \sqrt{41}$

Can we achieve a similar formula for 3-dimensional space? Do problem 15 of Sec. 4.3.

Circles. As a first instance of work with labels and the distance formula, let's try to capture the definition of a circle algebraically. Geometrically, a circle with center C and radius r is the set of all points P which lie at a distance r from C. Suppose C has coordinates (a, b), and represent an arbitrary point P by (x, y). Isn't the condition on distance precisely that

$$|CP| = \sqrt{(x - a)^2 + (y - b)^2} = r?$$

That is, x and y represent coordinates of a point on the circle if — and only if — they satisfy the (squared) equation

$$(x-a)^2 + (y-b)^2 = r^2. \tag{3}$$

EXAMPLE 1. Does the point $(2, 2)$ lie on the circle with center $(3, 0)$ and radius 1? Here $a = 3$, $b = 0$, $r = 1$. Substitute $x = 2$ and $y = 2$ in (3) to see whether the equation is satisfied:

$$(2-3)^2 + (2-0)^2 = 1^2 + 2^2 = 5 \neq 1^2.$$

It isn't; so $(2, 2)$ does not lie on the circle.

Now check yourself with some

4.3 PROBLEMS ON LABELING

1. Indicate, by shading on a straight line, all points whose real number labels x satisfy the following conditions:
   (a) *Sample:* $-1 < x \leq 2$.

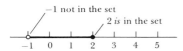

   (b) $|x| = 2$
   (c) x is in the interval $[-1, 3]$
   (d) x is in the interval $\langle 2, 4 \rangle$
   (e) $|x| > 0$
   (f) $|x-3| \leq 1$
   (g) $|x-1| > 2$
   (h) $|x+1| \leq 3$
   (i) $|x-1| = |x-5|$
   (j) $|x^2 - 1| = 3$
2. Write an algebraic statement describing each of the following sets:
   (a) *Sample:* The set of points on the number line whose distance from the origin is less than three units.
       Answer: The set of all real numbers x satisfying $|x| < 3$.
   (b) The set of points on the number line whose distance from the origin is at least 4.
   (c) The set of points on the number line whose distance from the point with label 2 is at most one unit.
   (d) The set of points on the number line whose distance from the point with label -2 is at least 1 and at most 3.
3. Replace the following double inequalities by equivalent single inequalities using absolute values.
   (a) *Sample:* $1 \leq x \leq 5$.
       Answer: $|x-3| \leq 2$.
   (b) $-2 < x < 2$
   (c) $-5 < x < -3$
   (d) $-3 \leq x \leq 1$

(e) $x < -2$ or $x > 2$

(f) $x < 0$ or $x > 4$

(g) $-1 \leqslant x \leqslant 0$

*(h) $c \leqslant x \leqslant d$ where c and d are fixed numbers, $c < d$.

4. Show that the midpoint of an interval $[a, b]$ is the point with label $c = \frac{1}{2}(a+b)$. [*Hint*: Check $|c-a|$ and $|b-c|$.]

5. Draw a set of coordinate axes and plot each of the following points:

$(-7, 0)$, $(0, -7)$, $(2, 5)$, $(-2, 5)$, $(-5, 2)$, $(-2, -5)$, $(0, 7)$, $(7, 0)$, $(5, -2)$, $(-5, -2)$.

6. Compute the distances between the following pairs of points in the plane:

(a) *Sample:* $(1, 2)$ and $(4, -2)$.

Answer:

$$\text{Distance} = \sqrt{(1-4)^2 + (2-(-2))^2}$$
$$= \sqrt{9+16} = \sqrt{25}$$
$$= 5.$$

(b) $(-1, -3)$ and $(2, 2)$

(c) $(4, 9)$ and $(-2, 1)$

(d) $(-1, -3)$ and $(2, -1)$

(e) $(1, 2)$ and $(1, -7)$

7. For each of the cases below draw a set of coordinate axes.

(a) Plot the given point P. Then

(b) Plot point Q such that the segment PQ is perpendicular to the x axis and is bisected by it. (The points P and Q are said to be *symmetric about the x axis.*)

(c) Plot a point R such that the segment PR is perpendicular to the y axis and is bisected by it. (The points P and R are said to be *symmetric about the y axis.*)

(d) Plot a point S such that the segment PS has the origin as its midpoint. (The points P and S are said to be *symmetric about the origin.*)

(i) *Sample:* $P = (2, -1)$.

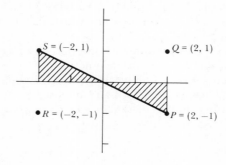

Answer: Note that the coordinates of S are found by considering the two shaded *congruent* triangles.

    (ii) $P = (-1, 2)$
   (iii) $P = (2, 0)$
   (iv) $P = (0, -1)$
    (v) $P = (-2, -1)$
   (vi) $P = (a, b)$ where a and b are positive.

*8. What symmetry statement, if any, can be made about the pairs of points $(2, -1)$ and $(-1, 2)$; $(2, 0)$ and $(0, 2)$; $(2, 3)$ and $(3, 2)$; $(-3, -1)$ and $(-1, -3)$; and in general (a, b) and (b, a)? [*Hint*: Plot all the points on the same coordinate axes. Draw the line segment joining the two points in each pair. Is there any common line or point about which all these pairs are symmetric?]

*9. Find the coordinates of the midpoint Q of the line segment from $P_1 = (x_1, y_1)$ to $P_2 = (x_2, y_2)$. Use the figure below, congruent triangles, and the result of Problem 4.

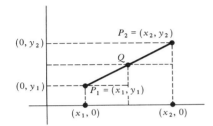

10. Give equations for the following circles:
   (a) *Sample:* Center $(-2, 0)$, containing the point $(1, 0)$.
      Answer: The distance from $(-2, 0)$ to $(1, 0)$ is 3. Thus, the radius of the circle is 3 and an equation for the circle is

$$(x + 2)^2 + y^2 = 9.$$

   (b) Center $(3, 4)$, radius 2.
   (c) Center $(-3, -3)$, containing the point $(3, 5)$.

11. Consider the circle with center $(-1, 2)$ and radius 4. Determine whether each of the following points lies on, inside or outside this circle. [*Note*: A point lies inside, if its distance from the center is less than the radius; outside, if its distance from the center is greater than the radius.]
   (a) $(3, 2)$
   (b) $(2, 5)$
   (c) $(-3, 5)$

12. At what points does the circle $(x + 1)^2 + (y - 2)^2 = 16$ intersect the x axis? the y axis?

13. Determine the centers and radii of the following circles:
   (a) *Sample:* $x^2 + y^2 + 2x + 2y = 0$.
      Complete the squares: $x^2 + 2x + 1 + y^2 + 2y + 1 = 2$
$$(x + 1)^2 + (y + 1)^2 = 2$$
      Thus, the center is $(-1, -1)$ and the radius is $\sqrt{2}$.
   (b) $x^2 + y^2 + 4x - 2y = 11$.
   (c) $x^2 + y^2 - 2y = 8$.

*14. Does every equation of the form $x^2+Ax+y^2+By+C=0$ where A, B, and C are fixed numbers, represent a circle? In particular, look at the equations:

(a) $x^2+y^2+4x-2y+14=0$

(b) $x^2+y^2+4x-2y+5=0$

Are there points (x,y) in the plane whose coordinates satisfy either of these equations?

*15. Let's try to extend the distance formula from two-dimensional to three-dimensionsl space:

(a) Project the points P_1 and P_2 into the xy plane (see figure) to obtain the points R_1 and R_2. What is the distance $|R_1R_2|$ in the xy plane?

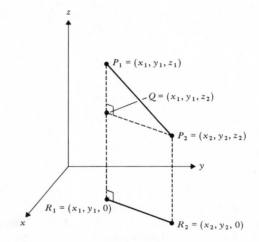

(b) A horizontal plane through P_2 will cut the vertical segment P_1R_1 at the point Q. Note that $|QP_2|=|R_1R_2|$. What is $|P_1Q|$ in terms of coordinates?

(c) Can you use the Pythagorean theorem for the right triangle P_1QP_2 to find the distance $|P_1P_2|$?

4.4 LINES

FIGURE 4-10

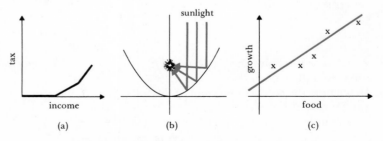

(a)   (b)   (c)

An algebraic hold on lines will be very helpful for studying functions. Let's look first at a (nonvertical) line which passes through the origin

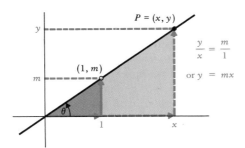

FIGURE 4-11

of a coordinate system, as in Fig. 4-11. (Here m is the altitude corresponding to $x = 1$.) Because the indicated triangles are similar, a point $P = (x, y)$ will be on the line if — and only if —

$$\frac{y}{x} = \frac{m}{1} \qquad (x \neq 0) \tag{1}$$

or

$$y = mx \tag{2}$$

(Equation (2) permits $x = 0$, $y = 0$ also.) In Fig. 4-11 I sketched the case $m > 0$, $x > 0$. For other cases — all leading to the same equation $y = mx$ — see Fig. 4-12, where I've indicated lengths of segments by

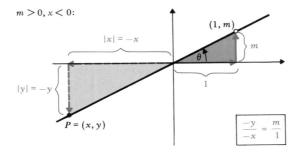

FIGURE 4-12

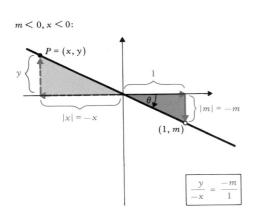

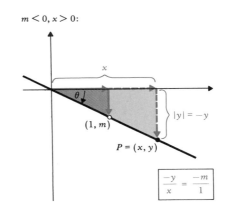

FIGURE **4-13**

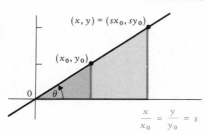

$$\frac{x}{x_0} = \frac{y}{y_0} = s$$

$$x = sx_0, \; y = sy_0$$

absolute values. In all these cases, the quantity m indicates the amount of vertical rise (or fall if $m < 0$) along the line per *unit* change in horizontal position—and is commonly called the *slope* of the line. (In trigonometric terms, $m = \tan\theta$, where θ is the angle which the line makes with the horizontal axis, as in Fig. 4-11.) The product mx is the change in altitude corresponding to x units of change in horizontal position. (See the green arrows in Figs. 4-11 and 4-12.)

Note also from Fig. 4-13 that, given any one point $(x_0, y_0) \neq (0, 0)$ on the line, we can express all others in the form (sx_0, sy_0) if we let s take on all real values—again because the triangles are similar.

Next, examine a nonvertical line which intersects the y axis at altitude b, as in Fig. 4-14. With m as indicated, a point $P = (x, y)$ will lie on the line if—and only if—its altitude y is the sum of the altitude b plus the change in altitude mx:

FIGURE **4-14**

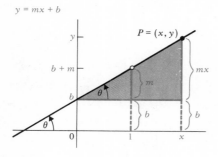

$$y = mx + b, \tag{3}$$

(no matter what the algebraic signs of mx and b). Thus we can completely describe a nonvertical line algebraically by an equation—just as for a circle.

Note that we can determine the slope m via any two points $P_1 = (x_1, y_1)$ and $P_2 = (x_2, y_2)$ on the line; namely, as a *difference ratio*

$$m = \frac{y_2 - y_1}{x_2 - x_1}. \tag{4}$$

Geometrically this follows again from the similarity of triangles, such as in Fig. 4-15. To see (4) algebraically, just write the conditions that P_1 and P_2 do lie on the line; namely,

$$y_1 = mx_1 + b \tag{5}$$
$$y_2 = mx_2 + b. \tag{6}$$

FIGURE **4-15**

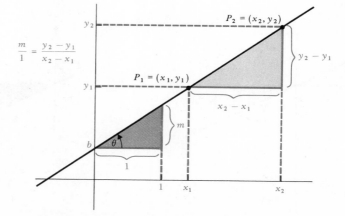

$$\frac{m}{1} = \frac{y_2 - y_1}{x_2 - x_1}$$

Then subtract (5) from (6) and divide by $x_2 - x_1$.

It doesn't matter which coordinates appear first in a difference ratio as long as the order is the same in both numerator and denominator, since

$$\frac{y_1 - y_2}{x_1 - x_2} = \frac{-(y_2 - y_1)}{-(x_2 - x_1)} = \frac{y_2 - y_1}{x_2 - x_1}.$$

For simplicity, I've sketched only lines with $m > 0$ and $b \geqslant 0$ in Fig. 4-14 and 4-15. If you haven't done so anywhere before, I invite you to sketch other cases and see that the equation $y = mx + b$ describes all nonvertical lines. Do Problem 1 of Sec. 4.6.

Horizontal lines are the special case $m = 0$. Then $y = mx + b$ reads

$$y = b \tag{7}$$

with no restriction on x.

Vertical lines. We can describe a vertical line (see Fig. 4-16) by a similar equation

$$x = a \tag{8}$$

with no restriction on y.

Note finally that all the above equations for lines are special cases of the form

$$Ax + By + C = 0. \tag{9}$$

For this reason, the left-hand side is called the "general linear expression" in x and y.

FIGURE 4-16

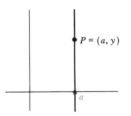

EXAMPLE 1. We can describe the line with slope $m = -2$ and passing through the point $(0, 3)$ algebraically as the set of all points whose coordinates (x, y) satisfy the equation

$$y = -2x + 3.$$

In particular, the point $(1, 1)$ lies on this line, and the point $(1, 2)$ doesn't, since $1 = -2 \cdot 1 + 3$ and $2 \neq -2 \cdot 1 + 3$.

EXAMPLE 2. Find an equation describing the line which passes through the points $P = (1, 2)$ and $Q = (4, 3)$. P and Q determine the difference quotient

$$\frac{y_2 - y_1}{x_2 - x_1} = \frac{3 - 2}{4 - 1} = \frac{1}{3} = m.$$

So the line in question is describable by an equation of the form

$$y = \tfrac{1}{3}x + b.$$

To determine b, substitute the coordinates of P

$$2 = \frac{1}{3} \cdot 1 + b$$

whence $b = 5/3$. Thus the equation is

$$y = \frac{1}{3}x + \frac{5}{3}. \tag{10}$$

EXAMPLE 3. Describe all points whose coordinates (x, y) satisfy the relationship

$$3x + 2y = 8 \qquad \text{where } 0 \leqslant x \leqslant 1. \tag{11}$$

Divide the equation through by 2 and rearrange as

$$y = -\frac{3}{2}x + 4. \tag{12}$$

By the reasoning above, the ordered pairs (x, y) satisfying (11) must lie on a line with slope $m = -3/2$ and passing through the point $(0, 4)$. I've sketched such a line in Fig. 4-17 by proceeding 2 units to the right from $(0, 4)$ while dropping 3 units of altitude, to assure a slope of $-3/2$. The dark segment indicates the set of points on the line which satisfy the added restriction $0 \leqslant x \leqslant 1$.

FIGURE 4-17

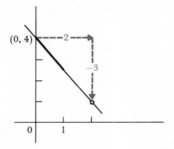

4.5 MORE CONNECTIONS BETWEEN GEOMETRY AND ALGEBRA

How can we check algebraically whether two lines are *parallel*? They must have the same slope m, because triangles as in Fig. 4-18 are similar. Hence the equations for the lines can differ only in the altitude constant b. And how does *perpendicularity* show up algebraically? Look at two perpendicular lines through the origin, with slopes m_1 and m_2 as in Fig. 4-19. Together with the vertical line $x = 1$, they

FIGURE 4-18

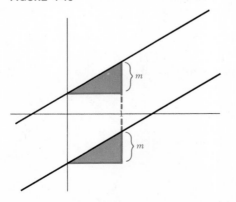

FIGURE 4-19

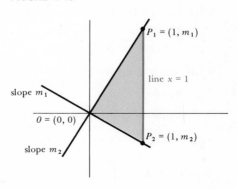

cut out a right triangle, for which

$$|P_1P_2|^2 = |OP_1|^2 + |OP_2|^2. \tag{1}$$

In terms of coordinates this reads

$$(m_2 - m_1)^2 = [1^2 + m_1{}^2] + [1^2 + m_2{}^2]. \tag{2}$$

Multiply out the left-hand side of (2) and cancel against the right-hand side to get simply

$$m_1 m_2 = -1. \tag{3}$$

Conversely, given (3) we could work backwards to (1), to show that the lines have to be perpendicular. And if our original lines didn't meet in the origin, we could pick a parallel pair which did. Conclusion: the algebraic relationship $m_1 m_2 = -1$ characterizes perpendicularity.

Here are two examples of geometry clarifying algebra:

EXAMPLE 1. How many "simultaneous solutions" (x_0, y_0) are there for the system of equations

$$\begin{aligned} 2x - 5y &= 7 \\ x + 3y &= 5. \end{aligned} \tag{4}$$

Rewrite the equations as

$$\begin{aligned} y &= \frac{2}{5}x - \frac{7}{5} \\ y &= -\frac{1}{3}x + \frac{5}{3}. \end{aligned} \tag{5}$$

A "simultaneous solution" of (4) or (5) is a specific pair of numbers (x_0, y_0) which satisfy both equations. Geometrically it corresponds to a point which lies on the line described by each of the equations in (5). Since $2/5 \neq -1/3$ these lines cannot be parallel; hence they intersect in *one* point. So there is one, and only one, simultaneous solution for the system (4). (We can find it by "eliminating" y in (5) to get $11x_0 = 46$, or $x_0 = 46/11$; and then $y_0 = 15/55$.)

EXAMPLE 2. The system of equations

$$\begin{aligned} 2x - 5y &= 7 \\ -4x + 10y &= 5 \end{aligned} \tag{6}$$

can have no "simultaneous solution" because, rewritten as

$$\begin{aligned} y &= \frac{2}{5}x - \frac{7}{5} \\ y &= \frac{2}{5}x + \frac{1}{2}, \end{aligned} \tag{7}$$

it describes two lines which have the same slope $m = 2/5$ and hence are parallel. The lines can't be identical since they intersect the vertical axis at different altitudes $-7/5$ and $1/2$. Two parallel lines can't pass through a common point $P = (x, y)$.

FIGURE 4-20

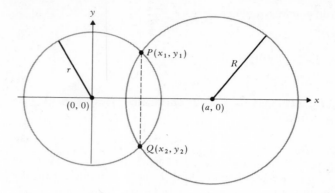

Finally, here is another example of algebra simplifying geometry.

EXAMPLE 3. Let's show that the line through the points of intersection of two circles is perpendicular to the line through the centers of the circles. It simplifies matters to take the horizontal coordinated axis as the line through the centers and to locate the origin $(0, 0)$ at one of the centers—as in Fig. 4-20. We must then show that the points of intersection, $P = (x_1, y_1)$ and $Q = (x_2, y_2)$ lie on a *vertical* line; that is, have the same x coordinate, $x_1 = x_2$.

Now, each point of intersection lies on both circles. Hence, its coordinates must simultaneously satisfy two equations:

$$x^2 + y^2 = r^2 \tag{8}$$

and

$$(x - a)^2 + y^2 = R^2. \tag{9}$$

Subtract (8) from (9) to get

$$-2ax + a^2 = R^2 - r^2$$

or

$$x = \frac{R^2 - r^2 - a^2}{-2a} \tag{10}$$

as the *unique* value for the x coordinate of any simultaneous solution. Thus, $x_1 = x_2$: P and Q do lie on the same vertical line, perpendicular to the axis of centers.

4.6 PROBLEMS ON LINES AND ANALYTIC GEOMETRY

1. For each of the cases below, draw a coordinate system. Then:
   (i) Locate the point $(0, b)$ and draw a line through it having slope m.
   (ii) Pick several arbitrary points $P = (x, y)$ on the line you drew and (using arrows) check that altitudes add (or cancel) correctly to give $y = mx + b$.

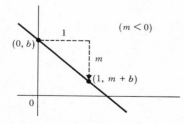

(a) *Sample:* $b = 2$, $m = -\frac{2}{3}$.

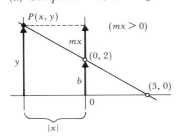 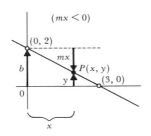 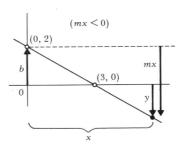

(b) $b = -4$, $m = 2$.
(c) $b = -3$, $m = -\frac{1}{2}$.
2. Find the slope of the line passing through each of the following
pairs of points:
(a) $(2, 3)$ and $(1, 2)$
(b) $(2, 3)$ and $(-1, 1)$
(c) $(-8, 5)$ and $(0, 3)$
3. Determine an equation for each of the following lines:
(a) *Sample:* The line passing through the point $(0, 4)$ and having
slope 3.
Answer: $y = 3x + 4$.
(b) *Sample:* The line through the point $(0, 4)$, perpendicular to
the line $y = \frac{1}{2}x + 3$.
Answer: The required line must have slope -2 and thus
equation $y = -2x + 4$.
(c) The line with slope 3 through the point $(1, 1)$.
(d) The line parallel to the line $y = -\frac{2}{3}x + 1$ and through the
point $(2, 1)$.
(e) The vertical line through $(-5, 6)$.
(f) The horizontal line through $(-5, 6)$.
(g) The line through the points $(1, 1)$ and $(2, 3)$.
(h) The line through the points $(-1, -3)$ and $(-2, 1)$.
(i) The line parallel to $y = 2x - 3$ through the origin.
(j) The line perpendicular to $y = 2x - 3$ through the origin.
4. Which of the lines in Problem 3 are rising? Which are falling?
5. Indicate, by shading, the region in the plane consisting of all
points (x, y) satisfying the given inequalities.
(a) *Sample:* $2 < x < 5$ and $y < x$. See the figure.
(b) $2 < x < 5$ *and* $0 < y \leqslant 4$
(c) $y \leqslant 1$
(d) $x \geqslant 0$
(e) $x < y$
(f) $xy = 0$

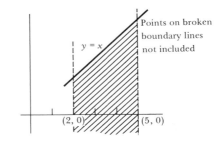

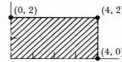

(0, 2)

(−2, 0)   (2, 0)

boundary
included

(0, −2)

(g) $|y| = |x|$
(h) $|xy| = xy$
(i) $|xy| > xy$
(j) *Sample:* $x^2 + y^2 \leqslant 4$.
    See the figure.
(k) $(x-2)^2 + (y-3)^2 > 1$
(l) $y \leqslant x+3$
(m) $x-y \leqslant 3$
(n) $|y-x| \leqslant 3$
(o) $y \leqslant x+3$ and $y \geqslant -x+3$

6. Write an algebraic statement describing each of the following sets:
   (a) *Sample:* The set of points in the plane above the x axis.
       Answer: All ordered pairs (x, y) with $y > 0$.
   (b) The set of points in the plane whose distance from the y axis is at most 2.
   (c) The set of points in the plane whose distance from the origin is less than 2.
   (d) The set of points contained in the shaded rectangular region (boundary included, see figure).

(0, 2)   (4, 2)

                (4, 0)

   (e) The set of points which are equidistant from the point $(0, 2)$ and the point $(0, 4)$.
   (f) The set of points contained in the shaded triangular region (boundary included, see figure).

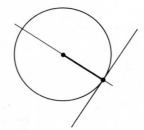

(2, 2)

(2, 0)

7. Find an equation for the line tangent to the circle
   $$(x-2)^2 + (y-3)^2 = 25$$
   at the point $(5, -1)$. [*Hint:* The line passing through the center of the circle and the point $(5, -1)$ is perpendicular to the tangent line at $(5, -1)$.]

8. Without actually solving, say whether simultaneous solutions exist for the following sets of equations, and if so, how many.
   (a) $2x - 4y = 7$
       $-x = 2y + 1$
   (b) $3y = x + 4$
       $3x + 4 = 9y$
   (c) $\frac{1}{7}x - \frac{3}{7}y = 1$
       $2y = 4x + 8$
   (d) $x = 3y - 4$
       $9y = 12 + 3x$

9. Find an algebraic equation describing all points (x, y) which are equidistant from the point $(0, 2)$ and the x axis. (The distance from a point to a line is measured along the perpendicular from the point to the line.) Plot some of the points with the described property. This is a special case of a "parabola."

10. Consider the two fixed points $(-2, 0)$ and $(2, 0)$. Find an algebraic expression describing all points $P = (x, y)$ such that the sum of the distances from P to $(2, 0)$ and from P to $(-2, 0)$ is 6. Can you complete the sketch of the set of points? This figure is called an "ellipse."

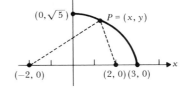

11. An old result of geometry is that the diagonals of a parallelogram intersect at their midpoints. Using the accompanying figure, demonstrate the result algebraically via the following steps:
    (a) Write an equation for the line OC.
    (b) Write an equation for the line AB.
    (c) Solve simultaneously to find the coordinates of D.
    (d) Use the distance formula to show that D is equidistant from O and C, and also D is equidistant from A and B. (Or alternately, use the result of Problem 9, Sec. 4.3.)

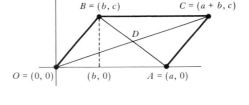

*12. Let P be a point on a circle. Show that a line l through P and perpendicular to a radius of the circle intersects the circle in no other point. Analysis: Place coordinate axes as in the figure, to simplify matters: The point P will have coordinates $(0, r)$; and the line l, being horizontal, will have equation

$$y = r.$$

Points on the circle must satisfy the equation

$$x^2 + y^2 = r^2.$$

Is there any simultaneous solution of these equations other than $(0, r)$?

*13. If $P = (x_0, y_0, z_0)$ is a point in 3-space different from the origin and L is the line through P and the origin, show that any point (x, y, z) on L is of the form (sx_0, sy_0, sz_0) for some real number s.

    (a) Project the points (x_0, y_0, z_0) and (x, y, z) into the xy plane (see the figure).
    (b) Project the points (x_0, y_0, z_0) and (x, y, z) into the yz plane.
    (c) Look at the triangles dashed in the figure. Use similarity to show that x/x_0, y/y_0, and z/z_0 must have the same value, s.

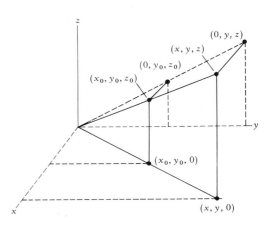

4.7 GRAPHS OF FUNCTIONS

In terms of a labeled plane, it's now easy to make precise what the "graph" of a function is.

Definition: Suppose that f is a function whose domain D consists of real numbers. Then by the *graph* of f let's mean the set of all points in the plane whose labels have the form $(x, f(x))$ where x is an input in D.

EXAMPLE 1. Let's look at the area function for a circle: $A(r) = \pi r^2$, with domain $D = \{$all real numbers $r \geq 0\}$. For a number of choices of input $r = 0, \frac{1}{2}, 1, \ldots$, we can calculate corresponding outputs $A(0), A(\frac{1}{2}), A(1), \ldots$, as in the table below:

r	$A(r)$
0	0
$\frac{1}{2}$	$\frac{1}{4}\pi$
1	π
$\frac{3}{2}$	$\frac{9}{4}\pi$
2	4π

Next, we can plot corresponding points on the graph of A: $(0, A(0))$, $(\frac{1}{2}, A(\frac{1}{2}))$, $(1, A(1)), \ldots$, as in Fig. 4-21. Since the domain D has infinitely many inputs, we could never hope actually to plot all points $(r, A(r))$ on graph. At this stage, we can only *guess* that they fill up a curve such as I've sketched in green in Fig. 4-21.

EXAMPLE 2. Suppose that the domain D of a function f consists of four numbers $D = \{1, 2, 3, 4\}$, and that $f(1) = 0.86$, $f(2) = 0.15$, $f(3) = 0.14$, and $f(4) = 0.02$. Then we can give a complete picture of the graph of f: it consists merely of four points, as in Fig. 4-22.

NOTE: Even if the objects composing the domain of a function f are not real numbers, we can often represent them by points on a

FIGURE 4-21

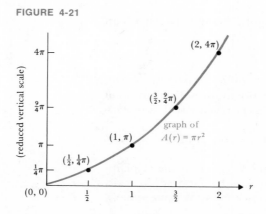

FIGURE 4-22

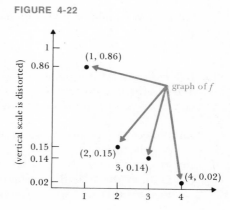

horizontal axis, and then picture the "graph" of f as a subset of the plane.

EXAMPLE 3. Studies have been made to see whether twins are more often affected by each other's troubles than nontwin pairs of related persons. Here is data from a study of schizophrenia. In the table below the right-hand fraction associated with each type of pair is the ratio of the number of pairs of that type with *both* members afflicted to the number of pairs of that type with *at least one* member afflicted.

Type of pair	Ratio (both ÷ at least one)
1. One-egg twins	0.86
2. Two-egg twins	0.15
3. Full siblings	0.14
4. Husband-wife	0.02

If we wanted to display these results graphically, then Fig. 4-22 already does the job. (Sometimes people draw in bars to guide the eye, as in Fig. 4-23.)

FIGURE 4-23

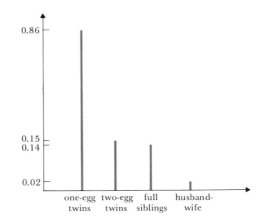

Linear functions. Thanks to the few results of "analytic geometry" above, we can single out a kind of function whose domain contains infinitely many inputs but whose graph we can picture completely and with little plotting.

Let's call a function f linear if its domain D is a set of real numbers and if its rule can be given by a formula

$$f(x) = mx + b \qquad \text{for all } x \text{ in } D, \tag{1}$$

where m and b are fixed constants. The reason for the name is that the graph of f must be a subset of the line described by the equation

$$y = mx + b. \tag{2}$$

What rule (1) says is precisely that the coordinates $(x, f(x))$ of a graph point do satisfy (2) for all x in D.

EXAMPLE 4. To sketch the graph of the function with domain $D = [0, 1]$ and rule $f(x) = -(3/2)x + 4$, draw a line of slope $m = -3/2$ passing through $(0, 4)$, as in Fig. 4-16 above. The graph of f is precisely that segment of the line lying above the interval $[0, 1]$ (shaded in Fig. 4-17).

Going in the opposite direction, we can recognize any (nonvertical) line segment as the graph of a linear function.

EXAMPLE 5. We describe the line passing through $P = (1, 2)$ and $Q = (4, 3)$ by the equation

$$y = \frac{1}{3}x + \frac{5}{3}, \tag{3}$$

as in Example 3 of Sec. 4.3. Hence the line segment between P and Q is the graph of the linear function

$$f(x) = \frac{1}{3}x + \frac{5}{3} \tag{4}$$

with domain $D = [1, 4]$. See Fig. 4-24.

FIGURE 4-24

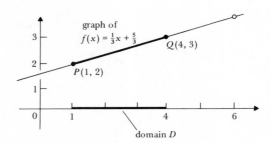

EXAMPLE 6. Suppose we see data showing that a certain family earned $2,000 in 1961 and $3,000 in 1964. If we suppose also that its income was increasing at a constant rate during the early and middle 1960's, how much can we guess that they earned in 1966?

Let's plot the known data. With a vertical axis marked off in thousands of dollars and a horizontal axis marked off in years x since 1960, the known data correspond to the points P and Q in Fig. 4-24. The line determined by P and Q has a constant rate of increase of altitude per unit change in x, namely its slope $m = \frac{1}{3}$. So, for integer values of $x = 0, 1, 2, 3, 4, 5, 6$, we can consider its altitude

$$f(x) = \frac{1}{3}x + \frac{5}{3}$$

to indicate the family's earnings for the year $1960 + x$. In particular,

$$f(6) = \frac{1}{3}6 + \frac{5}{3} = 3\frac{2}{3} \qquad \text{(thousand dollars).}$$

EXAMPLE 7. For the family of Example 6, suppose the data also show living expenses of \$1,000 in 1961 and \$2,500 in 1964. If living expenses also increased at a constant rate during the early and middle 1960's, by what year would the family's expenses exceed their income?

I've plotted the living expense data as points $A = (1, 1)$ and $B = (4, 2\frac{1}{2})$ in Fig. 4-25. They determine a (green) line with slope

$$\frac{(5/2) - 1}{4 - 1} = \frac{(3/2)}{3} = \frac{1}{2}.$$

FIGURE 4-25

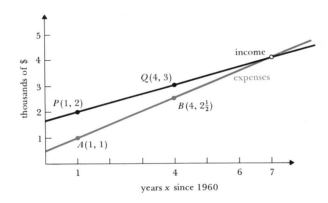

The line has equation

$$y = \frac{1}{2}x + b \qquad (5)$$

which must be satisfied by the coordinates of $A = (1, 1)$. Hence $1 = \frac{1}{2} \cdot 1 + b$, or $b = \frac{1}{2}$. Reasoning as for Example 6, we can suppose the family's expenses for the year $1960 + x$ to be describable by the function

$$g(x) = \frac{1}{2}x + \frac{1}{2} \qquad (6)$$

The problem is to find that x for which $g(x) = f(x)$ — where $f(x)$ is the "earnings function" of Example 6. Just let

$$\frac{1}{2}x + \frac{1}{2} = \frac{1}{3}x + \frac{5}{3} \qquad (7)$$

and solve for x: namely, $\frac{1}{6}x = \frac{7}{6}$, or $x = 7$. If all our assumptions were correct, the family just made do in 1967, and had a deficit thereafter.

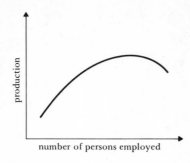

production

number of persons employed

4.8 PROBLEMS ON GRAPHS AND LINEAR FUNCTIONS

1. What story does the accompanying graph tell about an individual factory?

2. What story do the accompanying graphs tell?

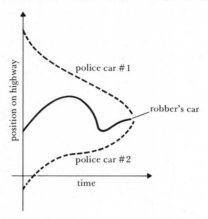

3. Graph the data in the accompanying table. What story does it tell?

U.S. Balance of Payments: Capital Transactions, 1961–1967

Year	1961	1962	1963	1964	1965	1966	1967–first 3 quarters
U.S. Private Capital, net [Billions of dollars]	−4.2	−3.4	−4.5	−6.5	−3.7	−4.2	−5.1

(*From Economic Report of the President, Transmitted to Congress February 1968*, Table 27, page 171.)

4. Sketch the graphs of the following functions. Show where the graph rises and where it falls. (Plot several points $(x, f(x))$ and follow any algebraic or other clues you may find.) If possible, determine the range of f and specify maximum and minimum values.

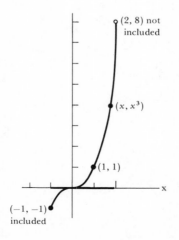

(a) *Sample:* $f(x) = x^3$; domain, the set $\{x: -1 \leq x < 2\}$. (See Appendix B for set notation $\{:\}$.) Since $a < b$ implies $a^3 < b^3$, the graph is rising over the whole domain. The range is the set $\{y: -1 \leq y < 8\}$ and thus the minimum value is -1 and occurs at $x = -1$. There is no maximum value.

(b) $f(x) = 1$; domain: the set $\{x: 1 \leqslant x < 4\}$.

(c) $f(x) = -3x + 1$; domain: the set $\{-1, 0, 1\}$.

(d)
$$f(x) = \begin{cases} x^2 & \text{if } x \geqslant 0 \\ -x^2 & \text{if } x < 0 \end{cases} \qquad \text{domain: } \{0, \pm 1, \pm 2, \pm 3\}.$$

(e) $f(x) = |x|$; domain: all real numbers.

(f) $f(x) = \dfrac{x}{1+x}$; domain: all positive integers.

(g) $f(x) = \dfrac{1}{x}$; domain: all numbers except zero.

5. (a) On the same set of coordinate axes graph the functions f_1, f_2, f_3, f_4 with domain all real numbers and rules $f_1(x) = x$, $f_2(x) = x^2$, $f_3(x) = x^3$, $f_4(x) = x^4$.

(b) Indicate, by shading, the region in the plane consisting of all points (x, y) satisfying each of the following conditions (use a different color or a different type of shading for each part):

   (i) $y > x^2$

   (ii) $x < y \leqslant x^3$

   (iii) $x^2 < y < x^4$

   (iv) $y \leqslant x^2$

   (v) $x^4 < y < x$

6. Give at least two reasons why the graph of $f(x) = x^2$ with domain all real numbers does not look like the figure. Hint: If $0 < a < b$, how is $f(a)$ related to $f(b)$? How do $f(a)$ and $f(-a)$ compare?

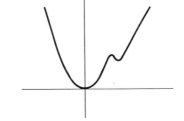

7.

Unemployment Rate (Percent)*

Group	1961	1965	1966	1967	1970
Total	6.7	4.5	3.8	3.8	—
Demographic Groups:					
White	6.0	4.1	3.3	3.4	—
Teenagers	15.3	13.4	11.2	11.0	—
Adult Males	5.1	2.9	2.2	2.1	—
Nonwhite	12.4	8.1	7.3	7.4	—
Teenagers	27.6	26.2	25.4	26.4	—
Adult Males	11.7	6.0	4.9	4.3	—

*Number unemployed in each group as percent of labor force for the group. Data relate to persons 16 years of age and over.

(*From: Economic Report of the President, Transmitted to Congress February* 1968, Table 4, page 53.)

(a) Draw coordinate axes and — using a different color for each group — plot the data from the table labeling the points as (year, percent).

(b) Draw a straight line to approximate the data trends for each group.

(c) If these trends continue, how should the "1970" column of the table be completed?

(d) What group showed the steepest decline in unemployment? What group the least?

8. Describe the domain, range, and rule for the linear functions whose graphs are the line segments joining the following pairs of points:

(a) *Sample:* $(1, 3)$ and $(4, 2)$.

Answer: domain: $[1, 4]$, range: $[2, 3]$. Rule: $f(x) = -\frac{1}{3}x + 3\frac{1}{3}$.

Graph:

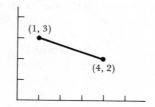

(b) $(0, 0)$ and $(4, 3)$

(c) $(2, 1)$ and $(-1, 3)$

(d) $(2, 1)$ and $(-7, 1)$

9. An exclusive fashion designer finds that his clients will pay more for limited edition dresses. Experience has shown him that if he makes 11 copies of a particular dress he can sell them for $100 each. If he reduces the quantity to 2 copies, he can get $1000 each. *If* he can assume that the price P per dress is a linear function of the number of copies made, how many copies should he make to maximize his receipts?

(a) Make a graph of P by plotting the points $(11, 100)$ and $(2, 1000)$ and drawing a line through them.

(b) Find a rule for the price P as a function of the number of copies, x.

(c) Find the income I (his receipts) as a function of x. (Assume he sells as many dresses as he makes.)

(d) Find the input x at which the function I has its maximum. (Hint: Complete the square.)

(e) Graph the function I on the same axes as P.

*10. In the example on family income and expenses (Examples 6 and 7 of Section 4.7), I assumed that these two quantities were increasing at a constant rate and I used linear functions to represent them — since we know that linear functions have constant rates of increase (slopes). Might there be other (nonlinear) functions which increase at constant rate?

11. (a) Is the line segment joining $(1, 2)$ and $(1, -7)$ the graph of a linear function?

(b) Consider the circle of radius 1 and center $(0, 0)$. Is this set of points the graph of a function? If so, find a rule for the function, and its domain.

(c) Can the graph of a function contain two points on the same vertical line?

(d) If a set of points in the plane contains at most one point on each vertical line, is it necessarily the graph of a function? If so, given the graph how would you find the domain and range of the function?

*12. If f is a one-to-one function, how many points of intersection can each *horizontal* line have with the graph of f?

13. A function is called *even* if $f(-x) = f(x)$ for each x in the domain. A function is called *odd* if $f(-x) = -f(x)$ for each x in the domain. *Sample:* $f(x) = 1/(x^2+2)$ for all real x is an even function, since

$$f(-x) = \frac{1}{(-x)^2+2} = \frac{1}{x^2+2} = f(x).$$

(a) If f is an even function, with inputs a and $-a$, what symmetry relation holds between the graph points $(a, f(a))$ and $(-a, f(-a))$? (Compare Problem 6 of Sec. 4.3.)

(b) Same question if f is an odd function, with inputs a and $-a$.

(c) Find a linear function which is odd. Find one which is even. Are there linear functions which are neither odd nor even? If so, give an example.

(d) Which of the functions in Problem 4(a)–(g) are odd, which even, which neither?

*14. Consider the function $f(x) = 1/x$, for $x > 0$. Show that if a and b are numbers such that $f(a) = b$, then $f(b) = a$, that is, whenever a point (a, b) is on the graph of f, the point (b, a) is also.

(a) What symmetry property does the graph of f have?

(b) Find another function with this property.

(c) If g is a linear function with this property, what is the slope of the graph of g?

(d) If a function has the property described above, what is $f(f(x))$?

*15. (a) Draw the graphs of $f(x) = ax^2+bx+c$ and $g(x) = -ax^2+bx+c$ where a is positive, b and c are arbitrary constants. Hint: Complete the square to help in analyzing the function.

(b) About what lines are the graphs symmetric?

16. What single condition on a set S of points in an xy plane will characterize S as the graph of some function f?

4.9 GEOMETRY AND PROBABILITY

Suppose that you are being chased by an enemy, and you want to escape by boarding a bus at a certain bus stop. Suppose also that buses pass the stop every 5 minutes, but that you don't know when you'll arrive within a 5 minute interval, and that you can afford to wait there only two minutes before taking other evasive action. What are your chances for escape by bus?

Focus on that particular five-minute interval between bus passages, during which you will arrive. If we start counting time at the beginning of that interval, then we can represent the interval as

FIGURE 4-26

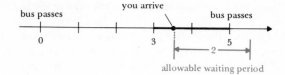

[0, 5]. Now think of your *exact arrival time* within that interval. Here is a situation involving "chance" which does not have finitely many possible outcomes as did those I discussed in Chapter 3. In fact, we could take all the numbers x in the interval [0, 5] as constituting a reasonable "list" Ω of possible times for your arrival.

For which subset A of Ω will you be successful in boarding a bus by waiting two minutes or less? Answer: for $A = [3, 5]$. See Fig. 4-26. Now, if you arrive "at random" in the interval [0, 5], doesn't it seem intuitively reasonable that the probability of your arriving in the subinterval [3, 5] should be

$$P([3, 5]) = \frac{\text{length of } [3, 5]}{\text{length of } [0, 5]} .$$ (1)

If so, then the probability for your escape by bus is 2/5.

More generally, shouldn't the probability for your arriving in any subinterval $[a, b]$ be the ratio

$$P([a, b]) = \frac{\text{length of } [a, b]}{\text{length of } [0, 5]} = \frac{b - a}{5} .$$ (2)

Formula (2) captures the idea that subintervals of equal length — no matter where they are located — have equal probabilities, which seems to be a reasonable interpretation of arrival "at random."

More generally still, if a subset A is the union of intervals which don't overlap, we can assign it the probability

$$P(A) = \frac{\text{sum of lengths of intervals in } A}{\text{length of } \Omega} .$$ (3)

EXAMPLE 1. The probability of arriving within two minutes of a bus passage (in Fig. 4-26) is

$$P([0, 2] \cup [3, 5]) = \frac{2 + 2}{5} = \frac{4}{5} .$$

NOTE: Formula (3) is not an example of assigning a probability number $P(A)$ to a subset A by summing "elementary probabilities" $p(x)$ for all outcomes x in A — as was my procedure in Chapter 3. In the present case the only real number we could assign as a common "elementary probability" for each single outcome x is zero. (Otherwise, if infinitely many points had $p(x) = c$, for some positive number c, we would have subsets of total probability exceeding 1.)

However, formula (3) is a direct analog of the formula

$$P(A) = \frac{\text{size of } A}{\text{size of } \Omega}$$

which I deduced in Chapter 3 for situations with finitely many *equally likely* outcomes. Moreover, if we use formula (3) to assign probabilities $P(A)$ to subsets A which are unions of nonoverlapping intervals, then the function P will still have the key properties of probability functions which I noted in Chapter 3, namely:

$$P(\Omega) = 1. \, P(\varnothing) = 0$$

$$0 \leqslant P(S) \leqslant 1 \text{ for any } S \subset \Omega$$

$$P(S \cup T) = P(S) + P(T) \text{ if } S \text{ and } T \text{ are mutually}$$
$$\text{exclusive subsets.}$$

(4)

(I invite you to check this claim in doing Problem 15 of Sec. 4.10.)

EXAMPLE 2. Suppose that, independently of you, your enemy will arrive at the same bus stop at a "random" time in the same 5-minute interval, and will spend two minutes there — or less if cut short by the arrival of the second bus. What is the probability that you will both be at the stop simultaneously?

One way to picture the possible outcomes in this situation is as the set of all ordered pairs (x, y) with $0 \leqslant x \leqslant 5$ and $0 \leqslant y \leqslant 5$ — where we can interpret x as your arrival time, and y as that of your enemy. The set — call it Ω — corresponds to a 5×5 square in a coordinate plane, as I've indicated in Fig. 4-27. For which subset A of points (x, y) in Ω will you and your enemy be at the bus stop simultaneously? *Answer*: precisely for those points (x, y) in Ω where the difference of arrival times (coordinates) is

$$|y - x| \leqslant 2.$$

(5)

As I've pointed out before, this inequality is equivalent to the simultaneous inequalities

$$x - 2 \leqslant y \quad \text{and} \quad y \leqslant x + 2.$$

(6)

That is, for a particular time x_0 when you might arrive, there will be points (x_0, y) in A corresponding to all altitudes y between $x_0 - 2$ and

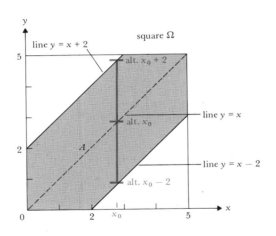

FIGURE 4-27

$x_0 + 2$ — provided also that $0 \leqslant y \leqslant 5$. See the green vertical segment in Fig. 4-27. For $x_0 \leqslant 3$, the highest such point lies on the line with equation

$$y = x + 2 \tag{7}$$

which has slope 1 and intersects the vertical axis at $(0, 2)$. And for $x_0 \geqslant 2$, the lowest such point lies on the line with equation

$$y = x - 2. \tag{8}$$

Considering all x_0's in $[0, 5]$, we can conclude that the set A consists of all points (x, y) lying between the two lines described in (7) and (8) and within the boundaries of the square: the shaded region in Fig. 4-27.

Finally, what probability $P(A)$ can we assign to A? Does the ratio

$$P(A) = \frac{\text{area of } A}{\text{area of } \Omega} \tag{9}$$

seem reasonable? It's analogous to the ratio of lengths (2) which I considered for the previous one-dimensional setup and to the rule in Chapter 3 for equally likely outcomes. To apply (9), just note that each triangle in $\Omega - A$ in Fig. 4-27 has area $= \frac{1}{2} \cdot 3 \cdot 3$. Hence the area of $A = 25 - 2(\frac{1}{2} \cdot 3 \cdot 3) = 16$, and $P(A) = 16/25$. The chances of meeting your enemy at the bus stop are a little better than 3 in 5.

Note that formula (9), like (3), is another instance of a probability function which is not defined in terms of "elementary probabilities." Nevertheless, we can expect probabilities $P(A)$ assigned by (9) to have the same general properties (4) as probabilities in Chapter 3. For example, $P(S) \geqslant 0$ for all subsets S of Ω, and $P(S \cup T) = P(S) + P(T)$ when S and T are mutually exclusive. This is because we expect areas of sets to be nonnegative, and we expect the area of $S \cup T$ to be the sum of the separate areas of S and T if S and T don't overlap.

To conclude this problem, let's ask whether the probability assignment (9), $P(A) = (\text{area of } A)/(\text{area of } \Omega)$, is consistent with the description of the arrival times x and y as being "independent" of each other. In Chapter 3, I argued that two subsets A and B can be interpreted as representing independent results — with respect to a given probability function $P(S)$ — if $P(A \cap B) = P(A)P(B)$. Let's check whether such a relationship holds.

Pick any two subintervals $[a, b]$ and $[c, d]$ of the interval $[0, 5]$. The result that you will arrive during $[a, b]$ — nothing being said about your enemy — corresponds to the subset

$$A = \{\text{all } (x, y) \text{ in } \Omega \text{ with } x \text{ in } [a, b] \text{ and } y \text{ unrestricted}\}. \tag{10}$$

The result that your enemy will arrive during $[c, d]$ — nothing being said about you — corresponds to the subset

$$B = \{\text{all } (x, y) \text{ in } \Omega \text{ with } y \text{ in } [c, d] \text{ and } x \text{ unrestricted}\}. \tag{11}$$

I've pictured these sets in Fig. 4-28. The sets A, B, and $A \cap B$ are all

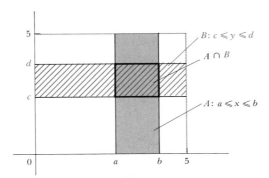

FIGURE 4-28

rectangular subsets of Ω. Let's check their probabilities according to formula (9):

$$P(A) = \frac{\text{area of } A}{\text{area of } \Omega} = \frac{(b-a)\cdot 5}{25} = \frac{b-a}{5}$$

$$P(B) = \frac{\text{area of } B}{\text{area of } \Omega} = \frac{5(d-c)}{25} = \frac{d-c}{5}$$

$$P(A \cap B) = \frac{\text{area of } A \cap B}{\text{area of } \Omega} = \frac{(b-a)(d-c)}{25} = P(A)P(B)$$

So formula (9) does yield independence between the arrivals of you and your enemy.

In this section I've presented two possible *models* to help analyze problems—one based on an interval, the other on a square, and each with an assumption about how to assign probabilities. They were both *idealizations*. (For example, of what realistic consequence could an overlap of one instant be, $y = x \pm 2$?) You may or may not have found yourself satisfied with the models. Either way, the question you should ask is, what more satisfactory models can one think of?

4.10 PROBLEMS ON GEOMETRIC PROBABILITY

1. Imagine spinning a pointer on the dial in the figure—and getting rewarded as follows: A pays \$5, B pays \$3, C pays \$5, D—you lose \$5. What should you expect to win "on the average" (per trial) in this game?

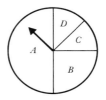

2. Imagine picking a point x at random from the unit interval, and writing x as a decimal.
   (a) What's the probability that the first digit in the decimal will be a 7?
   (b) What's the probability that the second digit in the decimal will be a 7?
   (c) What's the probability that both first and second digits will be 7's?

3. A penny is approximately $\frac{3}{8}$ inch in radius. Suppose you throw a penny down onto a floor made of parallel boards each $2\frac{1}{4}$ inches in width. What's the probability that the penny will touch a crack between two boards? Focus on that board—whichever it may be —on which the *center* of the penny will land. With some idealization, isn't the problem one of finding the probability that the center of the penny will land within $\frac{3}{8}$ inch of either edge of that board?

4. Generalization of Problem 3: What's the probability that a coin of radius r will hit a crack between floor boards of width w (where $2r < w$)?

5. Testing your answer in Problem 4: Toss a coin n times onto a floor of parallel boards, making sure you flip it well each time. Keep track of your "success ratio" N_n/n, where N_n is the number of times that your coin hit a crack during n tosses. Do the ratios, say,

$$\frac{N_{10}}{10}, \frac{N_{20}}{20}, \frac{N_{40}}{40}, \frac{N_{80}}{80}$$

seem to "tend" toward a "limiting value"?

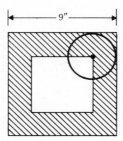

6. Suppose you throw down a coffee can cover of radius 2 inches onto a floor made of square tiles of 9 inches on a side. What's the probability that the cover will hit a crack between tiles?

Again, for an idealized model, disregard the edges of the room and the possibility that the center of the cover will lie exactly on some crack. Focus on that tile—whichever it may be—on which the center will land. What's the probability that the center will fall within 2 inches of the boundary of the tile?

7. Generalization of Problem 6: What's the probability that a disk of radius r will hit a crack between square tiles of width w (where $2r < w$)?

8. Testing your answer in Problem 7: Toss a disk n times onto a tiled floor. Keep track of your success ratio N_n/n, where N_n is the number of times that your coin hits a crack during the first n tosses. Do the ratios N_n/n appear to "tend" to a "limiting value"? —to the probability number you found in Problem 7 for a single toss?

9. Suppose that a city is roughly circular in shape with a ten-mile radius, and that it has a university at its center. If students' homes are distributed more or less uniformly throughout the city, what is the probability that a randomly chosen student lives within r miles from the university? ($0 \leqslant r \leqslant 10$)

What's the probability that a randomly chosen student lives between 5 and 6 miles from the university?

10. Suppose that two men — one junior and one senior — both plan to arrive at an appointed place, independently of one another, sometime between noon and one o'clock. Find the probability that they will meet—

   (a) If the junior will wait for the senior or until one o'clock, but the senior won't wait for the junior at all;

   Sample diagram
   of possible outcomes:

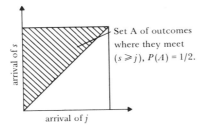

Set A of outcomes where they meet $(s \geq j)$, $P(A) = 1/2$.

   (b) if the junior will wait 10 minutes for the senior, or until one o'clock, but the senior won't wait at all;

   (c) if the junior must arrive before 12:30 and will wait until 12:30, but the senior won't wait at all;

   (d) if each will wait ten minutes or until one o'clock.

11. Suppose that, as a result of a storm, two airplanes find themselves in the same approach corridor to a city, each at some (random) altitude between 3,000 and 4,000 ft. What's the probability that their altitudes differ by no more than 200 ft?

12. Color green the open subinterval $\langle 1/3, 2/3 \rangle$ of the unit interval $[0, 1]$. It's length is $1/3$. There remain 2 flanking unpainted subintervals; color *their* middle $1/3$ rd intervals green, namely $\langle 1/9, 2/9 \rangle$ and $\langle 7/9, 8/9 \rangle$. These are each of length $1/3^2$. There remain 2^2 unpainted subintervals, color their middle $1/3$ rd intervals green. Those are each of length $1/3^3$. You — or someone — could go on and on, coloring green 2^{n-1} intervals of length $1/3^n$ for each positive integer n.

Now pick a point "at random" from the unit interval.

   (a) What's the probability that it will lie somewhere in the three largest green subintervals?

   (b) For any fixed integer n, let A_n denote the union of all green subintervals of size at least $1/3^n$. What's the probability that your randomly chosen point will lie somewhere in A_n? (See Appendix A for summation of terms in a "geometric sequence".)

   *(c) What's the probability that the randomly chosen point will be colored green — no matter in which of the infinitely

many possible green intervals it might lie? That is, what probability are you willing to associate to the union of all the green subintervals, of all sizes? Note that the partial unions A_n get larger and larger, $A_1 \subset A_2 \subset \cdots \subset$; and that any given green interval—say, of length $1/3^k$—will be a subset of A_n for all $n \geqslant k$.

*(d) What's the probability that your randomly chosen point will not be green?

*13. Answer the same questions as for Problem 11, except that this time at each stage choose the (open) middle quarters of the remaining subintervals to color green. Thus, there should be one green interval of length $1/4$, namely $\langle 3/8, 5/8 \rangle$; and two green intervals of $1/4^2$, namely $\langle 5/32, 7/32 \rangle$ and $\langle 25/32, 27/32 \rangle$; etc.

*14. Will the construction of Problem 12 leave *any* subinterval of $[0, 1]$ which is completely free of green points?

*15. Let $\Omega = [u, v]$ where $u < v$. And to any set S which is the union of finitely many disjoint subintervals of Ω,

$$S = [a_1, b_1] \cup [a_2, b_2] \cup \cdots \cup [a_n, b_n],$$

assign the probability

$$P(S) = \frac{(b_1 - a_1) + (b_2 - a_2) + \cdots + (b_n - a_n)}{v - u}.$$

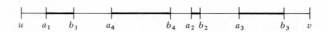

Show that the probability function P has the following properties:

(a) $P(\Omega) = 1$ and $P(\emptyset) = 0$
(b) $0 \leqslant P(S) \leqslant 1$ for any set S as above
(c) $P(S) \leqslant P(T)$ of S and T are two sets as above with $S \subset T$.

NOTE: Every subinterval $[a_i, b_i]$ of S must be contained in a subinterval—call it $[\bar{a}_j, \bar{b}_j]$—of T. And the length $\bar{b}_j - \bar{a}_j$ of any subinterval of T must be at least as great as the sum of the lengths of all subintervals of S which it contains. For example:

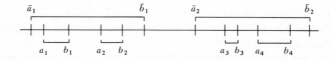

Can you conclude, therefore, that the complete numerator sum defining $P(T)$ must be $\geqslant$ the complete numerator sum defining $P(S)$?

(d) $P(S \cup T) = P(S) + P(T)$ if S and T are mutually exclusive unions of intervals.

4.11 HIGHER-DIMENSIONAL SPACES

We labeled points in 2-dimensional space by ordered pairs (x, y), and in 3-dimensional space by ordered triples (x, y, z). If you looked at Problem 15 of Sec. 4.3 and Problem 13 of Sec. 4.6, you may recall that other algebraic formulations extend from 2- to 3-dimensional space as well: We can describe a line through the origin in 3-dimensional space as a set of all triples of the form (sx_0, sy_0, sz_0) when s varies through all real numbers. We can determine the distance between points $P_1 = (x_1, y_1, z_1)$ and $P_2 = (x_2, y_2, z_2)$ by the formula

$$|P_1P_2| = \sqrt{(x_2 - x_1)^2 + (y_2 - y_1)^2 + (z_2 - z_1)^2} \, .$$

Having seen this, *let your imagination leap.* On to 4-dimensional space, on to 20-dimensional space, and—why not?—to n-dimensional space for any positive integer n.

Do such "spaces" really exist? Never mind. Why not make *models* for them anyway? Let's think of the set of all possible ordered "4-tuples" (x, y, z, t) of real numbers x, y, z, and t as a *model* for "4-dimensional space." This is how Albert Einstein conceived of his "space-time" model of the universe. It's nothing more mysterious than that. Einstein interpreted the x, y, and z coordinates as referring to ordinary physical space, and the t coordinate to time. Of course, it's hard to draw complete pictures for such a model. But we can sketch 1-, 2-, or 3-dimensional "subspaces" of it.

More generally, for a model of n-dimensional space, let's take as "points" the set of all possible ordered "n-tuples"

$$(x_1, x_2, x_3 \ldots, x_n) \tag{1}$$

of real numbers. (Here, I'm labeling all coordinates of a "point" by different subscripts, instead of by different letters $x, y, z, \ldots$, so we won't run out of letters.)

We can *define* a "line" passing through the origin $(0, 0, 0, \ldots, 0)$ and the point $(x_1, x_2, x_3, \ldots, x_n)$ as the set of all ordered n-tuples of the form $(sx_1, sx_2, sx_3, \ldots, sx_n)$ where s can be any real number.

How about the distance between two "points"

$$P = (x_1, x_2, x_3, \ldots, x_n) \quad \text{and} \quad Q = (y_1, y_2, y_3, \ldots, y_n)?$$

Since we are building the model, the "distance" isn't there yet until we *define* what it should be. Why not extend the old formula and use it now as a *definition*?

$$|PQ| = \sqrt{(y_1 - x_1)^2 + (y_2 - x_2)^2 + (y_3 - x_3)^2 + \cdots + (y_n - x_n)^2}. \tag{2}$$

I invite you to show that this definition still yields an old property: for any triangle PQR,

$$|PR| \leq |PQ| + |QR| \tag{3}$$

(See Problem 17 of Sec. 6.7.)

(NOTE: In his 4-dimensional space-time model, Einstein stuck in a negative constant before the time differences in his distance formula, to incorporate limitations on travel faster than the speed of light. As a result, the inequality (3) doesn't always hold in his model.

A consequence: you can go backwards in time by traveling faster than light.)

Can we include such concepts as "angle" in our model for n-dimensional space? What is an "angle," *precisely*, even in two dimensions? You may recall from trigonometry that in most computations "angles" don't enter except via their "trigonometric functions" $\cos \theta$, $\sin \theta$, and so on—and these relate to distances. For example, the so-called "law of cosines" for the triangle POQ in Fig. 4-29 reads

FIGURE 4-29

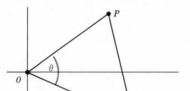

$$|PQ|^2 = |OP|^2 + |OQ|^2 - 2|OP| \cdot |OQ| \cos \theta$$

or

$$\cos \theta = \frac{|OP|^2 + |OQ|^2 - |PQ|^2}{2|OP| \cdot |OQ|}. \tag{4}$$

We know how to calculate distances in our n-dimensional model. So why not turn (4) around and regard it now as a *definition* for a quantity "$\cos \theta$" which we can then intuitively interpret as the "cosine of POQ"? If you were interested in actual computation with points $P = (x_1, x_2, x_3, \ldots, x_n)$ and $Q = (y_1, y_2, y_3, \ldots, y_n)$, you could substitute $|OP|$, $|OQ|$, and $|PQ|$ in (4) via the n-dimensional distance formula (2), cancel terms, and get

$$\cos \theta = \frac{x_1 y_1 + x_2 y_2 + x_3 y_3 + \cdots + x_n y_n}{\sqrt{x_1^2 + x_2^2 + x_3^2 + \cdots + x_n^2} \sqrt{y_1^2 + y_2^2 + y_3^2 + \cdots + y_n^2}}. \tag{5}$$

EXAMPLE 1: *How 20-dimensional space enters the public schools.* The problem is to determine whether two different "aptitude tests" give more or less the same results. Suppose that the two tests have been administered to a class of, say, 20 children. We can arrange the results as "ordered 20-tuples,"

$$P = (x_1, x_2, x_3, \ldots, x_i, \ldots, x_{20}) \tag{6}$$

and

$$Q = (y_1, y_2, y_3, \ldots, y_i, \ldots, y_{20}) \tag{7}$$

the scores x_i and y_i referring to the same (ith) child.

(We might first have adjusted the raw scores of the "P" test by subtracting a common constant so as to get an "average score"

$$\frac{x_1 + x_2 + x_3 + \cdots + x_{20}}{20} = 0,$$

and we might have treated the "Q" raw scores similarly, so that neither test would have an irrelevant advantage over the other in terms of "base score.")

Now, individual children may react differently to the different tests. Is there some quantity—some "index"—which will take due (but not undue) notice of these variations and measure whether the two tests are "closely related"? Here is a scheme which experimenters in many fields have adopted: In 20-dimensional space the point P determines a line through the origin O, namely, the set of all ordered 20-tuples of the form

$$(sx_1, sx_2, sx_3, \ldots, sx_i, \ldots, sx_{20}) . \tag{8}$$

Since any such 20-tuple represents a mere rescaling of the test scores by a factor s, let's think of the line itself as representing the test "P." Similarly, the point Q determines a line through the origin, which can represent the test "Q." The idea is to compute the $\cos \theta$ via (5) for the "angle POQ between the lines" and to say that the tests are "close" if $\cos \theta$ is a number of close to 1 ($= \cos 0$).

In the same way, a group of, say, five tests would correspond to five lines in 20-dimensional space; and we could check how these tests are "located" with respect to each other by calculating cosines between the various pairs of lines. The procedure is called "factor analysis." Computers can do the tedious computations. The main questions for an experimenter should be: Is the geometric model relevant? And when does one lose too much information by condensing data into one or several "indices"?

4.12 AXIOMS

After all I've said about "points" and "numbers," let's review the status of these concepts and the rules governing them.

What does one mean in geometry by a "point"? Some textbooks have definitions such as "a position in space." But then the question is what one means by "position" and "space." Other texts are worse still: "that which hath no length or width"—as if one could define something by naming a few properties which it doesn't possess. Of course, Euclid had a *visceral* feeling as to what a "point" and a "line" are, a feeling sound enough for him to develop a powerful theory—but not sound enough for a good definition. In fact can one ever have a good definition of "point," "line," and "plane" without getting into vicious circles?

You might say, "who cares, as long as one can get along?" That is just what mathematicians have said! They observed that as far as the development of results goes, one can consider "point," "line," and "plane," and even the notion of a "point lying on a line" as *undefined notions*. The key requirement is that one must have a workable set of axioms relating these undefined notions with each other.

Let's turn to algebra. What is an "integer" or "whole number"? You have seen a few, 1, 2, 3, and so on, but no one has seen them all. So how can we define "integer" or be confident about properties claimed for integers? (Perhaps the simplest property is that each integer is followed by another. A more complicated property is the so-called "principle of mathematical induction." See Chapter 6.)

More complicated still: How does one define "real number," "addition," etc., etc.? What mathematicians do here, at least currently, is the same as what they do in geometry. They regard certain numbers and operations as *undefined notions*. One can consider "integers" as undefined and then define "real numbers" in terms of integers, or one can even start by considering "real numbers" as undefined. In any case, one must come up with a *workable* set of axioms relating undefined numbers and operations. For example, we have every right to think of the old "rules" of algebra (which, after all, appear to be workable) as *axioms* relating "real numbers," "addition," and "multiplication." To cite just a few,

$$a + b = b + a$$
$$(a + b) + c = a + (b + c)$$
$$a + 0 = a$$
$$ab = ba$$
$$(ab)c = a(bc) \tag{1}$$
$$a \cdot 1 = a$$
$$a \cdot 0 = 0$$
$$a(b + c) = ab + ac$$
$$a + a = 2a.$$

From these axioms other results follow (all of them "theorems," if you like) such as

$$(a + b)^2 = a^2 + 2ab + b^2.$$

Still other rules or *axioms* relate to "order":

If $a < b$ and $b < c$, then $a < c$.
If $a \neq b$, then $a < b$ or $b < a$.
If $a < b$, then $a + c < b + c$. (2)
If $a < b$ and $0 < c$, then $ac < bc$.
If $a < b$ and $c < 0$, then $bc < ac$.

And here's a useful property noted by Archimedes:

If $0 < a$ and $0 < b$, then
$$b < na \tag{3}$$
for some positive integer n.

(Without Archimedes' "axiom," we couldn't even claim that ratios of the form $\frac{1}{2}, \frac{1}{3}, \frac{1}{4}, \ldots, 1/n, \ldots$ ultimately, get smaller than any given positive number a—the case $b = 1$.)

Suppose now that you're willing to assume the existence of "real numbers" as a set of objects satisfying all the above axioms plus others relating to subtraction and division. How, *precisely*, can you set these "numbers" into correspondence with geometric "points" on a line? To recall an earlier question: which "point" will correspond to $\sqrt[3]{\pi}$?

Here's one answer from an abstract approach: In the last section, I considered the set of all ordered "n-tuples" of real numbers as a *model* for n-dimensional space. Why not now let $n = 1$ and simply consider the set of real numbers itself as a *model* for one-dimensional space—for the set of "points" on a line? Then let the correspondence question vanish. Who needs "geometric points" at all?

Similarly, for $n = 2$, why not consider the set of all ordered pairs (x, y) as a model for the Euclidean plane—with lines *defined*, rather than described, by equations $Ax + By + C = 0$, where A or $B \neq 0$?

Does the prospect of all these undefined notions and arbitrary axioms—and of deducing results from them—seem full of pitfalls? Might the axioms possibly harbor some kind of inconsistency, as yet undiscovered? One project which helps dispel some doubts is to construct small concrete models to exemplify various axioms. I invite you to try it in doing Problems 6 and 7 of Sec. 4.13.

*4.13   PROBLEMS ON SPACES AND AXIOMS

A. Higher-dimensional space

1. Using the distance formula for 3-dimensional space, determine the distance between the points in each of the following pairs. Plot the points in each pair and sketch the line segment joining them.
   (a) *Sample:* $(-1, 1, 0)$ and $(1, 1, 7)$

   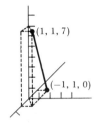

   Solution: Distance $= \sqrt{(-1-1)^2 + (1-1)^2 + (0-7)^2}$
   $$= \sqrt{4 + 49}$$
   $$= \sqrt{53}$$
   (b) $(0, 0, 0)$ and $(1, 1, 1)$
   (c) $(-1, 2, 4)$ and $(2, 3, 4)$
   (d) $(-1, 1, 0)$ and $(-3, 0, 1)$
   (e) $(5, -8, 7)$ and $(5, 3, 7)$
2. For 10-dimensional space, determine the distance between the following points:
   (a) The origin and $(1, 1, \ldots, 1) = P$
   (b) The point $(1, 1, \ldots, 1) = P$ and $(1, 0, 1, 1, \ldots, 1) = Q$
   (c) The origin and $(1, 0, 1, 1, \ldots, 1) = Q$
   Now, using these distances, show that the "triangle inequality" holds in this particular case: $|OP| \leq |OQ| + |QP|$.
3. In 5-dimensional space, find the "angle," $\angle POQ$, where $P = (1, 1, 0, 0, 0)$, $Q = (0, 0, 1, 1, 0)$ and O is the origin.
4. Can you guess what an equation corresponding to a circle or sphere would look like in a 3-space? in 4-space? in 20-space? Determine equations for the following spheres in 3-space.
   (a) Center $(0, 0, 0)$, radius 3
   (b) Center $(1, 2, -1)$, radius 2
   (c) Center $(-2, 0, 1)$, containing the point $(-1, 2, 2)$
5. Determine an equation for a sphere in 4-space having center $(1, 2, 3, 4)$ and radius 5. Is the origin inside, outside, or on the sphere?

B. Geometry—Axiomatics

6. Recall the axiom of plane geometry regarding "parallel" lines: "Given a line l_1 and a point P not on l_1, there is one and only one line l_2 such that P is on l_2 and l_2 is parallel to l_1." In Sec. 4.12 I

asserted that such an axiom was essentially a statement about the undefined notions "point," "line," a point being "on" a line, and "parallel." Can such undefined notions ever be made concrete so that we can check whether the axiom really does or doesn't hold? You may say: just look at points and parallel lines in "real space." But in "real space" — even if one could distinguish a "line" — one could never hope to get out to infinity to check whether "parallel" lines meet! So, for concreteness let's try a very small model.

Let the set {1, 2, 3, 4} of the first four integers be a model of "the plane." Call each number in the set a "point," and call any subset of size two a "line," for example, {1, 2} {1, 3} {2, 3}, and so on. In this model, let's say that a point lies "on" a line if that point is in the subset called the line. For example, the point 2 lies "on" the line {1, 2}. Call two lines "parallel" if they have no common point.

(a) How many lines does the model have?

(b) Check to see whether the above axiom about "parallel lines" holds for this model.

(c) Check other axioms which you may recall from geometry.

(d) This model can be pictured geometrically as a square but its diagonals are "constructed" so they do not intersect. Draw the figure.

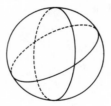

7. *Geometry on a sphere.* For this model let our "plane" be the surface of the sphere. "Lines" are arcs of great circles, and "points" are just points (in the Euclidean sense) on this sphere.

(a) Does the parallel axiom of Problem 1 hold? Do there even exist parallel lines?

(b) Do the other axioms of Euclidean geometry hold for this model?

(c) Do two points "determine" a line; that is, given two distinct points, is there one and only one line containing these two points? When will they meet, if ever?

C. Algebra — Axiomatics

8. About axioms — algebra: Since we can never hope to see all real numbers, we can't use them to check out the axiom set (1) in Sec. 4.12. We just have to *hope* that real numbers satisfy these axioms. More precisely, we should view mathematics as *conditional*; and add to every theorem of algebra the clause "provided *all* the real numbers satisfy our axioms."

However, we can try to check out the axioms on a pint sized number system. Even the smallest model should have two special "numbers" — denote them by O and I — to play roles analogous to the ordinary real numbers zero and one. Let's see if we can make do with only two "numbers." To specify a number system, we must also say how to "add" and how to "multiply" numbers. You may recall your addition and multiplication "tables" for integers. In principle they have infinitely many entries since there are infinitely many integers, and one could never write them all out to check axioms. But now, with only two numbers O and I the job should be simple. The "sum" or product of any two numbers must again be O or I, since there are no other numbers in the system.

(a) I've indicated below a table for "addition." Pick a row and a column and record in the square where they intersect the "number" which you think should be the "sum" of "numbers" appearing at the left of the row and the top of the column. For example, I have indicated my choice for $O+O$ to be O. Fill in the remaining three squares in such a way that the first three axioms of Sec. 4.12 hold:

  (i) $a+b=b+a$
  (ii) $(a+b)+c=a+(b+c)$
  (iii) $a+0=a$.

(To check an axiom you must see whether it holds for any choice of $a=O$ or I, $b=O$ or I, $c=O$ or I.)

+	O	I		×	O	I
O	O			O		
I				I		

(b) I've also indicated a "multiplication" table. Try to fill in the squares (with O or I) in such a way that *all* of the axioms (1) in Sec. 4.12 will hold. If you can do this successfully, there should be no logical inconsistency hidden in these axioms!

9. Axioms—more algebra: How can one tell whether or not one of the axioms (1) of Sec. 4.12, say

$$ab = ba,$$

could be *deduced* from the others, and therefore omitted from the list? One way to get a negative answer is to construct a model which satisfies all of the axioms *except* the axiom $ab = ba$. (For then, if "$ab = ba$" could be deduced from the others, how could it be false when the other axioms are all true?)

Here is one model: A "number" will now be a new sort of gadget, a 2 by 2 "matrix." (Later on I'll discuss a practical use for matrices.) A *2 by 2 matrix A* is *any* array of four real numbers (enclosed here by symbols $\| \|$), the *position* of each number being important

$$A = \begin{Vmatrix} a & b \\ c & d \end{Vmatrix}.$$

I hereby *define* how to "add" matrices:

$$\begin{Vmatrix} a_1 & b_1 \\ c_1 & d_1 \end{Vmatrix} \oplus \begin{Vmatrix} a_2 & b_2 \\ c_2 & d_2 \end{Vmatrix} = \begin{Vmatrix} a_1+a_2 & b_1+b_2 \\ c_1+c_2 & d_1+d_2 \end{Vmatrix}$$

In this expression the symbol $\oplus$ just indicates the new kind of addition. On the right-hand side $a_1 + a_2$ means the ordinary sum of real numbers a_1 and a_2. By definition, also, the "zero matrix" is

$$O = \begin{Vmatrix} 0 & 0 \\ 0 & 0 \end{Vmatrix}$$

and the "1 matrix" is

$$I = \begin{Vmatrix} 1 & 0 \\ 0 & 1 \end{Vmatrix}.$$

Finally, I define how to "multiply" two matrices:

$$\begin{Vmatrix} a_1 & b_1 \\ c_1 & d_1 \end{Vmatrix} \otimes \begin{Vmatrix} a_2 & b_2 \\ c_2 & d_2 \end{Vmatrix} = \begin{Vmatrix} a_1 a_2 + b_1 c_2 & a_1 b_2 + b_1 d_2 \\ c_1 a_2 + d_1 c_2 & c_1 b_2 + d_1 d_2 \end{Vmatrix}.$$

In this expression the $\otimes$ symbol just indicates the new kind of multiplication.

(a) Add $\begin{Vmatrix} 1 & -2 \\ 3 & 4 \end{Vmatrix} \oplus \begin{Vmatrix} 0 & 0 \\ 0 & 0 \end{Vmatrix} = \begin{Vmatrix} ? & ? \\ ? & ? \end{Vmatrix}$

(b) Add $\begin{Vmatrix} 1 & -2 \\ 3 & 4 \end{Vmatrix} \oplus \begin{Vmatrix} 3 & 0 \\ -1 & 0 \end{Vmatrix} = \begin{Vmatrix} ? & ? \\ ? & ? \end{Vmatrix}$

(c) Add $\begin{Vmatrix} 3 & 0 \\ -1 & 0 \end{Vmatrix} \oplus \begin{Vmatrix} 1 & -2 \\ 3 & 4 \end{Vmatrix} = \begin{Vmatrix} ? & ? \\ ? & ? \end{Vmatrix}$

(d) Multiply $\begin{Vmatrix} 1 & -2 \\ 3 & 4 \end{Vmatrix} \otimes \begin{Vmatrix} 1 & 0 \\ 0 & 1 \end{Vmatrix} = \begin{Vmatrix} ? & ? \\ ? & ? \end{Vmatrix}$

(e) Multiply $\begin{Vmatrix} 1 & -2 \\ 3 & 4 \end{Vmatrix} \otimes \begin{Vmatrix} 3 & 0 \\ -1 & 0 \end{Vmatrix} = \begin{Vmatrix} ? & ? \\ ? & ? \end{Vmatrix}$

(f) Multiply $\begin{Vmatrix} 3 & 0 \\ -1 & 0 \end{Vmatrix} \otimes \begin{Vmatrix} 1 & -2 \\ 3 & 4 \end{Vmatrix} = \begin{Vmatrix} ? & ? \\ ? & ? \end{Vmatrix}$

(g) Which of the following axioms hold?
$$A \oplus 0 = A$$
$$A \oplus B = B \oplus A$$
$$A \otimes I = A$$
$$A \otimes B = B \otimes A$$

(h) How about other axioms in the list (1) of Sec. 4.12? Is

$$ab = ba$$

deducible from the others?

4.14 SUMMARY OF CHAPTER 4

DEFINITIONS: Let's speak of the *number line* as the set of all real numbers, identified with—that is, put into one-to-one correspondence with—points on a Euclidean line; where we take as the *distance* between two numbers a and b (or their corresponding points) the absolute value $|b-a|$. (Sec. 4.1)

DEFINITIONS: *Closed interval* $[a, b]$: the set of all real numbers x with $a \leqslant x \leqslant b$. *Open interval* $\langle a, b \rangle$: the set of all real numbers x with $a < x < b$. (Sec. 4.1)

REMARK: The condition $|x-a| \leqslant d$ is equivalent to $a-d \leqslant x \leqslant a+d$; that is, x lies in the closed interval $[a-d, a+d]$. (Sec. 4.1)

DEFINITIONS: Let's speak of the *(rectangular) coordinate plane* as the set of all ordered pairs (x, y) of real numbers, identified with—that is, put into one-to-one correspondence with—points in a Euclidean plane; where we calculate *distance* between points (x_1, y_1) and (x_2, y_2) by the formula

$$\sqrt{(x_2-x_1)^2 + (y_2-y_1)^2} .$$

(Sec. 4.2)

ALGEBRAIC DESCRIPTION *of a circle of radius r and center* (a, b): the set of all points (x, y) whose coordinates x and y satisfy the equation

$$(x-a)^2 + (y-b)^2 = r^2.$$

(Sec. 4.2)

[Sec. 4.3, problems on labeling]

ALGEBRAIC DESCRIPTION of a *nonvertical line*: the set of all points (x, y) whose coordinates satisfy an equation of the form

$$y = mx + b.$$

The line intersects the vertical axis at $(0, b)$. The constant m is the *slope* of the line. It measures the change in vertical position along the line per unit change in horizontal position. (Sec. 4.4)

DEFINITION: The *difference ratio* determined by two points (x_1, y_1) and (x_2, y_2) where $x_1 \neq x_2$, is the ratio

$$\frac{y_2-y_1}{x_2-x_1} .$$

(Sec. 4.4)

REMARK: Any two distinct points (x_1, y_1) and (x_2, y_2) on a nonvertical line determine its slope by their difference ratio

$$m = \frac{y_2-y_1}{x_2-x_1} .$$

(Sec. 4.4)

ALGEBRAIC DESCRIPTION OF A VERTICAL LINE: the set of all points (x, y) whose coordinates satisfy an equation of the form

$$x = a.$$

(Sec. 4.4)

REMARK: Two lines with respective equations $y = m_1x + b_1$ and $y = m_2x + b_2$ are *parallel* if and only if $m_1 = m_2$. They are *perpendicular* if and only if $m_1m_2 = -1$. (Sec. 4.5)

[Sec. 4.6, problems on lines and analytic geometry]

DEFINITION: The *graph* of a function f, whose domain is a set of real numbers D, is the set of all ordered pairs of the form $(x, f(x))$ for inputs x in D. (Sec. 4.7)

DEFINITION: A *linear function* is one whose domain D is a set of real numbers, and whose rule can be written in the form

$$f(x) = mx + b$$

(Sec. 4.7)

REMARK: A function is linear if and only if its graph is a subset of a line with equation $y = mx + b$. (Sec. 4.7)

[Sec. 4.8, problems on graphs]

REMARK on *geometric probability*:
For an experiment whose possible outcomes comprise an interval $\Omega = [x_1, x_2]$, and a compound result $A = [a, b] \subset \Omega$, we can assign probability

$$P(A) = \frac{\text{length of } A}{\text{length of } \Omega} = \frac{b - a}{x_2 - x_1}$$

— in analogy with the formula

$$P(A) = \frac{\text{size of } A}{\text{size of } \Omega}$$

useful for *finitely* many *equally likely* outcomes. This definition makes all subintervals of the same length "equally likely." (Sec. 4.9)

For an experiment whose possible outcomes comprise, say, a square or rectangle Ω in the coordinate plane, we can assign probability

$$P(A) = \frac{\text{area of } A}{\text{area of } \Omega}$$

for reasonable subsets A — to preserve the same analogy. (This definition also yields independence of certain horizontal and vertical rectangles.) (Sec. 4.9)

[Sec. 4.10, problems on geometric probability]

For geometric-algebraic notions in higher-dimensional space, see Sec. 4.11.

Archimedes' axiom regarding order in the real number system: given any two positive numbers a and b, there exists a positive integer n such that

$$b < na.$$

(Sec. 4.12)

For other axioms, see Sec. 4.12.

[Sec. 4.13, problems on spaces and axioms]

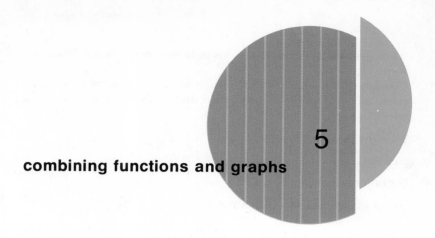

5

combining functions and graphs

In this chapter, I'll describe several ways to build a new function from given ones—or to view a given function as composed of simpler parts.

5.1 "SCALING," ADDITION, SUBTRACTION, MULTIPLICATION, DIVISION, AND "COMPOSITION" OF FUNCTIONS

I've defined and illustrated these operations—and the new functions to which they lead—in green in Figs. 5-1 through 5-7.

FIGURE 5-1   "SCALING" A FUNCTION (MULTIPLYING BY A CONSTANT): $h = cf$

$h(x) = cf(x)$

for each input x, and c a fixed constant

weight (in gms)

$h(x)$ = wt of sugar consumed per hour = $2f(x)$

$f(x)$ = wt of bacterial population

14.58

7.29

2
1

x in hours

Multiplying $f(x)$ by the constant c merely changes the vertical scale of the graph. In Fig. 5-1, where $c = 2$, the graph describes a population ("Escherichia coli") wherein each bacterium eats roughly twice its weight before splitting.

For a more concrete instance of scaling:

EXAMPLE 1. If $f(x) = 5x^3 - 7x + 2$ and $c = 3$, then

$$h(x) = 3f(x) = 15x^3 - 21x + 6.$$

ADDITION OF FUNCTIONS: $h = f + g$ **FIGURE 5-2**

$h(x) = f(x) + g(x)$

for each input x in
the common domain

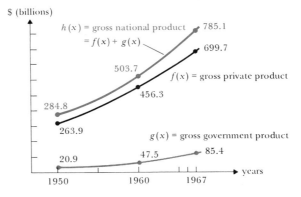

To graph the new function h, add graph heights for f and g above
each x.

EXAMPLE 2. If $f(x) = 5x^3 - 7x + 2$ and $g(x) = 3x^2 + x - 3$, then

$$h(x) = f(x) + g(x) = (5x^3 - 7x + 2) + (3x^2 + x - 3)$$

$$= 5x^3 + 3x^2 - 6x - 1.$$

SUBTRACTION OF FUNCTIONS: $h = f - g$ **FIGURE 5-3**

$h(x) = f(x) - g(x)$

for each input x in
the common domain

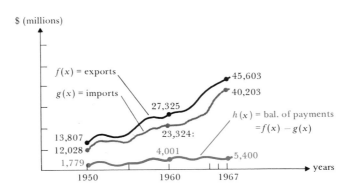

To graph the new function h, subtract graph heights for f and g
at each x.

EXAMPLE 3. If $f(x) = 5x^3 - 7x + 2$ and $g(x) = 3x^2 + x - 3$, then

$$h(x) = f(x) - g(x) = (5x^3 - 7x + 2) - (3x^2 + x - 3)$$

$$= 5x^3 - 3x^2 - 8x + 5.$$

FIGURE 5-4   MULTIPLICATION OF FUNCTIONS: $h = fg$

$h(x) = f(x) \cdot g(x)$

for each input x in
the common domain

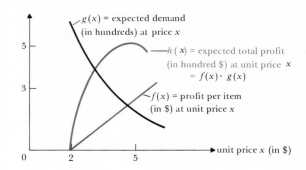

$g(x)$ = expected demand
(in hundreds) at price x

$h(x)$ = expected total profit
(in hundred \$) at unit price x
$= f(x) \cdot g(x)$

$f(x)$ = profit per item
(in \$) at unit price x

unit price x (in \$)

In Fig. 5-4 we can interpret the numbers $f(x)$ in the product $f(x)g(x)$ as scaling the graph heights $g(x)$, but differently for different inputs x.

EXAMPLE 4. If $f(x) = x - 2$ and $g(x) = (1000/x)$ for $x \geqslant 2$, then

$$h(x) = f(x)g(x) = (x-2)\frac{1000}{x} = 1000 - \frac{2000}{x} \qquad \text{for } x \geqslant 2.$$

FIGURE 5-5   DIVISION OF FUNCTIONS: $h = f/g$

$h(x) = f(x)/g(x)$

for each input x in
the common domain
$(g(x) \neq 0$ for all $x)$

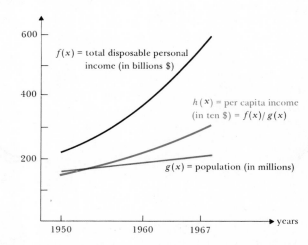

$f(x)$ = total disposable personal
income (in billions \$)

$h(x)$ = per capita income
(in ten \$) = $f(x)/g(x)$

$g(x)$ = population (in millions)

years

EXAMPLE 5. If $f(x) = x - 2$ and $g(x) = (1000/x)$ for $x \geqslant 2$, then

$$h(x) = \frac{f(x)}{g(x)} = \frac{x-2}{1000/x} = \frac{x^2 - 2x}{1000}.$$

$$h(x) = g(f(x))$$

FIGURE 5-6

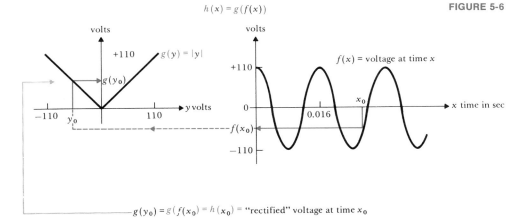

$g(y_0) = g(f(x_0)) = h(x_0) = $ "rectified" voltage at time x_0

"COMPOSITION" OF FUNCTIONS: $h = g(f)$

$$h(x) = g(f(x))$$

for each input x whose output $f(x)$ is itself an input of g.

To illustrate this operation, I've sketched an alternating current voltage $f(x)$ as a function of time x in the right-hand graph of Fig. 5-6. For some purposes such a current can be fed into a "voltage rectifier," a device which converts alternating into direct current. Ideally, a rectifier receives a voltage y (+ or −) and puts out the voltage $g(y) = |y|$. See the left-hand graph in Fig. 5-6.

To find the "rectified" voltage $h(x_0)$ at time x_0, just feed the value $f(x_0)$ into the g graph as an input—call it y_0—and find $g(y_0) = g(f(x_0)) = h(x_0)$. See Fig. 5-7 for the resulting graph of $h = g(f)$.

Here is another instance of composition:

EXAMPLE 6. If $f(x) = x^3 + 1$ for all real x and $g(y) = \sqrt{y}$ for all $y \geqslant 0$, then $h(x) = g(f(x)) = \sqrt{x^3 + 1}$ for all $x \geqslant -1$. For $x < -1$, $f(x)$ will be negative and not in the domain of g—so g won't "admit" the feed through for such x.

FIGURE 5-7

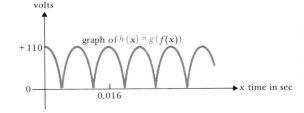

5.2 LINEAR FUNCTIONS

Note that if a function f is linear on an interval $[x_1, x_2]$, then any scaling of it must be also: if $f(x) = mx + b$, then

$$cf(x) = (cm)x + cb \qquad \text{for } x \text{ in } [x_1, x_2].$$

Moreover, if two functions f and g are linear on an interval $[x_1, x_2]$, then their sum must be also: if $f(x) = m_1 x + b_1$ and $g(x) = m_2 x + b_2$, then

$$(f + g)(x) = m_1 x + b_1 + m_2 x + b_2$$
$$= (m_1 + m_2)x + (b_1 + b_2) \qquad \text{for } x \text{ in } [x_1, x_2].$$

Similarly for $f - g$. These facts should simplify the drawing of graphs for the cases of cf and $f \pm g$.

5.3 REPEATED OPERATIONS

You yourself can synthesize complicated functions by applying several of the above operations repeatedly.

EXAMPLE 1. Take a function such as $f(x) = \frac{1}{4} + \frac{1}{4}x + \frac{1}{2}x^2$, for $0 \leqslant x \leqslant 1$, and compose it with itself several times to get higher degree polynomials,

$$f(f(x)) = \frac{1}{4} + \frac{1}{4}\left(\frac{1}{4} + \frac{1}{4}x + \frac{1}{2}x^2\right) + \frac{1}{2}\left(\frac{1}{4} + \frac{1}{4}x + \frac{1}{2}x^2\right)^2$$

$$= \frac{11}{32} + \frac{1}{8}x + \frac{9}{32}x^2 + \frac{1}{8}x^3 + \frac{1}{8}x^4, \tag{1}$$

$$f(f(f(x))) = \ldots, \text{ etc.}$$

The explicit formulas get messy, but to trace the fate of an original input x_0 during successive compositions, just follow the green staircase in Fig. 5-8.

FIGURE 5-8

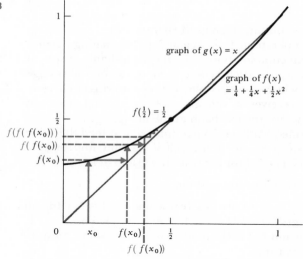

Each successive value

$$x_1 = f(x_0), \quad x_2 = f(f(x_0)), \quad x_3 = f(f(f(x_0))), \ldots \tag{2}$$

is an output

$$x_n = f(x_{n-1}) \tag{3}$$

of f corresponding to the previous value x_{n-1} as input. Note how the staircase is trapped between the graphs of $f(x)$ and $g(x) \equiv x$ — *provided* that I've drawn the graph of f correctly. The graphs meet at the point $(\frac{1}{2}, \frac{1}{2})$; so the sequence of numbers x_n would seem to "converge" to $\frac{1}{2}$ if we choose larger and larger n. And this seems to hold for *any* original input $x_0 \leqslant \frac{1}{2}$. Will there be similar convergence when $x_0 > \frac{1}{2}$?

In an opposite direction, you can try to *analyze* a given function as built (by someone else) via repeated applications of the operations above. In particular, all *polynomials* arise from the two simplest functions $f(x) \equiv 1$ and $g(x) \equiv x$ merely by successive multiplications, scalings, and additions.

EXAMPLE 2. With $f(x) \equiv 1$ and $g(x) \equiv x$ we can write the polynomial

$$P(x) = 2x^3 - 3x^2 + 4x - 5$$

as

$$P = 2(g \cdot g \cdot g) + (-3)(g \cdot g) + (4)g + (5)f. \tag{4}$$

Of what use is such analysis? Firstly: whenever we develop a new concept involving functions, it will always help to check how the concept works on the simplest functions, and then see how it carries over to more complicated ones built up from these.

Secondly: these are days of calculation by high speed computers — which, after all, are just enormous mindless machines. At one stage or another, someone must tell a machine exactly what operations to perform upon its input. And analyses such as in the above example suggest these instructions. See Fig. 5-9 for a "flow chart" picturing the operations in the polynomial (4) above.

FIGURE 5-9

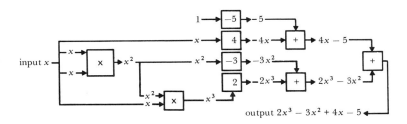

5.4 MACHINE DIAGRAMS

One of the ways I pictured a function in Chapter 2 was as a "machine" in a box, converting inputs into outputs. Now, given two functions f and g, it may help to picture a combining operation by suitably linking together the individual machine boxes of f and g and packaging the result as a new, bigger, machine box. See Fig. 5-10 for two examples.

FIGURE 5-10

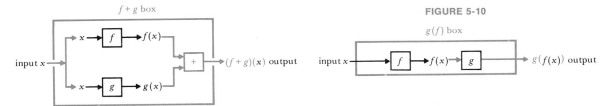

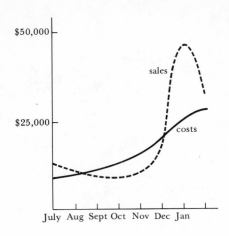

5.5 PROBLEMS ON COMBINING FUNCTIONS AND GRAPHS

°1. The accompanying graph illustrates a possible financial record for a toy manufacturing company for the second half of a year, July through December. Graph the company's profit curve for the same period of time.

°2. Let $f(x) = x$, $g(x) = 2x + 1$.

(a) *Sample.* Write a rule for $f + g$

$$(f+g)(x) = f(x) + g(x) = x + 2x + 1 = 3x + 1$$

(b) Write a rule for $2f$
(c) Write a rule for $f - g$
(d) Write a rule for $3f \cdot g - g$
(e) Evaluate (b) at $x = -1$
(f) Evaluate (c) at $x = 3$
(g) Evaluate (d) at $x = 2$.

3. Using the functions $f(x) = 1$, $g(x) = x$, and $h(x) = x^2$ as elementary components, show how each of the following functions can be built via *scaling* and *additions*. Then, graph each of the elementary components; and combine them graphically to obtain the graph of the synthesized function. (Use the set of all real numbers as the domain of each of the functions in this problem.)

(a) *Sample: $F(x) = 2x^2 - 1$.*
Answer: $F = 2h + (-1)f$

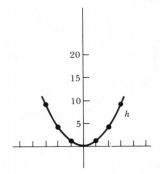

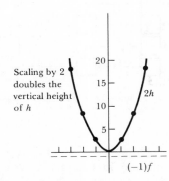

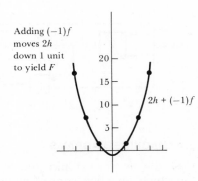

(b) $F(x) = x^2 + 1$ (c) $F(x) = 1 - 2x$ (d) $F(x) = x^2 + x$
(e) $F(x) = -x^2 - 4$ *(f) $F(x) = -x^2 + x$

4. Sketch the graph of each of the following functions by first sketching graphs for the two functions of which it is the *sum*, and then adding vertical heights.

(a) *Sample: $f(x) = x + \dfrac{1}{x}$ for all real $x \neq 0$*

Solution: Let $g(x) = x$

$$h(x) = \frac{1}{x}$$

Then $f = g + h$

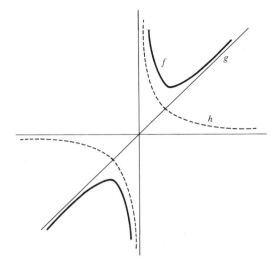

(b) $f(x) = |x| + x$ for all real x
(c) $f(x) = x - 1/x$ for all real $x \neq 0$
(d) $f(x) = |x| + |x|/x$ for all real $x \neq 0$
(e) $f(x) = x^3 + x$ for all real x
*(f) $f(x) = x^3 - x$ for all real x
(g) $f(x) = x^2 + 1/x^2$ for all real x
(h) $f(x) = x^2 - 1/x^2$ for all real x

5. On the same coordinate axes, graph $g(x) = 2x + 1$, $0 \leqslant x \leqslant 1$, and the functions defined by:

    (a) $G(x) = g(-x)$ $-1 \leqslant x \leqslant 0$
    (b) $G(x) = -g(-x)$ $-1 \leqslant x \leqslant 0$
    (c) $G(x) = g(x-7)$ $7 \leqslant x \leqslant 8$
    (d) $G(x) = 2g(x) - 1$ $0 \leqslant x \leqslant 1$
    (e) $G(x) = g(x/3)$ $0 \leqslant x \leqslant 3$
    (f) $G(x) = g(3x)$ $0 \leqslant x \leqslant \frac{1}{3}$

6. I noted in Sec. 5.2 that scaling of a linear function yields another linear function and that the sum and difference of two linear functions (with common domain) yield linear functions.
    (a) Under what conditions is the product of two linear functions linear?
    (b) Under what conditions is the composition of two linear functions linear?

7. (a) If f is a linear function how is the slope of the scaled function cf, where c is a constant, related to the slope of the graph of f?
    (b) If f and g are linear functions with common domain, how are the slopes of the graphs of $f + g$ and $f - g$ related to the slopes of the graphs of f and g?
    (c) How is the slope of the graph of the composite linear function $f(g)$ related to the slopes of the two functions f and g?

8. Let the graph of f be as shown in the figure, and let $g(x) = |x|$. Sketch the graph of

(a) $h(x) = g(f(x)) = |f(x)|$ (b) $h(x) = f(g(x)) = f(|x|)$

(c) $h(x) = f(-g(x)) = f(-|x|)$

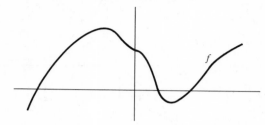

9. Consider the following linear functions:

$f(x) = \frac{1}{2}$ $0 \leqslant x \leqslant 3$

$g(x) = 2x + 1$ $0 \leqslant x \leqslant 1$

$h(x) = -\frac{1}{3}x + 1$ $0 \leqslant x \leqslant 3$

(a) On the same coordinate axes graph f, g, and each of the following functions where they are defined: $fg, -g, g+f, gh$.

(b) Determine and graph $f(g)$ and $g(f)$.

(c) Determine and graph $g(h)$ and $h(g)$.

10. Let $g(x) = \begin{cases} 1 & 0 \leqslant x \leqslant 2 \\ x & 2 < x \leqslant 3 \end{cases}$ and $h(x) = \begin{cases} 2x & 0 \leqslant x \leqslant 1 \\ 1/x & 1 < x \leqslant 3. \end{cases}$

(a) What is $h(g(x))$? $g(h(x))$? What are their respective domains?

(b) Draw graphs of g and h side by side, and use arrows to show how outputs of one function "feed" into inputs of the other to yield a composition function $h(g)$ or $g(h)$.

(c) Graph the two composition functions $h(g)$ and $g(h)$.

11. *A Staircase Problem*: Let $f(x) = x^2 - x + 1$, $g(x) = x$ for all real x.

(a) Plot the functions f and g on the same axes.

(b) What is $f(f(x))$?

(c) For the input $x = \frac{1}{2}$, calculate $f(x), f(f(x)), f(f(f(x)))$, and $f(f(f(f(x))))$.

(d) Draw a "staircase" composition as in Fig. 5-8.

(e) Let $x_0 = \frac{1}{2}$, $x_1 = f(x_0)$, and in general $x_n = f(x_{n-1})$, $n \geqslant 1$. What number does the sequence of numbers x_n seem to "converge" toward? *Hint*: Look at the "staircase" you drew in (d).

(f) For $x_0' = \frac{3}{2}$ and $x_n' = f(x_{n-1}')$, $n \geqslant 1$, calculate x_1', x_2', x_3', x_4'. Does the sequence of numbers x_n' also seem to tend to the same value that you found in (e)?

*12. Are there functions f such that $f(f(x)) = f(x)$ for each x in the domain of f?

13. (a) Show that under "scaling" by a positive constant c, the maximum and minimum of the new function cf occur at the same input values as for the original function f.

(b) What happens to the maximum and minimum if we scale by a negative constant?

(c) Under scaling, what happens to the "zeros" of f—those inputs x_0 such that $f(x_0) = 0$?

*14. Again call an input x_0 a "zero" of a function h if $h(x_0) = 0$. For each of the following cases determine how the zeros of h are related to those of f and g.

    (a) *Sample:* The product $h = fg$.

       Solution: $h(x) = fg(x) = f(x)g(x)$. For any $x_0, f(x_0)g(x_0) = 0$ if and only if $f(x_0) = 0$ *or* $g(x_0) = 0$. Therefore, the set of "zeros" of $h = fg$ is the *union* of the set of "zeros" of f and the set of "zeros" of g.

    (b) The sum $h = f + g$.

    (c) The composition $h = g(f)$.

*15. Review the definition of "even" and "odd" functions given in Problem 13 of Sec. 4.8. Determine whether $f + g$, $f \cdot g$, and $f(g)$ are even, odd, or not necessarily either in the cases:

    (a) f and g are both even.

    (b) f and g are both odd.

    (c) f is odd and g is even.

    (d) f is even and g is odd.

5.6 INVERSE FUNCTIONS

There is another approach sometimes for creating useful new functions from old ones: If a function is one-to-one on a given domain— that is, if no two different inputs can have the same output—then we can create a new function rule by exchanging the roles of inputs and outputs.

    EXAMPLE 1: *The square root function.* Let's start with the squaring function $f(x) = x^2$ on the domain $D = \{$all $x \geqslant 0\}$. f is one-to-one on D since $0 < a < b$ implies that $a^2 < b^2$. I've sketched the graph of f in Fig. 5-11. If we reverse the direction of the assignment arrows, as in Fig. 5-12, we see a new function $g(y)$ which treats each former output y_0 now as an input and assigns to it its square root $g(y_0) = \sqrt{y_0} = x_0$. The old range R of the function f (on the y axis) is now the domain of g, and the former domain D of f (all $x \geqslant 0$) is now the range of g.

FIGURE 5-11

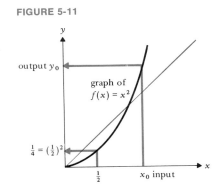

FIGURE 5-12

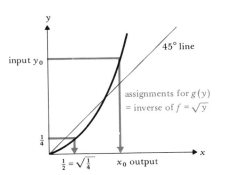

It's conventional to picture the domain of a function on the horizontal axis and the range on the vertical axis. To accomplish this format for g all we have to do is exchange the positions of the x and y axes in Fig. 5-12—say, by flipping the entire figure about the 45° line. Such a flip will display the graph of g (in green in Fig. 5-13) as an "image" of the old graph of f with the 45° line acting as "reflecting mirror."

FIGURE 5-13

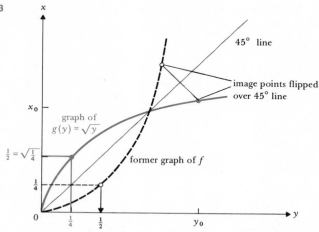

The new function $g(y) = \sqrt{y}$ is commonly called the *inverse* function of $f(x) = x^2$. We can also consider f as the "inverse" of g. In fact, each function undoes the work of the other. I've illustrated this process by machine diagrams in Fig. 5-14.

FIGURE 5-14

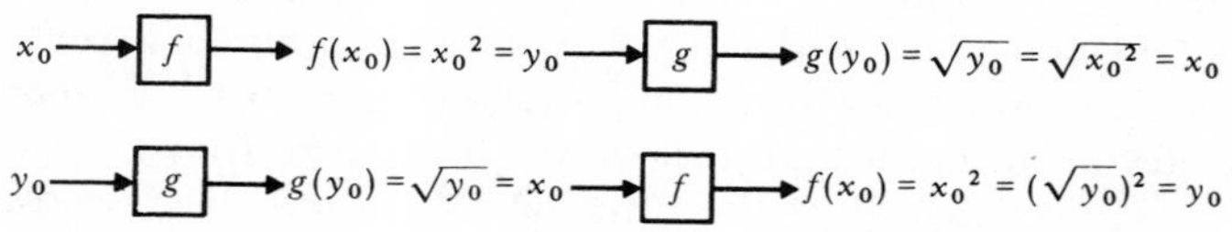

$$x_0 \longrightarrow \boxed{f} \longrightarrow f(x_0) = x_0{}^2 = y_0 \longrightarrow \boxed{g} \longrightarrow g(y_0) = \sqrt{y_0} = \sqrt{x_0{}^2} = x_0$$

$$y_0 \longrightarrow \boxed{g} \longrightarrow g(y_0) = \sqrt{y_0} = x_0 \longrightarrow \boxed{f} \longrightarrow f(x_0) = x_0{}^2 = (\sqrt{y_0})^2 = y_0$$

In symbols, these relationships read

$$g(f(x_0)) = x_0 \qquad \text{for all } x_0 \text{ in the domain of } f \tag{1}$$

and

$$f(g(y_0)) = y_0 \qquad \text{for all } y_0 \text{ in the domain of } g. \tag{2}$$

Definition. Let's call any two functions f and g *inverses* of each other if they are both one-to-one, if the range of f is the domain of g and the range of g is the domain of f and if (1) and (2) hold.

EXAMPLE 2. $f(x) = x^3$ for all real x, and $g(y) = \sqrt[3]{y}$ for all real y. Check that these are both one-to-one functions on their domains. I've indicated their graphs (in black and green) in Fig. 5-15, using a common pair of axes.

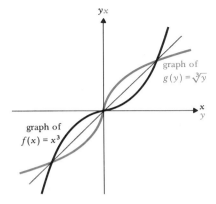

FIGURE 5-15

EXAMPLE 3. $f(x) = x^2$ for all $x \leqslant 0$, and $g(y) = -\sqrt{y}$ for all real y. See Fig. 5-16.

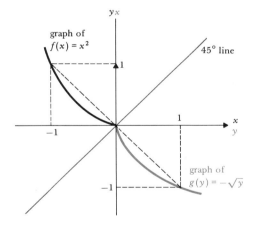

FIGURE 5-16

EXAMPLE 4. $f(x) = x^2$ for all real x, and $g(y) = ?$ It won't work: f is not one-to-one: $(-1)^2 = 1^2$.

5.7   PROBLEMS ON INVERSE FUNCTIONS

°1. Look at these mapping diagrams for functions with the domain in the left column and the range in the right column. Determine which functions have inverses and draw the mapping diagram for the inverse function.

(a) *Sample*:

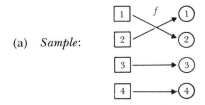

Solution: This function has an inverse since there is only one input mapped onto each output.

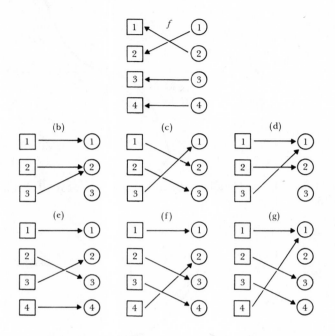

2. Which of the following functions have inverses? For those which do, graph the inverse function *g* and state its domain and rule.

(a) *Sample*: $f(x) = 3x + 2$ for $1 \le x \le 3$

  Solution: $y = 3x + 2$

  $3x = y - 2$

  $x = \dfrac{1}{3} y - \dfrac{2}{3}$

  $g(y) = \dfrac{1}{3} y - \dfrac{2}{3}$

  Domain of g = *Range* of f

  $= \{f(1) \le y \le f(3)\}$

  $= \{5 \le y \le 11\}$

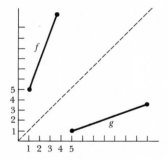

(b) $f(x) = 2x$ for all real x

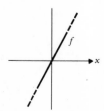

(c) $f(x) = |x|$ for all real x

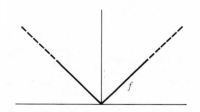

(d) $f(x) = |x| + 2$ for $-4 < x < 0$.

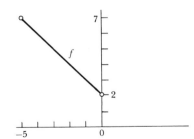

(e) $f(x) = x^3 + 3$ for all real x

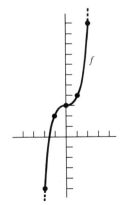

(f) $f(x) = x - 2$ for $1 \leqslant x \leqslant 6$

(g) $f(x) = \begin{cases} -2x \text{ for} -2 \leqslant x \leqslant 0 \\ x^2 \text{ for} \quad 0 < x \leqslant 2 \end{cases}$

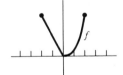

(h) $f(x) = \begin{cases} 2x \text{ for} -2 \leqslant x \leqslant 0 \\ x^2 \text{ for} \quad 0 < x \leqslant 2 \end{cases}$

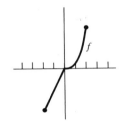

(i) $f(x) = x$ for all real x

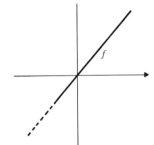

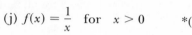

(j) $f(x) = \dfrac{1}{x}$ for $x > 0$ *(k) $f(x) = \begin{cases} 2x & -1 \leqslant x < 1 \\ 6 - 2x & 1 \leqslant x \leqslant 2 \end{cases}$

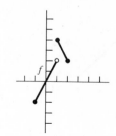

3. The general linear function has the form $f(x) = mx + b$ where m and b are fixed constants. Its graph is a straight line which crosses the y axis at $y = b$. What is its inverse? Does it always have an inverse? Is the inverse a straight line as well? If so, what is its slope and where does it cross the x axis?

4. Suppose the amount of food eaten per hour by a bacteria population of weight x is twice its weight. If you were a lab technician and had carefully measured the food consumed in an hour (call it y), how would you determine the bacterial population size for that hour?

5. The area of a circle as a function of its radius is given by the formula $A = \pi r^2$ for $r > 0$. Express the radius as a function of the area. What is the domain of this new function? What radius has area $A = 10$?

*6. Let f and g be inverses of each other. Show that if f is a *strictly increasing function*, then so is g. That is, show that if $y_1 > y_2$, then $g(y_1) > g(y_2)$. (Consider possible relations between $g(y_1)$ and $g(y_2)$ and apply f to them.)

*7. Can a function which is neither strictly increasing nor strictly decreasing have an inverse? If so, give an example.

5.8 AN APPLICATION OF COMPOSITION: THE PROBABILITY OF EXTINCTION

Suppose that an organism (call it "A") enters some host, lives for an hour, and then splits, leaving either *zero* viable offspring—with probability p_0, or *one* viable offspring—with probability p_1, or else *two* viable offspring—with probability p_2. Suppose also that, once born, each viable offspring will go on to live for an hour and to reproduce with the same probabilities as "A," completely *independently* of its siblings, cousins, and ancestors. Will the resultant disease die out or flourish ever more strongly?

What I have described is obviously an idealized model for a disease. Actual organisms don't split or lose viability " on the hour," and they don't live independently—but compete for food and space. Also they fight a complicated biochemical environment. However, in its abstract simplicity the model has generality: merely by changing terminology, we might use it to describe disintegration of atomic particles, or the evolution of family names in the English Peerage. (It was for this last purpose that Sir Francis Galton and Rev. Thomas Watson first studied it in the 1870's.)

Whether the disease ultimately explodes or becomes extinct should depend on the probabilities p_0, p_1, and p_2 for having viable offspring. For concreteness, suppose that $p_0 = \frac{1}{4}$, $p_1 = \frac{1}{4}$, and $p_2 = \frac{1}{2}$. Looking at a large number, say N, of independent parents, we might expect approximately $\frac{1}{4}N$ to leave zero viable offspring, $\frac{1}{4}N$ to leave one viable offspring, and $\frac{1}{2}N$ to leave two viable offspring—a grand total of

$$0 \times \tfrac{1}{4}N + 1 \times \tfrac{1}{4}N + 2 \times \tfrac{1}{2}N = \tfrac{5}{4}N \quad \text{viable offspring.}$$

Divide this total by N to get an *average* number of viable offspring *per parent* equal to

$$0 \times \frac{1}{4} + 1 \times \frac{1}{4} + 2 \times \frac{1}{2} = \frac{5}{4} \tag{1}$$

(a sum of products analogous to that for tossing a die, in Sec. 3.1). This average exceeds 1. Must the population therefore ultimately explode, or can it yet become extinct with some probability?

Here is a brief analysis: Let's call the original organism A together with all its future viable descendents a "dynasty," and let's represent a possible dynasty by arrows forming a horizontal family tree, as in Fig. 5-17 below. Suppose also that we can assign probabilities $P(S)$ to various sets S of possible dynasties. Let's try to find the probability— call it x_n—of the set of all dynasties that are extinct after n hours. This set splits into three *mutually exclusive* parts, according to whether organism A leaves zero, one, or two viable offspring. See the three cases in Fig. 5-17.

Each viable first generation offspring starts its own subdynasty. And if the original dynasty is to be extinct after n hours, then all such subdynasties must be extinct after an elapse of $n-1$ hours.

Now consider what the assumptions defining the model imply: Once a viable offspring is born at the end of hour # 1, the subsequent development of its subdynasty will be independent of what happened during hour # 1, and of simultaneous developments in any other subdynasty. For example, consider these three results:

(R_1) "A" produces two viable offspring (C and D) during hour # 1,

(R_2) subdynasty C is extinct after $n-1$ hours, and

(R_3) subdynasty D is extinct after $n-1$ hours.

FIGURE 5-17   Extinction of original dynasty after n hours

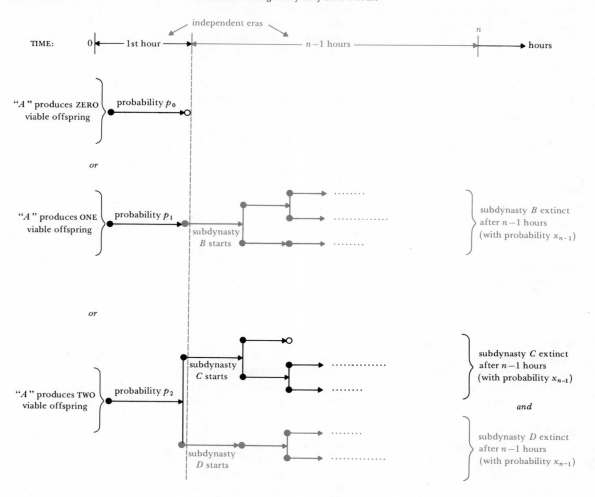

The results R_2 and R_3 should be independent of each other—given that C and D get born at all. Moreover, *if* C does get born, then the subsequent extinction of its dynasty (result R_2) should be independent of the fact that A had *two* offspring (result R_1). Similarly for D.

What does such "independence" mean in terms of probabilities? In Chapter 3, I argued that the probability for a *joint* occurrence of two "independent" results should be the product of their individual probabilities. *If* one could argue similarly about the three results here, we would have the probability

$$P(R_1 \text{ and } R_2 \text{ and } R_3) = P(R_1) \cdot P(R_2) \cdot P(R_3). \tag{2}$$

Let's suppose so, and see where (1) leads. (In Chapter 20, I'll discuss why (1) can hold even though R_2 and R_3 are conditional upon the births of C and D mentioned in R_1.)

Recall that mutually exclusive results have probabilities which add:

$$P(S_1 \ or \ S_2 \ or \ S_3) = P(S_1) + P(S_2) + P(S_3). \tag{3}$$

(See Problem 19 of Sec. 3.4.) We can apply (2) and (1) together to get a breakdown for the probability x_n of complete extinction by time n, as in Fig. 5-18.

FIGURE 5-18

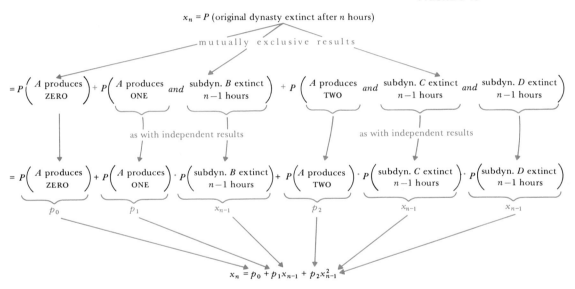

To get the last line in Fig. 5-18, I used the remaining assumption of the model: that all organisms reproduce with *exactly* the same probabilities as A. Should it not follow that the probability for any subdynasty to be extinct after $n-1$ hours will be the same as the probability x_{n-1} for the original dynasty to be extinct in the *same* elapse of time?

If so, then we can express each x_n in terms of the previous x_{n-1} via (3); and starting from x_1 we could calculate many x_n's, step by step. But for large n such cumulative work would be prohibitive. How then can we settle the question about "ultimate extinction" — about whether these extinction probabilities x_n converge to zero or to some larger number as time n goes on?

Just note in Fig. 5-18 that each x_n is an output

$$x_n = f(x_{n-1}) \tag{4}$$

corresponding to the input x_{n-1} via the function

$$f(x) = p_0 + p_1 x + p_2 x^2. \tag{5}$$

I traced just such a sequence of successive outputs, back in Fig. 5-8, for the case $p_0 = \frac{1}{4}$, $p_1 = \frac{1}{4}$, $p_2 = \frac{1}{2}$. There the x_n appeared to converge to $\frac{1}{2}$. Conclusion: for this case, even though the average number of viable offspring per parent exceeds 1, there still is probability $\frac{1}{2}$ for ultimate extinction rather than explosion of the population. Why? Because repeated chances for childlessness — each of weight $\frac{1}{4}$ — ultimately can take their toll.

5.9 *SUMMARY OF CHAPTER 5*

The following operations build new functions from given ones.

Operation	Given	New function	New rule	
Scaling	f, constant c	cf	$x \rightarrow cf(x)$	
Addition	f, g	$f + g$	$x \rightarrow f(x) + g(x)$	*
Subtraction	f, g	$f - g$	$x \rightarrow f(x) - g(x)$	*
Multiplication	f, g	fg	$x \rightarrow f(x)g(x)$	*
Division	f, g $(g(x) \neq 0)$	f/g	$x \rightarrow f(x)/g(x)$	*
Composition	f, g	$g(f)$	$x \rightarrow g(f(x))$	†

* indicates that two functions must have a common domain.
† indicates that the domain of g must contain the range of f.

See Sec. 5.4 for machine diagrams corresponding to several operations.

DEFINITION: Two functions f and g are *inverses* if they are each one-to-one, if the domain of g is the range of f and the range of f is the domain of g, and if

$$g(f(x_0)) = x_0 \qquad \text{for each } x_0 \text{ in the domain of } f$$

and

$$f(g(y_0)) = y_0 \qquad \text{for each } y_0 \text{ in the domain of } g.$$

(See Sec. 5.6)

A key principle: check out new concepts involving functions on simple examples first; then see how the concepts carry over to more complicated functions built up from simpler ones via the above operations.

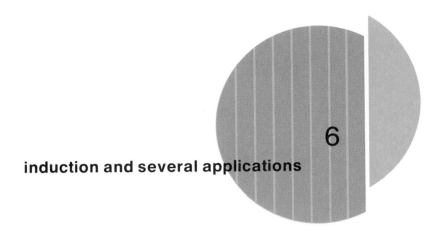

6

induction and several applications

In this chapter I'll discuss the notion of "induction," and apply it to such topics as compound interest, population growth, the probability addition rule for many mutually exclusive results, counting formulas, and the "binomial theorem."

6.1 INDUCTION

Think of a domino standing above each positive integer, as in Fig. 6-1.

FIGURE 6-1

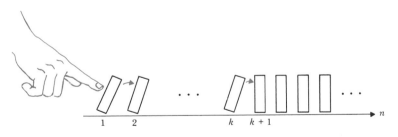

Suppose that
(a) domino Number 1 is pushed to the right, and
(b) the dominos stand so close to each other that *if* domino number k falls to the right it will cause domino number $k+1$ to fall rightwards also—for any given $k \geqslant 1$.

Intuitive conclusion: all dominos will fall, for all n along the line.

But no one has ever been all the way down the line to see whether the conclusion really holds. Therefore, we might best view the conclusion as an *axiom* about the positive integers—with the same status as other axioms about numbers.

Here is a more general version of the axiom, phrased to help in analyzing formulas and statements that depend on integers n: the so-called

"Principle" of mathematical induction: Suppose that we have a sequence of statements $\mathscr{S}_n$, one corresponding to each positive integer n. And suppose we can show two things:

(a) that $\mathscr{S}_1$ is true;
      and

(b) that for any k, the truth of $\mathscr{S}_k$ implies the truth of $\mathscr{S}_{k+1}$. Then we can conclude that *all* $\mathscr{S}_n$ must be true.

NOTE: To satisfy part (b) of the axiom we *don't* have to show that any $\mathscr{S}_k$ actually is true. We merely have to have some sort of argument—call it an "induction argument"—which will show that *if some $\mathscr{S}_k$ were true* then $\mathscr{S}_{k+1}$ would be also.

In the following sections, I'll discuss several examples of reasoning by induction.

6.2 THE GAME OF "TOWERS OF HANOI"

You have three spindles, and on one of them a stack of chips of decreasing radii (as in Fig. 6-2). Can you transfer the entire stack to another spindle by moving chips *one at a time*, from spindle to spindle, while never placing a larger chip above a smaller one?

FIGURE 6-2

FIGURE 6-3

An "induction argument"

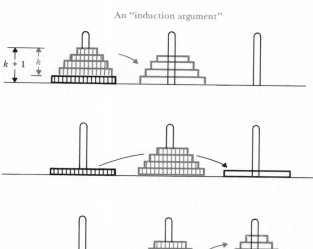

If the green transfers (⇢) are each possible in several steps, then the total transfer is too (for any k).

Answer: Yes, a stack of height n can be transferred, for any n. Why? (a) The assertion is true for $n = 1$. Moreover, (b) *if* it is true for stacks of height k, then it must be true for stacks of height $k+1$ — by the shifts I've indicated in Fig. 6-3. Hence the assertion is true for all n, by the induction axiom.

6.3 EXPONENTIAL INCREASE BEATS LINEAR, FOREVER

That is, $n < 2^n$ for all n; because

(a) $1 < 2^1$ $\qquad\qquad\qquad\qquad$ ($\mathscr{S}_1$ is true)

   and

(b)   If $k < 2^k$ $\qquad\qquad\qquad\qquad$ ($\mathscr{S}_k$

   add $1 < 2^k$ $\qquad\qquad\qquad\qquad\Downarrow$

   to get $k+1 < 2^k + 2^k = 2(2^k) = 2^{k+1}$ $\quad\mathscr{S}_{k+1}$)

6.4 COMPOUND INTEREST

Suppose you put N dollars in a bank that will pay you 5% interest on your money after one year. Then you will have $N + 0.05N$ dollars. More generally, if the annual interest rate is p, you will have $N + pN = (1+p)N$ dollars at the end of the year. You can get more from a bank that compounds the same annual interest rate p on a "semiannual basis" — that is, from a bank that will pay you $p/2$ interest after every $\frac{1}{2}$ year. After the first $\frac{1}{2}$ year, you will have

$$N_1 = N + \frac{p}{2}N = N\left(1 + \frac{p}{2}\right)$$

dollars with which to begin the second half year. By the end of the full year you will have

$$N_2 = N_1 + \frac{p}{2}N_1 = N_1\left(1+\frac{p}{2}\right) = N\left(1+\frac{p}{2}\right)^2$$

dollars. So $[1 + (p/2)]^2$ is the total factor by which each dollar is increased during the year. Similarly, if a bank pays $p/3$ interest every $\frac{1}{3}$ year, the amount N_1, N_2, and N_3 which you will have after the first, second, and third periods will be

$$N_1 = N\left(1+\frac{p}{3}\right), \qquad N_2 = N_1\left(1+\frac{p}{3}\right) = N\left(1+\frac{p}{3}\right)^2,$$

and

$$N_3 = N_2\left(1+\frac{p}{3}\right) = N\left(1+\frac{p}{3}\right)^3.$$

Some banks compound monthly, and some even daily. And you might guess a general formula: N dollars compounded m times a year at annual interest p will be worth

$$a_m = N\left(1+\frac{p}{m}\right)^m \tag{1}$$

dollars at the end of one year.

If you had doubts about formula (1), how could you prove it? By induction: let N_k be the amount present after k periods of length $1/m$. Then

$$N_1 = N + \frac{p}{m}N = N\left(1 + \frac{p}{m}\right);$$

and if

$$N_k = N\left(1 + \frac{p}{m}\right)^k,$$

then

$$N_{k+1} = N_k + \frac{p}{m}N_k = N_k\left(1 + \frac{p}{m}\right) = \left[N\left(1 + \frac{p}{m}\right)^k\right]\left(1 + \frac{p}{m}\right)$$
$$= N\left(1 + \frac{p}{m}\right)^{k+1}.$$

Hence $N_n = N[1 + (p/m)]^n$ for all n; and in particular, for $n = m$ (one year).

6.5 POPULATION GROWTH

Suppose we have a culture of N newly born bacteria, each of which will live for an hour and then split into two new similar organisms. Then the population size will double each hour, and will equal

$$a_h = N2^h \tag{2}$$

after h hours. (Induction again.)

Now compare the first culture with one containing a large number N of bacteria whose individual lifetimes may differ—though still "averaging" one hour. The organisms won't split simultaneously. But suppose they mature, on the average, as follows: During any short time interval of length, say, $(1/m)$th hour, there should occur splits in approximately $(1/m)$th of the population present at the beginning of *that* interval. How large will the resulting population be after one hour, and after h hours?

To get a manageable model for this situation let's choose an integer m, divide time into intervals of length $(1/m)$th hour, and pretend that all the splits due within a given interval occur only at its end. On the average, after the first interval there will be

$$N_1 = N + \frac{1}{m}N = N\left(1 + \frac{1}{m}\right)$$

bacteria present; and after the second, there will be

$$N_2 = N_1 + \frac{1}{m}N_1 = N_1\left(1 + \frac{1}{m}\right) = N\left(1 + \frac{1}{m}\right)^2,$$

and so on. It's exactly like compounding interest (in the previous section) with $p = 1$. Hence, for this model, there will be

$$N\left(1+\frac{1}{m}\right)^{n}$$

bacteria present after n time intervals of length $(1/m)$. In particular, (with $n = m$) there will be

$$b_{1} = N\left(1+\frac{1}{m}\right)^{m} \tag{3}$$

bacteria present at the end of one hour, and (with $n = hm$) there will be

$$b_{h} = N\left(1+\frac{1}{m}\right)^{hm} = N\left[\left(1+\frac{1}{m}\right)^{m}\right]^{h} \tag{4}$$

bacteria present after h hours. The hourly factor of increase, from hours h to $h+1$, will always be

$$\frac{b_{h+1}}{b_{h}} = \frac{N\{[1+(1/m)]^{m}\}^{h+1}}{N\{[1+(1/m)]^{m}\}^{h}} = \left(1+\frac{1}{m}\right)^{m}, \tag{5}$$

independently of h. For $m = 10$, the quantity $[1+(1/m)]^{m}$ is approximately 2.594—indicating that a population with mixed ages may do considerably more than double in an hour.

In Fig. 6-4 I've sketched in black a population graph for simultaneous hourly splitting ($m = 1$), and in green a population graph for $\frac{1}{10}$th—population splitting every $\frac{1}{10}$th hour ($m = 10$). Each graph is of height $N[1+(1/m)]^{n}$ over its $(n+1)$st interval of length $(1/m)$. Note how different the graphs are. Can we expect the one for $m = 10$ accurately to picture growth results for a real culture of mixed ages?

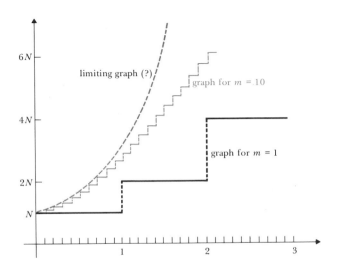

FIGURE 6-4

In actual cases, the starting size N is very large; for example, $N = 10^7$. Hence, for $m = 10$, there may be at least

$$\frac{1}{m}N = \frac{10^7}{10} = 10^6$$

bacteria splitting in each $\frac{1}{10}$th hour interval—and the idealization of lumping all these splits at the end of the interval may be a poor one. Perhaps we can improve our model by choosing shorter intervals, larger m's. Here are several choices for m, with corresponding hourly increase factors:

m	$\left(1 + \dfrac{1}{m}\right)^m$
10	2.594
10^2	2.704
10^3	2.717
10^4	2.7182
10^5	2.71827

(6)

Even with $m = 10^5$, there will be at least

$$\frac{1}{m}N = \frac{10^7}{10^5} = 100$$

splits within each interval. But note from the table (6) how the variation in hourly growth rates diminishes for large m. If we could choose m arbitrarily large, would the values $[1 + (1/m)]^m$ tend to a "limiting number"—a theoretical "upper bound" for hourly growth? And would the corresponding population graphs tend to a "limiting graph" for population growth (such as the dashed curve in Fig. 6-4)? Experimental growth records coincide remarkably well with the graphs for large values of m.

6.6 MUTUALLY EXCLUSIVE SUBSETS

Does the property of probability functions,

$$P(S \cup T) = P(S) + P(T) \tag{7}$$

for mutually exclusive subsets S and T, extend to *any* number of subsets?

For a fixed integer n, let $\mathscr{S}_n$ be the statement that

$$P(A_1 \cup A_2 \cup \cdots \cup A_n) = P(A_1) + P(A_2) + \cdots + P(A_n) \tag{8}$$

for any collection of n *mutually exclusive* subsets of a given set Ω. $\mathscr{S}_1$ just says that $P(S) = P(S)$; and $\mathscr{S}_2$ repeats (7). Moreover, we can unite any $k+1$ mutually exclusive sets $A_1, A_2, \ldots, A_k, A_{k+1}$ into two mutually exclusive parts,

$$S = A_1 \cup A_2 \cup \cdots \cup A_k \quad \text{and} \quad T = A_{k+1}, \tag{9}$$

to which (7) applies. See Fig. 6-5 for an induction scheme that uses this grouping idea to show that $\mathscr{S}_{k+1}$ will be true if $\mathscr{S}_k$ is.

FIGURE 6-5

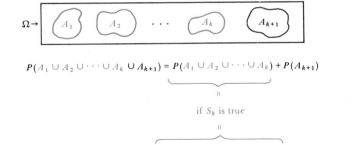

$$P(A_1 \cup A_2 \cup \cdots \cup A_k \cup A_{k+1}) = P(A_1 \cup A_2 \cup \cdots \cup A_k) + P(A_{k+1})$$

||

if S_k is true

||

$$= P(A_1) + P(A_2) + \cdots + P(A_k) + P(A_{k+1})$$

Conclusion: $\mathscr{S}_n$ is true for all n.

If you have read Sec. 3.5, you may recall a definition for the "independence" of two subsets, S and T, involving a *product* of probabilities:

$$P(S \cap T) = P(S)P(T). \tag{10}$$

Suppose now that we have n subsets, $S_1, S_2, \ldots, S_n$, each independent of any combination (via union, intersection, or complementation) of the others. I invite you to show, using induction as I did above for sums, that

$$P(S_1 \cap S_2 \cap \cdots \cap S_n) = P(S_1)P(S_2) \cdots P(S_n). \tag{11}$$

(Do Problem 4 of Sec. 6.7) I already discussed and used the case $n = 3$ in Example 3 of Sec. 3.5, in Problem 6 of Sec. 3.6, and in the population explosion example of Sec. 5.8.

6.7   PROBLEMS ON INDUCTION

1. Using the principle of mathematical induction, try to prove each of the following statements:

   (a) *Sample*: For each positive integer n,

   $$1^2 + 2^2 + 3^2 + \cdots + n^2 = \tfrac{1}{6}n(n+1)(2n+1).$$

   Reasoning: (i) $1^2 = \tfrac{1}{6} \cdot 1(1+1)(2 \cdot 1 + 1)$,

   $1^2 = \tfrac{1}{6} \cdot 1 \cdot 6 = 1.$ ($\mathscr{S}_1$ is true.)

   (ii) If $1^2 + 2^2 + 3^2 + \cdots + k^2 = \tfrac{1}{6}k(k+1)(2k+1)$ $\mathscr{S}_k$

   add $(k+1)^2 = (k+1)^2$

   to get

   $$1^2 + 2^2 + \cdots + k^2 + (k+1)^2 = \tfrac{1}{6}k(k+1)(2k+1) + (k+1)^2$$

   $$= \tfrac{1}{6}(k+1)(2k^2 + 7k + 6)$$

   $$= \tfrac{1}{6}(k+1)[(k+2)(2k+3)]$$

   $$1^2 + 2^2 + \cdots + k^2 + (k+1)^2 = \tfrac{1}{6}(k+1)[(k+1+1)(2(k+1)+1)]. \quad \mathscr{S}_{k+1}$$

Thus, by induction

$$1^2 + 2^2 + \cdots + n^2 = \tfrac{1}{6}n(n+1)(2n+1)$$

for every positive integer n.

(b) $1 + 2 + \cdots + n = \tfrac{1}{2}n(n+1)$ for each positive integer n.

(c) $1^3 + 2^3 + 3^3 + \cdots + n^3 = \dfrac{n^2(n+1)^2}{4}$ for each positive integer n.

(d) $2 + 4 + 6 + \cdots + 2n = n^2 + n$ for each positive integer n.

(e) $\dfrac{1}{2\cdot4} + \dfrac{1}{4\cdot6} + \cdots + \dfrac{1}{2n(2n+2)} = \dfrac{n}{4(n+1)}.$

(f) $5 + 5^2 + 5^3 + \cdots + 5^n = \tfrac{5}{4}(5^n - 1).$

2. (a) Note that
$$1 = 1$$
$$1 + 3 = 4$$
$$1 + 3 + 5 = 9$$
$$1 + 3 + 5 + 7 = 16.$$

Guess a general statement about the sum of the first n odd integers:

$$1 + 3 + 5 + 7 + \cdots + (2n - 1).$$

Prove it using mathematical induction.

(b) By calculating the sums for $n = 1, 2, 3,$ and 4 terms guess a general equation, for n any positive integer, of the numbers

$$\dfrac{1}{1\cdot2} + \dfrac{1}{2\cdot3} + \dfrac{1}{3\cdot4} + \cdots + \dfrac{1}{n(n+1)}$$

and prove it using mathematical induction.

(c) Guess a general equation for the product

$$\dfrac{2}{2}\cdot\dfrac{4}{3}\cdot\dfrac{6}{4}\cdot\dfrac{8}{5}\cdot\dfrac{10}{6}\cdots\cdots\dfrac{2n}{n+1}$$

and prove it using mathematical induction.

3. Prove that the following inequalities hold for every positive integer n.

(a) *Sample*: $2n \leqslant 2^n$.
   Reasoning: (i) $2\cdot1 \leqslant 2^1$
   $$2 \leqslant 2. \qquad (\mathscr{S}_1 \text{ is true.})$$
   (ii) If $2k \leqslant 2^k$
   add $\qquad 2 \leqslant 2^k$

   to get
   $$2k + 2 \leqslant 2^k + 2^k = 2^k(1+1)$$
   $$2(k+1) \leqslant 2^k\cdot2 = 2^{k+1}.$$

Thus, by induction $2n \leqslant 2^n$ for every positive integer n.

(b) $2n + 1 \leqslant 3^n$

(c) $3n \leqslant 3^n$

4. Suppose that we have a set of possible outcomes Ω, and a probability function P with domain the subsets of Ω. Suppose also that each of n subsets, $S_1, S_2, \ldots, S_n$, is independent of any combination of the others (via union, intersection, or complementation). Show that

$$P(S_1 \cap S_2 \cap \cdots \cap S_n) = P(S_1) \cdot P(S_2) \cdots \cdot P(S_n).$$

5. Prove each of the following equalities, either by direct multiplication and cancellation, or by induction:
(a) *Sample*: If x is a real number and n is any positive integer, then

$$x^n - 1 = (x-1)(1+x+x^2+\cdots+x^{n-1}).$$

Reasoning by induction:
(i) $x^1 - 1 = (x-1)\cdot 1.$ ($\mathscr{S}_1$ is true.)
(ii) If the statement is true for $n = k$, that is, if

$$x^k - 1 = (x-1)(1+x+x^2+\cdots+x^{k-1}),$$

then consider

$$x^{k+1} - 1.$$

Add and subtract x: $x^k\cdot x - x + x - 1 = x(x^k - 1) + (x-1).$ $\mathscr{S}_k$
Thus

$$\begin{aligned}
x^{k+1} - 1 &= x(x-1)(1+x+x^2+\cdots+x^{k-1}) + (x-1) \\
&= (x-1)[x+x^2+x^3+\cdots+x^k+1] \\
&= (x-1)(1+x+x^2+x^3+\cdots+x^{k+1-1}).
\end{aligned}$$

$\mathscr{S}_{k+1}$

Thus

$$x^n - 1 = (x-1)(1+x+x^2+\cdots+x^{n-1})   \text{for all } n.$$

(b) $b^n - a^n = (b-a)(b^{n-1} + ab^{n-2} + a^2 b^{n-3} + \cdots + a^{n-2}b + a^{n-1}).$
6. If $f_1, f_2, \ldots, f_n$ are n nonnegative functions with a common domain show that $f_1 + f_2 + \cdots + f_n$ is a nonnegative function. (Call a function f *nonnegative* if $f(x) \geq 0$ for all inputs x.)
7. If $f_1, f_2, \ldots, f_n$ are increasing functions with a common domain, show that $f_1 + f_2 + \cdots + f_n$ is increasing. (Call a function f *increasing* if $f(a) \leq f(b)$ for all inputs $a < b$.)
*8. (a) If f is a function with input x_0, such that $f(f(x_0)) = x_0$, what is

$$\underbrace{f(f(f(\ldots (f(x_0))\ldots)))}_{n \text{ times}}?$$

(b) If f is a function with input x_0 such that $f(f(x_0)) = f(x_0)$, what is

$$\underbrace{f(f(f(\ldots (f(x_0))\ldots)))}_{n \text{ times}}?$$

How would you prove these assertions?
9. Suppose f is a function, defined for all real numbers, which satisfies

$$f(x+y) = f(x) + f(y)$$

for all inputs x and y. Show that

$$f(x_1 + \cdots + x_n) = f(x_1) + \cdots + f(x_n)$$

where $x_1, \ldots, x_n$ are real numbers.

10. Let $A_1, A_2, \ldots, A_n$ be any n mutually exclusive finite sets. Let $N(A)$ denote the number of elements in the set A. Show that

$$N(A_1 \cup A_2 \cup \cdots \cup A_n) = N(A_1) + N(A_2) + \cdots + N(A_n).$$

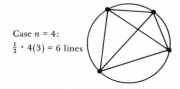

Case $n = 4$:
$\frac{1}{2} \cdot 4(3) = 6$ lines

11. Show that the number of lines formed by joining n distinct points lying on a circle is $\frac{1}{2}n(n-1)$.

12. Show that if n is any positive integer, then $n^3 + 2n$ is divisible by 3.

13. Suppose that $a_1, a_2, a_3, \ldots$ is a sequence of numbers (one for each positive integer n) such that $a_1 = 1$ and $a_n = 3a_{n-1} + 1$ for $n > 1$. Show that $a_n = \frac{1}{2}(3^n - 1)$.

14. Determine the minimum number of moves required to transfer a stack of n chips in the Tower of Hanoi game from one spindle to another. Let a_n be this minimum number.

   (a) Show that $a_1 = 1, a_2 = 3, a_3 = 7$.

   (b) Show that the minimum number of moves required for $k+1$ chips is related to that for k chips by the equation

   $$a_{k+1} = 2a_k + 1.$$

   (See Fig. 6-3.)

   (c) Use mathematical induction to show that $a_n = 2^n - 1$.

15. Let's now use induction to prove the contagiousness of being female: "whenever a group of people contains a female, it must consist exclusively of females." For $n = 1, 2, \ldots$, let $\mathscr{S}_n$ denote the statement: whenever a group of n people contains a female, it must consist exclusively of females. Let's show that $\mathscr{S}_n$ is true for every n. Clearly, $\mathscr{S}_1$ is true.

   To show that $\mathscr{S}_k$ implies $\mathscr{S}_{k+1}$, pick *any* group of $k+1$ people which contains a female. I've labeled the known female (there may be several) by the symbol "F" in the diagram.

Group of $k + 1$ people

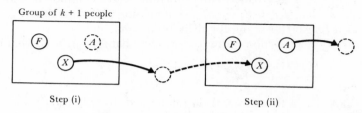

Step (i)   Step (ii)

Step (i): Extract some *other* person X from the group for a moment. This leaves a subset of k people, one of whom is F. If $\mathscr{S}_k$ is true, all k persons in this subset are females. There remains only the matter of determining the sex of X.

Step (ii): Return X to the group and extract some other person, say A, already known to be female by Step (i). This again leaves a subset of k people, one of whom is F. Again, these must all be females—in particular, X. So all of the original $k+1$ persons were females. And $\mathscr{S}_{k+1}$ follows from $\mathscr{S}_k$.

By induction, all $\mathscr{S}_n$ should be true. What's wrong with the proof?

16. For $n = 1, 2, 3, \ldots$ let $\mathscr{S}_n$ be the statement $n = n+7$. Note that if $\mathscr{S}_k$ is true $(k = k+7)$, then by adding 1 to each side of the equation we obtain $(k+1) = (k+1)+7$, that is, $\mathscr{S}_{k+1}$. Does it follow from the axiom of mathematical induction that $n = n+7$ for every positive integer n?

**17. Use induction to show that the "triangle inequality" for distance holds in n-dimensional space, for all n:

$$|PR| \leqslant |PQ| + |QR|,$$

or equivalently

$$|PR|^2 \leqslant |PQ|^2 + |QR|^2 + 2|PQ| \cdot |QR|, \qquad (1)$$

where P, Q, and R are any three "points" (n-tuples).

$P = (x_1, x_2, \ldots, x_n)$, $Q = (y_1, y_2, \ldots, y_n)$, and

$R = (z_1, z_2, \ldots, z_n)$,

and

$$|PQ|^2 = (x_1 - y_1)^2 + (z_2 - y_2)^2 + \cdots + (x_n - y_n)^2.$$

(a) Show that the assertion is true for $n = 1$.

(b) Suppose that the assertion holds for $n = k$. Pick any three points P, Q, and R in $(k+1)$-dimensional space, and saw off the $(k+1)$st coordinate of each to get corresponding points P', Q', and R' in k-dimensional space. For example,

$$P = (x_1, x_2, \ldots, x_k, x_{k+1}) \text{ and } P' = (x_1, x_2, \ldots, x_k).$$

(c) Write out the inequality (1) in detail for P', Q', and R'. Then write out a similar inequality for the sawed off coordinates:

$$(x_{k+1} - z_{k+1})^2 \leqslant (x_{k+1} - y_{k+1})^2 + (y_{k+1} - z_{k+1})^2$$

$$+ 2\sqrt{(x_{k+1} - y_{k+1})^2 (y_{k+1} - z_{k+1})^2}.$$

Add these two inequalities to get the inequality (1) for the original P, Q, R.

(d) For (c), you might find it convenient to use the inequality

$$\sqrt{a^2 b^2} + \sqrt{c^2 d^2} \leqslant \sqrt{(a^2 + c^2)(b^2 + d^2)} \qquad (2)$$

good for any nonnegative numbers a, b, c, and d. You can derive (2) from the inequality $(ad - bc)^2 \geqslant 0$, by squaring, making rearrangements and taking square roots.

(Let $a^2 = (x_1 - y_1)^2 + (x_2 - y_2)^2 + \cdots + (x_k - y_k)^2$,
$b^2 = (y_1 - z_1)^2 + (y_2 - z_2)^2 + \cdots + (y_k - z_k)^2$,
$c^2 = (x_{k+1} - y_{k+1})^2$ and $d^2 = (y_{k+1} - z_{k+1})^2$.)

6.8 COUNTING FORMULAS AND THE BINOMIAL THEOREM

The so-called "fundamental principle of counting" is the assertion that if you can do one task in m_1 distinct ways and if for each one of these you can accomplish a second task in m_2 distinct ways, then you can accomplish the joint task in $m_1 \times m_2$ distinct ways.

We can extend this "principle," again by induction, to a succession of n tasks, where you can accomplish the $(k+1)$st task in m_{k+1} distinct ways for any joint way of handling the first k tasks. You will have a total of

$$m_1 \times m_2 \times \cdots \times m_k \times \cdots \times m_n \tag{1}$$

distinct ways to accomplish the joint n-fold task.

Here are several applications of the counting principle.

Ordered samples. How many distinct ways are there for choosing r individuals out of a population of size n—if the *order* of choice is important and if no individual is to be chosen twice? Answer:

$$\underbrace{n(n-1)(n-2) \cdots (n-[r-1])}_{r \text{ factors}} \tag{2}$$

since there are n ways to accomplish the task of choosing the first individual; and once he is chosen, there are $n-1$ ways of choosing the second individual; and so on. A possible symbol for the product in (2) is

$$(n)_r = n(n-1)(n-2) \cdots (n-r+1) \qquad (\text{where } r \leq n). \tag{3}$$

EXAMPLE 1. Out of 10 contestants, how many different possibilities are there for first, second, and third prize winners? $(10)_3 = 10 \cdot 9 \cdot 8 = 720$. If all contestants are of equal ability, what's the probability that particular individuals A, B, and C win the first, second, and third prizes, respectively? Answer: Since the 720 possible outcomes seem equally likely, each should have elementary probability $1/720$—in particular, that A, B, C win as stated.

Permutations. How many distinct ways are there for arranging n individuals in left-to-right order? This is just a case of an ordered sample of size $r = n$ out of a population of size n. So, using a common symbol, $n!$—there should be

$$n! = n(n-1)(n-2) \cdots 2 \cdot 1 \tag{4}$$

distinct arrangements.

Here's how we could show this result directly by induction: (a) It's true when $n = 1$. (b) If the result were true for k individuals, then, given $k+1$ individuals, we could choose *one* of them (in $k+1$ different ways) to take first place, and then have $k!$ ways to arrange the remaining individuals—giving a total of

$$(k+1)k! = (k+1)k(k-1) \cdots 2 \cdot 1 = (k+1)!$$

possible arrangements. See Fig. 6-6. So for any n individuals there must be $n!$ distinct arrangements.

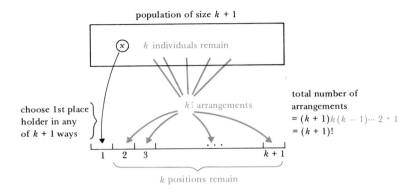

FIGURE 6-6

population of size $k + 1$

x

k individuals remain

$k!$ arrangements

choose 1st place holder in any of $k + 1$ ways

total number of arrangements

$= (k + 1)k(k - 1) \cdots 2 \cdot 1$

$= (k + 1)!$

1   2   3   . . . $k + 1$

k positions remain

Subsets of size r. How many distinct ways are there for choosing a subset of size r out of a population of size n — if the order of individuals within the subset is irrelevant?

One way to find this number — call it N — is to relate the N unordered subsets of size r with "*ordered* samples of size r" — all coming from the same population. Think of a given (unordered) subset of size r as a "cast of r characters." We can produce $r!$ distinct ordered samples of size r from this one cast of characters merely by arranging them in left-to-right order in the $r!$ possible permutations. Hence, choosing different casts of characters we can produce a grand total of $N \times r!$ distinct ordered samples of size r. But by a different argument above, I found this number to be $(n)_r$. Behold: an equation for the unknown $N: N \times r! = (n)_r$, or

$$N = \frac{(n)_r}{r!} \tag{5}$$

See Fig. 6-7 for the case $n = 3, r = 2$.

FIGURE 6-7

population $\boxed{A, B, C}$ of size $n = 3$

possible casts of characters of size $r = 2$

list of ordered samples of size $r = 2$

$N \left\{ \begin{array}{l} A, B \\ B, C \\ C, A \end{array} \right.$

A, B ——— yields $r! = 2$ ——→ $\left\{ \begin{array}{l} AB \\ BA \end{array} \right.$

B, C ——— yields $r! = 2$ ——→ $\left\{ \begin{array}{l} BC \\ CB \end{array} \right.$

C, A ——— yields $r! = 2$ ——→ $\left\{ \begin{array}{l} AC \\ CA \end{array} \right.$

$\left. \right\} (n)_r = (3)_r = 6$

$N \times r! = (n)_r$

A common symbol for the ratio in (5), used to show its dependence on n and r, is $\binom{n}{r}$. That is,

$$\binom{n}{r} = \frac{(n)_r}{r!} = \frac{n(n-1)\cdots(n-r+1)}{r!} \qquad \text{for } 1 \leqslant r \leqslant n. \tag{6}$$

Or, alternatively,

$$\binom{n}{r} = \frac{n(n-1)\cdots(n-r+1)}{r!} \cdot \frac{(n-r)(n-r-1)\cdots2\cdot1}{(n-r)(n-r-1)\cdots2\cdot1}$$

$$= \frac{n!}{r!(n-r)!} \qquad \text{for } 1 \leqslant r \leqslant n. \tag{7}$$

(To complete the symbolism for some formulas, let's also define $\binom{n}{0}$ as 1.)

EXAMPLE 2. In Sec. 4.11, I mentioned that test-score data for, say, five tests given to 20 school children could be viewed as determining 5 lines through the origin in 20-dimensional space. Part of a program for checking how "close" the tests are to each other involves calculating the cosines of the "angles" between each pair of lines.

According to (6), the computation must be made for

$$\binom{5}{2} = \frac{(5)_2}{2!} = \frac{5 \cdot 4}{1 \cdot 2} = 10 \text{ pairs of lines.}$$

I invite you to prove (6) directly by induction in doing Problem 6 of Sec. 6.9.

The "binomial expansion": Would compounding interest on a dollar 365 times a year really yield more money $\{\$[1+(p/365)]^{365}\}$ than compounding interest 52 times a year $\{\$[1+(p/52)]^{52}\}$ — and if so, is the difference significant?

To compare such quantities, it's helpful to have a scheme for writing powers of the form $(a+b)^n$ as orderly sums of simpler products. The earliest example of such a scheme is $(a+b)^2 = a^2+2ab+b^2$. How can we generalize such an expression for larger n? In Fig. 6-8, I've multiplied out the power $(a+b)^3$ to get a sum,

FIGURE 6-8

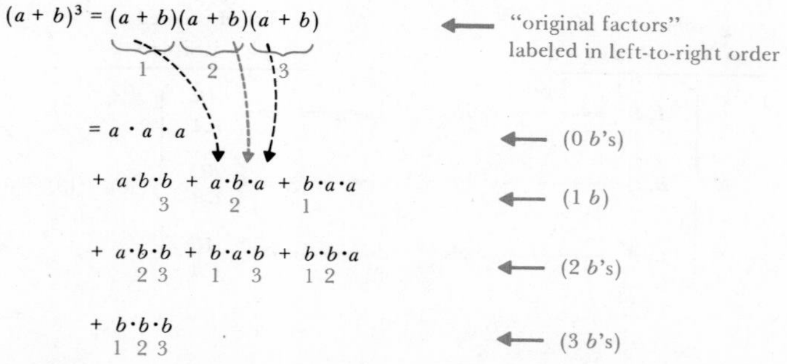

and I've classified each summand according to how many b's it contains and according to the origin of those b's from the original three $a+b$ factors—labeled in left-to-right order. Notice that each summand has $n=3$ factors—one from each of the original $a+b$ factors, and that the number, r, of possible b's in a summand varies from $r=0$ up to $r=n=3$. If there are r b's in a summand, there must be $n-r$ a's. For a given r, how many different summands can there be with exactly r b's? There can be as many as there are distinct ways to choose r of the original labeled $a+b$ factors to contribute the needed b's—namely $\binom{n}{r}$, the number of ways to choose a subset of size r from the "population" of n labeled original $a+b$ factors. Put these arguments together to get a sum of the form

$$(a+b)^3 = \binom{3}{0}a^3b^0 + \binom{3}{1}a^{3-1}b^1 + \binom{3}{2}a^{3-2}b^2 + \binom{3}{3}a^{3-3}b^3. \tag{8}$$

Why shouldn't the arguments also work for general n? If so, we should get a sum of the form

$$(a+b)^n =$$

$$\binom{n}{0}a^nb^0 + \binom{n}{1}a^{n-1}b^1 + \binom{n}{2}a^{n-2}b^2 + \cdots + \binom{n}{r}a^{n-r}b^r + \cdots + \binom{n}{n}a^{n-n}b^n, \tag{9}$$

the so-called "Binomial Expansion," where there are $n+1$ terms, one for each possible value of $r=0, 1, 2, \ldots, n$. I invite you to show that (9) holds for all positive integers n: write $(a+b)^{k+1} = (a+b)^k \cdot (a+b)$ and use induction—in Problem 7 of Sec. 6.9.

EXAMPLE 3. Is $(1+\tfrac{1}{2})^2 < (1+\tfrac{1}{3})^3$? Write

$$(1+\tfrac{1}{2})^2 = 1^2 + 2\cdot 1\cdot(\tfrac{1}{2}) \quad + (\tfrac{1}{2})^2 \tag{10}$$

and

$$(1+\tfrac{1}{3})^3 = 1^3 + 3\cdot 1^2\cdot(\tfrac{1}{3}) + 3\cdot 1\,(\tfrac{1}{3})^2 + (\tfrac{1}{3})^3 \tag{11}$$

Each of the first three terms in (11) is as large as the corresponding term in (10), and (11) even has one positive term left over—hence $(1+\tfrac{1}{2})^2 < (1+\tfrac{1}{3})^3$.

EXAMPLE 4. For any integer $m \geqslant 2$

$$\left(1+\frac{1}{m}\right)^m < \left(1+\frac{1}{m+1}\right)^{m+1} < 3. \tag{12}$$

(Hence the bacterial populations I discussed in Sec. 6.5 can't triple in size in one hour.) To see this, write the rth term in a "binomial sum" for $[1+(1/m)]^m$—namely the quantity

$$A_r = \binom{m}{r}1^{m-r}\left(\frac{1}{m}\right)^r = \frac{m(m-1)\cdots(m-r+2)(m-r+1)}{r!\,m^r} \tag{13}$$

(here $a = 1$, $b = 1/m$, and $n = m$). As in Example 3, compare A_r with the rth term in a "binomial sum" for

$$\left(1 + \frac{1}{m+1}\right)^{m+1}$$

namely the quantity

$$B_r = \binom{m+1}{r} 1^{m+1-r} \left(\frac{1}{m+1}\right)^r = \frac{(m+1)m(m-1)\cdots(m-r+2)}{r!\,(m+1)^r} \tag{14}$$

(here $a = 1$, $b = 1/(m+1)$ and $n = m+1$). I invite you to divide A_r by B_r and cancel various terms to check that $A_r \leqslant B_r$ for $r = 0, 1, 2, \ldots, m$. Hence the sum for $\{1 + [1/(m+1)]\}^{m+1}$ beats out that for $[1 + (1/m)]^m$, even having a positive term, $[1/(m+1)]^{m+1}$ left over.

To see that $[1 + (1/m)]^m < 3$ for any $m \geqslant 2$, note that for $2 \leqslant r \leqslant m$,

$$A_r = \frac{1}{r!} \frac{m(m-1)\cdots(m-r+1)}{m^r}$$

$$= \frac{1}{r!}\left(\frac{m}{m}\right)\left(\frac{m-1}{m}\right)\cdots\left(\frac{m-r+1}{m}\right) < \frac{1}{r!} \cdot 1 \cdot 1 \cdots 1 = \frac{1}{1 \cdot 2 \cdot 3 \cdots r}$$

$$< \underbrace{\frac{1}{1 \cdot 2 \cdot 2 \cdots 2}}_{r-1 \text{ factors}} = \frac{1}{2^{r-1}}. \tag{15}$$

Hence, comparing terms for each r, the binomial sum for $[1 + (1/m)]^m$ must be less than the sum

$$1 + 1 + \frac{1}{2} + \frac{1}{2^2} + \frac{1}{2^3} + \cdots + \frac{1}{2^{m-1}}. \tag{16}$$

Check that the "geometric" sum

$$\frac{1}{2} + \frac{1}{2^2} + \frac{1}{2^3} + \cdots + \frac{1}{2^{m-1}}$$

can't exceed 1. Hence the total sum in (16) can't exceed 3.
   I invite you to show in detail that, more generally,

$$\left(1 + \frac{p}{m}\right)^m < \left(1 + \frac{p}{m+1}\right)^{m+1} < 3 \tag{17}$$

for any positive $p \leqslant 1$ and for all $m \geqslant 2$. Do Problem 9 of the next section.

6.9 PROBLEMS ON COUNTING

°1. Evaluate:
   (a) *Sample*: $(11)_3$. *Answer*: $(11)_3 = 11 \cdot 10 \cdot 9 = 990$

   (b) $\dfrac{11!}{3!8!}$ (c) $\dfrac{(11)_3}{3!}$

(d) $(5)_5$ (e) $\binom{5}{4}$

(f) $\binom{10}{10}$ (g) $\binom{10}{1}$

°2. Write out a binomial expansion for:
   (a) $(a+b)^7$
   (b) $(a-b)^6$
   (c) $(2a-3b)^4$
°3. (a) Write in simplified form the term involving $a^3 b^9$ in $(2a-b)^{12}$.
   (b) In the expansion of $(x+y)^{50}$, what is the term that contains x^{30} as a factor?
   (c) In the expansion of $(x-y)^{13}$, what is the term that contains y^7 as a factor?
 4. By writing each of the following in the form $(1+b)^n$ or $(1-b)^n$ and expanding, find a numerical value for:
   (a) $(1.25)^4$
   (b) $(0.993)^3$
   (c) $(1.1)^6$
*5. (a) Using the binomial expansion, show that if n is a positive integer

$$\binom{n}{0}+\binom{n}{1}+\binom{n}{2}+\cdots+\binom{n}{n-1}+\binom{n}{n}=2^n.$$

   (b) What does this say about the total number of subsets of a set with n elements? (Include the empty set.)
*6. Use induction to show that, for any positive integers n and $r \le n$, a set of size n has exactly $\binom{n}{r}=\dfrac{n!}{r!\,(n-r)!}$ distinct subsets of size r.
**7. Use mathematical induction for a direct proof of the "Binomial Expansion": if a and b are real numbers and n is a positive integer, then

$$(a+b)^n = \binom{n}{0}a^n b^0 + \binom{n}{1}a^{n-1}b^1 + \binom{n}{2}a^{n-2}b^2 + \cdots + \binom{n}{r}a^{n-r}b^r$$

$$+\cdots+\binom{n}{n}a^0 b^n.$$

   Write $(a+b)^{k+1} = (a+b)^k(a+b)$. Show that

$$\binom{k}{r}+\binom{k}{r-1}=\binom{k+1}{r}.$$

 8. Use the binomial expansion to verify the intuitively obvious claim that, given any real numbers $A > 1$ and $B > 0$, there must be some integer n such that $A^n > B$.
   [Write $A = 1+C$, where $C > 0$. Show that $A^n > nC$ for any n, and recall "Archimedes' Axiom" in Sec. 4.12.]
**9. Paraphrase the reasoning in Example 4 of Sec. 6.8 to show that

$(1+p/m)^m < (1+p/(m+1))^{m+1} < 3$ for any positive $p \leq 1$ and any positive integer $m \geq 2$.

10. Suppose a rat is running a branching maze, so constructed that he first must choose one of a pair of doors, beyond each of these he must choose one of 3 doors, and beyond each of these he must choose one of 4 doors. After passing through a door he cannot return. How many paths are there from start to finish?

11. Five numbers 1, 3, 5, 6, and 8 are written on pieces of paper.
    (a) *Sample*: How many two-digit numbers less than 80 can be formed by placing two pieces of paper side by side? *Answer*: The digit in the "tens" place cannot be 8, thus there are 4 choices for the tens digit. For each of these choices there are 4 choices remaining for the "ones" digit. Thus $4 \cdot 4 = 16$ different two-digit numbers less than 80 are possible.
    (b) How many three-digit numbers can be formed?
    (c) How many two-digit odd numbers?
    (d) How many four-digit even numbers?
    (e) How many *numbers* less than 800?

12. Suppose there are 4 airlines providing service between Los Angeles and Phoenix; in how many ways can a person select airlines for a trip from Los Angeles to Phoenix and back if
    (a) he must travel both ways by the same airline?
    (b) he can, but need not, travel both ways by the same airline?
    (c) he cannot travel both ways by the same airline?

13. Suppose there are 30 men and 20 women at a party. Word comes that two persons at the affair are spies.
    (a) How many possible spies are there to consider?
    (b) If it is known that the spies are not of the same sex, how many possible pairs are there to consider?
    (c) If it is known that they are of the same sex, how many possible pairs are there to consider?

14. Suppose that 3 sections of a certain course are offered. If 15 students sign up for the course,
    (a) how many possibilities are there for the ways the students could distribute themselves in the sections?
    (b) how many of the ways would give the same number of students in each class?

15. A group of 9 people contains 4 boys and 5 girls.
    (a) How many ways can they be placed in a straight line?
    (b) How many ways can they be placed in a straight line so that the boys and girls alternate?

16. (a) How many different subcommittees of 3 can be formed from a group of 20?
    (b) If you are one of the 20 and a committee is chosen at random, what is the probability that you will be on the committee?
    (c) What is the probability you will not be on the committee?

17. Suppose a president, vice-president, and a secretary-treasurer are chosen at random from a group of 20 members of an organization.

(a) How many ways can this be done?

(b) If you are one of the members, what is the probability that you will be elected president?

(c) What is the probability that you will be one of the three officers?

18. There are 9 chairs in a row.

(a) In how many ways can 2 persons be seated?

(b) In how many of these ways will they be seated side by side?

19. Suppose 9 red poker chips and 2 white ones, all the same size, are thoroughly mixed and placed at random in a pile. Determine the probability

(a) that the 2 white ones are at the top.

(b) that the 2 white ones are together.

(c) If someone offers the following wager: he will pay you $3 if whites are together and you pay him $1 if not—should you take it?

20. How do living things transmit physical characteristics to their offspring? A host of experiments seems to indicate that the information is encoded for transmission via long molecules (called "DNA") which are chains made up of 4 possible chemical components ("bases"). Let's denote the components by letters A, B, C, and D. These act as a small alphabet for the coded "message" in the chain. Ⓐ—Ⓑ—Ⓑ—Ⓒ—Ⓐ—Ⓓ— ⋯

To transform the message into new living matter, the chains attract to themselves certain molecular building blocks called "amino acids," of which there seem to be exactly 20. A key problem is: which subsequences of bases along a DNA chain—call them "words"—attract which amino acids?

So far, no microscope is fine enough to expose the actual attractions. All the experiments are indirect. People visualize the situation in terms of a model, and try to guess features of the model which can be checked one way or another. Here are two of the many questions which have arisen:

(a) If "words" are all of the same length, what minimal length can that be in order that there be enough distinct words to correspond to each of the 20 amino acids?

(b) In one proposed model, "words" were all of length three, and were not separated by letters acting as spaces or punctuation. For example, see the diagram.

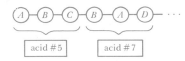

To avoid cases of confusion wherein acids might enter at the wrong point of the chain, this model excluded identical triplets, such as *AAA*, from having any "meaning" as far as attracting amino acids.

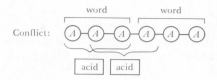

Moreover, for any "meaningful" word — say, *ABC* — the model excluded the two "cyclic" permutations of that word — *BCA* and *CAB* — from having "meaning," again to avoid confusion. With these exclusions, how many triplets are left to serve as "meaningful" words?

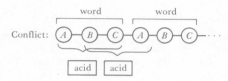

(The answer raised a furor. But this so-called "comma free" model has itself been excluded in the light of recent experiments.)

*21. Suppose that you are in a room with 23 people and that someone bets you even money that no 2 people in the room have the same birthday. Should you accept the bet?

(If you line the people up and ask them their birthday, how many possible patterns of answers can there be? How many patterns with no 2 dates the same?)

6.10 *SUMMARY OF CHAPTER 6*

INDUCTION AXIOM: For a sequence of statements $\mathscr{S}_n$, $n = 1, 2, 3, \ldots,$ if

(a) $\mathscr{S}_1$ is true,

and if

(b) for any k, the truth of $\mathscr{S}_k$ implies the truth of $\mathscr{S}_{k+1}$, then all $\mathscr{S}_n$ must be true.

(Sec. 6.1)

APPLICATIONS:

1. $n < 2^n$ for all n (Sec. 6.3)

2. *Compound interest*: one dollar compounded m times a year at interest rate p yields $\$[1 + (p/m)]^m$ at the end of a year. (Sec. 6.4)

3. *Biological populations* of uniformly mixed ages increase approximately by a factor of $[1+(1/m)]^m$ per unit time—where m is large. (Sec. 6.5)

4. $\left(1+\dfrac{1}{m}\right)^m < \left(1+\dfrac{1}{m+1}\right)^{m+1} < 3 \qquad$ for any $m \geqslant 2$.

   (Sec. 6.8, Example 4)

5. *Ordered samples* of size r from a population of size n: there are

   $$(n)_r = n(n-1)(n-2) \cdots (n-r+1) \qquad (r \text{ factors})$$

   such distinct samples. (Sec. 6.8)

6. *Permutations* of n individuals: there are

   $$n! = n(n-1)(n-2) \cdots 2 \cdot 1$$

   such distinct permutations. (Sec. 6.8).

7. *Unordered subsets* of size r from a population of size n: there are

   $$\binom{n}{r} = \frac{(n)_r}{r!} = \frac{n!}{r!(n-r)!} \qquad \text{for } 1 \leqslant r \leqslant n$$

   such distinct subsets.

   Notation: $\dbinom{n}{0} = 1$

   (Sec. 6.8)

8. The *binomial expansion*

   $$(a+b)^n = \binom{n}{0} a^n b^0 + \binom{n}{1} a^{n-1} b^1 + \binom{n}{2} a^{n-2} b^2 + \cdots$$

   $$+ \binom{n}{r} a^{n-r} b^r + \cdots + \binom{n}{n} a^0 b^n$$

   (Sec. 6.8)

9. "Addition rule" for probabilities of *mutually exclusive* subsets:

   $$P(S_1 \cup S_2 \cup \cdots \cup S_n) = P(S_1) + P(S_2) + \cdots + P(S_n)$$

   (Sec. 6.6)

10. "Multiplication rule" for probabilities of *independent subsets* $S_1, S_2, \ldots, S_n$ (each independent of any combination of the others):

    $$P(S_1 \cap S_2 \cap \cdots \cap S_n) = P(S_1) \cdot P(S_2) \cdots P(S_n)$$

    (Sec. 6.6 and Problem 4 of Sec. 6.7)

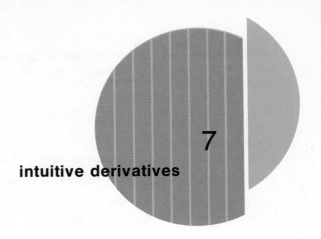

intuitive derivatives

7

In this chapter, I'll explore intuitively the idea of "slopes" of nonlinear graphs—"derivatives," and how this notion can be used to minimize costs, to describe "velocities" of moving objects, and to calculate the volume of a mountain.

7.1 HOW OFTEN TO ORDER BREAD

Suppose that you are the cook for a large outfit and that you will need 15,000 loaves of bread during a six-month period. You can order the loaves in small daily lots, or you can order larger lots less frequently by acquiring freezer storage space. There are costs associated with any plan. Storage costs for the total period are roughly proportional to the initial size of a lot stored—say, at $\frac{1}{2}\not c$ per loaf or \$5.00 for a lot of 1000 loaves. This means that ordering smaller but more frequent lots costs less in storage than fewer large lots. On the other hand, the placing and delivery of an order may cost some of your time or of other persons' time. Let's suppose that such costs may be accounted for at 30¢ per order. The smaller the lots the more the orders, and the more of this cost you have to pay. What's the optimal lot size, and corresponding number of orders you should place to cut total cost to a minimum?

Let's analyze the problem. Suppose that you order lots of size x. Then the total storage cost for the six-month period will be approximately

$$f(x) = x \cdot (\tfrac{1}{2} \text{ cents}) = 0.005\, x \text{ dollars.} \tag{1}$$

At x loaves per lot, you'll have to place about $15{,}000/x$ orders (or the nearest integer to it), and so you'll incur a total reorder cost of approximately

$$g(x) = \frac{15000}{x} \cdot (30 \text{ cents}) = 4500\frac{1}{x} \text{ dollars.} \tag{2}$$

Hence your overall total cost will be approximately

$$h(x) = f(x) + g(x) = 0.005x + 4500 \frac{1}{x} \text{ dollars.} \tag{3}$$

The problem is to find an input—call it x_{MIN}—which will make $h(x)$ an (absolute) minimum.

To get an answer you might program a high-speed computer to calculate $h(x)$ for 15,000 integer values of x and to search for the minimum output—an expensive job. Or you might yourself calculate several outputs such as

$$\begin{aligned}
h(100) &= \$45.50 & h(4000) &= \$21.13 \\
h(1000) &= \$9.50 & h(5000) &= \$25.90 \\
h(2000) &= \$12.25 & h(10000) &= \$50.45 \\
h(3000) &= \$16.50
\end{aligned} \tag{4}$$

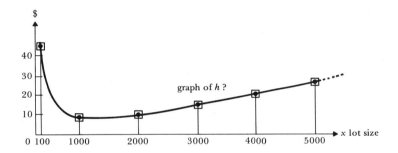

FIGURE 7-1

graph of h ?

x lot size

On the basis of these values you might guess that the graph of h lies on a curve such as I've sketched in Fig. 7-1. And looking at the curve you might *guess* that the minimum value of h occurs for x somewhere between, say, 500 and 1,000. But you would be dead wrong if the true graph of h fluctuates widely just at inputs which you didn't happen to plot and has its absolute minimum there. See Figs. 7-2, 7-3, and 7-4 for other possibilities using the same plotted data. Unless you calculate $h(x)$ for *every* input x how can you be certain that you have the true minimum?

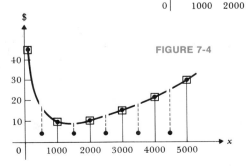

FIGURE 7-2

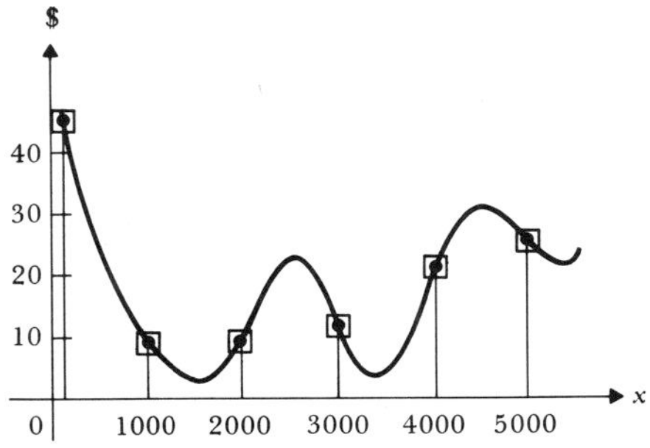

FIGURE 7-3

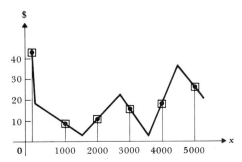

FIGURE 7-4

You may recall an algebraic method, "completing the square," for finding the minimum of a "quadratic" function (Problem 3 of Sec. 2.4).

To find the true minimum in the present example, here is a *general* approach — which dates back at least to Kepler and Leibnitz (in the 17th-century): Let's allow *all* real numbers x between 1 and 15,000 as inputs for the rule $h(x) = 0.005x + 4500/x$. Hopefully, the resulting function will have a "smooth" graph. In fact, let's suppose temporarily that the graph turns so smoothly that we'll be able to assign a "slope" to the graph at each of its points (a number which may vary from point to point). Whatever the precise rule for the assignment, let's suppose that "slopes" will be *negative* when the graph is falling from left to right and *positive* when the graph is rising — as is true for lines. See Fig. 7-5. In between stretches of falling and rising — at the bottoms of valleys and at the tops of hills — the "slope" should be *zero*.

FIGURE 7-5

Now *if* an absolute minimum exists, and *if* it doesn't occur at an end point of the graph, then it must be at the bottom of a valley — the deepest valley. Hence it should have a *special property*: it should have "zero slope," while being flanked on the left by points of negative "slope" (≤ 0) and on the right by points of positive "slope" (≥ 0). Given the formula for h, and a precise rule for calculating "slopes," we should be able to single out all points with this "special property" — as candidates for the true absolute minimum. And by comparing their altitudes, we could pick the winner.

To push such a program through we must concoct a workable definition of "slope" for nonlinear graphs. Let's build upon what we already have — slopes for lines. To capture the notion of "slope" *at* a graph point P_0, let's first flank P_0 by two nearby graph points, Q and R, and examine the slope of the line which they determine. See Fig. 7-6. This slope is the difference ratio

$$\frac{h(r) - h(q)}{r - q}. \tag{5}$$

Now think of moving Q and R into positions successively closer and closer to P_0. If the corresponding difference ratios (5) "tend" to a definite "limiting number," say m_0 — no matter which particular

FIGURE 7-6

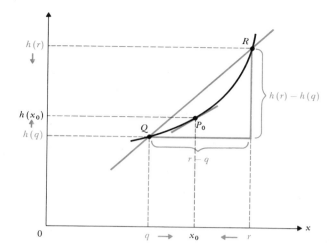

positions you may choose for Q and R—then wouldn't it be intuitively reasonable to assign m_0 as the "slope" *at* P_0?

Let's try it and see. Here's how the calculation goes for any point $P_0 = (x_0, h(x_0))$, not an end point, on the graph of $h(x) = ax + b/x$. (In the present example, $a = 0.005$, $b = 4500$, and $1 \le x \le 15{,}000$.) Pick any inputs $q < x_0$ and $r > x_0$. Then write out and simplify the corresponding difference quotient:

$$\frac{h(r) - h(q)}{r - q} = \frac{(ar + b/r) - (aq + b/q)}{r - q}$$

$$= \frac{a(r - q) + b(1/r - 1/q)}{r - q} \qquad \text{(factoring } a \text{ and } b\text{)}$$

$$= \frac{a(\cancel{r - q})}{\cancel{r - q}} + \frac{b(1/r - 1/q)}{r - q} \quad \text{(canceling)}$$

$$= a + \frac{b[(q - r)/(qr)]}{r - q} \qquad \begin{array}{l}\text{(forming a common} \\ \text{denominator } qr\text{)}\end{array}$$

$$= a + \frac{b(-1)(\cancel{r - q})1/qr}{\cancel{r - q}} \quad \text{(factoring } (-1) \text{ and canceling)}$$

$$= a - b\frac{1}{qr}. \tag{6}$$

If you let q "tend" to x_0 through *any* sequence of values $q_1, q_2, \ldots, q_n, \ldots$ and r "tend" to x_0 through *any* sequence of values $r_1, r_2, \ldots, r_n, \ldots$, shouldn't the products $q_1 r_1, q_2 r_2, \ldots, q_n r_n, \ldots$ "tend" to $x_0 x_0 = x_0{}^2$, and shouldn't their reciprocals tend to $1/x_0{}^2$? Finally, shouldn't the differences $a - b/q_n r_n$ "tend" to the unique "limit"

$a - b/x_0{}^2$? *If* so, then we *can* assign a "slope" *at* $P_0 = (x_0, h(x_0))$: namely

$$m_0 = a - b \frac{1}{x_0{}^2}. \tag{7}$$

Thanks to the general symbolism of algebra, we've just calculated — at one fell swoop — the "slopes" at each of the infinite host of points on the graph of h (except the end points).

To complete the search for an absolute minimum point, let's ask for which input x_0 the slope can be zero. Just set

$$m_0 = a - b \frac{1}{x_0{}^2} = 0; \tag{8}$$

and rearrange, to get

$$x_0{}^2 = \frac{b}{a}. \tag{9}$$

In the present example $b/a = 4500/0.005 = 9 \times 10^5$, and only positive numbers x_0 lie in the domain of h. Hence there is a *unique* input x_0 yielding zero slope; namely,

$$+ \sqrt{9 \times 10^5} = 300\sqrt{10}. \tag{10}$$

Check that for $x_0 < 300\sqrt{10}$, the slope $m_0 = 0.005 - 4500/x_0{}^2$ is negative; and for $x_0 > 300\sqrt{10}$, the slope $m_0 = 0.005 - 4500/x_0{}^2$ is positive. So the point P_0 with coordinate $x_0 = 300\sqrt{10}$ — and only that point — has what I called the "special property." Hence the absolute minimum must occur at this point, or else at an end point. At the end points, $h(1) = \$4500.01$ and $h(15,000) = \$45.30$; whereas $h(300\sqrt{10}) = \$9.50$ approximately. End of the search: $x_{MIN} = 300\sqrt{10} =$ a lot size of approximately 948 loaves.

The optimal number of orders should be one of the integers nearest the fraction

$$\frac{15,000}{x_{MIN}} = \frac{15,000}{300\sqrt{10}} = 5\sqrt{10} = 15.8.$$

Fifteen orders, each of size 1000 loaves, cost $15(\$0.30) + 1000(\$0.05) = \$9.50$; and sixteen orders, each of size 938, cost $16(\$0.30) + 938(\$0.05) = \$9.49$?

Now recall the "ifs": All these conclusions hold *provided* my arguments about "convergence" of products $q_n r_n$, reciprocals $1/q_n r_n$, and sums $a - b/q_n r_n$, were valid for establishing the assignment of "slopes" *at* points P_0. And *provided* that the "special property" (zero "slope," etc.) really holds true for minimum points when we define "slope" as above. And finally — *provided* that an absolute minimum *does* exist among the infinity of points $(x, h(x))$ for $1 \leq x \leq 15,000$. In later chapters I'll try to establish general results so that, given a function h, we can tell at a glance whether we're in the clear.

7.2   1 IS THE LARGEST INTEGER

In the last example: if I was able to calculate the minimizing input, $x_{\text{MIN}} = 300\sqrt{10}$, on the *assumption* that a minimum does exist, why need I doubt that assumption itself?

Here is an analogous case: *suppose* that there exists a largest integer—call it M. Then

$$M \geqslant 1. \tag{11}$$

Also, M^2 must be an integer; and since M is the largest integer,

$$M^2 \leqslant M. \tag{12}$$

Divide (12) through by M, a positive number, to get

$$M \leqslant 1. \tag{13}$$

Together, the inequalities (11) and (13) force $M = 1$.

Each algebraic step was valid. What's wrong?

7.3   "DERIVATIVES" FOR SEVERAL SIMPLE FUNCTIONS

The quantity m_0 that I used above to minimize order costs—the "slope" of a graph *at* a point $P_0 = (x_0, f(x_0))$—is commonly called the *derivative* of the function f at the input x_0. One of several common symbols for m_0 is "$f'(x_0)$"—a notation which highlights the fact that we are really *assigning* a "slope" to a graph point, or equivalently, to its input coordinate x_0.

Here again is the intuitive rule I used for the assignment: Let

$$f'(x_0) = \text{the "limit" of ratios } \frac{f(r_n) - f(q_n)}{r_n - q_n} \tag{1}$$

as we pick q_n and r_n closer and closer to x_0, with $q_n < x_0 < r_n$.

Apply the rule *provided* such a "limit" exists and doesn't depend on which particular sequence of pairs, q_n and r_n, we use as long as they squeeze toward x_0. (You might check Fig. 7-6 again.)

Linear functions. Since the notion of "slope" originates with lines—curves of constant slope—we should expect

$$f'(x_0) = m \qquad \text{for all } x_0, \tag{2}$$

whenever f is a linear function $f(x) \equiv mx + b$. And it seems to: For any fixed x_0, all flanking pairs of inputs $q_n < x_0 < r_n$ produce difference ratios

$$\frac{f(r_n) - f(q_n)}{r_n - q_n} = \frac{(mr_n + b) - (mq_n + b)}{r_n - q_n}$$

$$= \frac{m(r_n - q_n) + (b - b)}{r_n - q_n} = m \tag{3}$$

of the same value, m. If we pick q_n and r_n closer and closer to x_0, shouldn't the limit of all these m's be m?

EXAMPLE 1. If $f(x) = 3x - 5$ for all x, then $f'(x_0) = 3$ at any x_0.

The "quadratic" function $g(x) = x^2$. Here's how the calculation for $g'(x_0)$ goes in this case—for any fixed x_0. With $q_n < x_0 < r_n$, the difference ratio

$$\frac{g(r_n) - g(q_n)}{r_n - q_n} = \frac{r_n^2 - q_n^2}{r_n - q_n} = \frac{(r_n - q_n)(r_n + q_n)}{r_n - q_n} = r_n + q_n. \tag{4}$$

If we pick q_n and r_n closer and closer to x_0, shouldn't the sums $r_n + q_n$ "converge" to $x_0 + x_0 = 2x_0$? If so, then

$$g'(x_0) = 2x_0 \qquad \text{at any } x_0. \tag{5}$$

The formula (5) tells us that the slope of the graph is zero only at $x_0 = 0$, is negative for $x_0 < 0$, and is positive for $x_0 > 0$. Specifically, $g'(1) = 2 \cdot 1 = 2$, $g'(-1) = 2(-1) = -2$, $g'(2) = 2 \cdot 2 = 4$, and $g'(-2) = 2(-2) = -4$. With such facts to aid me, I sketched a graph for g in Fig. 7-7.

FIGURE 7-7

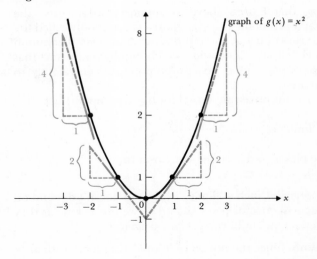

graph of $g(x) = x^2$

By the very rule for g, $g(x) = x^2$, you can tell that $x_0 = 0$ must provide the absolute minimum output—we needn't compute slopes for that purpose. But what about a quadratic such as $q(x) = x(1 - x) = x - x^2$? In order to find a maximizing output, you may previously have resorted to "completing the square" (Problem 3 of Sec. 2.4). Try finding the maximum now by computing slopes $q'(x_0)$ and locating the hilltops of the graph of q. Do Problem 3 of Sec. 7.4.

The cubic $h(x) = x^3$. For any fixed x_0, and flanking q_n and r_n,

$$\frac{h(r_n) - h(q_n)}{r_n - q_n} = \frac{r_n^3 - q_n^3}{r_n - q_n}. \tag{6}$$

What happens to the difference ratios (6) if we pick q_n and r_n closer and closer to x_0? As it stands, the right-hand fraction gives little

FIGURE 7-8

information: both numerator and denominator seem headed for zero. What's needed is an algebraic simplification of the ratio which will reveal its dependence on q_n and r_n more clearly—just as in the quadratic case (4). Do you recall the factoring identity

$$b^3 - a^3 = (b-a)(b^2 + ab + a^2)?\tag{7}$$

If not, just check it by multiplying out the right-hand side. Let's use this identity in the difference quotient for h, to get

$$\frac{h(r_n) - h(q_n)}{r_n - q_n} = \frac{r_n{}^3 - q_n{}^3}{r_n - q_n} = \frac{(\cancel{r_n - q_n})(r_n{}^2 + q_n r_n + q_n{}^2)}{\cancel{r_n - q_n}}.\tag{8}$$

As q_n and r_n get closer and closer to x_0, shouldn't all three quantities $r_n{}^2$, $q_n r_n$, and $q_n{}^2$ tend to $x_0{}^2$? And shouldn't their sum tend to $3x_0{}^2$? If so, then

$$h'(x_0) = 3x_0{}^2 \qquad \text{at any } x_0.\tag{9}$$

Again the slope is zero only at $x_0 = 0$, but is positive for all other x_0. Some particular values: $h'(1) = 3 \cdot 1^2 = 3$, $h'(-1) = 3(-1)^2 = 3$, $h'(2) = 3 \cdot 2^2 = 12$, $h'(-2) = 3(-2)^2 = 12$. I've used these slopes to draw a graph for h in Fig. 7-8. Note that the slope $h'(0) = 0$ even though $(0, 0)$ is neither a maximum nor a minimum point of the graph.

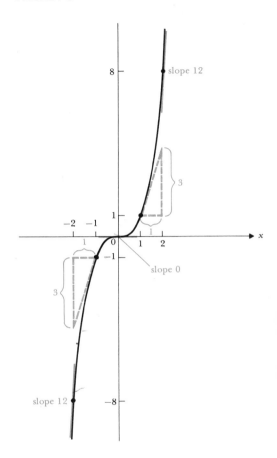

7.4 PROBLEMS ON DERIVATIVES AND OPTIMIZATION

°1. Find "derivatives" for the following:
   (a) *Sample*: $f(x) = x^2 + 2$.
       Answer: $f'(x) = 2x$, assuming that the derivative of a sum is the sum of the derivatives.
   (b) $f(x) = 1$
   (c) $f(x) = 2x - 3$
   (d) $f(x) = x + \dfrac{1}{x}$
   (e) $f(x) = x^3 + 1$
   (f) $f(x) = x^3 - 3x + 1$
   (g) $f(x) = -x^2 + x - 1$

°2. For the functions in Problem 1, find out for which inputs the "derivatives" are zero, and determine if these yield maxima, minima, or neither.
   (a) *Sample*: $f(x) = x^2 + 2$, $f'(x) = 2x$; f' is zero if and only if $x = 0$. $f'(-\frac{1}{2}) = -1$ and $f'(\frac{1}{2}) = 1$. So there is a "valley" at $x = 0$ and f has a minimum value, $f(0) = 2$, there.

3. Do you recall previously finding the minimum for a quadratic $f(x) = ax^2 + bx + c$, $a > 0$, by the method of "completing the square"? (Sec. 2.4) Now using "derivatives" find the input x_0 which yields a minimum.

*4. Can you find a minimum for $f(x) = ax + b \cdot (1/x)$ (where $x > 0$), by "completing a square"? (Note that $x = (\sqrt{x})^2$ and $\sqrt{x} \cdot (1/\sqrt{x}) = 1$.)

5. Show that for every positive integer n the derivative of $f(x) = x^n$ is $f'(x) = nx^{n-1}$. (*Hint*: Set up a difference ratio and use the factorization $b^n - a^n = (b-a)(b^{n-1} + \cdots + a^{n-1})$ from Problem 5 of Sec. 6.7.)

6. Suppose you had a square of cardboard 12 inches on each side and you were going to make an open box by cutting out squares (x inches on a side) from the corners and then folding up the sides. What size square should you remove from each corner to give you the largest volume? (Recall Problem 8 of Sec. 2.2.)

7. Suppose that an automobile manufacturing company wants to determine the optimal selling price for a car. For simplicity let's suppose also that, after the first several thousand cars, the cost of manufacture *per* car remains constant—at say, $1500. If the sales price is set at x dollars per car, then the profit will be $(x - 1500)$ per car sold. Now, the higher the unit price x, the more will be the unit profit. But the lower the unit price x, the larger the number of cars sold is likely to be. What unit price, if any, will maximize total profit?

   To answer such questions, industry analysts have tried to approximate customer reaction to prices by a *linear* "demand function," showing the anticipated number of cars desired $D(x)$ corresponding to a unit selling price of x dollars.

   (a) Suppose $D(\$1500) = 200,000$ and $D(\$2500) = 30,000$. Represent the total profit $T(x)$ as a function of the unit price x, for $\$1500 \leq x \leq \$2500$.

   (b) Try to find a maximizing input for T, using the method of slopes.

*8. *How can a group or company produce most effectively?* For an (idealized) economic model, let's focus on two key factors: the available amount of labor—say, x man-hours, and the available supply of capital for tools and machinery—say y dollars. Put the labor x and capital y together correctly, and you should get a corresponding amount of product p. We can think of this correspondence as a "function" $p(x, y)$ with two inputs, x and y—or as a function whose input is a pair (x, y).

   For concreteness, imagine a setup where the amount of product is proportional to each factor: say,

$$p(x, y) = xy \text{ units.} \tag{1}$$

   Suppose that labor costs $4 per man-hour, and that the company has a total of $1000 to allocate between labor x and capital y. What combination will give the greatest amount of product?

   The $1000 restriction imposes a linear relationship between x and y: namely, $\$4x + \$y = \$1000$, or

$$y = -4x + 1000. \tag{2}$$

On the other hand, if we ask how to produce a given number of units N, we get another relationship between x and y: $xy = N$, or

$$y = \frac{N}{x}. \tag{3}$$

On an $x-y$ coordinate system, graph the linear function in (2), and think how the graphs of the reciprocal functions in (3) might look for differing values of N. See the accompanying diagram (where the units differ on the two axes).

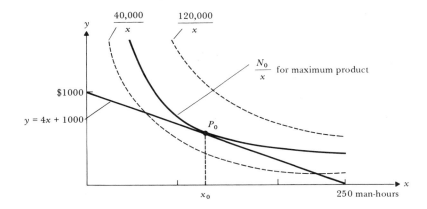

The larger the value of N, the higher the corresponding graph of N/x should sit.

(a) If there is a value of N_0 for which the graph of N/x touches the linear graph at a unique point $P_0 = (x_0, y_0)$, why should the coordinates of that point represent the amounts of labor and capital for maximum product?

(b) If there exists a unique contact point $P_0 = (x_0, y_0)$ as described in (a), do you believe intuitively that the *slopes* of the N_0/x and $-4x + 1000$ graphs should agree at P_0 as well as their altitudes? If so, set

$$\frac{N}{x} = -4x + 1000 \qquad \text{(equal altitudes)}, \tag{4}$$

and

$$\left(\frac{N}{x}\right)' = (-4x + 1000)' \qquad \text{(equal slopes)}; \tag{5}$$

evaluate the slopes in (5); and solve (4) and (5) simultaneously to find the maximizing labor input x_0 and the corresponding maximum product N_0.

7.5 MOTION

FIGURE 7-9

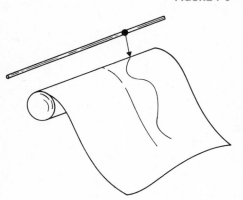

Think of an object moving along a line. How could you record and analyze its motion? If you could attach a pen to the object and move a stream of paper underneath, as in Fig. 7-9, you could get a trace of the motion. Of course, under sufficient magnification the trace would appear as blotches of ink. But in an *idealized* way we can think of such a trace as the graph of a function: a function p wherein we record all of the motion by assigning to each instant of time t the position $p(t)$ of the object at that instant. In Fig. 7-10 I've drawn a possible graph for such a "position function," with axes pointed in the usual directions.

FIGURE 7-10

$p(r) - p(q)$ is *net* change of position during time interval $[q,r]$

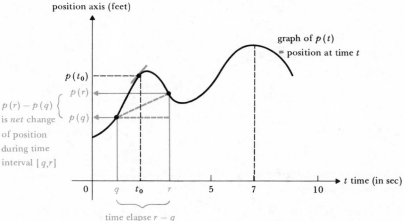

Remember, this graph is merely a convenient picture in a two-dimensional space-vs.-time plane. Don't confuse it with the line along which the actual motion takes place. From the graph we can read back many features of the motion. For example, an instant when the graph stops rising and begins to fall must be an instant when the object stopped traveling in a "forward" direction and changed to a backward direction ($t = 7$ in Fig. 7-10). Similarly, bottoms of valleys on the graph correspond to changes from backward to forward directions on the line of motion. (Move a vertical ruler to the right across Fig. 7-10, at one foot per second, and follow its point of intersection with the graph. The motion of that point along the ruler will duplicate the motion of the original object.)

Many other questions about motion involve "speed" or "velocity," and "acceleration." Here is how we can phrase these notions in terms of the position function p and its graph: The net change of position during a time interval $[q, r]$ is the difference $p(r) - p(q)$. For ages people have interpreted the ratio

$$\frac{\text{net change in position}}{\text{elapse of time}} = \frac{p(r) - p(q)}{r - q} \quad \text{(feet per second)} \qquad (1)$$

as the "average velocity" of the object during the interval $[q, r]$. Why "average"? Because intuitively they have accepted the idea that the object has a "true" or "instantaneous velocity" *at* each instant t_0, a quantity which may vary from instant to instant.

For example, how do you interpret the number indicated on the speedometer of a car at any instant?

Now, whether or not a *real* object has an "instantaneous velocity" at any instant t_0, how can we capture the notion precisely for our idealized "model" of motion? Why not as the "limiting value" of "average velocities" $[p(r_n) - p(q_n)]/[r_n - q_n]$, as we pick shorter and shorter time intervals $[q_n, r_n]$ containing t_0? —*provided* such a limit exists. In other words, let's make a

Definition. Let's define *(instantaneous) velocity at time* t_0 to be the derivative $p'(t_0)$ of the position function p, at t_0.

This means that on a graph of positions, as in Fig. 7-10, the (instantaneous) velocity at time t_0 will appear as the *slope* of the graph above t_0.

By definition, then, a position function determines its "velocities." Note also the common belief that velocities determine positions. For example, imagine two (idealized) horses running on parallel lines— and with respective position functions $f(t)$ and $g(t)$. If the horses start a race neck-and-neck (at $t = 0$) and have identical velocity records, then they should be neck-and-neck at *all* times. In symbols,

$$\left. \begin{array}{c} f(0) = g(0), \\ \text{and} \\ f'(t_0) = g'(t_0) \\ \text{at all } t_0 \end{array} \right\} \quad \text{imply that} \quad \left\{ \begin{array}{l} f(t_0) = g(t_0) \\ \text{at all } t_0. \end{array} \right. \qquad (2)$$

Let's call this the "*neck-and-neck race argument*."

Pictorially, the belief is that "slopes" capture the nature of graphs to such an extent that two graphs must coincide if they start at the same point and have equal slopes all along.

Let's go on to study how velocities themselves may change from time to time. To picture such change, think of velocities as outputs of a *new* function v: to each instant t, assign as output $v(t)$ the (instantaneous) velocity $p'(t)$ of the object at that instant. In Fig. 7-11, I've graphed a velocity function v corresponding to the position function p of Fig. 7-10.

The velocity $v(t)$ should be positive at inputs t where the position graph rises—that is, when the object moves "forward"—and $v(t)$ should be negative when the object retreats. $v(t)$ should read zero as the object makes an about face.

FIGURE 7-11

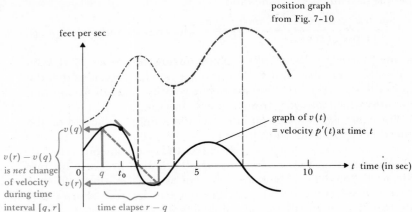

position graph
from Fig. 7–10

feet per sec

$v(q)$

graph of $v(t)$
= velocity $p'(t)$ at time t

$v(r) - v(q)$
is *net* change
of velocity
during time
interval $[q, r]$

$v(r)$

q t_0 r 5 10 t time (in sec)

time elapse $r - q$

Just as for net changes in position, people have interpreted the ratio

$$\frac{\text{net change in velocity}}{\text{elapse of time}} = \frac{v(r) - v(q)}{r - q} \qquad \text{(ft per sec per sec)} \qquad (3)$$

as an "average" — as the "average acceleration" of the object during the interval $[q, r]$. And they've believed in an "instantaneous acceleration" of the object at each instant t_0. How can we capture this notion precisely for our model of motion? Again, by a "limit" of ratios for shorter and shorter intervals — *provided* such a limit exists. Here's a second

Definition: Let's define *(instantaneous) acceleration at time* t_0 to be the derivative $v'(t_0)$ of the velocity function v, at t_0.

Instantaneous accelerations will show up as slopes on the velocity graph.

Now to the "provisos": do "limits" really exist for the "average velocity" and "average acceleration" ratios? If not, how could we even define "instantaneous velocity" and "acceleration"? What if a "true" graph of positions $f(t)$ has corners or breaks, as in Figs. 7-3 and 7-4 (Sec. 7.1), and isn't smooth enough to permit "slopes" at all of its points? Can we ever observe "true" motion accurately enough to tell?

Early workers, such as Newton and Laplace, didn't worry about such questions. They merely assumed that "true" position and velocity functions do have derivatives $p'(t_0)$ and $v'(t_0)$ at all times t_0, and they went on to get results. We needn't worry about these questions either if we stick to the view that the position function $p(t)$ represents a *model* of motion, not the ultimate picture of "true" motion itself. We can set forth as an *axiom* of the model that $p'(t_0)$ and $v'(t_0)$

exist at all instants t_0. And we need keep the model only as long as it seems consistent and useful.

What gives a model power, however, are other axioms—so-called "laws of nature"—which men have formulated from time to time while studying the real world. Here is an example.

EXAMPLE 1: FALLING OFF A CLIFF. Isaac Newton announced a "law of nature" regarding "forces": if an object of mass m moves in a straight line, a "force," $F(t_0)$, acting along that line at time t_0 will cause that object to accelerate according to the rule

$$mv'(t_0) = F(t_0). \tag{4}$$

You may recall that Newton also formulated another "law of nature" regarding the specific "force of gravity": two objects of masses m and M, attract each other at time t_0 with a "force"

$$F(t_0) = C\frac{mM}{[D(t_0)]^2} \tag{5}$$

where C is a constant depending on units of measurement and $D(t_0)$ is the distance between the objects at time t_0. (If the objects have considerable volume, we should measure $D(t_0)$ between suitably representative points in each.)

Here is an application: Suppose that you fall off a 100-ft cliff. How long before you hit the ground, and what will your velocity be at impact?

Start counting time the instant you leave the top $(t = 0)$; let T denote the (unknown) time of impact; and for $0 \leq t \leq T$, let $p(t)$ denote the number of feet you will have fallen in time t—your position down the cliff, as in Fig. 7-12.

To form a model of the incident, let's assume that derivatives $v(t) = p'(t)$ and $v'(t)$ exist for all $t < T$, and that Newton's "laws" hold—where m is your mass, M is the mass of the earth, and $D(t_0)$ is the distance between, say, the center of the earth and a point in your middle parts. We can eliminate "force" $F(t_0)$ between the two "laws" (4) and (5) to get

$$mv'(t_0) = C\frac{mM}{D(t_0)^2} \tag{6}$$

or, dividing by m,

$$v'(t_0) = C\frac{M}{D(t_0)^2} \qquad \text{for } 0 < t_0 < T. \tag{7}$$

During your entire fall, your distance $D(t)$ from the center of the earth will change only slightly (by 100 ft) compared to the radius of the earth (4000 miles). Hence the right-hand side of (7) is almost a constant. Note that the constant doesn't depend on your mass m or on anybody else's mass—merely on M and $D(t)$. Actual measurements

FIGURE 7-12

with inanimate falling objects show it to be approximately 32 ft per sec per sec.

So let's consider the following as an approximating model for the motion:

> a position function $p(t)$ with initial position $p(0) = 0$;
> and its velocity function $v(t) \equiv p'(t)$, with initial velocity $v(0) = 0$;
> and its acceleration $v'(t) = 32$ for $0 < t < T$.

The question is: what explicit forms must $p(t)$ and $v(t)$ have?

Recall that the linear function $g(t) \equiv 32t$ will have the *same* initial value and derivative properties

$$g(0) = 0 \quad \text{and} \quad g'(t) = 32 \quad \text{for } 0 < t < T \tag{8}$$

that we require of the velocity function $v(t)$. Is there a chance that we can identify the unknown $v(t)$ with $g(t)$? Yes: pretend for a moment that $v(t)$ and $g(t)$ are themselves position functions for two horses. They will have common initial positions and velocity records

$$v(0) = 0 = g(0) \quad \text{and} \quad v'(t) = 32 = g'(t) \quad \text{for all } t \tag{9}$$

—just the conditions for identity of position records $v(t) = g(t)$ at all times, by the "neck-and-neck race argument," (2).

If so, then we've determined your velocity

$$p'(t) = v(t) = 32t \quad \text{for all times } 0 < t < T. \tag{10}$$

What form does this fact imply for your position function p?

Let your mind roam once more. Do you recall from the last section that the quadratic function x^2 has derivative $2x_0$ at the input x_0? Now, if you multiply a function $h(x)$ by a constant, say 16, don't you thereby simply change its difference quotients by 16:

$$\frac{16h(r) - 16h(q)}{r - q} = 16\frac{h(r) - h(q)}{r - q}; \tag{11}$$

hence, won't you change its slopes $h'(x_0)$ by a factor of 16? If so, then —labeling inputs by t instead of x— the function $k(t) \equiv 16t^2$ should have slope

$$k'(t_0) = 16 \cdot 2t_0 = 32t_0 \tag{12}$$

at the input t_0. Note also that $k(0) = 0$.

Thus, we've determined an explicit function $k(t) \equiv 16t^2$ which shares the *same* initial position and velocity properties as the unknown position function $p(t)$:

$$k(0) = 0 = p(0) \quad \text{and} \quad k'(t) = 32t = p'(t) \quad \text{for all } t. \tag{13}$$

By the "neck-and-neck race argument," we should have $p(t) \equiv k(t) \equiv 16t^2$. If so, then we've succeeded in predicting your motion of fall from Newton's laws: after t seconds, you will have fallen approximately $16t^2$ feet, for any t up until impact time $t = T$.

To determine the impact time T, note that we must have $p(T) = 100$ ft, the total distance to ground level. Set

$$16T^2 = 100 \tag{14}$$

and solve to get

$$T = \sqrt{\frac{100}{16}} = \frac{10}{4} = 2.5 \text{ sec.}$$

At impact, your velocity will be

$$p'(T) = 32T = 32 \cdot \frac{10}{4} = 80 \text{ ft per sec.}$$

Concrete answers—which you can check experimentally—all based on Newton's axioms, on recalling the derivatives of linear and quadratic functions, and on the "neck-and-neck race argument."

Regarding Newton's axioms: When pushed or pulled you may have a visceral feeling about "force." But aside from people's feelings, what are "forces" *really*?

If you can't come up with a noncircular answer, how about regarding Newton's statement, force = mass × acceleration, merely as a *definition* of "force" in terms of the quantities mass and acceleration—rather than as a so-called "law"? If we do so, then the true axiom of our model above is $v'(t_0) = C[M/D(t_0)^2]$, (7) rather than (5) and (6).

7.6 HOW TO FIND THE VOLUME OF A MOUNTAIN

Let's work with an idealized mountain, say, one whose surface we could sweep out by rotating a graph about an axis as represented in Fig. 7-13. Although the goal is to find a *single* number, the volume of

FIGURE 7-13

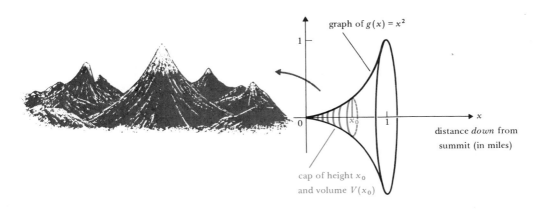

graph of $g(x) = x^2$

distance *down* from
summit (in miles)

cap of height x_0
and volume $V(x_0)$

the entire mountain, one of the most effective ways to do so is to *ask for more*: For each vertical distance *x* down from the summit ($0 \leqslant x \leqslant 1$ mile), think of the cap of the mountain of height *x* and denote its volume by $V(x)$. We know that $V(0) = 0$ and the number we seek is $V(1)$. Let's ask how the function $V(x)$ varies for *x* between 0 and 1. Specifically, at what *rate* do we increase the volume of a cap by increasing its height a given amount? For heights $q < r$, let's examine the "average rate"

$$\frac{\text{change of volume}}{\text{change of height}} = \frac{V(r) - V(q)}{r - q}. \qquad (1)$$

The numerator, $V(r) - V(q)$, is the volume of a slab of mountain, which I've indicated in black in Fig. 7-14.

FIGURE 7-14

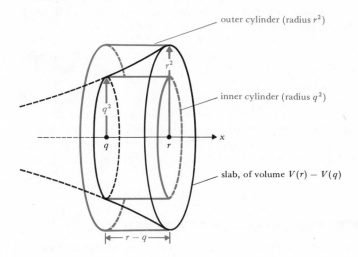

outer cylinder (radius r^2)

inner cylinder (radius q^2)

slab, of volume $V(r) - V(q)$

To estimate the volume of the slab, I've inscribed a (green) circular cylinder of height $r - q$ and radius q^2; and I've circumscribed a (green) circular cylinder of the same height, $r - q$, and of radius r^2. Will you accept from "high school" mathematics a formula for the volume of a right-circular cylinder; namely, $\pi R^2 h$, where R is the radius of the base and h is the height? And do you believe that the volume of the slab is a number lying between the volumes of the inscribed and circumscribed cylinders? If so, then we have inequalities

$$\pi (q^2)^2 (r - q) < V(r) - V(q) < \pi (r^2)^2 (r - q). \qquad (2)$$

To estimate the "average rate" of change of volume with respect to change in height, let's divide these inequalities through by $r - q$, to get

$$\pi q^4 < \frac{V(r) - V(q)}{r - q} < \pi r^4. \qquad (3)$$

If we pick pairs q_n and r_n flanking a fixed height x_0 and getting closer and closer to x_0, shouldn't the quantities $\pi(q_n)^4$ and $\pi(r_n)^4$ get closer and closer to $\pi x_0{}^4$? Hence, shouldn't the "average rates"

$$\frac{V(r_n) - V(q_n)}{(r_n - q_n)}$$

be squeezed to a "limiting," "instantaneous rate"

$$V'(x_0) = \pi x_0{}^4 \tag{4}$$

—a derivative for the cap-volume function $V(x)$ at x_0?

Suppose so. Then to find $V(x)$ itself, let's proceed as for "position functions" in the last section. Let's search for an explicit function $h(x)$ which will share the same "initial value" and derivative properties as $V(x)$, namely

$$h(0) = 0 = V(0) \quad \text{and} \quad h'(x) = \pi x^4 = V'(x) \qquad \text{for } 0 < x < 1. \tag{5}$$

Then we'll be able to identify $V(x)$ with $h(x)$, by the "neck-and-neck race argument."

A few functions for which you already know derivatives are

$$(x^1)' = 1, \quad (x^2)' = 2x, \quad (x^3)' = 3x^2. \tag{6}$$

Looking at this list, would you guess that

$$(x^4)' = 4x^3 \quad \text{and} \quad (x^5)' = 5x^4 \,(?) \tag{7}$$

If such results are correct, then couldn't we multiply x^5 by the constant $\pi/5$ to get

$$\left(\frac{\pi}{5}x^5\right)' = \left(\frac{\pi}{5}\right)(x^5)' = \left(\frac{\pi}{5}\right)5x^4 = \pi x^4 \,(?) \tag{8}$$

If so, then

$$h(x) \equiv \frac{\pi}{5}x^5$$

has the desired properties (5), and

$$V(x) \equiv h(x) \equiv \frac{\pi}{5}x^5.$$

In particular, the volume of the entire mountain is

$$V(1) = \frac{\pi}{5}1^5 = \frac{\pi}{5}$$

cubic miles.

A scheme which promises delivery of such concrete results seems worthy of clarification so that we'll know for which functions it works. All the "ifs" hark back to the basic notion of "limit"—to which I'll turn in the next chapter.

7.7 PROBLEMS ON VELOCITIES AND RATES

1. Suppose that the vertical position of a moving particle can be described by the formula $p(t) = -16t^2 + 8t + 1000, t > 0$.

(a) What is the velocity of the particle at any time t? Its acceleration?

(b) What is the maximum altitude of the particle and when does it attain this height?

2. The graph of a function F is given in the accompanying figure. Sketch the graph of the derivative F'.

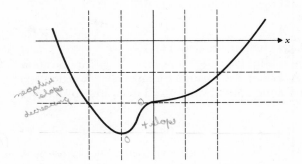

negative slope decreasing

positive to 0 again

+ slope

positive to 0 again

negative to zero

3. Suppose you were to shoot a sky rocket vertically into the air with an initial velocity of 1000 ft per sec. (For a simple model, ignore air resistance and assume that gravity ($g = -32$ ft per sec^2) is the only force acting on the rocket—as I did in Sec. 7.5.) When would the rocket touch ground again? How high would it reach? Graph its vertical altitude as a function of time.

4. (The Leaking Bucket): Suppose that an old five-gallon bucket steadily becomes more and more leaky, and loses water at a rate of $\frac{1}{2}t$ gallons per hour. (t is time in hours.) When will the bucket be empty if you filled it completely at time $t = 0$, and then left it alone?

5. Find the area of the shaded region—which is bounded above by the graph of $f(x) = x^2$. To use the method of Sec. 7.6, you might seek for the areas $A(x)$, where $1 \leqslant x \leqslant 2$, as indicated in the second figure. Note that $A(x_2) - A(x_1)$ can be estimated by inside and outside rectangles. Can you squeeze the difference ratio

$$? \leqslant \frac{A(x_2) - A(x_1)}{x_2 - x_1} \leqslant \; ? $$

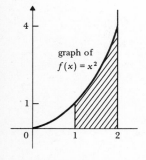

graph of
$f(x) = x^2$

FIGURE (i)

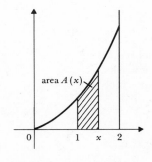

area $A(x)$

FIGURE (ii)

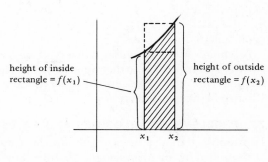

height of inside
rectangle = $f(x_1)$

height of outside
rectangle = $f(x_2)$

FIGURE (iii)

6. Find the area of the shaded region bounded above by the graph of $f(x) = 1/x^2$.

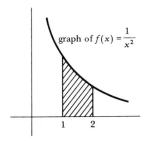

*7.8 CANTOR'S FUNCTION—A DARK HORSE?

The concrete results of the last several sections depended on what I called the "neck-and-neck race argument." Is that argument always applicable?

Around 1900, Georg Cantor suggested how we might construct a function on the unit interval whose graph rises from 0 to 1 with *no breaks*, yet whose slopes are almost all—if not all—zero. I've indicated his scheme in Fig. 7-15. Suppose that the pattern of plateaus in Fig. 7-15 can be filled in completely, leaving no breaks, as Cantor

FIGURE 7-15

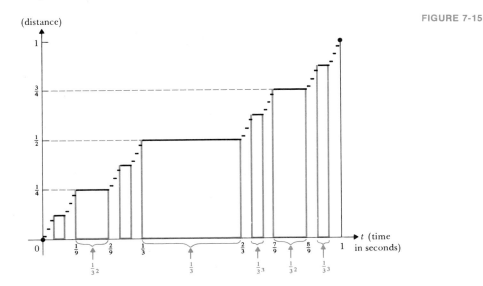

claimed. Then the slope will be *zero* over an infinite union of (green) subintervals. The total length of all the subintervals of size at least $1/3^n$ will be

$$L_n = \frac{1}{3} + 2\left(\frac{1}{9}\right) + 4\left(\frac{1}{27}\right) + \cdots + 2^{n-1}\left(\frac{1}{3^n}\right)$$

$$= \frac{1}{3} + \frac{1}{3}\left(\frac{2}{3}\right) + \frac{1}{3}\left(\frac{2}{3}\right)^2 + \cdots + \frac{1}{3}\left(\frac{2}{3}\right)^{n-1},$$

(1)

for any fixed integer n. Check that this "geometric sum" can be re-written as

$$L_n = \frac{1}{3}\left(\frac{1-(2/3)^n}{1-(2/3)}\right)$$
$$= 1-(2/3)^n. \qquad (2)$$

(Recall the scheme in Sec. 1.3, or see Appendix A.) We can include more and more intervals by choosing n larger and larger. Then the quantity $(\frac{2}{3})^n$ should get smaller and smaller, and L_n should "converge" to 1. It would appear, therefore, that the lengths of *all* the green intervals add up to *unit time*. And those instants—if any—that sit outside all the green intervals account for $1-1=0$ seconds, "no time at all."

How can we interpret such a result in terms of velocities? If Cantor's function described the positions of an idealized race horse, then the horse would have velocity *zero* at all instants in the unit interval—except possibly for some instants amounting to "no time at all." Yet the horse would move from 0 to 1 in unit time, and with no jumps! What can be happening at the instants outside the green intervals: can velocities exist there in the usual sense?

If Cantor's function can be constructed as claimed, what light or doubt does it shed on the "neck-and-neck race argument"? Cantor's horse would part company with a truly stationary horse, although both start at the same place and have identical (zero) velocities at all instants—except possibly for some amounting to "no time at all." If you felt sure about the "neck-and-neck race argument" when velocities were equal *all* the time, then why shouldn't it work here too? Pictorially, how can Cantor's graph rise above the zero level with no jumps?

All the matters in question here are based upon the properties of "limits" and of derivatives defined as "limits"—properties which I'll explore in coming chapters.

7.9 SUMMARY OF CHAPTER 7

DEFINITION: The average rate of change of a function over an interval $[q, r]$ is the difference ratio

$$\frac{f(r)-f(q)}{r-q}.$$

TENTATIVE DEFINITION: The *derivative of a function* $f(x)$ at an input x_0 is the "limit" (if it exists) of "average rates" of change

$$\frac{f(r_n)-f(q_n)}{(r_n-q_n)},$$

as we pick smaller and smaller intervals $[q_n, r_n]$ containing x_0. Notation for the "limiting" number: $f'(x_0)$.
(See Fig. 7-6 and Sec. 7.3.)

REMARK. If it exists, the derivative $f'(x_0)$ is usually interpreted as the *slope* of the graph of f *at* the point $(x_0, f(x_0))$ — generalizing the idea of "slopes" of lines.   (Sec. 7.1)

CONJECTURE (The "neck-and-neck race argument"): If $f(a) = g(a)$ and $f'(x) = g'(x)$ for $a < x < b$, then $f(x) \equiv g(x)$ on $[a, b]$. (Sec. 7.5)

Tentative specific derivatives:

$f(x)$	$f'(x_0)$
$mx + b$	m
x^2	$2x_0$
x^3	$3x_0{}^2$
x^{-1}	$-x_0{}^{-2}$ $(x_0 \neq 0)$

(Secs. 7.3 and 7.1)

TENTATIVE APPLICATIONS TO FINDING MAXIMA AND MINIMA: If the derivative $f'(x_0)$ of a function exists for all x_0 inside a domain $[a, b]$ and if an absolute maximum occurs at an input $x_0 \neq a$ or b, then we should expect $f'(x_0) = 0$, with $f'(x) \geq 0$ for inputs x neighboring x_0 on the left and $f'(x) \leq 0$ for inputs x neighboring x_0 on the right.

Similarly for a minimum input, except with $\geq$ and $\leq$ interchanged (Sec. 7.1).

TENTATIVE APPLICATIONS TO MOTION ALONG A STRAIGHT LINE: Let $p(t)$ denote the position of an object at time t.

DEFINITION: The (*instantaneous*) *velocity at time* t_0 is the derivative $p'(t_0)$ of p at t_0.

Considering velocity $v(t) = p'(t)$ as a function of the time input t,

DEFINITION: the (*instantaneous*) *acceleration at time* t_0 is the derivative $v'(t_0)$ of the velocity function v at t_0.

PROBLEM TYPE: how to find $p(t)$ and $v(t)$ given an explicit "law" for the acceleration $v'(t)$ and given "initial" values $p(0)$ and $v(0)$. (Sec. 7.4)

TENTATIVE APPLICATIONS TO FINDING VOLUME, ETC.: see Sec. 7.6.

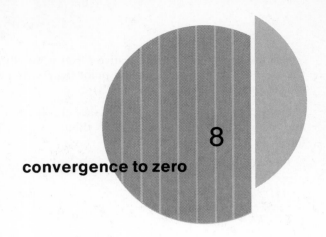

8 convergence to zero

Let's begin to examine the concept of numbers "converging" to a "limiting value." If we can build a framework of trustworthy results about "convergence," we can hope to dispel the doubts of Chapter 7 and to extend the methods I described there.

In this chapter, I'll mainly discuss the simplest case: sequences which "converge" to zero—call them *null* sequences. But first,

8.1 HOW TO DENOTE AND TO PICTURE A SEQUENCE

If we don't know or don't care to specify the nth term in a sequence, let's denote it by a letter with a subscript: a_n, for example. And let's denote the entire sequence by braces: $\{a_n\}$. We can specify a particular sequence such as

$$\frac{1}{2}, \frac{1}{4}, \frac{1}{8}, \ldots, \frac{1}{2^n}, \ldots$$

by writing "$a_n = 1/2^n$", or $\{a_n\} = \{1/2^n\}$.

One way to picture a specific sequence is to locate several of its numbers a_n on a coordinate line, as in Fig. 8-1.

FIGURE 8-1   the sequence $\left\{ \frac{1}{2^n} \right\}$

Another way—which better shows how a sequence changes from step to step—is to represent the sequence by points of the form (n, a_n) in a two-dimensional coordinate plane, as in Fig. 8-2. The vertical axis in Fig. 8-2 corresponds to the coordinate line in Fig. 8-1.

148

FIGURE 8-2

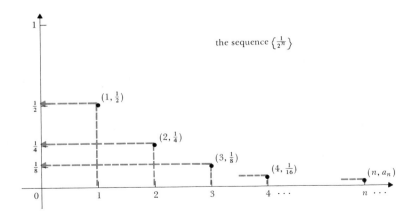

The points (n, a_n) in Fig. 8-2 constitute a "graph" for the sequence $\{a_n\}$. In fact, one way to *define* the notion of "sequence" is as a *function which assigns an output number a_n to each input n in the infinite domain of positive integers.* The set of points (n, a_n) is the graph of the function—as in Chapter 4.

We might say that a *subsequence* of a given sequence is merely a restriction of the original function to a smaller (but infinite) domain of integers. We can relabel the inputs of a subsequence so that it appears as a sequence in its own right. See the green subsequence in Fig. 8-3.

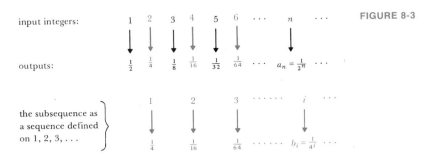

FIGURE 8-3

The ith member ("b_i") in the green subsequence has the subscript $2i$ in the original sequence $\{a_n\}$. The ith member in some other subsequence might have another original subscript—call it "n_i." In what follows, I'll often use the general notation

$$a_{n_1}, a_{n_2}, a_{n_3}, \ldots, a_{n_i}, \ldots$$

to denote a subsequence of an original sequence $a_1, a_2, a_3, \ldots, a_n, \ldots$ (See Problem 7 of Sec. 8.3 for another view of subsequences.)

8.2 PROPERTIES OF NULL SEQUENCES

FIGURE 8-4

Here now are more examples and pictures of sequences which appear to "converge" to zero. They display properties which we might conjecture to hold for all null sequences.

Example 1. $1, \frac{1}{2}, \frac{1}{3}, \frac{1}{4}, \frac{1}{5}, \frac{1}{6}, \frac{1}{7}, \frac{1}{8}, \frac{1}{9}, \ldots$

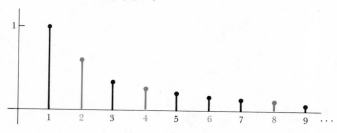

Property: *Any subsequence of a null sequence is itself a null sequence.*

FIGURE 8-5

Example 2. $1, \frac{1}{2}, \frac{1}{3}, \frac{1}{4}, \frac{1}{5}, \frac{1}{6}, \frac{1}{7}, \frac{1}{8}, \frac{1}{9}, \ldots$

$2, 2, 2, 2, \frac{1}{5}, \frac{1}{6}, \frac{1}{7}, \frac{1}{8}, \frac{1}{9}, \ldots$

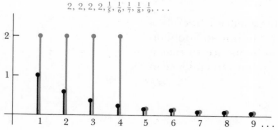

Property: *A sequence which differs from a null sequence in only finitely many places is itself a null sequence.*

In other words: only the "tail" of a sequence — starting at whatever term you wish — determines whether the sequence converges to zero.

FIGURE 8-6

Example 3. $1, \frac{1}{2}, \frac{1}{2}, \frac{1}{4}, \frac{1}{3}, \frac{1}{8}, \frac{1}{4}, \frac{1}{16}, \frac{1}{5}, \frac{1}{32}, \frac{1}{6}, \ldots$

Property: *If one interlaces two null sequences, the resulting sequence is null.*

(Note in Example 3 that the numbers in a sequence needn't get smaller at each step in order for the sequence to converge to zero.)

Example 4. $1, \frac{1}{2}, \frac{1}{3}, \frac{1}{4}, \frac{1}{5}, \cdots, \frac{1}{n}, \cdots$ **FIGURE 8-7**

$-2, -\frac{2}{2}, -\frac{2}{3}, -\frac{2}{4}, -\frac{2}{5}, \cdots, -\frac{2}{n}, \cdots$

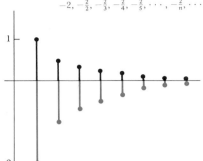

Property: *If one multiplies ("scales") all terms of a null sequence by a fixed real number, the resulting sequence is null.*

Example 5. $1 + \frac{1}{2}, \frac{1}{2} + \frac{1}{4}, \frac{1}{3} + \frac{1}{8}, \frac{1}{4} + \frac{1}{16}, \cdots, \frac{1}{n} + \frac{1}{2^n}, \cdots$ **FIGURE 8-8**

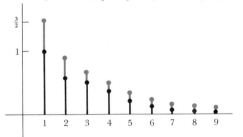

Property: *The (term-by-term) sum of two null sequences is a null sequence.*

Example 6. $1 \cdot 2, \frac{1}{2} \cdot (-3), \frac{1}{3} \cdot 2, \frac{1}{4}(-3), \ldots, \frac{1}{n} \cdot b_n, \cdots$ **FIGURE 8-9**
where $|b_n| \leq 3$ for all n

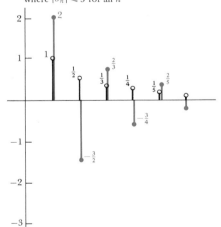

Property: *The (term-by-term) product $\{c_n = a_n b_n\}$ of a null sequence $\{a_n\}$ with another sequence $\{b_n\}$ will itself be a null sequence if the values b_n can't cancel the smallness of the a_n by becoming arbitrarily large—that is, if the sequence $\{b_n\}$ is "bounded":*

Definition: Let's call a sequence $\{b_n\}$ *bounded* if there is some number $b \geq 0$ (a "bound") such that

$$|b_n| \leq b \qquad \text{for all } n, \tag{1}$$

or equivalently,

$$-b \leq b_n \leq b \qquad \text{for all } n.$$ (2)

Boundedness means that all the numbers b_n lie in some fixed interval of finite width, about the origin, as in Fig. 8-10.

FIGURE 8-10

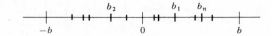

More pictorially still, boundedness means that the entire graph of the sequence $\{b_n\}$ lies trapped in a "tube" of width $2b$, as in Fig. 8-11. (The "tube" is the set of all points (x, y) in the coordinate plane with $x \geq 0$, and $|y| \leq b$.)

FIGURE 8-11

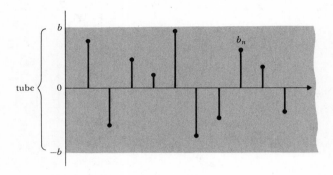

To be bounded, a sequence needn't converge to zero, but from all the examples above we might expect that

Property: *Every null sequence is bounded.*

Together, the last two properties should yield a third:

Property: *The (term-by-term) product $\{a_n b_n\}$ of two null sequences $\{a_n\}$ and $\{b_n\}$ is itself a null sequence.*

Here are several more examples and properties:

FIGURE 8-12

Example 7. $1, -\frac{1}{2}, \frac{1}{3}, -\frac{1}{4}, \frac{1}{5}, -\frac{1}{6}, \dots$

$1, \quad \frac{1}{2}, \frac{1}{3}, \quad \frac{1}{4}, \frac{1}{5}, \quad \frac{1}{6}, \dots$

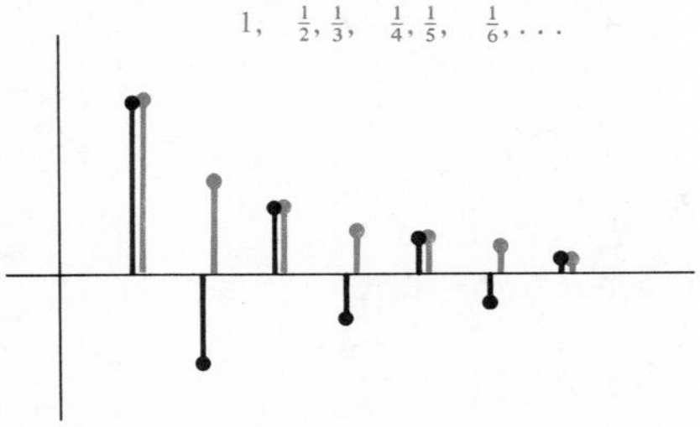

Property: *If a sequence $\{a_n\}$ is null, then so is the sequence of absolute values $\{|a_n|\}$, and conversely.*

Example 8. $1, \quad \frac{1}{2}, \quad \frac{1}{3}, \quad \frac{1}{4}, \quad \frac{1}{5}, \quad \frac{1}{6}, \quad \frac{1}{7}, \quad \frac{1}{8}, \quad \frac{1}{9}, \quad \dots$

$1^2, (\frac{1}{2})^2, (\frac{1}{3})^2, (\frac{1}{4})^2, (\frac{1}{5})^2, (\frac{1}{6})^2, (\frac{1}{7})^2, (\frac{1}{8})^2, (\frac{1}{9})^2, \dots$

$\sqrt{1}, \sqrt{\frac{1}{2}}, \sqrt{\frac{1}{3}}, \sqrt{\frac{1}{4}}, \sqrt{\frac{1}{5}}, \sqrt{\frac{1}{6}}, \sqrt{\frac{1}{7}}, \sqrt{\frac{1}{8}}, \sqrt{\frac{1}{9}}, \dots$

FIGURE 8-13

FIGURE 8-14

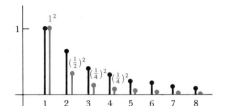

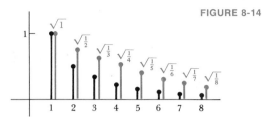

Property: *If $\{a_n\}$ is a null sequence of positive numbers, and r is any fixed positive rational number, then the sequence of powers $a_1{}^r, a_2{}^r, a_3{}^r, a_4{}^r, \dots, a_n{}^r, \dots$ is also a null sequence.*

FIGURE 8-15

Example 9. $1, \quad \frac{1}{2}, \quad \frac{1}{3}, \quad \frac{1}{4}, \quad \frac{1}{5}, \quad \dots, \quad \frac{1}{n}, \quad \dots$

$-\frac{1}{2}, \frac{1}{2+\sqrt{2}}, -\frac{1}{3+\sqrt{3}}, \frac{1}{4+\sqrt{4}}, -\frac{1}{5+\sqrt{5}}, \dots, \frac{(-1)^n}{n+\sqrt{n}}, \dots$

Here $\left| \dfrac{(-1)^n}{n+\sqrt{n}} \right| < \dfrac{1}{n}$ for all n.

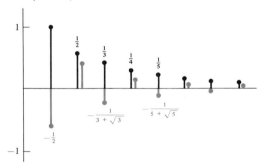

Property: *A sequence $\{b_n\}$ must be null if its absolute values term by term don't exceed the values in some null sequence $\{a_n\}$ — that is, if*

$$|b_n| \leq a_n \qquad \text{for all } n.$$

FIGURE 8-16

Example 10. $0, 0, 0, 0, 0, \dots$
$1, 1, 1, 1, 1, \dots$

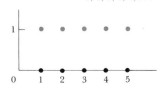

Property: *The only "constant" sequence $c, c, c, \dots$ which is null is for $c = 0$.*

Finally, regarding specific sequences, let's record that

Property: *The sequence $\{1/n\}$ is null, and so is $\{r^n\}$ for any fixed positive $r < 1$.*

So far, we don't have an actual working definition of what a null sequence is. I've merely pointed out "properties" which we might intuitively expect to hold for sequences "converging" to zero. Relying on such properties, here's how we could check whether a new sequence $\{a_n\}$ is null: let's see whether it's built up from simpler null sequences.

EXAMPLE 11. $a_n = \dfrac{3n-1}{n^2}$ for $n = 1, 2, 3, \ldots$. Write

$$a_n = \frac{3n}{n^2} - \frac{1}{n^2}$$

$$= 3\left(\frac{1}{n}\right) + (-1)\left(\frac{1}{n}\right)\left(\frac{1}{n}\right). \tag{3}$$

If $\{1/n\}$ is a null sequence, then $\{(1/n) \cdot (1/n)\}$ should be also, as the term-by-term product of null sequences. So also should be $\{3(1/n)\}$ and $\{(-1)(1/n) \cdot (1/n)\}$, got by scaling null sequences. Finally, $\{a_n\}$ is displayed in (3) as the sum of two null sequences, and so should be null. I invite you to test your intuition even further by deciding which sequences in the next problem section should be classified as "null."

If you believe that the above "properties" are completely self-evident, then one way we might proceed from here is as follows: We could accept the notion of "convergence to zero" as an undefined concept—just as with the notions of "point" and "line" in geometry. We could then regard the above properties as *axioms* describing the notion. And on this platform we could erect a framework of results on convergence and derivatives which will support the "calculus" begun in Chapter 7. If you wish to follow such a path, go on to Chapter 9 after doing the problems of the next section.

There is another road: We can try to capture the notion of "convergence to zero" by a precise *definition*, in terms of concepts already available. Then we can see whether the above properties all flow logically from the one definition—as "theorems." To follow this path, read the rest of this chapter before going on. (For use with either approach, I've listed the properties again in the Summary Section 8.11.)

8.3 PROBLEMS ON IDENTIFYING NULL SEQUENCES

For these problems, assume that the conjectures about the properties of null sequences (in Sec. 8.2) *are valid.*

°1. Show how these properties help us identify the following as null sequences. Sketch a graph of each sequence.

(a) $-\dfrac{1}{2}, -\dfrac{1}{3}, -\dfrac{1}{4}, -\dfrac{1}{5}, \ldots; a_n = \dfrac{-1}{n+1}.$

Sample reasoning: Since $n+1 > n$, we have $1/(n+1) < 1/n$, so that

$$|a_n| = \left|\dfrac{-1}{n+1}\right| = \dfrac{1}{n+1} < \dfrac{1}{n}.$$

Then the sequence $\{-1/(n+1)\}$ has its absolute values term by term less than the values of the null sequence $\{1/n\}$ and therefore is a null sequence.

(b) $2, \dfrac{1}{3}, \dfrac{2}{3}, \dfrac{1}{9}, \dfrac{2}{5}, \dfrac{1}{27}, \ldots; a_n = \begin{cases} \dfrac{2}{n} & \text{if } n \text{ is odd,} \\ \left(\dfrac{1}{3}\right)^{n/2} & \text{if } n \text{ is even.} \end{cases}$

Sample reasoning: The sequence $\{2/n\}$ is obtained by multiplying each term of the null sequence $\{1/n\}$ by the fixed real number 2 and hence is a null sequence. The sequence $\{(\tfrac{1}{3})^n\}$ is of the form $\{r^n\}$ with $r = \tfrac{1}{3}$ and so is a null sequence. We can obtain the given sequence $2, \tfrac{1}{3}, \tfrac{2}{3}, \tfrac{1}{9}, \ldots$, by interlacing these two null sequences, and so it will be a null sequence too.

(c) $100, \dfrac{100}{2}, \dfrac{100}{3}, \dfrac{100}{4}, \ldots; a_n = \dfrac{100}{n}.$

(d) $1, \dfrac{1}{3}, \dfrac{1}{5}, \dfrac{1}{7}, \ldots; a_n = \dfrac{1}{2n-1}.$

(e) $\dfrac{5}{2}, \dfrac{5}{4}, \dfrac{5}{6}, \dfrac{5}{8}, \ldots; a_n = \dfrac{5}{2n}.$

(f) $-1, \dfrac{1}{2}, -\dfrac{1}{3}, \dfrac{1}{4}, -\dfrac{1}{5}, \ldots; a_n = \dfrac{(-1)^n}{n}.$

(g) $1, \dfrac{1}{\sqrt{2}}, \dfrac{1}{\sqrt{3}}, \ldots; a_n = \dfrac{1}{\sqrt{n}}.$

(h) $10, 10, 10, \dfrac{1}{4}, \dfrac{1}{5}, \dfrac{1}{6}, \ldots; a_n = \begin{cases} 10 \text{ if } n = 1, 2, 3, \\ \dfrac{1}{n} \text{ if } n \geqslant 4. \end{cases}$

(i) $0, \dfrac{1}{4}, 0, \dfrac{1}{16}, 0, \dfrac{1}{64}, \ldots; a_n = \begin{cases} \dfrac{1}{2^n} \text{ if } n \text{ is even,} \\ 0 \text{ if } n \text{ is odd.} \end{cases}$

(j) $\dfrac{1}{3}, \dfrac{1}{16}, \dfrac{1}{45}, \dfrac{1}{96}, \ldots; a_n = \dfrac{1}{n^2}\left(\dfrac{1}{n+2}\right).$

(k) $\dfrac{1}{2}, \dfrac{4}{9}, \dfrac{9}{28}, \dfrac{16}{65}, \ldots; a_n = \dfrac{n^2}{n^3+1}.$

(l) $-\dfrac{1}{2}, -\dfrac{\sqrt{2}}{3}, -\dfrac{\sqrt{3}}{4}, \ldots; a_n = \dfrac{-\sqrt{n}}{n+1}.$

(m) $\dfrac{3}{2}, \dfrac{5}{6}, \dfrac{7}{12}, \dfrac{9}{20}, \ldots, a_n = \dfrac{1}{n}+\dfrac{1}{n+1}.$

(n) $\dfrac{13}{5}, \dfrac{13}{10}, \dfrac{13}{15}, \dfrac{13}{20}, \ldots; a_n = \dfrac{2}{n}+\dfrac{3}{5n}.$

(o) $\dfrac{1}{1\cdot 2}, \dfrac{1}{2\cdot 3}, \dfrac{1}{3\cdot 4}, \dfrac{1}{4\cdot 5}, \ldots; a_n = \dfrac{1}{n(n+1)}.$

$\left(\text{Note also: } a_n = \dfrac{1}{n}-\dfrac{1}{n+1}.\right)$

(p) $0, \dfrac{1}{4}, \dfrac{2}{9}, \dfrac{3}{16}, \ldots; a_n = \left(\dfrac{1}{n}-\dfrac{1}{n^2}\right).$

(q) $-1, -\dfrac{7}{8}, -\dfrac{17}{27}, -\dfrac{31}{64}, \ldots; a_n = \left(\dfrac{1}{n^3}-\dfrac{2}{n}\right).$

(r) $1, \dfrac{3}{4}, \dfrac{5}{9}, \dfrac{7}{16}, \ldots; a_n = \left(\dfrac{1}{n}\right)\left(2-\dfrac{1}{n}\right).$

(s) $-\dfrac{1}{2}, \dfrac{4}{15}, -\dfrac{3}{20}, \dfrac{8}{85}, \ldots; a_n = \left(\dfrac{2}{n^2+1}\right)(-1)^n\left(\dfrac{n}{n+1}\right).$

(t) $1, \left(\dfrac{1}{8}\right)^{1/2}, \left(\dfrac{1}{27}\right)^{1/2}, \dfrac{1}{8}, \ldots; a_n = \left(\dfrac{1}{n^3}\right)^{1/2}.$

(u) $-\dfrac{1}{2}, \dfrac{1}{5}, -\dfrac{1}{10}, \dfrac{1}{17}, \ldots; a_n = \dfrac{(-1)^n}{n^2+1}.$

*(v) $1, \dfrac{1}{2^{3/2}}, \dfrac{1}{3^{4/3}}, \dfrac{1}{4^{5/4}}, \ldots; a_n = \dfrac{1}{n^{[1+(1/n)]}}.$

°2. Find a "bound" b for each of the sequences in Problem 1. Explain why $|a_n| \leq b$ for all n.

Sample: in (1b) we have

$$2, \frac{1}{3}, \frac{2}{3}, \frac{1}{9}, \frac{2}{5}, \frac{1}{27}, \ldots; a_n = \begin{cases} \dfrac{2}{n} & \text{if } n \text{ is odd}, \\ \left(\dfrac{1}{3}\right)^{n/2} & \text{if } n \text{ is even}. \end{cases}$$

Since $2/n \le 2$ for all n, and $(\frac{1}{3})^{n/2} < 1$ for all n, we must have $|a_n| \le 2$ for all n. A bound is $b = 2$.

3. Show that each of the following is not a null sequence. What properties of null sequences do these fail to have? Sketch a graph of each sequence.

(a) $1, 2, 3, 4, \ldots; a_n = n$.

Sample reasoning: This sequence is not bounded. For any "would be" bound b, there will be an integer N_b larger than b; and $a_{N_b} > b$. Since the sequence is not bounded, it is not a null sequence.

(b) $1, \dfrac{1}{8}, 1, \dfrac{1}{64}, \dfrac{1}{125}, 1, \ldots, a_n = \begin{cases} 1 & \text{if } n \text{ is multiple of } 3, \\ \dfrac{1}{n^3} & \text{if } n \text{ is not multiple of } 3. \end{cases}$

Sample reasoning: This sequence contains the subsequence $1, 1, 1, \ldots$. Since the only constant sequence which is null is the sequence $0, 0, 0, \ldots$, we know that $1, 1, 1, \ldots$, is not null. But every subsequence of a null sequence is null, so the given sequence $1, \frac{1}{8}, 1, \frac{1}{64}, \ldots$ cannot be null.

(c) $1, -1, 1, -1, \ldots; a_n = \begin{cases} 1 & \text{if } n \text{ is odd}, \\ -1 & \text{if } n \text{ is even}. \end{cases}$

(Note that general term of this sequence can also be written as $a_n = (-1)^{n+1}$.)

(d) $1, 4, 9, 16, 25, 36, \ldots; a_n = n^2$.

(e) $1, \dfrac{1}{4}, 9, \dfrac{1}{16}, 25, \dfrac{1}{36}, \ldots; a_n = \begin{cases} \dfrac{1}{n^2} & \text{if } n \text{ is even}, \\ n^2 & \text{if } n \text{ is odd}. \end{cases}$

(f) $1, -2, 3, -4, \ldots; a_n = (-1)^{n+1}n$.

(g) $\dfrac{1}{2}, \dfrac{1}{4}, \dfrac{1}{2}, \dfrac{1}{16}, \dfrac{1}{2}, \dfrac{1}{64}, \ldots; a_n = \begin{cases} \left(\dfrac{1}{2}\right)^n & \text{if } n \text{ is even}, \\ \dfrac{1}{2} & \text{if } n \text{ is odd}. \end{cases}$

(h) $1, 0, \dfrac{1}{2}, \dfrac{1}{2}, \dfrac{1}{3}, \dfrac{2}{3}, \dfrac{1}{4}, \dfrac{3}{4}, \dfrac{1}{5}, \dfrac{4}{5}, \ldots ; a_n = \begin{cases} 1 - \dfrac{2}{n} & \text{if } n \text{ is even,} \\[2ex] \dfrac{2}{n+1} & \text{if } n \text{ is odd.} \end{cases}$

4. For the following pairs of sequences, decide which ones are null and which ones are not.

$$\begin{cases} 1, \dfrac{1}{4}, \dfrac{1}{9}, \dfrac{1}{16}, \ldots ; a_n = \dfrac{1}{n^2}, \\[2ex] 1, 4, 9, 16, \ldots ; \ b_n = n^2. \end{cases}$$

$$\begin{cases} 1, 8, 27, 64, \ldots ; \ a_n = n^3, \\[2ex] 1, \dfrac{1}{8}, \dfrac{1}{27}, \dfrac{1}{64}, \ldots ; b_n = \dfrac{1}{n^3}. \end{cases}$$

$$\begin{cases} 3, 3, 3, 3, \ldots ; \ a_n = 3, \\[2ex] \dfrac{1}{3}, \dfrac{1}{3}, \dfrac{1}{3}, \dfrac{1}{3}, \ldots ; b_n = \dfrac{1}{3}. \end{cases}$$

The first *two* pairs of sequences might suggest a conjecture about properties of null sequences. What is it? Does your conjecture hold for the third pair?

*5. We can be misled about the ultimate behavior of a sequence if we examine only the first few terms. As an example, consider the sequence whose general term a_n is $(24)^n/n!$. The first four terms of this sequence are 24, 288, 2304, and 13,824. In fact, the 10th term is greater than 17,000,000. Yet this is a null sequence! You might try to prove this surprising fact in a later exercise. Right now, show that this sequence is bounded and, moreover, that terms ultimately *decrease* in absolute value: that is, there is an integer N such that if $k > N$, then $a_{k+1} < a_k$. (Suggestion: look at a_{k+1}/a_k.)

*6. Suppose that $\{a_n\}$ is any null sequence with $a_n > 0$ for all n. Show that there is always another null sequence $\{b_n\}$ which converges to 0 much "faster" than $\{a_n\}$ and a null sequence $\{c_n\}$ which converges to 0 much "slower" than $\{a_n\}$, in the sense that $\lim_{n \to \infty} b_n/a_n = 0$ and $\lim_{n \to \infty} a_n/c_n = 0$.

*7. As I mentioned in Sec. 8.1, we can regard a sequence $\{a_n\}$ as a function with positive integer inputs n and corresponding outputs a_n, or "$a(n)$." Note that we can also regard a *subsequence* $a_{n_1}, a_{n_2}, \ldots, a_{n_k}, \ldots$ as a *composition of functions*, "$a(n(k))$," where the inside function $n(k)$ has the following rule: To each positive integer k assign the original subscript n_k, or "$n(k)$," of the kth member in the subsequence, a_{n_k}.

(a) Write out several sequences and subsequences, and for each case draw a diagram with arrows showing how inputs k lead to outputs $n(k)$, which lead to further outputs $a(n(k))$, or a_{n_k}.

(b) If k_1 and k_2 are two input integers for the function $n(k)$, with $k_1 < k_2$, what relation must hold between their corresponding outputs $n(k_1)$ and $n(k_2)$?

*8.4   DEFINITION OF CONVERGENCE TO ZERO

How can we make precise the notion of a sequence of numbers $\{a_n\}$ "converging" to zero—say, as pictured in Fig. 8-17 or in Fig. 8-18?

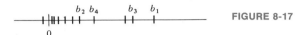

FIGURE 8-17

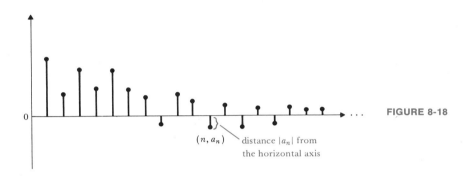

FIGURE 8-18

Intuitively, if we go *far enough* to the right in the sequence of Fig. 8-18, the values $|a_n|$ should get very small—the points should be very close to the horizontal axis. How far must we go? That depends on how small we want the values $|a_n|$ to be.

For example, if you claim that the sequence $\{1/n\}$ converges to zero, you should be prepared to answer challenges, as follows:

A challenger might ask: will the points ever stay within 10^{-6} units from the horizontal axis? Your answer: Yes, for *all* $n \geq 10^6 + 1$, you'll have

$$|a_n| = \frac{1}{n} < 10^{-6}.$$

The challenger could continue: will the points ever stay within 10^{-100} units from the horizontal axis? Your answer: Yes, for all $n \geq 10^{100} + 1$, you'll have

$$|a_n| = \frac{1}{n} < 10^{-100}.$$

And so on.

Here's how we can picture such a dialogue between you and a challenger about a sequence $\{a_n\}$: Your challenger has the right to pick *any* radius—call it ϵ—of a "tube" about the horizontal axis. (See the three cases in Fig. 8-19.)

FIGURE 8-19

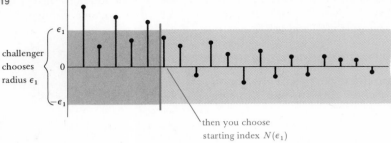

challenger
chooses
radius ϵ_1

then you choose
starting index $N(\epsilon_1)$

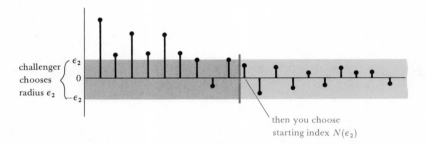

challenger
chooses
radius ϵ_2

then you choose
starting index $N(\epsilon_2)$

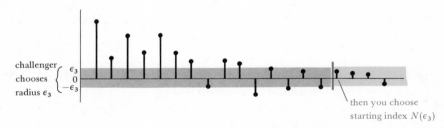

challenger
chooses
radius ϵ_3

then you choose
starting index $N(\epsilon_3)$

Once the challenger has chosen a radius ϵ, you must then choose a value of n—call it a "starting index" and denote it by $N(\epsilon)$—such that for all $n \geqslant N(\epsilon)$ the points (n, a_n) will lie within the challenger's tube. (See the green portions in Fig. 8-19.) Algebraically, you must be able to show that

$$|a_n| < \epsilon \qquad \text{for all } n \geqslant N(\epsilon).$$

Of course, the smaller the ϵ chosen by the challenger, the larger you may have to choose your starting index $N(\epsilon)$. The point is: you should be prepared *in advance* with a plan, a routine, for responding to challenger's ϵ's by producing suitable $N(\epsilon)$'s.

(Note, there need be no unique starting index in any given case: if one green strip traps the tail of the sequence, then any strip of the same radius and starting further to the right will trap it also.)

Let's try to capture these ideas with a precise

Definition: Let's say that a sequence $\{a_n\}$ *converges to zero*, or is a *null sequence*, if it is possible to devise a routine which will do the following: whenever you feed a positive number ϵ into the routine, the output will be an integer, call it $N(\epsilon)$, with the property that

$$|a_n| < \epsilon \qquad \text{for all } n \geqslant N(\epsilon).$$

The traditional notation for convergence to zero is: $\lim_{n \to \infty} a_n = 0$.

FIGURE 8-20

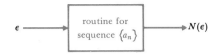

We can picture the routine itself as accomplished by a machine in a box, as in Fig. 8-20.

Here's what the definition means for a sequence displayed on a coordinate line, as in Fig. 8-21. If a challenger chooses an interval $(-\epsilon, \epsilon)$ about the origin, the routine will produce a corresponding "starting index" $N(\epsilon)$ such that the values a_n will lie inside $(-\epsilon, \epsilon)$ for all $n \geqslant N(\epsilon)$. ($|a_n| < \epsilon$ is equivalent to $-\epsilon < a_n < \epsilon$.)

FIGURE 8-21

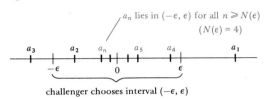

The above definition is man made. Is it a useful one? To decide, we should check whether it agrees with our intuition in classifying various basic sequences as null or not null. And we should see whether all the "properties" I conjectured for null sequences in Sec. 8.2 now follow logically from the definition itself.

*8.5   CHECKING THE DEFINITION AGAINST EXAMPLES

EXAMPLE 1. The sequence 1, 0, 1, 0, 1, 0, . . . is not null; because a challenger can choose $\epsilon = \frac{1}{2}$ and it will not be true that $|a_n| < \frac{1}{2}$ for all $n \geqslant$ some starting index $N(\epsilon)$.

EXAMPLE 2. To show that $\{1/n\}$ is a null sequence according to the precise definition, we must devise a routine. Given any challenger's ϵ, we need a special integer $N(\epsilon)$ with the property that

$$\frac{1}{n} < \epsilon \qquad \text{for all } n \geqslant N(\epsilon), \tag{1}$$

or, writing it differently,

$$\boxed{n \geqslant N(\epsilon)} \text{ should } \textit{imply} \text{ that } \boxed{\frac{1}{n} < \epsilon}. \tag{2}$$

To get at the symbol n more easily in the last inequality, let's invert, and get an equivalent statement:

$$\boxed{n \geqslant N(\epsilon)} \text{ should } \textit{imply} \text{ that } \boxed{n > \frac{1}{\epsilon}}. \tag{3}$$

FIGURE 8-22

Inspiration: Announce as $N(\epsilon)$, say, the first integer greater than the real number $1/\epsilon$. (Such an integer does exist, by Archimedes' axiom, Sec. 4.12.) Pictorially, we'll have Fig. 8-22. Then (since $a \geqslant b$ and

$b \geq c$ imply $a \geq c$) we'll have

$$\boxed{n \geq N(\epsilon)}\ \text{plus the fact}\ \boxed{N(\epsilon) > \frac{1}{\epsilon}}\ \textit{imply}\ \boxed{n > \frac{1}{\epsilon}}$$

$$\text{or equivalently}\ \boxed{\frac{1}{n} < \epsilon}. \tag{4}$$

And the routine accomplishes its mission.

Until we can use general "properties" of null sequences, this is the kind of detail we must go through in testing for convergence to zero if we are to stick with the precision of the definition.

EXAMPLE 3. $\{1/2^n\}$ is a null sequence. Given ϵ, let's find a $N(\epsilon)$ such that

$$\boxed{n \geq N(\epsilon)}\ \text{will}\ \textit{imply}\ \boxed{\frac{1}{2^n} < \epsilon}, \tag{5}$$

or equivalently,

$$\boxed{n \geq N(\epsilon)}\ \text{will}\ \textit{imply}\ \boxed{2^n > \frac{1}{\epsilon}}. \tag{6}$$

Inspiration: Announce as $N(\epsilon)$, say, the first integer N which will make $2^N > 1/\epsilon$. (There is such an N, as you might recall from Problem 3 of Sec. 6.7.) For a picture, see Fig. 8-23. Then

FIGURE 8-23

routine: $\epsilon \longrightarrow$ | pick 1st N such that $2^N > \frac{1}{\epsilon}$ | $\longrightarrow N(\epsilon)$

$$\boxed{n \geq N(\epsilon)}\ \text{implies}\ \left.\begin{array}{c}\boxed{2^n \geq 2^{N(\epsilon)}} \\[4pt] \text{plus} \\[4pt] \boxed{2^{N(\epsilon)} > \frac{1}{\epsilon}}\end{array}\right\}\ \textit{imply}\ \boxed{2^n > \frac{1}{\epsilon}}$$

$$\text{or equivalently}\ \boxed{\frac{1}{2^n} < \epsilon}. \tag{7}$$

The routine works.

EXAMPLE 4. $a_n = 2n/(n^2+1)$ for $n = 1, 2, 3, \ldots$. Intuitively $\{a_n\}$ should be a null sequence since the denominator overpowers the numerator more and more for larger and larger n. But let's again devise a routine. Given any $\epsilon > 0$, we need an index $N(\epsilon)$ such that

$$\boxed{n \geq N(\epsilon)}\ \text{will}\ \textit{imply}\ \boxed{\frac{2n}{n^2+1} < \epsilon}. \tag{8}$$

Let's again invert the second inequality to isolate n: namely,

$$\boxed{\frac{n^2+1}{2n} > \frac{1}{\epsilon}}\ \text{or}\ \boxed{n + \frac{1}{n} > \frac{2}{\epsilon}}. \tag{9}$$

Here is a new wrinkle: n still isn't isolated in (9) as it was in previous examples; there is an added $1/n$ term.

Inspiration: Don't mind the added term—it may help later. Announce as $N(\epsilon)$, say, the first integer greater than $2/\epsilon$ (Fig. 8-24). Let's check the routine:

FIGURE 8-24

$$\begin{rcases} \boxed{n \geq N(\epsilon)} \quad implies \quad \boxed{n + \frac{1}{n} \geq N(\epsilon)} \\[1em] plus \\[1em] \boxed{N(\epsilon) > \frac{2}{\epsilon}} \end{rcases} \quad imply \quad \boxed{n + \frac{1}{n} > \frac{2}{\epsilon}}$$

or equivalently

$$\boxed{\frac{2n}{n^2+1} < \epsilon}. \qquad (10)$$

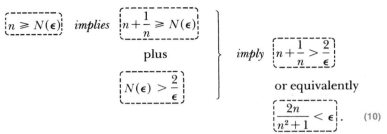

So $\{a_n\}$ is a null sequence.

This was my routine for devising routines: Start, say on scratch paper, with the desired inequality: $|a_n| < \epsilon$. In many cases a_n will be an algebraic expression involving n. By a sequence of algebraic operations try to convert the inequality into one of the form

$$n \geq \text{some expression involving } \epsilon. \qquad (11)$$

Then, *tentatively*, announce as $N(\epsilon)$ some value of n, say the smallest, for which (11) holds. But you will not yet have demonstrated that a routine exists until you *validate* it—until you check that

$$\boxed{n \geq N(\epsilon)} \quad plus \quad \boxed{N(\epsilon) \geq \cdots} \quad imply \quad \boxed{|a_n| < \epsilon}.$$

(I did such checking in (4), (7), and (10) above.) The reason for checking a routine—for perhaps working backward through your original steps—is that algebraic operations are not always reversible. (For example, $x > 2$ implies $x^2 > 4$ but not conversely.)

Now try your own hand at testing for convergence to zero and devising routines, in the problems of the next section.

*8.6   PROBLEMS ON CHECKING FOR CONVERGENCE TO ZERO

1. Look at several of the sequences in Problem 1 of Sec. 8.3. In each case, and for $\epsilon = 1/10$ and $\epsilon = 1/100$, find corresponding "starting indexes" $N(1/10)$ and $N(1/100)$ so that we'll have

$$|a_n| < \frac{1}{10} \quad \text{for all } n \geq N\!\left(\frac{1}{10}\right)$$

and

$$|a_n| < \frac{1}{100} \quad \text{for all } n \geq N\!\left(\frac{1}{100}\right).$$

Sample reasoning: (a) $-\frac{1}{2}, -\frac{1}{3}, -\frac{1}{4}, -\frac{1}{5}, \ldots; a_n = \frac{-1}{n+1}$.

When $n \geqslant 10$, we'll have $n+1 \geqslant 11$, and $1/(n+1) \leqslant 1/11 < 1/10$, and $|a_n| < 1/10$. So we can choose $N(1/10) = 10$. When $n \geqslant 100$, we'll have $n+1 \geqslant 101$, and $1/(n+1) \leqslant 1/101 < 1/100$, and $|a_n| < 1/100$. So we can choose $N(1/100) = 100$.

Sample reasoning: (b) $2, \dfrac{1}{3}, \dfrac{2}{3}, \dfrac{1}{9}, \dfrac{2}{5}, \dfrac{1}{27}, \ldots;$ $a_n = \begin{cases} \dfrac{2}{n} & \text{if } n \text{ is odd,} \\[2mm] \left(\dfrac{1}{3}\right)^{n/2} & \text{if } n \text{ is even.} \end{cases}$

For $\epsilon = 1/10$: If we pick n odd and $\geqslant 21$, then we'll have

$$|a_n| = \frac{2}{n} \leqslant \frac{2}{21} < \frac{1}{10}.$$

If we pick n even and such that $3^{n/2} > 10$, then again we'll have $|a_n| = (\frac{1}{3})^{n/2} < 1/10$. Since $3^3 > 10$, we'll have $3^{n/2} \geqslant 3^3 > 10$ when $n/2 \geqslant 3$ or $n \geqslant 6$. For $N(1/10)$, let's choose 21 (the larger of 21 and 6). Then we'll have $|a_n| < 1/10$ for all $n \geqslant N(1/10)$, odd or even. Similarly, with $\epsilon = 1/100$.

Sample reasoning: (j) $\dfrac{1}{3}, \dfrac{1}{16}, \dfrac{1}{45}, \dfrac{1}{96}, \ldots;$ $a_n = \dfrac{1}{n^2}\left(\dfrac{1}{n+2}\right).$

Let's note that $|a_n| < 1/n^3$ for all positive n. So if $n \geqslant 3 > \sqrt[3]{10}$, we'll have $n^3 > 10$ and $|a_n| < 1/n^3 < 1/10$. If $n \geqslant 5 > \sqrt[3]{100}$, we'll have $n^3 > 100$ and $|a_n| < 1/n^3 < 1/100$.

2. Use the definition of null sequence to show that each sequence in Problem 1 of Sec. 8.3 is a null sequence.

Sample reasoning: (a) $-\dfrac{1}{2}, -\dfrac{1}{3}, -\dfrac{1}{4}, -\dfrac{1}{5}, \ldots;$ $a_n = \dfrac{-1}{n+1}.$

Let ϵ be *any* given positive number. Choose the index $N(\epsilon)$ to be the first positive integer greater than $(1/\epsilon) - 1$; then if $n \geqslant N(\epsilon)$, we'll have $n+1 > (1/\epsilon)$ and $1/(n+1) < 1/\epsilon$, and $|a_n| < 1/\epsilon$.

Sample reasoning: (b) $2, \dfrac{1}{3}, \dfrac{2}{3}, \dfrac{1}{9}, \dfrac{2}{5}, \dfrac{1}{27}, \ldots;$ $a_n = \begin{cases} \dfrac{2}{n} & \text{if } n \text{ is odd,} \\[2mm] \left(\dfrac{1}{3}\right)^{n/2} & \text{if } n \text{ is even.} \end{cases}$

Let ϵ be *any* given positive number. Choose the index N_1 to be the first integer greater than $2/\epsilon$. Then $n > 2/\epsilon$ if $n > N_1$. And if n is *odd*, $a_n = 2/n < \epsilon$. Choose the index N_2 to be an integer such that $3^{N_2/2} > 1/\epsilon$. (There *is* such an integer: see Problem 8 of Sec. 6.9.) Then $3^{n/2} > 1/\epsilon$ if $n > N_2$. And n is *even*, $a_n = (\frac{1}{3})^{n/2} < \epsilon$. Finally, choose N to be the larger of the two integers N_1 and N_2. Whenever $n > N$, a_n will be less than ϵ.

Sample reasoning: (j) $\dfrac{1}{3}, \dfrac{1}{16}, \dfrac{1}{45}, \dfrac{1}{96}, \ldots;$ $a_n = \dfrac{1}{n^2}\left(\dfrac{1}{n+2}\right).$

Note that $|a_n| < 1/n^3$ for all positive n. Let ϵ be *any* given positive number. Choose the index $N(\epsilon)$ to be the first positive integer greater than $\sqrt[3]{1/\epsilon}$. Then if $n \geq N(\epsilon)$, we'll have $n > \sqrt[3]{1/\epsilon}$, and $n^3 > 1/\epsilon$, and $|a_n| < 1/n^3 < \epsilon$.

*8.7 RESULTS FLOWING FROM THE DEFINITION

Need we always devise an $\epsilon,N(\epsilon)$ routine to check whether a sequence is null? Not if the conjectured "properties" of Sec. 8.2 do follow from the definition of convergence to zero. If they do, then we can conclude that a sequence is null if we can display it as built up from simpler null sequences. You may recall the case

$$a_n = \frac{3n-1}{n^2}$$

$$= 3\left(\frac{1}{n}\right) + (-1)\left(\frac{1}{n}\right)\left(\frac{1}{n}\right)$$

(Example 11 in Sec. 8.2), and other cases in Sec. 8.3.

How, then, can we *prove* that the conjectured properties do hold for the infinite host of null sequences—that they are true "theorems"?

The question of what constitutes a proof is not an easy one. What Euclid felt was adequate proof did not convince Lobachevsky, and what Newton (1700) felt was adequate did not convince Cauchy (1800+). Presentation itself presents problems: in reading a "proof" you might be puzzled because of steps which were in fact omitted (often for the sake of economy); or you might wonder why many steps are included (often, to handle some special case you may have overlooked). Here again, experience helps.

Let's work through several proofs—the better to understand both null sequences and the present-day notion of "proof." Here is a plan for tackling a proof: Do scratch work first. Start by writing out what the hypotheses say in terms of basic definitions. Do the same for the conclusion. If possible, draw pictures representing hypotheses and conclusion. Then try to connect the two with logical steps—perhaps by working backward from the conclusion to a point where you can see how the hypotheses will help you.

NOTE: If you find that you don't need all the hypotheses, then you either have made a mistake, or else you have proved a stronger theorem than the one you started with.

If you find that the hypotheses are insufficient, then either you are failing to grasp something, or else the theorem is wrong. Don't always expect that *you* are the one in error.

If you can successfully pick your way between conclusion and hypotheses, then your scratch work is over. Write down a formal sequence of steps leading from hypotheses to conclusion.

Let's follow this plan first for the property of boundedness:

Theorem: If $\lim_{n\to\infty} a_n = 0$, then $\{a_n\}$ is a bounded sequence.

Scratch work:

Hypothesis says: There is a routine with the following property: given any $\epsilon > 0$, the routine will put out an index $N(\epsilon)$ such that

$$|a_n| < \epsilon \qquad \text{for all } n \geqslant N(\epsilon). \tag{1}$$

Conclusion says: There is a number $b \geqslant 0$ such that

$$|a_n| \leqslant b \qquad \text{for } \textit{all } n. \tag{2}$$

For pictures, see Figs. 8-25 and 8-26.

FIGURE 8-25

Hypotheses: (with $\epsilon = {}^1\!/_{10}$).

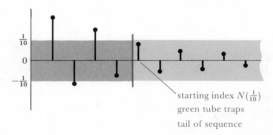

starting index $N(\frac{1}{10})$

green tube traps

tail of sequence

FIGURE 8-26

Conclusion: there is a radius b such that

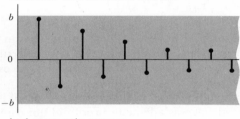

b tube traps entire sequence

Wherein does the tube of radius $\frac{1}{10}$ in Fig. 8-25 not suffice as the required b-tube in Fig. 8-26? Some of the points (n, a_n) might not be trapped for $n < N(\frac{1}{10})$. How much would we have to enlarge the radius $\frac{1}{10}$ tube to trap *all* points? Only enough to handle the largest of the finitely many values $|a_n|$ for $n < N\left(\frac{1}{10}\right)$. That's how large we should choose b.

Now let's try a formal write-up:

Proof: From the hypothesis, with $\epsilon = $ say, $\frac{1}{10}$, we know that there exists an integer $N\left(\frac{1}{10}\right)$ such that

$$|a_n| < \frac{1}{10} \qquad \text{for all } n \geqslant N\left(\frac{1}{10}\right). \tag{3}$$

Let b be the largest of the values

$$\frac{1}{10}, |a_1|, |a_2|, |a_3|, \ldots, |a_{N(1/10)-1}|. \tag{4}$$

Then

$$|a_n| \leqslant b \qquad \text{for } n < N\left(\frac{1}{10}\right), \tag{5}$$

and

$$|a_n| < \frac{1}{10} \leqslant b \qquad \text{for } n \geqslant N\left(\frac{1}{10}\right).$$

Hence

$$|a_n| \leqslant b \qquad \text{for } all \text{ } n.$$

End of the proof. (Note: any other fixed value of ϵ would have served equally well.)

Let's examine another property:

Theorem: If $\lim\limits_{n \to \infty} a_n = 0$ and if $\{b_n\}$ is a bounded sequence, then $\lim\limits_{n \to \infty} a_n b_n = 0$.

Scratch work:

The hypotheses say:

(i) There is a routine with the following property: given any $\epsilon > 0$, the routine will produce an index $N(\epsilon)$ such that

$$|a_n| < \epsilon \qquad \text{for all } n \geqslant N(\epsilon). \tag{6}$$

(ii) There is a bound $b \geqslant 0$ such that

$$|b_n| \leqslant b \qquad \text{for all } n. \tag{7}$$

The conclusion says: It's possible to devise a new routine with the following property: given any challenger's number—call it $\tilde{\epsilon}$ now, the routine will produce an index—call it $\tilde{N}(\tilde{\epsilon})$ now—such that

$$|a_n b_n| < \tilde{\epsilon} \qquad \text{for all } n \geqslant \tilde{N}(\tilde{\epsilon}). \tag{8}$$

How can we use the existing $\epsilon \to N(\epsilon)$ routine of (6) to create an $\tilde{\epsilon} \to \tilde{N}(\tilde{\epsilon})$ routine for (8)? See Fig. 8-27 for a picture of what's needed in the simple case $b_n = 2$ for all n, and $b = 2$.

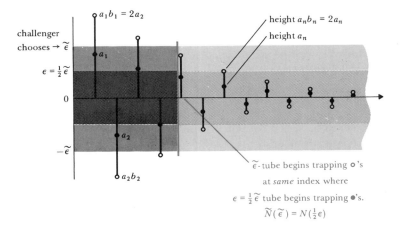

FIGURE 8-27

Figure 8-27 suggests how to build an $\tilde{\epsilon} \to \tilde{N}(\tilde{\epsilon})$ routine from the given $\epsilon \to N(\epsilon)$ routine: see Fig. 8-28. (Note: we'd need $b > 0$ to perform the indicated division.)

FIGURE 8-28

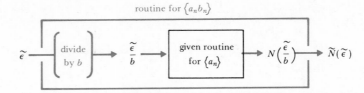

routine for $\{a_n b_n\}$

Now let's see whether we can validate such a routine by writing out a formal

Proof: If $b = 0$, then all $b_n = 0$ and $\{a_n b_n\}$ is null. So let's treat the case $b > 0$. Given a challenger's $\tilde{\epsilon} > 0$, let $\epsilon = \tilde{\epsilon}/b$. Then by hypothesis, there exists an index $N(\epsilon)$ such that

$$|a_n| < \epsilon = \frac{\tilde{\epsilon}}{b} \qquad \text{for all } n \geqslant N(\epsilon). \tag{9}$$

Multiply (9) by the inequality,

$$|b_n| \leqslant b \qquad \text{for all } n,$$

of the boundedness hypothesis, to get

$$|a_n| \cdot |b_n| < \frac{\tilde{\epsilon}}{b} \cdot b = \tilde{\epsilon} \qquad \text{for all } n \geqslant N(\epsilon). \tag{10}$$

Do you recall that $|x| \cdot |y| = |xy|$ for any real numbers x and y? (If not, see Appendix A.) We can use this fact in (10) to conclude that

$$|a_n b_n| < \frac{\tilde{\epsilon}}{b} \cdot b = \tilde{\epsilon} \qquad \text{for all } n \geqslant N(\epsilon). \tag{11}$$

Finally, announce $N(\epsilon)$ as the sought for $\tilde{N}(\tilde{\epsilon})$; and it will be true that

$$|a_n b_n| < \tilde{\epsilon} \qquad \text{for all } n \geqslant \tilde{N}(\tilde{\epsilon}).$$

End of the proof.

Once key results are established, others come more easily, such as the following two.

Theorem (on "scaling"): If $\lim_{n \to \infty} a_n = 0$ and c is any constant then $\lim_{n \to \infty} c a_n = 0$.

Proof: The statement is just a special case of the previous theorem, with $b_n = c$ for all n.

Theorem (on products of null sequences): If $\lim_{n \to 1} a_n = 0$ and $\lim_{n \to \infty} b_n = 0$, then $\lim_{n \to \infty} a_n b_n = 0$.

Proof: Since $\{b_n\}$ is null it must be bounded; hence $\{a_n b_n\}$ is null, by the key result above.

Let's derive one more useful property:

Theorem (on sums of null sequences): If $\lim_{n \to \infty} a_n = 0$ and $\lim_{n \to \infty} b_n = 0$, then $\lim_{n \to \infty} (a_n + b_n) = 0$.

Scratch work:

The hypotheses say: There are two routines, call them A and B. For any $\epsilon > 0$, routine A will produce an index $N_A(\epsilon)$ such that

$$|a_n| < \epsilon \qquad \text{for all } n \geq N_A(\epsilon), \tag{12}$$

and routine B will produce an index $N_B(\epsilon)$ such that

$$|b_n| < \epsilon \qquad \text{for all } n \geq N_B(\epsilon). \tag{13}$$

The conclusion says: it is possible to derive a new routine with the following property: given any challenger's $\tilde{\epsilon}$, the new routine will produce an index $\tilde{N}(\tilde{\epsilon})$ such that

$$|a_n + b_n| < \tilde{\epsilon} \qquad \text{for all } n \geq \tilde{N}(\tilde{\epsilon}). \tag{14}$$

How can we use the existing $\epsilon \to N_A(\epsilon)$ and $\epsilon \to N_B(\epsilon)$ routines to create an $\tilde{\epsilon} \to \tilde{N}(\tilde{\epsilon})$ for (13)? See Fig. 8-29 for a picture of what's needed in a simple case.

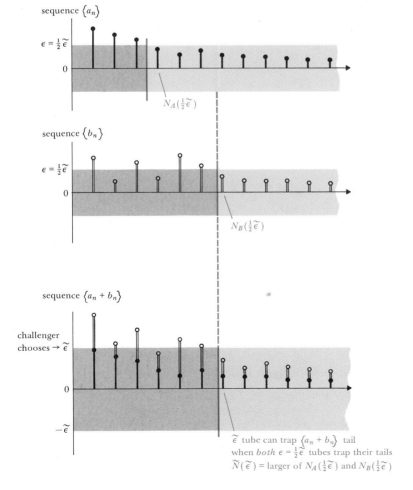

FIGURE 8-29

$\tilde{\epsilon}$ tube can trap $\{a_n + b_n\}$ tail when *both* $\epsilon = \frac{1}{2}\tilde{\epsilon}$ tubes trap their tails $\tilde{N}(\tilde{\epsilon}) =$ larger of $N_A(\frac{1}{2}\tilde{\epsilon})$ and $N_B(\frac{1}{2}\tilde{\epsilon})$

Figure 8-29 suggests how to build an $\tilde{\epsilon} \to \tilde{N}(\tilde{\epsilon})$ routine from the given A and B routines: see Fig. 8-30.

FIGURE 8-30

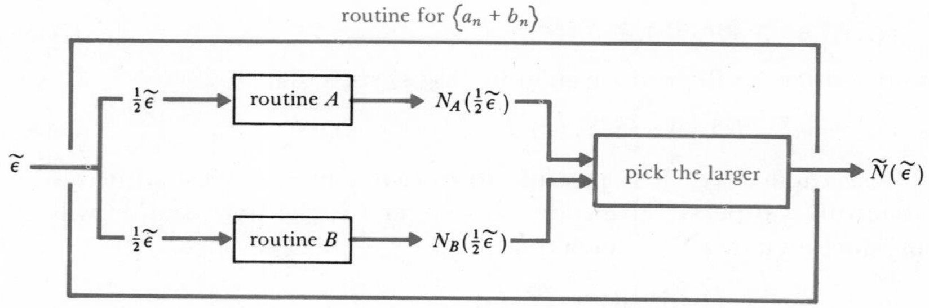

Finally, let's try a formal

Proof: Given a challenger's $\tilde{\epsilon} > 0$, let $\epsilon = \frac{1}{2}\tilde{\epsilon}$. Then by hypotheses there exist indices $N_A(\epsilon)$ and $N_B(\epsilon)$ such that

$$|a_n| < \epsilon = \tfrac{1}{2}\tilde{\epsilon} \qquad \text{for all } n \geqslant N_A(\epsilon) \tag{15}$$

and

$$|b_n| < \epsilon = \tfrac{1}{2}\tilde{\epsilon} \qquad \text{for all } n \geqslant N_B(\epsilon). \tag{16}$$

We can add the inequalities (15) and (16) to get

$$|a_n| + |b_n| < \tfrac{1}{2}\tilde{\epsilon} + \tfrac{1}{2}\tilde{\epsilon} = \tilde{\epsilon} \tag{17}$$

whenever $n \geqslant N_A(\epsilon)$ and $n \geqslant N_B(\epsilon)$ simultaneously.

Do you recall that $|a+b| \leqslant |a| + |b|$ for any real numbers a and b? (See Appendix A.) We can use this fact in (17) to conclude that

$$|a_n + b_n| < \tfrac{1}{2}\tilde{\epsilon} + \tfrac{1}{2}\tilde{\epsilon} = \tilde{\epsilon} \tag{18}$$

whenever $n \geqslant N_A(\epsilon)$ and $n \geqslant N_B(\epsilon)$ simultaneously.

Announce $\tilde{N}(\tilde{\epsilon})$ to be the *larger* of the two indices $N_A(\epsilon)$ and $N_B(\epsilon)$. Then

$$|a_n + b_n| < \tilde{\epsilon} \qquad \text{for all } n \geqslant \tilde{N}(\tilde{\epsilon}).$$

End of the proof.

All of the properties conjectured for null sequences in Sec. 8.2 can be deduced in more or less the same way from the above precise definition of convergence to zero. I invite you to try your own hand at proving several of them, in the problems of Sec. 8.9.

*8.8 HOW CAN CONVERGENCE TO ZERO FAIL?

Pictorially, a sequence $\{a_n\}$ fails of convergence to zero if for *some* challenger's ϵ—call it ϵ_0—the corresponding ϵ_0-tube fails to trap all the graph points (n, a_n), no matter what starting index $N(\epsilon_0)$ we might try. See Fig. 8-31. To the right of any would-be $N(\epsilon_0)$ there will always be some graph point "escaping" from the tube.

FIGURE 8-31

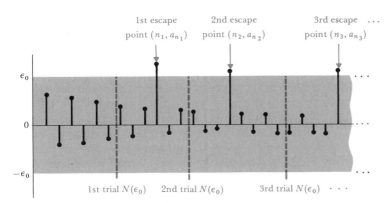

1st escape point (n_1, a_{n_1}) 2nd escape point (n_2, a_{n_2}) 3rd escape point (n_3, a_{n_3}) ...

ϵ_0

0

$-\epsilon_0$

1st trial $N(\epsilon_0)$ 2nd trial $N(\epsilon_0)$ 3rd trial $N(\epsilon_0)$ ...

As Fig. 8-31 suggests, we can pick a sequence of "escape points," and can state that

Theorem: If $\{a_n\}$ is not a null sequence, then there is an $\epsilon_0 > 0$ and a subsequence $a_{n_1}, a_{n_2}, \ldots, a_{n_k}, \ldots$ of $\{a_n\}$ such that

$$|a_{n_k}| \geq \epsilon_0 \qquad \text{for all } k.$$

On a coordinate line, what the theorem says is that all the a_{n_k}'s are excluded for an interval $(-\epsilon_0, \epsilon_0)$ surrounding the origin. See Fig. 8-32. Such was the case with the example $0, 1, 0, 1, 0, 1, \ldots$. For $\epsilon_0 = \frac{1}{2}$, the $\{a_{n_k}\} = \{1, 1, 1, \ldots\}$.

FIGURE 8-32

a_{n_k}'s excluded

$-\epsilon_0$ 0 ϵ_0

*8.9 PROBLEMS ON FAILURE OF CONVERGENCE TO ZERO, AND ON PROOFS

1. For each sequence $\{a_n\}$ of Problem 3 in Sec. 8.3, find an $\epsilon_0 > 0$ and a subsequence $\{a_{n_k}\}$ such that $|a_{n_k}| \geq \epsilon_0$ for all k. Thus $\{a_n\}$ can't be a null sequence.

   Sample reasoning: (a) $1, 2, 3, 4, \ldots$; $a_n = n$.

   Choose $\epsilon_0 = \frac{1}{2}$. Then $|a_n| = n > \frac{1}{2}$ for all n and we can use $\{a_n\}$ itself as the subsequence $\{a_{n_k}\}$.

   Sample reasoning:

   (b) $1, \dfrac{1}{8}, 1, \dfrac{1}{64}, \dfrac{1}{125}, 1, \ldots$; $a_n = \begin{cases} 1 \text{ if } n \text{ is a multiple of } 3, \\ \dfrac{1}{n^3} \text{ if } n \text{ is not a multiple of } 3. \end{cases}$

   Choose $\epsilon_0 = \frac{2}{3}$, and let n_k denote the integers which are multiples of 3 $(n_k = 3k)$. Then $|a_{n_k}| = 1 > \frac{2}{3}$ for all k.

2. Suppose $\{a_n\}$ is not a null sequence. Show that there is an $\epsilon_0 > 0$ and a subsequence $a_{n_1}, a_{n_2}, \ldots, a_{n_k}, \ldots$ of $\{a_n\}$ such that

   $$a_{n_k} \geq \epsilon_0 \qquad \text{for all } k$$

   or

   $$a_{n_k} \leq -\epsilon_0 \qquad \text{for all } k.$$

Sketch suitable "ε-tubes" and try to write out proofs for the following results about null sequences:

3. A sequence which differs from a null sequence in only finitely many places is a null sequence.

    Sample proof: Let $\{a_n\}$ be a null sequence and let $\{b_n\}$ be a sequence which differs in only finitely many places from $\{a_n\}$. This means that there is a finite collection of positive integers $J_1, J_2, \ldots, J_R$ such that $a_k = b_k$ unless k is equal to some J_i. Suppose ϵ is a given positive number. By hypothesis there must be an index $N_A(\epsilon)$ such that $|a_n| < \epsilon$ if $n \geq N_A(\epsilon)$. Choose $N_B(\epsilon)$ to be an integer which is greater than $N_A(\epsilon)$ and greater than the largest of the integers $J_1, J_2, \ldots, J_r$. If $n > N_B(\epsilon)$, then

    $$b_n = a_n \quad \text{and} \quad |a_n| < \epsilon.$$

    Hence $|b_n|$ will be $< \epsilon$ for all $n \geq N_B(\epsilon)$.

4. If one interlaces two null sequences, the resulting sequence is null.

    (For a given ϵ, how can you choose a "starting index" $N(\epsilon)$ for the interlaced sequence in terms of starting indexes for the original sequences?)

5. $\lim_{n \to \infty} a_n = 0$ if and only if $\lim_{n \to \infty} |a_n| = 0$.

6. If $\{a_n\}$ is a null sequence and each $a_n > 0$, then $\{a_n{}^r\}$ is a null sequence for any positive rational number r.

    (Note: $|a_n{}^r| < \epsilon$ is equivalent to $|a_n| < \epsilon^{1/r}$.)

7. If $\{a_n\}$ is a null sequence and $|b_n| \leq a_n$ for all n, then $\{b_n\}$ is a null sequence.

8. The sequence $c, c, c, \ldots, c, \ldots$ is null if, and only if, $c = 0$.

9. If $\{a_n\}$ is a null sequence, then $\{a_1, a_2{}^2, a_3{}^3, a_4{}^4, \ldots\}$ is a null sequence.

10. For any number r with $0 < r < 1$, $\{r^n\}$ is a null sequence $(n = 1, 2, 3, \ldots)$. (Suggestion: you might refer to Problem 8 of Sec. 6.9 and show first that $(1/r)^n > 1/\epsilon$ for any $\epsilon > 0$ and some n.)

11. Any subsequence of a null sequence is itself a null sequence. (Note that the kth member of a subsequence $\{a_{n_k}\}$ must appear in the original sequence with some subscript $\geq k$.)

12. Let $\{a_n\}$ and $\{b_n\}$ be null sequences. Shuffle them together to form a new sequence with the property that the order of the a_i's and of the b_i's is not changed; that is, a_i precedes a_{i+1} for all i, and similarly for b_i and b_{i+1}. The new sequence is a null sequence. (For example, such a shuffled sequence may start out as $a_1, a_2, b_1, a_3, b_2, b_3, b_4, a_4, b_5, a_5, b_6, b_7, a_6, \ldots$.)

*13. Let $\{a_1, a_2, a_3, \ldots\}$ be a null sequence with $|a_n| \leq 1$ for all n. Show that we can find a sequence of positive integers $K_1 \leq K_2 \leq K_3 \leq \cdots$ whose reciprocals $1/K_1, 1/K_2, 1/K_3, \ldots$ form a null sequence with

    $$-\frac{1}{K_n} \leq a_n \leq \frac{1}{K_n} \qquad \text{for all } n.$$

Suggestive picture:

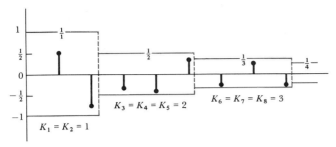

14. *(a) Let $\{a_1, a_2, a_3, \ldots\}$ be a sequence of positive numbers. Form a new sequence $\{b_1, b_2, b_3, \ldots\}$ where $b_n = a_{n+1}/a_n$. If $\{b_n\}$ is a null sequence, then $\{a_n\}$ is a null sequence.

(Suggestion: Choose N so that $b_n < \frac{1}{2}$ if $n \geqslant N$. Then the subsequence $\{a_N, a_{N+1}, \ldots\}$ is term-by-term smaller than the sequence $\{a_N, a_N(\frac{1}{2}), a_N(\frac{1}{2})^2, \ldots\}$.)

(b) Use this result to show that the sequence $\{24^n/n!\}$ is a null sequence.

*8.10   ANOTHER INSTANCE OF DIALOGUE

Imagine that to my right is an open window; in front of me, an empty basket; and to my left, a tub containing infinitely many billiard balls—one for each positive integer, with that integer painted on it.

FIGURE 8-33

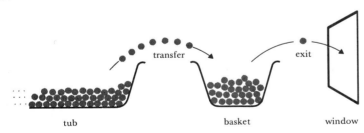

At one minute before noon, I transfer balls Number 1–10 from the tub to the basket. (Call this "Transfer Operation" # 1.)

At $\frac{1}{2}$ minute before noon, I select one of the balls in the basket and throw it out the window. (Call this "Exit Operation" # 1.)

At $\frac{1}{4}$ minute before noon, I transfer balls Number 11–20 from the tub to the basket. ("Transfer Operation" # 2.)

At $\frac{1}{8}$ minute before noon, I select one of the balls in the basket and throw it out the window. ("Exit Operation" # 2.)

I continue in this way, making an infinite number of alternate "transfer" and "exit" operations. Question: when noon comes, how many balls will I have left in the basket in front of me? (Think before reading on.)

Here's one answer: I can arrange it so that *no* balls will be left! I need only make sure to throw out ball Number n during Exit

Operation Number n, for each n. How can I *prove* then that no balls will be left? Again by a dialogue with any challenger. If you dispute my claim, the burden is on you to give me the *specific* number of a remaining ball. You can't just wave your hands and say, "*some ball must remain.*" If you give me a specific number—say, 147— I can tell you exactly when I threw that ball out: during Exit Operation Number 147. (Such is my routine.) So no balls can be left.

Can you devise an exit strategy for this game so that exactly three balls will be left? 27? infinitely many?

8.11 SUMMARY OF CHAPTER 8

DEFINITIONS: A *sequence* is a function assigning a real number a_n to each input n in an infinite domain of positive integers.

Notation: $\{a_n\}$ or $a_1, a_2, a_3, \ldots, a_n, \ldots$. A *subsequence* is the restriction of such an assignment to a smaller (infinite) domain of integers— which, after relabeling, appears as a sequence in its own right. Notation: $\{a_{n_i}\}$ or $a_{n_1}, a_{n_2}, a_{n_3}, \ldots, a_{n_i}, \ldots$. (See Sec. 8.1 and also Problem 7 of Sec. 8.3.)

Ways to picture a sequence: See Figs. 8-1 and 8-2 in Sec. 8.1.

DEFINITION: A sequence $\{a_n\}$ is *bounded* if there is a number $b \geq 0$ (a *bound*) such that

$$|a_n| \leq b \qquad \text{for all } n.$$

(Sec. 8.2.)

DEFINITION: A sequence $\{a_n\}$ *converges to zero*, or is a *null sequence*, if it is possible to devise a routine which will do the following: whenever you feed a positive number ϵ into the routine, the output will be an integer, call it $N(\epsilon)$, with the property that

$$|a_n| < \epsilon \qquad \text{for all } n \geq N(\epsilon).$$

Notation for convergence to zero: $\lim_{n \to \infty} a_n = 0$.
(Sec. 8.4.)

Ways to picture a null sequence: See Figs. 8-19 and 8-21 in Sec. 8-4.

Properties of null sequences

(following as theorems from the definition of convergence to zero)

Property a: Any subsequence of a null sequence is itself a null sequence.

Property b: ("the tail wags the dog"): A sequence which differs from a null sequence in only finitely many places is itself a null sequence.

Property c: If one interlaces two null sequences, the resulting sequence is null.

Property d (on "scaling"): If $\lim_{n \to \infty} a_n = 0$ and c is any constant, then $\lim_{n \to \infty} ca_n = 0$.

Property e (on "sums"): If $\lim_{n \to \infty} a_n = 0$ and $\lim_{n \to \infty} b_n = 0$, then $\lim_{n \to \infty} (a_n + b_n) = 0$.

Property f (on "products"): If $\lim_{n \to \infty} a_n = 0$ and if $\{b_n\}$ is a bounded sequence, then $\lim_{n \to \infty} a_n b_n = 0$.

Property g (on "boundedness"): If $\lim_{n \to \infty} a_n = 0$, then $\{a_n\}$ is bounded.

Property h (on "products"): If $\lim_{n \to \infty} a_n = 0$ and $\lim_{n \to \infty} b_n = 0$, then $\lim_{n \to \infty} a_n b_n = 0$.

Property i: $\lim_{n \to \infty} a_n = 0$ if, and only if, $\lim_{n \to \infty} |a_n| = 0$.

Property j: If $\lim_{n \to \infty} a_n = 0$ and $a_n > 0$ for all n, and if r is a positive rational number, then $\lim_{n \to \infty} (a_n)^r = 0$.

Property k (on "comparison"): If $\lim_{n \to \infty} a_n = 0$ and if $|b_n| \leq a_n$ for all n, then $\lim_{n \to \infty} b_n = 0$.

Property l: The sequence $c, c, c, \ldots, c, \ldots$ is null if, and only if, $c = 0$.

Property m: The sequence $\{1/n\}$ is null, and so is $\{r^n\}$ for any fixed positive $r < 1$.
(Secs. 8.1, 8.7, and 8.9.)

THEOREM (ON "ESCAPE"): If $\{a_n\}$ is not a null sequence, then there is an $\epsilon_0 > 0$ and a subsequence $a_{n_1}, a_{n_2}, a_{n_3}, \ldots, a_{n_k}, \ldots$ such that

$$|a_{n_k}| \geq \epsilon_0 \text{ for all } k.$$

(Sec. 8.8.)

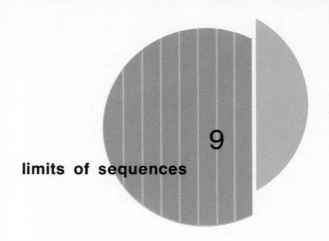

9

limits of sequences

In this chapter, I'll extend the notion of convergence to limits other than zero.

But first,

9.1 AN EXAMPLE: HOW GOVERNMENT SPENDING CAN AFFECT TOTAL INCOME

Suppose that a government introduces a dollar into the economy of a country, in paying for services or welfare. How will that dollar affect the total amount of income in the country?

For a simple model, let's suppose that each person spends about 90% of his income—for rent, groceries, clothes, services, etc.—and saves the rest. Thus the man who receives the original dollar will in time spend 90 cents of it. Suppose he gives 90 cents to his grocer—increasing the grocer's income by \$0.90. At this stage the total income generated by the original dollar is $1 + 0.90 = \$1.90$. In time the grocer will spend 90% of his 90 ¢—causing an increase in other persons' incomes of 81 ¢. At this stage the original dollar will have generated $1 + 0.9 + (0.9)^2 = \$2.71$ of income. The process goes on. After n stages, the total increase in income will be

$$S_n = 1 + 0.9 + (0.9)^2 + (0.9)^3 + \cdots + (0.9)^n \tag{1}$$

dollars.

If, ideally, the stages went on forever, would the sequence of amounts $\{S_n\}$ converge to some "limiting" amount of increase?

Intuitively people conjectured that the limit should exist as an "infinite sum"

$$S = 1 + (0.9) + (0.9)^2 + (0.9)^3 + \cdots \tag{2}$$

And some have attempted to evaluate S by the following device. They multiplied (2) on both sides by (0.9) and subtracted $(0.9)S$ from S:

$$S = 1 + (0.9) + (0.9)^2 + (0.9)^3 + \cdots \tag{3}$$
$$(0.9)S = (0.9) + (0.9)^2 + (0.9)^3 + (0.9)^4 + \cdots$$

If one could cancel corresponding terms in (3) all the way "out to infinity," one would be left with $S - (0.9)S = 1$, or $S = 1/0.1 = 10$ dollars. And one could conclude that the original dollar caused an increase of about $10 in total income.

But, is the notion of "infinite sum" in (2) really trouble-free, and are the infinitely many cancellations in (3) warranted? Let's test the same method on a fictitious scheme which should increase total income even more.

Suppose that the original dollar spurs its recipient to earn a matching dollar, and to spend the $2. And suppose that the recipients of the $2 earn a matching $2 and spend $4. And so on. Then after n stages people will have received a total of

$$T_n = 2 + 2^2 + 2^3 + \cdots + 2^{n+1} \tag{4}$$

dollars. If the stages went on forever, would the sequence $\{T_n\}$ converge to an "infinite sum"

$$T = 2 + 2^2 + 2^3 + \cdots \tag{5}$$

dollars? Let's try the above cancellation method. Multiply both sides of (5) by 2 and subtract $2T$ from T:

$$T = 2 + 2^2 + 2^3 + \cdots \tag{6}$$
$$2T = 2^2 + 2^3 + 2^4 + \cdots$$

If we could cancel all corresponding terms in (6), we would be left with $T - 2T = 2$, or $T = -2$ dollars, a *negative* total increase. Absurd! What's wrong?

It was such stumbling in the past which led people to formulate the notions of "convergence" and "infinite sums" with a little care. For example, we might try to see more clearly how the increase in income due to n transactions,

$$S_n = 1 + (0.9) + (0.9)^2 + \cdots + (0.9)^n,$$

depends on a given integer n—before we consider "limits" of such quantities. Why not apply the cancellation method directly to this *finite* sum? Write

$$S_n = 1 + (0.9) + (0.9)^2 + (0.9)^3 + \cdots + (0.9)^{n-1} + (0.9)^n \tag{7}$$

and

$$(0.9)S_n = (0.9) + (0.9)^2 + (0.9)^3 + (0.9)^4 + \cdots + (0.9)^n + (0.9)^{n+1}$$

Now a *finite* number of cancellations validly yields

$$S_n - (0.9)S_n = 1 - (0.9)^{n+1} \tag{8}$$

or

$$S_n = \frac{1 - (0.9)^{n+1}}{(0.1)} = 10 - 10(0.9)^{n+1}. \tag{9}$$

(This was the procedure I used in Chapter 1 to determine amounts of umbrella material.) Since the differences $S_n - 10 = -10(0.9)^{n+1}$ converge to zero as n increases (Property m of Chapter 8), we might well claim that the S_n "converge" to 10.

In no actual country will there be an infinite number of transactions; but we can interpret our results by saying that after a large number of transactions, the original dollar will have caused an income increase *approximately* equal to \$10.

How about the T_n's? By the same cancellation method, we could evaluate the sums $T_n = 2 + 2^2 + \cdots + 2^{n+1}$ as $T_n = 2^{n+2} - 2$, a sequence which grows without bound as n increases. So the symbol "$2 + 2^2 + 2^3 + \cdots$" can't represent a (finite) *real number* as limit of the $\{T_n\}$. We might well expect absurd results if we manipulate meaningless symbols with arithmetic operations designed for finite numbers.

9.2 DEFINITION OF CONVERGENCE

In the last example I argued that the sequence $\{S_n = 10 - 10(0.9)^{n+1}\}$ "converges" to the number 10 since the differences $S_n - 10 = -10(0.9)^{n+1}$ converge to zero. Why not use this approach and base a general concept of convergence on the notion of null sequences — which we've already explored in Chapter 8?

Definition: Let's say that a sequence $a_1, a_2, a_3, \ldots$, *converges* to a *limiting number A* if the sequence of differences

$$a_1 - A, a_2 - A, a_3 - A, \ldots, a_n - A, \ldots$$

converges to zero. If so, call the sequence $\{a_n\}$ *convergent* and call the number A its *limit*. Notation: $\lim\limits_{n \to \infty} a_n = A$.

On a coordinate line, we can picture the numbers a_n clustering around A, as in Fig. 9-1. And on a two-dimensional graph, the points (n, a_n) should get closer and closer to the horizontal line of height A, as n increases (rather than to the zero axis, as for null sequences). See Fig. 9-2.

FIGURE 9-1

FIGURE 9-2

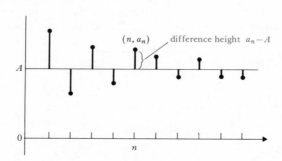

Here are several more examples:

EXAMPLE 1. To check that $\lim_{n \to \infty} (1 + (1/n)) = 1$, according to the precise definition above, just note that the sequence of differences $a_n - A = (1 + 1/n) - 1 = 1/n$ is null (the prime example of Chapter 8).

EXAMPLE 2. $a_n = 3n/(n+1)$ for $n = 1, 2, 3, \ldots$. First, let's guess a limit number A (supposing one exists). This is not always an easy matter, but in this example the ratios $n/(n+1)$ appear to converge to 1 as n increases (the first few values of $n/(n+1)$ are $\frac{1}{2}, \frac{2}{3}, \frac{3}{4}, \frac{4}{5}, \ldots$). Hence $3n/(n+1)$ should tend to $A = 3$. For a precise check, form the differences

$$a_n - A = \frac{3n}{n+1} - 3$$

$$= \frac{3n - 3(n+1)}{n+1} = \frac{-3}{n+1}$$

—a null sequence, by the results of Chapter 8. So $\lim_{n \to \infty} 3n/(n+1) = 3$, according to the definition.

EXAMPLE 3. $1, 0, 1, 0, 1, 0, \ldots$. Intuitively, no number A can be the limit of this sequence—and in particular, neither 0 nor 1—since the graph of the sequence never stays close to any *one* horizontal line, but oscillates between altitudes 0 and 1 forever. See Fig. 9-3.

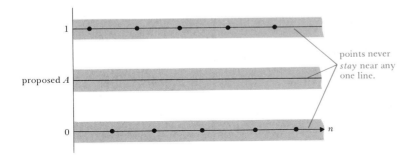

FIGURE 9-3

points never *stay* near any one line.

Using results we already have, here is a precise way to show that $1, 0, 1, 0, \ldots$ has no limit. Assume the contrary: that it has a limit A. By definition, then, the differences

$$1 - A, 0 - A, 1 - A, 0 - A, 1 - A, 0 - A, \ldots$$

constitute a null sequence. In particular, the two subsequences of alternate entries must be null:

$$1 - A, 1 - A, 1 - A, \ldots \tag{1}$$

and

$$0 - A, 0 - A, 0 - A, \ldots \tag{2}$$

Subsequence (1) can be null only if $1 - A = 0$; that is, if $A = 1$. Subsequence (2) can be null only if $0 - A = 0$; that is, if $A = 0$. An impossibility. Hence the assumption $\lim\limits_{n \to \infty} \{a_n\} = A$ is untenable in this case.

I invite you to try your own hand at checking limits in the problems of the next section.

9.3 PROBLEMS ON LIMITS

°1. Sketch a graph for each of the following sequences $\{a_n\}$ and show that $\lim\limits_{n \to \infty} a_n = A$, where A is given.

(a) $a_n = \dfrac{n}{3n+1}, A = \dfrac{1}{3}$.

Sample reasoning: Write

$$a_n - A = \frac{n}{3n+1} - \frac{1}{3} = \frac{3n - (3n+1)}{3(3n+1)} = \frac{-1}{3(3n+1)} = \left(\frac{-1}{3}\right)\frac{1}{3n+1}.$$

Now $\{(-1/3)1/(3n+1)\}$ is a null sequence (since $|(-1/3)1/(3n+1)| < 1/n$ for all n).

Hence $\lim\limits_{n \to \infty} \dfrac{n}{3n+1} = \dfrac{1}{3}$.

(b) $a_n = \dfrac{n-1}{n+1}, A = 1$.   (c) $a_n = \dfrac{3n}{n}, A = 3$.

(d) $a_n = \dfrac{3n+1}{n}, A = 3$.   (e) $a_n = \dfrac{2n^2+1}{n^3}, A = 0$.

*(f) $a_n = \dfrac{1}{1 \cdot 2} + \dfrac{1}{2 \cdot 3} + \dfrac{1}{3 \cdot 4} + \cdots + \dfrac{1}{n(n+1)}\bigg), A = 1$.

$\left(\text{Hint: } \dfrac{1}{n(n+1)} = \dfrac{1}{n} - \dfrac{1}{n+1}\right)$

(g) $a_n = \dfrac{2}{1 \cdot 3} + \dfrac{2}{2 \cdot 4} + \dfrac{2}{3 \cdot 5} + \cdots + \dfrac{2}{n(n+2)}, A = \dfrac{3}{2}$.

(h) $a_n = \left(\dfrac{n+1}{n}\right)\left(2 - \dfrac{1}{n}\right), A = 2$.

(i) $a_n = \left(\dfrac{3n}{n+2}\right)\left(\dfrac{5n+4}{n+1}\right); A = 15$.

(j) $a_n = \dfrac{1+2+3+\cdots+n}{n^2}, A = \dfrac{1}{2}$.

°2. Guess limits for the following sequences and check your guesses according to the definition (as in Problem 1).

(a) $a_n = \dfrac{2n+1}{n}$ (b) $a_n = \dfrac{2^n}{1+2^n}$

(c) $a_n = \dfrac{3n^2 - 7n + 1}{n^2}$

(d) $a_n = \dfrac{1}{n} + 2 - \dfrac{3000}{n^2}$

*(e) $\sqrt{n+1} - \sqrt{n}$

3. For each of the following sequences, determine whether or not it converges to some limit. If so, evaluate the limit; if not, state why.

(a) $a_n = n$.

Sample reasoning: If this sequence had a limit A, then the sequence of differences $b_n = n - A$ would be a null sequence, hence bounded. But $\{b_n\}$ isn't bounded: for any b, there is some integer N such that $b_N = N - A > b$. Conclusion: $\{n\}$ can't converge to any limit A.

(b) $a_n = \sqrt{n}$

(c) $a_n = \dfrac{1}{(1 + 1/n)^2}$

(d) $a_n = \left(\dfrac{n-1}{n} + \dfrac{2n}{n^2 + 3}\right)$

(e) $a_n = \left(\dfrac{n-1}{n}\right)\sqrt{n}$

(f) $a_n = \dfrac{1 + (-1)^n}{3}$

(g) $a_n = \dfrac{1 + (1/n)^n}{3}$

4. In the example of Sec. 9.1 on government spending, suppose that each person could and would spend only 80% of his income and would save the rest. How would $1 of government spending then affect the total national income?

5. Draw a circle of radius one inch, and inscribe a polygon each of whose sides is no greater than one inch. Measure the length of the perimeter of the polygon. Next inscribe a second polygon each of whose sides is no greater than $\frac{1}{2}$ inch, and measure its perimeter. Likewise for a third polygon of maximum side length no greater than $\frac{1}{4}$ inch. Do the perimeter lengths appear to be converging?

6. You may recall from Sec. 6.4 that if you put N dollars in a bank which compounds interest m times annually, then at the end of one year you will have $N(1 + p/m)^m$ dollars, where p is the "rate of interest." Compute $N(1 + p/m)^m$ for $N = \$1$, $p = 0.05$ (i.e., 5% interest), and $m = 1$ (annual compounding), $m = 2$ (semiannual), $m = 12$ (monthly) — and $m = 52$ (weekly), if you know how to use logs. Do the amounts of interest appear to converge?

7. In a coordinate plane, draw a straight line segment from $(0,0)$ to $(1, 1)$. Think of this segment as the side view of a ramp. Now let's approximate the ramp by a sequence of stairways, the nth of which is shown in profile in the accompanying figure. Its individual stairs and "risers" are each $1/n$ feet long.

You can get a stairway configuration whose vertical and horizontal differences from the ramp are all as small as you wish —

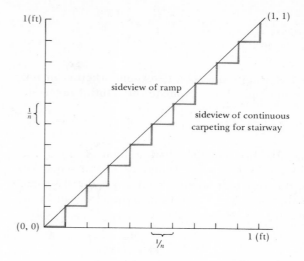

merely by choosing n large enough. Does this mean that any reasonable measurement associated with the nth stairway will "converge" to the corresponding measurement associated with the ramp as n gets larger and larger?

For example, let $a_n =$ the number of running feet of continuous carpeting required to cover the nth stairway. Is $\lim_{n \to \infty} a_n =$ the number of feet needed to carpet the ramp?

9.4 GETTING ACROSS A STREET

Long ago certain philosophers began worrying about the question of how one can ever succeed in getting across a street: before one can get across one must reach the half-way point; and if one gets to that point, one must still reach the half-way point of the remaining half—the $\frac{3}{4}$ point, and then one must reach the $\frac{7}{8}$ point, etc. So how can one ever get *all* the way across? Yet we do cross streets.

The successive half-way points $a_n = 1 - (1/2^n)$, $n = 1, 2, 3, \ldots$ constitute a sequence; and the mathematical analog of success in crossing the street is simply that $\lim_{n \to \infty} a_n = 1$. (Does this mathematical fact really answer the question?)

9.5 PROPERTIES OF LIMITS

If we define general limits, $\lim_{n \to \infty} a_n = A$, in terms of null sequences, $\lim_{n \to \infty} (a_n - A) = 0$, shouldn't many properties of general limits flow directly from those of null sequences, discussed in Chapter 8?

Here is a list of such results. Many closely resemble corresponding statements for null sequences in Chapter 8. Most of the results show how to recognize convergence of a sequence if it is put together from simpler convergent sequences—so that we needn't check each new example against the original definitions.

*Property A ("**uniqueness**"): A sequence can't have more than one limit.*

*Property B ("**limits of subsequences**"): If $\lim_{n \to \infty} a_n = A$, then any subsequence of $\{a_n\}$ converges to A also.*

(In particular, if we omit the first, say, k terms of a convergent sequence $\{a_n\}$, we can denote the limit of the remaining subsequence by $\lim_{n \to \infty} a_{k+n}$.)

*Property C ("**the tail wags the dog**"): If $\lim_{n \to \infty} a_n = A$ and if b_n differs from a_n for only finitely many n, then $\lim_{n \to \infty} b_n = A$.*

*Property D (on "**interlacing**"): If each of two sequences converges to the same limit A, and if one interlaces the two sequences to form a new sequence $\{a_n\}$, then $\lim_{n \to \infty} a_n = A$ also.*

*Property E (on "**boundedness**"): A convergent sequence is bounded.*

The next property, F — as well as K and L below — is not similar to any statements about null sequences in Chapter 8.

*Property F ("**boundedness of reciprocals**"): If $\lim_{n \to \infty} b_n = B$ and if $b_n \neq 0$ for all n and $B \neq 0$, then the sequence $\{1/b_n\}$ is bounded.*

Property G: The limit of a sequence of constants $a_n = a$ for $n = 1, 2, 3, \ldots$ is just a.

*Property H (on "**scaling**"): If $\lim_{n \to \infty} a_n = A$ and if c is a constant, then $\lim_{n \to \infty} ca_n = cA$.*

*Property I (on "**sums**"): If $\lim_{n \to \infty} a_n = A$ and $\lim_{n \to \infty} b_n = B$, then $\lim_{n \to \infty} (a_n + b_n) = A + B$. Also $\lim_{n \to \infty} (a_n - b_n) = A - B$.*

*Property J (on "**products**"): If $\lim_{n \to \infty} a_n = A$ and $\lim_{n \to \infty} b_n = B$, then $\lim_{n \to \infty} a_n b_n = AB$.*

*Property K (on "**reciprocals**"): If $\lim_{n \to \infty} b_n = B$ and if $b_n \neq 0$ for all n and $B \neq 0$, then $\lim_{n \to \infty} 1/b_n = 1/B$.*

*Property L (on "**quotients**"): If $\lim_{n \to \infty} a_n = A$, and if $\lim_{n \to \infty} b_n = B$ and $b_n \neq 0$ for all n and $B \neq 0$, then $\lim_{n \to \infty} a_n/b_n = A/B$.*

*Property M (on "**rational powers**"): If $a_n \geq 0$ for all n, with $\lim_{n \to \infty} a_n = A$, and if r is a fixed positive rational number, then $\lim_{n \to \infty} a_n^r = A^r$.*

*Property N (on "**exponent sequences**"): If a_n are rational numbers for all n, with $\lim_{n \to \infty} a_n = A$, a rational number, and if c is a fixed positive constant, then $\lim_{n \to \infty} c^{a_n} = c^A$.*

*Property O (on "**comparison**"): If $\lim_{n \to \infty} a_n = A$ and $\lim_{n \to \infty} b_n = B$, and if $a_n \leq b_n$ for all n, then $A \leq B$.*

*Property P (on "**squeezing**"): If $\lim_{n \to \infty} a_n = A$ and $\lim_{n \to \infty} c_n = A$ and if $a_n \leq b_n \leq c_n$ for all n, then $\lim_{n \to \infty} b_n = A$.*

EXAMPLE 1. If the above properties hold, here is an easy way to handle an earlier example, the sequence $a_n = 3n/(n+1)$ of Sec. 9.2. Factor an n out of both numerator and denominator:

$$a_n = \frac{3n}{n+1} = \frac{n}{n}\frac{3}{1+(1/n)} = \frac{3}{1+(1/n)}.$$

Since the sequence of constants $1, 1, 1, \ldots$ has limit 1 and also $\lim_{n\to\infty} 1/n = 0$, we have $\lim_{n\to\infty}(1+1/n) = 1$, by the property I on sums. Moreover, the sequence $3, 3, 3, \ldots$ has limit 3. Hence we have

$$\lim_{n\to\infty} \frac{3}{1+(1/n)} = \frac{3}{1} = 3$$

by Property L on quotients.

If valid, Properties A–P justify the specific calculations of "derivatives" in Chapter 7. Recall that to calculate the "slope" of a function $f(x)$ at an input x_0, I picked sequences of inputs $\{q_n\}$ and $\{r_n\}$ flanking x_0 ($q_n < x_0 < r_n$ for all n) and converging to x_0, $\lim_{n\to\infty} q_n = x_0$ and $\lim_{n\to\infty} r_n = x_0$. The "derivative" $f'(x_0)$ was to be the limit of difference ratios

$$f'(x_0) = \lim_{n\to\infty} \frac{f(r_n) - f(q_n)}{r_n - q_n}, \tag{1}$$

provided the limit existed and its value didn't depend on which particular approximating sequences $\{q_n\}$ and $\{r_n\}$ I chose (Sec. 7.3). Here are calculations of $f'(x_0)$ for two kinds of function f, which cover all the specific cases of Chapter 7.

EXAMPLE 2: The *power function* $f(x) = x^k$ with exponent k a fixed *positive integer*. Form the difference ratio

$$\frac{f(r_n) - f(q_n)}{r_n - q_n} = \frac{r_n^k - q_n^k}{r_n - q_n}. \tag{2}$$

As in Sec. 7.3, we can apply an algebraic identity in order to factor the quantity $r_n - q_n$ from the numerator; namely, the identity

$$a^k - b^k = (a - b)(a^{k-1} + a^{k-2}b^1 + a^{k-3}b^2 + \cdots + a^1 b^{k-2} + b^{k-1}). \tag{3}$$

(To check (3), just multiply out and cancel terms on the right-hand side.) Then the difference ratio becomes

$$\frac{f(r_n) - f(q_n)}{r_n - q_n} = \frac{(r_n - q_n)(r_n^{k-1} + r_n^{k-2}q_n^1 + \cdots + r_n^1 q_n^{k-2} + q_n^{k-1})}{r_n - q_n}$$

$$= r_n^{k-1} + r_n^{k-2}q_n^1 + \cdots + q_n^{k-1}. \tag{4}$$

Each of the $k+1$ terms on the right-hand side of (4) is of the form $r_n^{k-1-i}q_n^i$ for some fixed integer $i \geq 0$. Now

$$\lim_{n\to\infty} r_n^{k-1-i}q_n^i = (\lim_{n\to\infty} r_n)^{k-1-i}(\lim_{n\to\infty} q_n)^i$$

$$= x_0^{k-1-i}x_0^i = x_0^{k-1}, \tag{5}$$

by several applications of Property J (on the limit of products) or by

Property M (on rational powers). Hence

$$\lim_{n\to\infty} (r_n^{k-1} + r_n^{k-2}q_n + \cdots + r_nq_n^{k-2} + q_n^{k-1})$$

$$= \lim_{n\to\infty} r_n^{k-1} + \lim_{n\to\infty} r_n^{k-2}q_n + \cdots + \lim_{n\to\infty} q_n^{k-1}$$

$$= \underbrace{x_0^{k-1} + x_0^{k-1} + \cdots + x_0^{k-1}}_{k \text{ terms}} = kx_0^{k-1}, \tag{6}$$

by several applications of Property I (on sums). Conclusion:

$$f'(x_0) = kx_0^{k-1} \qquad \text{at any input } x_0. \tag{7}$$

EXAMPLE 3: The *power function* $g(x) = x^{-k}$ with *negative integer* exponent, defined for $x \neq 0$. To calculate $g'(x_0)$ at any fixed $x_0 \neq 0$, pick flanking and approximating sequences $\{q_n \neq 0\}$ and $\{r_n \neq 0\}$. As in Example 2, form the difference ratio, and try to cancel the factor $r_n - q_n$:

$$\frac{g(r_n) - g(q_n)}{r_n - q_n} = \frac{(1/r_n^k) - (1/q_n^k)}{r_n - q_n} = \frac{[(q_n^k - r_n^k)/r_n^k q_n^k]}{r_n - q_n}$$

$$= \left(\frac{1}{r_n^k q_n^k}\right)\left(\frac{q_n^k - r_n^k}{r_n - q_n}\right) = -\left(\frac{1}{r_n^k q_n^k}\right)\left(\frac{r_n^k - q_n^k}{r_n - q_n}\right)$$

$$= \left(-\frac{1}{r_n^k q_n^k}\right)\frac{(r_n - q_n)(r_n^{k-1} + r_n^{k-2}q_n^1 + \cdots + q_n^{k-1})}{(r_n - q_n)} \tag{8}$$

By Properties H, J, and K (on scaling, on products, and on reciprocals), we have

$$\lim_{n\to\infty} \left[(-1)\frac{1}{r_n^k q_n^k}\right] = (-1)\frac{1}{(\lim_{n\to\infty} r_n)^k (\lim_{n\to\infty} q_n)^k}$$

$$= (-1)\frac{1}{x_0^k x_0^k} = -\frac{1}{x_0^{2k}}. \tag{9}$$

And as in Example 2, $\lim_{n\to\infty} (r_n^{k-1} + r_n^{k-2}q_n + \cdots + q_n^{k-1}) = kx_0^{k-1}$. Hence, by Property J (on products), we can conclude that

$$g'(x_0) = \lim_{n\to\infty} \frac{g(r_n) - g(q_n)}{r_n - q_n} = \left(-\frac{1}{x_0^{2k}}\right)(kx_0^{k-1})$$

$$= (-k)x_0^{(-k)-1}. \tag{10}$$

Note that we can summarize the results of both Examples 2 and 3 in the expression

$$(x^p)'_{\text{at } x_0} = px_0^{p-1} \tag{11}$$

for p any positive or negative integer, and x_0 any input ($x_0 \neq 0$ when $p < 0$). The case $p = 0$ corresponds to the *constant* function $x^0 \equiv 1$, which has derivative

$$(x^0)' = \lim_{n\to\infty} \frac{1-1}{r_n - q_n} = 0 \qquad \text{at any } x_0. \tag{12}$$

Even this case fits into the expression (11), at least for $x_0 \neq 0$.

Will the formula (11) hold for any rational exponent p? Try the case $p = \frac{1}{2}$ in doing Problem 4 of Sec. 9.6.

But recall, the success of all these calculations depends on properties from the list A–P above. If you are interested in seeing how the properties follow from those for null sequences, I invite you to read Sec. 9.7 and 9.8.

9.6   MORE LIMIT PROBLEMS

°1. Use the properties of limits stated in Sec. 9.5 to show that each of the following sequences has the indicated limit.

(a) $\displaystyle\lim_{n \to \infty} \frac{n}{n+1} = 1$

Sample reasoning:

$$\frac{n}{n+1} = 1 - \frac{1}{n+1}.$$

By Property G, $\displaystyle\lim_{n \to \infty} 1 = 1$. Since $-1/(n+1)$ is a null sequence, $\displaystyle\lim_{n \to \infty} [-1/(n+1)] = 0$. Hence

$$\lim_{n \to \infty} \left[1 - \frac{1}{(n+1)} \right] = 1 - 0 = 1$$

by Property I.

(b) $\displaystyle\lim_{n \to \infty} \frac{n}{3n+1} = \frac{1}{3}$.

Sample reasoning:

$$\frac{3n+1}{n} = \frac{3n}{n} + \frac{1}{n} = 3 + \frac{1}{n}.$$

Thus $\displaystyle\lim_{n \to \infty} (3n+1)/n = 3$ by Properties G and I. Hence $\displaystyle\lim_{n \to \infty} n/(3n+1) = \frac{1}{3}$, by Property K.

(c) $\displaystyle\lim_{n \to \infty} \frac{n-1}{n+1} = 1$

(d) $\displaystyle\lim_{n \to \infty} \frac{2n^2+1}{n^3} = 0$

*(e) $\displaystyle\lim_{n \to \infty} \left(\frac{1}{1 \cdot 2} + \frac{1}{2 \cdot 3} + \cdots + \frac{1}{n(n+1)} \right) = 1$

(f) $\displaystyle\lim_{n \to \infty} \frac{2n+5}{n+2} = 2$

(g) $\displaystyle\lim_{n \to \infty} \left(\frac{2n+5}{n+2} \right)\left(3 + \frac{1}{n} \right) = 6$

(h) $\displaystyle\lim_{n \to \infty} \frac{7 - (1/n^2)}{-3 + (1/n)} = -\frac{7}{3}$

(i) $\displaystyle\lim_{n \to \infty} \frac{(1/n) + (1/n^2)}{2 - (1/n^2)} = 0$

(j) $\displaystyle\lim_{n \to \infty} \left(\frac{3n}{n+2} \right)^3 = 27$

(k) $\displaystyle\lim_{n \to \infty} \left(1 + \frac{1}{n} \right)^{3/2} = 1$

°2. Use properties of limits stated in Sec. 9.5 to find the limits of the following sequences:

(a) $a_n = \dfrac{2n+1}{n}$

(b) $a_n = \dfrac{2^n}{1+2^n}$

(c) $a_n = \dfrac{3n^2 - 7n + 1}{n^2}$ (d) $a_n = \dfrac{1}{n} + 2 - \dfrac{3000}{n^2}$

*(e) $\sqrt{n+1} - \sqrt{n}$ (f) $a_n = \dfrac{n-2}{3n+4}$

(g) $a_n = \dfrac{(-1)^n \, (n+1)}{n} \dfrac{}{(n+2)}$ (h) $a_n = \left(2 + \dfrac{1}{n^2}\right)\left(4 - \dfrac{1}{n^3}\right)\left(6 + \dfrac{1}{n^4}\right)$

(i) $a_n = \dfrac{1 + (2/n) - (3/n^2)}{4 - (2/n^2)}$ (j) $a_n = \dfrac{(1/n^2) - (1/n)}{10 + (1/n^3)}$

(k) $a_n = \left(2 - \dfrac{1}{n}\right)^4$

3. Show that the validity of Properties A–P implies the validity of the following additional properties of sequences.
   (a) If $\lim\limits_{n\to\infty} a_n = A$, $\lim\limits_{n\to\infty} b_n = B$ and $\lim\limits_{n\to\infty} c_n = C$,
      then $\lim\limits_{n\to\infty} (a_n + b_n + c_n) = A + B + C$,

      $\qquad\qquad \lim\limits_{n\to\infty} (a_n + b_n - c_n) = A + B - C$,
      and $\qquad \lim\limits_{n\to\infty} a_n \cdot b_n \cdot c_n = A \cdot B \cdot C$.

   (b) If $\lim\limits_{n\to\infty} a_n = A$, then $\lim\limits_{n\to\infty} a_n{}^2 = A^2$.
   (c) If $\lim\limits_{n\to\infty} a_n = A$ and k is a positive integer, then $\lim\limits_{n\to\infty} a_n{}^k = A^k$.
   (d) If $\lim\limits_{n\to\infty} a_n = A$, $\lim\limits_{n\to\infty} b_n = B$, $\lim\limits_{n\to\infty} c_n = C$ and $a_n \leqslant b_n \leqslant c_n$, then
      $A \leqslant B \leqslant C$.
   (e) If $\lim\limits_{n\to\infty} a_n = A$ and k is a positive integer, then $\lim\limits_{n\to\infty} a_{n+k} = A$.
      (Note: $a_{1+k}, a_{2+k}, a_{3+k}, \ldots$ is a subsequence of $\{a_n\}$.)

4. Show that the "slope" formula (11) of Sec. 9.5,

   $$(x^p)'_{\text{at } x_0} = p x_0{}^{p-1},$$

   holds in the case $p = \frac{1}{2}$ if x_0 is a positive number. (*Hint:* $(\sqrt{r_n} - \sqrt{q_n})/(r_n - q_n) = 1/(\sqrt{r_n} + \sqrt{q_n})$. Then use Property M, Property I, and Property L.)

*5. Show that $(x^p)'_{\text{at } x_0} = p x_0{}^{p-1}$ holds in the case $p = \frac{1}{3}$ and x_0 is any nonzero number.

*6. (a) Show that $(x^{q/r})'_{\text{at } x_0} = (q/r)x_0{}^{q/r-1}$ if q/r is a positive rational number and x_0 is a positive number.
   (b) Show that the result of (a) holds when x_0 is *any* nonzero number and q/r is a positive rational with r an odd integer.

7. More "slopes." Let $f(x) = 3x^2 - 5x + 4$ for all x. Calculate $\lim\limits_{n\to\infty} [f(r_n) - f(q_n)]/(r_n - q_n)$ in cases (a)–(d):

   (a) $q_n = 2 - \dfrac{1}{n}$ and $r_n = 2 + \dfrac{1}{n}$ for $n = 1, 2, 3, \ldots$.

   (b) $\{q_n\}$ and $\{r_n\}$ are arbitrary sequences with $q_n < 2 < r_n$ for all n, and $\lim\limits_{n\to\infty} q_n = \lim\limits_{n\to\infty} r_n = 2$.

(Write

$$\frac{f(r_n) - f(q_n)}{r_n - q_n} = \frac{3(r_n{}^2 - q_n{}^2) - 5(r_n - q_n) + (4 - 4)}{r_n - q_n};$$

then cancel $r_n - q_n$ and apply limit properties.)

(c) $q_n = 2$ and $r_n \neq 2$ for all n, but $\lim_{n \to \infty} r_n = 2$.

(d) $r_n = 2$ and $q_n \neq 2$ for all n, but $\lim_{n \to \infty} q_n = 2$.

(e) What can you say about the "slope" of f at $x_0 = 2$?

8. Repeat the cases of Problem 7 with $f(x) = 1/(x^2 + 1)$ for all x.

9. Repeat the cases of Problem 7 with $x_0 = 2$ replaced by $x_0 = -1$. (For example, in (a) let $q_n = (-1) - (1/n)$ and $r_n = (-1) + (1/n)$. In (b), let $q_n < -1 < r_n$ for all n, and $\lim_{n \to \infty} q_n = \lim_{n \to \infty} r_n = -1$.)

10. Let $f(x) = |x - 2|$ for all x. Calculate $\lim_{n \to \infty} [f(r_n) - f(q_n)]/(r_n - q_n)$ in cases (a) and (b):

   (a) $q_n = 2 - \dfrac{1}{n}$ and $r_n = 2 + \dfrac{1}{3n}$ for $n = 1, 2, 3, \ldots$.

   (b) $q_n = 2 - \dfrac{1}{3n}$ and $r_n = 2 + \dfrac{1}{n}$ for $n = 1, 2, 3, \ldots$.

   (c) Does f have a "slope" at $x_0 = 2$?

11. Use Properties J (on "products") and K (on "reciprocals") to prove Property L (on "quotients").

*12. Show that the definition for $\lim_{n \to \infty} a_n = A$ in Sec. 9.2—namely, that $\lim_{n \to \infty} (a_n - A) = 0$—is equivalent to the following: *for any $\epsilon > 0$ there is an integer $N(\epsilon)$ such that*

$$|a_n - A| < \epsilon \qquad \text{for all } n \geqslant N(\epsilon).$$

Draw a graph to illustrate this requirement.

*9.7 WHY THE PROPERTIES HOLD

In this section I'll show how several properties of general convergence follow from those of null sequences. In each case, I'll rewrite the relevant hypotheses and the conclusion in terms of null sequences. Then I'll try to work logically from the one to the other.

Let's begin with the property of "uniqueness."

Theorem (Property A): *A sequence can't have more than one limit.* In other words: if $\lim_{n \to \infty} a_n = A$ and $\lim_{n \to \infty} a_n = B$, then $A = B$.

Intuitively, the values in a convergent sequence can't *simultaneously* get close, and *stay* close, to two different numbers $A \neq B$. See Fig. 9-4. Now, let's try a more precise

FIGURE 9-4

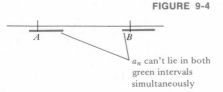

a_n can't lie in both green intervals simultaneously

Proof: *The hypothesis says*: $\lim_{n \to \infty} (a_n - A) = 0$ and $\lim_{n \to \infty} (a_n - B) = 0$. To get at A and B, let's cancel the a_n's by subtraction. That is, write

$$(a_n - A) + (-1)(a_n - B) = B - A \qquad \text{for all } n. \tag{1}$$

The quantities on the left-hand side form a null sequence—the sum of $\{a_n - A\}$ and $\{B - a_n\}$. Hence the right-hand constants constitute a null sequence $B - A, B - A, B - A, \ldots$. This can be the case only if $B - A = 0$ (Property 1 of Chapter 8). *Conclusion*: $A = B$. End of the proof.

Secondly, let's check boundedness.

Theorem (Property E). *A convergent sequence $\{a_n\}$ is bounded.* That is, there is a constant $b \geqslant 0$ such that $|a_n| \leqslant b$ for all n.

To find b intuitively, see Fig. 9-5.

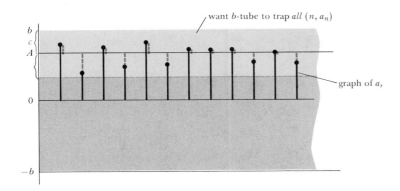

want b-tube to trap *all* (n, a_n)

graph of a,

FIGURE 9-5

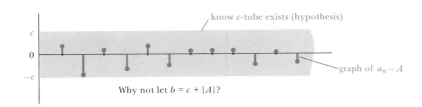

know c-tube exists (hypothesis)

graph of $a_n - A$

Why not let $b = c + |A|$?

For a precise

Proof: The *hypothesis says*: $\{a_n - A\}$ is a null sequence. Hence $\{a_n - A\}$ is bounded (Property g of Chapter 8): that is, there is some constant $c \geqslant 0$ such that

$$|a_n - A| \leqslant c \qquad \text{for all } n. \tag{2}$$

How can we get a bound b for the a_n's themselves, knowing a bound c for the $a_n - A$? Write

$$\begin{aligned} a_n &= a_n - A + A \\ &= (a_n - A) + A, \end{aligned} \tag{3}$$

and recall that $|u + v| \leqslant |u| + |v|$ for any real numbers u and v. Hence

$$|a_n| \leqslant |a_n - A| + |A|, \tag{4}$$

and we can conclude from (2) that

$$|a_n| \leqslant c + |A| \qquad \text{for all } n. \tag{5}$$

Why not let $b = c + |A|$? Then we have the required

Conclusion: $|a_n| \leqslant b$ for all n.   End of the proof.

It takes a somewhat longer argument to show why a sequence of reciprocals $\{1/b_n\}$ must be bounded if the $b_n \neq 0$, $B \neq 0$ and $\lim_{n \to \infty} b_n = B$ (Property F). So I'll postpone that proof to Sec. 9.10.

Here are several results on building new sequences from old.

Theorem (Property H): *If* $\lim_{n \to \infty} a_n = A$, *then* $\lim_{n \to \infty} ca_n = cA$.

Proof: *The hypothesis says:* $\lim_{n \to \infty} (a_n - A) = 0$.

The conclusion says: $\lim_{n \to \infty} (ca_n - cA) = 0$.

Just factor to see that $\{ca_n - cA\} = \{c(a_n - A)\}$ must converge to zero, by the scaling Property d of null sequences.   End of the proof.

Theorem (Property I): *If* $\lim_{n \to \infty} a_n = A$ *and* $\lim_{n \to \infty} b_n = B$, *then*

$$\lim_{n \to \infty} (a_n + b_n) = A + B \quad \text{and} \quad \lim_{n \to \infty} (a_n - b_n) = A - B.$$

Proof: *The hypotheses say*: $\lim_{n \to \infty} (a_n - A) = 0$ and $\lim_{n \to \infty} (b_n - B) = 0$.

The conclusions say:

$$\lim_{n \to \infty} [(a_n + b_n) - (A + B)] = 0 \quad \text{and} \quad \lim_{n \to \infty} [(a_n - b_n) - (A - B)] = 0.$$

To get from the hypotheses to the conclusion on addition, *add* the given null sequences, term-by-term, and rearrange: the numbers

$$(a_n - A) + (b_n - B) = (a_n + b_n) - (A + B) \tag{6}$$

must constitute a null sequence. (Property e on sums of null sequences, in Chapter 8.)

To get the result on subtraction, scale $\{b_n - B\}$ first by (-1) and then add. The numbers

$$(a_n - A) + (-1)(b_n - B) = (a_n - b_n) - (A - B) \tag{7}$$

must constitute a null sequence.   End of the proof.

Theorem (Property J): *If* $\lim_{n \to \infty} a_n = A$ *and* $\lim_{n \to \infty} b_n = B$, *then*

$$\lim_{n \to \infty} a_n b_n = AB.$$

Proof: *The hypotheses say*: $\lim_{n \to \infty} (a_n - A) = 0$ and $\lim_{n \to \infty} (b_n - B) = 0$.

The conclusion says: $\lim_{n \to \infty} (a_n b_n - AB) = 0$.

How can we get from $a_n - A$ and $b_n - B$ to $a_n b_n - AB$? Let's try an old tool: add and subtract suitable terms. Write, say,

$$a_n b_n - AB = a_n b_n - \underbrace{a_n B + a_n B} - AB. \tag{8}$$

$$\text{these terms cancel}$$

Then factor on the right-hand side to get

$$a_n b_n - AB = a_n(b_n - B) + (a_n - A)B. \tag{9}$$

Now, by the above results on boundedness, $\{a_n\}$ is bounded. Hence the sequence of products $\{a_n(b_n - B)\}$ is null. Similarly, $\{(a_n - A)B\}$ is a null sequence. Hence, as displayed in (9), the sequence $\{a_n b_n - AB\}$ is the sum of two null sequences, and must itself be null. End of the proof.

I'll conclude this sampling of proofs with the result on reciprocals.

Theorem (Property K): *If* $\lim_{n\to\infty} b_n = B$ *and if* $b_n \neq 0$ *for all n and* $B \neq 0$, *then* $\lim_{n\to\infty} 1/b_n = 1/B$.

Proof: *The hypotheses say:* $\lim_{n\to\infty}(b_n - B) = 0$; $b_n \neq 0, B \neq 0$.

The conclusion says: $\lim_{n\to\infty}(1/b_n - 1/B) = 0$.

How can we get from $b_n - B$ to $1/b_n - 1/B$? Let's convert the latter difference to a common denominator:

$$\frac{1}{b_n} - \frac{1}{B} = \frac{B - b_n}{b_n B} = \left(\frac{1}{b_n}\right)\left(-\frac{1}{B}\right)(b_n - B). \tag{10}$$

Thus we can display $\{(1/b_n) - (1/B)\}$ as resulting from a null sequence $\{-(1/B)(b_n - B)\}$ multiplied term-by-term by factors $\{1/b_n\}$. We could conclude that $\{(1/b_n) - (1/B)\}$ is itself null—and finish the proof—if we could be sure that the reciprocals $1/b_n$ form a *bounded* sequence (recall Property f of Chapter 8, on boundedness). That $\{1/b_n\}$ is bounded is just the claim of "Property F," whose proof I've postponed to Sec. 9.10.

All of the other properties of convergence follow from properties of null sequences by much the same kind of reasoning as I've sampled above. I invite you to try your own hand at proving several of the results—by doing problems in Sec. 9.8.

*9.8 PROBLEMS ON PROOFS

1. (a) Prove Property B: If $\lim_{n\to\infty} a_n = A$, then any subsequence of $\{a_n\}$ converges to A also.

   Sample proof: Let $a_{n_1}, a_{n_2}, a_{n_3}, \ldots$ be any subsequence of $\{a_n\}$. Since $\lim_{n\to\infty} a_n = A$, $b_n = a_n - A$ is a null sequence. Any subsequence of a null sequence is a null sequence so $b_{n_1}, b_{n_2}, b_{n_3}, \ldots$ is a null sequence; that is, $a_{n_1} - A, a_{n_2} - A, a_{n_3} - A, \ldots$ is a null sequence. Hence $\lim_{n\to\infty} a_{n_i} = A$ also.

   (b) Prove a corollary: if $\lim_{n\to\infty} a_n = A$, then $\lim_{n\to\infty} a_{n+k} = A$ for any fixed positive integer k. (Can you regard $\{a_{n+k}\}$ as a subsequence of $\{a_n\}$?)

2. Prove Property C, "the tail wags the dog."

3. Prove Property D, on "interlacing."

4. Prove Property G, on "$\{a, a, a, \ldots\}$ converging to a"; and Property L, on "quotients."

5. Prove Property O, on "comparison."

6. Prove Property P, on "squeezing."

*7. Suppose $\{a_n\}$ is a sequence and $\lim_{n\to\infty} a_n = A$. Show that there is an $\epsilon_0 > 0$ and a subsequence $a_{n_1}, a_{n_2}, \ldots, a_{n_k}, \ldots$ such that

$$a_{n_k} - A \geqslant \epsilon_0 \qquad \text{for all } k$$

or

$$A - a_{n_k} \geqslant \epsilon_0 \qquad \text{for all } k.$$

*8. Prove the following special case of Property M (on "rational powers"): Suppose $a_n \geqslant 0$ for all n with $\lim_{n\to\infty} a_n = A$, then $\lim_{n\to\infty} a_n^{1/2} = A^{1/2}$.

(Suggestion: show that

$$\{a_n^{1/2} - A^{1/2}\} \text{ is a null sequence.}$$

Case 1. $A = 0$: Apply Property j of null sequences.

Case 2. $A \neq 0$: Rewrite $|a_n^{1/2} - A^{1/2}|$ as $|a_n - A|/(\sqrt{a_n} + \sqrt{A})$. Since $\sqrt{a_n} + \sqrt{A} \geqslant \sqrt{A}$,

$$\frac{|a_n - A|}{\sqrt{a_n} + \sqrt{A}} \leqslant \frac{|a_n - A|}{\sqrt{A}}.$$

Given $\epsilon > 0$, choose N so that if $n \geqslant N$, $|a_n - A| < \sqrt{A}\epsilon$.)

**9. Prove Property M in case $r < 1/q$ where q is positive integer.

**10. Prove Property M.

*11. Here's an alternative, indirect way to prove Property M, on "rational powers":

Suppose $a_n \geqslant 0$ for all n with $\lim_{n\to\infty} a_n = A$ and r is a fixed positive rational number such that $\lim_{n\to\infty} a_n^r \neq A^r$. Write r as $r = p/q$ where p and q are positive integers. Suppose you apply the result of Problem 7 and obtain a positive number ϵ_0 and a subsequence $a_{n_1}, a_{n_2}, \ldots, a_{n_k}, \ldots$ of $\{a_n\}$ such that

$$a_{n_k}^r - A^r \geqslant \epsilon_0 \qquad \text{for all } k.$$

Then

$$a_{n_k}^{p/q} \geqslant A^{p/q} + \epsilon_0 \qquad \text{for all } k.$$

(a) Show that $a_{n_k}^p \geqslant A^p + \epsilon_0^q$ for all k.

(b) Show that this implies that $\lim_{k\to\infty} a_{n_k}^p \neq A^p$.

(c) Use Property B to show that this implies $\lim_{n\to\infty} a_n^p \neq A^p$.

(d) Use Property J (or Problem 3 of Sec. 9.6) to show that this implies $\lim_{n\to\infty} a_n \neq A$.

(e) Modify this proof to handle the case when the result of Problem 7 yields a subsequence with $A^r - a_{n_k}^r \geqslant \epsilon_0$.

**12. Use a proof similar to that of Problem 11 in order to prove Property N, on "exponent sequences."

(Suggestion: Consider separately the cases $c > 1$, $c = 1$, $c < 1$.

In the case where $c > 1$ and there is a subsequence $\{a_{n_k}\}$ of $\{a_n\}$ such that

$$c^{a_{n_k}} \geqslant c^A + \epsilon_0 \qquad \text{for all } k,$$

we have

$$c^{a_{n_k}} \geqslant c^A \cdot c^r = c^{A+r} \qquad \text{for some positive number } r.$$

Conclude from this that $a_{n_k} \geqslant A + r$ for all k.)

9.9 UNBOUNDED SEQUENCES

How can a sequence $\{a_n\}$ fail to converge? One way is for the a_n to oscillate, as in the example $1, 0, 1, 0, \ldots$. Another way is for some a_n's to lie farther and farther out on the coordinate line, as n increases. For example: $1, -2, 1, 3, 1, -4, 1, 5, 1, -6, 1, 7, \ldots$. In this case, no single finite interval $[-b, b]$ can contain all the a_n's: no single real number b can be a bound for the sequence—with $|a_n| \leqslant b$ for all n. See Fig. 9-6.

some a_n's escape from $[-b, b]$

FIGURE 9-6

In other words: *no matter what positive number b you might choose as a would-be bound, there will be a subscript—call it n_b—such that $|a_{n_b}| > b$.* Such is the meaning of a sequence being *not bounded* (or "un-bounded"). The numbers in an unbounded sequence can't ulti-mately get near, and *stay* near, any would-be limiting number A.

People have given a special name to the situation when a sequence $\{a_n\}$ is unbounded by virtue of *drifting to the right* on the coordinate line—not necessarily at every step—but in such a way as ultimately to leave any given number behind. For example: $1, 3, 2, 4, 3, 5, 4, 6, \ldots$.

Definition: Call a sequence $\{a_n\}$ *divergent positively* if it has the following property: for any given real number b, there is some integer—call it $N(b)$—such that

$$a_n > b \qquad \text{for all } n \geqslant N(b).$$

Notation: $\lim\limits_{n \to \infty} a_n = +\infty$.

For pictures, see Figs. 9-7 and 9-8. We could give a similar definition for *divergence negatively* ($\lim\limits_{n \to \infty} a_n = -\infty$).

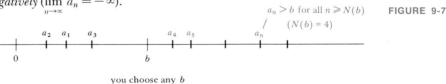

$a_n > b$ for all $n \geqslant N(b)$

($N(b) = 4$)

FIGURE 9-7

you choose any b

FIGURE 9-8

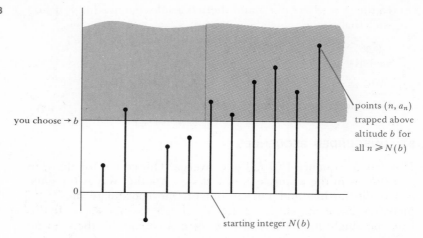

you choose → b

points (n, a_n) trapped above altitude b for all $n \geqslant N(b)$

0

starting integer $N(b)$

If you read the definition for $\lim_{n \to \infty} a_n = 0$ in Chapter 8, notice how analogous to it the present definition for $\lim_{n \to \infty} a_n = +\infty$ is. Although "$+\infty$" is just part of the symbol for divergence, the present definition almost reads as if "$+\infty$" represented a "point" at the right-hand end of the coordinate line, toward which a divergent sequence "converges."

The notion of divergence should help you analyze the sequences in the problems of Sec. 9.11.

*9.10 SPECIAL UNBOUNDED SUBSEQUENCES

Here is an even more specific statement which we can make about an unbounded sequence—merely by choosing *integers* k as would-be bounds b. I'll call it a

Theorem: If a sequence $a_1, a_2, a_3, \ldots, a_n, \ldots$ is unbounded, then we can extract from it a subsequence—label it

$$a_{n_1}, a_{n_2}, a_{n_3}, \ldots, a_{n_k}, \ldots$$

such that $|a_{n_k}| > k$ for each positive integer k, and moreover $|a_{n_{k+1}}| > |a_{n_k}|$.

EXAMPLE 1:
Original labels: $a_1 \quad a_2 \quad a_3 \quad a_4 \quad a_5 \quad a_6 \quad a_7 \quad a_8 \quad \ldots$

$\qquad\qquad\quad 1 \quad \boxed{-2} \quad 1 \quad \boxed{3} \quad 1 \quad \boxed{-4} \quad 1 \quad \boxed{5}$

New labels: $\qquad\quad a_{n_1} \qquad\quad a_{n_2} \qquad\quad a_{n_3} \qquad\quad a_{n_4} \quad \ldots$

Proof of the theorem: Given the unbounded sequence $\{a_n\}$. We try the integers k as would-be bounds b.

$k = 1$ can't be a bound. Hence there must be some subscript—choose the first and call it n_1—such that $|a_{n_1}| > 1$.

Next, $k = 2$ can't be a bound, nor can $|a_{n_1}|$. Hence there must be some subscript—choose the first and call it n_2—such that $|a_{n_2}| > 2$ and $|a_{n_2}| > |a_{n_1}|$.

Similarly, neither $k = 3$ nor $|a_{n_2}|$ can be a bound, so we can find an a_{n_3} with $|a_{n_3}| > 3$ and $|a_{n_3}| > |a_{n_2}|$. And we can carry the process on for all positive integers k to get a subsequence $\{a_{n_k}\}$ as claimed. I invite you to write out a complete proof using the principle of induction: do Problem 7 of Sec. 9.11. Here's how the selection process looks pictorially (for positive a_n's).

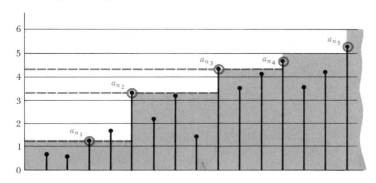

FIGURE 9-9

(Note that $a_{n_{k+1}}$ must always lie farther out in the original sequence than a_{n_k}, or else we would have chosen the value called $a_{n_{k+1}}$ to play the role of a_{n_k} in the first place.)

The above theorem will come in handy several times. Here's one application: a proof of

Property F: *If* $\lim_{n \to \infty} b_n = B$ *and if* $b_n \neq 0$ *for all* n *and* $B \neq 0$, *then the sequence* $\{1/b_n\}$ *is bounded.*

Proof: Suppose that the sequence $a_n = 1/b_n$ is not bounded. By the theorem above, we can extract a subsequence

$$\frac{1}{b_{n_1}}, \frac{1}{b_{n_2}}, \frac{1}{b_{n_3}}, \frac{1}{b_{n_4}}, \ldots, \frac{1}{b_{n_k}}, \ldots$$

such that

$$\left| \frac{1}{b_{n_k}} \right| > k \qquad \text{for all } k. \tag{1}$$

Taking reciprocals of both sides in (1), we can conclude that

$$|b_{n_k}| < \frac{1}{k} \qquad \text{for all } k. \tag{2}$$

Since $1/k$ converges to zero as k increases, b_{n_k} must also. (Recall Property k of Chapter 8, on comparing sequences.) But on the other hand, b_{n_k} converges to $B \neq 0$, as must any subsequence of the original $\{b_n\}$ (by Property B on limits of subsequences). A contradiction! To avoid it, we must reject the possibility that $\{b_n\}$ is not bounded. Conclusion: $\{b_n\}$ *is* bounded.   End of the proof.

I invite you to follow through an alternative, direct proof based on the *definition* of a null sequence: see Problem 8 of Sec. 9.11.

9.11 PROBLEMS ON UNBOUNDEDNESS

°1. Give a definition of what it might mean for a sequence $\{a_n\}$ to be "divergent negatively."
Notation: $\lim_{n\to\infty} a_n = -\infty$.

°2. Determine which of the following sequences are "unbounded." In particular, show whether they are "divergent positively" or "divergent negatively."

(a) $a_n = n^2$.

Sample reasoning: $\{a_n\}$ is unbounded and $\lim_{n\to\infty} a_n = \infty$ because for any given real number b, if $N(b)$ is chosen to be an integer greater than $\sqrt{b}$, then $a_n > b$ whenever $n \geq N(b)$.

*(b) $a_n = n^2 - n^3$.

Sample reasoning: $\{a_n\}$ is unbounded and $\lim_{n\to\infty} a_n = -\infty$. To see that this is true, note that $a_n = n^2(1 - n) \leq -n^2$ for $n > 1$. For any $b < 0$, let $N(b)$ be the first integer greater than $\sqrt{|b|}$ and greater than 1. Then $n \geq N(b)$ implies that $n > \sqrt{|b|}$ or $n^2 > |b|$. Hence $|a_n| \geq n^2 > |b|$, and moreover $a_n \leq -n^2 < b$, whenever $n \geq N(b)$.

(c) $a_n = (-1)^n n$.

Sample reasoning: $\{a_n\}$ is unbounded but it is neither divergent positively or divergent negatively. The $|a_n| = n$ increase beyond any bound $b > 0$. But we can't have $a_n > b$ or $a_n < -b$ for some $b > 0$ and for all $n \geq N(b)$, because the a_n alternate in sign.

(d) $a_n = 2^n$ (e) $a_n = (-1)(3^n)$

(f) $a_n = (-4)^n$ (g) $a_n = \dfrac{1}{2^n}$

(h) $a_n = 2^n + \dfrac{1}{2^n}$ (i) $a_n = n^2 + 2^n$

*(j) $a_n = n^2 - 2n$. (Suggestion: Recall that $2^k > k + 1$ for all $k \geq 2$, via Problem 3 of Sec. 6.7.)

(k) $a_n = \dfrac{n+1}{n}$ (l) $a_n = 2^n\left(\dfrac{n+1}{n}\right)$

(m) $a_n = (-1)^n$ (n) $a_n = (-1)^n\left(\dfrac{n+1}{n}\right)$

(o) $a_n = (-1)^n n^2$

(p) $a_n = \begin{cases} n^2 \text{ if } n \text{ is even,} \\ \dfrac{1}{n} \text{ if } n \text{ is odd} \end{cases}$ (q) $a_n = \begin{cases} -n \text{ if } n \text{ is even,} \\ \dfrac{n+1}{n} \text{ if } n \text{ is odd} \end{cases}$

(r) $a_n = \begin{cases} 2^n \text{ if } n \text{ is even,} \\ 2^{-n} \text{ if } n \text{ is odd} \end{cases}$ (s) $a_n = \begin{cases} 2^n \text{ if } n \text{ is even,} \\ -2^n \text{ if } n \text{ is odd} \end{cases}$

°3. Determine which of the following sequences converge and which ones fail to converge:

(a) $a_n = (-1)^n \dfrac{2n}{n+1}$

(b) $a_n = (-1)^n \dfrac{n}{n^2+1}$

(c) $a_n = 1 + (-1)^n$

(d) $a_n = \dfrac{1+(-1)^n}{n}$

(e) $a_n = \dfrac{n^2 - n}{2n^2 + (1/n^3)}$

(f) $a_n = 1 + \dfrac{(-1)^n}{2^n}$

(g) $a_n = \dfrac{10n^2 + 2n + 3}{4n+1} - \dfrac{5n^2 - 2}{2n}$

(h) $a_n = 2^{2-(1/n)}$

*(i) $a_n = \sqrt{n+1} - \sqrt{n}$

*(j) $a_n = \sqrt{n^2+2} - \sqrt{n^2+1}$

*(k) $a_n = \sqrt{n^2+1} - \sqrt{n}$

4. Give examples to show that each of the following statements about unbounded sequences is false:
   (a) Any subsequence of an unbounded sequence is unbounded.
   Sample: The sequence $1, 2, 1, 4, 1, 6, \ldots$ given by

   $$a_n = \begin{cases} n \text{ if } n \text{ is even,} \\ 1 \text{ if } n \text{ is odd,} \end{cases}$$

   is unbounded but has a convergent subsequence $1, 1, 1, \ldots$.
   (b) If $\{a_n\}$ and $\{b_n\}$ are unbounded sequences, then $\{a_n + b_n\}$ is unbounded.
   (c) If $a_n \neq 0$ for all n and $\{a_n\}$ is unbounded, then $\{1/a_n\}$ is unbounded.
   (d) If $\{a_n\}$ and $\{b_n\}$ are unbounded and $a_n \leq c_n \leq b_n$ for all n, then $\{c_n\}$ is unbounded.
5. If $\{a_n\}$ and $\{b_n\}$ are unbounded sequences, is $\{a_n b_n\}$ necessarily unbounded?
6. Show that the following statements about unbounded sequences are true:
   (a) If $\{a_n\}$ is an unbounded sequence and if b_n differs from a_n for only finitely many n, then $\{b_n\}$ is unbounded.
   (b) If each of two sequences is unbounded and if one interlaces the two sequences to form a new sequence, then the new sequence is unbounded.
   (c) If $\{a_n\}$ is an unbounded sequence and c is a nonzero constant, then $\{ca_n\}$ is unbounded.
*7. Write out a complete proof, based on the principle of mathematical induction, that the process for choosing a subsequence $\{a_{n_k}\}$ in the proof of the theorem in Sec. 9.10 can be carried out.
*8. Here's a direct way to prove Property F, on "boundedness of reciprocals":
   Suppose first that B is not 1 or -1. Since $\{b_n - B\}$ is a null sequence, then there is an integer N such that

   $$|b_n - B| < 1 \text{ if } n > N.$$

(a) Show that if $n > N$, then $B - 1 < b_n < B + 1$ and hence that

$$\frac{1}{B-1} > \frac{1}{b_n} > \frac{1}{B+1}.$$

(b) Show that the sequence $\{1/b_n\}$ is bounded.

(c) Modify the proof to handle the case when $B = 1$ or $B = -1$.

9.12   SUMMARY OF CHAPTER 9

DEFINITION: A sequence $\{a_n\}$ converges to a limit A if the sequence of differences $\{a_n - A\}$ converges to zero.   *Notation:* $\lim\limits_{n \to \infty} a_n = A$. (Sec. 2.2)

Properties of convergent sequences
(following as theorems from the definition)

Property A ("uniqueness"): A sequence can't have more than one limit.

Property B ("limits of subsequences"): If $\lim\limits_{n \to \infty} a_n = A$, then any subsequence of $\{a_n\}$ converges to A also.

Property C ("the tail wags the dog"): If $\lim\limits_{n \to \infty} a_n = A$ and if b_n differs from a_n for only finitely many n, then $\lim\limits_{n \to \infty} b_n = A$.

Property D (on "interlacing"): If each of two sequences converges to the same limit A, and if one interlaces the two sequences to form a new sequence $\{a_n\}$, then $\lim\limits_{n \to \infty} a_n = A$ also.

Property E (on "boundedness"): A convergent sequence is bounded.

Property F ("boundedness of reciprocals"): If $\lim\limits_{n \to \infty} b_n = B$ and if $b_n \neq 0$ for all n and $B \neq 0$, then the sequence $\{1/b_n\}$ is bounded.

Property G: The limit of a sequence of constants $a_n = a$ for $n = 1, 2, 3, \ldots$ is just a.

Property H (on "scaling"): If $\lim\limits_{n \to \infty} a_n = A$ and if c is a constant, then $\lim\limits_{n \to \infty} ca_n = cA$.

Property I (on "sums"): If $\lim\limits_{n \to \infty} a_n = A$ and $\lim\limits_{n \to \infty} b_n = B$, then $\lim\limits_{n \to \infty} (a_n + b_n) = A + B$. Also $\lim\limits_{n \to \infty} (a_n - b_n) = A - B$.

Property J (on "products"): If $\lim\limits_{n \to \infty} a_n = A$ and $\lim\limits_{n \to \infty} b_n = B$, then $\lim\limits_{n \to \infty} a_n b_n = AB$.

Property K (on "reciprocals"): If $\lim\limits_{n \to \infty} b_n = B$ and if $b_n \neq 0$ for all n and $B \neq 0$, then $\lim\limits_{n \to \infty} 1/b_n = 1/B$.

Property L (on "quotients"): If $\lim\limits_{n \to \infty} a_n = A$, and if $\lim\limits_{n \to \infty} b_n = B$ and $b_n \neq 0$ for all n and $B \neq 0$, then $\lim\limits_{n \to \infty} a_n/b_n = A/B$.

Property M (on "rational powers"): If $a_n \geq 0$ for all n, with $\lim\limits_{n \to \infty} a_n = A$, and if r is a fixed positive rational number, then $\lim\limits_{n \to \infty} a_n{}^r = A^r$.

Property N (on "exponent sequences"): If a_n are rational numbers for all n, with $\lim_{n \to \infty} a_n = A$, a rational number, and if c is a fixed positive constant, then $\lim_{n \to \infty} c^{a_n} = c^A$.

Property O (on "comparison"): If $\lim_{n \to \infty} a_n = A$ and $\lim_{n \to \infty} b_n = B$, and if $a_n \leq b_n$ for all n, then $A \leq B$.

Property P (on "squeezing"): If $\lim_{n \to \infty} a_n = A$ and $\lim_{n \to \infty} c_n = A$ and if $a_n \leq b_n \leq c_n$ for all n, then $\lim_{n \to \infty} b_n = A$.

(Sec. 9.5) (Proofs in Secs. 9.7, 9.8, and 9.10.)

Description of a sequence $\{a_n\}$ as *unbounded* (that is, not bounded): given any $b > 0$, there is a subscript n_b such that $|a_{n_b}| > b$.
(Sec. 9.9)

DEFINITION: Call a sequence $\{a_n\}$ *divergent positively* if it has the following property: for any given real number b, there is some integer — call it $N(b)$ — such that

$$a_n > b \qquad \text{for all } n \geq N(b).$$

Notation: $\lim_{n \to \infty} a_n = +\infty$.

(Sec. 9.9)

THEOREM: If a sequence $\{a_n\}$ is unbounded, then we can extract from it a subsequence — label it $a_{n_1}, a_{n_2}, a_{n_3}, \ldots a_{n_k}, \ldots$ — such that $|a_{n_k}| > k$ and $|a_{n_{k+1}}| > |a_{n_k}|$ for each positive integer k.
(Sec. 9.10)

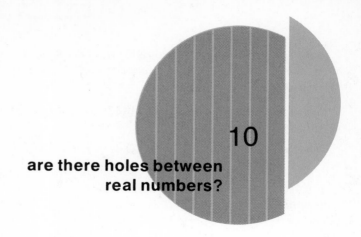

10

are there holes between
real numbers?

In this chapter I'll discuss several common examples of sequences, and whether there exist limiting numbers to which they can converge.

10.1 DOES A CIRCLE REALLY HAVE "LENGTH"?

FIGURE 10-1

I've been supposing that we know what we mean by the "length" of a straight line segment—in terms of some "unit." Hence we should know what we mean by the "length" of a polygon, as in Fig. 10-1: just add the lengths of its segments. But what can we mean by the "length" of a curve that isn't composed of straight line segments—such as a circle? Need every circle have "length"?

Intuitively one thinks of a string laid along a circle, then straightened and measured. But actual strings have width, and stretch. Although we might use a string in making approximate measurements, how could we rely on it for a *definition* of length?

(Is a good definition even necessary? Recall that a method for computation can lead to false results if the quantity to be computed doesn't exist in the first place. For example, in Sec. 7.2, I got the formula $M = 1$ from an assumption that a largest integer M exists.)

Note also that the old formula for the "length" L of a circle, $L = 2\pi r$, doesn't really *define* L. If anything, it defines $\pi = L/2r$, on the assumption that circles do have "length."

How then can we proceed? Do you recall the old procedure of inscribing polygons in a circle? Let us view it now as a means for defining "length," as well as for computing it approximately. Think of a sequence of polygons inscribed in a circle, fitting the circle, more and more closely—the $(n+1)$st polygon having all the vertices of the nth, plus others. See Fig. 10-2. Let's denote the

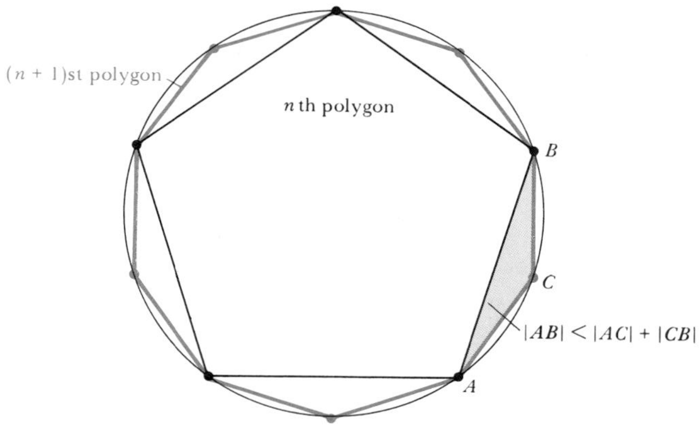

FIGURE 10-2

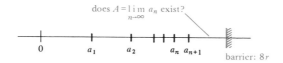

$(n + 1)$st polygon

nth polygon

B

C

$|AB| < |AC| + |CB|$

A

length of the nth polygon by a_n. In any one of the triangles such as
ABC, in Fig. 10-2, the nth polygon accounts for less length ($|AB|$)
than does the $(n+1)$st ($|AC|+|CB|$). Hence, summing over all
such triangles, we can conclude that the nth polygon has less total
length than does the $(n+1)$st: $a_n < a_{n+1}$ for any n. On a coordinate
line the a_n's march to the right, as in Fig. 10-3.

does $A = \lim\limits_{n \to \infty} a_n$ exist?

FIGURE 10-3

0 a_1 a_2 a_n a_{n+1} barrier: $8r$

Can they march out of sight? No. Look at Fig. 10-4 to see how we can
surround the nth polygon by a (green) polygon of length $b_n > a_n$,
which in turn sits in a square of perimeter $8r > b_n$. Thus $a_n < b_n < 8r$
for all n. The number $8r$ forms a barrier to the rightward march of
the a_n's in Fig. 10-3.

Can we conclude therefore that the a_n's converge—crowd onto—
some number A which lies $\leq 8r$? If so, why not *define* A as the

FIGURE 10-4

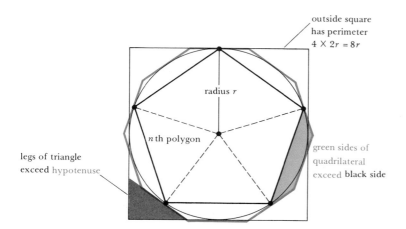

outside square
has perimeter
$4 \times 2r = 8r$

radius r

nth polygon

legs of triangle
exceed hypotenuse

green sides of
quadrilateral
exceed **black side**

"length" of the circle? For this to be a reasonable definition, we should check that *any* sequence of approximating inscribed polygons will have lengths converging to the same number A. And likewise for circumscribed polygons. (See Problem 13 of Sec. 10.5). So far, no one has come up with a better kind of definition. *Thus our very concept of "length," like that of instantaneous velocity, depends on the basic notion of limit.*

But what if no real number A exists to serve as the limit of the a_n's? What if—so to speak—the a_n's march right up to a "hole" in the coordinate line?

10.2   NO HOLES

To say that there are no "holes" in the real number system—in particular that all circles have "length"—is to assert a property of real numbers. Either this property follows from some *definition* of a "real number" in terms of simpler notions, or we should acknowledge it as a basic *axiom*—one which we should add to the list of Sec. 4.12. Let's take the latter path.

To formulate a "no holes" axiom let's consider only *bounded* sequences; since an unbounded sequence like $1, 2, 3, \ldots$ needn't crowd onto any limiting number. For simplicity, let's also focus on sequences which move only in one direction—as did the lengths of approximating polygons in the last section. More precisely:

Definition: Call a sequence $\{a_n\}$ *increasing* if $a_n \leqslant a_{n+1}$ for all n. Similarly, call a sequence a_n *decreasing* if $a_n \geqslant a_{n+1}$ for all n.

Here, then, is one way to state a "no holes" axiom:

Axiom A: If $\{a_n\}$ is a bounded increasing sequence, then there must exist a real number A such that $\lim_{n \to \infty} a_n = A$. (Similarly for bounded and decreasing sequences.) See Figs. 10-5 and 10-6.

FIGURE 10-5   increasing sequence $\{a_n\}$ bounded by b

$A = \lim_{n \to \infty} a_n$, also $a_n \leqslant A$ for all n

FIGURE 10-6   decreasing sequences $\{a_n\}$ bounded by b

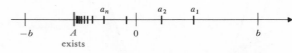

$A = \lim_{n \to \infty} a_n$, also $A \leqslant a_n$ for all n

On the basis of the axiom, we can assert the existence of many limits:

EXAMPLE 1. Circles have length. So do their subarcs (see Problem 14 of Sec. 10.5).

EXAMPLE 2: *Bacterial growth.* In Sec. 6.5 I showed how the quantities $a_n = [1 + (1/n)]^n$ form approximations to the hourly growth rate for a bacterial population of mixed ages, where each organism splits into two. And in Example 4 of Sec. 6.8 I argued that

$$\left(1 + \frac{1}{n}\right)^n < \left(1 + \frac{1}{n+1}\right)^{n+1} < 3 \qquad \text{for all } n \geqslant 2. \tag{1}$$

Thus $\{a_n\}$ is a bounded increasing sequence ($|a_n| \leqslant 3$ for all n) and by Axiom A, there must exist a limiting hourly growth rate. The standard symbol for that number is e:

$$e = \lim_{n \to \infty} \left(1 + \frac{1}{n}\right)^n \tag{2}$$

($e = 2.71827+$.)

EXAMPLE 3: *Compound interest:* In Sec. 6.4 I showed that the quantity $b_n = [1 + (p/n)]^n$ represents the amount of money you will have in your account at the end of one year if you deposit \$1 in a bank which compounds interest n times yearly at an annual rate of \$$p$ per dollar. If you worked Problem 9 of Sec. 6.9, you would have seen that, for any p with $0 < p < 1$,

$$\left(1 + \frac{p}{n}\right)^n < \left(1 + \frac{p}{n+1}\right)^{n+1} < 3 \qquad \text{for all } n \geqslant 2. \tag{3}$$

Hence $\{b_n\}$ is a bounded increasing sequence, too, and by Axiom A there must exist a limiting amount of principal-plus-interest,

$$B = \lim_{n \to \infty} [1 + (p/n)]^n.$$

We can get an actual formula for B: namely, $B = e^p$, where e is the special limiting value of the previous example ($e = 2.71827+$). From such a formula, you can conclude that if you put \$1 in a bank at 5\% interest ($p = 0.05$), you cannot hope to have more than $e^{0.05} = 1.0513$ dollars (approximately) at the end of one year — no matter how often the interest is compounded. (The advantages of frequent compounding become evident only after a longer time.)

Here's how to see that $B = e^p$, at least when p is a positive rational number, say, $p = i/j$. In such a case,

$$b_n = \left(1 + \frac{p}{n}\right)^n = \left(1 + \frac{i}{jn}\right)^n \qquad \text{for any } n. \tag{4}$$

How can we relate these quantities to the simpler ones $[1 + (1/n)]^n$? Pick a subsequence of multiples of i: $n_k = ki$, where $k = 1, 2, 3, \ldots$.

Then we can write

$$b_{n_k} = \left(1+\frac{i}{jn_k}\right)^{n_k} = \left(1+\frac{i}{jki}\right)^{ki}$$

$$= \left[\left(1+\frac{1}{jk}\right)^k\right]^i = \left[\left(1+\frac{1}{jk}\right)^{jk}\right]^{i/j} = \left[\left(1+\frac{1}{jk}\right)^{jk}\right]^p. \tag{5}$$

In the last line I introduced canceling numbers j/j so as to make appear in the $[\quad]^p$ brackets the quantities $\{[1+(1/jk)]^{jk}\}$. For $k = 1, 2, 3, \ldots$ these quantities form a subsequence of $\{[1+(1/n)]^n\}$. Hence they have the same limit

$$\lim_{k\to\infty}\left(1+\frac{1}{jk}\right)^{jk} = e. \tag{6}$$

Moreover, we can raise all quantities to the power p, to get

$$\lim_{k\to\infty} b_{n_k} = \lim_{k\to\infty}\left[\left(1+\frac{1}{jk}\right)^{jk}\right]^p = e^p, \tag{7}$$

by Property M of Chapter 9, on rational powers. But a subsequence such as $\{b_{n_k}\}$ must converge to the same limit as the full sequence $\{b_n\}$. Hence $B = e^p$.

10.3   LEAST UPPER BOUNDS

Note back in Fig. 10-5 that the limit A of a bounded increasing sequence $\{a_n\}$ appears to serve as a right-hand "barrier": $a_n \le A$ for all n. Of course, any number $A' > A$ can serve as such a barrier, too. But no number $A' < A$ appears to do the job. So A stands as a "leftmost right-hand barrier." Similarly, in Fig. 10-6 the limit A of a bounded decreasing sequence $\{a_n\}$ stands as a "rightmost left-hand barrier."

Such observations led people to formulate an alternative version of a "no holes" axiom—wherein the notion of "limit" is replaced by that of "barrier." Here are some standard names for one-sided barriers:

Definitions: Call a sequence $\{a_n\}$ *bounded above* if there is some number d such that

$\quad a_n \le d \qquad$ for all n;

and call d an *upper bound* for $\{a_n\}$. If $\{a_n\}$ has no other upper bound $d' < d$, then call d a *least upper bound*:

Similarly, call a sequence $\{a_n\}$ *bounded below* if there is some number c such that

$\quad c \le a_n \qquad$ for all n;

and call c a *lower bound* for $\{a_n\}$. If $\{a_n\}$ has no other lower bound $c' > c$, then call c a *greatest lower bound*.

(By the very definitions, no sequence can have more than one least upper bound, nor more than one greatest lower bound.)

Based on such notions, here is an alternative

Axiom A' (a "least upper bound" version): If $\{a_n\}$ is an increasing sequence which is bounded above, then there must exist a least upper bound d for $\{a_n\}$. (Similarly, a decreasing sequence, if bounded below, must have a greatest lower bound.)

Do you believe that Fig. 10-5 really suggests the truth? For a bounded increasing sequence $\{a_n\}$, does the limit A claimed by Axiom A coincide with the least upper bound d claimed by Axiom A'? In other words, are the two versions really equivalent to each other?

The answer is "yes," as you will see if you examine Theorems B and C at the end of this section. But first several examples and a note concerning one-sided bounds:

EXAMPLE 1. The sequence $1, 2, 3, \ldots$ has no upper bound, hence no least upper bound. But it is bounded below by 0 and all negative numbers. In particular, its greatest lower bound is 1.

EXAMPLE 2. The sequence $a_n = 1 - (1/n)$, for $n = 1, 2, 3, \ldots$ has 0 as its greatest lower bound and 1 as an upper bound. Although not itself in the sequence, 1 is a least upper bound. Why? If there were some other upper bound $d' < 1$, then we would have $1 - (1/n) \le d'$, or $1 - d' \le 1/n$, for all n. Invert the last inequality to get

$$\frac{1}{1-d'} \ge n \qquad \text{for all } n,$$

which is impossible (by Archimedes' axiom).

EXAMPLE 3. The limiting hourly rate of bacterial growth via splitting (of Example 2, Sec. 10.2), namely, the number $e = 2.71827+\ldots$, stands as the least upper bound of the increasing quantities $[1 + (1/n)]^n$, as well as their limit.

EXAMPLE 4. *Ultimate extinction.* In any model of growth which includes the possibility of individuals leaving no viable offspring, such as I discussed in Sec. 5.8, one can consider the probability—call it x_n—that the entire population be extinct by the nth generation. There is always at least as much probability for extinction by the $(n + 1)$st generation as by the nth; so the quantities x_n form an increasing sequence. Being probabilities, they are bounded above by 1. Hence—even without further specific assumptions as in Sec. 5.8— we can conclude that the x_n have a least upper bound x, which we might well interpret as the probability of ultimate extinction for the population. By the results of the last section, $x = \lim_{n \to \infty} x_n$ also.

NOTE: *Equivalent statements of boundedness.* As defined in Chapter 8, a *bounded* sequence $\{a_n\}$ is one for which $|a_n| \le b$, for all n. This means that all a_n's lie in the interval $[-b, b]$. It also implies that the sequence is both bounded *above* (by b) and *below* (by $-b$). Conversely, if a sequence has upper bound d and lower bound c, it must lie entirely in the interval $[c, d]$, and must be bounded in the sense of Chapter 8: $|a_n| \leqslant b$ for all n, where we can choose a "common bound" $b =$ the larger of $|c|$ and $|d|$. See Fig. 10-7.

FIGURE 10-7

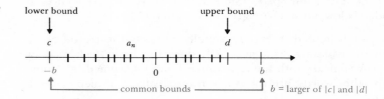

If d is the *least* upper bound of $\{a_n\}$ and c is the greatest lower bound, then $[c, d]$ is the *smallest* closed interval which can contain $\{a_n\}$ entirely.

I invite you now to view two results about limits, which imply that Axioms A and A' are equivalent:

Theorem B: *If* $A = \lim_{n \to \infty} a_n$ *for an increasing sequence* $\{a_n\}$, *then* A *must be the least upper bound of* $\{a_n\}$.

And

Theorem C: *If* d *is the least upper bound of an increasing sequence* $\{a_n\}$, *then* $\lim_{n \to \infty} a_n = d$.

Why theorem B holds: Suppose that $A = \lim_{n \to \infty} a_n$. Then A must be an upper bound, with $a_n \leqslant A$ for all n. Otherwise, $A < a_{n_0}$ for some subscript n_0. Since the a_n's increase, we would then have

$$A < a_{n_0} \leqslant a_{n_0+1} \leqslant a_{n_0+2} \leqslant \cdots$$

as in Fig. 10-8. For $n > n_0$ the distances $|a_n - A|$ could never be less

FIGURE 10-8

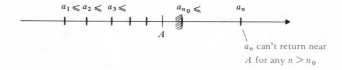

than $a_{n_0} - A$, a contradiction to $A = \lim_{n \to \infty} a_n$. So A must be an upper bound. It must be the least upper bound, too. Otherwise if $a_n \leqslant A'$ for all n, for some $A' < A$, then the distance $|a_n - A|$ could never be less than $A - A'$, again contradicting $A = \lim_{n \to \infty} a_n$. (See Fig. 10-9.)

FIGURE 10-9

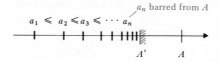

So A must be the least upper bound.   End of the proof.

Why theorem C holds: Suppose that d is the least upper bound of $\{a_n\}$. Then no smaller number can do the job. In particular, for any positive distance ϵ, the number $d-\epsilon$ is *not* an upper bound. So we must have $a_{n_0} > d-\epsilon$ for some subscript n_0. Since $\{a_n\}$ is increasing, all subsequent a_n's (for $n > n_0$) must be sandwiched between $d-\epsilon$ and d, as in Fig. 10-10. In terms of distances

$$|a_n - d| < \epsilon \qquad \text{for all } n \geq n_0.$$

By choosing smaller and smaller ϵ's we can force the differences $a_n - d$ toward zero. Thus $\lim_{n\to\infty} a_n = d$.   End of the proof.

FIGURE 10-10

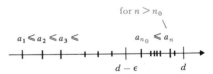

*10.4 HOW TO EXTRACT ONE-WAY SEQUENCES

What can we conclude from Axiom A about sequences which are bounded but neither increasing nor decreasing?

EXAMPLE 1. The sequence $\{1, \frac{1}{2}, 1, \frac{1}{3}, 1, \frac{1}{4}, 1, \frac{1}{5}, \ldots\}$ is bounded and has no limit. However it contains a decreasing subsequence $\{1, \frac{1}{2}, \frac{1}{3}, \frac{1}{4}, \frac{1}{5}, \ldots\}$ which, by the axiom, should have a limit, and does—namely 0. There is also an "increasing" subsequence $\{1, 1, 1, 1, \ldots\}$, which has the limit 1.

Does this situation hold more generally? Can we claim the following?

Theorem A ("on extracting subsequences"): Every sequence (bounded or not) contains either an increasing subsequence or a decreasing subsequence, if not both.

If such a result were true, we could apply it to any *bounded* sequence, and extract a one-way bounded subsequence. Then we could apply Axiom A to the subsequence. Conclusion:

Theorem B ("on convergent subsequences"): If $\{a_n\}$ is any bounded sequence—say, with $c \leq a_n \leq d$ for all n—then $\{a_n\}$ contains some (one-way) subsequence $\{a_{n_k}\}$ which converges to a limit A. The number A must itself lie between c and d. (See Fig. 10-11.)

an increasing subsequence $\{a_{n_k}\}$

limit A

FIGURE 10-11

What Theorem B says is that no sequence of numbers $\{a_n\}$ can be cooped up in an interval $[c, d]$ of finite length without "crowding" onto at least one inhabitant A of that interval.

Why must A lie in $[c, d]$? Because it must be either a least upper bound or a greatest lower bound of the one way subsequence $\{a_{n_k}\}$. Hence it must lie between the given upper and lower bounds, d and c.

And why should Theorem A (on extracting subsequences) be true? In Figs. 10-12 and 10-13, I've indicated a pictorial device which shows precisely how we can extract a one-way sequence from *any* given sequence $\{a_n\}$.

FIGURE 10-12

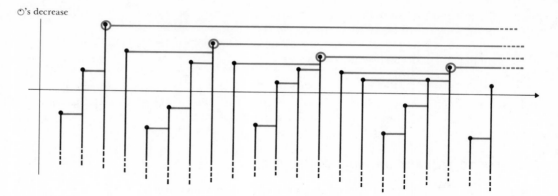

$\circlearrowleft$'s decrease

FIGURE 10-13

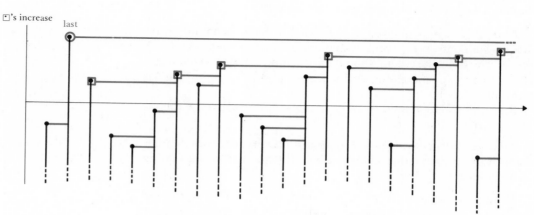

$\square$'s increase

last

In these figures I drew from each graph point (n, a_n) a black vertical line going *downward*. Then from each graph point I drew a green horizontal line going *rightward* as far as possible until interruption by some black vertical. I've encircled those graph points where green lines can go on forever. If there were infinitely many such points, as in Fig. 10-11, they correspond to a *decreasing* subsequence. Alternatively, there will be only finitely many circled points, as in Fig. 10-12. In this case, start *after the last* of these, and put a square about each point which stands at least as tall as all its predecessors. The squared points correspond to an *increasing* subsequence. There must be infinitely many of them, otherwise the last of them would be another circled point.   End of the proof.

10.5   PROBLEMS ON BOUNDS AND SEQUENCES

°1. Examine several of the sequences $\{a_n, n = 1, 2, 3, \ldots\}$ below in the following ways:
  (i)   Locate the first few terms on a coordinate line.
  (ii) Graph the first few points (n, a_n) on a coordinate plane.
  (iii) Find the least upper bound of $\{a_n\}$ (if it exists).
  (iv) Find the greatest lower bound (if it exists).
  (v)   Find a common bound (if it exists).

(vi) Draw horizontal lines on the graph in (ii) at altitudes representing the bounds in (iii), (iv), and (v).

(a) $a_n = n$

(b) $a_n = \dfrac{n-1}{n}$

> *Sample reasoning:* $a_n = 1 - (1/n)$ increases with n, so $a_1 = 0$ is the greatest lower bound. $a_n < 1$ for all n, so 1 is an upper bound. 1 is also a least upper bound, since for any $d' < 1$ there is an n such that $d' < 1 - (1/n)$.

(c) $a_n = \dfrac{2n-1}{2n}$

(d) $a_n = 2^{-n} + 3^{-n}$

(e) $a_n = -n$

(f) $a_n = (-1)^n n$

(g) $a_n = (-1)^n \dfrac{2n}{n+1}$

(h) $a_n = \dfrac{(-1)^n n}{n^2+1}$

(i) $a_n = \dfrac{3n^2 + 7n - 1}{n^2 + 1}$

(j) $a_n = \begin{cases} \dfrac{1}{n} & \text{if } n \text{ is odd,} \\ -\dfrac{1}{n^2} & \text{if } n \text{ is even} \end{cases}$

(k) $a_n = \begin{cases} n^2 & \text{if } n \leqslant 10, \\ 2 + \dfrac{1}{n} & \text{if } n > 10 \end{cases}$

(l) $a_n = \begin{cases} \dfrac{n+1}{n} & \text{if } n \text{ is odd,} \\ \dfrac{n}{n+1} & \text{if } n \text{ is even} \end{cases}$

(m) $a_n = \begin{cases} -\dfrac{3}{n^2+1} & \text{if } n \text{ is odd,} \\ -3n^2 & \text{if } n \text{ is even.} \end{cases}$

°2. For each of the sequences in Problem 1, point out a subsequence which is increasing, or one which is decreasing, or one of each kind.

°3. In Problem 5 of Sec. 9.3, I suggested that you compute several polygonal approximations to the length of a circle — call them a_1, a_2, a_3. Now,
(a) Mark these values on a coordinate line, and — looking at the points — guess at a least upper bound d for an infinite sequence of similar, but better and better, approximations $\{a_n\}$.
(b) Sketch the first few points (n, a_n) of the graph of $\{a_n\}$, and sketch a horizontal line at the altitude d you chose in (a). Does it appear that your graph points will approach the line as n increases?
(c) How does your value d compare with $2\pi = 6.28$ (approximately)?

°4. In Problem 6 of Sec. 9.3, I suggested that you compute the returns (a_n) on \$1 at 5% annual interest if computed yearly (a_1), semiannually (a_2), monthly (a_{12}) and weekly (a_{52}). Now,

(a) Plot the points (n, a_n) for $n = 1, 2, 12$, and 52 and guess at the locations for other points on the graph of $a_n = (1 + 0.05/n)^n$.

(b) Sketch a horizontal line which the points (n, a_n) might approach as n increases.

*(c) What relation does the height d of the horizontal line in (b) have with the number $e^{0.05}$?

5. Why can a given sequence have no more than one "least upper bound" and no more than one "greatest lower bound"?

6. Suppose that A is the least upper bound of some sequence $\{a_n\}$ and that B is the least upper bound of a sequence $\{b_n\}$.

(a) Let $c_n = a_n + b_n$. Need $A + B$ be an upper bound for $\{c_n\}$? Draw graphs to illustrate your answer.

(b) With $c_n = a_n + b_n$, need $A + B$ be a *least* upper bound for $\{c_n\}$? Can you find a counterexample?

(c) Let $a'_n = ca_n$ where $c > 0$. Need cA be the least upper bound for $\{a'_n\}$? Draw a graph to illustrate the case $c = 2$.

(d) Let $e_n = a_n \cdot b_n$. Need AB be a least upper bound for $\{e_n\}$?

7. Formulate definitions of "least upper bound" and "greatest lower bound" for a *set S* of numbers (as distinct from a sequence), and apply them to the sets $\{$all x with $0 < x \leqslant 1\}$ and $\{$all $x < 0\}$.

*8. Use the "least upper bound" Axiom A' of Sec. 10.3 and the theorem on "extracting one way sequences" in Sec. 10.4 to get a third version of a "no holes" axiom: *Every bounded sequence has a least upper bound and a greatest lower bound.*

*9. Show that if $A = \lim\limits_{n \to \infty} a_n$ for a decreasing sequence $\{a_n\}$, then A must be the greatest lower bound of $\{a_n\}$. (See the proof of Theorem B in Sec. 10.3.)

*10. Show that if c is the greatest lower bound of a decreasing sequence $\{a_n\}$, then $\lim\limits_{n \to \infty} a_n = c$. (See the proof of Theorem C in Sec. 10.3.)

*11. Look at a circle with center O and radius r. To any inscribed polygon $\mathscr{I}$ containing O in its interior we can associate a circumscribed polygon $\mathscr{C}$, and vice versa, as in the accompanying figure. Intuitively you might guess that the shorter and more numerous all the sides are, the better the polygons will "fit" the

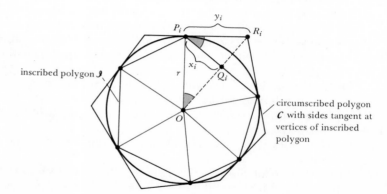

inscribed polygon $\mathscr{I}$

circumscribed polygon $\mathscr{C}$ with sides tangent at vertices of inscribed polygon

circle. So to measure closeness of fit for any such polygon $\mathscr{P}$ let's define the *mesh* $m(\mathscr{P})$ as the length of the longest side of $\mathscr{P}$.

Suppose now that we have a *sequence* of pairs of corresponding inside and outside polygons, $\mathscr{I}_1, \mathscr{C}_1, \mathscr{I}_2, \mathscr{C}_2, \mathscr{I}_3, \mathscr{C}_3, \ldots$.

(a) Show that if $\lim_{n\to\infty} m(\mathscr{I}_n) = 0$, then $\lim_{n\to\infty} m(\mathscr{C}_n) = 0$, and conversely. That is, "inside" and "outside" "fits" get better simultaneously.

(Note from the figure that for corresponding half-sides, $x_i < y_i$. Moreover, P_iOQ_i and R_iOP_i are similar triangles. Hence

$$\frac{y_i}{r} = \frac{x_i}{|OQ_i|} \quad \text{or} \quad y_i = \frac{r}{|OQ_i|}x_i = \frac{r}{\sqrt{r^2 - x_i^2}}x_i.$$

Also, $m(\mathscr{I}_n) =$ twice the largest x_i in $\mathscr{I}_n$, and $m(\mathscr{C}_n) =$ twice the largest y_i in $\mathscr{C}_n$.)

(b) Let a_n denote the perimeter length of $\mathscr{I}_n$ ($= x_1 + x_2 +$ etc. for all the half-sides in the figure); and let b_n denote the perimeter length of $\mathscr{C}_n$ ($= y_1 + y_2 +$ etc. in the figure). Show that if $\lim_{n\to\infty} m(\mathscr{I}_n) = 0$, then $\lim_{n\to\infty} (b_n - a_n) = 0$. That is, the better the polygonal "fit" to the circle, the closer the "inside" and "outside" approximations for "length."

(Note in the figure that $y_i < |Q_iR_i| + x_i$, or $y - x_i < |Q_iR_i|$. Moreover, P_iOQ_i and $R_iP_iQ_i$ are similar triangles. Hence

$$\frac{|Q_iR|}{y_i} = \frac{x_i}{r} \quad \text{or} \quad |Q_iR_i| = x_i\left(\frac{y_i}{r}\right).$$

Thus

$$y_i - x_i < x_i\left(\frac{y_i}{r}\right) \leqslant x_i\frac{m(\mathscr{C}_n)}{r}.$$

Recall that $a_n = x_1 + x_2 +$ etc. $< 8r$ for all n.)

*12. (a) Show that any two polygons $\mathscr{I}$ and $\mathscr{I}'$ inscribed in a circle (as in Problem 9) define a third inscribed polygon $\mathscr{I}''$ that has all the vertices of $\mathscr{I}$ and $\mathscr{I}'$, that has $m(\mathscr{I}'') \leqslant$ both $m(\mathscr{I})$ and $m(\mathscr{I}')$, and that has perimeter length *longer* ($\geqslant$) than either of the perimeters of $\mathscr{I}$ and $\mathscr{I}'$.

(b) Get a similar result for two circumscribed polygons $\mathscr{C}$ and $\mathscr{C}'$. Show that they define a $\mathscr{C}''$ with $m(\mathscr{C}'') \leqslant m(\mathscr{C})$ and $m(\mathscr{C}')$, and with *shorter* ($\leqslant$) perimeter length than in $\mathscr{C}$ or $\mathscr{C}'$.

*13. Use the results in Problems 11 and 12 to show that for a given circle there is a unique number A which will be the limit of the perimeter lengths of any sequence of inscribed polygons $\mathscr{I}_1, \mathscr{I}_2, \mathscr{I}_3, \ldots$ whose "fits" get better and better ($\lim_{n\to\infty} m(\mathscr{I}_n) = 0$), and will also be the limit of the perimeter lengths of any sequence of circumscribed polygons $\mathscr{C}_1, \mathscr{C}_2, \mathscr{C}_3, \ldots$ for which $\lim_{n\to\infty} m(\mathscr{C}_n) = 0$. Suggestions:

(a) Suppose that a sequence of inscribed polygons $\mathscr{I}_n$ have lengths a_n and have $\lim_{n\to\infty} m(\mathscr{I}_n) = 0$. Let $\mathscr{C}_n$ be corresponding circumscribed polygons, as in Problem 11, with lengths b_n. For each n form a new inscribed polygon $\tilde{\mathscr{I}}_n$ with all the vertices of $\mathscr{I}_k$ for $k \leqslant n$. It will have length $\tilde{a}_n \geqslant a_n$ (and $m(\tilde{\mathscr{I}}_n) \leqslant m(\mathscr{I}_n)$). And the corresponding circumscribed polygon $\tilde{\mathscr{C}}_n$ will have length $\tilde{b}_n \leqslant b_n$. So $a_n \leqslant \tilde{a}_n \leqslant \tilde{b}_n \leqslant b_n$. As in Secs. 10.1 and 10.2, show that the $\tilde{a}_n$ *increase* to a limit A. As in Problem 11, $\lim\limits_{n\to\infty} (b_n - a_n) = 0$. Show that all the sequences $\{a_n\}$, $\{\tilde{a}_n\}$, $\{\tilde{b}_n\}$, and $\{b_n\}$ must therefore converge to A.

(b) Suppose now that $\{\mathscr{I}'_n\}$ is a second sequence of inscribed polygons with lengths $\{a'_n\}$ and with $\lim\limits_{n\to\infty} m(\mathscr{I}'_n) = 0$. Let $\{\mathscr{C}'_n\}$ be the corresponding sequence of circumscribed polygons, with lengths $\{b'_n\}$ (as in Problem 9). Form third sequences $\{\mathscr{I}''_n\}$ with lengths $\{a''_n\}$ and $\{\mathscr{C}''_n\}$ with lengths $\{b''_n\}$, as in Problem 10. Note that

$$a_n \leqslant a''_n \leqslant b''_n \leqslant b_n \quad \text{and} \quad a'_n \leqslant a''_n \leqslant b''_n \leqslant b'_n$$

for each n; and show that $\{a_n\}$, $\{a''_n\}$, $\{a'_n\}$, $\{b_n\}$, $\{b''_n\}$, and $\{b'_n\}$ must all tend to the same limit A as in part (a).

(c) Note that this procedure holds just as well if we start first with circumscribed polygons $\{\mathscr{C}_n\}$.

*14. (a) Adapt the procedures of Problems 11, 12, and 13 to show that there exists a unique number $L(\overset{\frown}{AB})$ which we can interpret as the "length" of any given arc $\overset{\frown}{AB}$ of a circle.

(b) Show that such "arclength" has an "additive property": *if an arc $\overset{\frown}{AC}$ is composed of two adjacent arcs $\overset{\frown}{AB}$ and $\overset{\frown}{BC}$, then $L(\overset{\frown}{AC}) = L(\overset{\frown}{AB}) + L(\overset{\frown}{BC})$.*

(Suggestion: Consider polygons which include B as a vertex. Such polygons split into two parts, one fitting AB and one fitting BC. See the figure.)

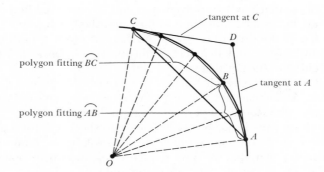

(c) Show that "arclength" has a "sandwich property": *the length of any arc $\overset{\frown}{AC}$ must always exceed the chord length $|AC|$. On the other hand, if $\overset{\frown}{AC}$ is less than a quarter circle, then $L(\overset{\frown}{AC})$ can never exceed the length of the exterior route along segments AD and DC, tangent to the circle at A and C, as in the figure.*

*15. Try to give a precise definition of "area" of a circle, and discuss whether a given circle necessarily has such "area."

*16. If a circle of radius R does have area, give plausible reasoning as to why that area A should equal $\frac{1}{2}RC$, where C is the length of the circumference.

*17. (a) Show that if $\lim_{n\to\infty} a_n = A$, then the numbers a_n must get "closer and closer to each other" as n increases, in the sense that

$$\left. \begin{array}{l} \text{for any } \epsilon > 0, \text{ there exists an integer } N_\epsilon \text{ such that} \\ |a_m - a_n| < \epsilon \text{ whenever } m \geqslant N_\epsilon \text{ and } n \geqslant N_\epsilon \end{array} \right\} \qquad (*)$$

(b) Show the converse: If a sequence $\{a_n\}$ has property $(*)$, then it must converge to some limit A.

(Suggestion: First choose $\epsilon =$ say, 1, and show that $\{a_n\}$ is bounded. Hence some subsequence $\{a_{n_k}\}$ must converge to some limit A. Use $(*)$ to show that the entire sequence $\{a_n\}$ must do the same.)

The property $(*)$ was studied by Augustin Cauchy (1800+) and bears his name.

10.6   DECIMALS AND INFINITE SERIES

A finite decimal, such as 0.385, denotes a specific rational number — in this case

$$\frac{3}{10} + \frac{8}{100} + \frac{5}{1000}.$$

We all know how to perform the finite number of additions indicated. But what do nonterminating decimals, such as 0.141591415914159 . . . denote? Does there exist a real number that deserves being described by the symbol

$$\frac{1}{10} + \frac{4}{10^2} + \frac{1}{10^3} + \frac{5}{10^4} + \frac{9}{10^5} + \cdots \qquad ? \qquad (1)$$

Here *infinitely many* additions are indicated. The same problem arose in the examples of Sec. 9.1, concerning the influence of government spending on income. You may also recall the billiard ball problem of Sec. 8.10, which suggested that the symbol

$$10 - 1 + 10 - 1 + 10 - 1 + 10 - 1 + \cdots \qquad (2)$$

might be interpreted equally well as 0, 3, 27, "∞," or any finite integer.

To clarify such matters, let's first try to formulate a precise general notion of "infinite sum" $s_1 + s_2 + s_3 + \cdots$. Afterward, we can ask whether such "sums" exist — in particular, infinite decimals. Why not base such a definition upon the sequence of *finite* sums

$$s_1, s_1 + s_2, s_1 + s_2 + s_3, s_1 + s_2 + s_3 + s_4, \ldots$$

whose meanings we do know, and then use our concept of "limit"?

Definitions: Let's call an indicated addition of an infinite sequence of numbers,

$$s_1 + s_2 + s_3 + \cdots + s_n + \cdots, \tag{3}$$

an *infinite series*. For $n = 1, 2, 3, \ldots$, call the (ordinary) sum of the first n terms of the series,

$$S_n = s_1 + s_2 + s_3 + \cdots + s_n, \tag{4}$$

its *n*th *partial sum*. If the sequence $\{S_n\}$ of partial sums converges to some limit S, call S the *sum of the series*, and call the series itself *summable*. In this case, write

$$S = s_1 + s_2 + s_3 + \cdots + s_n + \cdots \tag{5}$$

Again, the expression (5) means nothing more or less than that $\lim_{n \to \infty} S_n = S$. Note also: if minus signs appear, interpret these as addition of negative numbers. Thus $1 - \frac{1}{2} + \frac{1}{4} - \frac{1}{8} + \cdots$ means

$$1 + \left(-\frac{1}{2}\right) + \frac{1}{4} + \left(-\frac{1}{8}\right) + \cdots.$$

EXAMPLE 1 (from Sec. 9.1). The series $1 + 0.9 + (0.9)^2 + (0.9)^3 + \cdots$ has partial sums $S_n = 10 - 10(0.9)^{n+1}$, which converge to $S = 10$. So the series is "summable" and we can write "$1 + 0.9 + (0.9)^2 + \cdots = 10$."

EXAMPLE 2 (from Sec. 9.1). The series $1 + 2 + 2^2 + 2^3 + \cdots$ has partial sums $S_n = 2^{n+1} - 2$ which don't converge; so this series is not summable. In fact, the S_n increase beyond any given positive value as n increases. (In the notation of Sec. 9.9, we can write $\lim_{n \to \infty} S_n = \infty$.)

EXAMPLE 3: the general "*geometric series*" with "*ratio*" r:

$$a + ar + ar^2 + \cdots + ar^{n-1} + \cdots.$$

Once and for all, by cancellation we can get

$$S_n = a + ar + ar^2 + \cdots + ar^{n-1}$$

minus

$$rS_n = ar + ar^2 + \cdots + ar^{n-1} + ar^n,$$

or $(1 - r)S_n = a(1 - r^n)$. When $r \neq 1$, we can write

$$S_n = a\frac{1 - r^n}{1 - r}$$

$$= \frac{a}{1 - r} - \left(\frac{a}{1 - r}\right)r^n. \tag{6}$$

If $|r| < 1$, the $\lim_{n \to \infty} r^n = 0$; so $\lim_{n \to \infty} S_n = a/(1 - r)$, and the series is summable, with sum $a/(1 - r)$.

If $|r| > 1$, the sequence $\{S_n\}$ is unbounded and can have no limit. To see this, write

$$\frac{a}{1 - r}r^n = \frac{a}{1 - r} + (-S_n)$$

and take absolute values, to get

$$\left|\frac{a}{1-r}\right| \cdot |r^n| \leq \left|\frac{a}{1-r}\right| + |S_n|$$

or

$$\left|\frac{a}{1-r}\right| \cdot |r|^n - \left|\frac{a}{1-r}\right| \leq |S_n| . \tag{7}$$

As n increases, the left-hand side of (7) will increase without bound, forcing the $|S_n|$'s up as well.

If $r = 1$, then $S_n = an$, and the $\{S_n\}$ are unbounded, too. If $r = -1$, the S_n oscillate between the values 0 and a.

EXAMPLE 4: the series

$$\frac{1}{1 \cdot 2} + \frac{1}{2 \cdot 3} + \frac{1}{3 \cdot 4} + \cdots + \frac{1}{n(n+1)} + \cdots .$$

You may recall from Problem 1(o) of Sec. 8.3, that each term $1/n(n+1)$ can be written as a difference $1/n(n+1) = 1/n - 1/(n+1)$. Hence we can simplify the partial sums by cancellation:

$$S_n = \frac{1}{1 \cdot 2} + \frac{1}{2 \cdot 3} + \cdots + \frac{1}{(n-1)n} + \frac{1}{n(n+1)}$$

$$= \left(\frac{1}{1} - \frac{1}{2}\right) + \left(\frac{1}{2} - \frac{1}{3}\right) + \cdots + \frac{1}{n-1} - \frac{1}{n} + \frac{1}{n} - \frac{1}{n+1}$$

$$= 1 - \frac{1}{n+1} .$$

And $\lim\limits_{n \to \infty} S_n = 1$, or "$\dfrac{1}{1 \cdot 2} + \dfrac{1}{2 \cdot 3} + \dfrac{1}{3 \cdot 4} + \cdots = 1$."

Now let's apply the "series" concept to decimals. The symbol $0.d_1d_2d_3d_4. \ldots$, where the d_i's are digits between 0 and 9 denotes an infinite series

$$\frac{d_1}{10^1} + \frac{d_2}{10^2} + \frac{d_3}{10^3} + \cdots + \frac{d_n}{10^n} + \cdots \tag{8}$$

with partial sums

$$S_n = \frac{d_1}{10^1} + \frac{d_2}{10^2} + \cdots + \frac{d_n}{10^n} \qquad \text{for } n = 1, 2, 3, \ldots \tag{9}$$

These partial sums are all nonnegative, and moreover *increasing*, since

$$S_{n+1} = S_n + \frac{d_{n+1}}{10^{n+1}} \geq S_n \qquad \text{for any } n. \tag{10}$$

Hence by Axiom A, we'll know that there exists a limit number $S = \lim\limits_{n \to \infty} S_n$, the "sum of the sequence," if only we can show that the $\{S_n\}$ are bounded.

Why must $\{S_n\}$ be bounded? Note that the largest value any d_i can have is 9. Therefore,

$$S_n = \frac{d_1}{10^1} + \frac{d_2}{10^2} + \frac{d_3}{10^3} + \cdots + \frac{d_n}{10^n}$$

$$\leq \frac{9}{10^1} + \frac{9}{10^2} + \frac{9}{10^3} + \cdots + \frac{9}{10^n}$$

$$= \frac{9}{10} \cdot \frac{1 - (1/10)^n}{1 - (1/10)} = 1 - \left(\frac{1}{10}\right)^n. \tag{11}$$

To get the last line in (11), I evaluated the "geometric" partial sum with ratio $r = \frac{1}{10}$ as in Example 3 above. Thus the S_n are bounded:

$$0 \leq S_n \leq 1 - \left(\frac{1}{10}\right)^n < 1 \qquad \text{for any } n, \tag{12}$$

and the sequence $\{S_n\}$ has a (unique) limit S. Note that S must be a real number in the unit interval $0 \leq x \leq 1$ (since $\lim_{n\to\infty} 0 \leq \lim_{n\to\infty} S_n \leq \lim_{n\to\infty} 1$, by Property O of Chapter 9, on comparing limits).

To get an idea of how quickly the S_n can converge to S, look at the first few partial sums of the decimal $0.14159\ldots$ in Fig. 10-14.

FIGURE 10-14

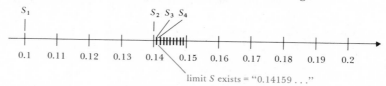

limit S exists = "0.14159 . . ."

In summary: if we assume Axiom A, we can say that every decimal $0.d_1d_2d_3 \ldots$ represents a unique number S between 0 and 1.

Is the converse true? Does every S in $[0, 1]$ have a decimal representation? And is it unique? To get a decimal corresponding to any given S, just work the scheme of Fig. 10-14 in reverse. Carve the unit interval into tenths. The given S must lie in one of these—with left-hand end point $d_1/10$. Carve this subinterval once more into tenths. The given S must also lie in one of these—with left-hand end point $d_1/10 + d_2/10^2$. Continue the process, forever if necessary, to get digits d_i, and partial sums

$$S_n = \frac{d_1}{10^1} + \frac{d_2}{10^2} + \cdots + \frac{d_n}{10^n}$$

converging to S.

Can two distinct decimal symbols represent the same sum S? What about 0.1 and 0.09999 . . .?

Since I defined "sums" of series in terms of limits, you might expect several properties of limits to carry over to series. They do. I invite you to explore such results in Problems 5–9 of the next section.

10.7   PROBLEMS ON DECIMALS AND INFINITE SERIES

°1. Which rational numbers do the following decimal series represent? In each case, locate several partial sums on a coordinate line.

(a) 0.123 123 123 . . .

Sample reasoning: Write

$$S = \left(\frac{1}{10} + \frac{2}{10^2} + \frac{3}{10^3}\right) + \left(\frac{1}{10^4} + \frac{2}{10^5} + \frac{3}{10^6}\right) = \frac{123}{10^3} + \frac{123}{10^6} + \frac{123}{10^9} + \cdots,$$

a geometric series with initial term $a = 123/1000$ and ratio $r_n = 1/1000$, as in Example 3 of Sec. 10.6. The partial sums S_n tend to

$$S = a\left(\frac{1}{1-r}\right) = \frac{123}{1000}\left[\frac{1}{1-(1/1000)}\right] = \frac{123}{999}.$$

(b) 0.11111 . . .   (c) 0.272727 . . .
(d) 0.242424 . . .   (e) 0.135135135 . . .
(f) 0.123412341234 . . .   (g) 0.285714285714 . . .

°2. Determine a decimal series for each of the following rational numbers. In each case locate several partial sums on a coordinate line.

(a) $\dfrac{2}{3}$ (b) $\dfrac{3}{4}$

(c) $\dfrac{1}{9}$ (d) $\dfrac{4}{11}$

(e) $\dfrac{3}{7}$ (f) $\dfrac{21}{8}$

(g) $\dfrac{14}{5}$

3. (a) Does every decimal series which repeats itself in blocks (as do the series in Problem 1) represent a rational number?
   (b) Can every positive rational number $x \leqslant 1$ be represented by a "repeating" decimal series?

°4. (a) Do the two distinct decimal symbols 0.1 and 0.09999 . . . represent the same sum S?
   *(b) Can three distinct decimal symbols represent the same sum?

5. Why can a series $s_1 + s_2 + s_3 + \cdots$ have at most one number S as its sum? (Recall the sequence of partial sums S_n.)

6. Suppose that $S = s_1 + s_2 + s_3 + \cdots$ and $T = t_1 + t_2 + t_3 + \cdots$ and c is a real number. Show that

(a) $cS = (cs_1) + (cs_2) + (cs_3) + \cdots$

and

(b) $S + T = (s_1 + t_1) + (s_2 + t_2) + (s_3 + t_3) + \cdots.$

(Consider the partial sums and their limits.)

*7. Suppose that $0 \leqslant s_k \leqslant t_k$ for all $k = 1, 2, 3, \ldots$. Show that if the series $t_1 + t_2 + t_3 + \cdots$ is summable, then the series $s_1 + s_2 + s_3 + \cdots$ is also. Equivalently, if the "lesser" s-series is not summable, then the "greater" t-series can't be either (compare the partial sums).

**8. The "ratio test" for summability: Suppose that $s_1 + s_2 + s_3 + \cdots$ is a series with all $s_n \geq 0$ for which there exists a limit $R = \lim\limits_{n \to \infty} s_{n+1}/s_n$. Show that

(a) the series is summable if $R < 1$;

(b) the series is not summable if $R > 1$.

   (Suggestion: Compare the partial sums $s_1 + s_2 + \cdots + s_n$ with corresponding geometric partial sums

$$A(1 + R + R^2 + \cdots + R^{n-1})$$

   for suitable A.)

**9. On "alternating series." Show that if a series $s_1 + s_2 + s_3 + \cdots$ has terms of alternating sign whose magnitudes $|s_n|$ form a decreasing sequence with $\lim\limits_{n \to \infty} |s_n| = 0$, then the series is summable.

   (Suggestion: Study how the partial sums must be located on a coordinate line.)

*10. *"Binary representations."* Nowadays electronic computers do a lot of our calculating. Although numbers may be fed into the machines in usual decimal form, still, inside the electronic mind of the machine—where it does its high speed computation—only two distinct inputs are receivable: plus-vs.-minus (or, alternatively, on-vs.-off). So the machine itself has to translate decimal representation into a representation which will involve only two symbols—which in turn will become, electronically, "plus" or "minus." Analogous to the decimal representation of numbers (which uses powers of 10) is the *binary representation*, which uses powers of 2. According to this representation the following compound symbol

   0.1011001 . . .

(which uses only *two* basic symbols 0 and 1) stands for the (possibly infinite) sum

$$\frac{1}{2^1} + \frac{0}{2^2} + \frac{1}{2^3} + \frac{1}{2^4} + \frac{0}{2^5} + \frac{0}{2^6} + \frac{1}{2^7} + \cdots \qquad (*)$$

(a) Show that any infinite binary representation

$$0.b_1 b_2 b_3 b_4 \cdots b_n \cdots, \qquad (**)$$

   where the b_n's are either 0 or 1, stands for a unique number in the unit interval $[0, 1]$.

(b) Can two distinct symbols of the form (**) stand for the same number in $[0, 1]$? If so, how many different examples can there be of such nonuniqueness of representation? Also, would such nonuniqueness contradict the uniqueness asserted in part (a)?

(c) Draw a picture of the unit interval $[0, 1]$. Divide $[0, 1]$ into *halves*, and these halves into halves, etc. Pick any number in $[0, 1]$ and show that you can approximate it by a sum such as in (*); hence that number *has* a binary representation.

*11. Imagine an experiment consisting of infinitely many tosses of a true coin. Any conceivable outcome of this experiment may be described by an infinite sequence of H's and T's. For example,

$$H, T, H, H, T, T, H, \ldots .$$

If we agree to the following code: 1 means H and 0 means T, then the symbol 0.1011001 ... of Problem 10 also constitutes a description of the possible outcome of our experiment. This suggests a close connection between coin tossing and numbers in [0, 1]: Draw a picture of [0, 1] as in the accompanying figure. Now perform the experiment. If the first toss results in a head, restrict attention to the *right-hand* half, $[\frac{1}{2}, 1]$, of [0, 1]. If the second toss results in a tail, restrict further attention to the *left-hand* half of $[\frac{1}{2}, 1]$; etc., etc. (H indicates right-hand half; and T the left-hand half.) With each successive toss your attention is narrowed down to an interval of one-half the length of the previous interval.

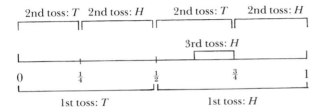

(a) With more and more tosses, will you zero in on a single number? Will it be the one represented in (*) of Problem 10, if our results are $H, T, H, H, T, T, H, \ldots$?

(b) Gather together *all* the possible outcomes of the experiment which share this one property: *an H on the 2nd toss*. To what subset of points in [0, 1] do they correspond? What is the total length of that subset? Considering the coin to be true, what should the "probability" be of getting a head on the 2nd toss regardless of what you get on other tosses?

(c) Gather together *all* the possible outcomes of the experiment which share the following property: *an H on the 1st toss and a T on the 2nd*. To what subset of points in [0, 1] do these correspond? What is its length? What should the probability be for an H on the 1st toss *and* "independently" a T on the 2nd, regardless of the rest?
Any general conclusions?

*12. Are there as many integers as points on a line? Looking at representations of numbers such as in Problem 10, we might *conjecture* that there are as many points in [0, 1] as there are different sequences of 1's and 0's (of course we would have to settle the nonuniqueness question in part (b) of Problem 10 before we could speak with certainty). Following this conjecture, we might try to discover whether the set of integers

{1, 2, 3, . . .} can be put into a one-to-one correspondence with the set of *all* sequences of 1's and 0's.

Suppose that such a correspondence were possible, and that someone knowing the details of this correspondence had already listed *each and every* 0, 1 sequence on a row labeled by the very integer to which that sequence is supposed to correspond—as in the accompanying table.

Integer						Corresponding sequence						
1	[1]	0	0	1	1	0	1	1	1	. . .	1	1 . . .
2	0	[1]	1	1	0	0	0	0	1	. . .	0	0 . . .
3	1	0	[0]	0	1	1	0	0	0	. . .		
4	0	0	1	[1]	1	0	1	0	1	. . .		
5					[ ]							
						[ ]						
							[ ]					
⋮									⋱			
n											[a_n]	
⋮												⋱

Now record the sequence of numbers which appear in the diagonal squares. In the table, the sequence is

$$1, 1, 0, 1, \ldots, a_n, \ldots \qquad (*)$$

Whatever this diagonal sequence may be, manufacture a new one by replacing each 1 with a 0 and each 0 with a 1. Under this transformation the particular sequence (*) becomes

$$0, 0, 1, 0, \ldots, b_n, \ldots \qquad (**)$$

where $b_n = 0$ if $a_n = 1$ and $b_n = 1$ if $a_n = 0$. Here is one of the most basic questions faced by mathematical logic in the last century: on which *row* of the table can we find the sequence (**)? We've assumed that *every* sequence is on some definite row. So suppose the new sequence (**) is on, say, the 101st row. Then what about the 101st entry in the sequence? It must be in a diagonal box. Call its value a_{101}. But by the way we manufactured the sequence (**), its 101st entry must be different from a_{101}—a contradiction. Hence the sequence (*) must be on some other—but nevertheless *definite*—row; it can't be on a "floating" row whose integer label can't be ascertained even in principle. Which row?

(The above procedure was invented by Georg Cantor (1845–1918) and is known as the "Cantor diagonal process.")

10.8 *SUMMARY OF CHAPTER 10*

DEFINITIONS: Call a sequence $\{a_n\}$ *increasing* if $a_n \leqslant a_{n+1}$ for all n. Similarly, call a sequence $\{a_n\}$ *decreasing* if $a_n \geqslant a_{n+1}$ for all n. (Sec. 10.2)

DEFINITIONS: Call a sequence $\{a_n\}$ *bounded above* if there is some number d such that $a_n \leqslant d$ for all n, and call d an *upper bound* for $\{a_n\}$. Similarly, call a sequence $\{a_n\}$ *bounded below* if there is some number c such that $c \leqslant a_n$ for all n, and call c a *lower bound* for $\{a_n\}$. (Sec. 10.3)

REMARK: Three equivalent statements of boundedness:
   (i) $\{a_n\}$ is "bounded": $|a_n| \leqslant b$ for all n.
   (ii) $\{a_n\}$ is both bounded above and bounded below.
   (iii) $\{a_n\}$ lies entirely in some interval $[c, d]$.
(Sec. 10.3)

DEFINITIONS: A number d is a *least upper bound* for a sequence $\{a_n\}$ if d is an upper bound and if no number $d' < d$ is also an upper bound. Similarly, a number c is a *greatest lower bound* for a sequence $\{a_n\}$ if c is a lower bound and if no number $c' > c$ is also a lower bound. (Sec. 10.3)

REMARK: If a sequence $\{a_n\}$ has a least upper bound at all, then it can have only one. Similarly regarding a greatest lower bound. (Sec. 10.3)

THEOREM: If $A = \lim_{n \to \infty} a_n$ for an increasing sequence $\{a_n\}$, then A must be the least upper bound of $\{a_n\}$. (Sec. 10.3, Theorem B)

THEOREM: If d is the least upper bound of an increasing sequence $\{a_n\}$, then $\lim_{n \to \infty} a_n = d$. (Sec. 10.3, Theorem C)

Two *equivalent* axioms:

AXIOM A : If $\{a_n\}$ is a bounded increasing sequence, then there *must exist* a real number A such that $\lim_{n \to \infty} a_n = A$. (Similarly for bounded and decreasing sequences.) (Sec. 10.2)

AXIOM A': (A "LEAST UPPER BOUND AXIOM"): If $\{a_n\}$ is an increasing sequence which is bounded above, then there *must exist* a number d which is a least upper bound for $\{a_n\}$. (Similarly, a decreasing sequence, if bounded below, must have a greatest lower bound.) (Sec. 10.3)

Applications of the axioms:
   To the length of circles (Sec. 10.1)
   To bacterial growth rate (Sec. 10.2 and 10.3)
   To compound interest (Sec. 10.2)
   To infinite decimals (Sec. 10.6)

DEFINITION: $e = \lim\limits_{n\to\infty} \left(1 + \dfrac{1}{n}\right)^n$.

REMARK: the limit e exists, by Axioms A and A′. Furthermore, for any positive rational number p,

$$e^p = \lim\limits_{n\to\infty} \left(1 + \dfrac{p}{n}\right)^n.$$

THEOREM (ON "EXTRACTING SUBSEQUENCES"): Every sequence contains either an increasing or a decreasing subsequence, if not both. (Sec. 10.4)

THEOREM (ON "CONVERGENT SUBSEQUENCES"): If $\{a_n\}$ is any bounded sequence, with $c \leq a_n \leq d$ for all n, then $\{a_n\}$ contains either an increasing or a decreasing subsequence which converges to some number A in the interval $[c, d]$.
(Sec. 10.4)

DEFINITIONS: Call an indicated addition of an infinite sequence of numbers $s_1 + s_2 + s_3 + \cdots$, an *infinite series*. For $n = 1, 2, 3, \ldots$, call the sum of the first n terms of the series, $S_n = s_1 + s_2 + \cdots + s_n$, its nth *partial sum*. If the sequence $\{S_n\}$ of partial sums converges to a limit S, call S the *sum of the series*, and call the series itself *summable*. Notation: $S = s_1 + s_2 + s_3 + \cdots$.
(Sec. 10.6)

DEFINITION: A *geometric series with ratio r* is any series of the form $a + ar + ar^2 + \cdots + ar^n + \cdots$.

REMARK: A geometric series with ratio r is summable if $|r| < 1$, not summable if $|r| \geq 1$.
(Sec. 10.6, Example 3)

For application to "infinite decimals" and for further properties of series, see Sec. 10.6 and the problems of Sec. 10.7.

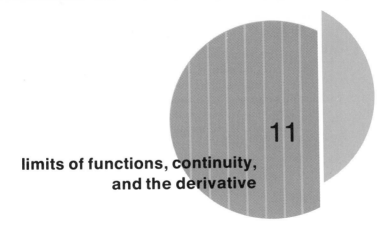

11
limits of functions, continuity, and the derivative

In this chapter I define limits for functions in terms of limits for sequences. We can then give a precise meaning for the notion of a graph having no breaks ("continuity") and for the instantaneous rate of change of a function (its "derivative"). Useful results about these concepts then follow from properties of sequences.

11.1 LIMITS OF FUNCTIONS

What precise meaning can we give to the notion of a function output $f(x)$ "converging" to some limit A as we "move" the input x toward some fixed value x_0—as in Fig. 11-1? Why not consider successive values x_n for the input variable, converging to x_0, as in Fig. 11-2?

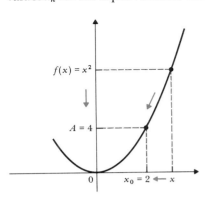

FIGURE 11-1

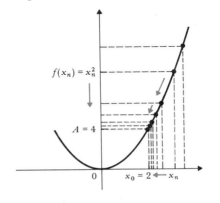

FIGURE 11-2

We know precisely what convergence means for such a *sequence*. And what should we demand for the corresponding output values $f(x_n)$? Simply, that they too should form a convergent sequence, with $\lim_{n\to\infty} f(x_n) = A$.

223

For the function $f(x) = x^2$ in Fig. 11-2, we needn't pick the x_n's always to one side of x_0. *Every* sequence with $\lim_{n\to\infty} x_n = 2$ will have $\lim_{n\to\infty} x_n^2 = 4$. Shouldn't we demand the same more generally: that *every* input sequence $\{x_n\}$ converging to the fixed value x_0 should yield outputs $\{f(x_n)\}$ converging to the *same* value A?

A caution: there might be some functions—such as I've pictured in Figs. 11-3 and 11-4—for which it would be impossible or *misleading* to pick $x_n = x_0$.

FIGURE 11-3

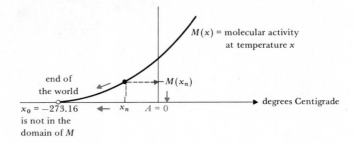

In Fig. 11-3, I've indicated a function M whose domain doesn't include the value x_0—although x_0 is a limit of sequences $\{x_n\}$ in the domain. In Fig. 11-4, the value $x_0 = 0$ *is* in the domain of the function T, but the output value $T(x_0)$ differs greatly from what we might reasonably call the limit of $T(x)$ as x *approaches* x_0.

FIGURE 11-4

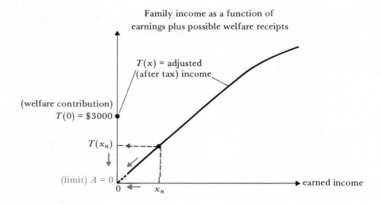

FIGURE 11-5

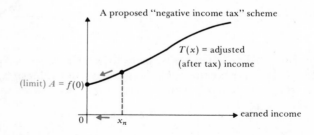

To accommodate many such examples with one limit definition, let's agree never to let "approaching" inputs x_n actually take on the value x_0—although they should get closer and closer to it. Here is a definition which takes all the above requirements into account:

Definition I: Suppose that f is a function with domain $\mathcal{D}$ consisting of real numbers, and that x_0 is a real number (either in $\mathcal{D}$ or not) which is the limit of at least one sequence of inputs in $\mathcal{D}$, all distinct from x_0. Let's say that a *limit of* $f(x)$ *exists as x converges to* x_0 if there is some real number A such that $\lim_{n\to\infty} f(x_n) = A$ for EVERY sequence $\{x_n\}$ of inputs distinct from x_0 and converging to x_0. Call A the *limit of* $f(x)$, and say that $f(x)$ *converges to A as x converges to* x_0.

Once more,

$$
\begin{array}{c}
\boxed{\begin{array}{l} \lim_{n\to\infty} x_n = x_0 \\[4pt] x_n \neq x_0 \text{ for all } n \end{array}} \quad \textit{always implies} \quad \boxed{\lim_{n\to\infty} f(x_n) = A} \qquad (1) \\[10pt]
\text{(inputs)} \qquad\qquad\qquad\qquad\qquad\qquad \text{(outputs)}
\end{array}
$$

Notation: $\lim_{x\to x_0} f(x) = A$, or $\lim_{y\to x_0} f(y) = A$ (the choice of symbol, x or y, for the "moving" variable is immaterial).

A definition is a tool which we, or others before us, build in order to handle ideas and problems. Its merit depends on how effective it is. Let's see how Definition I works.

EXAMPLE 1: *A specific polynomial*: $f(x) = \frac{1}{2}x^3 + 3$ for all real x. Intuitively, we might expect that as x tends, say, to -1, x^3 will tend to $(-1)^3$ and $f(x)$ will tend to $\frac{1}{2}(-1)^3 + 3 = 5/2$. Definition I completely supports this line of reasoning, basing it upon the precise results of Chapters 8 and 9. Namely, for *any sequence* $\{x_n\}$ with $\lim_{n\to\infty} x_n = -1$ (and $x_n \neq -1$ for all n), we can conclude that

$$
\lim_{n\to\infty} f(x_n) = \lim_{n\to\infty} \left[\frac{1}{2}(x_n)^3 + 3 \right] = \frac{1}{2}[\lim_{n\to\infty} x_n]^3 + \lim_{n\to\infty} 3
$$

$$
= \frac{1}{2}(-1)^3 + 3 = \frac{5}{2}. \qquad (2)
$$

Here I used properties about limits of constant sequences, of scaled sequences, and of sums and products of sequences (Properties G, H, I, and J of Chapter 9). The result is just the condition which warrants description as "$\lim_{x\to -1} f(x) = 5/2$", according to Definition I.

Let's check for a limit of the same function at some other output; say, at $x_0 = 2$. For *any* sequence $\{x_n\}$ with $\lim_{n\to\infty} x_n = 2$ and $x_n \neq 2$ we must have

$$
\lim_{n\to\infty} f(x_n) = \lim_{n\to\infty} \left[\frac{1}{2}x_n^3 + 3 \right] = \frac{1}{2}[\lim_{n\to\infty} x_n]^3 + \lim_{n\to\infty} 3
$$

$$
= \frac{1}{2}(2)^3 + 3 = 7. \qquad (3)
$$

Thus "$\lim_{x\to 2} f(x) = 7$".

To test the working of Definition I further, let's look at

EXAMPLE 2: *The polynomial slightly mutilated.* Construct a function g identical to the polynomial f in Example 1 *except at $x_0 = -1$.* Say,

$$g(x) = \begin{cases} \frac{1}{2}x^3 + 3 & \text{for all } x \neq -1. \\ -2 & \text{for all } x = -1. \end{cases}$$

Will such a change alter the limit as *x approaches* -1? It shouldn't. A requirement of Definition I was not to allow approaching inputs x to equal -1. How, then, could corresponding outputs $g(x)$ differ from the $f(x)$ of Example 1 in their convergence to 5/2? See Figs. 11-6 and 11-7.

FIGURE 11-6

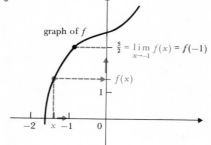

FIGURE 11-7

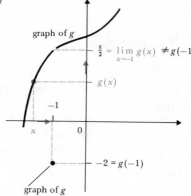

More precisely, according to Definition I, we must again examine every sequence $\{x_n\}$ with $\lim_{n\to\infty} x_n = -1$ and $x_n \neq -1$ for all n. Now, with $x_n \neq -1$, exactly the same calculations apply as in Example 1:

$$\lim_{n\to\infty} g(x_n) = \lim_{n\to\infty} \left[\frac{1}{2}(x_n)^3 + 3 \right] = \frac{1}{2} [\lim_{n\to\infty} x_n]^3 + \lim_{n\to\infty} 3$$

$$= \frac{1}{2}(-1)^3 + 3 = \frac{5}{2}. \tag{4}$$

Hence "$\lim_{x\to-1} g(x) = 5/2$", according to the definition. The only difference from Example 1 is that

$$\lim_{x\to-1} f(x) = \frac{5}{2} = f(-1) \qquad \text{in Example 1,} \tag{5}$$

whereas

$$\lim_{x\to-1} g(x) = \frac{5}{2} \neq g(-1) \qquad \text{here.} \tag{6}$$

How about $\lim_{x\to2} g(x)$? Shouldn't it be the same as $\lim_{x\to2} f(x)$, since $g(x) = f(x)$ for all $x \neq -1$? Yes. Pick any sequence $\{x_n\}$ with $\lim_{n\to\infty} x_n = 2$

and $x_n \neq 2$. Now, only finitely many x_n's can $= -1$ (otherwise, we'd have a subsequence with limit -1 rather than 2). Hence for all $n \geqslant$ some index N we must have $x_n \neq -1$, and $g(x_n) = \frac{1}{2}x_n{}^3 + 3$. Since only the tail of a sequence influences its limit (Property C of Chapter 9), we have again

$$\lim_{n \to \infty} g(x_n) = \lim_{n \to \infty} \left[\frac{1}{2}x_n{}^3 + 3 \right] = \frac{1}{2} [\lim_{n \to \infty} x_n]^3 + \lim_{n \to \infty} 3$$

$$= \frac{1}{2}2^3 + 3 = 7 \tag{7}$$

Thus "$\lim_{x \to 2} g(x) = 7$." Here the limit coincides with $g(2)$.

We can extend the arguments of Example 1 to

EXAMPLE 3: *Any polynomial*

$$P(x) = a_0 + a_1 x + a_2 x^2 + \cdots + a_k x^k.$$

Choose any real input x_0, and let's check the existence of "$\lim_{x \to x_0} P(x)$." Think again of an *arbitrary* sequence $\{x_n\}$ with $\lim x_n = x_0$ (and $x_n \neq x_0$ for all n). By the same properties which I invoked for Example 1, we can conclude that

$$\lim_{n \to \infty} P(x_n) = \lim_{n \to \infty} [a_0 + a_1 x_n + a_2(x_n)^2 + \cdots + a_k(x_n)^k]$$

$$= \lim_{n \to \infty} a_0 + a_1 \lim_{n \to \infty} x_n + a_2 [\lim_{n \to \infty} x_n]^2 + \cdots + a_k [\lim_{n \to \infty} x_n]^k$$

$$= a_0 + a_1 x_0 + a_2 x_0{}^2 + \cdots + a_k x_0{}^k$$

$$= P(x_0). \tag{8}$$

What does equation (8) say? It says that the single number $A = P(x_0)$ serves as the limit of outputs corresponding to any input sequence $\{x_n\}$ converging to, but distinct from, x_0 — just the condition we should denote by

$$\lim_{x \to x_0} P(x) = P(x_0). \tag{9}$$

(For an equivalent definition of "$\lim_{x \to x_0} f(x) = A$," using the notion of interval "neighborhoods" $(A - \epsilon, A + \epsilon)$ and $(x_0 - \delta, x_0 + \delta)$, see Problem 8 of Sec. 11.3.)

11.2 CONTINUITY

How do the graphs in Figs. 11-6 and 11-7 differ? The right-hand graph clearly has a "break" — a "discontinuity" corresponding to the input $x_0 = -1$, whereas the left-hand one *appears* "continuously" drawn. Of course, under high enough magnification any picture of a graph will separate into blotches of ink. But now, using the idea of limit, we can avoid reliance on pictures. We can give a precise mathematical meaning to the notion of a graph having no "break" at a point $(x_0, f(x_0))$. Let's simply focus upon the essential difference between Examples 1 and 2 above.

Definition II: Let's call a function f *continuous at the input* x_0 if a $\lim_{x \to x_0} f(x)$ exists and moreover its value coincides with the output value $f(x_0)$ at x_0:

$$\lim_{x \to x_0} f(x) = f(x_0). \tag{1}$$

Call a function f *continuous* (without specifying x_0) if f is continuous at x_0 for every input x_0 in the domain of f. If $\lim_{x \to x_0} f(x)$ fails to exist or fails to equal $f(x_0)$, call f *discontinuous* at x_0 (or say that f has a *discontinuity* at x_0).

In the last section the polynomial $f(x) = \frac{1}{2}x^3 + 3$ of Example 1 was continuous at $x_0 = -1$ and at $x_0 = 2$, since $\lim_{x \to -1} f(x) = 5/3 = f(-1)$ and $\lim_{x \to 2} f(x) = 7 = f(2)$. But the mutilated polynomial g of Example 2 was *not* continuous at $x_0 = -1$, since $\lim_{x \to -1} g(x) = 5/3 \neq -2 = g(-1)$. (Recall the "break" in Fig. 11-7.) However g *was* continuous at $x_0 = 2$.

More generally, we can rephrase the result $\lim_{x \to x_0} P(x) = P(x_0)$ of Example 3 of the last section, as a

Theorem A: Every polynomial is continuous (at all inputs).

If we ever seek to find the absolute maximum or minimum of a function it will be helpful to know beforehand that the function is continuous.

EXAMPLE 1. Recall the ordering-cost function for loaves of bread (from Sec. 7.1):

$$h(x) = (0.005)x + (4500)\frac{1}{x} \quad \text{(dollars)} \tag{2}$$

for a lot of size x, where $1 \leq x \leq 1500$. In searching for a lot size x_{MIN} which would minimize cost, I previously *hoped* (in Sec. 7.1) that the graph of h was "continuous" (as suggested in Fig. 11-8) rather than with "breaks" (a possibility pictured in Fig. 11-9). If the true graph

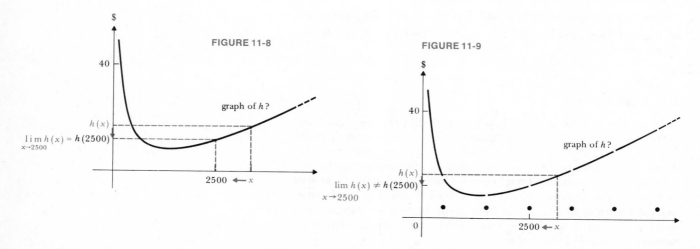

FIGURE 11-8

FIGURE 11-9

of h had discontinuities (as in Fig. 11-9), then I might well have missed the absolute minimum of h while searching for valley bottoms — as I did in Sec. 7.1.

But now we can check that h is continuous — at least in the sense of Definition II: Choose any input x_0 $(1 \leq x_0 \leq 1500)$; and consider any sequence $\{x_n\}$ converging to, but distinct from, x_0. We can conclude that

$$\lim_{n \to \infty} h(x_n) = \lim_{n \to \infty} \left[(0.005)x_n + \frac{4500}{x_n} \right] = (0.005) \lim_{n \to \infty} x_n + \frac{4500}{\lim_{n \to \infty} x_n}$$

$$= 0.005x_0 + \frac{4500}{x_0} = h(x_0), \tag{3}$$

again, by properties on scaling, reciprocals, and addition for limits of sequences (Chapter 9). Thus

$$\lim_{x \to x_0} h(x) = h(x_0), \tag{4}$$

and h is continuous at x_0.

In coming sections, I'll discuss more about how continuity affects the search for maxima and minima of functions. And we'll be able to extend the catalog of continuous functions to include not only polynomials and simple combinations $ax + b/x$ as in (2) above, but hosts of other functions too.

Here is an alternate characterization of continuity which can help us recognize general properties of continuous functions. It's phrased purely in terms of sequences; and you may have guessed it while reading the examples above.

Theorem B (an alternate definition of continuity at x_0): The requirement

$$\lim_{x \to x_0} f(x) = f(x_0) \tag{5}$$

is equivalent to the requirement:

$$\boxed{\lim_{n \to \infty} x_n = x_0} \ \textit{always implies} \ \boxed{\lim_{n \to \infty} f(x_n) = f(x_0)} \tag{6}$$

— whether $x_n = x_0$ or not.

Essentially, requirements (5) and (6) differ *only* with respect to sequences $\{x_n\}$ where x_n's $= x_0$. Such x_n's have outputs already equal to $f(x_0)$. So they do no harm; they merely guarantee that

$$\lim_{n \to \infty} f(x_n) = f(x_0).$$

Here are more particulars regarding

A proof of Theorem B: If we rewrite (5) in terms of the basic definition (I) of limits, it reads

$$\boxed{\begin{aligned} &\lim_{n \to \infty} x_n = x_0 \\ &x_n \neq x_0 \text{ for all } n \end{aligned}} \quad \textit{always implies} \quad \boxed{\lim_{n \to \infty} f(x_n) = f(x_0).} \tag{5'}$$

Requirement (6) involves *more* sequences $\{x_n\}$; namely, those for which some $x_n = x_0$. Hence if (6) holds, it implies (5′) — and (5). On the other hand, suppose that (5′) holds. Pick any sequence $\{x_n\}$ with $\lim\limits_{n\to\infty} x_n = x_0$. Even if there are infinitely many x_n's $\neq x_0$, they form a subsequence — call it $\{x_{n_k}\}$. And we can conclude that $\lim\limits_{k\to\infty} f(x_{n_k}) = f(x_0)$ by (5′). The remaining outputs all equal $f(x_0)$. Even if there are infinitely many of these, the full sequence $\{f(x_n)\}$ must converge to $f(x_0)$ — by the "interlacing" property for limits (Property D in Chapter 9). Thus requirement (6) will be satisfied. See Fig. 11-10 for a sample sequence (and f continuous at $x_0 = 1$).

FIGURE 11-10

| inputs | $\frac{1}{2}$, | 1, | $\frac{3}{4}$, | 1, | $\frac{5}{6}$, | 1, | $\frac{7}{8}$, | ... | converge to 1 |

outputs $\Bigg\{$

$f(\tfrac{1}{2})$, $\qquad$ $f(\tfrac{3}{4})$, $\qquad$ $f(\tfrac{5}{6})$, $\qquad$ $f(\tfrac{7}{8})$, ... $\quad$ converge to $f(1)$, by requirement (5′)

$f(1)$, $\qquad$ $f(1)$, $\qquad$ $f(1)$, $\qquad$ ... $\quad$ also converge to $f(1)$ (a sequence of constants)

hence the interlaced output sequence

$$f(\tfrac{1}{2}), f(1), f(\tfrac{3}{4}), f(1), f(\tfrac{5}{6}), f(1), f(\tfrac{7}{8}), \ldots \quad \text{converges to } f(1).$$

I invite you to help complete the proof by including the cases where only finitely many x_n's appear in either the black or the green subsequence: do Problem 11 of Sec. 11.3.

For still another equivalent definition of "continuity," using "neighborhoods" $(f(x_0) - \epsilon, f(x_0) + \epsilon)$ and $(x_0 - \delta, x_0 + \delta)$, see Problem 10 of Sec. 11.3.

11.3 PROBLEMS ON LIMITS AND CONTINUITY

°1. For some of the following choices of f and x_0, sketch a graph of f and estimate what $\lim\limits_{x\to x_0} f(x) = A$ should be. Then check your estimate according to Definition I. The domain $\mathscr{D}$ in each case is the set of all real numbers, unless otherwise indicated.

(a) $f(x) = \begin{cases} |x| & \text{if } x \neq 0 \\ 1 & \text{if } x = 0 \end{cases}$; $x_0 = 0$.

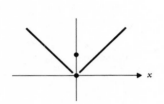

Sample reasoning: The graph looks as in the accompanying figure.

Estimate: $\lim\limits_{x\to x_0} f(x) = 0$.

Check: If $\lim\limits_{n\to\infty} x_n = 0$ and $x_n \neq 0$ for all n, then $\lim\limits_{n\to\infty} f(x_n) = \lim\limits_{n\to\infty} |x_n| = 0$, since $|x_n| = x_n b_n$ where $b_n = 1$ if $x_n > 0$ and $b_n = -1$ if $x_n < 0$. (The b_n are bounded. Recall Property f of Chapter 8.)

(b) $f(x) = 2x + 1$; $x_0 = 1$.

(c) $f(x) = \begin{cases} 2x+1 & \text{if } x \neq 1 \\ 4 & \text{if } x = 1 \end{cases}$; $x_0 = 1$.

(d) $f(x) = 2x + 1$ if $x \neq 1$; $x_0 = 1$. The domain $\mathscr{D}$ is the set of real numbers not equal to $+1$.

(e) $f(x) = 2x + 1$ if $-1 < x < 0$; $x_0 = 1$.

(Suggestion: What is $\mathscr{D}$? Is x_0 the limit of any sequence of inputs in $\mathscr{D}$?)

(f) $f(x) = (x-1)^2$; $x_0 = 1$.

(g) $f(x) = 3$; $x_0 = 1$.

(h) $f(x) = x^3 - 2x^2 + x - 5$; $x_0 = 2$.

(i) $f(x) = \dfrac{x+1}{x^2+1}$; $x_0 = -1$.

(j) $f(x) = \begin{cases} \dfrac{x+1}{x^2-1} & \text{if } x \neq \pm 1 \\ 1 & \text{if } x = \pm 1 \end{cases}$; $x_0 = 0$. How about $x_0 = 1$?

(k) $f(x) = (3x+5)x^2$; $x_0 = 1$, $x_0 = 0$.

(l) $f(x) = 2^x$; $x_0 = 1$, $x_0 = -1$, and $x_0 = 0$.

(m) $f(x) = g(x) - h(x)$ where

$$g(x) = \begin{cases} 0 & \text{if } x \neq 0 \\ 1 & \text{if } x = 1 \end{cases}, \text{ and } h(x) = \begin{cases} 3 & \text{if } x \geq 0 \\ 0 & \text{if } x < 0 \end{cases}; \text{ and } x_0 = 0$$

(n) $f(x) = \begin{cases} 1 & \text{if } x \leq 1 \\ |x| & \text{if } x > 1 \end{cases}$; and $x_0 = 1$.

°2. For some of the choices of f and x_0 in Problem 1, determine whether f is continuous at x_0.

Sample reasoning for (a): f is not continuous at $x_0 = 0$ because $\lim_{x \to 0} f(x) = 0 \neq 1 = f(0)$.

3. For each $x \geq 0$, let $f(x)$ equal the greatest integer not larger than x. This function is often denoted by $[x]$.
For example, $[2.1] = 2$, $[2.99] = 2$, $[2] = 2$, $[\frac{1}{2}] = 0$, $[1.4] = 1$.
Graph $[x]$. Is it continuous at $x_0 = \frac{1}{2}$? at $x_0 = 1$?

4. For each of the following choices of f and x_0, sketch a graph of f.
Use Definition I to show that no limit of $f(x)$ exists as x converges to x_0.

(a) $f(x) = \begin{cases} 1 & \text{if } x \geq 0 \\ -1 & \text{if } x < 0 \end{cases}$; $x_0 = 0$.

Sample: See the accompanying graph.

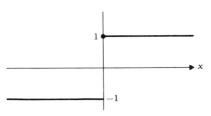

A $\lim_{x \to 0} f(x)$ can't exist because we can find at least two sequences $\{x_n \neq 0\}$ with $\lim_{n \to \infty} x_n = 0$ for which the corresponding output sequences $\{f(x_n)\}$ don't have a common limit. For example: if $a_n = 1/n$, then $\lim_{n \to \infty} a_n = 0$ and $\lim_{n \to \infty} f(1/n) = \lim_{n \to \infty} 1 = 1$. But for $b_n = -1/n$, $\lim_{n \to \infty} (-1/n) = 0$ whereas

$$\lim_{n \to \infty} f(-1/n) = \lim_{n \to \infty} (-1) = -1.$$

(b) $f(x) = \dfrac{1}{x^2}$ if $x \neq 0$; $x_0 = 0$.

Sample: See the accompanying graph.

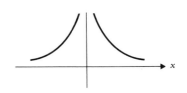

A $\lim_{x \to 0} f(x)$ can't exist because there doesn't exist a $\lim_{n \to \infty} f(x_n)$ for every subsequence $\{x_n \neq 0\}$ with $\lim_{n \to \infty} x_n = 0$. For example, let $x_n = 1/n$. Then the sequence $f(x_n) = 1/(1/n)^2 = n^2$ isn't even *bounded* and so can't have a limit (Property E of Chapter 9). (In particular, for any $A > 0$, if $n \geq \sqrt{A}$ then $f(x_n) > A$.)

(c) $f(x) = x + [x]$; $x_0 = 1$ ([] as in Problem 3).

(d) $f(x) = \dfrac{1}{x}$ if $x \neq 0$; $x_0 = 0$.

(e) $f(x) = \dfrac{1}{x^2 - x}$ if $x \neq 0, 1$; $x_0 = 0$, $x_0 = 1$.

(f) $f(x) = \begin{cases} 1 & \text{if } x \text{ is rational,} \\ 0 & \text{if } x \text{ is irrational.} \end{cases}$

(g) $f(x) = [x] - x^2$; $x_0 = 1$.

(h) $f(x) = \begin{cases} \dfrac{2}{x(x^2 - 1)} & \text{if } x \neq 0, 1, -1 \\ 2 & \text{if } x = 0, 1, -1 \end{cases}$; $x_0 = 0, 1, -1$.

5. Consider the set of points $\{P_n\}$ in the plane given by

$$P_n = \begin{cases} \left(\dfrac{1}{n}, 1\right) & \text{if } n \text{ is odd,} \\ \left(\dfrac{1}{n}, 0\right) & \text{if } n \text{ is even.} \end{cases}$$

We can obtain the graph of a function f by joining each P_n to P_{n+1} by a straight line segment.
(a) Sketch the graph of f. Does f have a limit at $x_0 = 0$?
(b) Let $g(x) = xf(x)$ for $x > 0$ where f is given in (a). Does g have a limit at $x_0 = 0$? If we define $g(0) = 0$, is g continuous at 0? (Suggestion: Notice that $0 \leq f(x) \leq 1$ for all $x > 0$.)

6. Consider the function f defined by

$$f(x) = \begin{cases} 1 & \text{if } x = 0 \\ x & \text{if } -1 \leq x < 0 \text{ or } 0 < x \leq 1 \\ x^2 & \text{if } x > 1 \text{ or } x < -1. \end{cases}$$

(a) Sketch a graph of f.
(b) By finding the limit of f at each of the following inputs x_0, tell whether f is continuous at x_0; $x_0 = -1, 0, 1, 2$.

7. Consider the function f defined by

$$f(x) = \begin{cases} \dfrac{1}{2}x^2 + \dfrac{1}{2} & \text{if } x > 1 \\ |x| & \text{if } -1 \leq x \leq 1 \\ \dfrac{1}{x+1} & \text{if } -2 \leq x < -1 \\ -x - 2 & \text{if } x < -2. \end{cases}$$

(a) Sketch a graph of f.
(b) Is f continuous at $-2, -1, 0, 1$?

*8. In Problem 12 of Section 9.6, I gave an alternate definition for $\lim_{n \to \infty} a_n = A$; namely: for any $\epsilon > 0$, there is an integer $N(\epsilon)$ such that

$$|a_n - A| < \epsilon \text{ for all } n \geq N(\epsilon).$$

Now for a function f and an input x_0, I invite you to consider a similarly phrased alternate definition for $\lim_{x \to x_0} f(x) = A$. Namely:

Definition I′ : *For any $\epsilon > 0$, there is a positive number δ_ϵ such that $|f(x) - A| < \epsilon$ for all inputs $x \neq x_0$ with distance $|x - x_0| < \delta_\epsilon$.*

(See the accompanying figure.)

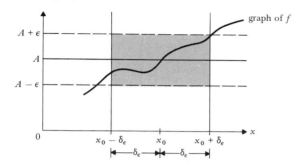

What the inequalities in this definition require is that, except perhaps at x_0, the graph of f must be between altitudes $A - \epsilon$ and $A + \epsilon$ above the interval $(x - \delta_\epsilon, x + \delta_\epsilon)$ — that is, inside the shaded rectangle.

(a) Show that if $\lim_{x \to x_0} f(x) = A$ according to Definition I′, then $\lim_{x \to x_0} f(x) = A$ according to Definition I in Sec. 11.1.

   Suggestion: Let $\{x_n \neq x_0\}$ be a sequence of inputs converging to x_0. To show that $\lim_{n \to \infty} f(x_n) = A$, pick any $\epsilon > 0$ and feed it into Definition I′—to get a δ_ϵ. Will there be an $N(\epsilon)$ such that $|x_n - x_0| < \delta_\epsilon$ for $n \geq N(\epsilon)$? If so, what about $|f(x_n) - A|$ for such n?

(b) Suppose $\lim_{x \to x_0} f(x) \neq A$ according to Definition I′. Show that there must be a "bad apple" value for ϵ—call it ϵ_0—such that no matter what positive δ one might choose (as candidate for δ_{ϵ_0}) there will be an input x_δ with $x_\delta \neq x_0$ and $|x_\delta - x_0| < \delta$ but $|f(x_\delta) - A| \geq \epsilon_0$. See the diagram.

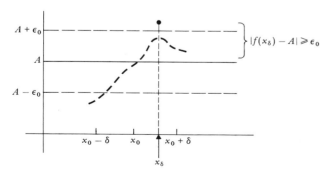

Choosing $\delta = 1, \frac{1}{2}, \frac{1}{3}, \ldots, 1/n, \ldots$, select a corresponding sequence $x_1, x_2, \ldots, x_n, \ldots$.

Show that $\{x_n\}$ converges to $\{x_0\}$, but $\{f(x_n)\}$ does not converge to A.

(c) If $\lim_{x \to x_0} f(x) \neq A$ according to Definition I', can $\lim_{x \to x_0} f(x) = A$ according to Definition I?

(d) Show that Definitions I and I' are equivalent.

9. Examples for the alternate Definition I' of $\lim_{x \to x_0} f(x) = A$ in Problem 8: For each of the following choices of f, x_0, A, and ϵ, find a corresponding δ_ϵ such that $|f(x) - A| < \epsilon$ for inputs $x \neq x_0$ with $|x - x_0| < \delta_\epsilon$. Graph f and shade the rectangle determined by $x_0 \pm \delta_\epsilon$ and $A \pm \epsilon$.

(a) $f(x) = 3x$; $x_0 = 1, A = 3$; $\qquad \epsilon = \frac{1}{2}, \epsilon = \frac{1}{10}$.

(b) $f(x) = x^2$; $x_0 = 1, A = 1$; $\qquad \epsilon = \frac{1}{2}, \epsilon = \frac{1}{10}$;

$\qquad\qquad\qquad x_0 = 2, A = 4$; $\qquad \epsilon = \frac{1}{2}, \epsilon = \frac{1}{10}$.

(c) $f(x) = \begin{cases} x^2 & \text{for } x \neq 1 \\ 2 & \text{for } x = 1 \end{cases}$; $x_0 = 1$; $A = 2$; $\epsilon = \frac{1}{2}, \frac{1}{10}$.

*10. By analogy with Definition I' for $\lim_{x \to x_0} f(x) = A$ in Problem 8, we might also formulate an alternate definition for continuity.

> ***Definition II'***. Call f *continuous at the input* x_0 if for every $\epsilon > 0$ there is a $\delta_\epsilon > 0$ such that $|f(x) - f(x_0)| < \epsilon$ for all inputs x with $|x - x_0| < \delta_\epsilon$.

(a) Sketch a graph to illustrate this definition.

(b) Show that this definition is equivalent to Definition II in Sec. 11.2 (and thus also to the continuity definition in Theorem B of Sec. 11.2). (Suggestion: Use the equivalence of Definitions I and I' shown in Problem 8, with $A = f(x_0)$; and eliminate the condition $x \neq x_0$.)

(c) Check the cases in Problem 9 for continuity of f at x_0 according to Definition II'.

*11. A few details are needed to complete the proof of Theorem B ("an alternate definition of continuity at x_0") in Sec. 11.2.

(a) Suppose $\{a_n\}$ is a sequence which converges to A and $b_1, b_2, \ldots, b_k$ are any k numbers. If we construct a new "expanded" sequence from the a_n's by inserting the b_i's at arbitrary points, show that this new sequence also converges to A. Possible candidates for the start of the expanded sequence are

$$a_1, a_2, b_1, b_2, b_3, a_3, b_4, a_4, a_5, \ldots$$

or

$$b_1, b_2, b_3, a_1, b_4, b_5, a_2, a_3, a_4, b_6, \ldots$$

(b) In proving Theorem B, I had a sequence $\{x_n\}$ which converged to x_0. I labeled the elements of the sequence which differed from x_0 by $\{x_{n_k}\}$. Show that if there are only finitely many such x_{n_k}'s or if there are only finitely many x_n's *not* in the subsequence $\{x_{n_k}\}$, then the result of (a) can be used to prove that $\lim\limits_{n\to\infty} f(x_n) = f(x_0)$.

12. In many applications, especially when the inputs correspond to different "times," we may be interested in the behavior of the outputs when the inputs become arbitrarily large. By analogy with the definition for $\lim\limits_{x\to x_0} f(x) = A$, let's define

$$\lim_{x\to\infty} f(x) = A.$$

If for every positively divergent sequence of inputs $\{x_n\}$, we'll have $\lim\limits_{n\to\infty} f(x_n) = A$.

For each of the following functions f, find a number A such that $\lim\limits_{n\to\infty} f(x) = A$.

(a) $f(x) = 1 - \dfrac{1}{x}$ for $x > 0$.

    Sample reasoning: Let $\{x_n\}$ be a positively divergent sequence. Then

$$\lim_{n\to\infty} f(x_n) = \lim_{n\to\infty} \left(1 - \frac{1}{x_n}\right) = 1 - \lim_{n\to\infty} \frac{1}{x_n} = 1 - 0 = 1.$$

    Hence $A = 1$.

(b) $f(x) = \dfrac{1}{x^2}$ for $x > 0$.

(c) $f(x) = \dfrac{x}{x^2+1}$.

(d) $f(x) = \dfrac{-x^2+1}{2x^2+3}$.

(e) $f(x) = \dfrac{x+1}{x}\left(3 - \dfrac{2}{x}\right)$ for $x > 0$.

(f) $f(x) = 4 - \dfrac{2}{x^3} + \dfrac{5}{x^2} - \dfrac{7}{x}$ for $x > 0$.

13. Formulate a definition for $\lim\limits_{x\to-\infty} f(x) = A$ in analogy to the definition in Problem 10.

*14. Does it make sense to try to define "f is continuous at infinity"?

11.4 A NEW LOOK AT DERIVATIVES

The recurrent theme in Chapter 7 was that of finding the *rate* at which one quantity — call it $f(x)$ — changes in response to changes in another quantity x. (The examples there were cost-vs.-lot size, position-vs.-time, velocity-vs.-time, and volume-vs.-altitude.) For a change in x from values q to r, $f(x)$ changes from $f(q)$ to $f(r)$; and I considered the so-called "average" rate of change of f over the interval $[q, r]$, namely, the difference ratio $[f(r)-f(q)]/(r-q)$. Then, to arrive at an "instantaneous" rate of change of f at a given input x_0, I picked pairs q_n, r_n flanking x_0, and converging to it, and tentatively defined the "derivative" as the limit

$$f'(x_0) = \lim_{n \to \infty} \frac{f(r_n) - f(q_n)}{r_n - q_n},$$ (1)

provided the limit exists.

Although a ratio $[f(r_n) - f(q_n)]/(r_n - q_n)$, $q_n < x < r_n$, may measure "average" rate of change in f as we step *past* x_0 (from q_n to r_n), note that the ratio doesn't involve the output $f(x_0)$ itself. Thus, under the tentative definition (1), the discontinuous function g in Fig. 11-11 can have the same (zero) slope at x_0 as the smooth function h in Fig. 11-12—although $g(x_0)$ is not a minimum output and $h(x_0)$ is.

FIGURE 11-11

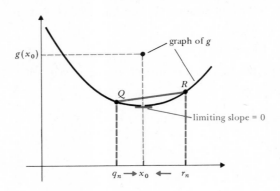

FIGURE 11-12

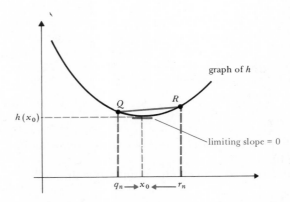

Here is one way to take an output $f(x_0)$ into account, while even simplifying the procedure for convergence toward the input x_0: Let's abandon flanking intervals $[q_n, r_n]$, and instead anchor one end point at x_0. Let's examine difference ratios of the form

$$R(x) = \frac{f(x) - f(x_0)}{x - x_0} \qquad \text{for all } x \neq x_0$$ (2)
$$\text{(x in the domain of f).}$$

If $x > x_0$, the ratio R represents the average rate of change of f over the interval $[x_0, x]$. The same is true for the interval $[x, x_0]$ when $x < x_0$,

since
$$\frac{f(x_0) - f(x)}{x_0 - x} = \frac{f(x) - f(x_0)}{x - x_0}.$$

How will such "average slopes" over intervals $[x_0, x]$ and $[x, x_0]$ compare with "average slopes" over flanking intervals $[q_n, r_n]$? See Figs. 11-13 and 11-14 for an indication—in the case of a function *continuous* at x_0.

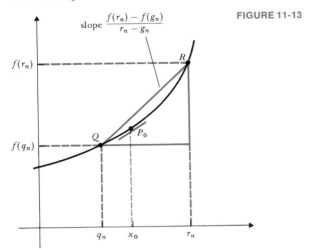

slope $\dfrac{f(r_n) - f(q_n)}{r_n - g_n}$

FIGURE 11-13

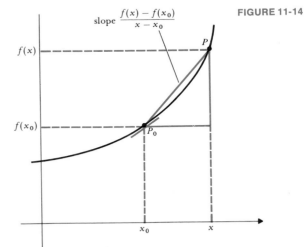

slope $\dfrac{f(x) - f(x_0)}{x - x_0}$

FIGURE 11-14

As we move x toward x_0 from the right or the left, or even in an oscillating fashion, shouldn't the slope of P_0P in Fig. 11-14 approach the same limiting value, $f'(x_0)$, as does the slope of QR in Fig. 11-13 when we squeeze the pair q_n, r_n toward x_0? The answer is yes. (Theorems A and B at the end of this section supply a proof.)

Why not then use the concept of limit for a function to provide a new definition of "derivative"?

Definitions III: Suppose that $f(x)$ is a function with domain $\mathcal{D}$ and that x_0 is an input in $\mathcal{D}$ such that $x_0 = \lim_{n \to \infty} x_n$ for some sequence of inputs $x_n \neq x_0$. Let's define the *difference ratio* function

$$R(x) = \frac{f(x) - f(x_0)}{x - x_0} \quad \text{for all } x \neq x_0, x \text{ in } \mathcal{D}.$$

If $\lim_{x \to x_0} R(x)$ exists, let's call its value the *derivative of f at x_0*, and denote it by the symbol $f'(x_0)$. We can say that f is *differentiable at x_0*.

This definition is a prime example of considering a limit for a function—here $R(x)$—as x converges to a value x_0 where the function is *not even defined.*

If limits for functions have properties similar to those for limits of sequences, then we should be able to calculate derivatives according to the new definition just as we did for the old.

EXAMPLE 1. $f(x) = x^k$ where k is a positive integer. Pick an input x_0. To find $f'(x_0)$, let's evaluate the difference ratio function $R(x)$ at $x \neq x_0$. Namely,

$$R(x) = \frac{x^k - x_0^k}{x - x_0} = \frac{(x - x_0)(x^{k-1} + x^{k-2}x_0 + \cdots + xx_0^{k-2} + x_0^{k-1})}{x - x_0}$$

$$= x^{k-1} + x^{k-2}x_0 + \cdots + xx_0^{k-2} + x_0^{k-1}. \qquad (3)$$

For any fixed integer i $(0 \leq i \leq k-1)$, we might expect that

$$\lim_{x \to x_0} x^{(k-1)-i}x_0^i = (x_0^i) \lim_{x \to x_0} x^{(k-1)-i} = (x_0^i) \left[\lim_{x \to x_0} x \right]^{(k-1)-i}$$

$$= x_0^i (x_0)^{(k-1)-i} = x_0^{k-1} \qquad (4)$$

(by properties on "scaling" and limits of products). Hence, we might expect that

$$f'(x_0) = \lim_{x \to x_0} R(x) = \lim_{x \to x_0} \left[x^{k-1} + x^{k-2}x_0 + \cdots + xx_0^{k-2} + x_0^{k-1} \right]$$

$$= \lim_{x \to x_0} x^{k-1} + \lim_{x \to x_0} x^{k-2}x_0 + \cdots + \lim_{x \to x_0} x_0^{k-1}$$

$$= x_0^{k-1} + x_0^{k-1} + \cdots + x_0^{k-1}$$

$$= k x_0^{k-1} \qquad (5)$$

by a further property, on limits of sums. We need no longer check against all sequences of inputs $\{x_n \neq x_0\}$ with $\lim_{n \to \infty} x_n = x_0$, as I did for similar calculations in Example 3 of Sec. 11.1, regarding polynomials.

I'll discuss properties of limits of functions in Sec. 11.7, and in later sections I'll check whether the "derivative"—à la Definition III above—really fulfills the promises of Chapter 7. (Must $f'(x_0) = 0$ always hold at peaks and valleys of a graph? Is the "neck-and-neck race argument" valid?)

If you are interested, either now or at a later reading, here are results which relate limits of the form $\lim_{x \to x_0} [f(x) - f(x_0)]/(x - x_0)$ with limits of the form

$$\lim_{n \to \infty} \frac{f(r_n) - f(q_n)}{r_n - q_n}, \, q_n < x_0 < r_n.$$

Theorem A: If there exists a limit

$$\lim_{x \to x_0} \frac{f(x) - f(x_0)}{x - x_0} = A, \qquad (6)$$

then for any sequence of inputs $\{q_n\}$ and $\{r_n\}$ converging to x_0, with $q_n < x_0 < r_n$, we must have

$$\lim_{n \to \infty} \frac{f(r_n) - f(q_n)}{r_n - q_n} = A. \qquad (7)$$

Moreover, in the other direction:

Theorem B: Suppose that f is continuous at x_0. If the limit (7) exists for all $\{q_n\}$ and $\{r_n\}$ sequences flanking and converging to x_0, then (6) must hold too — with the same limiting value A.

A proof of Theorem A: The hypothesis (6) says that

$$\lim_{n\to\infty} \frac{f(x_n)-f(x_0)}{x_n-x_0} = A \tag{8}$$

for any sequence $\{x_n\}$ converging to x_0 (with $x_n \neq x_0$ for all n). How can we make use of (8) to show that (7) holds? Let's manipulate the difference ratios $[f(r_n)-f(q_n)]/(r_n-q_n)$ into a helpful form. Given $q_n < x_0 < r_n$, write

$$\frac{f(r_n)-f(q_n)}{r_n-q_n} = \frac{[f(r_n)-f(x_0)]+[f(x_0)-f(q_n)]}{r_n-q_n}$$

$$= \frac{f(r_n)-f(x_0)}{r_n-q_n} + \frac{f(x_0)-f(q_n)}{r_n-q_n}$$

$$= \left(\frac{r_n-x_0}{r_n-q_n}\right)\left[\frac{f(r_n)-f(x_0)}{r_n-x_0}\right] + \left(\frac{x_0-q_n}{r_n-q_n}\right)\left[\frac{f(x_0)-f(q_n)}{x_0-q_n}\right]$$

$$= \underbrace{\left(\frac{r_n-x_0}{r_n-q_n}\right)}_{a_n}\left[\frac{f(r_n)-f(x_0)}{r_n-x_0}\right] + \underbrace{\left(\frac{x_0-q_n}{r_n-q_n}\right)}_{b_n}\left[\frac{f(q_n)-f(x_0)}{q_n-x_0}\right]. \tag{9}$$

Note that the quantities

$$a_n = \frac{r_n-x_0}{r_n-q_n} \quad \text{and} \quad b_n = \frac{x_0-q_n}{r_n-q_n}$$

are both ≥ 0 and add to 1. Check that the ratio $[f(r_n)-f(q_n)]/(r_n-q_n)$ must therefore lie somewhere between the ratios

$$\left[\frac{f(r_n)-f(x_0)}{r_n-x_0}\right] \quad \text{and} \quad \left[\frac{f(q_n)-f(x_0)}{q_n-x_0}\right] \tag{10}$$

on the coordinate line — say, as in Fig. 11-15. Now let n increase. The two outside ratios will approach the limit A — by hypothesis. Hence the ratio sandwiched in between must converge to A also. That is, (7) holds.

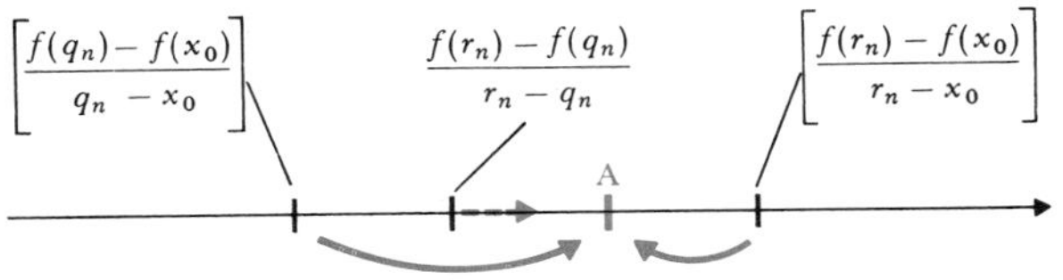

FIGURE 11-15

I invite you to supply further details for this proof, and also to prove the converse Theorem B, in doing Problems 5 and 6 of Sec. 11.6.

11.5 A ROGUES' GALLERY

Before listing general properties of function limits which do exist, let's see how limits can fail to exist. I've pictured two main types of failure in Figs. 11-16 through 11-19. Other examples may involve mixtures of these types.

FIGURE 11-16   (no limit)

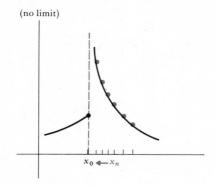

FIGURE 11-17   (no limit)

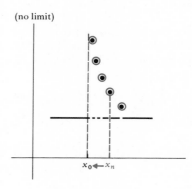

FIGURE 11-18   (no limit)

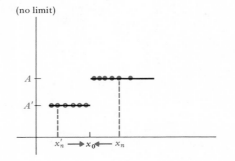

FIGURE 11-19   (no limit)

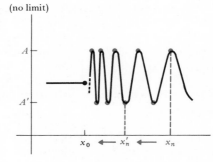

In Figs. 11-16 and 11-17, limits fail to exist at x_0 because, in each case, there is at least one sequence of inputs $\{x_n\}$ converging to x_0 for which the corresponding sequence of outputs $\{f(x_n)\}$ is *unbounded*—and thus can have no limit. In Figs. 11-18 and 11-19, limits fail to exist at x_0 because, in each case, there are (at least) two input sequences $\{x_n\}$ and $\{x'_n\}$ converging to x_0 (and distinct from x_0) for which the corresponding output sequences $\{f(x_n)\}$ and $\{f(x'_n)\}$ converge to *different* limits A and A'—so no common limit can exist for all output sequences.

I invite you, in doing Problem 4 of Sec. 11.6, to show that I've in fact pictured the only causes for nonexistence of a function limit: either the presence of an unbounded output sequence $\{f(x_n)\}$, or the presence of two sequences $\{f(x_n)\}$ and $\{f(x'_n)\}$ converging to different limits.

Note that all of the above examples of functions without limits at x_0 are also examples of functions which are *discontinuous* at x_0;

since to be continuous at x_0, a function f must at least have a $\lim\limits_{x \to x_0} f(x)$ existing — by definition. The other possibility for discontinuity at x_0 is that a $\lim\limits_{x \to x_0} f(x)$ does exist but fails to equal $f(x_0)$ — as in Fig. 11-20 (or in Figs. 11-7 and 11-9 earlier).

FIGURE 11-20

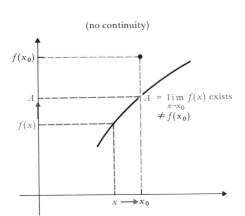

(no continuity)

$A = \lim\limits_{x \to x_0} f(x)$ exists $\neq f(x_0)$

FIGURE 11-21

(no derivative)

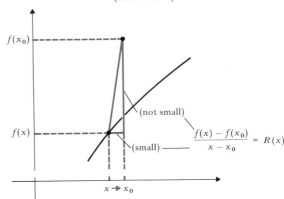

(not small)

$\dfrac{f(x) - f(x_0)}{x - x_0} = R(x)$

(small)

Now how can a derivative $f'(x_0)$ fail to exist? Check in any of the above figures that difference ratios calculated at a discontinuity input x_0 can become large without bound, and approach no limiting "slope" $f'(x_0)$. I've pictured this situation in Fig. 11-21 — a blowup of Fig. 11-20. At a discontinuity, the numerator of the difference ratio function $R(x) = [f(x) - f(x_0)]/(x - x_0)$ is kept from becoming small as we move x toward x_0, whereas the denominator does approach 0. Thus $R(x)$ has no limit "$f'(x_0)$" at x_0.

A final rogue: even when f is continuous it can fail to have a derivative $f'(x_0)$ if the graph of f has a "corner" at the point $(x_0, f(x_0))$, as in Fig. 11-22. Intuitively speaking, what definite "slope" value could we reasonably assign to the graph of f above $x_0 = 1$ in Fig. 11-22? More precisely, if we calculate

$$R(x) = \frac{f(x) - f(1)}{x - 1}$$

we get $R(x) = 1$ for $x < 1$ and $R(x) = 0$ for $x > 1$ (Fig. 11-23). Thus R itself can have no limit "$f'(1)$" at $x_0 = 1$.

(no derivative)   **FIGURE 11-22**

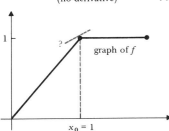

graph of f

$x_0 = 1$

FIGURE 11-23

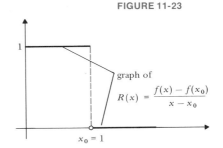

graph of

$R(x) = \dfrac{f(x) - f(x_0)}{x - x_0}$

$x_0 = 1$

11.6 PROBLEMS ON THE EXISTENCE OF LIMITS

°1. For each of the following functions f, I've tried to find $f'(x_0)$ by using properties of limits of functions which I might expect to be true. In each case, formulate what properties are necessary for the argument given.

(a) $f(x) = x^2 + x$.

Argument:

$$R(x) = \frac{f(x) - f(x_0)}{x - x_0} = \frac{(x^2 + x) - (x_0{}^2 + x_0)}{x - x_0} = \frac{x^2 - x_0{}^2 + x - x_0}{x - x_0}$$

$$= \frac{(x - x_0)[x + x_0 + 1]}{x - x_0} = x + x_0 + 1.$$

Then

$$f'(x_0) = \lim_{x \to x_0} R(x) = \lim_{x \to x_0} (x + x_0 + 1) = \lim_{x \to x_0} (x_0 + 1) + \lim_{x \to x_0} x$$

$$= x_0 + 1 + x_0 = 2x_0 + 1.$$

Sample reasoning: I would need a property that a limit of a sum is equal to the sum of limits of terms and a property that the limit of a constant (in this case, $x_0 + 1$) is that constant.

(b) $f(x) = \frac{1}{x}, \quad x > 0$.

Argument:

$$R(x) = \frac{(1/x) - (1/x_0)}{x - x_0} = \frac{x_0 - x}{xx_0(x - x_0)} = \frac{-1}{xx_0}.$$

Then

$$f'(x_0) = \lim_{x \to x_0} R(x) = \lim_{x \to x_0} \frac{-1}{xx_0} = -\frac{1}{x_0} \lim_{x \to x_0} \frac{1}{x} = -\frac{1}{x_0} \cdot \frac{1}{x_0} = -\frac{1}{x_0{}^2}.$$

(c) $f(x) = \sqrt{x}, x > 0$.

Argument:

$$R(x) = \frac{\sqrt{x} - \sqrt{x_0}}{x - x_0} = \frac{\sqrt{x} - \sqrt{x_0}}{x - x_0} \cdot \frac{\sqrt{x} + \sqrt{x_0}}{\sqrt{x} + \sqrt{x_0}}$$

$$= \frac{x - x_0}{(x - x_0)(\sqrt{x} + \sqrt{x_0})} = \frac{1}{\sqrt{x} + \sqrt{x_0}}.$$

Now

$$\lim_{x \to x_0} (\sqrt{x} + \sqrt{x_0}) = \lim_{x \to x_0} \sqrt{x} + \lim_{x \to x_0} \sqrt{x_0} = \sqrt{x_0} + \sqrt{x_0} = 2\sqrt{x_0}.$$

So

$$f'(x_0) = \lim_{x \to x_0} \frac{1}{\sqrt{x} + \sqrt{x_0}} = \lim_{x \to x_0} \frac{1}{\sqrt{x} + \sqrt{x_0}} = \frac{1}{2\sqrt{x_0}}.$$

(d) $f(x) = (x + 1)(x^2 - 2)$.

Argument:

$$R(x) = \frac{(x+1)(x^2-2) - (x_0+1)(x_0^2-2)}{x-x_0}$$

$$= \frac{(x+1)(x^2-2) - (x+1)(x_0^2-2) + (x+1)(x_0^2-2) - (x_0+1)(x_0^2-2)}{x-x_0}$$

$$= \frac{(x+1)[(x^2-2) - (x_0^2-2)]}{x-x_0}$$

$$+ \frac{[(x+1) - (x_0+1)](x_0^2-2)}{x-x_0}$$

$$= (x+1)(x+x_0) + (x_0^2-2).$$

Hence

$$f'(x_0) = \lim_{x \to x_0} [(x+1)(x+x_0) + x_0^2 - 2] = \lim_{x \to x_0} (x+1)(x+x_0)$$

$$+ \lim_{x \to x_0} (x_0^2 - 2)$$

$$= \lim_{x \to x_0} (x+1) \lim_{x \to x_0} (x+x_0) + \lim_{x \to x_0} (x_0^2 - 2)$$

$$= (x_0+1)(x_0+x_0) + (x_0^2-2) = (x_0+1)(2x_0) + (x_0^2-2).$$

2. Let f be defined by

$$f(x) = \begin{cases} 1 \text{ if } x \neq 0 \\ 0 \text{ if } x = 0 \end{cases},$$

and let $x_0 = 0$.
   (a) Show that $\lim_{n \to \infty} [f(r_n) - f(q_n)]/(r_n - q_n) = 0$ for all $\{q_n\}$ and $\{r_n\}$ sequences flanking and converging to x_0.
   (b) Show that $\lim_{x \to x_0} [f(x) - f(x_0)]/(x - x_0)$ does not exist for any sequence $\{x_n\}$, $x_n \neq x_0$, which converges to x_0.
   (c) Does this contradict Theorem B of Sec. 11.4? Why not?
3. Give examples of the following:
   (a) a function which has a limit at each real number;
   (b) a function which fails to have a limit at only finitely many numbers;
   (c) a function which fails to have a limit at infinitely many numbers;
   (d) a function which has a limit at each number, but fails to be continuous at only finitely many numbers;
   (e) a function which has a limit at each number, but fails to be continuous at infinitely many numbers;
   (f) a function which has a derivative at each real number;
   (g) a function which is continuous at each number, but which fails to have a derivative for only finitely many numbers;
   (h) a function which is continuous at each number, but fails to have a derivative for infinitely many numbers.
*4. In Sec. 11.5, I claimed that there are only two causes for non-existence of a function limit, $\lim_{x \to x_0} f(x)$: either (i) there is a sequence of inputs $\{x_n \neq x_0\}$ converging to x_0 for which the output

sequence $\{f(x_n)\}$ is *unbounded*; or (ii) there are two sequences $\{x_n \neq x_0\}$ and $\{x'_n \neq x_0\}$ converging to x_0 for which $\{f(x_n)\}$ and $\{f(x'_n)\}$ converge to *different* limits. To see that there are no other causes, suppose that (i) and (ii) are impossible for a given function f and input x_0. Via the following steps, show that there must therefore exist a number A such that $\lim_{n \to \infty} f(x_n) = A$ for any sequence $\{x_n \neq x_0\}$ with $\lim_{n \to \infty} x_n = x_0$.

(a) To get at a candidate for "A," pick a particular sequence $\{a_n \neq x_0\}$ with $\lim_{n \to \infty} a_n = x_0$. Show that, because $\{f(a_n)\}$ is bounded, some subsequence of its outputs—call it $\{f(a_{n_k})\}$ must converge to a limit—call it A. (Recall Theorem B of Sec. 10.4 on convergent subsequences.)

(b) Now pick any other sequence $\{x_n \neq x_0\}$ with $\lim_{n \to \infty} x_n = x_0$. Show that if $\lim_{n \to \infty} f(x_n) \neq A$, then for some subsequence, and some $\epsilon > 0$, either $f(x_{n_k}) \leq A - \epsilon$ or $f(x_{n_k}) \geq A + \epsilon$, for all k. (Recall Problem 7 of Sec. 9.8.)

(c) By repeating the argument in (a) show that some further subsequence of the $\{f(x_{n_k})\}$ in (b) must converge to a limit $B \neq A$. This contradicts the supposition that (ii) can't be true.

5. (a) Let x and y be real numbers with $x \leq y$. Suppose a and b are nonnegative real numbers and $a + b = 1$. Show that

$$x \leq ax + by \leq y.$$

(Suggestion: $x = (a + b)x$ and $bx \leq by$.)

*(b) Use (a) to verify that, in the proof of Theorem A in Sec. 11.4, the ratio

$$\frac{f(r_n) - f(q_n)}{r_n - q_n}$$

lies between the ratios

$$\frac{f(r_n) - f(x_0)}{r_n - x_0} \quad \text{and} \quad \frac{f(q_n) - f(x_0)}{q_n - x_0}.$$

**6. Prove Theorem B of Sec. 11.4: if f is continuous at x_0 and if

$$\lim_{n \to \infty} \frac{f(r_n) - f(q_n)}{r_n - q_n} = A$$

for all $\{q_n\}$ and $\{r_n\}$ sequences flanking and converging to x_0, then $\lim_{n \to \infty} [f(x_n) - f(x_0)]/(x_n - x_0) = A$ for all sequences $\{x_n \neq x_0\}$ converging to x_0.

Suggestions:

(a) Suppose $x_n > x_0$ for all n, with $\lim_{n \to \infty} x_n = x_0$. Thus the x_n's play the role of r_n's. *Choose* a sequence of inputs $q_n < x_0$ converging to x_0 much faster than the x_n's do—so that

$$\lim_{n \to \infty} \frac{q_n - x_0}{x_n - x_0} = 0 \quad \text{and} \quad \lim_{n \to \infty} \frac{f(q_n) - f(x_0)}{x_n - x_0} = 0.$$

Then write

$$\frac{f(x_n) - f(x_0)}{x_n - x_0} = \left[1 - \frac{q_n - x_0}{x_n - x_0}\right]\frac{f(x_n) - f(q_n)}{x_n - q_n} + \left[\frac{f(q_n) - f(x_0)}{x_n - x_0}\right]$$

and take limits.

(b) Proceed similarly if $x_n < x_0$ for all n. Then (c) "interlace" sequences to get the general case.

11.7   PROPERTIES OF LIMITS OF FUNCTIONS

Since I defined the concept "$\lim_{x \to x_0} f(x)$" in terms of limits of sequences, you might expect that many properties of sequence limits will translate into corresponding properties for function limits. In particular, we might look for general results which will relate limits of complicated functions to limits of their component parts.

Here is a partial list of properties, all flowing from those in Chapter 9. (I've labeled them with corresponding letters $\hat{A}$, $\hat{B}$, etc.)

*Property $\hat{A}$ ("**uniqueness**"): A function can't have more than one limit at a given input.* That is, if $\lim_{x \to x_0} f(x) = A$ and $\lim_{x \to x_0} f(x) = B$, then $A = B$.

*Property $\hat{B}$ (on "**restricting the domain**"): If $\lim_{x \to x_0} f(x) = A$, and if we restrict the domain $\mathcal{D}$ of f to a smaller set $\mathcal{D}_0$, then we shall still have* $\lim_{x \to x_0} f(x) = A$ (provided some subsequence $\{x_n \neq x_0\}$ of inputs in $\mathcal{D}_0$ still converges to x_0).

*Property $\hat{C}$ (**limits are determined "locally"**): If $\lim_{x \to x_0} f(x) = A$, and if $g(x)$ differs from $f(x)$ only outside some interval $[x_0 - \delta, x_0 + \delta]$, then* $\lim_{x \to x_0} g(x) = A$.

*Property $\hat{D}$ (on "**interlacing**"): Suppose that $f(x)$ is defined on an interval (a, x_0) and $g(x)$ is defined on an interval (x_0, b); and that* $\lim_{x \to x_0} f(x) = A$ and $\lim_{x \to x_0} g(x) = A$. *If we have*

$$h(x) = \begin{cases} f(x) & \text{for } a < x < x_0 \\ g(x) & \text{for } x_0 < x < b, \end{cases}$$

then $\lim_{x \to x_0} h(x) = A$ *also.*

*Property $\hat{G}$ (on "**constant functions**"): If $f(x) = c$ for all x in some interval (a, b) then* $\lim_{x \to x_0} f(x) = c$ *at any x_0 in (a, b).*

*Property $\hat{H}$ (on "**scaling**"): If $\lim_{x \to x_0} f(x) = A$ and if c is a constant, then* $\lim_{x \to x_0} cf(x) = cA$.

*Property $\hat{I}$ (on "**sums**"): If f and g have a common domain, and* $\lim_{x \to x_0} f(x) = A$ *and* $\lim_{x \to x_0} g(x) = B$, *then* $\lim_{x \to x_0} [f(x) + g(x)] = A + B$. *Also,* $\lim_{x \to x_0} [f(x) - g(x)] = A - B$.

*Property $\hat{J}$ (on "**products**"): If f and g have a common domain, and* $\lim_{x \to x_0} f(x) = A$ *and* $\lim_{x \to x_0} g(x) = B$, *then* $\lim_{x \to x_0} f(x)g(x) = AB$.

*Property $\hat{L}$ (on "**quotients**"): If f and g have a common domain where g never $= 0$, and if* $\lim_{x \to x_0} f(x) = A$ *and* $\lim_{x \to x_0} g(x) = B \neq 0$, *then* $\lim_{x \to x_0} f(x)/g(x) = A/B$.

Property $\hat{M}$ (on "rational powers"): If $f(x) = x^r$ for $x \geq 0$, where r is a positive rational number, then $\lim_{x \to x_0} f(x) = x_0{}^r$ at any $x_0 \geq 0$.

Property $\hat{O}$ (on "comparison"): If $f(x) \leq g(x)$ for all x in a common domain, and if $\lim_{x \to x_0} f(x) = A$ and $\lim_{x \to x_0} g(x) = B$, then $A \leq B$.

Property $\hat{P}$ (on "squeezing"): If $f(x) \leq g(x) \leq h(x)$ for all x in a common domain, and if $\lim_{x \to x_0} f(x) = A$ and $\lim_{x \to x_0} h(x) = A$, then $\lim_{x \to x_0} g(x) = A$.

EXAMPLE 1. If the above properties are true, we can easily calculate limits for a function whose rule is given by different formulas in different portions of its domain. Suppose

$$f(x) = \begin{cases} x^2 + 1 & \text{for} & 0 \leq x \leq 1 \\ 3 - x & \text{for} & 1 < x \leq 2. \end{cases}$$

To evaluate $\lim_{x \to \frac{1}{2}} f(x)$ we need only consider f on the restricted domain $0 \leq x \leq 1$, where we can use the formula $f(x) = x^2 + 1$—by Property $\hat{B}$ on "restricting the domain." Hence

$$\lim_{x \to \frac{1}{2}} f(x) = \lim_{x \to \frac{1}{2}} (x^2 + 1) = [\lim_{x \to \frac{1}{2}} x]^2 + \lim_{x \to \frac{1}{2}} 1 = \left(\frac{1}{2}\right)^2 + 1 = \frac{5}{4}, \tag{1}$$

by Properties $\hat{G}$, $\hat{J}$, and $\hat{I}$ on limits of constants, of products and of sums.

Now how about $\lim_{x \to 1} f(x)$? We can restrict f to separate domains $(0, 1)$ and $(1, 2)$. Looking at $(0, 1)$ only, we have

$$\lim_{x \to 1} f(x) = \lim_{x \to 1} (x^2 + 1) = 1^2 + 1 = 2. \tag{2}$$

Looking at $(1, 2)$ only, we have

$$\lim_{x \to 2} f(x) = \lim_{x \to 2} (3 - x) = 3 - 1 = 2. \tag{3}$$

Hence for the original function f defined on $[0, 2]$ we can claim that $\lim_{x \to 1} f(x) = 2$, by the "interlacing" property of limits, $\hat{D}$.

EXAMPLE 2: The *absolute value function*

$$|x| = \begin{cases} x & \text{for } x \geq 0 \\ -x & \text{for } x \leq 0. \end{cases} \tag{4}$$

As in Example 1 we can restrict the domain to show that

for $x_0 > 0$: $\lim_{x \to x_0} |x| = \lim_{x \to x_0} x = x_0 = |x_0|$

and (5)

for $x_0 < 0$: $\lim_{x \to x_0} |x| = \lim_{x \to x_0} (-x) = -\lim_{x \to x_0} x = -x_0 = |x_0|$.

Note also that

on $0 < x < \infty$: $\lim_{x \to 0} |x| = \lim_{x \to 0} x = 0$

and (6)

on $-\infty < x < 0$: $\lim_{x \to 0} |x| = \lim_{x \to 0} (-x) = 0$.

Hence by Property $\hat{D}$ on "interlacing," we have $\lim_{x \to 0} |x| = 0 = |0|$.

In summary,

$$\lim_{x \to x_0} |x| = |x_0| \qquad \text{at any real } x_0. \tag{7}$$

EXAMPLE 3. Consider a ratio of polynomials $f(x) = P(x)/Q(x)$ defined for some interval $[a, b]$ where Q is never zero. For any x_0 in $[a, b]$, we can claim that

$$\lim_{x \to x_0} f(x) = \frac{\lim_{x \to x_0} P(x)}{\lim_{x \to x_0} Q(x)} = \frac{P(x_0)}{Q(x_0)} = f(x_0), \tag{8}$$

provided Property $\hat{L}$ on quotients is always valid.

EXAMPLE 4. If the above properties hold true, what can we say about the $\lim_{x \to 2} [(2x^3 + 3)/x^2 + 4)]^{1/3}$? Here we have a *composition* of functions, $h(x) = g(f(x))$, where

$$f(x) = \frac{2x^3 + 3}{x^2 + 4} \quad \text{and} \quad g(y) = y^{1/3}. \tag{9}$$
$$\text{(for all } x) \qquad\qquad \text{(for all } y)$$

By the result of Example 3, we can conclude that

$$\lim_{x \to 2} f(x) = \lim_{x \to 2} \frac{2x^3 + 3}{x^2 + 4} = f(2) = \frac{2 \cdot 2^3 + 3}{2^2 + 4} = \frac{19}{8}. \tag{10}$$

Moreover,

$$\lim_{y \to 19/8} g(y) = \lim_{y \to 19/8} y^{1/3} = \left(\frac{19}{8}\right)^{1/3}, \tag{11}$$

by Property $\hat{M}$ on rational powers. Can we conclude that

$$\lim_{x \to 2} g(f(x)) = \lim_{y \to 19/8} g(y) = \left(\frac{19}{8}\right)^{1/3} ? \tag{12}$$

In this case: yes — as we could see by going back to input sequences $\{x_n \neq 2\}$ with $\lim_{n \to \infty} x_n = 2$, and checking corresponding output sequences $\{gf(x_n)\}$. But is it *always* true for functions f and g that if $\lim_{x \to x_0} f(x) = A$ and $\lim_{y \to A} g(y) = B$, then $\lim_{x \to x_0} g(f(x)) = B$? Look at Fig. 11-24 to see how trouble can arise.

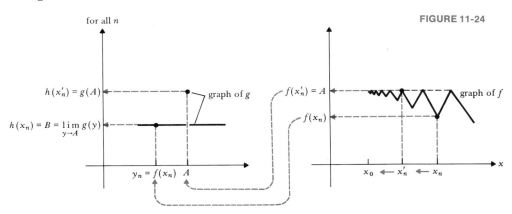

FIGURE 11-24

In Fig. 11-24, I could pick different sequences $\{x_n\}$ and $\{x_n'\}$ converging to x_0 whose corresponding outputs

$$h(x_n) = g(f(x_n)) = B$$

and

$$h(x_n') = g(f(x_n')) = g(A)$$

would never have a common limit. Why? Because the $\lim_{y \to A} g(y) = B$ doesn't coincide with $g(A)$: g is *discontinuous* at A.

Excluding such possibilities, we might conjecture:

Property $\hat{Q}$ (on "composition"): If $\lim_{x \to x_0} f(x) = A$, and if g is defined on the range of f and is continuous at A, then

$$\lim_{x \to x_0} g(f(x)) = g(A). \tag{13}$$

I'll argue in favor of Property $\hat{Q}$ in the next section. But first, another, very particular, kind of composition:

EXAMPLE 5. Since $\lim_{x \to 3} x^2 = 9$, shouldn't $\lim_{t \to 0} (3+t)^2 = 9$? It does. More generally,

Property $\hat{R}$ (on "shifting input variables"): Suppose that g is a function, with domain $\mathscr{D}$, such that $\lim_{y \to y_0} g(y) = B$. If we let $h(x) = g(y_0 + x)$ (for all x such that $y = y_0 + x$ is an input in $\mathscr{D}$), then $\lim_{x \to 0} h(x) = B$.

*11.8 DO THE PROPERTIES HOLD TRUE?

Here are three sample proofs to show how the above properties follow from those for limits of sequences (in Chapter 9).

A proof of Property $\hat{I}$ (on "sums"): If $\lim_{x \to x_0} f(x) = A$ and $\lim_{x \to x_0} g(x) = B$, then $\lim_{x \to x_0} [f(x) + g(x)] = A + B$.

In Fig. 11-25, I've indicated what the hypotheses and the conclusion mean in terms of input and output sequences.

FIGURE 11-25

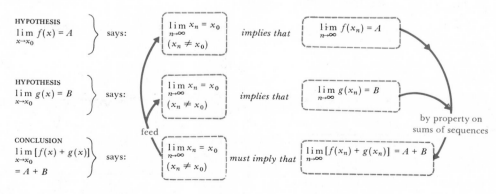

Given any input sequence $\{x_n \neq x_0\}$ with $\lim_{n\to\infty} x_n = x_0$, we can feed the $\{x_n\}$ separately into the f function and into the g function, to get output sequences $\{f(x_n)\}$ and $\{g(x_n)\}$. The hypotheses say that

$$\lim_{n\to\infty} f(x_n) = A \quad \text{and} \quad \lim_{n\to\infty} g(x_n) = B.$$

By courtesy of Property I on limits of sums of sequences (Chapter 9), we can immediately say that

$$\lim_{n\to\infty} [f(x_n) + g(x_n)] = A + B$$

—which is all that's needed for the conclusion.   End of the proof.

A proof of Property $\hat{Q}$ (on "composition"): if $\lim_{x\to x_0} f(x) = A$ and g is defined on the range of f and is continuous at A, then $\lim_{x\to x_0} g(f(x)) = g(A)$.

If we use the characterization of continuity via sequences (Theorem B of Sec. 11.2), we can write the meaning of the hypotheses and the conclusion as in Fig. 11-26. Follow the green lines for a proof.

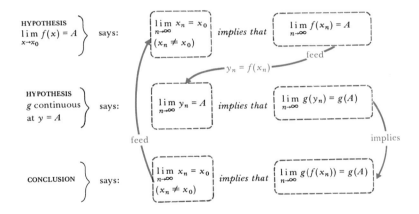

FIGURE 11-26

A proof of Property $\hat{C}$ (limits are determined "locally"): If $\lim_{x\to x_0} f(x) = A$ and if $g(x)$ differs from $f(x)$ only outside some interval $[x_0 - \delta, x_0 + \delta]$, then $\lim_{x\to x_0} g(x) = A$. (See Fig. 11-27.)

For any sequence $\{x_n\}$ with $\lim_{n\to\infty} x_n = x_0$, note that the x_n's must lie in the interval $[x_0 - \delta, x_0 + \delta]$ for all $n \geqslant$ some N. Otherwise there would be a subsequence—call it $\{x_{n_k}\}$—excluded from the interval, with distances $|x_{n_k} - x_0|$ all greater than δ. This subsequence couldn't converge to x_0—which contradicts $\lim_{n\to\infty} x_n = x_0$ (by Property B on subsequences, in Chapter 9). But once x_n lies in $[x_0 - \delta, x_0 + \delta]$ we have $f(x_n) = g(x_n)$, by hypothesis.

I've indicated the remaining hypothesis and the conclusion of Property $\hat{C}$ in Fig. 11-28.

FIGURE 11-27

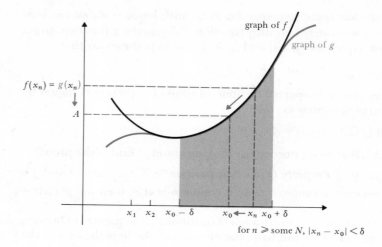

for $n \geqslant$ some N, $|x_n - x_0| < \delta$

FIGURE 11-28

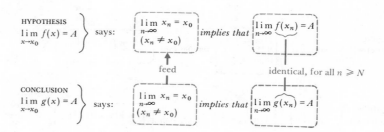

Now, limits of sequences are determined only by their *tails*— Property C of Chapter 9. So we need examine the outputs in Fig. 11-28 only for large n, where $f(x_n) = g(x_n)$. If we feed any input sequence $\{x_n \neq x_0\}$ (with $\lim_{n \to \infty} x_n = x_0$) along the green line, we can conclude that $\lim_{n \to \infty} g(x_n) = A$.   End of the proof.

I invite you to try your own hand at validating others of the above properties, in doing Problems 3–13 of the next section.

11.9 PROBLEMS ON LIMITS AND THEIR PROPERTIES

1. Use the properties of limits of functions to determine whether $\lim_{x \to x_0} f(x)$ exists or not for each of the following choices of f and x_0.

(a) $f(x) = \begin{cases} |x|^3 & \text{if } x \neq 0 \\ 1 & \text{if } x = 0 \end{cases}$; $x_0 = 0$.

Sample reasoning: Let $h(x) = x^3$ and $g(x) = (-x)^3$. Then

$$f(x) = \begin{cases} h(x) & \text{for } x > 0 \\ g(x) & \text{for } x < 0 \\ 1 & \text{for } x = 0. \end{cases}$$

Now $\lim_{x \to 0} h(x) = \lim_{x \to 0} x^3 = 0^3 = 0$ by Property $\hat{M}$ and $\lim_{x \to 0} g(x) =$
$\lim_{x \to 0} (-x)^3 = \lim_{x \to 0} -(x)^3 = -\lim_{x \to 0} x^3 = 0$ by Properties $\hat{G}$ and $\hat{M}$.
Thus, by Property $\hat{D}$, $\lim_{x \to 0} f(x) = 0$.

Note: Alternately we can use Property $\hat{Q}$ and the fact that $\lim_{x \to 0} |x| = 0$.

(b) $f(x) = \dfrac{x^2 + 1}{x}$ for $x \neq 0$; $x_0 = 0$.

Sample reasoning: The $\lim_{x \to 0} f(x)$ can't exist. A direct way to get the answer is to pick $x_n = 1/n$ and get $f(x_n) = n + (1/n^2)$, a sequence which can't converge to any finite number A. Here is an alternate method: write $xf(x) = x^2 + 1$. If $\lim_{x \to 0} f(x) = A$, then we would have the contradiction $0 = 0A = \lim_{x \to 0} xf(x) = \lim_{x \to 0} (x^2 + 1) = 0 + 1 = 1$, by Properties $\hat{I}$ and $\hat{J}$.

(c) $f(x) = \dfrac{x^2 + 3}{x^2 - x - 6}$; $x_0 = 0$.   (d) $f(x) = \dfrac{x^2 - 1}{x - 1}$; $x_0 = 1$.

(e) $f(x) = \dfrac{x^2}{x - 1}$; $x_0 = 1$.   (f) $f(x) = \dfrac{x}{|x|}$ for $x \neq 0$; $x_0 = 0$.

(g) $f(x) = \dfrac{x}{|x|^2}$ for $x \neq 0$; $x_0 = 0$.

(h) $f(x) = x \sin \dfrac{1}{x}$; $x_0 = 0$.

(i) $f(x) = \begin{cases} 1 & \text{if } x \text{ is rational} \\ 0 & \text{if } x \text{ is irrational} \end{cases}$; $x_0 = \frac{1}{2}$.

(j) $f(x) = \dfrac{3^x}{1 + x^2}$; $x_0 = -1$.

(k) $f(x) = \begin{cases} x^3 + 1 & \text{for } x < 0 \\ \dfrac{x^5 + 4x^3 + 1}{x^3 - x^2 + 1} & \text{for } x > 0 \end{cases}$; $x_0 = 0$.

2. For each f in Problem 1, is it possible to define $f(x_0)$ so that f is continuous at x_0?

In Problems 3–14, record the hypothesis and the conclusion, and, if necessary, rewrite them in terms of sequences, as I did in Figs. 11-25–11-28. Then show how to pass from the one to the other.

*3. Try to prove Property $\hat{A}$ ("uniqueness").
*4. Try to prove Property $\hat{B}$ (on "restricting the domain").
*5. Try to prove Property $\hat{D}$ (on "interlacing").
*6. Try to prove Property $\hat{G}$ (on "constant functions").
*7. Try to prove Property $\hat{H}$ (on "scaling").
*8. Try to prove Property $\hat{J}$ (on "products").
*9. Try to prove Property $\hat{L}$ (on "quotients").
*10. Try to prove Property $\hat{M}$ (on "rational powers").
*11. Try to prove Property $\hat{O}$ (on "comparison").
*12. Try to prove Property $\hat{P}$ (on "squeezing").

*13. Try to prove Property $\hat{R}$ (on "shifting input variables").

*14. Suppose g is *bounded* on its domain $\mathscr{D}$ (that is, there is a constant M such that $|g(x)| \leqslant M$ for all x in $\mathscr{D}$). Suppose also that f has the same domain $\mathscr{D}$, that x_0 is in $\mathscr{D}$, and that $\lim_{x \to x_0} f(x) = 0$. Show that $\lim_{x \to x_0} f(x)g(x) = 0$.

11.10 A CATALOG OF CONTINUOUS FUNCTIONS

We already have results which certify various specific functions as being continuous:

Theorem A:
  (i) Any ratio of polynomials $P(x)/Q(x)$ is continuous on any domain where $Q(x)$ never equals zero;
  (ii) any function of the form $f(x) = x^r$, where r is a positive rational, is continuous at any $x_0 \geqslant 0$; and
  (iii) the absolute value function $|x|$ is continuous everywhere.

(For (i), recall Example 3 of Sec. 11.7; for (ii) recall Property $\hat{M}$ on rational powers; and for (iii) see Example 2 of Sec. 11.7.)

Shouldn't we be able to recognize more complicated functions as being continuous if they are built up from simpler continuous functions by scaling, addition, multiplication, division, and composition? We know how these operations relate to limits—namely, Properties $\hat{H}, \hat{I}, \hat{J}, \hat{L}$, and $\hat{Q}$. Here is a list of results which you might expect:

Theorem B (on "scaling"): If c is a constant and the function f is continuous (or continuous at x_0), then $cf(x)$ is also.

Theorem C (on "sums and products"): If f and g have a common domain and are continuous (or continuous at x_0), then $f + g$, $f - g$, and fg are also.

Theorem D (on "quotients"): If f and g have a common domain where g is never zero, and if f and g are continuous (or continuous at x_0), then so is f/g.

Theorem E (on "composition"): If f is continuous, with range $\mathscr{R}$, and if g is continuous on $\mathscr{R}$, then $h(x) = g(f(x))$ is continuous.

EXAMPLE 1: *Negative rational powers.* Suppose $f(x) = x^{-r}$ for $x > 0$, where r is a positive rational. Then f is continuous at any $x_0 > 0$—provided Theorem D on quotients is true—since $f(x) = 1/x^r$, and x^r is positive and continuous for $x > 0$ (Theorem A, part (ii)).

EXAMPLE 2. $h(x) = x^{1/m}$ for all real x, where m is an *odd* positive integer. Check that for $x < 0$,

$$h(x) = -|x|^{1/m}, \tag{1}$$

a composition wherein the continuous function $|x|$, with nonnegative outputs, is fed into the function $y^{1/m}$, which is continuous at nonnegative inputs (Theorem A, part (ii)). If Theorems E (on composition) and B (on scaling) are true, then h must be continuous at all $x_0 < 0$.

We already knew from Theorem A that h was continuous at $x_0 > 0$. I invite you to check that h is continuous at $x_0 = 0$, by using the "interlacing" property of limits ($\hat{D}$ in Sec. 11.7): do Problem 6 of Sec. 11.11. Thus h is continuous everywhere.

EXAMPLE 3. $h(x) = [5x - (x^3 + 7)^{1/3}]/\sqrt{1 - x^2}$ is continuous at all x_0 with $|x_0| < 1$, provided the above results are true; because h is built up from polynomials by composition, subtraction, and division. Note that in the numerator the composition is definable and continuous for all real x, since $y^{1/3}$ is continuous at all real y (Example 2). But in the denominator, the composition $\sqrt{1 - x^2}$ is definable (and continuous) only for $|x| \leq 1$. We must restrict $|x| \neq 1$, otherwise $\sqrt{1 - x^2} = 0$ and the quotient makes no sense.

Why are the theorems true? Here is a sample bit of reasoning:

A proof of part of Theorem C: If f and g are continuous at x_0, then $f + g$ is also.

The hypothesis says: $\lim_{x \to x_0} f(x) = f(x_0)$ and $\lim_{x \to x_0} g(x) = g(x_0)$. We have to consider the sum function $h(x) = f(x) + g(x)$, which has the particular output $h(x_0) = f(x_0) + g(x_0)$; and we must CONCLUDE that

$$\lim_{x \to x_0} h(x) = h(x_0). \tag{2}$$

By Property $\hat{I}$ on the limits of sums (plus the hypothesis) we have

$$\lim_{x \to x_0} h(x) = \lim_{x \to x_0} [f(x) + g(x)] = \lim_{x \to x_0} f(x) + \lim_{x \to x_0} g(x)$$
$$= f(x_0) + g(x_0) = h(x_0). \tag{3}$$

End of the proof.

I invite you to supply similar reasoning for the remaining results of Theorems B–E in doing Problems 1–4 of the next section.

11.11 MORE PROBLEMS ON CONTINUITY

1. Try to prove Theorem B of Sec. 11.10, on "scaling."
2. Show that if f and g have a common domain and are continuous (or continuous at x_0), then $f - g$ and fg are also.
3. Try to prove Theorem D of Sec. 11.10, on "quotients."
4. Try to prove Theorem E of Sec. 11.10, on "composition."
5. Show that if f is continuous on the domain $\mathscr{D}$ and $\mathscr{D}_0$ is a smaller set, then f restricted to $\mathscr{D}_0$ is also continuous.
6. Suppose that $f(x)$ is defined on an interval (a, x_0) and $g(x)$ is defined on an interval (x_0, b). Suppose also that $\lim_{x \to x_0} f(x) = A = \lim_{x \to x_0} g(x)$, and that $h(x)$ is defined by

$$h(x) = \begin{cases} f(x) & \text{for } a < x < x_0 \\ A & \text{for } x = x_0 \\ g(x) & \text{for } x_0 < x < b. \end{cases}$$

Show that h is continuous at x_0.
7. In my discussion of Example 2 in Sec. 11.10, I invited you to show that the function $h(x) = x^{1/m}$ where m is an *odd* positive

integer is continuous at $x_0 = 0$. One way you can do this is to write h as

$$h(x) = \begin{cases} x^{1/m} & \text{if } x > 0 \\ 0 & \text{if } x = 0 \\ -|x|^{1/m} & \text{if } x < 0 \end{cases}$$

and use the result of Problem 6.

8. Let $f(x) = x^{1/m}$, where m is an even positive integer and $x \geqslant 0$. Show that f is continuous at each $x_0 \geqslant 0$.

9. A philosophical problem. Some people have argued that any quantity having to do with the real world can change with time only in a continuous fashion; and that any apparent abruptness or discontinuity would, if inspected closely enough, be revealed as a steep but smooth transition. See Figure (a).

FIGURE (a)

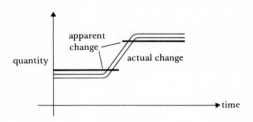

Others have argued contrariwise—that all real change may be just a jumping from stage to stage; and that what appear to be continuous transitions are merely rapid successions of jumps so small as to be individually undetected. See Figure (b).

FIGURE (b)

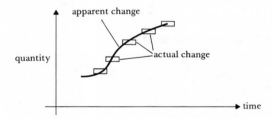

Question: Could any physical observations or experiments ever give final preference to one of the opposing theories over the other?

Can you give more detailed arguments to support either philosophical position for the specific issues of population growth, speed of a moving object, or change in human body weight?

10. Experiment with continuous functions defined on the interval $0 \leqslant x \leqslant 1$.

(a) For any such function f is there always a number B (depending on f) such that

$$|f(x)| \leqslant B \text{ for all } x \text{ in } [0, 1]?$$

(b) For any such function, does there always exist an input value x_0 such that

$$f(x_0) \geqslant f(x) \text{ for all other } x \text{ in } [0, 1]?$$

11. Experiment with continuous functions defined on $[0, 1]$ which have the further restriction that their range is contained in $[0, 1]$. See the figure for a picture of the graph of such a function. Will the graph of f always cross or touch the $45°$ line L above some point x_0 in $[0, 1]$? Equivalently, does there always exist an x_0 in $[0, 1]$ such that $f(x_0) = x_0$?

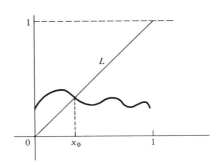

11.12 SUMMARY OF CHAPTER 11

DEFINITION: LIMIT OF A FUNCTION: Let f be a function with domain $\mathscr{D}$, and x_0 be a number which is the limit of at least one sequence of inputs in $\mathscr{D}$, all distinct from x_0. Let's say that *a limit of $f(x)$ exists as x converges to x_0* if there is some real number A such that $\lim_{n \to \infty} f(x_n) = A$ for EVERY sequence $\{x_n\}$ of inputs with $\lim_{n \to \infty} x_n = x_0$ and $x_n \neq x_0$. Call A the *limit of $f(x)$*, and say that $f(x)$ *converges to A as x converges to x_0.*

Notation: $\lim_{x \to x_0} f(x) = A$.
(Sec. 11.1)

(For an alternate definition of $\lim_{x \to x_0} f(x) = A$, involving "$\epsilon$'s" and "$\delta$'s", see Problem 8 of Sec. 11.3.)

DEFINITIONS: CONTINUITY: Call a function f *continuous at the input x_0* if a $\lim_{x \to x_0} f(x)$ exists and equals $f(x_0)$. Call a function f *continuous* (without specifying x_0) if f is continuous at x_0 for every input x_0 in the domain of f. If $\lim_{x \to x_0} f(x)$ fails to exist or fails to equal $f(x_0)$, call f *discontinuous at x_0* (or say that f has a *discontinuity* at x_0).
(Sec. 11.2)

THEOREM (ALTERNATE DEFINITION OF CONTINUITY): The requirement that $\lim_{x \to x_0} f(x) = f(x_0)$ is equivalent to the requirement that

$$\lim_{n \to \infty} x_n = x_0 \text{ always implies } \lim_{n \to \infty} f(x_n) = f(x_0),$$

whether $x_n = x_0$ or not.
(Sec. 11.2)

(For still another definition of continuity, involving "ϵ's" and "δ's", see Problem 10 of Sec. 11.3.)

Properties of limits of functions (Sec. 11.7)

Property $\hat{A}$ ("uniqueness"): A function can't have more than one limit at a given input. That is, if $\lim_{x \to x_0} f(x) = A$ and $\lim_{x \to x_0} f(x) = B$, then $A = B$.

Property $\hat{B}$ (on "restricting the domain"): If $\lim_{x \to x_0} f(x) = A$, and if we restrict the domain $\mathscr{D}$ of f to a smaller set $\mathscr{D}_0$, then we shall still have

$\lim_{x \to x_0} f(x) = A$ (provided some subsequence $\{x_n \neq x_0\}$ of inputs in $\mathcal{D}_0$ *still converges to x_0*).

Property $\hat{C}$ (limits are determined "locally"): If $\lim_{x \to x_0} f(x) = A$ and if $g(x)$ *differs from $f(x)$ only outside some interval* $[x_0 - \delta, x_0 + \delta]$, *then* $\lim_{x \to x_0} g(x) = A$.

Property $\hat{D}$ (on "interlacing"): Suppose that $f(x)$ is defined on an interval (a, x_0) and $g(x)$ is defined on an interval (x_0, b); and that $\lim_{x \to x_0} f(x) = A$ and $\lim_{x \to x_0} g(x) = A$. If we have

$$h(x) = \begin{cases} f(x) & \text{for } a < x < x_0 \\ g(x) & \text{for } x_0 < x < b, \end{cases}$$

then $\lim_{x \to x_0} h(x) = A$ *also.*

Property $\hat{G}$ (on "constant functions"): If $f(x) = c$ for all x in some interval (a, b) then $\lim_{x \to x_0} f(x) = c$ at any x_0 in (a, b).

Property $\hat{H}$ (on "scaling"): If $\lim_{x \to x_0} f(x) = A$ and if c is a constant, then $\lim_{x \to x_0} cf(x) = cA$.

Property $\hat{I}$ (on "sums"): If f and g have a common domain, and $\lim_{x \to x_0} f(x) = A$ and $\lim_{x \to x_0} g(x) = B$, then $\lim_{x \to x_0} [f(x) + g(x)] = A + B$. Also, $\lim_{x \to x_0} [f(x) - g(x)] = A - B$.

Property $\hat{J}$ (on "products"): If f and g have a common domain, and $\lim_{x \to x_0} f(x) = A$ and $\lim_{x \to x_0} g(x) = B$, then $\lim_{x \to x_0} f(x)g(x) = AB$.

Property $\hat{L}$ (on "quotients"): If f and g have a common domain where g *never* $= 0$, and if $\lim_{x \to x_0} f(x) = A$ and $\lim_{x \to x_0} g(x) = B \neq 0$, then

$$\lim_{x \to x_0} f(x)/g(x) = A/B.$$

Property $\hat{M}$ (on "rational powers"): If $f(x) = x^r$ for $x \geq 0$, where r is a positive rational number, then $\lim_{x \to x_0} f(x) = x_0{}^r$ at any $x_0 \geq 0$.

Property $\hat{O}$ (on "comparison"): If $f(x) \leq g(x)$ for all x in a common domain, and if $\lim_{x \to x_0} f(x) = A$ and $\lim_{x \to x_0} g(x) = B$, then $A \leq B$.

Property $\hat{P}$ (on "squeezing"): If $f(x) \leq g(x) \leq h(x)$ for all x in a common domain, and if $\lim_{x \to x_0} f(x) = A$ and $\lim_{x \to x_0} h(x) = A$, then $\lim_{x \to x_0} g(x) = A$.

Property $\hat{Q}$ (on "composition"): If $\lim_{x \to x_0} f(x) = A$, and if g is defined on the range of f and is continuous at A, then

$$\lim_{x \to x_0} g(f(x)) = g(A).$$

Property $\hat{R}$ (on "shifting input variables"): Suppose that g is a function, with domain $\mathcal{D}$, such that $\lim_{y \to y_0} g(y) = B$. If we let $h(x) = g(y_0 + x)$ (for all x such that $y = y_0 + x$ is an input in $\mathcal{D}$), then $\lim_{x \to 0} h(x) = B$.

Results on continuity (from Sec. 11.2 and Sec. 11.10):

THEOREM: Every polynomial is continuous. (Sec. 11.2)

THEOREM: (i) Any ratio of polynomials P/Q is continuous on any domain where Q never equals zero; (ii) any function of the form $f(x) = x^r$, where r is a positive rational, is continuous at any $x_0 \geqslant 0$; (iii) the absolute value function $|x|$ is continuous everywhere.

THEOREM (ON "SCALING"): If c is a constant and f is continuous (or continuous at x_0), then cf is also.

THEOREM (ON "SUMS AND PRODUCTS"): If f and g are continuous (or continuous at x_0), then $f + g$, $f - g$, and fg are also.

THEOREM (ON "QUOTIENTS"): If f and g have a common domain where g is never zero, and if f and g are continuous (or continuous at x_0), then so is f/g.

THEOREM (ON "COMPOSITION"): If f is continuous, with range $\mathcal{R}$, and if g is continuous on $\mathcal{R}$, then $h(x) = g(f(x))$ is continuous.

THEOREM: x^{-r} (where r is a positive rational) is continuous at any $x_0 > 0$.
(Sec. 11.10, Example 1)

THEOREM: $x^{1/m}$ (where m is an odd positive integer) is continuous at any real x_0.
(Sec. 11.10, Example 2)

DEFINITIONS: THE DERIVATIVE: Let f be a function with domain $\mathcal{D}$ and let x_0 be an input in $\mathcal{D}$ such that $x_0 = \lim_{n \to \infty} x_n$ for some sequence of inputs $x_n \neq x_0$. For x in $\mathcal{D}$ and $x \neq x_0$, define the *difference ratio function*

$$R(x) = \frac{f(x) - f(x_0)}{x - x_0}.$$

If $\lim_{x \to x_0} R(x)$ exists, call its value the *derivative of f at x_0*, and denote it by the symbol $f'(x_0)$. We can call f *differentiable at x_0*.
(Sec. 11.4)

THEOREM: If $\lim_{x \to x_0} [f(x) - f(x_0)]/(x - x_0) = A$, then

$$\lim_{n \to \infty} [f(r_n) - f(q_n)]/(r_n - q_n) = A$$

for any sequences of inputs $\{q_n\}$ and $\{r_n\}$ converging to x_0, with $q_n < x_0 < r_n$. The converse holds if f is continuous at x_0 (Theorems A and B of Sec. 11.4).

For examples showing failure of limits to exist, failure of continuity, and failure of a derivative to exist, see Sec. 11.5.

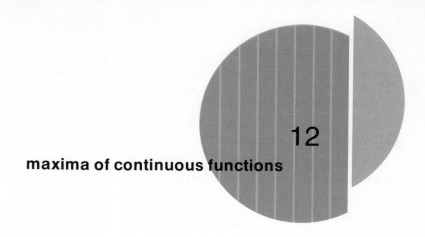

12

maxima of continuous functions

In the loaves-of-bread example of Chapter 7, I found a "lot" size which minimized the total ordering cost. Whenever the goal is similar—to find a maximum or a minimum output for some given function—it would be comforting to know that a maximum or minimum output *does* exist, before one bothers to search for it.

In this chapter I'll show how continuity helps *guarantee* the existence of such outputs. Then I'll return to the derivative, as a tool for finding the outputs.

Let's begin with an example regarding maxima.

12.1 HOW LARGE TO DIG A HOLE

You may perhaps recall this problem from Chapter 2: With what radius should one dig a cylindrical hole for a swimming pool so as to achieve a *maximum* volume of water, while keeping the vertical side area at, say, 100 square feet? See Fig. 12-1 (and Problem 9 of Sec. 2.2 and Problem 2 of Sec. 2.4). If we dig with radius r ft, the resulting volume will be $V(r) = 50r$ cu ft. As a function of possible radii $r > 0$, V is linear—with graph as in Fig. 12-2. And V has *no*

FIGURE 12-1

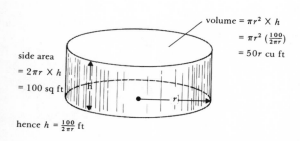

side area
$= 2\pi r \times h$
$= 100$ sq ft

hence $h = \frac{100}{2\pi r}$ ft

volume $= \pi r^2 \times h$
$= \pi r^2 \left(\frac{100}{2\pi r}\right)$
$= 50r$ cu ft

FIGURE 12-2   (reduced units)

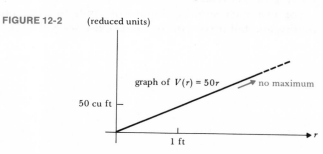

graph of $V(r) = 50r$ no maximum

50 cu ft

1 ft

maximum: we can make $V(r)$ as large as we wish by choosing r large enough. We could contain all the waters on earth with only 100 sq ft of siding material, were it not for physical limitations. Except for such physical drawbacks, would you have guessed at the outset that *in principle* the restriction to 100 sq ft side area imposes no bound on the volume?

The function V is "well behaved" — it's continuous at all r, and its graph rises only a finite amount over any interval $a \leqslant r \leqslant b$ of finite length. How do the outputs $V(r)$ get to increase "without bound"? Simply because the domain, all $r \geqslant 0$, is of "infinite" length and permits the graph to escape upward indefinitely.

But even over domains of finite length, there can be functions with no maxima. Here is a rogues' gallery:

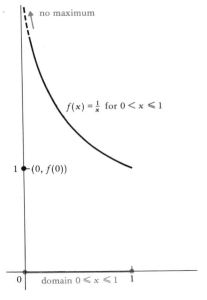

FIGURE 12-3

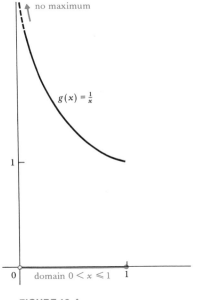

FIGURE 12-4

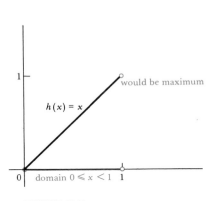

FIGURE 12-5

In Fig. 12-3 the outputs $f(x)$ get a chance to increase without bound, as x approaches the input 0, because f is *discontinuous* at 0. Its graph isn't tied down to the point $(0, f(0))$, and so can escape upward.

The function g in Fig. 12-4 *is* continuous at all inputs, but still its graph climbs without bound. Why? Because the domain $0 < x \leqslant 1$ doesn't contain an end point 0. So, again, the graph needn't approach — or be "tied" — to some point $(0, f(0))$.

Fig. 12-5 shows the tamest case: the outputs $h(x)$ don't increase without bound. There is no maximum merely because the domain is short an end point — just the input where a maximum should occur.

How can we find general requirements for a function which will guarantee that a maximum *will* exist? Looking at the four cases above—and trying to avoid their pitfalls—would you CONJECTURE that any *continuous* function f defined on a *closed* interval $a \leqslant x \leqslant b$ of *finite* length must have an absolute maximum value $f(x_0)$ attained at some input x_0?

Such a conjecture seems plausible on the basis of any graph one might actually *draw*, tied down at both end points, and having no "breaks." But must it hold for the infinite host of continuous functions, whose graphs—some with wild contortions—we can never hope to inspect minutely? In other words, must the truth of the conjecture follow logically from the manmade definition of "continuity" (in Sec. 11.2)?

12.2   BOUNDS FOR SETS

To ask whether a function f has a *maximum* output value is to ask a question about the *set* of all output values of f—the "range" of f: does that set contain a largest number? So to settle the above conjecture about the maxima for continuous functions, let's first try to extend to *sets* the precise results on least upper bounds for sequences. By analogy with sequences,

Definitions: Call a set S of real numbers *bounded above* if there is some *real number d* such that

$$s \leqslant d \qquad \text{for all } s \text{ in } S, \tag{1}$$

and call d an *upper bound* for S. If S has no other upper bound d' less than d, then call d a *least upper bound*.

Similarly, call a set S *bounded below* if there is some real number c such that

$$c \leqslant s \qquad \text{for all } s \text{ in } S, \tag{2}$$

and call c a *lower bound* for S. If S has no other lower bound c' greater than c, then call c a *greatest lower bound*.

Call a set S *bounded* if there is some real number b such that

$$|s| \leqslant b \qquad \text{for all } s \text{ in } S. \tag{3}$$

REMARKS: Just as for sequences, upper and lower bounds are not unique; but—by their very definition—a *least* upper bound and a *greatest* lower bound must be unique.

Also as for sequences, to say that S is "bounded" is equivalent to saying that S is *bounded both above and below*. Another equivalent statement of boundedness is that S *is contained in some interval* $[c, d]$ *of finite length* (here c and d are lower and upper bounds).

If a set S has a least upper bound d_0 and a greatest lower bound c_0, then $[c_0, d_0]$ is the smallest closed interval which contains S entirely. See Fig. 12.6.

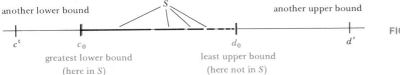

FIGURE 12-6

another lower bound

c^t c_0

greatest lower bound
(here in S)

S

another upper bound

d_0 d'

least upper bound
(here not in S)

Check that if a set S has an upper bound d which lies *in* S, then d must be a *least* upper bound. Similarly for lower bounds. (Do Problem 2 of Sec. 12.4.)

EXAMPLE 1. The function $h(x) = x$ (where $0 \leqslant x < 1$), in Fig. 12-5, has range $R = \{y: 0 \leqslant y < 1\}$. R is bounded below by $c = 0$ and above by $d = 1$. c is in R but d is not. R is also bounded below by $c' = -\frac{1}{2}$ and above by $d' = 3/2$. But R is not bounded below by any $c'' > 0$ nor above by any $d'' < 1$. Thus $c = 0$ is a *greatest* lower bound and $d = 1$ is a *least* upper bound.

What can a set be like if it is *not* bounded (or is "unbounded")? Just as for unbounded sequences (in Sec. 9.10), no integer n can then be a bound for S. In particular, the integer 1 can't be a bound, with $|s| \leqslant 1$ for all s in S. Hence there must be some number in S—call it s_1—such that $|s_1| > 1$. Moreover, neither the value $|s_1|$ nor the integer 2 can be a bound for S; so there must be some number in S—call it s_2—such that $|s_2| > |s_1|$ and $|s_2| > 2$. Proceeding by induction, we could conclude that

Theorem A (on "unbounded sets"): If S is an unbounded set of real numbers, then we can extract a sequence of numbers $\{s_n\}$ from S such that $|s_n| > n$ for each positive integer n, and moreover, $|s_{n+1}| > |s_n|$.

EXAMPLE 2. The function $g(x) = 1/x$ (where $0 < x \leqslant 1$), in Fig. 12-4 has range $R = \{y: 1 \leqslant y < \infty\}$. R is not bounded, and we can extract the unbounded sequence $\{y_n = n + 1\}$ from R to illustrate Theorem A. The function f in Fig. 12-3 has the same unbounded range.

Now if the range of a function does have an upper bound—as in Fig. 12-5—must it have a *least* upper bound? Recall the "least upper bound axiom" (Axiom A' of Sec. 10.3) for *sequences*: any increasing sequence, if bounded above, has a least upper bound. Does a similar result hold for *sets*? If a set S has an upper bound d, can't we locate a suitable increasing sequence $\{s_n\}$ of numbers in S whose least upper bound should also be a least upper bound for S? See Fig. 12-7.

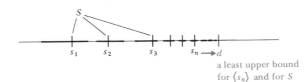

S

s_1 s_2 s_3 $s_n \longrightarrow d$

FIGURE 12-7

a least upper bound
for $\{s_n\}$ and for S

The answer is yes:

Theorem B (on least upper bounds for sets): If a set S of real numbers is bounded above, then it has a least upper bound d. In that case: either d is itself a number in S; or there is an increasing sequence $\{s_n\}$ of numbers in S such that $\lim_{n \to \infty} s_n = d$; or both may be true.

Similarly, if S is bounded below, then it has a greatest lower bound c which must either lie in S or be the limit of a decreasing sequence $\{s_n\}$ of numbers in S, or both. (See Fig. 12-8.)

FIGURE 12-8

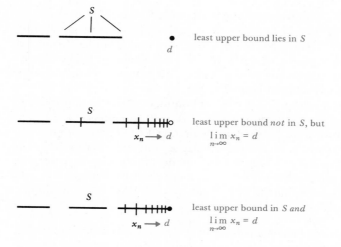

In Fig. 12-9, I've indicated a precise scheme for picking out an increasing sequence $\{s_n\}$ which will lead to a least upper bound for a set S, and won't fall short.

If you are interested in more details, here is a

Proof of half of Theorem B: Let's suppose that we are given an upper bound d_0 for a set S. If d_0 also happens to be a number in S, then d_0 must be the *least* upper bound of S; and we need seek no further. Otherwise, pick some number s_0 in S. If s_0 happens to be an upper bound, then again we need seek no further. So suppose neither s_0 nor d_0 are the sought-for least upper bound. To carry on the search, think of a sequence of vertical copies of S, as I've pictured in Fig. 12-9.

Here's a rule for going from one copy of S to the next, each time focusing on a smaller interval $[s_n, d_n]$, where d_n is always an upper bound for S and s_n is a number in S. Let m_n be the midpoint of $[s_n, d_n]$. If m_n happens to be an upper bound for S (as is m_1 in Fig. 12-9), then pick $d_{n+1} = m_n$ and $s_{n+1} = s_n$. On the other hand, if m_n is not an upper bound for S (e.g., m_2 in Fig. 12-9), choose s_{n+1} as some number in S with $s_{n+1} > m_n$. In this case, let $d_{n+1} = d_n$.

Now some m_n might simultaneously be an upper bound for S and a number in S. In such a case, stop the game—the search is over: m_n is the least upper bound of S. But otherwise, let the game go on

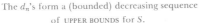

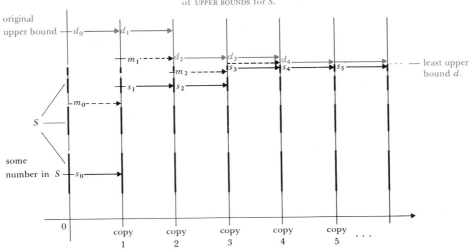

The d_n's form a (bounded) decreasing sequence **FIGURE 12-9**
of UPPER BOUNDS for S.

the s_n's form a (bounded) increasing sequence
of numbers in S.

forever. Note that the sequence $\{s_n\}$ is bounded and increasing. Hence it must converge to some limit, call it $\bar{s}$ (by Axiom A of Sec. 10.2). On the other hand, the sequence $\{d_n\}$ is bounded and decreasing. So it must converge to a limit, say $\bar{d}$. Since the interval $[s_{n+1}, d_{n+1}]$ is always at most half as long as the interval $[s_n, d_n]$, the lengths $d_n - s_n$ tend to zero; and

$$\bar{d} - \bar{s} = \lim_{n \to \infty} d_n - \lim_{n \to \infty} s_n = \lim_{n \to \infty} (d_n - s_n) = 0.$$

That is, $\{s_n\}$ and $\{d_n\}$ converge to a common limit $d = d = \bar{s}$. See Fig. 12-10 for a picture of the successive intervals $[s_n, d_n]$ on a common horizontal coordinate line. I invite you to check that d must be an upper bound for S and in fact the *least* such bound. Do Problem 8 of Sec. 12.4.

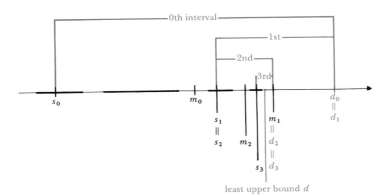

FIGURE 12-10

least upper bound d

Try also to write out a similar scheme for convergence to the greatest lower bound of a set S, if S is known to be bounded below. (Problem 9 of Sec. 12.4.)

12.3 BOUNDS FOR FUNCTIONS

Now let's apply the above results on sets to the case of functions. Suppose that f is a function with domain D. In the spirit of the last section, let's call f *bounded*, or *bounded above* or *below*, if its range

$$\{\text{all outputs } s = f(x) \text{ for } x \text{ in } D\}$$

is correspondingly bounded, or bounded above or below, as a *set*. (See Fig. 12-11.)

FIGURE 12-11

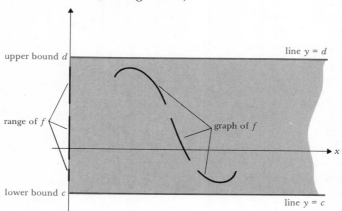

With this interpretation, here's how the definitions of the last section translate in terms of inputs x and outputs $s = f(x)$:

Definitions: Call a function f (with domain D) *bounded above* if there is some real number d such that

$$f(x) \leqslant d \qquad \text{for all } x \text{ in } D, \tag{1}$$

and call d an *upper bound* for f. If f has no other upper bound d' less than d, then call d a *least upper bound*.

Similarly, call a function f (with domain D) *bounded below* if there is some real number c such that

$$c \leqslant f(x) \qquad \text{for all } x \text{ in } D, \tag{2}$$

and call c a *lower bound* for f. If f has no other lower bound c' greater than c, then call c a *greatest lower bound*.

Call a function f (with domain D) *bounded* if there is some real number b such that

$$|f(x)| \leqslant b \qquad \text{for all } x \text{ in } D. \tag{3}$$

REMARKS: As for sets, upper and lower bounds of functions are not unique, but *least* upper bounds and *greatest* lower bounds are.

To say that f is "bounded" is equivalent to saying that f is *bounded both above and below*: that is, that inequalities

$$c \leqslant f(x) \quad \text{and} \quad f(x) \leqslant d \qquad \text{hold for all } x \text{ in } D$$

simultaneously. Pictorially, boundedness means that the graph of f lies entirely in a horizontal "tube," between lines with equations $y = c$ and $y = d$, as in Fig. 12-11.

If f has a least upper bound d_0 and a greatest lower bound c_0, then the lines $y = c_0$ and $y = d_0$ determine the smallest tube which can contain the graph of f.

Here are translations, in terms of functions, of the two theorems of the last section:

Theorem A' (on "unbounded functions"): If a function f is *not* bounded (or is "unbounded"), then we can extract a sequence of outputs $s_n = f(x_n)$ such that $|f(x_n)| > n$ for each positive integer n, and moreover, $|f(x_{n+1})| > |f(x_n)|$. (See Fig. 12-12.)

FIGURE 12-12

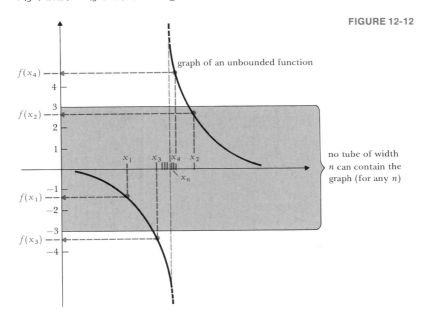

graph of an unbounded function

no tube of width n can contain the graph (for any n)

Theorem B' (on "least upper bounds for functions"): If a function f is bounded above, then it has a least upper bound d. In that case: either d is itself an output $d = f(x_0)$ for some input x_0; or there is an increasing sequence of outputs $f(x_n)$ such that $\lim_{n \to \infty} f(x_n) = d$; or both may be true.

Similarly, if f is bounded below, then it has a greatest lower bound c which must either be itself an output $c = f(x_1)$, or the limit of a decreasing sequence of outputs, $c = \lim_{n \to \infty} f(x_n)$; or both. (See Fig. 12-13.)

FIGURE 12-13

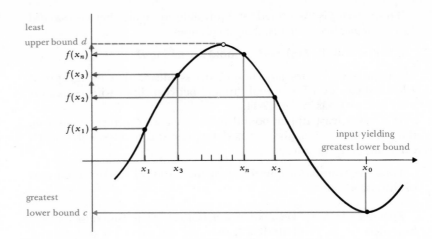

Now, check your understanding of bounds by trying some of the problems in the next section.

12.4 PROBLEMS ON BOUNDS FOR SETS AND FUNCTIONS

°1. For each of the following examples of a set S, determine a least upper bound and a greatest lower bound, if they exist. State whether the set S is bounded or unbounded.

(a) $S = \{1, 2, 3, \ldots\}$ (b) $S = \{-2, -4, -6, \ldots\}$

(c) $S = \left\{1, \dfrac{1}{2}, \dfrac{1}{3}, \ldots\right\}$ (d) $S = \left\{\dfrac{1}{4}, \dfrac{3}{4}, \dfrac{1}{8}, \dfrac{7}{8}, \dfrac{1}{16}, \dfrac{15}{16}, \ldots\right\}$

(e) $S = \{x\colon 1 < |x| < 2\}$

(f) $S = \left\{a_n\colon a_n = \dfrac{(-1)^n}{1 + n^2}, \; n = 1, 2, 3, \ldots\right\}$

(g) $S = \{$all rational numbers in $[0, 1]\}$

(h) $\{$all irrational numbers in $[0, 1]\}$

(i) $S = \{x\colon x^2 < 2\}$

2. (a) Show that if d is an upper bound for a set S and d lies in S, then d must be the *least* upper bound for S. (Suggestion: If d is not the least upper bound, then choose d' to be an upper bound for S with $d' < d$. But if d lies in S, what must be true about the relative sizes of d and d'?)

   (b) If c is a lower bound for a set S and c lies in S, show that c is the greatest lower bound for S.

°3. For each of the following sets S, determine the least upper bound d. State whether d is in S or not. Find, if possible, an increasing sequence $\{s_n\}$ of numbers of S such that $\lim\limits_{n \to \infty} s_n = d$.

(a) $S = \{x\colon 0 < x < 1\}$

(b) $S = \{x: 0 < x \leqslant 2\}$

(c) $S = \left\{\dfrac{1}{3}, \dfrac{2}{3}, \dfrac{1}{9}, \dfrac{8}{9}, \dfrac{1}{27}, \dfrac{26}{27}, \ldots\right\}$

(d) $S = \{$all rational numbers in $[-1, 0]\}$

°4. For each of the following sets S, find a sequence $\{s_n\}$ from S such that $|s_n| > n$ for each positive integer n and $|s_{n+1}| > |s_n|$.

(a) $S = \{1, 2, 1, 3, 1, 4, 1, 5, \ldots\}$

(b) $S = \{1, -4, +9, -16, \ldots\}$

(c) $S = \{-1, -2, 10, -3, -4, 100, -5, -6, 1000, \ldots\}$

(d) $S = \{$all positive irrational numbers$\}$

°5. For each of the following examples of a function f with domain $\mathscr{D}$, determine a least upper bound and a greatest lower bound — or show why they don't exist. If the function is bounded, show how to enclose its graph in a horizontal "tube" as in Fig. 12-11.

(a) $f(x) = x$; $\mathscr{D} = [-1, 1]$, $\mathscr{D} = \{$all $x \geqslant 0\}$

(b) $f(x) = x$; $\mathscr{D} = [-1, 1\rangle$

(c) $f(x) = |x|$; $\mathscr{D} = [-1, 1]$

(d) $f(x) = 1 - |x|$; $\mathscr{D} = [-1, 1]$

(e) $f(x) = 1 - |x|$; $\mathscr{D} = \langle -1, 1]$

(f) $f(x) = \begin{cases} 0 & \text{for } -1 \leqslant x < 0 \\ 1 & \text{for } 0 \leqslant x < 1 \\ 2 & \text{for } x = 1 \end{cases}$

(g) $f(x) = \dfrac{1}{x}$; $\mathscr{D} = \langle -1, 0\rangle$, $\mathscr{D} = \{$all $x < 0\}$, $\mathscr{D} = [-2, -1]$

(h) $f(x) = 2^{-|x|}$; $\mathscr{D} = [-1, 1]$, $\mathscr{D} = \{$all $x\}$

(i) $f(x) = (x-1)^2$; $\mathscr{D} = \left[\dfrac{1}{2}, 2\right]$

(j) $f(x) = (x-1)^2$; $\mathscr{D} = \left\langle \dfrac{1}{2}, 2\right\rangle$

**6. (a) Show that the lengths of all polygons inscribed in a given circle, as in Fig. (a), constitute a set having a least upper bound d.

(b) Show that the lengths of all polygons circumscribed about the same circle, as in Fig. (b), constitute a set having a greatest lower bound c.

(c) Show that $c = d$, and that the common value is the same as the "length" A of Problem 13 in Sec. 10.5. (You might want to use the method of Problem 12 of Sec. 10.5.)

FIGURE (a)   FIGURE (b)

*7. Let $S = \{$all x with $x \geqslant 0$ and $x^2 < 2\}$.

Follow the rule given in the proof of Theorem B of Sec. 12.2 to construct the first two terms of an increasing sequence $\{s_n\}$ of numbers of S such that $\lim_{n\to\infty} s_n = $ least upper bound of S.

*8. Check that the number $d = \bar{d} = \bar{s}$ constructed in the proof of Theorem B of Sec. 12.2 actually is (i) an upper bound for S and

(ii) the *least* such bound. (Suggestion for (i): If d is not an upper bound for S, then you may choose an s in S with $d < s$. Let $\epsilon = s - d$ and pick N so that if $n > N$, then $d_n - d < \epsilon/2$. Compare the sizes of d_{N+1} and s. Part (ii) follows by similar reasoning.)

*9. Write out the proof for the half of Theorem B of Sec. 12.2 dealing with convergence to the greatest lower bound of a set S, if S is known to be bounded below.

12.5 A GUARANTEE FOR MAXIMA AND MINIMA

On the strength of the above results about bounds, we can now settle the conjecture (of Sec. 12.1) that a *continuous* function for a *closed* interval $[a, b]$ (of *finite* length) must be well behaved. Firstly, the output values $f(x)$ can't get arbitrarily large:

> **Theorem C (on "bounds for continuous functions"):** Suppose that a function f has as domain a closed interval $[a, b]$, and that f is continuous on $[a, b]$. Then f must be bounded.

I invite you to inspect the next three figures (Figs. 12-14, 12-15, 12-16) for a

Proof of Theorem C. Let's start with the supposition that f is *not* bounded, and see how that leads to a logical impossibility.

Note how Figs. 12-14 and 12-16 conflict: the *convergent* subsequence of outputs $f(x_{n_k})$ in Fig. 12-16 must be bounded. On the other hand, in Fig. 12-14 the same subsequence has $|f(x_{n_k})| > n_k$ for all k, and so must be unbounded ($\lim\limits_{k \to \infty} n_k = \infty$). To avoid this contradiction we must reject the starting assumption that f is unbounded. *Conclusion: f* must be bounded.   End of proof.

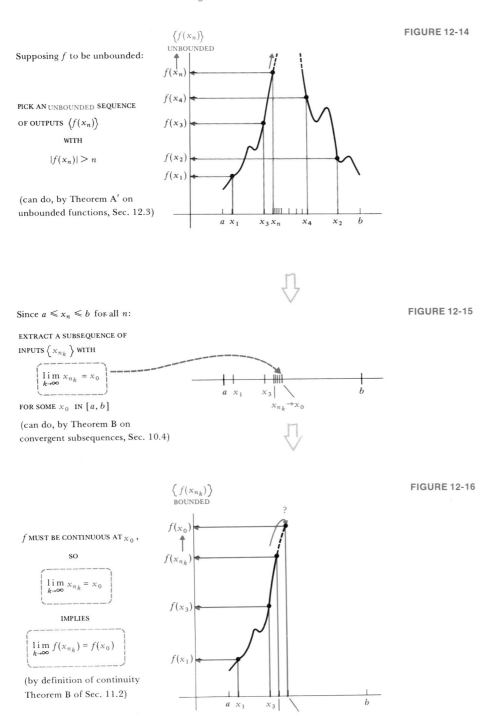

FIGURE 12-14

Supposing f to be unbounded:

PICK AN UNBOUNDED SEQUENCE OF OUTPUTS $\langle f(x_n) \rangle$

WITH

$$|f(x_n)| > n$$

(can do, by Theorem A' on unbounded functions, Sec. 12.3)

$\langle f(x_n) \rangle$ UNBOUNDED

$f(x_n)$
$f(x_4)$
$f(x_3)$
$f(x_2)$
$f(x_1)$

a x_1 x_3 x_n x_4 x_2 b

FIGURE 12-15

Since $a \leqslant x_n \leqslant b$ for all n:

EXTRACT A SUBSEQUENCE OF INPUTS $\langle x_{n_k} \rangle$ WITH

$$\lim_{k \to \infty} x_{n_k} = x_0$$

FOR SOME x_0 IN $[a, b]$

(can do, by Theorem B on convergent subsequences, Sec. 10.4)

a x_1 x_3 b

$x_{n_k} \to x_0$

FIGURE 12-16

f MUST BE CONTINUOUS AT x_0,

SO

$$\lim_{k \to \infty} x_{n_k} = x_0$$

IMPLIES

$$\lim_{k \to \infty} f(x_{n_k}) = f(x_0)$$

(by definition of continuity Theorem B of Sec. 11.2)

$\langle f(x_{n_k}) \rangle$ BOUNDED

?

$f(x_0)$
$f(x_{n_k})$
$f(x_3)$
$f(x_1)$

a x_1 x_3 b

$x_{n_k} \to x_0$

Finally, a GUARANTEE to support future searches for maxima and minima:

Theorem D ("guaranteeing maxima and minima"): Suppose that a function f has as domain a closed interval $[a, b]$ and that f is continuous on $[a, b]$. Then there exists an input x_{max} such that $f(x_{max})$ is an (absolute) maximum for f:

$$f(x) \leq f(x_{max}) \qquad \text{for all } x \text{ in } [a, b].$$

Similarly, there exists an input x_{min} such that $f(x_{min})$ is an (absolute) minimum for f:

$$f(x_{min}) \leq f(x) \qquad \text{for all } x \text{ in } [a, b].$$

(There may exist several inputs yielding the same maximum or minimum output value.)

Why must the guarantee hold? The previous result (Theorem C) tells us that f must be *bounded*. Therefore f must have a *least* upper bound d and a *greatest* lower bound c. (Such was the message of Theorem B$'$ of Sec. 12.3, on "least upper bounds for functions.") Will the least upper bound itself be a maximum output, $d = f(x_{max})$; and will the greatest lower bound be a minimum output, $c = f(x_{min})$?

These questions point the way to a

Proof of Theorem D: Recall that the same result which assures us that d exists also tells us that either $d = f(x_0)$ for some input x_0, or

$$d = \lim_{n \to \infty} f(x_n)$$

for suitable inputs x_n in $[a, b]$. (Theorem B$'$ of Sec. 12.3, again.) Let's show that even in the second case, $d = \lim_{n \to \infty} f(x_n)$, we must have $d = f(x_0)$ for some input x_0 — which we can then label $x_0 = x_{max}$.

See the next three figures — analogous to those for Theorem C — on how to extract a subsequence of inputs $\{x_{n_k}\}$ leading the way to x_0 (Figs. 12-17, 12-18, 12-19).

On the one hand, the continuity of f forces $\lim_{k \to \infty} f(x_{n_k}) = f(x_0)$. On the other hand, $\{f(x_{n_k})\}$ is a subsequence of $\{f(x_n)\}$, and so must have $\lim_{k \to \infty} f(x_{n_k}) = d$ (by Property B on limits of subsequences, of Chap. 9). Thus $d = f(x_0)$: d is attained at some input $x_0 = x_{max}$.

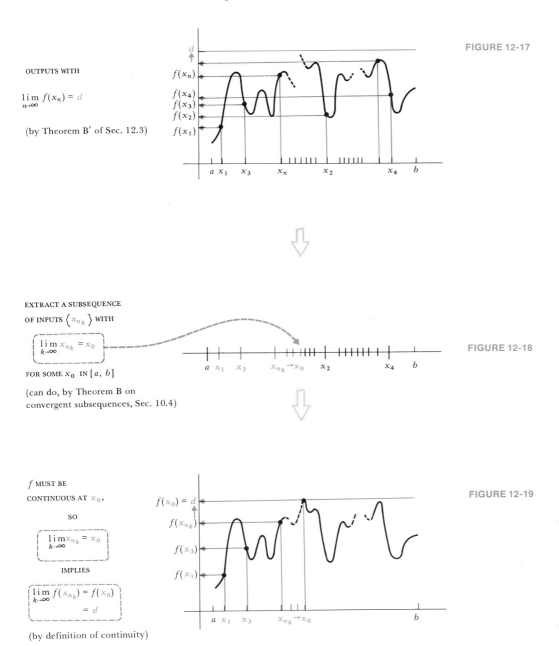

FIGURE 12-17

OUTPUTS WITH

$$\lim_{n\to\infty} f(x_n) = d$$

(by Theorem B' of Sec. 12.3)

FIGURE 12-18

EXTRACT A SUBSEQUENCE

OF INPUTS $\left\{x_{n_k}\right\}$ WITH

$$\lim_{k\to\infty} x_{n_k} = x_0$$

FOR SOME x_0 IN $[a, b]$

(can do, by Theorem B on
convergent subsequences, Sec. 10.4)

FIGURE 12-19

f MUST BE

CONTINUOUS AT x_0,

SO

$$\lim_{k\to\infty} x_{n_k} = x_0$$

IMPLIES

$$\lim_{k\to\infty} f(x_{n_k}) = f(x_0)$$
$$= d$$

(by definition of continuity)

I invite you to draw pictures and give a similar argument to show that the greatest lower bound $c = f(x_{\min})$. Do Problem 13 of Sec. 12.8.

EXAMPLE 1. The ordering cost function for loaves of bread (from Sec. 7.1),

$$h(x) = (0.005)x + (4500)\frac{1}{x} \text{ dollars,}$$

which I considered for lot sizes x in the interval $1 \leq x \leq 1500$, must have an (absolute) minimum—since the interval $[1,1500]$ is closed and h is continuous there. Thus, *even before I entered upon the elaborate search for x_{MIN} in Sec. 7.1, I knew that the search had a valid goal.* (You may recall that I checked the continuity of h in Example 1 of Sec. 11.2.)

12.6 RELATIVE MAXIMA AND MINIMA

When we inspect a function for a maximum or a minimum value, we may also find minor peaks and valleys in the graph of the function, as in Fig. 12-20.

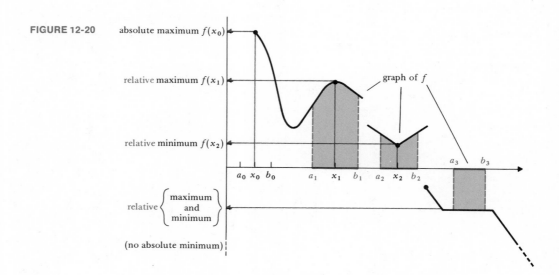

FIGURE 12-20

If we cut the full domain of f in Fig. 12-20 down to a subinterval such as $[a_1, b_1]$, *surrounding* the input x_1, then the output $f(x_1)$ appears as an (absolute) maximum over $[a_1, b_1]$—although it's not an absolute maximum for the original domain. Here are standard names to distinguish such outputs:

Definitions: Call an output $f(x_1)$ a *relative maximum* of a function f if there is an interval $[a_1, b_1]$, with $a_1 < x_1 < b_1$, such that

$$f(x) \leq f(x_1) \qquad \text{for all inputs } x \text{ in } [a_1, b_1].$$

Similarly, call an output $f(x_2)$ a *relative minimum* of f if there is an interval $[a_2, b_2]$, with $a_2 < x_2 < b_2$, such that

$$f(x_2) \leq f(x) \qquad \text{for all inputs } x \text{ in } [a_2, b_2].$$

With this definition, absolute maxima and minima qualify as "relative" too. (And an end point of the original domain of the function, such as x_0 in Fig. 12-20, can be a relative maximum: $f(x) \leq f(x_0)$ for all inputs in $[a_0, b_0]$—although there are no inputs to the left of x_0.)

REMARK: In the last section, I deduced that bounds and absolute maxima must exist for continuous functions whose domains are closed intervals. We can apply the same results to a discontinuous function too, if we can restrict the function to some closed interval $[a, b]$ on which it is continuous.

EXAMPLE 1. The function f whose graph I've pictured in Fig. 12-20 above is not continuous everywhere. But if we think of f as restricted to the interval $[a_1, b_1]$, it is continuous there—and so must have an absolute maximum for the interval $[a_1, b_1]$. As I noted, that maximum occurs at the input x_1: $f(x) \leq f(x_1)$ for all x in $[a_1, b_1]$. Since the interval $[a_1, b_1]$ *surrounds* x_1, we can also call the value $f(x_1)$ a "relative maximum" for f on its original domain—according to the definition just above.

Note that the function f in Fig. 12-20 must also have an absolute minimum on the restricted interval $[a_1, b_1]$—by the results of the last section. However, this minimum occurs at a_1, an end point of $[a_1, b_1]$, not *inside* $[a_1, b_1]$. So $f(a_1)$ doesn't qualify as a "relative minimum" of f in the original domain.

12.7   THE DERIVATIVE AT A MAXIMUM OR MINIMUM

Back in Sec. 7.1, when I sought a minimum ordering cost for loaves of bread, I based my search on this CONJECTURE: *the derivative $f'(x_0)$ should be zero at a valley bottom or at a hilltop of the graph of a function f*—provided the derivative exists at all.

For example, in Fig. 12-20, we might expect $f'(x_1) = 0$ corresponding to the *relative maximum* $f(x_1)$. Intuitively this is because, as one goes from left to right past x_1, the outputs $f(x)$ stop increasing and begin decreasing. So—if an instantaneous rate of change $f'(x_1)$ exists—it should be zero.

Note, however, that no derivative exists at all at the relative minimum $f(x_2)$ in Fig. 12-20, because the graph has too sharp a "corner" there. Also, at an *end point* of the domain—such as x_0 in Fig. 12-20—a graph can begin falling from an absolute maximum height with a rate of change $f'(x_0) \neq 0$.

Can we rely on the above conjecture in all future searches for maxima and minima — if we keep away from end points and inputs where derivatives don't exist? Yes:

Theorem E (on "derivatives at maxima and minima"): Suppose that a function f is defined for $a \leqslant x \leqslant b$ and that x_0 is an input with $a < x_0 < b$. If $f(x_0)$ is a relative maximum or minimum and if $f'(x_0)$ exists, then we must have $f'(x_0) = 0$.

EXAMPLE 1. $f(x) = x^4$ for $-1 \leqslant x \leqslant 1$. The absolute minimum occurs at $x_0 = 0$, and sure enough $f'(x_0) = 4x_0{}^3 = 4 \cdot 0^3 = 0$.

EXAMPLE 2. The ordering cost function again (from Sec. 7.1):

$$h(x) = (0.005)x + (4500)\frac{1}{x} \quad \text{for } 1 \leqslant x \leqslant 1500.$$

At any input x_0, $h'(x_0)$ exists. I'll review the calculation:

$$
\begin{aligned}
h'(x_0) &= \lim_{x \to x_0} \frac{h(x) - h(x_0)}{x - x_0} \\[2mm]
&= \lim_{x \to x_0} \frac{[(0.005)x + (4500)/x] - [(0.005)x_0 + (4500)/x_0]}{x - x_0} \\[2mm]
&= \lim_{x \to x_0} \frac{(0.005)(x - x_0) + (4500)[(1/x) - (1/x_0)]}{x - x_0} \\[2mm]
&= \lim_{x \to x_0} \frac{(0.005)(x - x_0)}{x - x_0} + \lim_{x \to x_0} \frac{(4500)[(1/x) - (1/x_0)]}{x - x_0} \\[2mm]
&= (0.005) + (4500) \lim_{x \to x_0} \frac{[(x_0 - x)/(xx_0)]}{x - x_0} \\[2mm]
&= (0.005) + (4500) \lim_{x \to x_0} \left(-\frac{1}{xx_0}\right)\left(\frac{x - x_0}{x - x_0}\right) \\[2mm]
&= (0.005) - \frac{(4500)}{x_0} \lim_{x \to x_0} \left(\frac{1}{x}\right) = 0.005 - \frac{4500}{x_0{}^2}.
\end{aligned}
$$

Now recall the SEARCH PLAN:

We know that an absolute minimum exists, because h is continuous on the closed interval $[1, 15,000]$. Either a minimizing input $x_{\min}$ occurs at an end point (1 or 15,000) or it must lie in between. *If* Theorem E is true and *if* $1 < x_{\min} < 1500$, then we must have

$$h'(x_{\min}) = 0.005 - \frac{4500}{(x_{\min})^2} = 0,$$

or

$$x_{\min} = \sqrt{\frac{4500}{0.005}} = 300\sqrt{10}.$$

That is, the only possible candidates for $x_{\min}$ are the end points 1 and 15,000, and the interior input $300\sqrt{10}$. As you may recall from Sec. 7.1, $300\sqrt{10}$ wins.

Here is how we can support our intuition and give

A proof for Theorem E (on "derivatives at maxima and minima"):
Suppose that $a < x_0 < b$ and x_0 is a relative maximum for a function
f. That is, for some subinterval $[a_0, b_0]$ contained in $[a, b]$, with
$a_0 < x_0 < b_0$, we must have $f(x) \leqslant f(x_0)$, or

$$f(x) - f(x_0) \leqslant 0 \qquad \text{for all } x \text{ in } [a_0, b_0].$$ (1)

See Figs. 12-21 and 12-22.

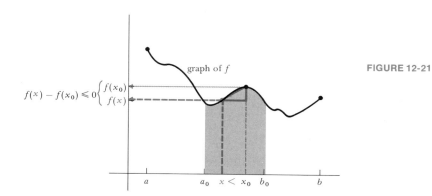

FIGURE 12-21

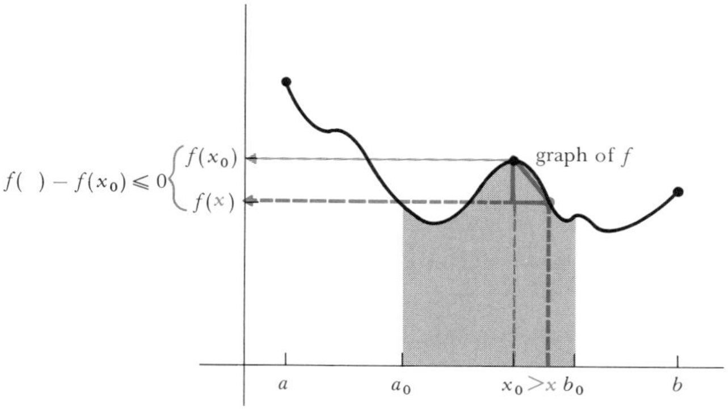

FIGURE 12-22

Note in Fig. 12-21 that for x slightly to the left of x_0, the approximating slope between the points $(x, f(x))$ and $(x_0, f(x_0))$ is positive. More precisely, the difference ratio function

$$R(x) = \frac{f(x) - f(x_0)}{x - x_0} \geq 0 \qquad \text{for } a_0 < x < x_0, \tag{2}$$

since its numerator $f(x) - f(x_0)$ is nonpositive and its denominator $x - x_0$ is negative. On the other hand, for x slightly to the right of x_0, as in Fig. 12-22, the approximating slope is negative:

$$R(x) = \frac{f(x) - f(x_0)}{x - x_0} \leq 0 \qquad \text{for } x_0 < x < b_0, \tag{3}$$

since the numerator $f(x) - f(x_0)$ is still nonpositive, but now the demoninator *is* positive. Thus a graph of $R(x)$ must look like the sketch in Fig. 12-23. Now, by hypothesis, the limit

FIGURE 12-23

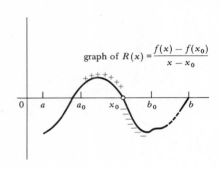

graph of $R(x) = \dfrac{f(x) - f(x_0)}{x - x_0}$

$$\lim_{x \to x_0} R(x) = \lim_{x \to x_0} \frac{f(x) - f(x_0)}{x - x_0} = f'(x_0)$$

exists. If we restrict R to the subinterval (a_0, x_0) we can see that $f'(x_0)$ must be ≥ 0. (Recall Property $\hat{B}$ on "restricting the domain".) Similarly, if we restrict R to the subinterval (x_0, b_0) we can see that $f'(x_0)$ must be ≤ 0. Conclusion: $f'(x_0)$ must be $= 0$. End of the proof.

WARNING: Just because $f'(x_0) = 0$, it needn't follow that $f(x_0)$ is a relative maximum or minimum, even if x_0 isn't an end point of the domain.

EXAMPLE 3. $f(x) = x^3$ for all x. At $x_0 = 0$, $f'(x_0) = 3x_0^2 = 3 \cdot 0^2 = 0$; but $f(x) > 0$ for all $x > 0$, and $f(x) < 0$ for all $x < 0$.

12.8 PROBLEMS ON MAXIMA AND MINIMA

°1. Try to sketch graphs for each of the following cases of a function f and a domain $\mathscr{D}$. Then, by comparing different outputs, determine whether an absolute maximum exists. If so, find its value. Do the same for the absolute minima.

(a) $f(x) = x$; $\mathscr{D} = [-1, 1]$, $\mathscr{D} = [-1, 1\rangle$, $\mathscr{D} = \{\text{all } x > 0\}$

(b) $f(x) = |x|$; $\mathscr{D} = [-1, 1]$, $\mathscr{D} = [-1, 1\rangle$

(c) $f(x) = 1 - |x|$; $\mathscr{D} = [-1, 1]$, $\mathscr{D} = \langle-1, 1\rangle$, $\mathscr{D} = [-1, 1\rangle$

(d) $f(x) = \begin{cases} 0 & \text{for } -1 \leq x < 0 \\ 1 & \text{for } 0 \leq x < 1 \\ 2 & \text{for } x = 1 \end{cases}$

(e) $f(x) = \dfrac{1}{x}$; $\mathscr{D} = [-1, 0\rangle$, $\mathscr{D} = \langle-1, 0\rangle$, $\mathscr{D} = \{\text{all } x < 0\}$

(f) $f(x) = \begin{cases} \dfrac{1}{x} & \text{for } 1 \leq x < 0 \\ 0 & \text{for } x = 0 \end{cases}$

(g) $f(x) = 2^{-|x|}$; $\mathscr{D} = [-1, 1]$, $\mathscr{D} = \{\text{all } x\}$

(h) $f(x) = (x-1)^2$; $\mathscr{D} = [\frac{1}{2}, 2]$, $\mathscr{D} = \langle \frac{1}{2}, 2 \rangle$, $\mathscr{D} = \{\text{all } x\}$

(i) $f(x) = \begin{cases} -x & \text{for } -1 \leqslant x < 0 \\ 2x & \text{for } 0 \leqslant x \leqslant 1 \end{cases}$

(j) $f(x) = \begin{cases} x^2 & \text{for } -1 \leqslant x \leqslant 1 \\ 2-x & \text{for } 1 < x \leqslant 3 \end{cases}$

*(k) $f(x) = \begin{cases} 0 & \text{for } 0 \leqslant x < \dfrac{1}{2} \\ x + \dfrac{1}{x} & \text{for } \dfrac{1}{2} \leqslant x \leqslant \dfrac{3}{2} \end{cases}$

°2. In which of the cases of Problem 1 was the function f *unbounded* on the domain $\mathscr{D}$? For each such case, which hypotheses of Theorem C (on "bounds for continuous functions") in Sec. 12.5 were violated?

°3. For those cases of Problem 1 where absolute maxima or minima *failed* to exist, which hypotheses of Theorem D ("guaranteeing maxima and minima") in Sec. 12.5 were violated?

°4. In which cases of Problem 1 did there exist relative maxima or minima $f(x_0)$ which were *not* absolute?

°5. Are there cases in Problem 1 where relative maxima or minima $f(x_0)$ existed *without* $f'(x_0) = 0$? (Recall the "rogues' gallery" of Sec. 11.5.)

6. (a) Suppose that a function f is defined on an interval $[a, b]$, that $[c, d]$ is a *subinterval*, and that x_0 is an input in $[c, d]$. Show that if $f(x_0)$ is an absolute maximum for f on the *restricted domain* $[c, d]$, then $f(x_0)$ is at least a relative maximum on the larger domain $[a, b]$. Similarly for absolute and relative minima.

   (b) Sketch examples where $f(x_0)$ will not be an absolute maximum or minimum in the larger domain.

7. Assume rules for differentiation such as $(cf(x))' = cf'(x)$, $(f(x) + g(x))' = f'(x) + g'(x)$, and $(x^n)' = nx^{n-1}$ — as in Sec. 7.3 and Sec. 11.4. Then, for each of the following cases, calculate $f'(x)$ and try to determine all inputs which yield relative or absolute maxima or minima.

   (a) $f(x) = x^3 - 6x^2 + 9x + 1$ for $0 \leqslant x \leqslant 5$.
   Sample reasoning: $f'(x) = 3x^2 - 12x + 9$ at all x in $[0, 5]$. Hence, by Theorem E (on "derivatives at maxima and minima") in Sec. 12.7, the *only* inputs x_0 which can provide relative maxima or minima are the end points $x_0 = 0$ or 5, or values such that

   $$f'(x_0) = 3(x_0^2 - 4x_0 + 3) = 3(x_0 - 1)(x_0 - 3) = 0$$

— namely, $x_0 = 1$ or 3. Make a table for these values:

x_0	0	1	3	5
$f(x_0)$	1	5	1	21

By Theorem D ("guaranteeing maxima and minima") in Sec. 12.5, an absolute (hence also "relative") maximum *must exist*, since f is continuous on $[0, 5]$. Hence it must appear among the possibilities in the table, and we can identify it as $f(5) = 21$. Similarly, an absolute minimum must exist, and we can identify it with $f(0) = f(3) = 1$. What about the remaining $f(1) = 5$? Note that on the *restricted domain* $[0, 3], f(1) = 5$ appears as an absolute maximum, by the same reasoning as before. Hence on the larger domain $[0, 5]$, $f(1) = 5$ must be a relative maximum — by the result of Problem 6(a). (Alternatively, note that $f'(x) = 3(x - 3)(x - 1) > 0$ for $0 < x < 1$ and $f'(x) < 0$ for $1 < x < 3$ — and apply the slope arguments of Sec. 7.1.)

(b) $f(x) = x^2 - 2x + 5$, $\mathscr{D} = [0, 4]$
(c) $f(x) = -x^2 + 4x - 2$, $\mathscr{D} = [0, 4]$
(d) $f(x) = x^3 + 2x - 1$, $\mathscr{D} = [-1, 2]$
(e) $f(x) = x^4 + 2x^3$, $\mathscr{D} = [-3, 3]$
(f) $f(x) = x^4 - 4x^3 + 4x^2$, $\mathscr{D} = [-4, 4]$
(g) $f(x) = x + 1/x$, $\mathscr{D} = [\frac{1}{2}, 2]$

8. (a) Suppose that a function f has as domain $\mathscr{D}$ either an open interval $a < x < b$ or a half-line such as $\{$all $x > a\}$. And suppose that x_0 is an input with the property that whenever we restrict $\mathscr{D}$ to a closed subinterval $[c, d]$ containing x_0, $f(x_0)$ appears as an absolute maximum for f over $[c, d]$. Show that $f(x_0)$ is an absolute maximum for f over the entire domain $\mathscr{D}$. Similarly for absolute minima.

   (b) Use the result of part (a) to find absolute maxima and minima — if they exist — for the functions in Problem 6 and the domains $\mathscr{D} = \{$ all $x > 0\}$ and $\mathscr{D} = \{$all $x < 0\}$.

9. Among all rectangles having a given area, is there one shape which provides a minimum perimeter?

   (Suggestion: Label the length of one side x, and express the corresponding perimeter $p(x)$ in terms of A and x. Look for x_0 such that $p'(x_0) = 0$. Use Problem 7(a) if necessary.)

10. Suppose that a handbill is to contain 36 square inches of printed matter surrounded by a 2-inch margin on all sides. Need there exist dimensions for a rectangular sheet of paper whereby it can satisfy the handbill specifications while having a *minimum* amount of area? If so, find them.

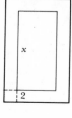

11. Light reaching a point P from some point source S is usually directly proportional to the "intensity" of the source S and inversely proportional to the distance between P and S. Suppose that two sources S_1 and S_2 are 1 mile apart, and that S_2 has twice

the "intensity" of S_1. Among all the points P on the line segment between S_1 and S_2, is there one which receives a minimum *total* light? If so, which?

12. Must there be a point on the graph of the function $f(x) = x^2$ (for all x) which lies closest to the point $(0, 2)$ in the xy plane? If so, which?

*13. Parallel the proof of Theorem D ("guaranteeing maxima and minima") of Sec. 12.5, to show that an absolute minimum must exist for a continuous function on a closed interval.

*12.9   UNIFORM CONTINUITY

For later use, I'll include here a result which follows from the very same kind of reasoning as I pictured in Figs. 12-14 through 12-16 and in Figs. 12-17 through 12-19.

EXAMPLE 1. Look at the graph of $f(x) = 1/x$, for $0 < x \leqslant 3$, in Fig. 12-24.

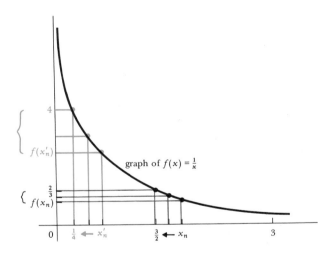

FIGURE 12-24

graph of $f(x) = \frac{1}{x}$

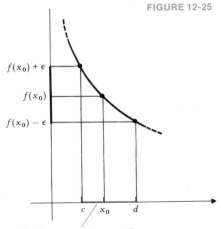

FIGURE 12-25

$f(x_0) + \epsilon$

$f(x_0)$

$f(x_0) - \epsilon$

$c \quad x_0 \quad d$

The "guarantee distance" δ

Although f is continuous both at 3/2 and at 1/4, note that as the x_n approach 3/2 the vertical distances $|f(x_n) - f(3/2)|$ tend to zero "more quickly" then do the (green) distances $|f(x_n') - f(1/4)|$ as the similarly spaced x_n' approach $\frac{1}{4}$. The nearer an input x_0 is to zero, the steeper the graph is above x_0, and the "slower" the convergence of $|f(x_n) - f(x_0)|$ to zero should be as x_n tends to x_0.

More specifically, let's choose any vertical distance $\epsilon > 0$; and let's ask how close we must pick an input x_n to a given x_0 in order to have a *guarantee* that $|f(x_n) - f(x_0)| \leqslant \epsilon$. See Fig. 12-25. Since the graph falls as x increases, we can choose as a "guarantee distance" — call it δ — the shorter of the two (green) distances $x_0 - c$ and $d - x_0$ in Fig.

12-25. Whenever an input x_n lies closer to x_0 than δ, we'll know that $c < x_n < d$. Hence $f(c) > f(x_n) > f(d)$. That is

$$f(x_0) + \epsilon > f(x_n) > f(x_0) - \epsilon \tag{1}$$

or

$$|f(x_n) - f(x_0)| < \epsilon. \tag{2}$$

Moreover, if we choose δ as in Fig. 12-25, it represents the *most generous guarantee distance* from x_0. Because if we permit ourselves to exceed δ, we can pick $x_n < c$ and get $f(x_n) > f(c) = f(x_0) + \epsilon$, or $|f(x_n) - f(x_0)| > \epsilon$.

To evaluate δ in this example, just invert the equalities

$$f(c) = \frac{1}{c} = f(x_0) + \epsilon = \frac{1}{x_0} + \epsilon = \frac{1 + \epsilon x_0}{x_0} \tag{3}$$

and

$$f(d) = \frac{1}{d} = f(x_0) - \epsilon = \frac{1}{x_0} - \epsilon = \frac{1 - \epsilon x_0}{x_0}, \tag{4}$$

to get

$$c = \frac{x_0}{1 + \epsilon x_0} \quad \text{and} \quad d = \frac{x_0}{1 - \epsilon x_0}. \tag{5}$$

$$x_0 - c = x_0 - \frac{x_0}{1 + \epsilon x_0} = \frac{(1 + \epsilon x_0)x_0 - x_0}{1 + \epsilon x_0} = \left(\frac{\epsilon}{1 + \epsilon x_0}\right) x_0{}^2 \tag{6}$$

and

$$d - x_0 = \frac{x_0}{1 - \epsilon x_0} - x_0 = \frac{x_0 - (1 - \epsilon x_0)x_0}{1 - \epsilon x_0} = \left(\frac{\epsilon}{1 - \epsilon x_0}\right) x_0{}^2. \tag{7}$$

The smaller of the two distances in (6) and (7) is

$$\delta = \left(\frac{\epsilon}{1 + \epsilon x_0}\right) x_0{}^2. \tag{8}$$

Note that δ depends on the allowed vertical distance ϵ. Moreover, it depends on x_0 too. And the closer x_0 is to 0, the smaller δ is—so the closer x_n must be to x_0 to have $|f(x_n) - f(x_0)| \leq \epsilon$ (see Problem 10 of Sec. 11.3 for an alternate definition of continuity in terms of such δ's).

Would you CONJECTURE that if the graph of f couldn't rise without bound—if it were "tied down" to a point $(0, f(0))$—then (given ϵ) we could find one single guarantee distance δ which would work at *all* inputs x_0? See Fig. 12-26.

EXAMPLE 2. For $f(x) = 1/x$ on the domain $1 \leq x \leq 3$, and any fixed $\epsilon > 0$, the most generous guarantee distance δ remains as calculated in Example 1, (8) above:

$$\delta = \left(\frac{\epsilon}{1 + \epsilon x_0}\right) x_0{}^2$$

FIGURE 12-26

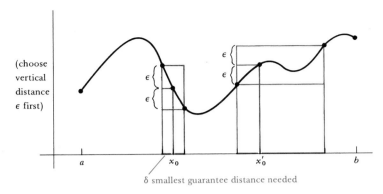

δ smallest guarantee distance needed

at the input x_0. For fixed ϵ, δ is a *function* of x_0. Check that this function decreases as we decrease x_0: if $x_0 < x_0'$ then

$$\frac{\epsilon}{1 + \epsilon x_0} x_0{}^2 < \frac{\epsilon}{1 + \epsilon x_0'} (x_0')^2$$

(Problem 3 of Sec. 12.10). Hence for $1 \leqslant x_0 \leqslant 3$, the smallest δ must correspond to $x_0 = 1$,

$$\delta_{\text{MIN}} = \frac{\epsilon}{1 + \epsilon}. \tag{9}$$

No matter what other inputs x_0 and x_n we might choose in the interval $[1, 3]$, as long as $|x_n - x_0| < \delta_{\text{MIN}} = \epsilon/(1 + \epsilon)$, we must have $|f(x_n) - f(x_0)| < \epsilon$.

Note that even the smallest guarantee distance δ still depends on the originally chosen vertical distance ϵ. Let's henceforth denote such dependence by a subscript, δ_ϵ.

Here is a standard name for situations where a single δ_ϵ can serve at all x_0's:

Definition: Call a function f *uniformly continuous* on an interval $[a, b]$ if, given any $\epsilon > 0$, there exists a positive number δ_ϵ such that $|f(x) - f(x')| < \epsilon$ whenever x and x' are two inputs in $[a, b]$ with $|x - x'| < \delta_\epsilon$.

And the conjecture above? It's correct:

Theorem F (on "uniform continuity"): Any function continuous on a closed interval $[a, b]$ must also be uniformly continuous on $[a, b]$.

I invite you to inspect the next three figures for a

Proof of Theorem F. Choose an $\epsilon > 0$. We must show that a positive number δ_ϵ exists such that

$$|f(x) - f(x')| < \epsilon \text{ whenever } x \text{ and } x' \text{ are in } [a, b] \text{ and } |x - x'| < \delta_\epsilon. \tag{10}$$

Let's start with the supposition that *no* such number exists, and see how that leads to a logical impossibility.

FIGURE 12-27

PICK INPUT PAIRS
x_n and x_n'

WITH

$|f(x_n) - f(x_n')| \geqslant \epsilon \begin{cases} f(x_n) \\ f(x_n') \end{cases}$

AND

$|x_n - x_n'| < \frac{1}{n}$

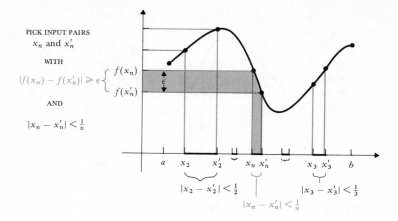

$|x_2 - x_2'| < \frac{1}{2}$ $|x_3 - x_3'| < \frac{1}{3}$

$|x_n - x_n'| < \frac{1}{n}$

FIGURE 12-28

EXTRACT FROM $\left\{ x_n \right\}$
A SUBSEQUENCE OF
INPUTS $\left\{ x_{n_k} \right\}$ WITH

$\lim\limits_{k\to\infty} x_{n_k} = x_0$

FOR SOME x_0 IN $[a, b]$

(Can do by Theorem B on
convergent subsequences,
Sec. 10.4)

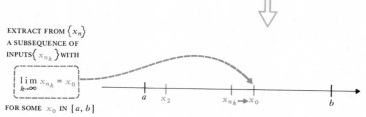

FIGURE 12-29

f MUST BE
CONTINUOUS AT x_0

SO

$\lim\limits_{k\to\infty} x_{n_k} = x_0 = \lim\limits_{k\to\infty} x_{n_k}'$

IMPLIES

$\lim\limits_{k\to\infty} f(x_{n_k}) = f(x_0) = \lim\limits_{k\to\infty} f(x_{n_k}')$

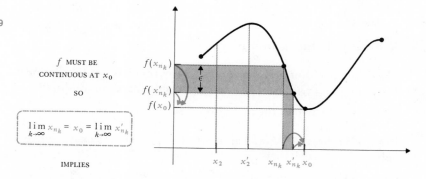

In particular, no reciprocal $1/n$ can serve as δ_ϵ. Hence for each n, there must be two inputs — call them x_n and x'_n — in $[a, b]$ with

$$|x_n - x'_n| < \frac{1}{n}, \tag{11}$$

but also with

$$|f(x_n) - f(x'_n)| \geq \epsilon. \tag{12}$$

(See Figs. 12-27 and 12-28.)

Note that for the subsequence of partners $\{x'_{n_k}\}$ we must have

$$\lim_{k \to \infty} x'_{n_k} = x_0 \tag{13}$$

also. This is because

$$x'_{n_k} - x_0 = (x'_{n_k} - x_{n_k}) + (x_{n_k} - x_0) \tag{14}$$

and both $\{x'_{n_k} - x_{n_k}\}$ and $\{x_{n_k} - x_0\}$ are null sequences. Hence, Fig. 12-29.

But how can $f(x_{n_k})$ and $f(x'_{n_k})$ both converge to $f(x_0)$ while always staying at least ϵ units apart? We must have

$$\lim_{k \to \infty} [f(x_{n_k}) - f(x'_{n_k})]$$
$$= \lim_{k \to \infty} [f(x_{n_k}) - f(x_0)] + \lim_{k \to \infty} [f(x_0) - f(x'_{n_k})] = 0 + 0 = 0. \tag{15}$$

So we've arrived at a logical impossibility from the supposition that no δ_ϵ exists as required. *Conclusion:* a suitable δ_ϵ must exist.   End of the proof.

*12.10 PROBLEMS ON UNIFORM CONTINUITY

1. For each of the following functions f, and for values $\epsilon = 1/10$ and $\epsilon = 1/100$, find if possible a $\delta_\epsilon > 0$ such that $|f(x) - f(x')| < \epsilon$ whenever $|x - x'| < \delta_\epsilon$.
   (a) $f(x) = x$ for all x (b) $f(x) = x^2$ for all x
   (c) $f(x) = x^2$ for $0 \leq x \leq 1$
   (d) $f(x) = x^2$ for $0 \leq x \leq 10$

   (e) $f(x) = \begin{cases} 0 & \text{for } -1 \leq x < 0 \\ 1 & \text{for } 0 \leq x \leq 1 \end{cases}$ (f) $f(x) = \dfrac{1}{1+x^2}$

   (g) $f(x) = x^2 + x - 2$ for $0 \leq x \leq 1$ (h) $f(x) = x + \dfrac{1}{x}$ for $x > 0$

   (i) $f(x) = x - \dfrac{1}{x}$ for $x > 0$.

2. Show that if a function f is uniformly continuous on an interval $[a, b]$, then it must also be just plain continuous on $[a, b]$.

3. (a) If a, b, and c are positive numbers and $a < b$ show that

   $$\frac{a^2}{1+ca} < \frac{b^2}{1+cb}.$$

   (Suggestion: Show that $b^2/(1 + cb) - a^2/(1 + cb)$ can be written as $(b - a)$ times a factor which is always positive.)

(b) Show that the inequality

$$\frac{\epsilon}{1 + \epsilon x_0} x_0^2 < \frac{\epsilon}{1 + \epsilon x_0'} (x_0')^2$$

of Example 2 of Sec. 12.9 is valid.

4. If f and g are functions uniformly continuous on a domain $\mathscr{D}$, which of the following functions must also be uniformly continuous on $\mathscr{D}$?

(a) cf, where c is an arbitrary constant.

(b) $f + g$ (c) fg

(d) f/g if $g(x) \neq 0$ for all inputs x in $\mathscr{D}$.

*5. Can the *graph* of any continuous function f on $[0, 1]$ be enclosed in a finite set of rectangles of *arbitrarily small total area*? See the shaded rectangles in the accompanying figure.

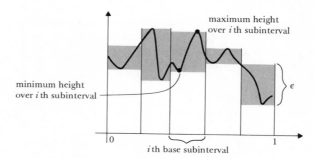

maximum height over ith subinterval

minimum height over ith subinterval

ϵ

0 1

ith base subinterval

(Given an $\epsilon > 0$, can you use the *uniform* continuity of f to determine a size for base subintervals so that the graph of f won't change altitude by more than ϵ over any base subinterval?)

**6. What ordinary continuity of a function f at all points x_0 in $[a, b]$ means is that, given $\epsilon > 0$, each x_0 in $[a, b]$ is contained in an open interval I_{x_0}, whose length *depends* on x_0, such that $|f(x) - f(x_0)| < \epsilon$ for all x in I_{x_0}. (See the figure.) Uniform continuity means that such I's can be found all of the *same* length. Here is an alternate way of showing that ordinary continuity implies uniform continuity on a finite closed interval $[a, b]$, based on the "$\epsilon - \delta$" notion of Problem 10 in Sec. 11.3.

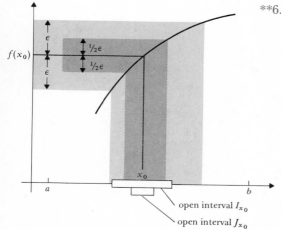

$f(x_0)$

ϵ

$\frac{1}{2}\epsilon$

$\frac{1}{2}\epsilon$

ϵ

x_0

a b

open interval I_{x_0}

open interval J_{x_0}

(a) Let's say that a (possibly infinite) collection of *open* intervals $\{I\}$ "*covers*" $[a, b]$ if each x in $[a, b]$ is contained in at least one of the I's. Show that any such collection must contain a *finite* subcollection of I's which do the job of covering $[a, b]$.

(One procedure: Let C be the set of all c's in $[a, b]$ with the property that the subinterval $[a, c]$ is already covered by finitely many of the I's. And let d be the least upper bound of C. Show that d is in C, and that $d = b$.)

(b) Given $\epsilon > 0$, pick for each x_0 in $[a, b]$ a suitably small open interval J_{x_0}, as in the figure. By part (a), finitely many of the J_{x_0}'s must cover $[a, b]$. Let δ_ϵ be $\frac{1}{2}$ the length of the shortest of these. And show that $|f(x) - f(x')| < \epsilon$ for any x and x' in $[a, b]$ with $|x - x'| < \delta_\epsilon$.

12.11   SUMMARY OF CHAPTER 12

Bounds for sets (Sec. 12.2)

DEFINITIONS: Call a set S of real numbers *bounded above* if there is some real number d such that $s \leq d$ for all s in S, and call d an *upper bound* for S. If S has no other upper bound $d' < d$, then call d a *least upper bound*.

Similarly, call a set S *bounded below* if there is some real number c such that $c \leq s$ for all s in S, and call c a *lower bound* for S. If S has no other lower bound $c' > c$, then call c a *greatest lower bound*.

Call a set S *bounded* if there is some real number b such that $|s| \leq b$ for all s in S.

REMARK: Three equivalent statements of boundedness:

(i) S is "bounded": $|s| \leq b$ for all s in S

(ii) S is bounded above and below

(iii) S lies entirely in some interval $[c, d]$.

REMARK: If a set S has a least upper bound it can have only one. If a set S has an upper bound d which lies *in* S, then d must be a least upper bound. Similarly for lower bounds.

THEOREM (ON "UNBOUNDED SETS"): If S is an unbounded (that is, not bounded) set of real numbers, then we can extract a sequence of numbers $\{s_n\}$ from S such that $|s_n| > n$ for each positive integer n, and moreover, $|s_{n+1}| > |s_n|$.

THEOREM (ON "LEAST UPPER BOUNDS FOR SETS"): If a set S of real numbers is bounded above, then it has a least upper bound d. In that case: either d is itself a number in S, or there is an increasing sequence $\{s_n\}$ of numbers in S such that $\lim_{n \to \infty} s_n = d$; or both may be true. Similarly for a set bounded below and its greatest lower bound.

Bounds for functions (Sec. 12.3)

DEFINITIONS: Call a function f (with domain D) *bounded above* if there is some number d such that $f(x) \leq d$ for all x in D, and call d an *upper bound* for f. If f has no other upper bound $d' < d$, then call d a *least upper bound*.

Similarly, call a function f (with domain D) *bounded below* if there is some real number c such that $c \leq f(x)$ for all x in D, and call c a *lower bound* for f. If f has no other lower bound $c' > c$, then call c a *greatest lower bound*.

Call a function f (with domain D) *bounded* if there is some real number b such that $|f(x)| \leq b$ for all x in D.

REMARK: Four equivalent statements of boundedness:

(i) f is "bounded": $|f(x)| \leq b$ for all x in D.

(ii) f is bounded above and below.

(iii) the range of f lies entirely in some interval $[c, d]$.

(iv) the graph of f lies entirely in a horizontal "tube" in the plane, between lines with equations $y = c$ and $y = d$.

THEOREM (ON "UNBOUNDED FUNCTIONS"): If a function f is unbounded (that is, not bounded) then we can extract a sequence of outputs $f(x_n)$ such that $|f(x_n)| > n$ for each positive integer n, and moreover, $|f(x_{n+1})| > |f(x_n)|$.

THEOREM (ON "LEAST UPPER BOUNDS FOR FUNCTIONS"): If a function f is bounded above, then it has a least upper bound d. In that case: either d is itself an output $d = f(x_0)$ for some input x_0; or there is an increasing sequence of outputs $f(x_n)$ such that $\lim_{n\to\infty} f(x_n) = d$; or both may be true.

Results on maxima and minima

THEOREM (ON "BOUNDS FOR CONTINUOUS FUNCTIONS"): Suppose that a function f has as domain a closed interval $[a, b]$ (of finite length) and that f is continuous on $[a, b]$. Then f must be bounded. (Sec. 12.4)

THEOREM ("GUARANTEEING MAXIMA AND MINIMA"): Suppose that a function f has as domain a closed interval $[a, b]$ (of finite length) and that f is continuous on $[a, b]$. Then there exists an input $x_{\max}$ such that $f(x_{\max})$ is a (absolute) maximum for f: $f(x) \leq f(x_{\max})$ for all x in $[a, b]$. Similarly, there exists an input $x_{\min}$ such that $f(x_{\min})$ is an (absolute) minimum for f: $f(x_{\min}) \leq f(x)$ for all x in $[a, b]$. (Sec. 12.4)

DEFINITIONS: Call an output $f(x_1)$ a *relative maximum* of a function f if there is an interval $[a_1, b_1]$, with $a_1 < x_1 < b_1$, such that $f(x) \leq f(x_1)$ for all inputs x in $[a_1, b_1]$. Similarly, call an output $f(x_2)$ a *relative minimum* of f if there is an interval $[a_2, b_2]$, with $a_2 < x_2 < b_2$, such that $f(x_2) \leq f(x)$ for all inputs x in $[a_2, b_2]$.

(Remark: Absolute maxima and minima are "relative" also.) (Sec. 12.6)

THEOREM (ON "DERIVATIVES AT MAXIMA AND MINIMA"): Suppose that a function f is defined for $a \leq x \leq b$ and that x_0 is an input with $a < x_0 < b$. If $f(x_0)$ is a relative maximum or minimum and if $f'(x_0)$ exists, then we must have $f'(x_0) = 0$.

DEFINITION: Call a function f *uniformly continuous* on an interval $[a, b]$ if, given any $\epsilon > 0$, there exists a positive number δ_ϵ such that $|f(x) - f(x')| < \epsilon$ whenever x and x' are two inputs in $[a, b]$ with $|x - x'| < \delta_\epsilon$.

THEOREM (ON "UNIFORM CONTINUITY"): Any function continuous on a closed interval $[a, b]$ must also be uniformly continuous on $[a, b]$.

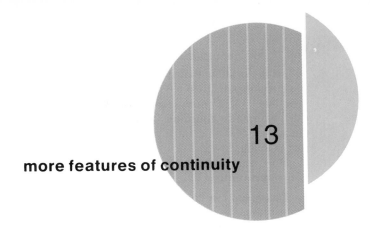

more features of continuity

13

In this chapter I'll use the notion of continuity to show that all sorts of roots of numbers exist. Then I can define irrational exponents, and logarithms. We'll be able to include "exponential" functions, "log" functions, and other inverses, in the catalog of continuous functions.

13.1 CAN CONTINUOUS FUNCTIONS SOMEHOW SKIP VALUES? MUST $\sqrt[3]{\pi}$ EXIST?

Intuitively, a "continuous" function is one whose graph has no "breaks." Thus, if a function f is continuous at each x in some interval $[x_1, x_2]$, you might expect its graph *to pass at least once through every altitude between the two input altitudes $f(x_1)$ and $f(x_2)$* — as in Figs. 13-1 and 13-2.

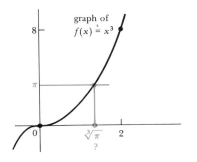

FIGURE 13-1

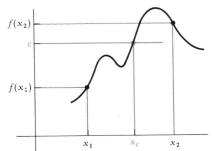

FIGURE 13-2

   Must such a conclusion follow from the particular definition of continuity in Sec. 11.2? What I recorded there was a formulation whereby people have tried to capture the notion of a graph having no "break" *at a particular point* $(x_0, f(x_0))$, namely: $\lim_{x \to x_0} f(x) = f(x_0)$. Even if we know that the graph of $f(x) = x^3$ has no break for every existing input x_0, do we really know yet whether an input deserving the label "$\sqrt[3]{\pi}$" does exist? And if one doesn't, what power lies in the manmade continuity definition to force a conclusion that the graph of $f(x) = x^3$ must make an appearance exactly at the altitude π? (See Fig. 13-1.)

Here is a result which shows that the continuity definition doesn't fail our intuition:

Theorem A (on "intermediate values"): Suppose that a function f is continuous at all x in some interval $[x_1, x_2]$, and that $f(x_1) \neq f(x_2)$. Pick any number c between $f(x_1)$ and $f(x_2)$. Then there exists at least one input — call it x_c — with $x_1 < x_c < x_2$ and $f(x_c) = c$.

I'll give arguments for Theorem A in the next section. But first, let's see how we can use Theorem A itself as foolproof evidence for quantities — such as $\sqrt[3]{\pi}$ — whose existence you may for years have taken merely on faith.

EXAMPLE 1: *Odd roots.* Every real number c has a unique "nth root," $c^{1/n}$, if n is an *odd* positive integer. Why? Because the power function $f(x) = x^n$ is continuous at all x. In particular, for $c > 0$, f is continuous on the interval $0 \le x \le c + 1$. And c lies between the outputs $f(0) = 0$ and $f(c+1) = (c+1)^n$. Hence there exists an input x_c (with $0 < x_c < c + 1$), such that

$$f(x_c) = x_c{}^n = c. \tag{1}$$

This equality is the precise meaning of the symbolism $x_c = c^{1/n}$. (See Fig. 13-3.) For the case $c < 0$: merely inspect f over the interval $[c-1, 0]$. (For the case $c = 0$: $0^n = 0$; hence $0 = 0^{1/n}$.) Finally, the *uniqueness* of the nth roots follows from the fact that f is one-to-one, since $x_1{}^n < x_2{}^n$, when $x_1 < x_2$.

FIGURE 13-3

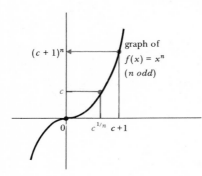

graph of
$f(x) = x^n$
(n odd)

$(c+1)^n$

c

0 $c^{1/n}$ $c+1$

FIGURE 13-4

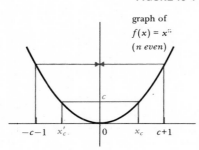

graph of
$f(x) = x^{..}$
(n even)

c

$-c-1$ x_c' 0 x_c $c+1$

EXAMPLE 2: *Even roots.* If n is an *even* positive integer, then every positive number c has exactly two roots, one positive and one negative. (See Fig. 13-4.) Merely apply the argument of Example 1 to the intervals $[0, c+1]$ and $[-c-1, 0]$ separately.

Here is another instance wherein the "result on intermediate values" will support what seems intuitively reasonable.

A corollary (on "changes of sign"): If a function f has outputs $f(x_1)$ and $f(x_2)$ of *opposite sign* and is continuous on the interval $[x_1, x_2]$, then $f(x_0) = 0$ for some input x_0 with $x_1 < x_0 < x_2$. Put in other terms: If f is continuous and never zero on some interval (open, closed, or half-infinite), then all outputs must have the *same sign* there.

Why? Because whenever two outputs $f(x_1)$ and $f(x_2)$ do have opposite sign, then the value $c = 0$ is intermediate between them. And we're forced to have $f(x_0) = 0$ for some x_0 between x_1 and x_2.

EXAMPLE 3: A polynomial such as $x^2 + 1$ has no real root, but *every polynomial of* ODD *degree must have at least one real root.* Why? Consider a polynomial

$$P(x) = a_0 + a_1 x + a_2 x^2 + \cdots + a_{n-1} x^{n-1} + a_n x^n \qquad (a_n \neq 0).$$

When $|x|$ is very large, the term $a_n x^n$ "dominates" all the others. More precisely, we can write $P(x)$ in the form

$$P(x) = (a_n x^n) \left[\frac{a_0}{a_n} \frac{1}{x^n} + \frac{a_1}{a_n} \frac{1}{x^{n-1}} + \frac{a_2}{a_n} \frac{1}{x^{n-2}} + \cdots + \frac{a_{n-1}}{a_n} \frac{1}{x^{n-1}} + 1 \right].$$

And when $|x|$ is very large, the factor [ ] must be a number close to 1, since its first n terms are all very small. Now, if n is *odd*, the factor $(a_n x^n)$ takes on *opposite signs* according to whether x is positive or negative. Hence, when $|x|$ is very large, the product $P(x) = (a_n x^n)[\ ]$ must also take on opposite signs according to whether x is positive or negative. Conclusion: there must exist an input x_0 in between with $P(x_0) = 0$.

Regarding signs of outputs, note also this basic feature of limits — which I'll label

Theorem B (on "nearby signs"): If $\lim\limits_{x \to x_0} f(x) = A > 0$, then $f(x) > 0$ for all inputs $x \neq x_0$ which lie in some interval $[x_0 - \delta, x_0 + \delta]$ surrounding x_0. In particular, if a function f is continuous at an input x_0 and $f(x_0) > 0$, then $f(x) > 0$ for *all* x in some interval $[x_0 - \delta, x_0 + \delta]$. (See Fig. 13-5.)

FIGURE 13-5

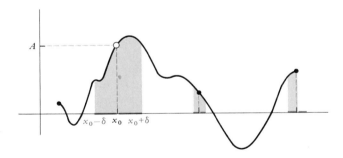

Why? Because otherwise every interval of the form

$$\left[x_0 - \left(\frac{1}{n} \right), x_0 + \left(\frac{1}{n} \right) \right], \quad \text{for } n = 1, 2, 3, \ldots$$

would contain some input — call it x_n — with $x_n \neq x_0$ and $f(x_n) \leq 0$. Since $|x_n - x_0| < 1/n$, we would have $\lim\limits_{n \to \infty} x_n = x_0$. Hence $\lim\limits_{n \to \infty} f(x_n) = A$. Hence the contradiction that $A \leq 0$, as the limit of $f(x_n) \leq 0$. In case f is continuous at x_0, the role of A is played by $f(x_0)$.

(You might also recall Problems 8 and 10 of Sec. 11.3 on alternate definitions of limit and continuity involving $[x_0 - \delta, x_0 + \delta]$ intervals.)

Now for an instance where the result on "intermediate values" may not support your intuition:

EXAMPLE 4. Imagine that you have a friend in a hypnotic state of rigidity whom you must send home on a lurching trolley car. No seats are available, so you must implant him on a spot on the floor — say with wads of chewing gum under his soles to fix him there. As the car lurches his body will sway back and forth; the angle between his body and the floor will keep changing. See Fig. 13-6.

FIGURE 13-6

Question: Is there a beginning angle at which you can place him so that when he comes to his home stop his body will be at 90° from the floor?

Answer: Yes, if Theorem A on "intermediate values" is true, and if you reason like this:

Think of a plot of how the angle θ changes with time t, as in Fig. 13-7. For a specific beginning angle, say $\theta = x$, there will be a corresponding angle at the stopping time — call it $\theta = f(x)$. In other words the motion of the problem defines a function f with possible beginning angles as inputs and finishing angles as outputs. We don't know a precise formula for f — that would depend on all the aspects of the motion. But it seems reasonable to *assume* that whatever the precise rule f may be, it will be true that if we make only the slightest of changes in the starting angle x, then the result will be only a slight change in the stopping angle — via, say, the dotted plot in Fig. 13-7. Physicists usually make such assumptions — for better or worse. But what does such an assumption amount to? I indicate a possible graph for f in Fig. 13-8. If x_1 and x_2 are any starting angles that are close together, then their corresponding stopping angles

FIGURE 13-7

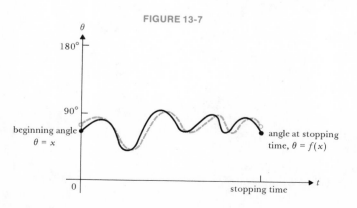

FIGURE 13-8

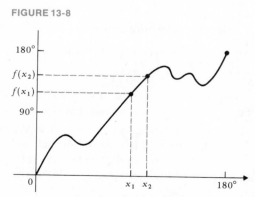

$f(x_1)$ and $f(x_2)$ should be close together; which means that there can be no breaks in the graph — otherwise there could be a situation as in Fig. 13-9. So the assumption is that f must be *continuous*.

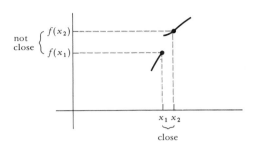

FIGURE 13-9

Now if the starting angle x is 0, your friend must be lying on his stomach and will remain so; hence $f(0) = 0$. If $x = 180°$, he is lying on his back and will remain so; hence $f(180°) = 180°$. See Fig. 13-8. If Theorem A "on intermediate values" is true, there must be some starting angle x_{90} such that $f(x_{90}) = 90°$.   End of the argument.

13.2 WHY SHOULD THE RESULT ON "INTERMEDIATE VALUES" BE TRUE?

Look at Fig. 13-10 where $f(x_1) < c < f(x_2)$. How can we find an input x_c that will yield $c = f(x_c)$? (There may be several candidates. How can we locate, say, the largest of them?) Why not separate all inputs in $[x_1, x_2]$ into two sets, according to whether their outputs don't or do lie above the value c (black vs. green in Fig. 13-10).

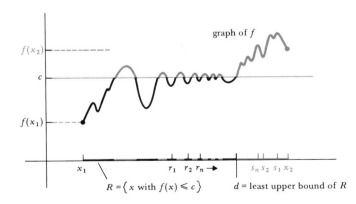

FIGURE 13-10

If we can locate some input d which sits on a "boundary" between the two sets, shouldn't the continuity of f at d force the output $f(d)$ to be exactly equal to c? If so, then d will be the sought for input x_c.

Here are a few more details for a

Proof of Theorem A: Let R be the set of all (black) inputs x in $[x_1, x_2]$ with $f(x) \leq c$. The remaining (green) inputs x with $f(x) > c$ constitute a set S. Note that x_1 lies in R, and x_2 lies in S. Being bounded above (by x_2) the set R must have a *least upper bound*—call it d. And d must lie in R, or at least d must be the limit of an increasing sequence $\{r_n\}$ of inputs in r (by Theorem B on "least upper bounds for sets," in Sec. 12.2). Even in the latter case we can conclude that d must lie in R: Because f is continuous at d, we must have

$$\lim_{n \to \infty} f(r_n) = f(d). \tag{1}$$

Moreover, $f(r_n) \leq c$ for all n. Hence

$$f(d) = \lim_{n \to \infty} f(r_n) \leq c,$$

and d qualifies for membership in R. (The inequality (1) follows from Property O on "comparison" of limits of sequences, in Chap. 9.)

Note that $d \neq x_2$, because x_2 is in S. Moreover, since d is an *upper* bound for R, all the inputs x with $d < x < x_2$ must lie in S. Pick any sequence $\{s_n\}$ with $d < s_n < x_2$ and $\lim_{n \to \infty} s_n = d$ (for example,

$$s_n = d + (1/n)(x_2 - d), \quad \text{for } n = 1, 2, \ldots).$$

Let's appeal again to the continuity of f at d to conclude that

$$\lim_{n \to \infty} f(s_n) = f(d). \tag{2}$$

This time $f(s_n) > c$ for all n, and we must have

$$f(d) = \lim_{n \to \infty} f(s_n) \geq c. \tag{3}$$

Together, the two inequalities $f(d) \leq c$ and $f(d) \geq c$ force $f(d) = c$. (Note therefore that $d > x_1$, since $f(x_1) < c$.) We've shown that the input d qualifies for the label x_c: $x_1 < d < x_2$, and $f(d) = c$. A similar argument will work for the case $f(x_1) > c > f(x_2)$.   End of the proof.

13.3 EXPONENTIAL FUNCTIONS

In Sec. 13.1 (Examples 1 and 2), I noted why each positive number c must possess a unique positive root $c^{1/n}$ for every positive integer n. That result justifies the definitions of all *rational powers of c*:

$$c^{i/j} = [c^i]^{1/j}, \tag{1}$$

where i is any integer and j is a positive integer. (You should check that $[c^i]^{1/j}$ always is identical to $[c^{1/j}]^i$. See Problem 4 of Sec. 13.5.) Actually, I presupposed such definitions in Chapters 8 and 9, in formulating properties about sequences with rational exponents. Now we know that the quantities I spoke of there always make sense.

But how can we assign a reasonable meaning to an *irrational power*, such as 2^π? In Fig. 13-11 I've sketched the graph of the function $f(x) = 2^x$ defined only for *rational* inputs x. To define 2^π, let's borrow the black-set-vs.-green-set idea from Fig. 13-10 of the last section, and apply it now on the *vertical* axis, to the range of $f(x) = 2^x$: Color black all the outputs $f(r)$ for rational $r < \pi$. They form a set—call it R—which is bounded above. (Any number 2^s, where $s > \pi$, will serve as an upper bound.) Hence R must have a least upper bound (by Theorem B on least upper bounds for sets, in Sec. 12.2). Color green

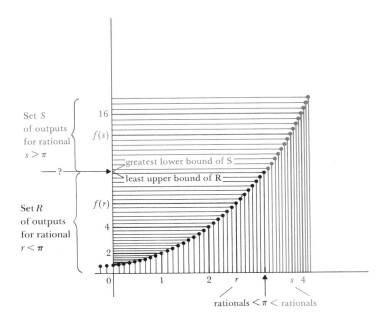

Set S
of outputs
for rational
$s > \pi$

16

$f(s)$

—?—

greatest lower bound of S

least upper bound of R

Set R
of outputs
for rational
$r < \pi$

$f(r)$

4

2

0   1   2 r s 4

rationals $< \pi <$ rationals

FIGURE 13-11

all the outputs $f(s)$ for rational $s > \pi$. They form a set—call it S—
which is bounded below, and must have a *greatest lower bound*. I invite
you to check that the least upper bound of R and the greatest lower
bound of S must be identical. (Do Problem 10 of Sec. 13.5.) Why not
define their common value as "2^π"?

We could make a similar definition for "c^x" where c is any positive
number and x is any irrational. And we might then verify that old
intuitive rules for exponents do follow from the precise definitions—
such as,

$$c^{x+y} = c^x c^y \tag{2}$$

and

$$c^{xy} = (c^x)^y = (c^y)^x \tag{3}$$

for all real x and y; and

$$c^x < c^y \qquad \text{if } x < y \text{ and } c > 1,$$

and

$$c^x > c^y \qquad \text{if } x < y \text{ and } 0 < c < 1. \tag{4}$$

(Try your hand at Problems 8–13 of Sec. 13.5.) In what follows, I'll
suppose that all such properties have been checked, and that we can
use numbers of the form c^x for any real x without fear of hidden
pitfalls.

In fact, for any *positive* number c, let's

Define: *the exponential function (with base c) as the rule assigning to
each real input x the output number c^x.*

You might visualize the graph of the exponential function 2^x as
obtainable from the graph in Fig. 13-11 by filling in the spaces—the

result being a curve with no breaks. More generally, you might conjecture that

Theorem C (on "the continuity of exponential functions"): For any positive number $c \neq 1$, the exponential function c^x is continuous at every real input x_0.

The conjecture is true. If you seek a proof, I'll present arguments in the next section. But first, here is a prime example of the use of exponential functions.

EXAMPLE 1. Population growth and the function e^t, where

$$e = \lim_{n \to \infty} [1 + (1/n)]^n.$$

Do you perhaps recall (from Sec. 6.5) the models I discussed for the growth of a large population of bacteria of mixed ages, wherein each organism lives for one hour (on the average) and then splits into two new organisms? For the mth approximation, I divided time into intervals of length $(1/m)$th hour. Let's let $S_m(t)$ be the average population size after t hours, according to the mth model. At $t = 0$, I started with a large number N of bacteria, so $S_m(0) = N$. Then, my basic *assumption* for the mth model was that *at the end of any interval of length $1/m$ splitting took place for approximately $(1/m)$th of the organisms present at the beginning of that interval.* For the ith interval $[(i-1)/m \leqslant t < (i/m)]$:

$$S_m\left(\frac{i}{m}\right) - S_m\left(\frac{i-1}{m}\right) = \frac{1}{m} S_m\left(\frac{i-1}{m}\right). \tag{5}$$

(Recall that an individual bacterial split causes a net increase of *one* in the population size.) From this relationship, I concluded in Sec. 6.5

FIGURE 13-12

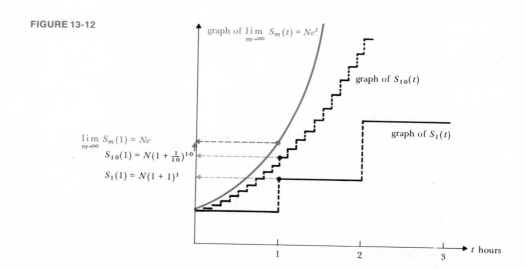

that the average population should have

$$S_m(t) = N\left(1 + \frac{1}{m}\right)^{i-1} \tag{6}$$

bacteria during the ith time interval, $(i-1)/m \leq t < i/m$—for any $i = 1, 2, 3, \ldots$. Thus the graph of $S_m(t)$ is composed of "steps" of width $1/m$, as in Fig. 13-12 (which repeats Fig. 6-4).

Will the graphs of $S_m(t)$ approach a limiting curve if we pick m larger and larger? From Sec. 10.2 we have evidence concerning the function outputs $S_m(t)$ for the particular time $t = 1$ hour: In the mth model, the time $t = 1$ hour begins the $(m+1)$st time interval. Hence (in (6) above)

$$S_m(1) = N\left(1 + \frac{1}{m}\right)^m, \tag{7}$$

and

$$\lim_{m \to \infty} S_m(1) = N \lim_{m \to \infty} \left(1 + \frac{1}{m}\right)^m$$
$$= Ne. \tag{8}$$

(See Example 2 of Sec. 10.2.)

How about the population sizes $\{S_m(t)\}$ at any other fixed time t, if we pick m larger and larger?

Answer:

$$\lim_{m \to \infty} S_m(t) = Ne^t \qquad \text{for } every \text{ fixed } t \geq 0. \tag{9}$$

I invite you to check that (9) holds for *rational* t's, in doing Problem 14 of Sec. 13.5. You might then use the *continuity* of the function Ne^t to help extend the result to all irrational t's—in Problem 15 of Sec. 13.5.

The values $S_m(t)$ approach Ne^t very quickly—as you may have noted for the case $t = 1$, in Sec. 6.5, table (6). Biologists almost universally use the continuous function Ne^t to approximate the growth of a large population where ages are well mixed, where organisms don't die, and where each organism lives for an average of one hour before splitting into two.

Note that if organisms had an average lifetime of *two* hours before splitting, the growth would take place half as fast. And we should expect the population to grow from size N to size Ne^t in $2t$ hours—for any t. Let $T = 2t$ (or $t = \frac{1}{2}T$) to see that the population will grow from size N to size $Ne^{T/2}$ in T hours.

More generally, if organisms have an average lifetime of L hours before splitting (for some fixed $L > 0$), then we might expect the population to grow from size N to size $Ne^{T/L}$ in T hours.

If at noon you become host to 1000 bacteria that produce a certain disease, and if the average bacterial lifetime is 45 minutes before splitting, to how many of these organisms will you be host at 6 p.m. of the same day?

Answer: Here the average lifetime is $L = \frac{3}{4}$ hours; so after $T = 6$ hours we can expect $1000\, e^{6/(3/4)} = 1000\, e^8$ bacteria. Since $e > 2.5$, $e^8 > (5/2)^8 = 1526$ (approximately). Hence $1000\, e^8 > (1000)(1526) = 1.5$ million, approximately.

EXAMPLE 2: The *rate* of population growth: the *derivative* of an exponential function. For the models in Example 1, the basic assumption on how population size $S_m(t)$ increases during a time interval $(i-1)/m \leqslant t \leqslant i/m$ was

$$S_m\!\left(\frac{i}{m}\right) - S_m\!\left(\frac{i-1}{m}\right) = \frac{1}{m} S_m\!\left(\frac{i-1}{m}\right) \tag{5}$$

or equivalently,

$$\frac{S_m(i/m) - S_m[(i-1)/m]}{1/m} = S_m\!\left(\frac{i-1}{m}\right). \tag{10}$$

In this second form, the left-hand side appears as nothing other than the *"average" rate of increase of population* (in the mth model) *during the time interval* $(i-1)/m \leqslant t \leqslant i/m$. And the basic assumption was merely that this *average rate* is equal to the population size itself at the start of the interval, $t = (i-1)/m$.

In Example 1, I argued that if we choose models based on smaller and smaller time intervals $1/m$, the corresponding population functions $S_m(t)$ should tend to a limiting function $S(t) = Ne^t$, for each fixed time t. Would you conjecture that this limiting function should have the property that its *instantaneous rate* of change *at* any time t_0—its derivative $S'(t_0)$—is equal to the population size itself, $S(t_0)$, at t_0? That is

$$S'(t_0) = S(t_0) \qquad \text{at any } t_0 \geqslant 0. \tag{11}$$

Let's use the algebraic properties of exponents to explore the conjecture. For convenience, we'll let $S(t) = Ne^t$ for *all* real t (including negative inputs); and let's choose some input t_0. For $t \neq t_0$, form the difference ratio

$$\frac{S(t) - S(t_0)}{t - t_0} = \frac{Ne^t - Ne^{t_0}}{t - t_0} = \frac{Ne^{t_0 + (t - t_0)} - Ne^{t_0}}{t - t_0}$$

$$= \frac{Ne^{t_0} e^{(t-t_0)} - Ne^{t_0}}{t - t_0} = Ne^{t_0} \left\{ \frac{e^{(t-t_0)} - 1}{t - t_0} \right\}$$

$$= S(t_0) \left\{ \frac{e^{(t-t_0)} - 1}{t - t_0} \right\}. \tag{12}$$

The derivative

$$S'(t_0) = \lim_{t \to t_0} \frac{S(t) - S(t_0)}{t - t_0} = S(t_0) \lim_{t \to t_0} \left\{ \frac{e^{(t-t_0)} - 1}{t - t_0} \right\} \tag{13}$$

will exist and will equal $S(t_0)$ itself provided the

$$\lim_{t \to t_0} \left\{ \frac{e^{(t-t_0)} - 1}{t - t_0} \right\} \text{ exists and equals 1.} \tag{14}$$

For convenience, we can relabel $x = t - t_0$ and consider limits as x converges to 0 (recall Property $\hat{R}$ on "shifting inputs," in Chapter 11). Thus

$$\lim_{t \to t_0} \left\{ \frac{e^{(t-t_0)} - 1}{t - t_0} \right\} = \lim_{x \to 0} \left[\frac{e^x - 1}{x} \right] = \lim_{x \to 0} \left[\frac{e^x - e^0}{x - 0} \right], \tag{15}$$

provided the right-hand limit exists. Note that the right-hand limit in (15) is completely independent of the input t_0; and — if it exists — is nothing other than the derivative of the function $f(x) = e^x$ at $x = 0$. *Conclusion*: $S'(t_0) = S(t_0)$ at any t_0 if $f'(0) = 1$. I'll calculate $f'(0)$ in the next chapter.

EXAMPLE 3. To calculate $f'(0)$ for $f(x) = e^x$, it will be helpful to know whether quantities of the form $[1 + (1/n)]^n$ must still converge to e if we replace the n's by any sequence $\{x_n\}$ which increases without bound. (From the last section, we know how to assign a meaning to a power $[1 + (1/x)]^x$ even if x is irrational.)

Here's how to show that

$$\boxed{\lim_{n \to \infty} x_n = \infty} \quad \text{implies that} \quad \boxed{\lim_{n \to \infty} \left(1 + \frac{1}{x_n} \right)^{x_n} = e.} \tag{16}$$

For each $x_n \geq 1$, find the integers — call them M_n and $M_n + 1$ — that flank x_n on the coordinate line: that is, for which

$$M_n \leq x_n < M_n + 1. \tag{17}$$

Since the x_n increase without bound, the M_n's must too, as n increases. Let's estimate the quantity $(1 + 1/x_n)^{x_n}$ in terms of M_n. From the inequalities (17), we can conclude that

$$\frac{1}{M_n} \geq \frac{1}{x_n} > \frac{1}{M_n + 1},$$

and

$$1 + \frac{1}{M_n} \geq 1 + \frac{1}{x_n} > 1 + \frac{1}{M_n + 1},$$

and

$$\left(1 + \frac{1}{M_n} \right)^{x_n} \geq \left(1 + \frac{1}{x_n} \right)^{x_n} > \left(1 + \frac{1}{M_n + 1} \right)^{x_n}. \tag{18}$$

Moreover, since $M_n + 1 > x_n$, we have

$$\left(1 + \frac{1}{x_n} \right)^{x_n} \leq \left(1 + \frac{1}{M_n} \right)^{x_n} < \left(1 + \frac{1}{M_n} \right)^{M_n + 1} = \left(1 + \frac{1}{M_n} \right) \left(1 + \frac{1}{M_n} \right)^{M_n}. \tag{19}$$

Similarly, since $M_n \leqslant x_n$, we have

$$\left(1+\frac{1}{x_n}\right)^{x_n} > \left(1+\frac{1}{M_n+1}\right)^{x_n} \geqslant \left(1+\frac{1}{M_n+1}\right)^{M_n}$$

$$= \left(1+\frac{1}{M_n+1}\right)^{M_n+1}\left(1+\frac{1}{M_n+1}\right)^{-1}. \tag{20}$$

Taking the extreme terms in (19) and (20), we can get a squeeze on $[1+(1/x_n)]^{x_n}$ for larger and larger n:

$$\underbrace{\left(1+\frac{1}{M_n}\right)}_{\downarrow}\underbrace{\left(1+\frac{1}{M_n}\right)^{M_n}}_{\downarrow} > \underbrace{\left(1+\frac{1}{x_n}\right)^{x_n}}_{\downarrow} > \underbrace{\left(1+\frac{1}{M_n+1}\right)^{M_n+1}}_{\downarrow}\underbrace{\left(1+\frac{1}{M_n+1}\right)^{-1}}_{\downarrow}.$$

$$\begin{array}{ccccc} 1 & e & \text{squeezed} & e & 1 \\ & & \text{to} & & \\ & & \downarrow & & \\ & & e & & \end{array} \tag{21}$$

(Recall Property P, on "squeezing," in Chapter 9.) End of the proof.

We can replace the x_n by $x_n = 1/t_n$ with $\lim_{n\to\infty} t_n = 0$, and reformulate the result as

$$\lim_{t\to 0} (1+t)^{1/t} = e. \tag{22}$$

(Here the domain is all $t > 0$.)

*13.4 WHY EXPONENTIAL FUNCTIONS ARE CONTINUOUS

Here are steps leading to a

Proof of Theorem C (on "the continuity of exponential functions"):
Let's examine $f(x) = c^x$ for a fixed $c > 1$, and a fixed input x_0. We must show that $\lim_{n\to\infty} c^{x_n} = c^{x_0}$ whenever $\lim_{n\to\infty} x_n = x_0$.

Step 1. Let's take perhaps the simplest case: $x_0 = 0$ and $x_n = 1/K_n$ where K_n is an increasing sequence of positive integers—with possible repetitions—and $\lim_{n\to\infty} K_n = \infty$. Since $0 < K_n \leqslant K_{n+1}$ we must have $1/K_n \geqslant 1/K_{n+1} > 0$ and

$$c^{(1/K_n)} \geqslant c^{(1/K_{n+1})} > c^0 = 1. \tag{1}$$

Being a decreasing sequence, bounded below, $\{c^{1/K_n}\}$ must have a limit $A = \lim_{n\to\infty} c^{1/K_n}$, which also serves as its greatest lower bound:

$$c^{(1/K_n)} \geqslant A \geqslant 1 \qquad \text{for all } n. \tag{2}$$

But we can't have $A > 1$. Why? Just raise both sides of the inequality (2) to the K_nth power, to get

$$c = (c^{1/K_n})^{K_n} \geqslant A^{K_n} \qquad \text{for all } n. $$

If $A > 1$, then the quantities A^{K_n} would increase without bound for larger and larger n—violating the inequality (2). Hence $\lim_{n\to\infty} c^{1/K_n} = A = 1$.

Step 2. Another special case: let $x_0 = 0$ and $x_n = -1/K_n$, with K_n as in Step 1. Then again

$$\lim_{n\to\infty} c^{-1/K_n} = \lim_{n\to\infty} [c^{1/K_n}]^{-1} = [\lim_{n\to\infty} c^{1/K_n}]^{-1} = \frac{1}{1} = 1. \tag{3}$$

Step 3. A more general case: let $x_0 = 0$, and pick any sequence $\{x_n\}$ with $\lim_{n\to\infty} x_n = 0$. Since $\lim_{n\to\infty} x_n = 0$, we must have $|x_n| \le 1$ for all $n \ge$ some index N. Moreover, for $n \ge N$, we can find a sequence of integers—say, K_n—that increase without bound and whose reciprocals $\pm 1/K_n$ flank the corresponding x_n:

$$-\frac{1}{K_n} \le x_n \le \frac{1}{K_n} \qquad \text{for all } n \ge N, \tag{4}$$

as in Fig. 13-13 (see Problem 13 of Sec. 8.6). Note that $\lim_{n\to\infty} 1/K_n = 0$ and $\lim_{n\to\infty} (-1/K_n) = 0$. Hence from Steps 1 and 2 we can conclude that $\lim_{n\to\infty} c^{1/K_n} = 1$ and $\lim_{n\to\infty} c^{-1/K_n} = 1$. But

$$c^{-(1/K_n)} \le c^{x_n} \le c^{(1/K_n)} \qquad \text{for all } n \ge N. \tag{5}$$

Hence $\lim_{n\to\infty} c^{x_n} = 1$, by the "squeezing" property for limits of sequences (Property P, in Chapter 9). Conclusion: $\lim_{x\to0} c^x = 1$.

Step 4. The general case with $c > 1$: For any fixed x_0, and any input x, we can write

$$c^x = c^{x_0 + (x - x_0)} = c^{x_0} c^{x - x_0}. \tag{6}$$

Hence

$$\lim_{x\to x_0} c^x = c^{x_0} \lim_{x\to x_0} c^{x - x_0}$$

$$= c^{x_0} \lim_{t\to0} c^t = c^{x_0} 1 = c^{x_0}. \tag{7}$$

To get the last line of (7), I shifted inputs, writing $t = x - x_0$ or $x = x_0 + t$. (Recall Property $\hat{\text{R}}$ on "shifting inputs," in Chapter 10.) And I used the result $\lim_{t\to0} c^t = 1$ from Step 3. Conclusion: $\lim_{x\to x_0} c^x = c^{x_0}$ at any x_0.

Step 5. Suppose $0 < c < 1$. Then

$$c^x = \left(\frac{1}{c}\right)^{-x} = \frac{1}{(1/c)^x}, \tag{8}$$

where $1/c > 1$. By Step 4, we must have once more,

$$\lim_{x\to x_0} c^x = \frac{1}{\lim_{x\to x_0} (1/c)^x} = \frac{1}{(1/c)^{x_0}} = \left(\frac{1}{c}\right)^{-x_0} = c^{x_0} \tag{9}$$

at any x_0.   End of the proof.

FIGURE 13-13

13.5   PROBLEMS ON ROOTS AND EXPONENTIALS

1. Sketch a graph for the function $f(x) = x^n$ where n is an even integer, and fill in the details for Example 2 of Sec. 13.1 to show that every positive number has *exactly* two real numbers as nth roots—one positive and one negative.

2. Suppose $P(x) = a_0 + a_1x + a_2x^2 + \cdots + a_nx^n$ is a polynomial of even degree n, with $a_n > 0$. Use the corollary (on "changes of sign") in Sec. 13.1 to determine whether
   (a) $P(x)$ must have at least one positive root and one negative root in case the constant term a_0 is negative.
   (b) Same as (a) with $a_0 > 0$.
   (c) $P(x)$ must have at least one positive root in case $a_0 + a_1 + \cdots + a_n < 0$.
   (d) $P(x)$ must have at least two positive roots in case both $a_0 > 0$ and $a_0 + a_1 + \cdots + a_n < 0$.
   (e) Same as (d) if either $a_0 < 0$ or $a_0 + a_1 + \cdots + a_n > 0$.
   (Suggestion: Consider the signs of $P(0)$ and $P(1)$.)

°3. Sketch graphs for the following exponential functions:
   (a) $f(x) = 3^x$ (b) $f(x) = 5^x$
   (c) $f(x) = (\frac{1}{2})^x$ (d) $f(x) = 1^x$
   (e) $f(x) = (\frac{1}{3})^x$ (f) $f(x) = 2^{-x}$
   (g) $f(x) = 2^{x+1}$ (h) $f(x) = 2^{x^2}$
   (i) $f(x) = 2^{2^x}$

4. Recall that for a positive number $c \neq 1$, and a positive integer k, "$c^{1/k}$" is *by definition* the *unique* positive number b such that $b^k = c$. Use this definition—and basic rules of algebra, such as $a^k < b^k$ if $0 < a < b$—to check out some old properties of rational exponents:
   (a) $(c^i)^{1/j} = (c^{1/j})^i$.
   (b) For rational numbers r and s, $c^{r+s} = c^r c^s$.
   (c) For rational numbers r and s, $(c^r)^s = c^{rs}$.
   (d) If $c > 1$ and r is a positive rational number, then $c^r > 1$.
   (e) If $c > 1$ and r and s are rational numbers with $r < s$, then $c^r < c^s$.

5. Suppose that at 8 a.m. there are 200 organisms in a bacterial culture, and that organisms will live for an average of one and a half hours before splitting. How many of these organisms will be present at 8 p.m. of the next day?
   (Recall the population growth approximation $Ne^{(1/L)T}$ in Example 1 of Sec. 13.3.)

6. Suppose that you are now host to 1 million bacteria, which have an average lifetime of 30 minutes before splitting. To how many of these bacteria will you be host two hours from now? How many were alive an hour ago?

7. Think of what happens in a jar of radioactive material during a very short interval of time. Suppose that the amount of mass which leaves the jar via radiation during that interval is approximately proportional to the total amount of mass in the jar at the beginning of the interval and to the length of the interval:

(a) Set up a relationship describing *loss* of mass during an interval (perhaps similar to that for increase of population, in (5) of Sec. 13.3).

(b) What can you say about the *average rate* of change of mass per unit time?

(c) Guess at a relationship between the amount of mass $M(t)$ present at any time t and its instantaneous rate of change $M'(t)$.

*8. Let c be > 1 and let x and y be real numbers with $x < y$. Just as I defined "2^{π}" in Sec. 13.3, let's now define "c^{x}" as the least upper bound of the set X of all numbers of the form c^{r} where r is rational and $r < x$, and "c^{y}" as the least upper bound of the set Y of all real numbers of the form c^{s} where s is rational and $s < y$. Show that $c^{x} < c^{y}$.

   (Suggestion: Pick rational numbers u and v with $x < u < v < y$, and show why $c^{x} \leqslant c^{u} < c^{v} \leqslant c^{y}$.)

*9. By analogy with Problem 8, show that $c^{x} > c^{y}$ if $x < y$ and $0 < c < 1$.

*10. Help fill in the details of my argument in Sec. 13.3 to show that 2^{π} exists. You might recall from Fig. 13-11 that R was the set of numbers of the form 2^{r} where r is a rational number and $r < \pi$. And S was the set of numbers 2^{s} where s is rational and $s > \pi$.

(a) Show that each number in S is an upper bound for R and that each number in R is a lower bound for S. (Recall Problem 4(e).)

(b) Let a be the *least* upper bound of R and b the *greatest* lower bound of S. Show that $a \leqslant b$. (If $b < a$, wouldn't there be an r and an s with $2^{s} < 2^{r}$?)

   The remaining steps show one method for proving that $a = b$, so that we can call the common value "2^{π}." (This method will also work for constants c other than 2.)

(c) Suppose $a < b$. Let $\epsilon_{1} = \sqrt{b}(\sqrt{b} - \sqrt{a})$. Choose a number a' in R which is in the open interval $\langle a - \epsilon_{1}, \pi \rangle$ and a number b' in S in the interval $\langle b, b + \epsilon_{1} \rangle$. Show that

$$b' - \sqrt{b'a'} = \sqrt{b'}(\sqrt{b'} - \sqrt{a'}) > \sqrt{b}(\sqrt{b} - \sqrt{a}) = \epsilon_{1}$$

and hence that $\sqrt{b'a'} < b$. (See the figure.)

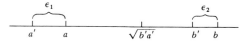

(d) Suppose again that $a < b$ and let $\epsilon_{2} = \sqrt{a/2}(\sqrt{b} - \sqrt{a})$. Choose a' on $\langle a - \epsilon_{2}, a \rangle$ with $a' > a/2$ and b' in $\langle b, b + \epsilon_{2} \rangle$. Show that

$$\sqrt{a'b'} - a' = \sqrt{a'}(\sqrt{b'} - \sqrt{a'}) > \sqrt{\frac{a}{2}}(\sqrt{b} - \sqrt{a}) = \epsilon_{2}$$

and hence that $\sqrt{b'a'} > a$.

(e) Show that if $a < b$, then there is a single positive number ϵ such that if $a - \epsilon < a' < a$ and $b < b' < b + \epsilon$, then

$$a < \sqrt{a'b'} < b.$$

(f) Show that if a' is in R and b' is in S, then $\sqrt{a'b'}$ is in R or in S.

(g) Show that no number 2^k in R or in S can satisfy the inequalities $a < 2^k < b$.

(h) Conclude that $a = b$.

**11. Help extend the equality $c^{r+s} = c^r c^s$ in Problem 4(c) to the case $c^{r+x} = c^r c^x$, where r is still rational but now x may be *irrational*. Here are some steps to follow, patterned on the ideas in Sec. 13.3. Let U be the set of numbers of the form c^u whose u is rational and $u < x$. Let V be the set of numbers of the form c^v where v is rational and $v < r+x$. Then by definition, c^x is the least upper bound of U and c^{r+x} is the least upper bound of v.

(a) Use the fact that c^x is an upper bound of U to show that $c^r c^x$ is an upper bound of V. (Note that if c^v is in V, then c^{v-r} is in U.)

(b) Use the fact that c^x is the *least* upper bound of U to show that no number b which is smaller than $c^r c^x$ can be an upper bound of V. (Consider any number c^u which is in U and in the interval $\langle b/c^r, c^x \rangle$.)

(c) Use the fact that least upper bounds are *unique* to conclude that $c^{r+x} = c^r c^x$.

**12. Now help extend the equality of Problem 11 to the case $c^{x+y} = c^x c^y$ where both x and y may be irrational.

Let R be the set of numbers c^r, r rational and $r < x$.

Let S be the set of numbers c^s, s rational and $s < y$.

Let T be the set of numbers c^t, t rational and $t < x+y$.

Then $c^x =$ least upper bound of R, $c^y =$ least upper bound of S and $c^{x+y} =$ least upper bound of T.

(a) Suppose t is a rational number with $t < x+y$. Show that you can always find rational numbers r and s such that $r+s = t$, $r < x$, $s < y$. (Suggestion: Choose r in the interval $\langle t-y, x \rangle$.)

(b) Use (a) and the fact that c^x and c^y are upper bounds, respectively, of the sets R and S to show that $c^x c^y$ is an upper bound of T.

(c) Use the fact that c^x and c^y are the *least* upper bounds, respectively, of R and S to show that no number b smaller than $c^x c^y$ can be an upper bound for T.

(Suggestion: Let $\epsilon = c^x c^y - b$. Choose a number c^s in S which is in the interval $\langle c^y - (\epsilon/2c^x), c^y \rangle$ and then choose c^r in R so that c^r is in the interval $\langle c^x - (\epsilon/2c^s), c^x \rangle$. Show that $c^r c^s$ is in the interval $\langle b, c^x c^y \rangle$ and that $c^r c^s$ is in T.)

***13. Use reasoning similar to that in Problems 11 and 12 to show that $c^{xy} = (c^x)^y = (c^y)^x$ for all real x and y and for any positive number c.

*14. For the mth model of bacterial growth which I considered in Example 1 of Sec. 13.3, the average population size after an integer number of hours h will be

$$S_m(h) = N \left[1 + \frac{1}{m} \right]^{hm} = N \left\{ \left[1 + \frac{1}{m} \right]^m \right\}^h.$$

(Recall also Sec. 6.5.)

(a) Show that $\lim\limits_{n \to \infty} S_m(h) = Ne^h$. (Recall Property M of sequences in Chapter 9.)

(b) Now suppose we examine the population size after time $t = p/q$ where p and q are integers, and — following the same scheme I used for compound interest in Example 3 of Sec. 10.2 — let's look at a subsequence of models involving intervals of length $1/m_k$ where $m_k = kq$, $k = 1, 2, 3, \ldots$. The time $t = p/q = kp/kq$ will consist of kp intervals of length $1/m_k$. Hence

$$S_{m_k}(t) = N\left(1 + \frac{1}{m_k}\right)^{kp} = N\left[\left(1 + \frac{1}{m_k}\right)^{kq}\right]^{p/q} = N\left[\left(1 + \frac{1}{m_k}\right)^{m_k}\right]^t.$$

Show that $\lim\limits_{k \to \infty} S_{m_k}(t) = Ne^t$.

(c) For the case (b), where t is rational, show moreover that for the full sequence of models, $\lim\limits_{m \to \infty} S_m(t) = Ne^t$. (Use the fact that

$$\left(1 + \frac{1}{m}\right)^m \le \left(1 + \frac{1}{m+1}\right)^{m+1} \le 3 \qquad \text{for all } m \ge 2,$$

as in Sec. 10.2.)

**15. Here is how we can use the continuity of exponential functions (Theorem C of Sec. 3.3) to show that even for an *irrational* lapse of time t_0, the population size approximations of Problem 14(c) have $\lim\limits_{m \to \infty} S_m(t_0) = Ne^{t_0}$.

(a) For any $\epsilon > 0$, show that there exist rational numbers r and s, with $0 < r < t_0 < s$, such that

$$Ne^r > Ne^{t_0} - \frac{1}{2}\epsilon \quad \text{and} \quad Ne^s < Ne^{t_0} + \frac{1}{2}\epsilon.$$

(b) Use the result of Problem 14(c) to show that there must be some integer M_ϵ such that

$$S_m(r) > Ne^r - \frac{1}{2}\epsilon \qquad \text{for all } m \ge M_\epsilon.$$

(c) Put the results (a) and (b) together with the facts that $S_m(s) \le Ne^s$ and that

$$S_m(r) \le S_m(t_0) \le S_m(s) \qquad \text{for each } m,$$

to show that

$$Ne^{t_0} - \frac{1}{2}\epsilon - \frac{1}{2}\epsilon < S_m(t_0) < Ne^{t_0} + \frac{1}{2}\epsilon$$

for all $m \ge M_\epsilon$.

See the accompanying figure.

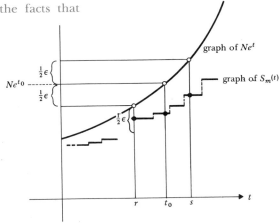

13.6 STILL MORE CONTINUOUS FUNCTIONS: INVERSES

You may perhaps recall (from Sec. 5.6) the relationship between a one-to-one function $f(x)$ and its inverse function $g(y)$: the domain of g is the range of f; and

$$g(f(x)) = x \qquad \text{for all } x \text{ in the domain of } f, \tag{1}$$

and

$$f(g(y)) = y \qquad \text{for all } y \text{ in the domain of } g. \tag{2}$$

Pictorially, we can get the graph of g by flipping the graph of f over the 45° line—as in Figs. 13-14 and 13-15.

FIGURE 13-14   FIGURE 13-15

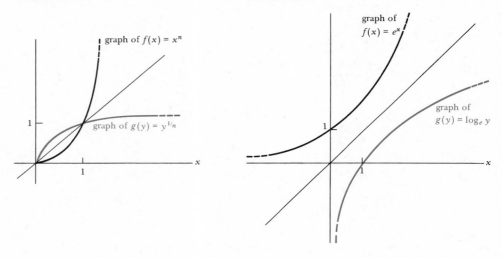

If the function f is continuous—that is, if the graph of f has no "breaks"—shouldn't the flipped over graph of the inverse function g also have no "breaks"? If so, we can increase our catalog of continuous functions by including inverses g of many one-to-one functions f.

EXAMPLE 1: The *root function* $g(y) = y^{1/n}$, where n is any positive integer. The power function $f(x) = x^n$ is one-to-one and continuous for all $x \geqslant 0$. Moreover, I showed earlier—via the "intermediate values" result—that every real number $y \geqslant 0$ is the output $y = x^n$ for some input $x \geqslant 0$ (Examples 1 and 2 of Sec. 13.1). Hence the power function $f(x) = x^n$ (for $x \geqslant 0$) has its inverse function $g(y) = y^{1/n}$ defined for all $y \geqslant 0$. And the inverse function *is* continuous at all such y: $\lim_{n \to \infty} y_n^{1/n} = y_0^{1/n}$ for all sequences $\{y_n \geqslant 0\}$ with $\lim_{n \to \infty} y_n = y_0$ (by Property M on "rational exponents," Chap. 9).

EXAMPLE 2: *Logarithms.* Suppose that c is positive and not 1. If a number y has the form $y = c^x$, it has long been traditional to call x the *logarithm of y to the base c.* Notation: $x = \log_c y$. Note that the logarithm x must be unique because

$$c^{x_1} < c^{x_2} \qquad \text{if } x_1 < x_2 \quad \text{and} \quad c > 1 \tag{3}$$

and

$$c^{x_1} > c^{x_2} \qquad \text{if } x_1 < x_2 \quad \text{and} \quad 0 < c < 1. \tag{4}$$

If we let $y_1 = c^{x_1}$ and $y_2 = c^{x_2}$, then we can get inequalities which are equivalent to the inequalities (3) and (4), namely:

$$\log_c y_1 < \log_c y_2 \qquad \text{if } y_1 < y_2 \quad \text{and} \quad c > 1 \tag{5}$$

and

$$\log_c y_1 > \log_c y_2 \qquad \text{if } y_1 > y_2 \quad \text{and} \quad 0 < c < 1. \tag{6}$$

Similarly we can translate other familiar properties of exponentials — such as $c^0 = 1$, $(c^{x_1})^p = c^{px_1}$, $(c^{x_1})(c^{x_2}) = c^{x_1+x_2}$, and $c^{x_1}/c^{x_2} = c^{x_1-x_2}$ — in terms of logarithms:

$$\log_c 1 = 0, \tag{7}$$
$$\log_c (y_1{}^p) = p \log_c y_1, \tag{8}$$
$$\log_c (y_1 y_2) = \log_c y_1 + \log_c y_2, \tag{9}$$

and

$$\log_c \left(\frac{y_1}{y_2}\right) = \log_c y_1 - \log_c y_2. \tag{10}$$

Thus,

$$\log_2 8 = \log_2 2^3 = 3,$$

and

$$\log_2 \frac{32}{8} = \log_2 2^5 - \log_2 2^3 = 5 - 3 = 2 = \log_2 2^2 = \log_2 4.$$

Now in order to have a logarithm, a number y must be positive, since numbers of the form c^x are always positive. Thanks to the theorem on intermediate values (of Sec. 13.1), we can say more: *Every* positive y must have a logarithm to a given base c; y must equal c^x for some real x. See Fig. 13-16. Check that for $c > 1$ and a given

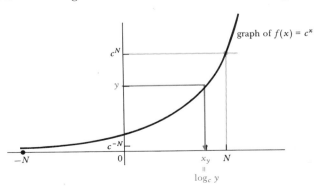

FIGURE 13-16

$y > 0$, there must be some positive integer N such that

$$\frac{1}{c^N} = c^{-N} < y < c^N. \tag{11}$$

That is,

$$f(-N) < y < f(N),$$

where $f(x) = c^x$. Since exponential functions are continuous everywhere (Theorem C of Sec. 13.3), there must be some input x_y with $-N < x_y < N$ such that

$$f(x_y) = c^{x_y} = y.$$

In the present notation: $x_y = \log_c y$. (Similarly for the case $c < 1$.)

If we *assign* to each positive number y (as input) its unique logarithm

$$g(y) = \log_c y$$

(as output), we have a function g — the *inverse* of $f(x) = c^x$. Note that

$$g(f(x)) = \log_c (c^x) = x \quad \text{and} \quad f(g(y)) = c^{\log_c y} = y. \tag{12}$$

Let's call g the *log function for the base c*.

I've sketched the graph of $f(x) = e^x$ in black in Fig. 13-11 and the graph of its inverse, $g(y) = \log_e y$, in green. f is continuous. Must g be continuous also? Although its graph *appears* to have no breaks, we have as yet no property of limits which applies to logarithms and which would guarantee continuity (as did Property M for root functions).

Why worry whether $\log_e y$ is a continuous function? Consider

EXAMPLE 3. How long will it take for a bacterial population to increase its size by a factor of 25 — if organisms live for an average of one hour? In Example 1 of Sec. 13.3, I argued that the population size might well be approximated by the function $S(t) = Ne^t$, where t denotes the lapse of time (in hours) from a starting instant when there were N bacteria. To answer the question, we must find a value $t = T$ such that $S(T) = 25\, S(0)$; that is,

$$Ne^T = 25Ne^0, \tag{13}$$

or $e^T = 25$, or

$$T = \log_e 25. \tag{14}$$

How can you actually evaluate the quantity $\log_e 25$? You might try to approximate it by $\log_e y$ for values y close to 25 for which you can compute $\log_e y$ — such as $y_0 = e^3 = (2.71\ldots)^3$. Or you might turn to a "table of logarithms" wherein approximations made by other people are recorded. Or you might program a computer to approximate $\log_e y$ — but how? All these methods would lead nowhere if log functions were not suitably continuous, and if their derivatives didn't exist.

I'll discuss derivatives of log functions in the next chapter. Let's first see why log functions, as well as other inverses, should be continuous.

Does the continuity of an inverse function g somehow follow primarily from the continuity of the original function f—as perhaps suggested by Figs. 13-14 and 13-15?

Look at the discontinuous function f in Fig. 13-17. The function f assigns to each input x in the interval $[a, b]$ a unique output, and so an inverse function g exists. It's true that the domain of g doesn't consist of a *single* interval as did that of f. Nevertheless, g *appears to be continuous at each input in its domain*—even at an "inside end point" such as c. (There is no sequence of *inputs* $y_n < c$ with $\lim_{n\to\infty} y_n = c$ to cause trouble.)

What property do the functions f in Figs. 13-14, 13-15, and 13-17 have in common which might insure continuity for their inverses?

Can it be merely the fact that the graph of each f *rises* from left to right?

Note that if a function f is itself continuous on an interval $[a, b]$ and if f is to have an inverse, then its graph must either exclusively rise or exclusively fall over $[a, b]$. For otherwise, f wouldn't be one-to-one (as we can conclude from the "intermediate value" result of Sec. 13.1). See Fig. 13-18.

Here are standard names for the properties of exclusive rise and exclusive fall.

Definitions: Call a function f *increasing* (over a subset S in its domain) if

$$f(x_1) \le f(x_2) \quad \text{whenever } x_1 < x_2 \text{ and } x_1 \text{ and } x_2 \text{ are inputs in } S. \quad (15)$$

If the inequality $f(x_1) < f(x_2)$ always holds in (15), call f *strictly increasing*. Similarly, call a function f *decreasing* (over a subset S in its domain) if

$$f(x_1) \ge f(x_2) \quad \text{whenever } x_1 < x_2 \text{ and } x_1 \text{ and } x_2 \text{ are inputs in } S. \quad (16)$$

If the inequality $f(x_1) > f(x_2)$ always holds in (16), call f *strictly decreasing*.

I've used the fact that power functions x^n (for $x \ge 0$) and exponentials c^x (for $c > 1$) are strictly increasing to conclude that those functions do have inverses. More generally, we can say that

Theorem D (on "the existence of inverse functions"): Any function $f(x)$ that is strictly increasing over its domain must have an inverse function $g(y)$ that is also strictly increasing. Similarly, any strictly decreasing f must have a strictly decreasing inverse g.

Recall that for $y = f(x)$ we need merely define $g(y) = x$. When x_1 and x_2 are inputs of f,

$$y_1 = f(x_1) \quad \text{and} \quad y_2 = f(x_2)$$

FIGURE 13-17

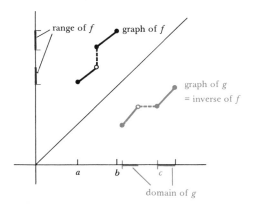

FIGURE 13-18

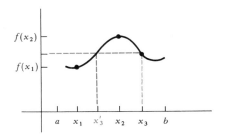

will be inputs for g. And if f is strictly increasing, then

$$y_1 < y_2 \quad \text{only if} \quad x_1 = g(y_1) < x_2 = g(y_2) \tag{17}$$

as in Fig. 13-19.

FIGURE 13-19   strictly increasing functions

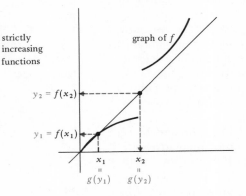
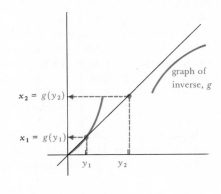

If f is strictly decreasing, then

$$y_1 < y_2 \text{ only if } x_1 = g(y_1) > x_2 = g(y_2) \tag{18}$$

as in Fig. 13-20.

FIGURE 13-20   strictly decreasing functions

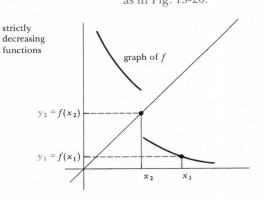
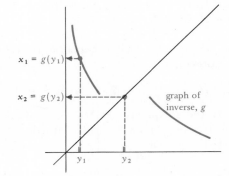

More is true: For a function f defined on an interval, the property of strict increase, by itself, does guarantee that the inverse function g must be *continuous*—at least at all of its inputs that don't stand "isolated" (as are the inputs y_2 in Figs. 13-19 and 13-20).

Theorem E (on "the continuity of inverse functions"): If a function f is defined on an interval (or a line or a half line) and is strictly increasing on its domain, then its inverse function g is continuous at each input $y_0 = f(x_0)$ — provided that y_0 is itself the limit of some sequence of other inputs $\{y_n = f(x_n)\}$. Similarly for strictly decreasing functions.

In other words, if a sequence of g-*inputs* $y_n = f(x_n)$ converges to a g-input $y_0 = f(x_0)$, as in Fig. 13-21, then the corresponding sequence of g-*outputs* $x_n = g(y_n)$ should converge to $x_0 = g(y_0)$.

FIGURE 13-21

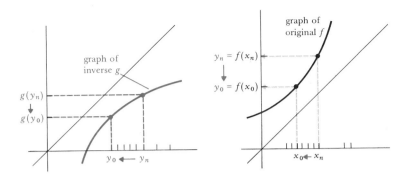

If you are interested in a

Proof of theorem E: Let's suppose that for *some* sequence $\{y_n = f(x_n)\}$ converging to $y_0 = f(x_0)$ the corresponding sequence $\{x_n = g(y_n)\}$ *fails* to converge to x_0. What logical havoc must follow? How can the x_n's fail to converge to x_0? Some subsequence of the x_n's—call them x_{n_k}'s—must remain separated from x_0 by some positive distance—call it ϵ: $|x_{n_k} - x_0| \geq \epsilon$ for all k, as in Fig. 13-22. (You might recall Problem 7 of Sec. 9.8.)

FIGURE 13-22

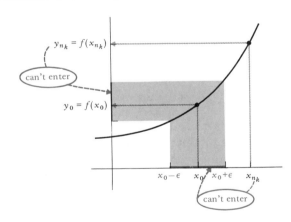

Now if f is strictly increasing, and the x_{n_k}'s are excluded from the interval $[x_0 - \epsilon, x_0 + \epsilon]$, then the outputs $y_{n_k} = f(x_{n_k})$ must be excluded from an interval on the vertical axis containing $y_0 = f(x_0)$. For example, if both numbers $x_0 - \epsilon$ and $x_0 + \epsilon$ are themselves in the domain of f, then for any x_{n_k}, either

$$x_{n_k} < x_0 - \epsilon < x_0 \quad \text{and} \quad f(x_{n_k}) < f(x_0 - \epsilon) < f(x_0), \tag{19}$$

or

$$x_{n_k} > x_0 + \epsilon > x_0 \quad \text{and} \quad f(x_{n_k}) > f(x_0 + \epsilon) > f(x_0). \tag{20}$$

So all $y_{n_k} = f(x_{n_k})$ are excluded from the interval

$$[f(x_0 - \epsilon), f(x_0 + \epsilon)].$$

I invite you to check that a similar argument holds even if both numbers $x_0-\epsilon$ and $x_0+\epsilon$ are not in the domain of f. So long as that domain is an interval (or a line or a half line), we should be able to replace the subinterval $[x_0-\epsilon, x_0+\epsilon]$ by a suitably smaller subinterval which does lie entirely in the domain. Check also that similar arguments hold if f is strictly decreasing. (Do Problem 15 of Sec. 13.7.)

Conclusion: The subsequence $\{y_{n_k}=f(x_{n_k})\}$ can't converge to $y_0=f(x_0)$. Hence the full sequence $y_n=f(x_n)$ can't either—in contradiction to the way we chose $\{y_n\}$. It was the original supposition that g was not continuous at y_0 that caused the trouble—so it must go.   End of the proof.

For an alternate proof, see Problem 16 of the next section.

13.7 PROBLEMS ON INVERSES

1. Use the relations in (12) of Sec. 13.6 to change the equations in parts (a)–(d) to logarithmic form, and the equations in parts (e)–(h) to exponential form.
   (a) $2^3=8$ (b) $3^2=9$ (c) $10^{-4}=0.0001$ (d) $x^y=z$
   (e) $\log_3 27=3$ (f) $\log_4 (1/16)=-2$
   (g) $\log_e 1=0$ (h) $\log_x z=y$

°2. Evaluate the following numbers:
   (a) $\log_2 (1/8)$ (b) $\log_5 (625)$
   (c) $\log_{10} (1,000,000)$ (d) $\log_{1/3} 9$
   (e) $4^{\log_4 7}$ (f) $\log_9 (1/9)$ (g) $\log_8 \sqrt[5]{8}$ (h) $10^{5\log_2 3}$

°3. Simplify the following expressions:
   (a) $e^{(\log_e x)}$ (b) $e^{(-\log_e x^2)}$ (c) $\log_e (e^{1/x})$ (d) $e^{(\log_e (1/x))}$
   (e) $e^{(2\log_e x)}$ (f) $\log_e [e^{(x+x^2+1)}]$ (g) $\log_e [xe^{(-3x^2)}]$

°4. Sketch graphs of the following functions side by side with graphs of their inverses—if they exist. Use arrows to show how various inputs lead to corresponding outputs—as in Figs. 13-19 and 13-20.
   (a) $f(x)=x$ for all x (b) $f(x)=x^2$ for all $x\geq 0$
   (c) $f(x)=x^2$ for all $x\leq 0$ (d) $f(x)=x^2$ for all x
   (e) $f(x)=x^3$ for all x (f) $f(x)=2^x$ for all x
   (g) $f(x)=\left(\frac{1}{2}\right)^x$ for all x (h) $f(x)=\log_2 x$ for all $x>0$
   (i) $f(x)=\log_{1/2} x$ for all $x>0$
   (j) $f(x)=\begin{cases} x & \text{for } 0\leq x\leq 1 \\ x+1 & \text{for } x>1 \end{cases}$
   (k) $f(x)=\begin{cases} x^2 & \text{for } 0\leq x<1 \\ 2 & \text{for } x=1 \\ x^2+2 & \text{for } x>1 \end{cases}$
   (l) $f(x)=\begin{cases} -x-1 & \text{for } -1\leq x<0 \\ 1-x & \text{for } 0\leq x\leq 1 \end{cases}$
   (m) $f(x)=\begin{cases} x+1 & \text{for } -2\leq x<1 \\ x-1 & \text{for } 1\leq x\leq 2 \end{cases}$

(n) $f(x) = \begin{cases} x+1 & \text{for } -2 \leqslant x < 1 \\ 0 & \text{for } x = 1 \\ x-1 & \text{for } 1 < x \leqslant 2 \end{cases}$

(o) $f(x) = \begin{cases} -x-2 & \text{for } -2 \leqslant x \leqslant -1 \\ 1-x & \text{for } 0 \leqslant x \leqslant 1 \end{cases}$

(p) $f(x) = \begin{cases} 0 & \text{for } -1 \leqslant x < 0 \\ x & \text{for } 0 \leqslant x \leqslant 1 \end{cases}$

5. (a) If inverse functions failed to exist for cases in Problem 4, why was Theorem D (on "the existence of inverse functions") in Sec. 13.6 not applicable?

   (b) If inverse functions failed to be strictly increasing or strictly decreasing for cases in Problem 4, why was Theorem D again not applicable?

6. For which f's in Problem 4 were the corresponding inverse functions *not continuous* at all inputs? What hypothesis of Theorem E (on "the continuity of inverse functions") in Sec. 13.6 failed to apply?

°7. If $c > d > 1$, is $\log_c x > \log_d x$ for all $x > 0$?

8. Can you make sense of the idea of "the logarithm to the base $c = 1$"?

9. Show that for $c > 1$ and a given $y > 0$, there must be some positive integer N such that

$$c^{-N} < y < c^N.$$

10. For the case $0 < y < 1$, show that the range of c^x is the set of all positive numbers if the domain is the set of all real numbers.

11. Does $f(x) = e^{-x^2/2}$ have an inverse function on the domain $\mathcal{D}$

   (a) if $\mathcal{D} = [0, \infty)$?   (b) if $\mathcal{D} = \langle -\infty, \infty \rangle$?

   (c) if $\mathcal{D} = [0, 1]$?   (d) if $\mathcal{D} = [-1, 0] \cup [2, 3]$?

12. Suppose that organisms in a population of bacteria live an average of one hour before splitting; and that someone divides the population into two groups, one of size N_A and the other of size N_B. Show that each group requires the same amount of time to double its size.

13. Suppose you are host to a population of bacteria which have an average lifetime of 3 hours before splitting. How much time will it take before the population is doubled? How much longer after that will it take to double the population again? How long ago was the population half the size it is now?

*14. Consider two groups of bacteria. Group A has a population of N_A organisms which live for an average of 1 hour before splitting. Group B has a population of $N_B = 2N_A$ organisms which live for an average of 2 hours before splitting. Which group will double its population first?

*15. Write out a proof for Theorem E of Sec. 13.6 on "the continuity of inverse functions" in case f is a strictly decreasing function.

*16. If you read the alternate "$\epsilon - \delta$" definition of continuity in Problem 10 of Sec. 11.3, try now to rephrase the statement of Theorem E (of Sec. 13.6) on "the continuity of inverse functions" in terms of that alternate definition. Explain the statement via a picture, as in the accompanying figure.

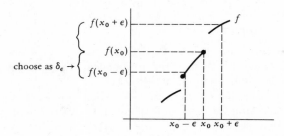

Try to prove Theorem E via the alternate definition of continuity.

13.8 "FIXED POINTS" OF CONTINUOUS FUNCTIONS

FIGURE 13-23

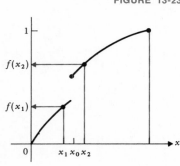

Suppose that I rearrange numbers in the interval $[0, 1]$ in any devilish way I please — even piling numbers on top of one another — subject only to one *condition:* if two numbers x and x' were close together before rearrangement they should be tolerably close together after the rearrangement. We can describe the rearrangement by a function f which assigns to each original number x in $[0, 1]$ a new position called $f(x)$ — again a number in $[0, 1]$. We can interpret the condition above simply as a requirement that f be a *continuous* function. Otherwise, if the graph of f had a break at some x_0, then two numbers originally very near to x_0 and very near to each other might be separated considerably by the rearrangement. See Fig. 13-23.

Question: Can I create such a rearranging function f which will move every number in $[0, 1]$ to a new position? Or must there be at least one number — or "point" — x_0 which stays *fixed*?

What does "staying fixed" mean in terms of the function f? Simply that

FIGURE 13-24

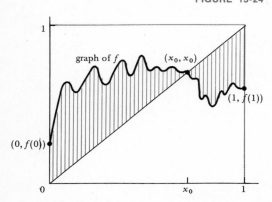

$$f(x_0) = x_0. \tag{1}$$

This equality means nothing other than that the graph of f intersects the 45° line in the point (x_0, x_0), as in Fig. 13-24.

Thinking intuitively, you might ask: How can the graph of f travel from the point $(0, f(0))$ to the point $(1, f(1))$ with no breaks and without crossing the 45° line? You're right; it can't.

Theorem F (on "fixed points"): If f is a continuous function on $[0, 1]$ with range contained in $[0, 1]$, then there must be at least one input x_0 in $[0, 1]$ such that $f(x_0) = x_0$.

The idea is similar to that appearing in the "intermediate values" result (Theorem A) in Sec. 13.1: the graph of a continuous function

FIGURE 13-25

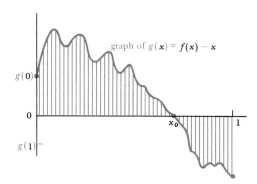

graph of $g(x) = f(x) - x$

$g(0)$

0

x_0 1

$g(1)$

can't go from one altitude to another without intersecting all *horizontal* lines in between. Why not try to reduce the present question, involving a 45° line, to one involving a horizontal line? One way to do so might be to consider the function $g(x) = f(x) - x$ which measures the difference in altitude between the graph of f and the 45° line. See Fig. 13-25. For

A proof of theorem F. Let's note three possibilities: Either $f(0) = 0$ — in which case 0 is a fixed point; or $f(1) = 1$ — in which case 1 is a fixed point; or $f(0) > 0$ and $f(1) < 1$ — as in Fig. 13-24. But in the last case, the function $g(x) = f(x) - x$ has outputs $g(0) = f(0) - 0 > 0$ and $g(1) = f(1) - 1 < 0$. Being the difference of two continuous functions, $f(x)$ and x, $g(x)$ is continuous. And the value $c = 0$ lies between $g(0)$ and $g(1)$. Hence there must be some input x_0 in $[0, 1]$ such that $g(x_0) = 0$. In terms of f, $g(x_0) = f(x_0) - x_0 = 0$ means that $f(x_0) = x_0$. x_0 must be a "fixed point" of f.   End of the proof.

Here are some applications and nonapplications.

EXAMPLE 1. A continuous rearrangement of points on a circle need not have a fixed point. For example, just rotate the circle by 10°. See Fig. 13-26.

EXAMPLE 2. If it is true, however, that any continuous rearrangement of points on the surface of a sphere must have a fixed point, then one can conclude the following: at any one time there must be some spot on earth where the wind is not blowing. Why? Here is an intuitive argument: At a fixed instant in time, t_0, imagine each point on the surface of the earth has suddenly become loose and ready to be blown elsewhere by the slightest puff of wind acting after that instant. Points close enough together should be blown not far from each other. Thus, in a very short elapse of time after t_0, the wind effects a *continuous* rearrangement of the surface of the earth. So, if an analog of Theorem F holds for this situation (and it *does*), then there should be some point which doesn't get moved — which means that no wind was blowing there at time t_0.

(Why should this result be so different from that of Example 1?)

FIGURE 13-26

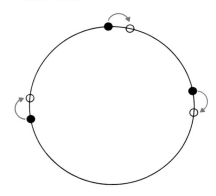

EXAMPLE 3: *Extinction of dynasties with many children.* You may recall, from Sec. 5.8, the problem of finding the probability of ultimate extinction of a dynasty wherein each parent, independently of all others, contributed either 0 viable offspring (with probability p_0), or 1 viable offspring (with probability p_1), or else 2 viable offspring (with probability p_2). I argued that the probability of ultimate extinction could be regarded as a limit $x = \lim_{n\to\infty} x_n$, of the probabilities x_n for extinction of the dynasty by the nth generation. And I argued that we could find each successive x_n in terms of the previous x_{n-1},

$$x_n = f(x_{n-1}) \qquad \text{for all } n, \tag{2}$$

via the polynomial

$$f(x) = p_0 + p_1 x + p_2 x^2 \tag{3}$$

whose coefficients were the given probabilities of offspring. (The products and sums defining the polynomial corresponded to calculating probabilities of jointly independent results and of mutually exclusive results. Recall Fig. 5-18.)

Now, what if parents can have more than two children? Suppose that each parent can contribute any number k of viable offspring (with corresponding probability p_k) where $0 \leqslant k \leqslant n$, and n is some large integer. What will be the probability of ultimate extinction for such a model?

The probabilities p_k for different numbers of offspring should again add to 1 (see Sec. 6.6); and to avoid special cases we might again suppose all the p_k's > 0. I claim that if you will check back through the arguments I gave in Sec. 5.8, you will find that all of them still hold for the present, more general, situation. In particular, the probability x_n that everyone will be dead by the nth generation must still be related to x_{n-1} via a polynomial, $x_n = f(x_{n-1})$. The only new feature—as you might guess—is that the polynomial f must now be of degree n to incorporate all the different probabilities of offspring:

$$f(x) = p_0 + p_1 x + p_2 x^2 + \cdots + p_n x^n. \tag{4}$$

Note that $f(0) = p_0 > 0$ and $f(1) = p_0 + p_1 + p_2 + \cdots + p_n = 1$. Moreover, since all the p_k's are positive we must have $f(x) < f(x')$ whenever $0 \leqslant x < x' \leqslant 1$. That is, f must be *strictly increasing* over $[0, 1]$.

The probability x_1 of extinction by the first generation is just $f(0) = p_0$, the probability that the originator of the dynasty leaves no offspring. For $n > 1$, the heights $x_n = f(x_{n-1})$ must again form a staircase, as in Fig. 13-27 or in Fig. 13-28. If the graph of f sits *above* the 45° line as in Fig. 13-27, it would appear that the probability of ultimate extinction, the $\lim_{n\to\infty} x_n$, must be 1. However, if the graph of f dips below the 45° line near $x = 1$, then f must have a *fixed point* $q < 1$, with $f(q) = q$. (Why? Because if we altered f a little near $x = 1$, as in Fig. 13-29, then the new version would have a fixed point q with $0 < q < 1$. And q must be a fixed point of the original

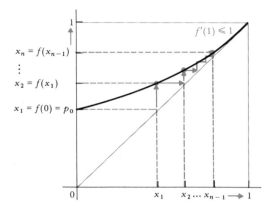

FIGURE 13-27

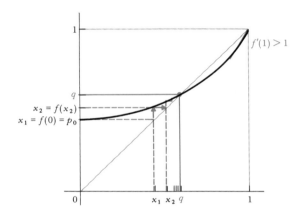

FIGURE 13-28

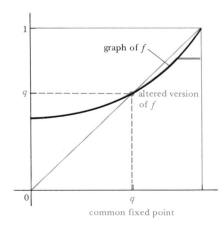

FIGURE 13-29

f, too.) What does the fixed point q do in Fig. 13-28? It traps the increasing values $x_n = f(x_{n-1})$. For the case I pictured in Fig. 13-28, the ultimate probability of extinction is $\lim_{n \to \infty} x_n = q < 1$. And the dynasty will survive forever with probability $1 - q > 0$.

What simple numerical distinction might there be between the two cases in Figs. 13-27 and 13-28? How about the slope $f'(1)$? Does $f'(1)$ have some special meaning in terms of the original probabilities p_k for k offspring? To evaluate $f'(1)$, recall that $(x^k)' = kx^{k-1}$ for any k (from Sec. 9.5). If the derivative of a sum of functions is the sum of their separate derivatives, we can conclude that

$$f'(x_0) = 0 + p_1 + 2p_2 x_0^{2-1} + 3p_3 x_0^{3-1} + \cdots + np_n x_0^{n-1} \tag{5}$$

at any x_0. In particular, for $x_0 = 1$, $f'(1)$ has the form

$$f'(1) = 0 \cdot p_0 + 1 \cdot p_1 + 2 \cdot p_2 + 3 \cdot p_3 + \cdots + n \cdot p_n, \tag{6}$$

a sum wherein *each possible number of offspring k is multiplied by its probability p_k*. In connection with betting, I argued in Sec. 3.1 that we might consider such a sum as an "average" — in this case, as the *average number of offspring per parent*.

Conclusion: From Figs. 13-27 and 13-28, if the average number of offspring per parent is no greater than one, the population must die out with probability 1. If the average number of offspring per parent exceeds one, then the population can still die out with a positive probability q, but can survive with positive probability $1 - q$, where q is the unique solution of the equation $f(x) = x$ in the interval $0 < x < 1$.

Of course, such deductions depend on there being no cases other than those I pictured in Fig. 13-27 corresponding to $f'(1) \leqslant 1$ and in Fig. 13-28 corresponding to $f'(1) > 1$. What if f has a graph as in Fig. 13-30? Can there be more than one fixed point q? In the next chapter we'll be able to rule out all cases other than those in Figs. 13-27 and 13-28 — by appealing to a few simple results on derivatives.

FIGURE 13-30

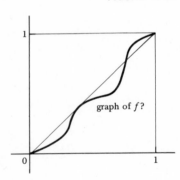

graph of f?

13.9 PROBLEMS ON FIXED POINTS

1. For each of the following functions f defined on $[0, 1]$, determine
    (i) whether the range of f is contained in $[0, 1]$;
    (ii) whether f leaves any points "fixed" ($f(x) = x$); and
    (iii) which points these are, if any.

    (a) $f(x) = x^2$

    (b) $f(x) = \sqrt{x}$

    (c) $f(x) = x^2 - 3x + 1$

    (d) $f(x) = \dfrac{1}{2}x^2 - x + \dfrac{3}{4}$

$$(\text{e})\ f(x) = \begin{cases} \dfrac{1}{2} & \text{for } 0 \leqslant x < \dfrac{1}{2} \\[2mm] \dfrac{1}{4} & \text{for } \dfrac{1}{2} \leqslant x \leqslant 1 \end{cases}$$

$$(\text{f})\ f(x) = \begin{cases} 0 & \text{for } x \text{ a rational number with } 0 < x \leqslant 1 \\[2mm] 1 & \text{for } x = 0 \text{ or } x = \text{an irrational number with } 0 < x < 1 \end{cases}$$

2. Let f be the function $f(x) = x^2$ whose domain is the open interval $\langle 0, 1 \rangle$.
   (a) Show that f does not satisfy the conclusion of Theorem F on "fixed points" in Sec. 13.8; that is, there is no x_0 in $(0, 1)$ with $f(x_0) = x_0$.
   (b) Show that f *does* satisfy the conclusion of Theorem A on "intermediate values" in Sec. 13.1; that is, if x_1 and x_2 are any two inputs in $(0, 1)$ and if c is a number between $f(x_1)$ and $f(x_2)$, then there is an input x_c with $x_1 < x_c < x_2$ such that $f(x_c) = e$.

3. Suppose that fissionable material is composed of active particles each of which moves freely for a short period of time and then either becomes inactive (with probability $\frac{1}{3}$) or splits into 2 new active particles (with probability $\frac{2}{3}$). What is the probability of an ultimate explosion?
   As in Example 2 of Sec. 13.8, you might proceed by these steps:
   (a) Define $f(x) = \frac{1}{3} + \frac{2}{3}x^2$ on $[0, 1]$, calculate $f'(x)$ — especially $f'(1)$, and sketch a graph of f.
   (b) Find a "fixed point" q of f with $0 < q < 1$.
   (c) Check graphically whether the sequence

   $$x_0 = f(0), x_1 = f(x_0), \ldots, x_n = f(x_{n-1}), \ldots$$

   converges to q — as in Fig. 13-28.

4. (a) "On the average" over many generations, the male members of the Euclid family have fathered families of the following composition.

number of male children	corresponding probability
4	0.07
3	0.13
2	0.11
1	0.09
0	0.60

   What is the probability that the Euclid name will die out?
   (b) What does the phrase "on the average" mean anyway?

5. Suppose f is continuous on the interval $[a, b]$ and x_0 is an input in $[a, b]$ such that $f(x_0) \neq x_0$. Show that there is an open interval $x_0 - \delta < x < x_0 + \delta$ which contains no fixed points of f.
   (Suggestion: Recall Theorem B on "nearby signs" in Sec. 13.1. Can you apply it in this case to the function $g(x) = f(x) - x$?)

*6. Another way to prove Theorem F on "fixed points" (in Sec. 13.8) begins thus: Suppose f has no fixed points. Then let A be the set of all inputs x such that $f(x) > x$ and B the set of all inputs x such that $f(x) < x$. Can you discover how to continue the argument so as to arrive at a contradiction to the assumption that f has no fixed points?

*7. Let f be a function whose domain is a circle and whose range is an interval. (For example, if C is the circle with center at the origin and radius 1, f could be the function which assigns to each point on C the real number which measures the distance of the point from the x axis.)

(a) What would it mean to say that f is a continuous function? (See the first paragraph of Section 13.8.)

(b) Can you use your definition to show that, if f is continuous, then it satisfies an "Intermediate Value Theorem" (analogous to Theorem A in Sec. 13.1)?

(c) Suppose that every continuous function from the circle to an interval satisfies an "Intermediate Value Theorem." If f is such a function, show that there is at least one pair of diametrically opposed points P and P' on the circle such that $f(P) = f(P')$. (Suggestion: Let $g(P) = f(P) - f(P')$.)

(d) At any one time there are *two* points at the equator on opposite sides of the earth which have the same wind velocity. Why?

**8. Suppose that f is a continuous function on $[0, 1]$ with range contained in $[0, 1]$ with the additional property that

$$|f(x) - f(x')| < \tfrac{1}{2}|x - x'|$$

for all inputs x and x' in $[0, 1]$.

Let x_0 be any input in $[0, 1]$, let $x_1 = f(x_0)$, $x_2 = f(x_1)$, and so forth, with $x_{n+1} = f(x_n)$ for $n = 1, 2, 3, 4, 5, \ldots$

(a) Show that the sequence $x_0, x_1, x_2, \ldots, x_n, \ldots$ converges to an input $\hat{x}$ in $[0, 1]$.

(Suggestions: Is $\{x_n\}$ bounded? If so, why must some subsequence $\{x_{n_k}\}$ converge to some $\hat{x}$ in $[0, 1]$? For any integer m and for $n_k > m$, can you estimate the distance

$$|x_m - \hat{x}| = |x_m - x_{n_k} + x_{n_k} - \hat{x}| \leq |x_m - x_{n_k}| + |x_{n_k} - x_m|?)$$

(b) Show that $\hat{x}$ is a fixed point of f.

13.10 SUMMARY OF CHAPTER 13

THEOREM (ON "INTERMEDIATE VALUES"): Suppose that a function f is continuous at all x in some interval $[x_1, x_2]$, and that $f(x_1) \neq f(x_2)$. Pick any number c between $f(x_1)$ and $f(x_2)$. Then there exists at least one input—call it x_c—with $x_1 < x_c < x_2$ and $f(x_c) = c$. (Sec. 13.1)

A COROLLARY (ON "CHANGES OF SIGN"): If a function f has outputs $f(x_1)$ and $f(x_2)$ of opposite sign, and is continuous on the interval $[x_1, x_2]$, then $f(x_0) = 0$ for some input x_0 with $x_1 < x_0 < x_2$. Alternately, if f is continuous and never zero on some interval (open, closed, or half-infinite), then all outputs must have the same sign there.
(Sec. 13.1)

THEOREM (ON "NEARBY SIGNS"): If $\lim_{x \to x_0} f(x) = A > 0$, then $f(x) > 0$ for all inputs $x \neq x_0$ and which lie in some interval $[x_0 - \delta, x_0 + \delta]$ surrounding x_0. In particular, if a function f is continuous at an input x_0, and $f(x_0) > 0$, then $f(x) > 0$ for *all* x in some interval $[x_0 - \delta, x_0 + \delta]$.

Other applications:

Every real number c has a unique positive root $c^{1/n}$, where n is any odd positive integer (Sec. 13.1).

Every positive number c has a unique root $c^{1/n}$, where n is any even positive integer (Sec. 13.1).

Every positive number $c \neq 1$ has a unique power c^x for any real number x (Sec. 13.3).

For properties and applications of exponential functions c^x, see Sec. 13.3.

THEOREM (ON "THE CONTINUITY OF EXPONENTIAL FUNCTIONS"): For any positive $c \neq 1$, the exponential function c^x is continuous at every real input x_0.
(Sec. 13.3)

DEFINITIONS: Call a function f *increasing* (over a subset S in its domain) if $f(x_1) \leq f(x_2)$ whenever $x_1 < x_2$, and x_1 and x_2 are inputs in S. If the inequality $f(x_1) < f(x_2)$ always holds when $x_1 < x_2$, call f *strictly increasing*.

Similarly, call a function f *decreasing* (over a subset S in its domain) if $f(x_1) \geq f(x_2)$ whenever $x_1 < x_2$, and x_1 and x_2 are inputs in S. If the inequality $f(x_1) > f(x_2)$ always holds when $x_1 < x_2$, call f *strictly decreasing*.
(Sec. 13.6)

THEOREM (ON "THE EXISTENCE OF INVERSE FUNCTIONS"): Any function that is strictly increasing over its domain must have an inverse function that is also strictly increasing. Similarly, any strictly decreasing function must have a strictly decreasing inverse.
(Sec. 13.6)

THEOREM (ON "THE CONTINUITY OF INVERSE FUNCTIONS"): If a function f is defined on an interval (or a line or a half line) and is strictly increasing over its domain, then its inverse function g is continuous at each input $y_0 = f(x_0)$ — provided only that y_0 is itself the limit of some sequence of other inputs $\{y_n = f(x_n)\}$.
(Sec. 13.6)

Applications:

$g(y) = y^{1/n}$, where n is any positive integer, is continuous at any $y_0 \geq 0$.

(Sec. 13.6)

For any $c > 0$, the function $f(x) = c^x$ has an inverse

$$g(y) = \log_c y$$

which is continuous at any $y_0 > 0$. For definition and other properties of *logarithms*, see Sec. 13.6.

THEOREM (ON "FIXED POINTS"): If f is a continuous function on $[0, 1]$ with range contained in $[0, 1]$, then there must be at least one input x_0 in $[0, 1]$ such that $f(x_0) = x_0$.

(Sec. 13.8)

For an application to extinction probabilities of populations with many children, see Sec. 13.8.

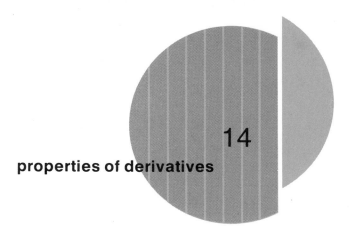

properties of derivatives

14

In this chapter I'll explore properties which will enable us to calculate derivatives for complicated functions in terms of the derivatives of their simpler parts.

14.1 A REVIEW OF DEFINITIONS: "RATES"

In Sec. 11.4 — improving upon the tentative definition of Chapter 7 — I defined the *derivative* of a function f at an input x_0 as the limit

$$f'(x_0) = \lim_{x \to x_0} \frac{f(x) - f(x_0)}{x - x_0},$$

(1)

provided the limit exists. I suggested that for $x \neq x_0$ the *difference ratio*

$$R(x) = \frac{f(x) - f(x_0)}{x - x_0}$$

(2)

measured an "average *rate* of change" for the function f over the interval between x_0 and x. And I interpreted a limiting value $f'(x_0)$ as representing an "instantaneous *rate* of change" of the function f at x_0.

Here is another example showing how the notion of *rate* is commonly used.

EXAMPLE 1: *The effects of nitrogen on wheat yield.* In the table of Fig. 14-1, I've recorded various amounts of nitrogen fertilizer which were

FIGURE 14-1

Applied nitrogen (in lb)	Wheat yield (in bushels)
0	20
20	24
40	25
60	24.5

FIGURE 14-2

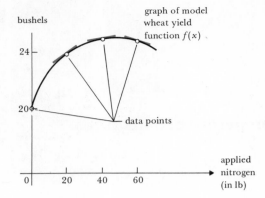

applied experimentally to similar one-acre plots of land. Corresponding to each such amount, you'll find indicated the crop growth which resulted. I've also pictured the same data by circled points in Fig. 14-2.

How can we evaluate the effect on wheat yield of a single pound of applied nitrogen?

The crudest way might be to divide the extra wheat yield due to 60 lbs. of nitrogen by 60, to get an *average rate* of "extra wheat yield per pound of nitrogen":

$$\frac{24.5 \text{ bushels} - 20 \text{ bushels}}{60 \text{ lb} - 0 \text{ lb}} = 0.075 \text{ bushels/lb.} \tag{3}$$

But such a number doesn't display the useful fact that the extra amount of wheat you can expect by adding a single pound of nitrogen depends on *how many pounds of nitrogen you have already used*. Thus, if you've already applied 40 lb of nitrogen to a one-acre plot then adding 20 lb more may well increase your yield at the *negative* rate of

$$\frac{24.5 \text{ bushels} - 25 \text{ bushels}}{60 \text{ lb} - 40 \text{ lb}} = -0.025 \text{ bushels/lb}$$

—at least according to the results in Figs. 14-1 and 14-2. Presumably the soil is already saturated with nitrogen.

On the other hand, the *first* 20 lb of nitrogen added produce extra crop yield at an "average" *rate* of

$$\frac{24 \text{ bushels} - 20 \text{ bushels}}{20 \text{ lb} - 0 \text{ lb}} = 0.2 \text{ bushels/lb.} \tag{4}$$

Now, a man who plans to apply, say, 10 lb of nitrogen might also wonder at what rate an 11th pound *by itself* will increase the yield — not when averaged with 10 other pounds. Or at what rate a single extra $\frac{1}{2}$ lb or $\frac{1}{4}$ lb — or even a single extra drop — will increase the yield.

The data in Fig. 14-1 are inadequate for answering such questions exactly. But let's try to capture the main features of the situation by a mathematical "model." Let's suppose that the "true" dependence of wheat yield upon the amount x of applied nitrogen can be represented by a function—call it $f(x)$—with graph as in Fig. 14-2. If so, then the rates in question are just difference ratios such as

$$R(10\tfrac{1}{2}) = \frac{f(10\tfrac{1}{2}) - f(10)}{10\tfrac{1}{2} - 10} \quad \text{and} \quad R(10\tfrac{1}{4}) = \frac{f(10\tfrac{1}{4}) - f(10)}{10\tfrac{1}{4} - 10}, \tag{5}$$

in bushels per pound. And if there existed a limit

$$f'(10) = \lim_{x \to 10} R(x) = \lim_{x \to 10} \frac{f(x) - f(10)}{x - 10} \text{ bushels/lb}, \tag{6}$$

would it not be reasonable to interpret $f'(10)$ as *the (instantaneous) rate at which the slightest extra drop beyond 10 lb of nitrogen increases the wheat yield*—still expressed in units of *bushels per pound*?

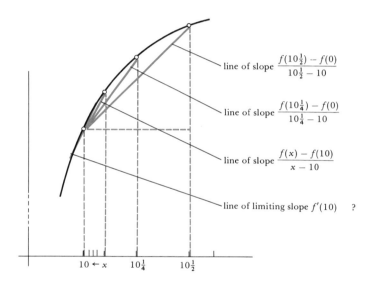

line of slope $\dfrac{f(10\tfrac{1}{2}) - f(0)}{10\tfrac{1}{2} - 10}$

line of slope $\dfrac{f(10\tfrac{1}{4}) - f(0)}{10\tfrac{1}{4} - 10}$

line of slope $\dfrac{f(x) - f(10)}{x - 10}$

line of limiting slope $f'(10)$?

FIGURE 14-3

$10 \leftarrow x$ $10\tfrac{1}{4}$ $10\tfrac{1}{2}$

In Fig. 14-3, which is a blowup of Fig. 14-2, I've represented the rates $R(10\tfrac{1}{2})$, $R(10\tfrac{1}{4})$, and so on, as slopes of lines through the graph point $(10, f(10))$. If a limiting rate $f'(10)$ did exist, we could represent it via a "limiting line"—namely, the line through the point $(10, f(10))$ with slope $m = f'(10)$. (Recall Sec. 4.4.)

For the hypothetical graph which I "fitted" to the given data in Fig. 14-2, I supposed $f'(20) = 0.125$ bushels/lb, $f'(40) = 0.031$ bushels/lb, and $f'(60) = -0.062$ bushels/lb. If the "model" approximates well to the "true" fertilizer story, then we can say that *an extra drop of nitrogen added onto a solution containing 20 lb is four times more potent than a corresponding extra drop added onto a solution containing 40 lb of nitrogen.*

Of what further use can it be to have a model with instantaneous rates $f'(x_0)$ for differing amounts x_0 of nitrogen?

One use is for determining the *most economical* amount of nitrogen to add. Of course, there is no sense in applying any amount x beyond, say, 45 lb—the input where the graph in Fig. 14-2 begins to fall, the "point of diminishing (wheat) returns." But even for values of $x < 45$ lb, every drop of nitrogen costs something. And if x is too large, the total cost of the applied nitrogen may reduce the user's net profit from what it might have been for smaller values of x. (Recall a similar problem of how to minimize ordering costs, in Sec. 7.1.)

Let's analyze the matter. To keep specific numbers from masking the main features, I'll use letters. Let's suppose that the wheat sells at A dollars per bushel, and that nitrogen costs M dollars per pound. And let's suppose that all other costs for producing the crop in the given field amount to B dollars. What will the net profit be if we apply x pounds of nitrogen (where $0 \leqslant x \leqslant 45$)? We can expect $f(x)$ bushels of wheat to bring in $Af(x)$ dollars. And our total expense will be $Mx + B$ dollars—yielding a net profit of

$$p(x) = Af(x) - (Mx + B) \text{ dollars.} \tag{7}$$

The graph of the "net profit function" p might look like the curve in Fig. 14-4.

FIGURE 14-4

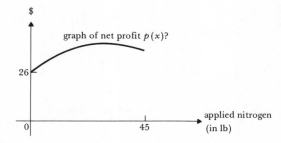

If $p(x)$ is continuous on the interval $[0, 45]$ then it must have at least one maximum output $p(x_{max})$. Where can a maximizing input lie? Either at one of the end points (0 or 45) or in between. If $p(x)$ has a derivative at each x, and if $0 < x_{max} < 45$ then we must have the slope $p'(x_{max}) = 0$ (as I argued in Sec. 12.7). That is, at $x = x_{max}$, the *instantaneous rate at which the next extra drop of nitrogen will increase the net profit* is zero.

If the derivative of a difference of functions is the difference of their separate derivatives (as it was, say, in Sec. 7.1), we can conclude from (7) that

$$p'(x_{max}) = Af'(x_{max}) - M = 0 \tag{8}$$

—since a linear function $Mx + B$ should have slope M. If we knew the crop selling price A (in dollars per bushel), and if we knew values for the rates $f'(x)$ (in bushels per pound) for $0 \leqslant x \leqslant 45$, we could solve (8) for a maximizing input x_{max}. It must be an input x_0 for which

$$Af'(x_0) - M = 0 \quad \text{or} \quad f'(x_0) = \frac{M}{A}. \tag{9}$$

Even without actually solving for x_{max} in a concrete case, let's note what the requirement

$$f'(x_{max}) = \frac{M}{A} \tag{10}$$

says in intuitive terms: Let's pick any input x very close to x_{max} (say with $x > x_{max}$), so that the difference ratio

$$\frac{f(x) - f(x_{max})}{x - x_{max}} \quad \textit{approximates closely to } f'(x_{max}) = \frac{M}{A}. \tag{11}$$

Multiplying the quantities in (11) by A/M we should find that

$$\frac{Af(x) - Af(x_{max})}{Mx - Mx_{max}} \quad \textit{approximates closely to } 1. \tag{12}$$

The numerator in (12) represents the *change in income* we would get by using the nearby amount of nitrogen x instead of x_{max} itself. And the denominator represents the corresponding *change in cost*. Hence (12) displays this property of a profit-maximizing input x_{max}: slight changes in input away from x_{max} must produce only equal (or approximately equal) changes in income and cost. These changes will cancel each other out so that no profit exceeding $p(x_{max})$ can be realized.

More concretely, suppose that wheat sells for $A = \$1.30$ per bushel, and that nitrogen costs $M = \$0.16$ per lb. Then we might expect an optimum input x_{max} to correspond to an instantaneous rate

$$f'(x_{max}) = \frac{M}{A} = \frac{\$0.16 \text{ per lb}}{\$1.30 \text{ per bushel}} = 0.123 \text{ bushels/lb}$$

(if x_{max} doesn't occur at an end point, 0 or 45). For the graph of f that I sketched in Fig. 14-2, the value $f' = 0.123$ occurs at approximately $x = 20$ lb, and only there.

To check whether x_{max} is the value 20 or one of the end points, 0 or 45, let's calculate the corresponding amounts of profit:

$$p(0) = (\$1.30 \text{ per bushel})(20 \text{ bushel}) - \$B = \$26 - B$$
$$p(45) = (\$1.30 \text{ per bushel})(25 \text{ bushel}) - (\$0.16 \text{ per lb})(45 \text{ lb}) - B$$
$$ = \$32.50 - \$4.80 - B$$
$$ = \$27.05 - B$$
$$p(20) = (\$1.30 \text{ per bushel})(24 \text{ bushel}) - (\$0.16 \text{ per lb})(30 \text{ lb}) - B$$
$$ = \$31.20 - \$3.20 - B$$
$$ = \$28.00 - B$$

The highest value of p occurs for $x = 20$. Hence x_{max} is not an end point; $x_{max} = 20$ lb.

Conclusion: If a user has soil and other conditions similar to those of the experimental plots for which the data in Fig. 14-1 were collected — then by applying 20 lb rather than 45 lb of nitrogen per acre, he may not only cut his springtime expenditures on nitrogen by more than half, but also increase his total season's profit by about $1 per acre.

14.2 DERIVATIVES DEFINE NEW FUNCTIONS

Whenever a function f has a derivative

$$f'(x_0) = \lim_{x \to x_0} \frac{f(x) - f(x_0)}{x - x_0} \tag{1}$$

existing at an input x_0, that number $f'(x_0)$ must be unique—since limits (if they exist) are always unique. And if the derivative $f'(x_0)$ exists at each x_0 in some set S of real numbers, then we can think of the definition (1) as a rule defining a *new function* with domain S:

to each x_0 (as input) *assign the value $f'(x_0)$* (as output) $\qquad$ (2)

Definitions: If $f'(x_0)$ exists at all x_0 in some set S of real numbers, let's call f *differentiable* (on S), and let's use the term *derivative function f' of f* to refer to the assignment in (2).

Although by definition a derivative $f'(x_0)$ is a limit to be computed at a fixed input x_0, once $f'(x_0)$ has been calculated (in principle) for *all* x_0's in some set S, then we can be free to use any labels we want for the inputs of the new derivative function—such as x's without subscripts: $f'(x)$.

EXAMPLE 1. You may recall the problem of a person falling from the top of a cliff. In Sec. 7.5 I argued that after t seconds of fall, the victim's vertical position down the cliff would be (approximately)

$$p(t) = 16t^2 \text{ feet}, \tag{3}$$

for all t up until the time T of impact with the ground. At any particular instant $t_0 < T$, the victim's *velocity*—that is, his *instantaneous rate of change of position*—is the derivative

$$v(t_0) = p'(t_0) = 32t_0 \text{ ft/sec}. \tag{4}$$

Recall that the relationship $v(t_0) = p'(t_0)$ constitutes a *definition* of "velocity," not merely a result following from other concepts. And for all $0 \leq t < T$, it defines a *velocity function $v(t) = 32t$.*

We can go further:

Definitions: If a function f is differentiable (on some set S) and its derivative function f' itself has a derivative at an input x_0, let's call that quantity the *second derivative* of f at x_0, and denote it by $f''(x_0)$:

$$f''(x_0) = \lim_{x \to x_0} \frac{f'(x) - f'(x_0)}{x - x_0}. \tag{5}$$

If $f''(x_0)$ exists at all x_0 in some subset T, we can use the term *second derivative function f'' of f* to refer to the rule assigning the number $f''(x)$ to each input x in T. Similarly, for "third derivatives," and so on.

The process of calculating derivatives has been called *differentiation*.

EXAMPLE 2. At what *rate* does the falling victim in Example 1 increase his downward velocity? You may recall (from Sec. 7.5 again) that, by definition, the *acceleration* of a body at any particular instant

t_1 is the *instantaneous rate of change of its velocity function*, the derivative

$$a(t_1) = v'(t_1). \tag{6}$$

With $v(t) = 32t$ in Example 1, we must have

$$v'(t_1) = 32 \text{ ft/sec}^2 \tag{7}$$

at any instant $t_1 < T$. In the notation above,

$$a(t_1) = p''(t_1). \tag{8}$$

Here is still another NOTATION for derivatives — which goes back to Leibnitz (1700), one of the originators of calculus. It will come in handy for distinguishing the derivatives of several functions appearing in the same problem but with differently labeled inputs. For a function f with inputs labeled x, we can denote $f'(a)$ by the alternate symbol "$(df/dx)(a)$." Similarly for a function $g(y)$ we can denote $g'(b)$ by "$(dg/dy)(b)$." The appearances of x and y in the symbols

$$\frac{df}{dx}(a) \quad \text{and} \quad \frac{dg}{dy}(b)$$

serve to recall the original labeling. And to Leibnitz, the "fractional form" of the symbols served to recall the difference ratios

$$\frac{f(x) - f(a)}{x - a} \quad \text{and} \quad \frac{g(y) - g(b)}{y - b}$$

whose limits define $f'(a)$ and $g'(b)$. But his symbols have *no* other algebraic meaning; they are not themselves ratios of numbers.

EXAMPLE 3. If $f(x) = x^3$, then $(df/dx)(a) = 3a^2$. If $g(y) = y^{-1}$, then $(dg/dy)(b) = -b^{-2}$. These expressions are sometimes written more simply as

$$\frac{df}{dx} = 3x^2 \quad \text{and} \quad \frac{dg}{dy} = -y^{-2}.$$

14.3 PROBLEMS ON RATES AND DERIVATIVE FUNCTIONS

°1. For each of the following functions f and inputs x_0, compute the corresponding slope-ratio function

$$R(x) = \frac{f(x) - f(x_0)}{x - x_0},$$

and sketch its graph.

(a) $f(x) = x^3$, $x_0 = 2$.

    Sample:

$$R(x) = \frac{x^3 - 8}{x - 2} = x^2 + 2x + 4, \text{ for } x \neq 2.$$

(b) $f(x) = x^2 + 2x$, $x_0 = 1$

(c) $f(x) = x^2 + 1$, $x_0 = 1$

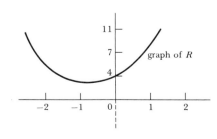

(d) $f(x) = x + 3$, $x_0 = 5$ (e) $f(x) = x + 3$, $x_0 =$ any integer

(f) $f(x) = \dfrac{1}{x^2}$, $x_0 = 1$

°2. For each of the following functions f and inputs x_0, determine whether or not $f'(x_0)$ exists. If it does, evaluate it.

(a) $f(x) = x^2 + 1$ at $x_0 = 1$

Sample:

$$f'(1) = \lim_{x \to 1} \frac{x^2 + 1 - 2}{x - 1} = \lim_{x \to 1} \frac{(x+1)(x-1)}{(x-1)} = 2.$$

(b) $f(x) = x^2 + 2x + 1$, $x_0 = 4$

(c) $f(x) = x^3 + 3x^2 + 1$, $x_0 = 3$

(d) $f(x) = \dfrac{x}{(x+1)^2}$, $x_0 = 1$

*(e) $f(x) = |x + 3|$, $x_0 = -3$

*(f) $f(x) = \dfrac{\sqrt{x+1}}{x}$, $x_0 = 1$

°3. Suppose that each of the following graphs represents the position x of an object moving along a straight line, as it depends on time t. Measure with a ruler if necessary, and estimate the *average* velocity of the object over the various intervals $[t_0, t_i]$. Then estimate the *instantaneous* velocity at t_0.

(a)

(b)

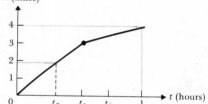

(c)

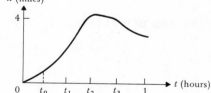

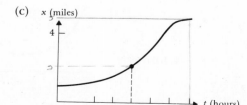

(d)

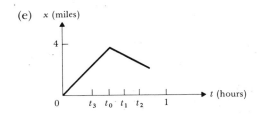

(e)

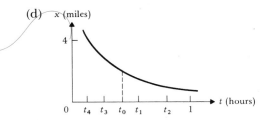

°4. Estimate slopes at several more points of the graphs in Problem 3, and determine during which time intervals the moving object had positive acceleration, and during which it had negative acceleration.

°5. "Fit", smooth graphs through each of the following sets of data. Then estimate inputs yielding maximum and/or minimum rates of change for the graphs.

(a)   average water temperature
(degrees centigrade) in a pond

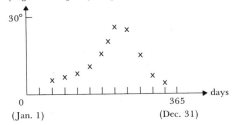

(b)   department store sales (in $ millions)

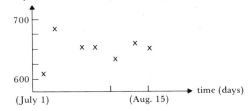

(c)

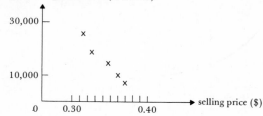

gallons of gasoline sold (in a week)

(d)

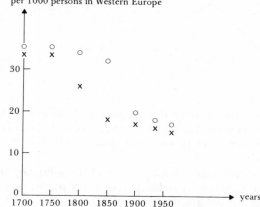

approx. numbers of births (○) and deaths (×) per 1000 persons in Western Europe

6. The data in Problem 5(c) represent the experience of a gasoline station in selling fuel at different prices. Suppose that for each gallon of gasoline sold, the station must pay $0.30 to its distributor and approximately $0.02 for labor and other costs. Suppose also that mortgage and utility payments, and so on, amount to $150 a week. Let the curve you fitted in Problem 5(c) be the graph of a function $f(x)$.

(a) Show that the station's weekly profit will be approximately

$$p(x) = (x - 0.32)f(x) - 150 \text{ dollars}$$

if it sells gasoline at x dollars per gallon.

(b) Sketch a graph of the function $p(x)$ and estimate the selling price x_0 which would maximize weekly profit.

(c) Why might one expect x_0 to be the input at which

$$[(x - 0.32)f(x)]' = 0?$$ (*)

(If we could write the condition (*) directly in terms of $f(x_0)$ and $f'(x_0)$, we could estimate x_0 directly from the graph of f, rather than going through step (b).)

7. Looking at the graphs in Problem 5(d), during what decades between 1700 and 1950 would you expect to find the greatest emigration rate from Western Europe?

8. Suppose that the price of nitrogen fertilizer changes to $0.18 per lb from the value I quoted in the fertilizer example of Sec. 14.1. How will that change the optimal amount of fertilizer to use?

9. For the "limiting" bacterial growth model which I discussed in Example 1 of Sec. 13.3 — wherein organisms lived for one hour before splitting — I conjectured that at any time t the instantaneous rate of change of population size $S(t)$ should equal $S(t)$ itself:

$$S'(t) = S(t) \qquad \text{for } t > 0. \tag{*}$$

Which of the following two sets of growth data approximately satisfy the relationship (*)?

(a)
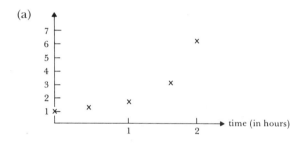

(b)   population (in millions)
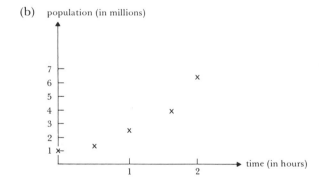

°10. Suppose that each of the following functions gives an object's position along a straight line $p(t)$ as a function of time t. For each case, find the velocity and acceleration.

(a) $p(t) = 3t^2 - 4t + 1$

(b) $p(t) = \frac{1}{2}gt^2 + v_0 t + p_0$ (g, v_0, p_0 are constants)

(c) $p(t) = 2t - 7$

(d) $p(t) = t^2 - 5t + 2$

(e) $p(t) = 3 - 3t - 3t^2$

(f) $p(t) = (5t - 1)^2$

$v = p'(t)$

$a = p''(t)$

(g) $p(t) = (1-t)^3$
(h) $p(t) = 6 - t^4$
(i) $p(t) = 8t - 2t^2$

11. For each of the following functions f, try to find df/dx by using limits of difference ratios:

(a) $f(x) = x^3$, for all x (b) $f(x) = x^2 + x + 1$,   for all x

(c) $f(x) = \dfrac{-1}{x}$, $x \neq 0$ (d) $f(x) = \dfrac{1}{x^2}$, $x \neq 0$

(e) $f(x) = \dfrac{x}{x+1}$, $x \neq -1$ (f) $f(x) = \sqrt{2x}$, $x > 0$

(g) $f(x) = x + \dfrac{1}{x}$, $x \neq 0$

14.4 COMBINATIONS OF LINEAR FUNCTIONS

Let's look again at the simplest kind of function for which one can calculate a derivative—a linear function, $L(x) = mx + b$. The graph of f is a line of slope m, which quantity is given by the difference ratio

$$R(x) = \frac{L(x) - L(x_0)}{x - x_0} = \frac{(mx+b) - (mx_0+b)}{x - x_0} = \frac{mx - mx_0}{x - x_0}$$

$$= \frac{m(x - x_0)}{x - x_0} = m, \tag{1}$$

no matter which two distinct inputs x_0 and x we may choose. See the similar triangles in Fig. 14-5.

FIGURE 14-5

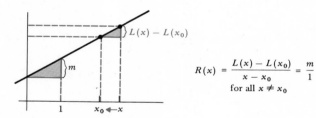

$$R(x) = \frac{L(x) - L(x_0)}{x - x_0} = \frac{m}{1}$$
for all $x \neq x_0$

FIGURE 14-6

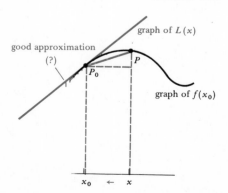

good approximation (?)

graph of $L(x)$

graph of $f(x_0)$

The limit

$$\lim_{x \to x_0} R(x) = \lim_{x \to x_0} m = m \tag{2}$$

exists at each input x_0, and is always the same: the slope of the line.

It was from the linear case that people got the idea of the "derivative" for more general functions f. They *hoped* that if a function was "smooth enough," then somehow it's graph could be approximated *close* to a point $P_0 = (x_0, f(x_0))$ by a line through that point—as in Fig. 14-6.

They thought of assigning the overall slope of the approximating line as an "instantaneous" or "local" slope $f'(x_0)$ for the graph of f at P_0.

In practice, these notations are useful only in the reverse order: If we *first* know (somehow) that a derivative $f'(x_0)$ exists at an input x_0, we can *then* consider the line passing through the point $(x_0, f(x_0))$ and having slope $m = f'(x_0)$; and we can ask how closely it approximates the graph of f. I'll discuss such approximations in later sections.

Perhaps we can learn what to expect of derivatives for various combinations of general functions — such as $f+g$, $f \cdot g$, and so on — if we think of approximating f by a linear function L and g by another linear function Q, and then ask about combinations of these linear functions — such as $L+Q$, $L \cdot Q$, and so on. Here are several examples:

1. *Scaling:* If $L(x) = mx + b$ is linear and c is a constant, then the scaled function $cL(x) = cmx + cb$ is linear too, with slope cm. That is

$$\boxed{(cL)'(x_0) = cL'(x_0)} \quad \text{at any input } x_0. \tag{3}$$

2. *Sums:* If $L(x) = mx + b$ and $Q(x) = Mx + B$, then their sum $L(x) + Q(x) = (m+M)x + (b+B)$ is again linear, with slope $m+M$. Hence

$$\boxed{(L+Q)'(x_0) = L'(x_0) + Q'(x_0)} \quad \text{at any input } x_0. \tag{4}$$

3. *Products:* If $L(x) = mx + b$ and $Q(x) = Mx + B$, then their product

$$\begin{aligned} L(x)Q(x) &= (mx+b)(Mx+B) \\ &= mMx^2 + (mB + Mb)x + bB \end{aligned} \tag{5}$$

is a quadratic polynomial. If we recall that $(x^k)' = kx^{k-1}$ for any integer k, and if the above scaling and addition rules apply generally, then we should have

$$(LQ)'(x_0) = mM(2x_0) + (mB + Mb). \tag{6}$$

To recognize the right-hand side in terms of the functions L and Q, let's regroup it as

$$\begin{aligned} &mMx_0 + mMx_0 + mB + Mb \\ &= m(Mx_0 + B) + M(mx_0 + b). \end{aligned} \tag{7}$$

Since $m = L'(x_0)$ and $M = Q'(x_0)$, we can rewrite (7) as

$$\boxed{(LQ)'(x_0) = L'(x_0)Q(x_0) + Q'(x_0)L(x_0)} \tag{8}$$

at any input x_0.

4. *Composition:* If $L(x) = mx + b$ and $Q(y) = My + B$, then their composition

$$Q(L(x)) = M(mx + b) + B = (Mm)x + (Mb + B) \tag{9}$$

is again linear, with slope Mm. That is,

$$\boxed{(Q(L))'(x_0) = Q'(y_0)L'(x_0).} \tag{10}$$

(Here it doesn't matter at which inputs x_0 and y_0 we evaluate the derivatives, since all the functions $L(x)$, $Q(y)$, and $Q(L(x))$ are linear.)

Will the above results also hold for functions f and g which might be approximated "closely" by the linear L and Q? More precisely, are such results valid for general differentiable functions?

14.5 PROPERTIES OF DERIVATIVES

Depending on the function f and the input x_0, the limit

$$\lim_{x \to x_0} \frac{f(x) - f(x_0)}{x - x_0}$$

defining the derivative $f'(x_0)$ may, or may not, exist. In Sec. 11.5 I gave examples of functions with discontinuities and with "corners" where derivatives could not exist. Now let's see whether results such as those for linear functions in the last section *must* hold whenever derivatives *do* exist.

First, let's note a basic requirement:

Theorem ("differentiability implies continuity"): If a derivative $f'(x_0)$ is to exist at an input x_0, then the function f must be continuous at x_0.

We can buttress the argument I previously gave for this result (recall Fig. 11-20) by a simple appeal to the property on limits of products — as in Fig. 14-7.

FIGURE 14-7

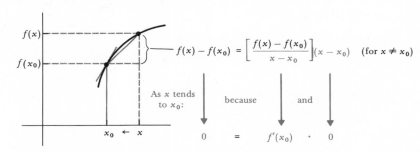

Conclusion: $\lim_{x \to x_0} [f(x) - f(x_0)] = 0$, or $\lim_{x \to x_0} f(x) = f(x_0)$.

Since derivatives are limits, wouldn't you expect the list of limit properties (in Chapter 11) to yield forth a number of further results about differentiation?

Here they come. (Where possible, I've labeled them to correspond with the limit properties from which they flow.)

Property A' ("uniqueness"). The derivative $f'(x_0)$ of a function f at an input x_0 — if it exists at all — must be a unique number.

Property B' (on "restricting the domain"). If $f'(x_0) = A$ and we restrict the domain $\mathscr{D}$ of f to a smaller set $\mathscr{D}_0$ containing x_0, then we shall *have* $f'(x_0) = A$ (provided some subsequence $\{x_n \neq x_0\}$ of inputs in $\mathscr{D}_0$ still converges to x_0).

Property C′ (*derivatives are determined "locally"*). *If* $f'(x_0) = A$ *and if* $g(x)$ *differs from* $f(x)$ *only outside some interval* $[x_0 - \delta, x_0 + \delta]$, *then* $g'(x_0) = A$.

Property D′ (*on "interlacing"*). *Suppose that* $f(x)$ *is defined on an interval* $[a, x_0]$ *and* $g(x)$ *is defined on an interval* $[x_0, b]$, *and that* $f(x_0) = g(x_0)$, *and* $f'(x_0) = g'(x_0) = A$. *If we have*

$$h(x) = \begin{cases} f(x) & \text{for } a \leqslant x \leqslant x_0 \\ g(x) & \text{for } x_0 \leqslant x \leqslant b, \end{cases}$$

then $h'(x_0) = A$ *also.* (See Fig. 14-8.)

FIGURE 14-8

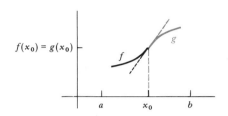

Property G′ (*on "linear functions"*). *If* f *is a linear function,* $f(x) = mx + b$, *then* $f'(x_0) = m$ *at any input* x_0. *In particular,* $f'(x) = 0$, *if* $f(x)$ *is a constant function,* $f(x) \equiv b$.

(Recall the last section on linear functions.)

Next, as predicted,

Property H′ (*on "scaling"*). *If* $f'(x_0) = A$ *and if* c *is a constant, then* $(cf)'(x_0) = cA$ (see Fig. 14-9).

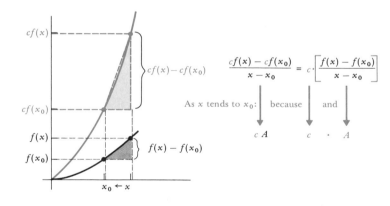

FIGURE 14-9

$$\frac{cf(x) - cf(x_0)}{x - x_0} = c \cdot \left[\frac{f(x) - f(x_0)}{x - x_0} \right]$$

As x tends to x_0:   because   and

$c\,A$ c $\cdot$ A

Again, as predicted,

Property I′ (*on "sums"*). *If* f *and* g *have a common domain, and*

$$f'(x_0) = A \quad \text{and} \quad g'(x_0) = B,$$

then $(f + g)'(x_0) = A + B$. *Also* $(f - g)'(x_0) = A - B$.

More generally: if $h(x) = f_1(x) + f_2(x) + \cdots + f_n(x)$, *where all the* f_i's *have a common domain and all the derivatives* $f_i'(x_0)$ *exist for* $i = 1, 2, \ldots, n$, *then*

$$\boxed{h'(x_0) = f_1'(x_0) + f_2'(x_0) + \cdots + f_n'(x_0).}$$

(See Fig. 14-10 for the case $n = 2$.)

FIGURE 14-10

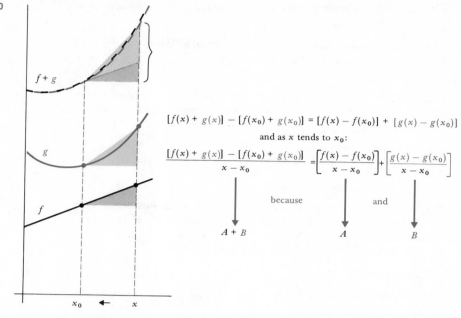

$$[f(x) + g(x)] - [f(x_0) + g(x_0)] = [f(x) - f(x_0)] + [g(x) - g(x_0)]$$

and as x tends to x_0:

$$\frac{[f(x) + g(x)] - [f(x_0) + g(x_0)]}{x - x_0} = \left[\frac{f(x) - f(x_0)}{x - x_0}\right] + \left[\frac{g(x) - g(x_0)}{x - x_0}\right]$$

because

$A + B$ and A B

Once more, as predicted,

> **Property J′ (Leibnitz's "product rule").** *If f and g have a common domain, and $f'(x_0) = A$ and $g'(x_0) = B$, then $(fg)'(x_0) = Ag(x_0) + Bf(x_0)$. That is,*

$$\boxed{(fg)'(x_0) = f'(x_0)g(x_0) + f(x_0)g'(x_0).}$$

(See Fig. 14-11.)

FIGURE 14-11   To separate f differences from g differences

write

$$f(x)g(x) - f(x_0)g(x_0) = [f(x)g(x) - f(x_0)g(x)] + [f(x_0)g(x) - f(x_0)g(x_0)]$$

$$= [f(x) - f(x_0)]g(x) + [g(x) - g(x_0)]f(x_0)$$

As x tends to x_0:

$$\frac{f(x)g(x) - f(x_0)g(x_0)}{x - x_0} = \left[\frac{f(x) - f(x_0)}{x - x_0}\right]g(x) + \left[\frac{g(x) - g(x_0)}{x - x_0}\right]f(x_0)$$

because   and   and   and

$Ag(x_0) + Bf(x_0)$ A · $g(x_0)$ + B · $f(x_0)$

(Why is $\lim\limits_{x \to x_0} g(x) = g(x_0)$ in Fig. 14-11? Because g must be continuous at x_0, since it has a derivative there.)

Property K′ (derivative of a reciprocal). *If g is never zero and $g'(x_0) = A$, then $(1/g)'(x_0) = -A/[g(x_0)]^2$. That is,*

$$\boxed{\left(\frac{1}{g}\right)'(x_0) = -\frac{g'(x_0)}{[g(x_0)]^2}.}$$

(See Fig. 14-12.)

FIGURE 14-12

To convert $\dfrac{1}{g}$ differences into g differences

write

$$\frac{1}{g(x)} - \frac{1}{g(x_0)} = \frac{g(x_0) - g(x)}{g(x)g(x_0)} = -\frac{1}{g(x_0)}\frac{1}{g(x)}[g(x) - g(x_0)]$$

As x tends to x_0:

$$\frac{[1/g(x)] - [1/g(x_0)]}{x - x_0} = -\frac{1}{g(x_0)}\frac{1}{g(x)}\left[\frac{g(x) - g(x_0)}{x - x_0}\right]$$

because   and   and

$$-\frac{A}{[g(x_0)]^2} = -\frac{1}{g(x_0)}\frac{1}{g(x_0)} \cdot A$$

Together, Properties J′ and K′ yield

Property L′ (derivatives of quotients). *If f and g have a common domain where g is never zero, and if $f'(x_0) = A$ and $g'(x_0) = B$, then*

$$\left(\frac{f}{g}\right)'(x_0) = A\left[\frac{1}{g(x_0)}\right] + \left[\frac{-B}{g(x_0)^2}\right]f(x_0);$$

or more compactly:

$$\boxed{\left(\frac{f}{g}\right)'(x_0) = \frac{f'(x_0)g(x_0) - g'(x_0)f(x_0)}{[g(x_0)]^2}.}$$

I invite you to try your hand at deducing those of the above results which I haven't proved in the figures. (Do Problems 4–6 of the next section.)

But first, here are several examples of how we can use the properties.

EXAMPLE 1. The absolute value function $f(x) = |x|$, for all x. To find $f'(2)$ we can restrict the domain, say, to the interval $[1, 3]$ around $x_0 = 1$—by Property B′ on restricting the domain. On $[1, 3]$, $|x| = x$; hence $f'(2) = 1$. See Fig. 14-13. Similarly, to find $f'(-2)$, we can restrict f to the interval $[-3, -1]$, where $|x| = -x$. Hence $f'(-2) = -1$. (Recall that the "corner" in the graph at $x_0 = 0$

FIGURE 14-13

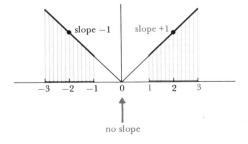

slope -1 | slope $+1$

no slope

prevents $f'(0)$ from existing. That is, $R(x) = [f(x)-f(0)]/(x-0) = 1$ if $x > 0$, and -1 if $x < 0$. Hence $R(x)$ has no limit as x tends to 0.)

EXAMPLE 2. Suppose that

$$f(x) = \begin{cases} x^2 & \text{for } x \geqslant 0 \\ 2x^2 & \text{for } x \leqslant 0. \end{cases}$$

FIGURE 14-14

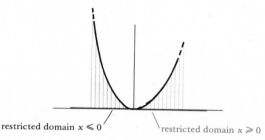

restricted domain $x \leqslant 0$ restricted domain $x \geqslant 0$

(See Fig. 14-14.) On the restricted domain $x \geqslant 0$, $f'(x) = 2x$. In particular, $f'(0) = 2(0) = 0$. On the restricted domain $x \leqslant 0$, $f'(x) = 4x$. In particular, $f'(0) = 4(0^3) = 0$. Hence for the original function $f'(0) = 0$, by Property D' on "interlacing."

EXAMPLE 3: *Polynomials.* If $f(x) = 4x^3 - 5x$, then

$$f'(x_0) = 12x_0{}^2 - 5$$

at any x_0. Here I've used the fact that $(x^k)' = kx^{k-1}$ for any integer $k \geqslant 0$ (recall Sec. 11.4), and I've appealed to Properties H' (on "scaling") and I' (on "sums"). By applying Property I for a longer sum of functions, we can conclude, more generally, that any polynomial

$$P(x) = a_0 + a_1x + a_2x^2 + a_3x^3 + \cdots + a_nx^n \tag{1}$$

must have a derivative of the form

$$P'(x_0) = a_1 + 2a_2x_0 + 3a_3x_0{}^2 + \cdots + na_nx_0{}^{n-1} \qquad \text{at any input } x_0. \tag{2}$$

You may recall from Sec. 13.8 (Example 3), that if $a_k = p_k =$ the probability that a parent will have k children, and if $p_0 + p_1 + p_2 + \cdots + p_n = 1$, then the derivative

$$P'(1) = p_1 + 2p_2 + 3p_3 + \cdots + np_n$$

represents the "average" number of children per parent.

EXAMPLE 4. If

$$h(x) = \frac{4x^3 + 3x^2 - 5x + 10}{x^4 - 1},$$

then we can write $h(x)$ as a quotient $h(x) = f(x)/g(x)$, where

$$f(x) = 4x^3 + 3x^2 - 5x + 10 \quad \text{and} \quad g(x) = x^4 - 1.$$

Note that the denominator polynomial $g(x) = 0$ only for $x = \pm 1$. For h to be reasonably defined, let's consider $+1$ and -1 as excluded from its domain. At any other value x_0, we can calculate

$f'(x_0) = 12x_0^2 + 6x_0 - 5$ and $g'(x_0) = 4x_0^3$. Hence, by Property L' on quotients,

$$h'(x_0) = \frac{f'(x_0)g(x_0) - g'(x_0)f(x_0)}{[g(x_0)]^2}$$

$$= \frac{(12x_0^2 + 6x_0 - 5)(x_0^4 - 1) - 4x_0^3(4x_0^3 + 3x_0^2 - 5x_0 + 10)}{(x_0^4 - 1)^2}. \quad (3)$$

In particular, for $x_0 = 0$,

$$h'(0) = \frac{(-5)(-1) - 0}{(-1)^2} = 5.$$

Considering the complexity of the function h, is it not an amazing coup of the human mind that — in just a few lines of computation — we could arrive at the concrete number 5 as the limiting value of difference quotients, $\lim_{x \to 0} [h(x) - h(0)]/(x - 0)$!

EXAMPLE 5. Here's another way to check that the formula

$$(x^k)' = kx^{k-1}$$

holds for *power functions with $k < 0$*. (Recall Example 2 of Sec. 9.5.) If $k < 0$ then $-k > 0$; and we can write

$$f(x) = x^k = \frac{1}{x^{(-k)}} = \frac{1}{g(x)}, \qquad \text{where } g(x) = x^{-k}.$$

Now, at any x_0, $g'(x_0) = (-k)x^{(-k)-1}$ (from Sec. 11.4). By appealing to Property K' on reciprocals, we can conclude that for $x_0 \neq 0$,

$$f'(x_0) = -\frac{g'(x_0)}{[g(x_0)]^2}$$

$$= -\frac{(-k)x_0^{(-k)-1}}{[x_0^{(-k)}]^2}$$

$$= +k\frac{x_0^{-k-1}}{x_0^{-2k}}$$

$$= kx_0^{2k-k-1} = kx_0^{k-1}. \quad (4)$$

Summarizing all cases, including $x^0 = $ constant, we have

$$(x^k)' = kx^{k-1} \qquad \text{for all integers } k = 0, \pm 1, \pm 2, \dots . \quad (5)$$

EXAMPLE 6. Intuitively we make extensive use of the sum rule for rates. For example, if each of the 25 sizeable towns bordering Lake Michigan deposits waste products into the lake at a certain rate — say $f_i'(t_0)$ tons per day for the ith town at the instant t_0 — then the overall rate at which the lake receives wastes from these towns at time t_0 is just

$$f_1'(t_0) + f_2'(t_0) + \cdots + f_{25}'(t_0) \qquad \text{tons per day.}$$

(Here we can interpret the function $f_i(t)$ itself as measuring the total waste contributed by the ith town between, say, the beginning of the year and time t.)

14.6 PROBLEMS ON DERIVATIVES

°1. Use various properties of Sec. 14.5 to calculate the derivative functions $f'(x)$ for each of the following functions $f(x)$:

(a) $f(x) = x^4 - 5x^3 + 6x^2 - 11x + 1$, for all x
(b) $f(x) = 7x^5 - 5x^7$, for all x
(c) $f(x) = \dfrac{x^4}{4} + \dfrac{x^3}{3} + \dfrac{x^2}{2} + x + 1$, for all x
(d) $f(x) = x^3(x^2 - 1)$, for all x
(e) $f(x) = (x - 3)(x + 2)$, for all x
(f) $f(x) = (3x + 1)(2x - 7)$, for all x
(g) $f(x) = \dfrac{x^2 - 1}{x^2}$, for $x \neq 0$
(h) $f(x) = \dfrac{x^2 + 1}{x^2 - 1}$, or $x \neq \pm 1$
(i) $f(x) = \dfrac{ax + b}{cx + d}$, for $x \neq -d/c$ (ab, c, d constants)
(j) $f(x) = \left(x + \dfrac{1}{x}\right)^2$, for $x \neq 0$
(k) $f(x) = \begin{cases} 3x^2 - 3x^3, & \text{for } x \leq 1 \\ -3x + 2, & \text{for } x > 1 \end{cases}$ $f'(x)$ does not exist at $x=1$?
(l) $f(x) = \begin{cases} \dfrac{x + 2}{x + 3}, & \text{for } -1 \leq x \leq 0 \\ \left(x + \dfrac{1}{12}\right)\left(x + \dfrac{1}{36}\right), & \text{for } x > 0 \end{cases}$
(m) $f(x) = \dfrac{x^2 - 1}{x^2} + x^3(x^2 - 1)$, for $x \neq 0$
(n) $f(x) = \dfrac{x^2 - 1}{x^2} + \dfrac{x^2 + 1}{x^2 - 1}$, for $x \neq 0, \pm 1$.

°2. Restate each of the properties of Sec. 14.5 in terms of the Leibnitz notation.

Sample: Property J′ can be stated as

$$\frac{d}{dx}(fg) = g\frac{df}{dx} + f\frac{dg}{dx}.$$

3. (a) Suppose that f, g, and h have a common domain and that $f'(x_0) = A$, $g'(x_0) = B$, and $h'(x_0) = C$. Show that

$$(fgh)'(x_0) = Ag(x_0)h(x_0) + Bf(x_0)h(x_0) + Cf(x_0)g(x_0).$$

(b) Formulate a generalization of Leibnitz's product rule (Property J′ in Sec. 14.5) for a product of n functions $f_1, f_2, \dots, f_n$.

*(c) Try to prove your generalization by induction.

4. Using corresponding properties of limits, show that the following properties (in Sec. 14.6) about derivatives must hold:
(a) Property A′ ("uniqueness")
(b) Property B′ (on "restricting the domain")

(c) Property C′ ("derivatives are determined locally")

(d) Property D′ (on "interlacing")

5. Try to write out a complete proof for Property L′ (on "derivatives of quotients") via two methods:

   (a) by using Properties J′ and K′ of Sec. 14.5,

   (b) by directly calculating the limit of the ratio

$$\frac{(f/g)(x) - (f/g)(x_0)}{x - x_0} = \frac{g(x_0)f(x) - g(x)f(x_0)}{g(x)g(x_0)(x - x_0)}$$

   (Rewrite the numerator of this ratio as

$$g(x_0)f(x) - g(x_0)f(x_0) + g(x_0)f(x_0) - g(x)f(x_0).)$$

6. Use induction to show that if

$$h(x) = f_1(x) + f_2(x) + \cdots + f_n(x),$$

   then

$$h'(x_0) = f_1'(x_0) + f_2'(x_0) + \cdots + f_n'(x_0)$$

   provided all the derivatives $f_i'(x_0)$ exist ($i = 1, 2, \ldots, n$). (This completes Property I′ (on "sums") in Sec. 14.5.)

*7. Can you find *any* pair of functions f and g with common domain $\mathscr{D}$ such that

$$(fg)'(x_0) = f'(x_0)g'(x_0)$$

   for all x_0 in $\mathscr{D}$?

14.7 COMPOSITION

When f and g were linear functions,

$$f(x) = mx + b \quad \text{and} \quad g(y) = My + B,$$

I noted in Sec. 14.4 that their composition $h(x) = g(f(x))$ was again linear — with slope $h' = Mm = g'f'$. Let's see now whether this simple relationship holds for nonlinear f's and g's, too.

   Here is an intuitive argument why it should: Suppose that $f(x_0) = y_0$, and that $f'(x_0) = A$ and $g'(y_0) = B$. If we pick an input x close to x_0, the difference ratio

$$\frac{f(x) - f(x_0)}{x - x_0} \quad \textit{should be close to } f'(x_0) = A. \tag{1}$$

If we multiply through by $x - x_0$, the difference

$$f(x) - f(x_0) \quad \textit{should be close to } A(x - x_0). \tag{2}$$

Thus the derivative $f'(x_0) = A$ represents a kind of "magnification factor" whereby the difference of inputs $x - x_0$ is multiplied to approximate the difference of outputs $f(x) - f(x_0)$. Similarly, for the function g: If we use $y_0 = f(x_0)$ and $y = f(x)$ now as inputs to g, and if y is close to y_0, then the difference

$$g(y) - g(y_0) \quad \textit{should be close to } B(y - y_0). \tag{3}$$

What might we expect the overall magnification effect to be for the composition function $h(x) = g(f(x))$? See Fig. 14-15.

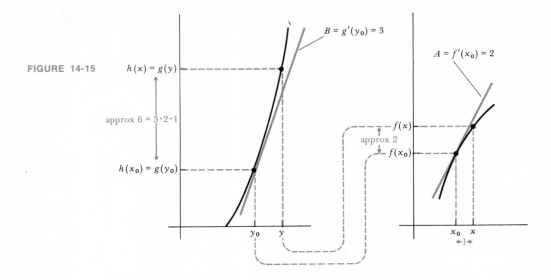

FIGURE 14-15

The difference

$$h(x) - h(x_0) = g(f(x)) - g(f(x_0)) = g(y) - g(y_0), \text{ which}$$

$$\text{approximately} = B(y - y_0) \qquad\qquad = B[f(x) - f(x_0)], \text{ which}$$

$$\text{approximately} = B[A(x - x_0)] \qquad = BA(x - x_0). \qquad (4)$$

So overall magnification does appear to be the product of the magnifications at each step. If we divide the last equation by the original input difference $x - x_0$, we should find that the difference ratio for h

$$\frac{h(x) - h(x_0)}{x - x_0} \quad \text{approximately} = BA = g'(y_0)f'(x_0). \qquad (5)$$

CONJECTURE: $h'(x_0) = g'(y_0)f'(x_0)$ for *any* functions f and g for which the composition $h(x) = g(f(x))$ makes sense, and for which derivatives $f'(x_0)$ and $g'(y_0)$ exist—where $y_0 = f(x_0)$.

But was all the above approximation reliable? Why not test it against our precise results for limits? To do so, let's pick *any* sequence $\{x_n \neq x_0\}$ which converges to x_0, and label the outputs $f(x_n) = y_n$. Will the corresponding sequence of h values,

$$h(x_n) = g(f(x_n)) = g(y_n)$$

give us difference ratios

$$\frac{h(x_n) - h(x_0)}{x_n - x_0} = \frac{g(y_n) - g(y_0)}{x_n - x_0}$$

which converge to $g'(y_0)f'(x_0)$? If yes, then

$$h'(x_0) = \lim_{x \to x_0} \frac{h(x) - h(x_0)}{x - x_0} = g'(y_0)f'(x_0),$$

To separate f and g difference quotients

FIGURE 14-16

write

$$\frac{h(x_n) - h(x_0)}{x_n - x_0} = \frac{g(y_n) - g(y_0)}{y_n - y_0} \cdot \frac{f(x_n) - f(x_0)}{x_n - x_0}$$

As x_n tends to x_0:   because   and

$$h'(x_0) \quad = \quad g'(y_0) \quad \cdot \quad f'(x_0)$$

and the conjecture is true. See Fig. 14-16. Is there any flaw in the argument in Fig. 14-16? If not, then we can announce

Property Q' (the "chain rule" for composition): If $f'(x_0) = A$ and if g is defined on the range of f and has derivative $g'(y_0) = B$ at $y_0 = f(x_0)$, then the composition $h(x) = g(f(x))$ has derivative $h'(x_0) = BA$. That is,

$$[g(f)]'(x_0) = g'(f(x_0))f'(x_0). \qquad (6)$$

In the notation of Sec. 14.2 we can also write the result as

$$\frac{dh}{dx}(x_0) = \frac{dg}{dy}(y_0)\frac{df}{dx}(x_0), \qquad (7)$$

or more simply as $dh/dx = dh/dy \cdot dy/dx$, to recall the labels ($x$ or y) for the inputs to the several functions.

NOTE: Suppose we can feed the composition $h(x) = gf(x)$ into a third function $k(z)$ to get a double composition $l(x) = k(h(x)) = k(g(f(x)))$. If $z_0 = h(x_0) = g(f(x_0))$ and if a derivative $k'(z_0)$ exists, then we can apply the above result first to the composition

$$l(x) = k(h(x)),$$

to get

$$\frac{dl}{dx}(x_0) = \frac{dk}{dz}(z_0)\frac{dh}{dx}(x_0). \qquad (8)$$

Next we can substitute the value of $(dh/dx)(x_0)$ from (7), to evaluate

$$\frac{dl}{dx}(x_0) = \frac{dk}{dz}(z_0)\frac{dg}{dy}(y_0)\frac{df}{dx}(x_0) \qquad (9)$$

again as a *product* of the individual derivatives of the component functions f, g, and k—calculated at appropriate inputs. (Because someone thought that the string of derivatives in (9) looks like a chain, Property Q' has been called the "chain rule.")

Did you find a flaw in the argument in Fig. 14-16? There is one: namely, that division by the (green) quantity $y_n - y_0 = f(x_n) - f(x_0)$ will make no sense if perchance $f(x_n) - f(x_0) = 0$. Such a calamity can't occur if, say, the function f is strictly increasing (as in Fig. 14-15) or if f is strictly decreasing. The argument works for such cases. But the calamity is only an apparent one. I'll show how to get around it in the next section. Here are examples of how we can use the "chain rule."

EXAMPLE 1. Consider the frightening function

$$h(x) = (x^{31} + 2x^{14} + x^7 - 9)^{143}.$$

We can write this function as $h(x) = g(f(x))$ where

$$f(x) = x^{31} - 2x^{14} + x^7 - 9 \quad \text{and} \quad g(y) = y^{143}.$$

Now,

$$f'(x_0) = 31x_0^{30} - 28x_0^{13} + 7x_0^6$$

at any x_0 and $g'(y_0) = 143y_0^{142}$ at

$$y_0 = f(x_0) = x_0^{31} - 2x_0^{14} + x_0^7 - 9.$$

Hence

$$h'(x_0) = g'(y_0)f'(x_0) = (143y_0^{142})(31x_0^{30} - 28x_0^{13} + 7x_0^6)$$
$$= 143(x_0^{31} - 2x_0^{14} + x_0^7 - 9)^{142}(31x_0^{30} - 28x_0^{13} + 7x_0^6) \text{ at any } x_0. \tag{10}$$

To arrive at the same result by appealing merely to rules on sums and products would take nearly 100 pages of calculation.

EXAMPLE 2. The simplest composition: When the *input* variable appears scaled. How can we find the derivatives of a function $h(x) = g(cx)$ if we know the function g and if c is a fixed constant? Let's just consider the expression cx as a linear function $f(x) = cx$, with $f'(x_0) = c$ at any x_0. Let's let $y_0 = cx_0$. Then

$$h'(x_0) = g'(y_0)f'(x_0) = g'(cx_0) \cdot c. \tag{11}$$

For instance,

$$[(5x)^{33}]' = 33(5x)^{32} \cdot 5. \tag{12}$$

EXAMPLE 3. Income tax. During 1969, single persons in the United States who had taxable incomes between $4,000 and $6,000 were taxed by the Federal Government at the rate of 22% for every dollar in excess of $4,000. More specifically, if such a person's taxable income for the entire year amounted to x dollars, where $4,000 < x \le \$6,000$, then he had to pay

$$T(x) = 690 + 0.22x \text{ dollars} \tag{13}$$

in federal taxes for the year. Suppose that an individual earned $4,500 during the first six months of 1969, and then was without work until December, at which time he got a job paying $2 an hour. At what hourly rate did his work increase his total federal tax bill during December?

Answer: We need merely multiply the *rate*, $2 per hour, at which the man receives income while working in December by the rate, $0.22 per dollar, at which such income is taxed. This is just the "chain rule" in action. Here is how the calculation results from the full tax *function* $T(x)$ in (13). Let's denote by $I(t)$ the total taxable income which the person earned from the beginning of 1969 up to the time t. Then the man's earning rate was

$$I'(t) = \$2 \text{ per hour} \tag{14}$$

for all t referring to working time in December. What burden of taxes did the man accumulate from the beginning of 1969 up to a given instant t in December? Exactly the amount

$$H(t) = T(I(t)), \tag{15}$$

the tax corresponding to a total taxable income of $I(t)$. At what rate did the amount $H(t)$ increase at any instant t_0 of work in December? By the "chain rule,"

$$H'(t_0) = T'(I(t_0))I'(t_0)$$
$$= (0.22)(2) = \$0.44 \text{ per hour.} \tag{16}$$

EXAMPLE 4. Suppose that the course of an airplane passes within 3 miles of a storm center. If the plane flies at 8 miles per minute, at what rate will it be receding from the center—say, one minute after the time of closest approach? See Fig. 14-17 for the geometry of the situation. At t minutes after the *instant* of closest approach, the plane will be $x = 8t$ from the *point* of closest approach. Hence, at that instant, it will be

FIGURE 14-17

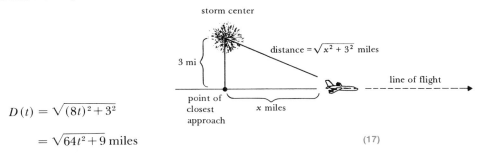

storm center

distance $= \sqrt{x^2 + 3^2}$ miles

3 mi

line of flight

point of closest approach

x miles

$$D(t) = \sqrt{(8t)^2 + 3^2}$$
$$= \sqrt{64t^2 + 9} \text{ miles} \tag{17}$$

from the storm center. The problem is to find the instantaneous rate of change $D'(t_0)$ at $t_0 = 1$ min provided such a rate exists.

We can think of $D(t)$ as a composition $D(t) = g(f(t))$, where $f(t) = 64t^2 + 9$ is a polynomial, and $g(y) = \sqrt{y}$ for $y \geqslant 0$. By previous results, $f'(t) = 128t$ at any t. What can we say about $g'(y)$? If it exists at any $y > 0$, then by the "chain rule" we'll have

$$D'(1) = g'(f(1))f'(1) = g'(73)(128) \text{ miles/min} \tag{18}$$

since $f(1) = 64 \cdot 1^2 + 9 = 73$ miles, and $f'(1) = 128 \cdot 1 = 128$ miles/min.

In Sec. 14.10 I'll discuss derivatives of power functions y^r for general r. Meanwhile, why not try to evaluate $g'(y) = (\sqrt{y})'$ directly from the definition of derivative? Let's pick $y_0 > 0$ and form the difference ratio $R(y) = (\sqrt{y} - \sqrt{y_0})/(y - y_0)$, for positive $y \neq y_0$. How can we rewrite $R(y)$ so as to see what $\lim_{y \to y_0} R(y)$ might be? Here's an old trick: let's consider y as $(\sqrt{y})^2$ and y_0 as $(\sqrt{y_0})^2$. Then

$$y - y_0 = (\sqrt{y})^2 - (\sqrt{y_0})^2 = (\sqrt{y} - \sqrt{y_0})(\sqrt{y} + \sqrt{y_0}) \tag{19}$$

and

$$R(y) = \frac{\sqrt{y} - \sqrt{y_0}}{y - y_0} = \frac{\sqrt{y} - \sqrt{y_0}}{(\sqrt{y} - \sqrt{y_0})(\sqrt{y} + \sqrt{y_0})} = \frac{1}{\sqrt{y} + \sqrt{y_0}}. \tag{20}$$

Hence, by the properties of limits in Chapter 11,

$$g'(y_0) = \lim_{y \to y_0} R(y) = \lim_{y \to y_0}\left(\frac{1}{\sqrt{y} + \sqrt{y_0}}\right) = \frac{1}{(\lim_{y \to y_0}\sqrt{y}) + \sqrt{y_0}}$$

$$= \frac{1}{\sqrt{\lim_{y \to y_0} y} + \sqrt{y_0}} = \frac{1}{\sqrt{y_0} + \sqrt{y_0}} = \frac{1}{2\sqrt{y_0}}. \tag{21}$$

Conclusion: One minute after its closest approach the plane will be leaving the storm center behind at the rate of

$$D'(1) = \frac{1}{2\sqrt{73}}(128) = 7.44 \text{ miles/min} \tag{22}$$

— *less* than the 8 miles/min speed of the plane. Note that earlier, just at the instant of closest approach, the escape speed was zero:

$$D'(0) = g'(f(0))f'(0) = \frac{1}{2\sqrt{3}}(128)(0) = 0 \text{ miles/hr}. \tag{23}$$

Can the escape speed $D'(t_0)$ ever equal the full speed of the plane, 8 miles per hour?

*14.8 A PROOF OF THE CHAIN RULE

Here is one way to patch up the argument for the "chain rule" as I gave it in Fig. 14-16. We had a composition $h(x) = g(f(x))$ with derivatives $f'(x_0)$ and $g'(y_0)$ existing, where $y_0 = f(x_0)$. I had chosen any sequence $\{x_n \neq x_0\}$ with $\lim_{n \to \infty} x_n = x_0$. The problem was

$$\frac{h(x_n) - h(x_0)}{x_n - x_0} = \left(\frac{g(y_n) - g(y_0)}{y_n - y_0}\right)\left(\frac{f(x_n) - f(x_0)}{x_n - x_0}\right). \tag{1}$$

The ratio

$$R_n = \frac{g(y_n) - g(y_0)}{y_n - y_0},$$

has no meaning for those n where the denominator $y_n - y_0 = 0$. Note that matters are really simpler for these supposedly "troublesome" n: namely,

$$\frac{h(x_n) - h(x_0)}{x_n - x_0} = \frac{g(y_n) - g(y_0)}{x_n - x_0} = \frac{g(y_0) - g(y_0)}{x_n - x_0} = 0, \tag{2}$$

and

$$\frac{f(x_n) - f(x_0)}{x_n - x_0} = \frac{y_n - y_0}{x_n - x_0} = 0. \tag{3}$$

To write equations (2) and (3) in the same form as the previous equation (1) let's define the quantity R_n as *equal to* $g'(y_0)$ for the "troublesome" n where $y_n - y_0 = 0$, while leaving

$$R_n = \frac{g(y_n) - g(y_0)}{y_n - y_0}$$

for the "nontroublesome" n where $y_n - y_0 \neq 0$. For the troublesome n, we can write the zero quantities in (2) and (3) as

$$\frac{h(x_n) - h(x_0)}{x_n - x_0} = R_n \left[\frac{f(x_n) - f(x_0)}{x_n - x_0} \right]. \tag{4}$$

But note now that the form (4) also describes the expression (1) for nontroublesome n. In other words, (4) holds for *all* n. Do the R_n's now converge to $g'(y_0)$? Yes: for the subsequence with non-troublesome subscripts—label them n_k—we must have

$$\lim_{n \to \infty} \frac{g(y_{n_k}) - g(y_0)}{y_{n_k} - y_0} = g'(y_0),$$

by definition of the derivative. And on the subsequence with troublesome subscripts, $R_n = g'(y_0)$ identically. Hence

$$\lim_{n \to \infty} R_n = g'(y_0)$$

by the "interlacing property" of limits (Property D of Chap. 9). And

$$h'(x_0) = \lim_{n \to \infty} \frac{h(x_n) - h(x_0)}{x_n - x_0} = \lim_{n \to \infty} R_n \lim_{n \to \infty} \frac{f(x_n) - f(x_0)}{x_n - x_0} = g'(y_0) f'(x_0).$$

End of the proof.

14.9 PROBLEMS ON RELATED RATES

1. For each of the following pairs of functions $f(x)$ and $g(y)$, write a formula for $h(x) = g(f(x))$. Then calculate $h'(x)$, $f'(x)$, $g'(y)$, and $g'(f(x))$; and verify the "chain rule" (of Sec. 14.8) for that example. (Consider the functions as defined for all inputs where the formulas make sense.)
   (a) $f(x) = 2x - 3$, $g(y) = -3y + 4$
   (b) $f(x) = 3x^2 + 1$, $g(y) = y^3$
   (c) $f(x) = 2x + 1$, $g(y) = \dfrac{y}{y^2 + 1}$ (d) $f(x) = \dfrac{3x - 2}{2x - 6}$, $g(y) = y^2$

2. For each of the pairs $f(x)$ and $g(y)$ in Problem 1:
   (a) Draw graphs of g and f side by side, as in Fig. 14-15; and use arrows to trace the route from $x_0 = 1$ to $y_0 = f(x_0)$ to $h(x_0) = g(y_0)$, and from $x_1 = 1.1$ to $y_1 = f(x_1)$ to $h(x_1) = g(y_1)$.

   (b) Compare (numerically) $\dfrac{y_1 - y_0}{x_1 - x_0}$ with $f'(x_0)$,

   $$\frac{g(y_1) - g(y_0)}{y_1 - y_0} \quad \text{with } g'(y_0),$$

   and $\dfrac{h(x_1) - h(x_0)}{x_1 - x_0}$ with $h'(x_0)$.

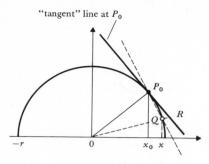

"tangent" line at P_0

FIGURE (a)

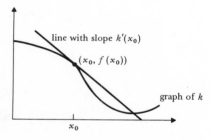

line with slope $k'(x_0)$

$(x_0, f(x_0))$

graph of k

x_0

FIGURE (b)

3. Do you recall the notion of a line "tangent" to a circle at a point P_0—as in the accompanying Fig. (a)?

You may recall a *definition* for the "tangent line at P_0"—namely as:

(i) "the line which touches the circle at P_0 and at no other points"; or as

(ii) "the line passing through P_0 and perpendicular to the radius OP"; or as

(iii) "the limiting position of lines determined by P_0 and Q as a point Q approaches P_0 along the circle."

Via the (right) triangle P_0OR in Fig. (a), you can check that definition (ii) implies definition (i). Now let's look at definition (iii), since it embodies the key idea of "slopes." Think of the semicircle in Fig. (a) as the graph of the function $h(x) = \sqrt{r^2 - x^2}$ for $-r \leqslant x \leqslant r$. (Recall that $x^2 + y^2 = x^2 + [h(x)]^2 = r^2$.) People have felt intuitively that a "limiting line" through P_0 should have a "limiting slope"

$$h'(x_0) = \lim_{x \to x_0} \frac{h(x) - h(x_0)}{x - x_0}. \qquad (*)$$

To be more precise, they *defined* the "tangent line" as *the (unique) line passing through the point $P_0 = (x_0, f(x_0))$ and having slope $h'(x_0)$*. (See Sec. 4.4.) Note that such a definition depends on the *existence* of the limit $h'(x_0)$ in (*). Then people went on to apply the same definition of "tangent line" to other graphs—such as in Fig. (b)—although for other graphs the properties in definitions (i) and (ii) need no longer hold, even if the limit $k'(t_0)$ exists.

You are now in a position to validate definition (iii) for the tangent to a circle, and to show that it implies definition (ii).

(a) Show that the derivative $h'(x_0)$ exists at each x_0 with $-r < x_0 < r$. (Suggestion: Write $h(x) = \sqrt{r^2 - x^2} = g(f(x))$, where $f(x) = r^2 - x^2$ for all x in $[-r, r]$ and $g(y) = \sqrt{y}$ for all $y \geqslant 0$, and apply the "chain rule" (Property Q') of Sec. 14.7. See Example 4 of Sec. 14.7 for $(\sqrt{y})'$.)

(b) Compare the slope $h'(x_0)$ with the slope of the radius OP_0 in Figure (a) and show that the tangent and the radius are perpendicular. (Recall the criterion for perpendicularity in Sec. 4.5.)

°4. Use the "chain rule" (one or more times) to evaluate $h'(x)$ for each of the following functions. (Consider the domains to consist of all numbers for which the formulas make sense.)

(a) $h(x) = (3x + 5)^{10}$

Sample reasoning: Write $h(x) = g(f(x))$ where $f(x) = 3x + 5$ and $g(y) = y^{10}$. Then $h'(x) = g'(f(x))f'(x) = 10(3x + 5)^9 3$.

(b) $h(x) = (6 - 3x)^7$

(c) $h(x) = (x + 5)^{-3}$

(d) $h(x) = (x^4 + 5x - 6x^{-1})^3$

(e) $h(x) = (3x^3 + 2x^2 - 6x^{-4})^{-4}$

(f) $h(x) = \dfrac{(2x + 1)}{(2x + 1)^2 + 1}$

(g) $h(x) = \dfrac{(5x^3 - 1)}{(5x^3 - 1)^2 + 1}$

(h) $h(x) = \dfrac{(3x-2)^2}{(3x^2-6)^3}$

Sample reasoning: Write

$$h(x) = \frac{f(x)}{g(x)} = \frac{(3x-2)^2}{(2x^2-6)^3}.$$

Then (by Property L' on quotients, in Sec. 14.7),

$$h'(x) = \frac{f'(x)g(x) - f(x)g'(x)}{[g(x)]^3}$$

$$= \frac{[2(3x-2)\cdot 3](2x^2-6)^3 - (3x-2)^2[3(2x^2-6)^2\cdot 4x]}{(2x^2-6)^6}$$

(i) $h(x) = \dfrac{(2x-6)^4}{(x+1)^7}$ (j) $f(x) = \dfrac{(x^2+2)^2}{(x^2+x^{-1})}$

(k) $f(x) = \dfrac{(x^{-1}+x^2)^{-1}}{(x^3-x^{-2})^{-2}}$ (l) $k(x) = \left[\dfrac{x^2+1}{(x^2+1)^3+4}\right]^{27}$

Sample reasoning: Write

$$k(x) = h(g(f(x))), \qquad f(x) = x^2 + 1,$$

$$g(y) = \frac{y}{y^3+4}, \qquad h(z) = z^{27}.$$

(m) $k(x)\left[\dfrac{x^3+1}{x^6-x^3+1}\right]^4$ (n) $k(x) = \left[\dfrac{x+1/x}{1+(x+1/x)^2}\right]^3$

(o) $f(x) = \dfrac{(x^2+2x-1)(x^3+3x-4)^2}{(2x+6)^2}$

(p) $f(x) = \dfrac{(x^{-2}+3x^{-4}+7x^{-5})^{-8}}{(x^2+x^{-2})^{-4}(x^{-1}+x^{-2})^{-3}}$

5. A pebble thrown into a still pond produces concentric circular ripples. If the radius of the largest ripple increases at 2 ft/sec, how fast is the area of disturbance within the ripple increasing when the radius is 15 feet?

6. A bacterial culture growing on a food medium in a shallow dish will generally have the shape of a circular disk whose area is proportional to the number of organisms. Suppose that at noon of one day such a culture has a diameter of 1 millimeter. If the organisms grow according to the model and the conjecture I discussed in Examples 1 and 2 of Sec. 13.3, then as a function of time t (hours from noon) the population size will be approximately $S(t) = Ne^t$, where N is the number of bacteria present at noon. And at any instant t_0 the population will be changing at the rate $S'(t_0) = S(t_0)$. Find the rate at which the *diameter of the culture* should be changing at 3 p.m. of the same day. (Suggestion: the relation between diameter and area is

$$d(A) = 2\sqrt{\frac{A}{\pi}} = \frac{2}{\sqrt{\pi}}\sqrt{A}.$$

For the derivative of $\sqrt{A}$, see Example 4 of Sec. 14.7.)

7. Suppose that a man 5 ft tall runs past a lamppost 15 ft high at the rate of 8 miles per hour. How fast is his shadow lengthening when he is 24 ft from the pole?

8. Suppose that a man stands at the top of an almost vertical 10-ft ladder which leans slightly against a wall. If the foot of the ladder were to begin sliding (say at 1 ft/sec) away from the wall, the man would come sliding down the wall. At what rate would he be traveling when he's halfway down? — when he's almost to the ground?

9. Suppose that an object is thrust from ground level vertically into the air with an initial velocity of 100 ft/sec, and that "gravity" causes it to accelerate (negatively) at -32 ft/sec².

   (a) Show why its altitude can be described in terms of the time t from lift-off by the function $f(t) = 100t - 16t^2$, at least until such time as the object hits the ground again. (You might recall the discussion I gave of a falling object, in Example 1 of Sec. 7.5.)

   (b) Find the maximum altitude which the object will reach, and the time, t_{max}, at which it does so.

   (c) Suppose that a 5-ft observer stands at a distance of 50 ft from where the object is launched. Describe the approximate distance $d(t)$ between the object and the observer's eyes as a function of time t, for $0 \leqslant t \leqslant t_{max}$.

   (d) Calculate the rate $d'(t)$ for $0 \leqslant t \leqslant t_{max}$.

10. Picture a man-made dam as creating behind it a large reservoir for water, roughly in the shape of a triangular trough — with dimensions as in the accompanying figure.

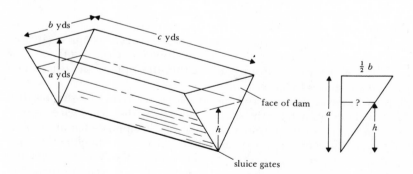

Let's begin counting time in days from the completion of the dam. And let's suppose that by any given time $t > 0$, a total of $F(t)$ cubic yards of water will have *entered* the reservoir via feeding streams and rainfall, and a total of $G(t)$ cubic yards of water will have left the reservoir via evaporation and via drainage through the sluice gates at the bottom of the dam. Denote by $H(t)$ the water level h at time t; and develop a formula for the *rate* $H'(t)$ at which that level is changing at time t—in terms of the constants a, b, c, the rates $F'(t)$ and $G'(t)$, and the level $H(t)$ itself.

(Suggestion: Express the water volume V in terms of h; and inversely, h as a function of V. Then write $V = F(t) = G(t)$.)

*11. If the interest rate for mortgages goes up, then the number of new buildings constructed goes down, bringing down the orders to lumber mills. This causes a decrease in revenues of states whose primary industry is lumber, and makes less state money available, say, for education. Here is a greatly simplified version of how such a chain of effects might look:

We might be able to express approximately the expected number of buildings, $h(r)$, constructed during a year when the interest rate r prevails, as a function

$$h(r) = \frac{10^5}{1+r} \qquad \text{for } 3\% \leqslant r \leqslant 10\%.$$

Suppose that an average building requires $3,000 worth of lumber. Suppose (a great simplification) that the lumber industry depends primarily on such orders, and that they are shared almost equally by, say, 50 companies in all, each making a 5% profit on its sales. Suppose that these companies pay taxes according to a formula

$$T(y) = 5 \times 10^{-2}y + 25 \times 10^{-7}y^2 \text{ dollars}$$

for incomes $y \leqslant$ one million dollars. Finally, suppose that 10 cents of each revenue dollar goes for educational needs.

(a) Put all these items together to get an expression showing how the amount of money available for education in states whose primary industry is lumber—call it $A(r)$—depends on the mortgage interest rate r. You may have to include undetermined constants in your formula, to denote other state revenues, and so on.

(b) Calculate at which rate educational funds diminish as the mortgage interest rate increases, assuming other factors are constant. Do you have sufficient data to complete the calculation?

12. Let $f(x) = \sqrt{x+1}$ for $x \geqslant -1$ and $g(y) = y^2 - 1$. Let $h(x) = g(f(x))$ and $k(y) = f(g(y))$. Show that $h(x) = x$ for all x and $k(y) = y$ for all $y \geqslant 0$. Verify the chain rule and sketch the graphs of f, g, h, and k.

13. Suppose that

$$h(x) = f_n(f_{n-1}(\cdots f_2(f_1(x)) \cdots)).$$

Let

$$x_1 = f_1(x_0), \quad x_2 = f_2(x_1), \quad x_3 = f_3(x_2), \ldots,$$

and

$$x_{n-1} = f_{n-1}(x_{n-2}).$$

And suppose that all derivatives $f_i'(x_{i-1})$ exist for $i = 1, 2,$ $3, \ldots, n$. Using induction, show that

$$h'(x_0) = f_n'(x_{n-1}) \cdot f_{n-1}'(x_{n-2}) \cdots f_2'(x_1)f_1'(x_0).$$

14.10 DERIVATIVES OF INVERSE FUNCTIONS

So far, our catalog of differentiable functions contains only power functions x^n, polynomials, and ratios of these. Can we extend it? You may recall other functions from Chap. 13: root functions $y^{1/n}$—the inverses of power functions, exponentials c^x, and logs $\log_c y$—the inverses of exponentials. Are all these functions differentiable too?

In Fig. 14-18 I've sketched (in black) the graph of a strictly increasing function f, and (in green) the graph of its inverse function g.

FIGURE 14-18

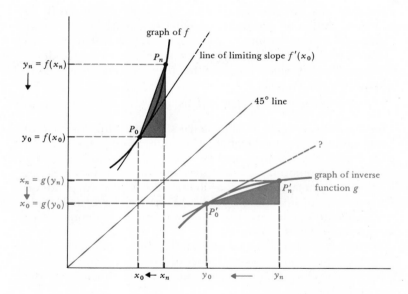

I got the green graph by flipping the black one over the 45° line. Suppose that the slopes of the line segments P_0P_n approach a limiting value $f'(x_0)$ as we move the point P_n toward P_0. Doesn't it seem as if the slopes of the corresponding line segments $P_0'P_n'$ should approach some limiting value $g'(y_0)$, too? And what might $g'(y_0)$ be? Notice that essentially the shaded green triangle differs from the black only by an interchange of vertical and horizontal sides. Hence the slope of $P_0'P_n'$ should be the *reciprocal* of the slope of P_0P_n. And why not the same for the corresponding limits,

$$g'(y_0) = \frac{1}{f'(x_0)}?$$

More precisely:

Theorem A (on "derivatives of inverses"): Suppose that f is defined on some interval, line, or half-line; that f is a strictly increasing or a strictly decreasing function; and that g is its inverse. If $f'(x_0)$ exists and is not zero, then $g'(y_0)$ exists at $y_0 = f(x_0)$ and

$$g'(y_0) = \frac{1}{f'(x_0)}. \tag{1}$$

Can we trust the picture in Fig. 14-17? We needn't. For a

Proof of theorem A: we need merely pick any sequence $\{y_n \neq y_0\}$ converging to y_0, and show that

$$\lim_{n \to \infty} \frac{g(y_n) - g(y_0)}{y_n - y_0} = \frac{1}{f'(x_0)}. \tag{2}$$

But since f and g are inverses, we must have

$$x_0 = g(y_0) \quad \text{when } y_0 = f(x_0) \tag{3}$$

and

$$y_n = f(x_n) \quad \text{when } x_n = g(y_n). \tag{4}$$

(See Fig. 14-17.) Hence we can write

$$\frac{g(y_n) - g(y_0)}{y_n - y_0} = \frac{x_n - x_0}{f(x_n) - f(x_0)}$$
$$= \frac{1}{\{[f(x_n) - f(x_0)]/(x_n - x_0)\}}. \tag{5}$$

Moreover, the sequence $x_n = g(y_n)$ must converge to $x_0 = g(y_0)$ when y_n tends to y_0, because the inverse g is *continuous* — such was the message of Theorem E in Sec. 13.6. Hence

$$g'(y_0) = \lim_{n \to \infty} \frac{g(y_n) - g(y_0)}{y_n - y_0}$$
$$= \frac{1}{\lim_{n \to \infty} \{[f(x_n) - f(x_0)]/(x_n - x_0)\}} = \frac{1}{f'(x_0)}, \tag{6}$$

by the property on "limits of reciprocals" (Property K in Chap. 9). End of the proof.

Now let's apply the new result to increase our store of differentiable functions:

EXAMPLE 1: *Root functions.* If n is a positive integer, the function $g(y) = y^{1/n}$, defined for all $y \geq 0$, is the inverse of $f(x) = x^n$. Hence, for $y_0 > 0$,

$$g'(y_0) = \frac{1}{f'(x_0)} = \frac{1}{nx_0^{n-1}}, \tag{7}$$

where $y_0 = f(x_0) = x_0^n$, or equivalently, $x_0 = g(y_0) = y_0^{1/n}$. \qquad (8)

We can substitute this last expression for x_0 into (7) to get

$$g'(y_0) = \frac{1}{nx_0^{n-1}} = \frac{1}{n(y_0^{1/n})^{n-1}} = \frac{1}{ny_0^{1-1/n}}$$

$$= \frac{1}{n} y_0^{1/n-1}. \tag{9}$$

That is,

$$\boxed{(y^{1/n})' = \frac{1}{n} y^{1/n-1}} \qquad \text{at any } y > 0. \tag{10}$$

Note that the same formula, $(x^p)' = px^{p-1}$, describes this result (with $p = 1/n$) and also the previous power function cases ($p =$ any integer).

We can push the application still further:

EXAMPLE 2: *Rational powers.* Let $h(x) = x^r$ for all $x > 0$, where $r = k/n$ is the ratio of any integer k (positive or negative or zero) and n is a positive integer. We can think of h as a composition $h(x) = g(f(x))$ where $f(x) = x^k$ and $g(y) = y^{1/n}$. So to differentiate h at any $x_0 > 0$, let's use the "chain rule":

$$h'(x_0) = g'(y_0)f'(x_0), \quad \text{where } y_0 = f(x_0) = x_0^k. \tag{11}$$

Now

$$f'(x_0) = kx_0^{k-1} \quad \text{and} \quad g'(y_0) = \frac{1}{n} y_0^{1/n-1}. \tag{12}$$

Putting all these notes together, we can conclude that

$$h'(x_0) = \frac{1}{n} y_0^{1/n-1} kx_0^{k-1} = \frac{1}{n} (x_0^k)^{1/n-1} kx_0^{k-1}$$

$$= \frac{k}{n} x_0^{k/n-k+k-1} = \frac{k}{n} x_0^{k/n-1}. \tag{13}$$

That is,

$$\boxed{(x^r)' = rx^{r-1}} \qquad \text{at any } x > 0, \tag{14}$$

again, the same formula as for the simpler power and root functions.

Now, how about the exponential c^x and its inverse $\log_c y$? If only we knew derivatives for one of them, we could take reciprocals and find derivatives for the other. Recall the distinctive properties of these functions such as

$$c^{x_1+x_2} = c^{x_1}c^{x_2} \quad \text{and} \quad (c^x)^p = c^{px}, \tag{15}$$

and

$$\log_c y_1 + \log_c y_2 = \log_c y_1 y_2 \quad \text{and} \quad p \log_c y = \log_c y^p. \tag{16}$$

The last two equalities, with $p = -1$, yield a formula for *differences*,

$$\log_c y_1 - \log_c y_2 = \log_c \frac{y_1}{y_2}. \tag{17}$$

And since differences play a key role in the definition of derivatives, it may be worthwhile to seek for the derivative of a log function first.

Pick a "base" $c > 0$ ($c \neq 1$), and an input $y_0 > 0$. And let's try to approach y_0 along a specially simple sequence of inputs, say $y_n = (1 + 1/n)y_0$. What will happen to the difference ratios

$$\frac{\log_c y_n - \log_c y_0}{y_n - y_0}?$$

Let's write

$$R(y_n) = \frac{\log_c y_n - \log_c y_0}{y_n - y_0} = \frac{\log_c (y_n/y_0)}{y_n - y_0} = \frac{\log_c [y_0(1 + 1/n)/y_0]}{y_n - y_0}$$

$$= \frac{\log_c (1 + 1/n)}{(1 + 1/n)y_0 - y_0} = \frac{\log_c (1 + 1/n)}{(1/n) y_0} = \frac{1}{y_0}\left[n \log_c \left(1 + \frac{1}{n}\right)\right]$$

$$= \frac{1}{y_0} \log_c \left[\left(1 + \frac{1}{n}\right)^n\right]. \tag{18}$$

To get the last line in (18), I used the property $p \log_c y = \log_c y^p$, with $p = n$. To find what a derivative might be for $\log_c y$ at y_0, let's examine the limit of the difference ratios

$$\lim_{n \to \infty} R(y_n) = \lim_{n \to \infty} \frac{1}{y_0} \log_c \left[\left(1 + \frac{1}{n}\right)^n\right]$$

$$= \frac{1}{y_0} \lim_{n \to \infty} \log_c \left[\left(1 + \frac{1}{n}\right)^n\right]. \tag{19}$$

What can the last limit be? Recall that the function $g(y) = \log_c y$ — being the inverse function of c^x — is *continuous* at all its inputs: for any sequence, say, $\{a_n\}$ converging to an input A, $\lim_{n \to \infty} g(a_n) = g(A)$. In particular, the inputs

$$a_n = \left(1 + \frac{1}{n}\right)^n$$

converge to $e = 2.71 \ldots$. Hence

$$\lim_{n \to \infty} R(y_n) = \frac{1}{y_0} \lim_{n \to \infty} \log_c \left[\left(1 + \frac{1}{n}\right)^n\right] = \frac{1}{y_0} \log_c e. \tag{20}$$

If the same result were true for *any* sequence $\{y_n \neq y_0\}$ converging to y_0, not just for

$$y_n = \left(1 + \frac{1}{n}\right)y_0,$$

then we could conclude that

$$\lim_{y \to y_0} \frac{\log_c y - \log_c y_0}{y - y_0} = \frac{1}{y_0} \log_c e, \tag{21}$$

and we would have a

Theorem B (on "derivatives of logs"): If c is any positive constant, and y_0 is > 0, then the log function $g(y) = \log_c y$ has derivative

$g'(y_0) = (\log_c e)/y_0$. In particular, if $c = e$, then $\log_e e = 1$ and $g'(y_0) = 1/y_0$.

I'll indicate in the next section why the above argument does hold for all sequences $\{y_n\}$ converging to y_0. But first, here are a few consequences of Theorem B.

EXAMPLE 3: *The simplest exponential.* Since $f(x) = e^x$ (for all x) and $g(y) = \log_e y$ (for all $y > 0$) are inverses of each other, we can now compute $f'(x_0)$ at any $x_0 = g(y_0)$. Namely,

$$f'(x_0) = \frac{1}{g'(y_0)} = \frac{1}{(1/y_0)} = y_0. \tag{22}$$

Since $x_0 = g(y_0)$, we must have

$$y_0 = f(x_0) = \exp x_0. \tag{23}$$

Putting the last two equations together, we can conclude that

$$\boxed{(e^x)' = e^x} \quad \text{at any real input } x. \tag{24}$$

If we multiply (24) through by any constant b, we get

$$(be^x)' = b(e^x)' = be^x, \tag{25}$$

by the scaling property of derivatives.

In particular, if we let $b = N$, the number of bacteria at time $t = 0$ in a population such as I discussed in Sec. 13.3 (Examples 1 and 2), then we can verify an earlier conjecture: It must indeed be true that the idealized population-size function $S(t) = Ne^t$ has an instantaneous rate of increase at any instant t_0 which exactly equals the population size at that instant: $S'(t_0) = S(t_0)$.

That formulation was for bacteria having an average lifetime of one hour. How about the population size function

$$\hat{S}(t) = Ne^{t/H}$$

for bacteria having an average lifetime of H hours? Let's use the "chain rule" (as in Example 3 of Sec. 14.7): consider

$$\hat{S}(t) = Ne^{t/H}$$

as a composition $S(L(t))$ where $S(x) = Ne^x$ as above, and

$$L(t) = \frac{1}{H}t.$$

With

$$x_0 = L(t_0) = \frac{1}{H}t_0,$$

we must have

$$\hat{S}'(t_0) = S'(x_0)L'(t_0). \tag{26}$$

Here $L'(t_0) = 1/H$, and

$$S'(x_0) = S(x_0) = Ne^{x_0} = Ne^{t_0/H}. \tag{27}$$

Hence

$$\hat{S}'(t_0) = [Ne^{t_0/H}]\left(\frac{1}{H}\right) = \frac{1}{H}\hat{S}(t_0). \qquad (28)$$

Conclusion: If bacteria have an average lifetime of H hours, then the instantaneous rate of increase of population is directly proportional to the population size at t_0 and inversely proportional to the average lifetime H.

EXAMPLE 4: *Other exponentials.* The same chain rule argument as in the last example gives, for any constant a, the result

$$\boxed{(e^{at})' = ae^{at}} \qquad \text{at any real } t. \qquad (29)$$

(Here $e^{at} = f(L(t))$, where $f(x) = e^x$ and $L(t) = at$.)

Moreover we can write any positive constant c in the form $c = e^a$, where $a = \log_e c$. Hence $c^x = e^{ax}$ and equation (29) now reads

$$\boxed{(c^x)' = (\log_e c)c^x} \qquad \text{for any } x. \qquad (30)$$

EXAMPLE 5: *Arbitrary positive powers.* We can now check whether the formula $(x^p)' = px^{p-1}$ holds for any real number p, not just for rational values. The reason is that we can write any positive x in the form $x = e^{\log_e x}$. Hence

$$h(x) = x^p = [e^{\log_e x}]^p = e^{p \log_e x}, \qquad (31)$$

and we can write $h(x)$ as a composition $h(x) = G(F(x))$, where $G(y) = e^y$ and $F(x) = p \log_e x$. Now $G'(y) = e^y$ and $F'(x) = p(\log_e x)' = p(1/x)$. If we let $y_0 = F(x_0) = p \log_e x_0$, the chain rule yields

$$\begin{aligned}
h'(x_0) = G'(y_0)F'(x_0) &= (e^{y_0})\left(p\frac{1}{x_0}\right) \\
&= [e^{p\log_e x_0}]\left(p\frac{1}{x_0}\right) = (x_0{}^p)p\left(\frac{1}{x_0}\right) \\
&= px_0{}^{p-1}
\end{aligned}$$

once more.

By scaling, adding, multiplying, dividing, and composing polynomials and exponentials and logs, we can now build a mountain of differentiable functions.

One more example:

EXAMPLE 6. The frightening function

$$f(x) = e^{(x^2/\sqrt{1+x^2})}. \qquad (32)$$

Let's write $f(x) = A(B(x))$ where

$$A(y) = e^y \quad \text{and} \quad B(x) = \frac{x^2}{\sqrt{1+x^2}}.$$

Since $A'(y) = e^y$, the chain rule yields

$$f'(x) = A'(B(x))B'(x) = A(B(x))B'(x) = e^{(x^2/\sqrt{1+x^2})} B'(x). \qquad (33)$$

Next write $B(x) = C(x)/D(x)$, where $C(x) = x^2$ and $D(x) = \sqrt{1+x^2}$. By the property on division,

$$B'(x) = \frac{C'(x)D(x) - D'(x)C(x)}{D^2(x)} = \frac{2x\sqrt{1+x^2} - D'(x)x^2}{1+x^2}. \tag{34}$$

Next write $D(x) = E(F(x))$, where $E(y) = y^{1/2}$ and $F(x) = 1+x^2$. Since

$$E'(y) = \frac{1}{2}y^{1/2-1} = \frac{1}{2}y^{-1/2} = \frac{1}{2}\frac{1}{\sqrt{y}},$$

the chain rule yields

$$D'(x) = E'(F(x))F'(x) = \frac{1}{2}\frac{1}{\sqrt{1+x^2}}F'(x). \tag{35}$$

Finally $F'(x) = 2x$. Putting all the parts together, we have

$$f'(x) = e^{(x^2/\sqrt{1+x^2})}\left[\frac{2x\sqrt{1+x^2} - \frac{1}{2}(1/\sqrt{1+x^2})(2x)x^2}{1+x^2}\right].$$

Would you have guessed it?

Some people view such manipulations as a kind of game, like doing crossword puzzles. I invite you to try your hand at it in doing the problems of Sec. 14.12.

*14.11 WHY THE FORMULA FOR LOG FUNCTIONS IS VALID

To prove that $(\log_c y)' = (1/y)\log_c e$ (Theorem B of the last section), we might try to write the difference ratio

$$R(y) = \frac{\log_c y - \log_c y_0}{y - y_0}$$

for general positive $y \neq y_0$ in a similar form as for the special

$$y_n = y_0\left(1 + \frac{1}{n}\right).$$

Recall that I used properties of logs to write

$$R(y_n) = \frac{\log_c(y_n/y_0)}{y_n - y_0} = \frac{\log_c(1 + 1/n)}{y_0(1/n)}$$

$$= \left(\frac{1}{y_0}\right)(n)\log_c\left(1 + \frac{1}{n}\right) = \left(\frac{1}{y_0}\right)\log_c\left\{\left(1 + \frac{1}{n}\right)^n\right\}. \tag{1}$$

For general $y > y_0$, let's now write

$$R(y) = \frac{\log_c(y/y_0)}{y - y_0} = \frac{\log_c[1 + (y/y_0 - 1)]}{y_0(y/y_0 - 1)}$$

$$= \frac{1}{y_0}\left(\frac{1}{y/y_0 - 1}\right)\log_c\left[1 + \left(\frac{y}{y_0} - 1\right)\right]$$

$$= \frac{1}{y_0}\log_c\left\{\left[1 + \left(\frac{y}{y_0} - 1\right)\right]^{1/[(y/y_0)-1]}\right\}. \tag{2}$$

We can view the complicated expression on the last line more simply as a composition

$$R(y) = \frac{1}{y_0} \log_c G(F(y)),$$ (3)

where

$$F(y) = \frac{y}{y_0} - 1 \qquad \text{for } y > y_0$$ (4)

and

$$G(t) = (1+t)^{1/t} \qquad \text{for } t > 0.$$ (5)

You might recall from Sec. 13.3 (Example 3) that $\lim\limits_{t \to 0} G(t) = e$. So if we define $G(0) = e$, G will be a continuous function at $t = 0$. Now, on the domain $\{\text{all } y > y_0\}$ we have $\lim\limits_{y \to y_0} F(y) = 0$. Hence

$$\lim_{y \to y_0} G(F(y)) = G(0) = e,$$ (6)

by our result on limits of compositions (Property Q of Chap. 11). Hence on the domain $\{\text{all } y > y_0\}$,

$$\lim_{y \to y_0} R(y) = \frac{1}{y_0} \lim_{y \to y_0} \log_c G(F(y)) = \frac{1}{y_0} \log_c e,$$ (7)

by the same property.

For positive $y < y_0$, write

$$R(y) = \frac{\log_c y_0 - \log_c y}{y_0 - y}$$

$$= \frac{1}{y} \log_c \left\{ \left[1 + \left(\frac{y_0}{y} - 1 \right) \right]^{1/[(y_0/y)-1]} \right\}.$$ (8)

The expression in the last line is the same as that in (2), except with y and y_0 in interchanged roles. Now define

$$F(y) = \frac{y}{y_0} - 1 \qquad \text{for } 0 < y < y_0,$$ (9)

and let $G(t)$ be as before. On the domain $\{0 < y < y_0\}$, $\lim\limits_{y \to y_0} G(F(y)) = e$, as before. Hence on $\{0 < y < y_0\}$,

$$\lim_{y \to y_0} R(y) = \lim_{y \to y_0} \left(\frac{1}{y} \right) \lim_{y \to y_0} \log_c (G(F(y))) = \frac{1}{y_0} \log_c e$$ (10)

as before. Conclusion: on the full domain $\{\text{all } y \neq y_0\}$,

$$\lim_{y \to y_0} R(y) = \frac{1}{y_0} \log_c e,$$ (11)

by the "interlacing property of limits" (Property D of Chap. 11). That is,

$$(\log_c y)' = \frac{1}{y} \log_c e \text{ at any } y > 0. \quad \text{End of the proof.}$$

14.12 PROBLEMS ON DERIVATIVES OF POWERS, EXPONENTIALS, AND LOGS: A FREE-FOR-ALL

°1. Draw graphs, as in Fig. 14-18, for each of the following pairs of inverse functions, $f(x)$ and $g(y)$. Use arrows to relate $y_0 = f(x_0)$ and $x_0 = g(y_0)$ for the indicated values of x_0. Draw line segments to represent the slopes $f'(x_0)$ and $g'(y_0)$. And check graphically whether $g'(y_0) = 1/f'(x_0)$ as claimed in Theorem A (on "derivatives of inverses") in Sec. 14.10.

(a) $f(x) = x^3$ for all x, $g(y) = y^{1/3}$ for all y; $x = 2$.
(b) $f(x) = e^{2x}$ for all x, $g(y) = \frac{1}{2}\log_e y$ for $y > 0$; $x_0 = 1$.

°2. Calculate derivative functions $f'(x)$ for each of the following functions f. (Consider the domains to consist of all values of x for which the functions f and f' make sense.)

(a) $f(x) = x^{1/3}$
(Suggestion: for $x < 0$, write $x^{1/3} = -(-x)^{1/3}$ and use the chain rule.)
(b) $f(x) = x^{-1/4}$, for $x > 0$
(c) $f(x) = (x+2)^{3/5}$, for $x > -2$
(Suggestion: Use the chain rule.)
(d) $f(x) = (x^3+2)^{-1/2}$, for $x > -\sqrt[3]{2}$
(e) $f(x) = x^\pi$, for $x > 0$

(f) $f(x) = \dfrac{x^{1/3} + 2x^{-1/3}}{x^{1/2} + 3x^{-1/2}}$, for $x > 0$

(Recall Property L', on quotients, in Sec. 14.7.)

(g) $f(x) = \log_e (ax+b)$
Sample: Write $f(x) = g(h(x))$ where $g(y) = \log_e y$ and

$h(x) = ax + b$.

Then $f'(x) = g'(h(x))h'(x) = a/(ax+b)$.
(h) $f(x) = \log_e (ax+b)^2$ (i) $f(x = \log_e ax^n$
(j) $f(x) = \log_e (x + \sqrt{1+x^2})$
Sample: Write $f(x) = g(h(x))$ where $g(y) = \log_e y$ and

$h(x) = x + \sqrt{1+x^2}$.

Then

$$f'(x) = g'(h(x))h'(x) = \frac{1 + \frac{1}{2}(2x/\sqrt{1+x^2})}{x + \sqrt{1+x^2}}.$$

(k) $f(x) = \log_e \sqrt{9 - 2x^2}$ (l) $f(x) = \log_e \sqrt{\dfrac{a+bx}{a-bx}}$

(m) $f(x) = 10^{nx}$

(Suggestion: Write $10^{nx} = (e^{(\log_e 10)})^{nx} = e^{(n \log_e 10)x}$.)

(n) $f(x) = e^{x^2}$ (o) $f(x) = \dfrac{2}{e^x}$

(p) $f(x) = x^2 \log_e x^2$ (q) $f(x) = \dfrac{e^x - 1}{e^x + 1}$

(r) $f(x) = xe^{-x}$ (s) $f(x) = x^2 e^{-x}$

(t) $f(x) = \log_e \dfrac{\sqrt{x^2+1}-x}{\sqrt{x^2+1}+x}$

(u) $f(x) = \log_e (\log x)$ (v) $f(x) = \log_e (e^x)$

(w) $f(x) = \log_{10} ax^n$

   (Recall that $10^y = e^{(e^{\log_e 10})^y}$; hence

   $\log_{10} ax^n = (\log_{10} e)(\log_e ax^n).$)

°3. Sketch the graphs of each of the following functions. Then try to find all relative maxima and relative minima. (Consider the domains to consist of all numbers for which the formulas make sense.)

(a) $f(x) = \log_e (x+2)$ (b) $f(x) = \log_e x^2$
(c) $f(x) = \log_e (x^2+1)$ (d) $f(x) = x^2 - \ln x^2$
(e) $f(x) = e^{3x}$ (f) $f(x) = x \log_e x$
(g) $f(x) = \dfrac{\log x}{x}$ (h) $f(x) = xe^{-x}$
(i) $f(x) = x^2 e^{-x}$ (j) $f(x) = e^{-x^2}$

4. If a bacterial population contains 10^6 organisms (of mixed ages) at a given instant, and if organisms have an average lifetime of approximately 45 minutes before splitting, how large will the population be three hours later?

5. Suppose that a bacterial culture has the shape of a circular disk one millimeter in diameter at noon. If organisms have an average lifetime of 45 minutes, what diameter will the disk have at 3 p.m.? (See the discussion in Problem 6 of Sec. 14.9.)

6. There are some cases of functions f where we may know an identity which relates inputs x and outputs $f(x)$ in some interval, but where we may not have an actual formula expressing $f(x)$ explicitly in terms of x—or where such a formula may be very mes y. Nevertheless, *if* we can assume that a derivative $f'(x_0)$ exists at some input x_0, we may be able to evaluate $f'(x_0)$ in terms of the numbers x_0 and $f(x_0)$ without ever using an explicit formula for $f(x)$. The procedure for doing so is called *implicit differentiation* and is based on the "chain rule." Here is an example:

(a) Evaluate $f'(x_0)$ in terms of x_0 and $f(x_0)$ if we know that

$$3f(x) - 2[f(x)]^3 + [f(x)]^5 = 15x^2 \qquad (*)$$

for all x in some interval containing x_0.

Sample reasoning: Regard the left-hand side of (*) as a *composition* $h(x) = g(f(x))$, where $g(y) = 3y - 2y^3 + y^5$. Then $h'(x) = g'(f(x))f'(x) = (15x^2)'$ at each input x_0. In particular

$$\{3 - 2 \cdot 3[f(x)]^2 + 5[f(x)^4]\}f'(x) = 15 \cdot 2x$$

or

$$f'(x_0) = \dfrac{30x_0}{3 - 6[f(x_0)]^2 + 5[f(x_0)]^4} \qquad (**)$$

—at least for x_0 where (*) and (**) make sense.

(b) Evaluate $f'(x)$ in terms of x and $f(x)$ if

$$x^2 f(x) - [f(x)]^3 + x^{1/2}[f(x)]^5 = 15x^2. \qquad (\text{***})$$

Sample reasoning: In this case, first apply Leibnitz's product rule and then the chain rule to *each term*:

$$\{x^2 f(x)\}' - \{[f(x)]^3\}' + \{x^{1/2}[f(x)]^5\}' = \{15x^2\}'$$

or

$$(2x)f(x) + (x^2)f'(x) - 3[f(x)]^2 f'(x) + (\tfrac{1}{2}x^{-1/2})[f(x)]^5$$
$$+ (x^{1/2})5[f(x)]^4 f'(x) = 30x.$$

Next, collect terms containing $f'(x)$:

$$\{x^2 - 3[f(x)]^2 + 5x^{1/2}[f(x)]^4\}f'(x) + 2xf(x) + \tfrac{1}{2}x^{-1/2}[f(x)]^5$$
$$= 30x.$$

Then solve for $f'(x)$:

$$f'(x) = \frac{30x - 2xf(x) - \tfrac{1}{2}x^{-1/2}[f(x)]^5}{x^2 - 3[f(x)]^2 + 5x^{1/2}[f(x)]^4}$$

—where such an expression makes sense.

Evaluate $f'(x)$ in terms of x and $f(x)$ in the following cases:

(c) $x = \sqrt{f(x)} + \sqrt[3]{f(x)}$

(d) $f^2(x) = 2px$

(e) $x^3 - 3x(f(x))^2 + (f(x))^3 = 10$

(f) $x + 2\sqrt{xf(x)} + f(x) = a$

(g) $ax^3 - 3b^2 xf(x) + c(f(x))^3 = 1$

(h) $\sqrt{\dfrac{f(x)}{x}} + \sqrt{\dfrac{x}{f(x)}} = 6$

(i) $x^{2/3} + (f(x))^{2/3} = a^{2/3}$

(j) $\sqrt{f(x)} + \sqrt{x} = \sqrt{a}$

(k) $x^3 - 3axf(x) + (f(x))^3 = 0$

7. For each of the following identities, use the method of implicit differentiation to evaluate $f'(x_0)$ concretely corresponding to the given values of x_0 and $f(x_0)$.

(a) $x^2 + 2xf(x) - 3(f(x))^2 + 11 = 0$, $x_0 = 2, f(x_0) = 3$.

Sample reasoning: Using implicit differentiation, we find

$$2x + 2f(x) + 2xf'(x) - 3 \cdot 2f(x) \cdot f'(x) = 0,$$

and substituting in $f(2) = 3$, we find that

$$4 + 2 \cdot 3 + 2 \cdot 2 \cdot f'(2) - 3 \cdot 2 \cdot 3f'(2) = 0$$

or

$$f'(2) = \frac{-10}{4-18} = \frac{5}{7}.$$

(b) $x^3 + 3x^2 f(x) + (f(x))^3 = 3$ at $x_0 = -1$, $f(x_0) = 1$.

(c) $\sqrt{2x} + \sqrt{3f(x)} = 5$ at $x_0 = 2$, $f(x_0) = 3$.

(d) $x^2 + 4\sqrt{xf(x)} + (f(x))^2 = 25$ at $x_0 = 1$, $f(x_0) = 4$.

(e) $[f(x)]^2 = x(x+6)$ at $x_0 = 2$, $f(x_0) = 4$.

(f) $\log f(x) = x^2$, $x_0 = 0$, $f(x_0) = 1$.

8. Prove that the tangent to a circle at a point P_0 and the radius to the same point are perpendicular — part (b) of Problem 3 in Sec. 14.9 — by applying implicit differentiation directly to the identity

$$x^2 + [h(x)]^2 = r^2 \qquad \text{for} -r \leqslant x \leqslant r,$$

instead of first solving for h in terms of x and using facts about $(\sqrt{y})'$, as in the earlier problem.

9. (a) Verify that the formula $(x^p)' = px^{p-1}$ (in Examples 1 and 2 of Sec. 14.10) holds even for $x < 0$ when $p = 1/n$ and n is an *odd* positive integer.
   (Suggestion: Write $x^{1/n} = -(-x)^{1/n}$ as in Problem 2(a).)
   (b) Extend the result of part (a) to expressions of the form $x^{k/n}$, where n is an odd positive integer and k is any integer, positive or negative.
   (c) Find $f'(x)$ for $f(x) = (x+2)^{3/5}$ and $x < -2$.
   (Compare with Problem 2(c).)

14.13 SUMMARY OF CHAPTER 14

DEFINITION (REPEAT): The *derivative* of a function f at an input x_0 is the limit

$$f'(x_0) = \lim_{x \to x_0} \frac{f(x) - f(x_0)}{x - x_0},$$

provided the limit exists (Sec. 14.1).

Alternate notation: $f'(x_0) = \dfrac{df}{dx}(x_0)$.

(Sec. 14.2)

DEFINITIONS: If $f'(x_0)$ exists at all x_0 in some set S of real numbers, let's call f *differentiable* (on S), and let's use the term *derivative function* f' of f to refer to the rule assigning to each x_0 (input) in S the value $f'(x_0)$ (as output).

The process of calculating derivatives is called *differentiation*. (Sec. 14.2)

See Sec. 14.2 for repeated derivatives, $f''(x)$, and so on. For special properties of derivatives of linear functions, see Sec. 14.4.

General properties of derivatives (Secs. 14.5 and 14.7)

Property A' ("uniqueness"). The derivative $f'(x_0)$ of a function f at an input x_0 — if it exists at all — must be a unique number.

Property B' (on "restricting the domain"). If $f'(x_0) = A$ and we restrict the domain $\mathscr{D}$ to a smaller set $\mathscr{D}_0$ containing x_0, then we still have $f'(x_0) = A$ (provided some subsequence $\{x_n \neq x_0\}$ in $\mathscr{D}_0$ still converges to x_0).

Property C' (derivatives are determined "locally"). If $f'(x_0) = A$ and if $g(x)$ differs from $f(x)$ only outside some interval $[x_0 - \delta, x_0 + \delta]$, then $g'(x_0) = A$.

Property D' (*on "interlacing"*). Suppose that $f(x)$ is defined on an interval $[a, x_0]$ and $g(x)$ is defined on an interval $[x_0, b]$, and that $f(x_0) = g(x_0)$, and $f'(x_0) = g'(x_0) = A$. If we have

$$h(x) = \begin{cases} f(x) & \text{for } a \leq x \leq x_0, \\ g(x) & \text{for } x_0 \leq x \leq b, \end{cases} \quad \text{then } h'(x_0) = A \text{ also.}$$

Property G' (*on "linear functions"*). If f is a linear function $f(x) = mx + b$, then $f'(x_0) = m$ at any x_0. In particular, $f'(x) = 0$ if f is a constant function, $f(x) \equiv b$.

Property H' (*on "scaling"*). If c is a constant, then

$$\boxed{(cf)'(x_0) = c \cdot f'(x_0).}$$

Property I' (*on "sums"*). If f and g have a common domain, and if $f'(x_0)$ and $g'(x_0)$ exist, then

$$(f+g)'(x_0) = f'(x_0) + g'(x_0), \quad \text{and} \quad (f-g)'(x_0) = f'(x_0) - g'(x_0).$$

More generally,

$$\boxed{(f_1 + f_2 + \cdots + f_n)'(x_0) = f_1'(x_0) + f_2'(x_0) + \cdots + f_n'(x_0).}$$

Property J' (*Leibnitz's "product rule"*). If f and g have a common domain, and if $f'(x_0)$ and $g'(x_0)$ exist, then

$$\boxed{(fg)'(x_0) = f'(x_0)g(x_0) + f(x_0)g'(x_0).}$$

Property K' (*"derivative of a reciprocal"*). If g is never zero, and $g'(x_0)$ exists,

$$\boxed{\left(\frac{1}{g}\right)'(x_0) = -\frac{g'(x_0)}{[g(x_0)]^2}.}$$

Property L' (*"derivatives of quotients"*). If f and g have a common domain where g is never zero, and if $f'(x_0)$ and $g'(x_0)$ exist, then

$$\boxed{\left(\frac{f}{g}\right)'(x_0) = \frac{f'(x_0)g(x_0) - g'(x_0)f(x_0)}{[g(x_0)]^2}.}$$

Property Q' (*the "chain rule" for composition*). If $f'(x_0)$ exists and if g is defined on the range of f and has derivative $g'(y_0)$ at $y_0 = f(x_0)$, then

$$\boxed{[g(f)]'(x_0) = g'(f(x_0))f'(x_0).}$$

A corollary: if c is a constant and $h(x) = g(cx)$, then

$$h'(x_0) = cg'(cx_0)$$

(provided the derivatives exist). (Sec. 14.7, Example 2.)

THEOREM (ON "DERIVATIVES OF INVERSE FUNCTIONS"): Suppose that f is defined on some interval, line, or half-line; that f is a strictly increasing or a strictly decreasing function; and that g is its inverse. If $f'(x_0)$ exists and is not zero, then $g'(y_0)$ exists at $y_0 = f(x_0)$, and

$$\boxed{g'(x_0) = \frac{1}{f'(x_0)}.}$$

(Sec. 14.10)

APPLICATIONS OF THE THEOREM (Sec. 14.10):

$(x^p)' = px^{p-1}$ at any $x > 0$, for any real p.

$(e^x)' = e^x$ at any real x.

$(e^{ax})' = ae^{ax}$ at any real x.

$(c^x)' = (\log_e c)c^x$ at any real x, for any $c > 0$.

$(\log_e x)' = \dfrac{1}{x}$ at any $x > 0$.

$(\log_c x)' = \dfrac{1}{x}(\log_c e)$ at any $x > 0$, for any $c > 0$.

For the method of *implicit differentiation*, see Problem 6 of Sec. 14.12.

the mean value theorem
and applications

In this chapter I'll explore a relation between a difference of outputs $f(b) - f(a)$ and values of the derivative $f'(x)$ at inputs x between a and b. Such information will lead to improved methods for finding maxima and minima and intervals of increase and decrease of functions. It will lead to a way of computing approximate output values for various functions. And it will validate the "neck-and-neck race argument" — which was a key tool for solving problems in Chapter 7.

I'll also note methods for finding an "antiderivative" for a given function f; that is, a function F such that $F' = f$.

15.1 HOW DERIVATIVES INFLUENCE FUNCTIONS

All of the precise results on derivatives so far have been in one direction: if you know changes in a function, such as $f(x) - f(x_0)$ over intervals $[x_0, x]$, then you can (in principle) determine the derivative

$$f'(x_0) = \lim_{x \to x_0} \frac{f(x) - f(x_0)}{x - x_0},$$

provided it exists. But what about the opposite direction? If you know the values of the derivative $f'(x)$ for all x in an interval $[a, b]$ *can you (in principle) put those infinitely many quantities together to determine the change $f(b) - f(a)$?*

Here are two other versions of the question: If an object moves along a straight line, and you know its velocity record $p'(t)$ for *all* instants t in an interval $[a, b]$, can there in principle be any ambiguity as to its overall change in position $p(b) - p(a)$? Or: if two graphs start out at the same altitude $f(a) = g(a)$, and if they have identical slopes over an entire interval, $f'(x) = g'(x)$ for $a \leqslant x \leqslant b$, then shouldn't they arrive at the same altitude $f(b) = g(b)$? (Such was the "neck-and-neck race argument" I used in Chap. 7.)

But here are some doubts: a graph can never change altitude *AT* a point — even though we may assign a nonzero slope $f'(x)$ there. *Actual change* can only occur BETWEEN points. If so, and if we are told of some wild function with $f'(x) > 0$ for $a \leqslant x \leqslant b$, how can we be sure that there will be a change in altitude $f(b) - f(a)$ if there was no *actual change AT* any of the graph points $(x, f(x))$ between $(a, f(a))$ and $(b, f(b))$? The Greeks worried about such problems in connection with motion. Zeno asked: how can there be motion of an object through space, if at each instant of time the object is — so to speak — stationed at some particular point?

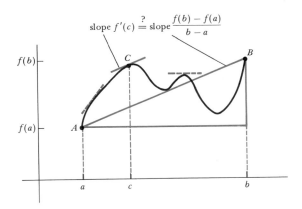

slope $f'(c) \overset{?}{=}$ slope $\dfrac{f(b) - f(a)}{b - a}$

FIGURE 15-1

How can an amount of overall change $f(b) - f(a)$ be *recovered* from, or related to, instantaneous rates of change $f'(x)$ for $a \leqslant x \leqslant b$? To get an idea, let's examine the graph of a differentiable function — such as I've sketched in Fig. 15-1. As we move from A to B along the graph shouldn't we encounter some point $C = (c, f(c))$ where a limiting line of slope $f'(c)$ will be parallel to the line segment AB? Suppose the graph of f represents the path of a drunkard wending his way from tavern (A) to home (B). If the drunkard doesn't move with sharp corners (so that f' always exists), must there not be at least one point in his journey where he aims in the same direction as the shortest path AB? If so, since parallel lines have identical slopes, we must have

$$f'(c) = \text{slope of } AB = \frac{f(b) - f(a)}{b - a}. \tag{1}$$

Note that such a result does relate the overall change $f(b) - f(a)$ with the instantaneous rate $f'(c)$ for *at least one input c* between a and b:

$$f(b) - f(a) = f'(c)(b - a), \quad \text{where } a < c < b. \tag{2}$$

EXAMPLE 1. Consider $f(x) = x^2$ on the interval $[0, 1]$. Here

$$\frac{f(1) - f(0)}{1 - 0} = \frac{1^2 - 0^2}{1 - 0} = 1.$$

Is there an input c between 0 and 1 such that $f'(c) = 2c = 1$? Yes: $c = \frac{1}{2}$. See Fig. 15-2.

FIGURE 15-2

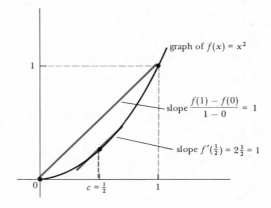

For a general statement:

Theorem A (the "mean value theorem"): If a function f has derivatives $f'(x)$ at all inputs in an interval $[a, b]$, then there must be some input c with $a < c < b$ such that

$$f'(c) = \frac{f(b) - f(a)}{b - a}$$

or equivalently,

$$f(b) - f(a) = f'(c)(b - a).$$

NOTE: This claim has been called the "mean value theorem" because historically people have used the word "mean" as synonymous with "average"; and the theorem asserts that the "average" rate $[f(b) - f(a)]/(b - a)$ must coincide with some instantaneous rate $f'(c)$.

But can we trust the pictorial reasoning above? If you glance at the cases I've pictured in Figs. 15-3, you might guess that we already have enough results about derivatives to yield a precise

Proof of theorem A:

FIGURE 15-3

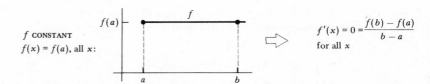

f CONSTANT
$f(x) = f(a)$, all x:

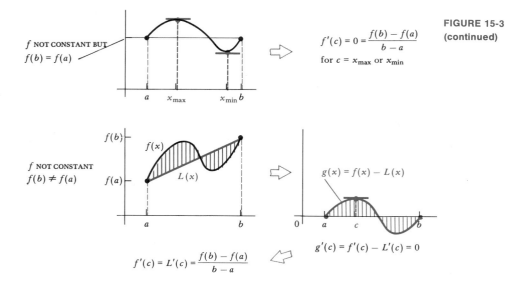

FIGURE 15-3
(continued)

f NOT CONSTANT BUT
$f(b) = f(a)$

$$f'(c) = 0 = \frac{f(b) - f(a)}{b - a}$$

for $c = x_{\max}$ or $x_{\min}$

f NOT CONSTANT
$f(b) \neq f(a)$

$g(x) = f(x) - L(x)$

$g'(c) = f'(c) - L'(c) = 0$

$$f'(c) = L'(c) = \frac{f(b) - f(a)}{b - a}$$

In the second case, if $f(b) = f(a)$ but f is not constant, then either $f(x) > f(a)$ or $f(x) < f(a)$ (or both) for some inputs x *between a and b*. Hence an absolute maximum output or an absolute minimum output must occur at some c *between a and b*, and there $f'(c) = 0 = [f(b) - f(a)]/(b - a)$. This is because f must be *continuous* on $[a, b]$, since it is differentiable there (by the theorem of Sec. 14.5). And a continuous function must have maximizing and minimizing inputs (by Theorem D of Sec. 12.5). And $f' = 0$ at such inputs, when they are *not* end points (by Theorem E of Sec. 12.7). (By itself, this second case has been called "Rolle's theorem.")

As I indicated in Fig. 15-3, we can transform a general differentiable function f into one which fits the second case merely by subtracting from f the linear function $L(x)$ whose graph is the segment between $(a, f(a))$ and $(b, f(b))$. Then $g(x) = f(x) - L(x)$ has $g(a) = 0 = g(b)$; and we must have $g'(c) = f'(c) - L'(c) = 0$ at some input c between a and b, or equivalently, $f'(c) = L'(c)$. Since L has constant slope $L' = [f(b) - f(a)]/(b - a)$, we must have $f'(c) = [f(b) - f(a)]/(b - a)$.   End of the proof.

Note that this theorem doesn't specify *which* input c between a and b will do the job of recovering the overall change $f(b) - f(a)$ from the instantaneous rates $f'(x)$. Can we nevertheless squeeze usable information from the result? That's the purpose of the rest of this chapter.

15.2   INFORMATION ABOUT INCREASE AND DECREASE

Intuitively, I've argued (in Chap. 7) that when a differentiable function f increases we should find a positive rate of change $f' \geqslant 0$, and vice versa. Similarly, decrease of f should go with negative values of f'. Such notions arose from the simplest cases, where f was a linear function and f' was the slope of its graph.

Now, with the relationship $f(b) - f(a) = f'(c)(b-a)$ provided by the mean value theorem, we can settle such questions of increase and decrease for all possible differentiable functions.

Here are precise statements of the claims. In one direction:

Theorem B ("_increase controls derivative sign_"): Suppose that f is a differentiable function on the interval $[a, b]$.

If f is constant on $[a, b]$, then $f'(x) = 0$ for all x in $[a, b]$.
If f is increasing on $[a, b]$, then $f'(x) \geqslant 0$ for all x in $[a, b]$.
If f is decreasing on $[a, b]$, then $f'(x) \leqslant 0$ for all x in $[a, b]$.
In the opposite direction:

Theorem C ("_derivative sign controls increase_"): Suppose that f is a differentiable function on the interval $[a, b]$.

If $f'(x) = 0$ for all x in $[a, b]$, then f is constant on $[a, b]$.

If $f'(x) \geqslant 0$ for all x in $[a, b]$, then f is increasing on $[a, b]$. Moreover, if $f'(x) > 0$ for all x in the open interval $\langle a, b \rangle$, then f is _strictly_ increasing on $[a, b]$.

If $f'(x) \leqslant 0$ for all x in $[a, b]$, then f is decreasing on $[a, b]$. Moreover, if $f'(x) < 0$ for all x in the open interval $\langle a, b \rangle$, then f is _strictly_ decreasing on $[a, b]$.

(I gave precise definitions of the terms "strictly increasing" and "strictly decreasing" in Sec. 13.6.)

In the first direction, going from differences to derivatives, you already know that a constant function has zero slopes. For a more general increasing or decreasing function f, shouldn't we be able to determine the sign of the limit $f'(x_0) = \lim\limits_{x \to x_0} [f(x) - f(x_0)]/(x - x_0)$ merely by checking the signs of the difference ratios

$$R(x) = \frac{f(x) - f(x_0)}{x - x_0} ?$$

For a

Proof of theorem B ("_increase controls derivative sign_"): Note that an _increasing_ function f on an interval $[a, b]$ must have outputs

$$f(x_1) \leqslant f(x_2) \quad \text{whenever } x_1 < x_2. \tag{1}$$

Or equivalently,

$$f(x_2) - f(x_1) \geqslant 0 \quad \text{whenever } x_2 - x_1 > 0, \tag{2}$$

and

$$f(x_2) - f(x_1) \leqslant 0 \quad \text{whenever } x_2 - x_1 < 0. \tag{3}$$

What signs can the difference ratio function

$$R(x) = \frac{f(x) - f(x_0)}{x - x_0}$$

have, therefore, if we pick inputs x and x_0 from $[a, b]$? $R(x)$ must always be ≥ 0, since its numerator and denominator are always of the *same sign*. At any input x_0 in $[a, b]$, we can evaluate $f'(x_0) = \lim_{x \to x_0} R(x)$ by restricting x to $[a, b]$ — since derivatives are determined "locally" (Properties C' and D' of Chap. 14). Hence $f'(x_0) \geq 0$, too, as the limit of a nonnegative function (Property O on "comparison" of limits, in Chap. 11).

For decreasing f, the difference ratio function $R(x)$ must always have numerator and denominator of *opposite sign*, and thus be ≤ 0. Conclusion: $f'(x_0) \leq 0$, too.   End of the proof.

In going from differences to derivatives we didn't need a "mean value" relationship. But see how handy it is in the other direction:

A proof of theorem C ("derivative sign controls increase"): Suppose first that $f'(x) \equiv 0$ on an interval $[a, b]$. What would it mean for f to be constant on $[a, b]$? Merely that $f(x) = f(a)$ for all x in $[a, b]$; or in terms of differences, that $f(x) - f(a) = 0$ for all x in $[a, b]$. Thanks to the mean value theorem — applicable to any given subinterval $[a, x]$ — we can relate the difference $f(x) - f(a)$ to derivatives f'; namely,

$$f(x) - f(a) = f'(c)(x - a)$$
$$= 0(x - a) = 0, \tag{4}$$

where c is some input *between* a and x. Since we can reach such a conclusion for *every* x with $a < x \leq b$, we must have $f(x) = f(a)$ on all of $[a, b]$ if $f' \equiv 0$ there.

More generally, as long as f is differentiable on $[a, b]$, why not apply the mean value theorem to any subinterval $[x_1, x_2]$ of $[a, b]$? Then we'll have

$$f(x_2) - f(x_1) = f'(c)(x_2 - x_1) \tag{5}$$

for some input c between x_1 and x_2. With $x_1 < x_2$ and thus $x_2 - x_1 > 0$, it must follow that the difference $f(x_2) - f(x_1)$ will have the *same sign* as $f'(c)$.

If we know that $f'(x) \geq 0$ for *all* x in $[a, b]$, then in particular $f'(c) \geq 0$. So we can conclude that $f(x_2) - f(x_1) \geq 0$, or equivalently, $f(x_2) \geq f(x_1)$. And this for any inputs $x_1 < x_2$ in $[a, b]$. f must be *increasing* on $[a, b]$.

Similarly, if $f'(x) > 0$ for all x in the open interval $\langle a, b \rangle$, then $f'(c) > 0$ and $f(x_2) - f(x_1) > 0$, and $f(x_2) > f(x_1)$. Conclusion: f is *strictly increasing* on $[a, b]$. Likewise, $f' \leq 0$ on $[a, b]$ implies *decrease*, and $f' < 0$ on $\langle a, b \rangle$ implies *strict decrease*.   End of the proof.

Note that in going from derivatives to differences (Theorem C), *strictly* positive derivatives $f' > 0$ imply *strict* increase. Why not the converse claim in Theorem B? Because it isn't true: recall that $f(x) = x^3$ is always strictly increasing, but $f'(0) = 3 \cdot 0^2 = 0$.

Now let's apply the results.

EXAMPLE 1. The ordering cost function for loaves of bread

$$h(x) = 0.005x + 4500\frac{1}{x}$$

for lot sizes x between 1 and 15,000. In Sec. 7.1 (and again in Sec. 12.7), I calculated the derivative

$$h'(x) = 0.005 - \frac{4500}{x^2} = \frac{0.005}{x^2}\left(x^2 - \frac{4500}{0.005}\right) \quad \text{in a factored form.} \tag{6}$$

And I noted that $h'(x_0) = 0$ for $x_0 = \sqrt{4500/0.005}$; and that $h'(x) < 0$ for $1 \leq x < x_0$, and $h'(x) > 0$ for $x_0 < x \leq 15{,}000$. By Theorem C ("derivative sign controls increase"), we can conclude that h is strictly decreasing on the entire interval $[1, x_0]$ and strictly increasing on the entire interval $[x_0, 15{,}000]$. Hence we can say that $h(x_0)$ is an *absolute minimum* — without even comparing it with outputs $h(1)$ and $h(15{,}000)$ at the end points.

EXAMPLE 2. Is $e^x > x$ for all $x \geq 0$? Yes: The difference $f(x) = e^x - x$ has value $f(0) = 1 > 0$, and has derivative $f'(x) = e^x - 1 > 0$ for all $x > 0$. Hence $f(x)$ is strictly increasing over any interval $[0, x_0]$, and $f(x_0) > f(0) = 1$. That is, $e^{x_0} - x_0 > 1$, and $e^{x_0} > x_0 + 1$ for all $x_0 > 0$.

EXAMPLE 3. In seeking the probability of ultimate extinction of a dynasty, in Secs. 5.8 and 13.8, I was led to consider a polynomial

$$P(x) = p_0 + p_1 x + p_2 x^2 + p_3 x^3 + \cdots + p_n x^n \quad \text{for } 0 \leq x \leq 1,$$

where $p_k = $ the probability that a parent would have k children. ($P(1) = p_0 + p_1 + \cdots + p_n = 1$.) The question was whether and where the graph of P might cross the 45° line. In Figs. 13-27 and 13-28 I sketched P as a *strictly increasing* function on $[0, 1]$. For what reason? Because the probabilities p_k were positive. Hence

$$P'(x) = p_1 + 2p_2 + 3p_3 x^2 + \cdots + np_n x^{n-1} > 0 \quad \text{for all } 0 < x \leq 1. \tag{7}$$

You may also recall from Sec. 14.5 (Example 3) that we can interpret the special value

$$P'(1) = 0 \cdot p_0 + 1 \cdot p_1 + 2 \cdot p_2 + 3 \cdot p_3 + \cdots + np_n \tag{8}$$

as the "average number of children per parent." And in Sec. 13.8, I argued intuitively that if $P'(1) > 1$, then the graph of $P(x)$ must *lie below the 45° line for x near 1.* From that fact it would follow that the graph of P had to intersect the 45° line at a point (q, q), where $0 < q < 1$. The value q would be revealed as the probability of ultimate extinction of the dynasty.

Here's one way to be absolutely certain that $P(x) < x$ for x close to 1 if $P'(1) > 1$: let's show that the polynomial $Q(x) = P(x) - x$ is *negative* for x close to 1. Now $Q'(x) = P'(x) - 1$ for all x. In particular $Q'(1) = P'(1) - 1 > 0$. Since $Q'(x)$ is itself a polynomial and continuous everywhere, we can conclude that $Q'(x) > 0$ for all x in some interval $[1-\delta, 1+\delta]$, where $\delta > 0$. (Recall the result "on nearby signs," in Sec. 13.1.) Hence $Q(x)$ must be *strictly increasing* on $[1-\delta, 1+\delta]$. Since $Q(1) = P(1) - 1 = 0$, we must have

$$Q(x) = P(x) - x < 0 \quad \text{for } 1 - \delta \leq x < 1. \tag{9}$$

Thus $P(x) < x$ for $1 - \delta \le x < 1$.

EXAMPLE 4. Where does the polynomial $P(x) = x^3 - 2x^2 - x + 2$ increase and where does it decrease? To answer, let's examine $P'(x) = 3x^2 - 4x - 1$. Using the quadratic formula we can check that $P'(x) = 0$ *only* at the inputs $x_1 = \frac{2}{3} - \frac{1}{6}\sqrt{28}$ and $x_2 = \frac{2}{3} + \frac{1}{6}\sqrt{28}$. Hence all outputs $P'(x)$ must be of the *same* sign for $x_1 < x < x_2$. (Recall the "corollary on changes of sign" in Sec. 13.1.) To determine that sign, let's just check $P'(\frac{2}{3}) = 3(\frac{2}{3})^2 - 4(\frac{2}{3}) - 1 = -\frac{7}{3}$. Thus $P'(x) < 0$ for all $x_1 < x < x_2$. Similarly, $P'(x) > 0$ for all $x < x_1$ and for all $x > x_2$ (as we might see by checking the signs of, say, $P'(\pm 100)$).

Conclusions: the original polynomial is strictly decreasing on $[x_1, x_2]$ and strictly increasing on any subinterval of the set $\{$all $x \le x_1\}$ and of the set $\{$all $x \ge x_2\}$.

From the facts $P'(x_1) = 0$ and $P'(x_2) = 0$ we might have suspected relative maxima or minima of P to occur at x_1 and x_2. Now we can check the matter. From the information on increase and decrease we just got, we can conclude in particular that

$$P(x) < P(x_1) \qquad \text{for all } x < x_1 \tag{10}$$

and

$$P(x) > P(x_2) \qquad \text{for all } x > x_2. \tag{11}$$

So $P(x_1)$ is a relative maximum and $P(x_2)$ is a relative minimum. See Fig. 15-4.

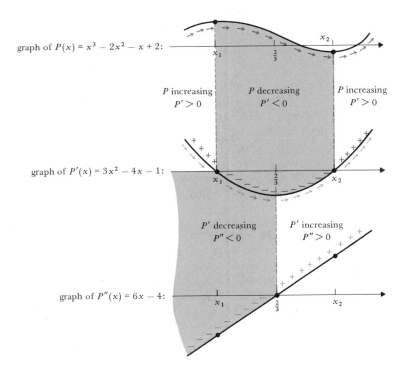

graph of $P(x) = x^3 - 2x^2 - x + 2$:

P increasing $P' > 0$

P decreasing $P' < 0$

P increasing $P' > 0$

graph of $P'(x) = 3x^2 - 4x - 1$:

P' decreasing $P'' < 0$

P' increasing $P'' > 0$

graph of $P''(x) = 6x - 4$:

FIGURE 15-4

15.3 INFORMATION FROM THE SECOND DERIVATIVE

On the graph of the polynomial $P(x)$ just above, as you look from left to right past the relative maximum $P(x_1)$, note that the slopes $P'(x)$ change from positive (where P is increasing) to negative (where P is decreasing). So it's reasonable to find that the rate of change of the slope function $P'(x)$ itself *at* x_1—namely, $P''(x_1)$—is *negative*. Similarly, we might expect $P''(x_2) \geq 0$ at the relative minimum $P(x_2)$, where slopes change from negative to positive.

Shouldn't such conclusions also be valid for more general functions f—provided f' and f'' exist? Moreover, might we not be able to *turn the results around*, and conclude from information such as $f'(x_0) = 0$ and $f''(x_0) < 0$ that $f(x_0)$ is a relative maximum? More precisely, we might conjecture

Theorem D ("at the sign of the second derivative"): Suppose that f is differentiable on $[a, b]$, that $f'(x_0) = 0$ at some input x_0 with $a < x_0 < b$, and that $f''(x_0)$ exists.

If $f(x_0)$ is a relative maximum, then $f''(x_0) \leq 0$; and
if $f(x_0)$ is a relative minimum, then $f''(x_0) \geq 0$.
On the other hand,
if $f''(x_0) < 0$, then $f(x_0)$ is a relative maximum; and
if $f''(x_0) > 0$, then $f(x_0)$ is a relative minimum.

EXAMPLE 1. The difference of functions $f(x) = (x^2 + x + 3) - e^x$ has derivative $f'(x) = (2x + 1) - e^x$. In particular, $f(0) = 3 - 1 = 2$ and $f'(0) = 1 - 1 = 0$. Is $f(0)$ a relative maximum, a relative minimum, or neither? Let's calculate

$$f''(x) = 2 - e^x, \quad \text{and specifically,} \quad f''(0) = 2 - 1 = 1 > 0.$$

If Theorem D is true, we can answer immediately: $f(0)$ *is a relative minimum.* Would you have believed such information could be got so easily?

What more can we guess from pictures of P, P', and P'' as in Fig. 15-4 above? Note that as long as $P''(x)$ remains negative throughout an interval (such as all $x < \frac{2}{3}$ in Fig. 15-4), and $P'(x)$ keeps decreasing, then the graph of $P(x)$ itself seems forced to "bow downward." Likewise, when $P''(x)$ remains positive (at all $x > \frac{2}{3}$ in Fig. 15-4), and $P'(x)$ keeps increasing, then the graph of $P(x)$ itself "bows upward."

If we are given the formula for a new function f, and if we always can trust the sign of f'' to govern the "bowing" properties of the graph of f, then we can use such information to help picture that graph. For this reason, people have tried to capture the intuitive notion of "bowing" precisely. A geometrical formulation of what one might mean by the graph of a function f "bowing upward" is that *any* line segment connecting two points P_1 and P_2 of the graph should lie *above* the graph—as in Fig. 15-5. Similarly, for "bowing downward" *any* segment $P_1 P_2$ should lie below the graph. (See Fig. 15-6.)

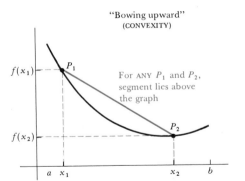

"Bowing upward"
(CONVEXITY)

FIGURE 15-5

For ANY P_1 and P_2,
segment lies above
the graph

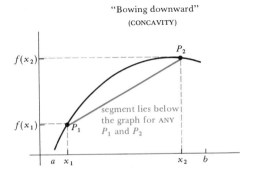

"Bowing downward"
(CONCAVITY)

FIGURE 15-6

segment lies below
the graph for ANY
P_1 and P_2

Since a line segment $P_1 P_2$ is the graph of a *linear* function, we might translate the geometric ideas in terms of inputs x and outputs $f(x)$ by the following

Definitions I: Let's call a function f *convex* on an interval $[a, b]$ if, given any two inputs $x_1 < x_2$ in $[a, b]$, we have

$$f(x) \leqslant L(x) \qquad \text{for all } x \text{ in the subinterval } [x_1, x_2], \tag{1}$$

where $L(x)$ is the unique linear function with outputs $L(x_1) = f(x_1)$ and $L(x_2) = f(x_2)$. Let's call f *concave* on $[a, b]$ if, given any two inputs $x_1 < x_2$ in $[a, b]$, we have

$$f(x) \geqslant L(x) \qquad \text{for all } x \text{ in the subinterval } [x_1, x_2]. \tag{2}$$

You might recall from Chap. 4 that, given $f(x_1)$ and $f(x_2)$, we can describe $L(x)$ by either of the formulas

$$L(x) = f(x_1) + \left[\frac{f(x_2) - f(x_1)}{x_2 - x_1}\right](x - x_1) \tag{3}$$

or

$$L(x) = f(x_2) + \left[\frac{f(x_2) - f(x_1)}{x_2 - x_1}\right](x - x_2). \tag{4}$$

Now the conjecture suggested by the pictures in Fig. 15-4:

Theorem E (on "convexity"): If $f''(x) \geq 0$ for all x in an interval $[a, b]$, then f is convex there. If $f''(x) \leq 0$ for all x in $[a, b]$, then f is concave there.

EXAMPLE 2. The ordering cost function

$$h(x) = 0.005x + 4500\frac{1}{x}$$

for loaves of bread in lots $x(1 \leq x \leq 15{,}000)$ has derivatives

$$h'(x) = 0.005 - \frac{4500}{x^2},$$

and

$$h''(x) = -4500(x^{-2})' = -4500(-2x^{-2-1})$$
$$= 9000(x^{-3}) > 0 \quad \text{for } 1 \leq x \leq 15{,}000.$$

If Theorem E is true, then I was correct in sketching the graph of h as convex in Fig. 7-1.

EXAMPLE 3. If the average number of children per parent exceeds 1, then the probability of ultimate extinction of the population must be a number $q < 1$ which is the coordinate of a point (q, q) where the graph of the polynomial

$$P(x) = p_0 + p_1 x + p_2 x^2 + p_3 x^3 + \cdots + p_n x^n \tag{5}$$

intersects the 45° line ($p_k =$ the probability for a parent to have k children). Such was the result I claimed for the dynasty model in Sec. 13.8 (Example 3) and in Sec. 15.2 (Example 2) above. Put another way, q must lie between 0 and 1 and must satisfy the equation

$$P(q) = q. \tag{6}$$

From Fig. 13-28 you might guess that q is the only—or at least the smallest number between 0 and 1 which satisfies this equation. Can there be two, or more? If so, and if we somehow can determine one of them, how will we know that it is the true extinction probability?

These problems disappear if Theorem E on "convexity" is true: there can be only one point (q, q), with $0 < q < 1$, where the graph of P intersects the 45° line. Why? Just note that

$$P'(x) = p_1 + 2p_2 x + 3p_3 x^2 + \cdots + np_n x^{n-1},$$

and

$$P''(x) = 2p_2 + 6p_3 x + \cdots + n(n-1)p_n x^{n-2} \geq 0 \quad \text{for all } x \text{ in } [0, 1]. \tag{7}$$

Hence P is *convex* on $[0, 1]$—and my sketch of the graph of P in Fig. 13-28 was correct in that respect. Recall that the graph of P does intersect the 45° line at $(1, 1)$ and lies *below* it near $(1, 1)$ (by Example 2 of Sec. 15.2). If the graph of P intersected the 45° line at two other points $Q = (q, q)$ and $Q' = (q', q')$, where q and q' lie between 0 and

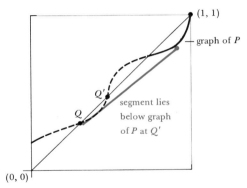

FIGURE 15-7

1, then — as in Fig. 15-7 — we could draw a segment from one of them which would lie below the other and would contradict the convexity of P.

If all p_i's are > 0, as I've supposed previously, then $P''(x) > 0$ on $[0, 1]$. I invite you to check that, when the average number of children per parent $P'(1) \leq 1$, the positivity of P'' rules out any solution of $P(q) = q$ except $q = 1$ — so the population must surely become extinct. Do Problem 21 of Sec. 15.6.

I'll give arguments for Theorems D and E in the next section — arguments based again on the mean value theorem.

*15.4 WHY THE RESULTS ABOUT f'' ARE VALID

A proof of theorem D ("at the sign of the second derivative"). We are to suppose that f is differentiable on $[a, b]$, that $f'(x_0) = 0$ at some input x_0 with $a < x_0 < b$, and that $f''(x_0)$ exists. And we should show that

(i) if $f(x_0)$ is a relative maximum, then $f''(x_0) \leq 0$;
(ii) if $f(x_0)$ is a relative minimum, then $f''(x_0) \geq 0$;
(iii) if $f''(x_0) < 0$, then $f(x_0)$ is a relative maximum; and
(iv) if $f''(x_0) > 0$, then $f(x_0)$ is a relative minimum.

First let's see why $f''(x_0) > 0$ forces $f(x_0)$ to be a relative minimum. Recall that

$$f''(x_0) = \lim_{x \to x_0} \frac{f'(x) - f'(x_0)}{x - x_0}. \tag{1}$$

From this very limit statement we can conclude that the difference ratio function

$$R(x) = \frac{f'(x) - f'(x_0)}{x - x_0} = \frac{f'(x) - 0}{x - x_0} = \frac{f'(x)}{x - x_0} \tag{2}$$

must be > 0 for all inputs $x \neq x_0$ in some interval $[x_0 - \delta, x_0 + \delta]$. (Recall the result "on nearby signs," in Sec. 13.1.) Hence the numerator $f'(x)$ and the denominator $x - x_0$ must be of the same sign for all such inputs. That is,

$$f'(x) < 0 \qquad \text{for } x_0 - \delta < x < x_0 \tag{3}$$

and

$$f'(x) > 0 \qquad \text{for} \quad x_0 < x < x_0 + \delta. \tag{4}$$

Conclusion: f itself must be strictly decreasing on the interval $[x_0 - \delta, x_0]$ and strictly increasing on the interval $[x_0, x_0 + \delta]$; and $f(x_0)$ must be a *relative minimum*. This proves (iv). And we could prove (iii) — regarding maxima — similarly.

On the other hand, suppose that $f(x_0)$ is a relative minimum; that is

$$f(x) \geq f(x_0) \text{ for all inputs } x \text{ in some subinterval } [x_0 - \delta, x_0 + \delta] \text{ of } [a, b]. \tag{5}$$

Why should $f''(x_0)$ be ≥ 0? To get at the second derivative via first derivatives, let's pick a sequence of inputs $\{x_n\}$ converging to x_0 and, say, with

$$x_0 < x_n < x_0 + \delta \qquad \text{for all } n. \tag{6}$$

We can relate the nonnegative differences $f(x_n) - f(x_0)$ to derivatives via the "mean value" relationship:

$$f(x_n) - f(x_0) = f'(y_n)(x_n - x_0), \qquad \text{where } x_0 < y_n < x_n \text{ for all } n. \tag{7}$$

Since the right-hand side of (7) must be nonnegative too, and since $x_n - x_0 > 0$, we can conclude that $f'(y_n) \geq 0$ for all n. Now, the y_n's are squeezed between x_0 and the x_n's, so we must have $\lim_{n \to \infty} y_n = x_0$. Hence we can relate the derivatives $f'(y_n)$ to $f''(x_0)$ via the basic definition

$$f''(x_0) = \lim_{n \to \infty} \frac{f'(y_n) - f'(x_0)}{y_n - x_0}. \tag{8}$$

The ratios

$$\frac{f'(y_n) - f'(x_0)}{y_n - x_0} = \frac{f'(y_n) - 0}{y_n - x_0} = \frac{f'(y_n)}{y_n - x_0} \tag{9}$$

have numerator $f'(y_n) \geq 0$ and denominator $y_n - x_0 > 0$. Hence $f''(x_0) \geq 0$ as the limit of nonnegative numbers. This proves (i). And we could prove (ii) similarly.

NOTE: Why can't we allow $\geqq$ signs in (iii) and (iv), just as in (i) and (ii)? Because then the claims would not be true: Recall the old example $f(x) = x^3$. $f'(0) = 3 \cdot 0^2 = 0$ and $f''(0) = 3 \cdot 2 \cdot 0 = 0$, but f is always strictly increasing and has no relative maximum or minimum at $x = 0$.

Next, a

Proof of theorem E (on "convexity"): which says that if $f''(x) \geq 0$ for all x in an interval $[a, b]$, then f is convex there. And if $f''(x) \leq 0$ for all x in $[a, b]$, then f is concave there.

Let's suppose that $f''(x) \geq 0$ for all x in $[a, b]$. To prove convexity, we must show that for *any* inputs x_1 and x_2 in $[a, b]$, with $x_1 < x_2$, we shall have

$$f(x) \leq L(x) \qquad \text{for all } x_1 \leq x \leq x_2 \tag{10}$$

— where L is the linear function whose graph passes through the points $(x_1, f(x_1))$ and $(x_2, f(x_2))$ on the graph of f. By the mean value theorem, we can relate the slope of L to a derivative of f:

$$\frac{f(x_2) - f(x_1)}{x_2 - x_1} = f'(c) \qquad \text{for some input } c \text{ with } x_1 < c < x_2. \qquad (11)$$

Hence we can describe L by the formula

$$L(x) = f(x_1) + f'(c)(x - x_1), \qquad (12)$$

and the requirement $f(x) \leqslant L(x)$ becomes

$$f(x) \leqslant f(x_1) + f'(c)(x - x_1). \qquad (13)$$

Equality holds when $x = x_1$. Now pick $x > x_1$. Let's rearrange terms in (13) and divide by $x - x_1$ to get the *equivalent requirement*

$$\frac{f(x) - f(x_1)}{x - x_1} \leqslant f'(c), \qquad (14)$$

which however displays a difference ratio. Does (14) hold? If we appeal again to the mean value theorem, we can express the ratio on the left-hand side of (14) as a derivative:

$$\frac{f(x) - f(x_1)}{x - x_1} = f'(d), \qquad \text{for some input } d \text{ with } x_1 < d < x. \qquad (15)$$

And (14) takes the form

$$f'(d) \leqslant f'(c). \qquad (16)$$

For $x \leqslant c$, we shall have $d < x \leqslant c$; and (16) *will* be true. Why? Because the condition $f''(x) \geqslant 0$ in $[a, b]$ implies that the function $f'(x)$ is increasing. Conclusion: for any x with $x_1 \leqslant x \leqslant c$ (and for corresponding d), we must have

$$\frac{f(x) - f(x_1)}{x - x_1} = f'(d) \leqslant f'(c) = \frac{f(x_2) - f(x_1)}{x_2 - x_1}.$$

That is,

$$f(x) \leqslant f(x_1) + \left[\frac{f(x_2) - f(x_1)}{x_2 - x_1}\right](x - x_1) = L(x).$$

I invite you to show a similar result for any x with $c \leqslant x \leqslant x_2$, using the expression

$$L(x) = f(x_2) + f'(c)(x - x_2).$$

(Do Problem 26 of Sec. 15.6.)   End of the proof.

15.5   A PROGRAM FOR SKETCHING GRAPHS AND FINDING MAXIMA AND MINIMA

Except for linear functions—and a few others defined via geometric notions—*no one knows what the graph of a specific function looks like in all its infinite detail.* All the graphs which I've sketched for specific functions are just *guesses* based on mathematical "clues."

The results of the preceding sections and chapters, plus some "common sense," suggest a *detective procedure* that you yourself might follow when given a formula or formulas defining some function f. Here are items to investigate:

A. General clues:

Continuity: Try to determine inputs at which f is not continuous and intervals on which f is continuous.

Bounds: Check for obvious upper and lower bounds for f—if any.

Large inputs: Check the size and sign of outputs $f(x)$ for inputs x which are large negatively or positively. Do these outputs converge to some finite limits, or do they grow large (positively or negatively) without bound?

"Symmetry": Check to see if, for some numbers x, $f(-x) = f(x)$ or $f(-x) = -f(x)$. If so, then you can learn about the graph for negative inputs from what you know about it for positive inputs.

Convenient values: Calculate $f(x)$ for several convenient values of x, such as $x = 0$, $x = \pm 1$, and so on.

Zeros and signs of f: Try to determine inputs x for which $f(x) = 0$ and on which $f(x) > 0$ or $f(x) < 0$.

Increase: Check whether the formula indicates directly certain intervals on which f is increasing or decreasing.

B. Clues via f'.

Try to determine inputs at which f' may not exist and intervals on which it does—on these intervals try to calculate a formula for $f'(x)$.

Examine the function $f'(x)$ in its own right, checking off items as above; *especially, try to find inputs x for which $f'(x) = 0$ and intervals on which $f'(x) > 0$ or $f'(x) < 0$.*

C. Clues via f''.

Try to determine inputs at which f'' may not exist and intervals on which it does—on these, try to calculate a formula for $f''(x)$.

Examine the function $f''(x)$ in its own right, checking off items as above; and again, *expecially, try to find inputs x for which $f''(x) = 0$ and intervals on which $f''(x) > 0$ or $f''(x) < 0$.*

D. Putting the clues together.

On a horizontal axis, mark off special inputs and intervals about which you may have information—as obtained in previous items. Pay special attention to inputs x at which $f'(x) = 0$ and to intervals where $f'(x) > 0$ or $f'(x) < 0$, and to intervals where $f''(x) > 0$ and $f''(x) < 0$.

Increase: If $f'(x) \geq 0$ on some interval, sketch the graph of f as increasing; if $f'(x) \leq 0$, then decreasing.

Convexity: If $f''(x) \geq 0$ on some interval, sketch the graph of f as convex; if $f''(x) \leq 0$, then concave.

If f' and f'' each do not change sign on some subinterval, then there are essentially four possibilities, as pictured in Fig. 15-8.

FIGURE 15-8

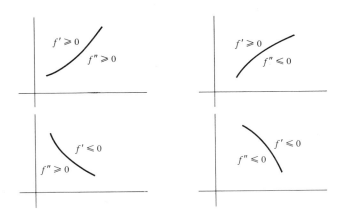

$f'' > 0$ convex

$f'' < 0$ concave

Relative maxima: If x_0 is not an end point of the domain and $f'(x_0) = 0$ then $f(x_0)$ will be a relative maximum either

if $f' \geq 0$ on some interval $[a_0, x_0]$ where $a_0 < x_0$, and $f' \leq 0$ on some interval $[x_0, b_0]$ where $b_0 > x_0$; or

if $f''(x_0) < 0$.

Relative minima: If x_0 is not an end point of the domain and $f'(x_0) = 0$, then $f(x_0)$ will be a relative minimum either

if $f' \leq 0$ on some interval $[a_0, x_0]$ where $a_0 < x_0$, and $f' \geq 0$ on some interval $[x_0, b_0]$ where $b_0 > x_0$; or

if $f''(x_0) > 0$.

Absolute maxima: To determine an absolute maximum for f, examine $f(x)$ at all relative maxima, at all inputs where f is not continuous or not differentiable, at all end points of intervals in the domain; and if the domain is not a bounded set, check the outputs for large $|x|$. Pick the largest of these output values if there is one.

Absolute minima: To determine an absolute minimum for f, examine $f(x)$ at all relative minima, and so on, and choose the smallest input if there is one.

Now fill in a picture of the graph.

I am not suggesting that you check each of the many items above for every function you meet. Depending on the particular case, some of the items are much more relevant or easy to check than others. But have these points in mind.

Here are two examples.

EXAMPLE 1. Let's investigate the function defined by

$$f(x) = \begin{cases} 0 & \text{for } x = 0 \\ x + \dfrac{1}{x} & \text{for } x \neq 0. \end{cases}$$

Note that if x is very small and positive $f(x)$ will be very large and positive. Since $f(0) = 0$, f is discontinuous at $x = 0$. But f is continuous at all other x. For x very large positively, the term $1/x$ will be very small, so $f(x) = x + 1/x$ will be large. And for large x the graph of f should lie slightly above the graph of the linear function $L(x) = x$. We should expect no absolute maximum.

Note also that

$$f(-x) = (-x + 1/-x) = -(x + 1/x) = -f(x) \qquad \text{for all } x \neq 0.$$

So we can copy the graph of f for $x < 0$ from its form for $x > 0$. In particular, we should expect no absolute minimum.

Now let's check f' and f'':

$$f'(x) = (x + x^{-1})' = 1 + (-1)x^{-2}$$

$$= 1 - \frac{1}{x^2} = \frac{x^2 - 1}{x^2} \qquad \text{for all } x \neq 0 \tag{1}$$

and

$$f''(x) = (1 - x^{-2})' = (-1)(-2)x^{-3} = \frac{2}{x^3} \qquad \text{for all } x \neq 0. \tag{2}$$

$f'(x) = 0$ only at $x = \pm 1$; $f'(x) < 0$ for $0 < x^2 < 1$; $f'(x) > 0$ when $x^2 > 1$. Thus f is decreasing on any subinterval of the set {all x with $0 < x \leq 1$} or of the set {all x with $-1 \leq x < 0$}. f is increasing on any subinterval of the set {all $x \geq 1$} or of the set {all $x \leq -1$}. Hence $f(1)$ is a relative minimum and $f(-1)$ is a relative maximum. These conclusions are confirmed by the fact that $f''(1) = 2/1^3 > 0$ and $f''(-1) = 2/(-1)^3 < 0$.

Since $f''(x) = 2/x^3 > 0$ for all $x > 0$, f must be convex on any subinterval of the set {all $x > 0$}. And since $f''(x) < 0$ for all $x < 0$, f must be concave there.

I've put all these clues together, and plotted one point $(2, f(2))$, to sketch the graph of f in Fig. 15-9.

FIGURE 15-9   sketch of the graph of f:

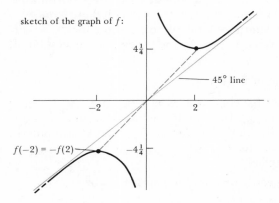

EXAMPLE 2. What does the graph of

$$f(x) = e^{2x} - e^x, \qquad \text{for all real } x, \tag{3}$$

look like? f is continuous everywhere (since e^{ax} is, for any constant a).

Note that when x is large positively, e^x and $f(x) = e^x(e^x - 1)$ are too. We should expect no absolute maximum. When x is large negatively, e^{-x} is large positively, so e^x is very small positively, and $e^x - 1$ will be close to -1. Hence $f(x)$ will be small negatively.

For more information, let's calculate derivatives (recalling that $(e^{ax})' = a(e^{ax})$):

$$f'(x) = 2e^{2x} - e^x \qquad \text{at all real } x, \tag{4}$$

and

$$f''(x) = 2(2e^{2x}) - e^x$$
$$= 4e^{2x} - e^x \qquad \text{at all real } x. \tag{5}$$

These are continuous everywhere also. To determine the zeros and signs of f, f', and f'', let's write e^{2x} as $e^x e^x$ and factor the above expressions:

$$f(x) = e^x e^x - e^x = e^x(e^x - 1), \tag{6}$$

$$f'(x) = 2e^x e^x - 2\frac{1}{2}e^x = 2e^x\left(e^x - \frac{1}{2}\right) \tag{7}$$

and

$$f''(x) = 4e^x e^x - 4\frac{1}{4}e^x = 4e^x\left(e^x - \frac{1}{4}\right). \tag{8}$$

Now e^x is always positive and increasing. Hence $f(x) = 0$ only when the factor $e^x - 1 = 0$; that is, only when $e^x = 1$; that is, only for $x = 0$. If $x < 0$, then $e^x < 1$ and $e^x - 1 < 0$ and $f(x) < 0$. If $x > 0$, then $f(x) > 0$.

Similarly, $f'(x) = 0$ only when $e^x - \frac{1}{2} = 0$; that is, only when $e^x = \frac{1}{2}$; that is, only for $x = \log_e \frac{1}{2} = -\log_e 2 (= -0.693 \text{ approx.})$. If

$$x < \log_e \tfrac{1}{2},$$

then $f'(x) < 0$; and if $x > \log_e \frac{1}{2}$, then $f'(x) > 0$. Conclusion: f is *strictly decreasing* on any subinterval of the set $\{$all $x \leq \log_e \frac{1}{2}\}$ and f is *strictly increasing* on any subinterval of the set

$$\{\text{all } x \geq \log_e \tfrac{1}{2}\}.$$

Hence at $x_1 = \log_e \frac{1}{2}$, the output

$$f(x_1) = e^{x_1} e^{x_1} - e^{x_1} = \tfrac{1}{2} \cdot \tfrac{1}{2} - \tfrac{1}{2} = -\tfrac{1}{4}$$

is an *absolute minimum*.

Similarly, $f''(x) = 0$ only when $e^x - \frac{1}{4} = 0$; that is, for $x = \log_e \frac{1}{4} = -2\log_e 2 (= -1.386 \text{ approx.})$. If $x < \log_e \frac{1}{4}$, then $f''(x) < 0$; and if $x > \log_e \frac{1}{4}$, then $f''(x) > 0$. Now if Theorem E on "convexity" is true, then f must be concave ("bowing downward") *on any subinterval of the set* $\{$all $x \leq \log_e \frac{1}{4}\}$, *and* f *must be convex* ("bowing upward") *on any subinterval of the set* $\{$all $x \geq \log_e \frac{1}{4}\}$.

Some further notes: $f'(0) = 2e^0 - e^0 = 1$. And at $x_2 = \log_e \frac{1}{4}$: $f(x_2) = e^{x_2} e^{x_2} - e^{x_2} = \frac{1}{4} \cdot \frac{1}{4} - \frac{1}{4} = -\frac{3}{16}$ and $f'(x_2) = 2(\frac{1}{4})^2 - \frac{1}{4} = -\frac{1}{8}$.

FIGURE 15-10

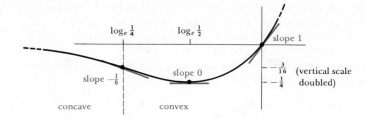

I've used all these facts to sketch the graph of f in Fig. 15-10. I actually plotted only three points!

I invite you to try your own hand at such detective work in doing the problems of the next section.

15.6 PROBLEMS ON INCREASE, MAXIMA, CONVEXITY, AND SKETCHING GRAPHS

°1. For each of the following intervals $[a, b]$ and functions f, find all inputs x_0 with $a < x_0 < b$ such that $f'(x_0) = [f(b)-f(a)]/(b-a)$.

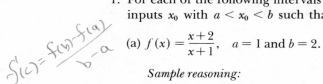

(a) $f(x) = \dfrac{x+2}{x+1}$, $a = 1$ and $b = 2$.

Sample reasoning:

$$f'(x) = \frac{(x+1)\cdot 1 - (x+2)\cdot 1}{(x+1)^2} = \frac{-1}{(x+1)^2},$$

$$f(1) = \frac{3}{2}, f(2) = \frac{4}{3}, \frac{f(2)-f(1)}{b-1} = -\frac{1}{6},$$

hence we need to find inputs x_0 such that

$$\frac{-1}{(x_0+1)^2} = -\frac{1}{6} \quad \text{or} \quad x_0{}^2 + 2x_0 - 5 = 0$$

or

$$x_0 = \frac{-2 \pm \sqrt{24}}{2} = -1 \pm \sqrt{6}.$$

The only one of these values in $[1, 2]$ is $-1 + \sqrt{6}$; hence

$$x_0 = -1 + \sqrt{6}.$$

(b) $f(x) = x^2 - 2x - 3$, $a = -1, b = 3$

(c) $f(x) = x^3 + x^2 - x$, $a = -2, b = 1$

(d) $f(x) = \dfrac{x-1}{x+1}$, $a = 0, b = 3$

(e) $f(x) = \dfrac{2x+3}{3x-2}$, $a = 1, b = 4$

(f) $f(x) = \sqrt{25 - x^2}$, $a = -3, b = 4$

(g) $f(x) = x^4 - 2x^3 + x^2 - 2x$, $a = -1, b = 2$

(h) $f(x) = \dfrac{x^2 - 3x - 4}{x + 5}$, $a = -1, b = 4$

(i) $f(x) = e^x$, $a = 0, b = 1$

*(j) $f(x) = \dfrac{\log x}{x}$, $a = 1, b = e$

2. If a function is differentiable on the closed interval $[a, b]$ and $f(b) > f(a)$, why must f' be positive at some input between a and b?

3. Let $f(x) = 1/x^{1/3}$, $a = -1$, $b = +8$. Show that the conclusion of the mean value theorem does not hold in this situation. Which of the hypotheses doesn't apply? Sketch the graph of the function.

4. Let $f(x) = x^{1/3}$, $a = -1$, $b = +8$. Show that the conclusion of the mean value theorem holds in this situation, although the hypotheses fail. Sketch the graph of the function.

5. The Ohio Turnpike is 240 miles long. When you enter the road at the Westgate you are given a card indicating the date and time that your journey begins and the toll charges at each exit. Suppose you start out at Westgate at 2:00 p.m. and arrive at Eastgate at 5:10 p.m. You hand the card to the toll booth attendant at Eastgate along with the correct toll. He glances at your card and then at his watch and says, "this will cost you an additional $25. The maximum legal speed on the Turnpike is 70 mph and I know that you have driven at least 75 mph at one point." You protest that he has not seen you violate the speed limit. He shows you a printed copy of the mean value theorem. How does it imply your guilt?

°6. For several of the following functions f determine

   (i) intervals on which f is increasing and intervals on which f is decreasing (say whether the increase or decrease is *strict*);
   (ii) inputs at which relative maxima and minima occur, and
   (iii) inputs at which absolute maxima or minima occur.

   Use this information to sketch the graph of f.

   (a) $f(x) = \dfrac{1}{3}x^3 - x^2 - 3x + 3$ for x in $[-4, 4]$,

   Sample reasoning: $f'(x) = x^2 - 2x - 3 = (x - 3)(x + 1)$ at each x. Thus $f'(x) = 0$ only at $x = 3$ or -1 (and these are the only input candidates for relative maxima and minima inside $[-4, 4]$). Now $f'(x) > 0$ only when both factors $x - 3$ and $x + 1$ have the same sign; otherwise $f'(x) < 0$. See Fig. (a).

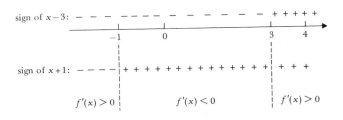

FIGURE (a)

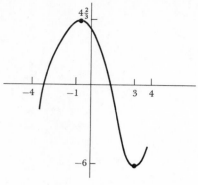

FIGURE (b)

Thus, by Theorem C ("derivative sign controls increase") in Sec. 15.2, f must be strictly increasing on $[-4, -1]$, and on $[3, 4]$, and strictly decreasing on $[-1, 3]$. Hence also $f(-1)$ must be an absolute maximum and $f(3)$ must be an absolute minimum. See Fig. (b) for a crude sketch of the graph.

(b) $f(x) = x^2 + 4x + 2$, for x in $[0, 4]$

(c) $f(x) = -x^2 + 3x + 4$, for x in $[-4, 0]$

(d) $f(x) = -\frac{1}{3}x^3 - x^2 + 2x$. for x in $[-4, 4]$

(e) $f(x) = x^3 + 2x^2 - 3x + 2$, for x in $[-4, 4]$

(f) $f(x) = \frac{x-1}{x+1}$, for x in $\left[-\frac{1}{2}, \frac{1}{2}\right]$

(g) $f(x) = \frac{2x+3}{3x-2}$, for x in $\left[-\frac{1}{2}, \frac{1}{2}\right]$

(h) $f(x) = xe^{-x}$, for x in $[-100, 100]$

(i) $f(x) = x^n e^{-x^2/2}$, for x in $[-100, 100]$, and n a positive integer

(j) $f(x) = x^{-1}e^x$, for x in $\left[\frac{1}{100}, 100\right]$

(k) $f(x) = -x \log e^x$, for x in $\left[\frac{1}{100}, 100\right]$

(l) $f(x) = x^2/\sqrt{x+1}$, for x in $\left[-\frac{1}{2}, \frac{1}{2}\right]$

(m) $f(x) = x^{2/3}(x+3)^{1/3}$ for x in $[-2, 2]$

(n) $f(x) = \begin{cases} x^2 & \text{for } 1 \leqslant x \leqslant 2 \\ x^3 & \text{for } -1 \leqslant x < 1 \end{cases}$

(o) $f(x) = \begin{cases} 3 & \text{for } 2 \leqslant x \leqslant 3 \\ x & \text{for } 0 \leqslant x \leqslant 2 \\ x^2 & \text{for } -1 \leqslant x < 0 \end{cases}$

(Suggestion: Consider f' on separate closed subintervals.)

(p) $f(x) = x\sqrt{2 - x^2}$, for x in $[-\sqrt{2}, \sqrt{2}]$

(q) $f(x) = \frac{x^2 - 3x - 4}{x - 2}$, for $x \neq 2$ and x in $[-100, 100]$

7. Show that all the results of Theorem B ("increase controls derivative sign") and Theorem C ("derivative sign controls increase"), in Sec. 15.2, remain valid if we replace the interval $[a, b]$ in the statements by an open interval $\langle a, b \rangle$, by a half-open interval $[a, b\rangle$ or $\langle b, a]$, by a "half-line" {all $x \geqslant a$} or {all $x \leqslant b$}, or by {all real x}. (For example: If $f'(x) > 0$ for all $x > a$, then f is strictly increasing on the set {all $x \geqslant a$}.)

(Suggestion: To compare any two outputs $f(x_1)$ and $f(x_2)$, where $x_1 < x_2$ you can always restrict f to the interval $[x_1, x_2]$ and apply Theorem C.)

°8. Redo several parts of Problem 6, considering the functions f as defined now for all real values x where the formulas make sense. (You may choose to piece together information from subintervals $[a, b]$, or to use the results of Problem 7.)

Sample:

(a) $f(x) = \frac{1}{3}x^3 - x^2 - 3x + 3$,

now defined for *all* real x. The same calculations hold as in 6(a). Now $f'(x) > 0$ for all $x > 3$ and for all $x < -1$. Hence f is strictly increasing on the half-lines $[3, \infty)$ and $\langle -\infty, 1]$. Note that $|f(x)|^3$ grows without bound as $|x|$ does. Hence there is no absolute maximum or minimum on the new domain. $f(-1)$ is now a relative maximum and $f(3)$ is now a relative minimum.

°9. For each of the following functions, determine
   (i) intervals of convexity, and
   (ii) intervals of concavity.
   Sketch the graph of each function.

(a) $f(x) = \frac{1}{4}x^4 - \frac{3}{2}x^2$ for x in $[-2, 2]$.

   Sample reasoning: $f'(x) = x^3 - 3x$ and $f''(x) = 3x^2 - 3$. Thus $f''(x) = 0$ if $x = \pm 1$; $f''(x) \geq 0$ for x in $[-2, -1]$ and $[1, 2]$ and $f''(x) \leq 0$ for x in $[-1, 1]$. Hence f is convex on $[-2, -1]$ and $[1, 2]$, and concave on $[-1, 1]$.

(b) $f(x) = 2x^2 - 6x + 5$,   for x in $[-4, 4]$

(c) $f(x) = x^3 - 3x + 2$,   for x in $[-4, 4]$

(d) $f(x) = x^2 + \frac{1}{x^2}$,   for x in $\left[\frac{1}{2}, 2\right]$

(e) $f(x) = x^3 - \frac{3}{2}x^2 - 6x + 2$,   for x in $[-100, 100]$

(f) $f(x) = |x|$,   for x in $[-100, 100]$

(g) $f(x) = \frac{4x}{x^2 + 4}$,   for x in $[-100, 100]$

(h) $f(x) = (x + 2)(x - 2)^3$,   for x in $[-100, 100]$

(i) $f(x) = e^x$,   for x in $[-100, 100]$

(j) $f(x) = e^{-x}$,   for x in $[-100, 100]$

(k) $f(x) = e^{-|x|}$,   for x in $[-100, 100]$

(l) $f(x) = \log_e x$,   for x in $\left[\frac{1}{100}, 100\right]$

(m) $f(x) = -x \log_e x$,   for x in $\left[\frac{1}{100}, 100\right]$

(n) $f(x) = x^2 e^{-x^2/2}$,   for x in $[-100, 100]$

10. (a) How would you define the notions of "convexity" and "concavity" on an open interval $\langle a, b \rangle$, or a half open interval $[a, b\rangle$ or $\langle a, b]$, on a "half-line" $\{$all $x \geq a\}$ or $\{$all $x \leq b\}$, and on $\{$all real $x\}$?

(b) Show that Theorem E (on "convexity"), in Sec. 15.3, remains valid if we replace the interval $[a, b]$ in its statement by any of the domains I mentioned in part (a).

(Suggestion: when considering the line L connecting two graph points $(x_1, f(x_1))$ and $(x_2, f(x_2))$, you can think of the domain of f as restricted to $[x_1, x_2]$, and apply Theorem E.)

°11. Redo several parts of Problem 9 considering the functions f as defined now for all real values x where the formulas make sense. (You may choose to piece together information about various subintervals $[a, b]$, or to use the results of Problem 10.)

Sample:

(a) $f(x) = \frac{1}{4}x^4 - \frac{3}{2}x^2$

now defined for all real x. The same calculations hold as in 9(a). Now $f''(x) \geq 0$ for all $x \leq -1$ and ≥ 2. Hence f is convex on $\langle -\infty, 1]$ and on $[2, \infty\rangle$.

*12. Is it possible to have a function f which is convex over the interval $[0, 1]$ but which is not continuous at some input x_0 with

$$0 < x_0 < 1?$$

(Try to sketch the graph of such an f.)

°13. Give as complete a discussion as you can for each of the following functions, determining continuity or lack thereof, increase, decrease, convexity, concavity, boundedness, maxima, minima, and so on. Sketch a graph using all the clues you have. (Consider the domain to consist of all numbers x for which the formulas make sense, unless defined otherwise.)

(a) $f(x) = x^{4/3} + 4x^{1/3}$.

Sample reasoning: $f(x)$ gets arbitrarily large positively when x gets arbitrarily large positively or negatively. Hence no absolute maximum can exist. f is continuous at all x (by the results of Sec. 11.10). At each $x \neq 0$, there exist derivatives

$$f'(x) = \frac{4}{3}x^{1/3} + \frac{4}{3}x^{-2/3} = \frac{4}{3}x^{-2/3}(x+1)$$

and

$$f''(x) = \frac{4}{9}x^{-2/3} - \frac{8}{9}x^{-5/3} = \frac{4}{9}x^{-5/3}(x-2).$$

(Recall Example 2 of Sec. 14.10 for $(x^p)'$ at $x > 0$, and see Problem 9 of Sec. 14.15 for $x < 0$.) Since $f'(-1) = 0$ and $f''(-1) > 0$, $f(-1)$ must be a relative minimum. Moreover, $f'(x) > 0$ for all $x > -1$ $(x \neq 0)$ and $f'(x) < 0$ for all $x < -1$.

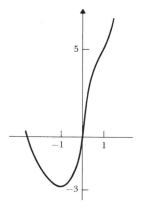

Hence f is strictly increasing on $[-1, 0]$ and on any subinterval of $[0, \infty)$, hence on $[-1, \infty)$. Similarly, f is strictly decreasing on $\langle -\infty, 1]$. Thus $f(-1) = -3$ is an *absolute minimum*; and there are no other relative maxima or minima. To check for convexity, note that $f''(x) \geq 0$ for $x \geq 2$ and for $x < 0$. Hence f is convex on any subinterval $[a, b]$ of $[2, \infty)$ or of $\langle -\infty, 0 \rangle$. (According to Problem 10, we can say that f is convex on all of $[2, \infty)$ and of $\langle -\infty, 0 \rangle$.) $f'(x) \leq 0$ for $0 < x < 2$. Hence f is concave on $\langle 0, 2 \rangle$.

Two more specific output values are $f(0) = 0$, $f(1) = 5$. Also $f'(1) = 8/3$. See the accompanying figure for a graph of the function.

(b) $f(x) = -3x^2 + 2x - 1$ (c) $f(x) = x^2 + 2x + 19$

(d) $f(x) = 2x^2 - \dfrac{1}{x^2}$ (e) $f(x) = x\sqrt{x+3}$

(f) $f(x) = x - 3 + \dfrac{2}{x+1}$ (g) $f(x) = \dfrac{4x}{x^2 + 4}$

(h) $f(x) = x^{2/3}(x+2)^{-1}$ (i) $f(x) = \dfrac{x+1}{x-1}$

(j) $f(x) = \begin{cases} x^2, & x < -2 \\ 1, & -2 \leq x < 1 \\ x, & x > 1 \end{cases}$

(k) $f(x) = \begin{cases} -2x & \text{for } x < -1 \\ x^2, & \text{for } -1 \leq x \leq 0 \\ 3x^4, & \text{for } 0 < x \leq 1 \\ 1/(x-1), & \text{for } 1 < x \leq 2 \\ 1, & \text{for } x > 2 \end{cases}$

(l) $f(x) = |x|e^{-|x|}$ (m) $f(x) = e^{-3x} - e^{2x}$

(n) $f(x) = \begin{cases} x \log_e x - x, & \text{for } x > 0 \\ x, & \text{for } x \leq 0 \end{cases}$

*(o) $f(x) = x^{\log_e x}$,   for $x > 0$

14. Suppose that your job is to plan the flight of an aircraft, and you are informed that the amount of turbulence $T(h)$ which the craft will experience when flying at altitude h has a graph as in the accompanying figure. At which altitude should the aircraft fly?

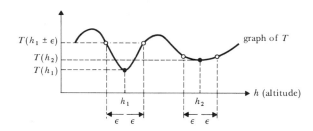

The turbulence would appear to be at an absolute minimum for $h = h_1$, and only at a relative, nonabsolute, minimum for $h = h_2$. But is it wiser to choose h_1 rather than h_2? Only if you can guarantee that the aircraft will make no deviations from the chosen altitude—deviations due to "chance" or whatever cause. However, if deviations are probable—say, of magnitude $\pm\epsilon$, as pictured in the figure, then the aircraft may be safer flying at altitudes near h_2—with corresponding turbulence differing only slightly from $T(h_2)$, than it would be flying at altitudes near h_1 with possible turbulence up to $T(h_1 \pm \epsilon)$.

Discuss what role the second derivative T'' can play in such decisions.

*15. I've been using the function $f(x) = x^2$ repeatedly in examples. Its graph (reproduced again in Figure (a)) is an example of what's called a "parabola"—which is not only a "convex" curve, but one which has a special "focusing" property. You may have heard of "parabolic mirrors." Here is how they work:

Suppose that we have a highly polished reflecting surface as sketched in Figure (b), whose cross sections are all parabolas as in (a) below.

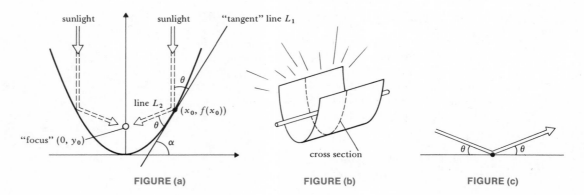

FIGURE (a)   FIGURE (b)   FIGURE (c)

If a copper pipe is inserted at just the correct level above the surface then water which runs through the pipe can be turned to steam by the intense heat of sunlight "focused" upon the pipe by the reflecting "parabolic surface." Why is there such a "focusing" effect? The main physical principle involved is that a light ray will bounce off a flat reflecting surface with the same angle—say θ—as that whereby it arrived, as in Figure (c). Now look at the cross section in Figure (a). An idealized, thin shaft of sunlight coming down vertically to the point $(x_0, f(x_0))$ will not find the parabola to be completely flat there, but almost so. Very near the point $(x_0, f(x_0))$ the parabola would appear to be approximated rather well by the "tangent line" through $(x_0, f(x_0))$ with slope $f'(x_0)$. So the shaft of sunlight may be expected to bounce off the parabola in a direction making an angle θ with the tangent line equal to the angle of its arrival. See Figure (a). It will then cross the midway axis of the parabola at a point $(0, y_0)$. Now here's the amazing mathematical aspect of the parabola: the point $(0, y_0)$ is the same no matter which arrival point $(x_0, f(x_0))$ we might have been considering. Thus vertical shafts of light hitting at various different points of the parabola all come together at the same point, after reflection. This is what "focusing" means. And most of the heat energy of the individual shafts of light comes together intensely around $(0, y_0)$. What's true for one cross section is true all along the 3-dimensional surface.

I invite you now to verify my assertion about the property of focusing:

(a) Suppose that the "tangent line" L_1 makes an angle α with the positive x axis as in Figure (a). Show that the rebound line L_2 makes an angle $\beta = \alpha - \theta$ with the positive x axis.

**(b) Calculate the slope of the rebound line L_2 in terms of

$$f'(x_0) = \tan \alpha.$$

(c) Write an equation for the rebound line L_2.

(d) Determine the height y_0 at which the line L_2 intersects the vertical $(x = 0)$ axis.

16. Suppose that on May 1, a man has 10,000 lb of ice stored in such a way that 35 lb of it melts every day. Initially the price is 10c per hundred pounds and it goes up 1¢ per hundred pounds every week as the weather gets warmer.

(a) On what date should he sell his ice to make maximum profit? What should be his corresponding selling price?

(b) If the price went up $\frac{1}{7}$¢ per hundred pounds every day, how would this change the result in (a)?

(c) Suppose the ice is stored in such a way that 1% of the remaining ice melts each day. On which day should the owner sell the ice?

17. Suppose that a fuel company expects to use 1,000,000 gallons of fuel oil in a year, that a gallon's worth of storage capacity costs 1¢ for a year, and that *each* shipment of oil to the company's tanks will cost $100 if there are fewer than 12 shipments in all, and $60 if there are more than 12 shipments in all.

(a) Determine the most economical number of shipments, and their size.

(b) How much is lost if there is a deviation by one or two shipments from the optimum?

18. Economists like to analyze phenomena via idealized models, just as physicists do. In such models they sometimes try to picture how "rational" economic behavior might look, so that they can compare it with — and perhaps predict — actual behavior. One component of some of these models is a "utility function," which

is supposed to represent how much usefulness or gratification ("utility") a given person has for differing amounts of a given thing or "good." Thus for differing amounts x of ice cream (as measured, say, in dollars), we might think of corresponding amounts $f(x)$ of your enjoyment (as measured, say, in mythical units, "utils"). For convenience we might suppose $f(x)$ to be differentiable. The derivative $f'(x_0)$ describes the *rate* at which your utility will change when you increase the amount of goods ever so slightly above x_0. (Since economists traditionally spoke of differences in amounts as "marginal" changes, they've taken to calling $f'(x)$ the "marginal utility function.")

(a) One can have enough, and even too much, ice cream in the house. How would you describe a "point x_0 of diminishing returns" in terms of $f'(x)$?

(b) Suppose that $f(x)$ is your utility function for amounts x of ice cream and $g(y)$ is your utility function for amounts y of coffee. Suppose also that you have a total of \$2 to spend on both ice cream and coffee, and that neither utility function reaches its maximum for inputs $<$ \$2. How should you split the \$2 between ice cream and coffee so as to maximize your *total* utility?

Now, some pairs of goods might interfere with each other, and then total utility might not be the sum of their individual utilities—for example, coffee and tea. But suppose that this is not the case with ice cream and coffee, that corresponding amounts x and y of these goods lead to a total utility

$$f(x) + g(y).$$

Let $y = \$2 - x$, and show why the best amounts x_0 and $y_0 = 2 - x_0$ of ice cream and coffee to buy are those which equalize the corresponding marginal utilities:

$$f'(x_0) = g'(y_0). \tag{*}$$

(c) Can you interpret the condition (*) in terms of what would happen if you spent slightly more (or less) than x_0 on ice cream, and correspondingly slightly less (or more) than y_0 on coffee?

19. Suppose that $f(p)$ represents the amount of a given produce which will be demanded by the buying public when the product is sold at price p dollars. (For examples, see Problem 7 of Sec. 7.4 and Problem 6 of Sec. 14.3.) If the product is sold at price p, the public will then spend a total of $pf(p)$ dollars on it.

(a) Suppose that f is a differentiable and that $pf(p)$ has a unique maximum for some price $p_0 > 0$. Show that p_0 must be such that the ratio

$$E(p_0) = -\frac{f'(p_0)}{f(p_0)} p_0 \tag{*}$$

has value $E(p_0) = 1$.

(b) Show that for any price p_0 and nearby price p, the right-hand side of (*) (except for the minus sign) measures the *ratio* of the *percentagewise change in demand* $\{[f(p)-f(p_0)]/f(p_0)\}$ to the *percentagewise change in price* $[(p-p_0)/p_0]$.

(c) Economists call the ratio $E(p)$ the *elasticity* of the product at price p. Show that if $E(p_0) > 1$, then a slight increase in price above p_0 will decrease the total expenditure, and if $E(p_0) < 1$ then a slight decrease in price from p_0 will increase the total expenditure.

(d) Compute the elasticity at $p = \$0.50$ for a foreign chocolate bar whose "demand function" has been estimated for the U.S. public as $f(p) = -4000 + 7000/p$. Would the imposition of a tariff on this item serve to cut down or to increase total public expenditures on it?

20. Suppose that a printer agrees to produce notes for a new experimental course—in which 200 and 300 students are expected to enroll. The printer must manufacture the notes prior to the week of registration in order that they be ready for class. He will, however, suffer a penalty in total profits if he prints more sets of notes or less sets of notes than the actual demand: each superfluous set will lose him, say, \$2. On the other hand, for each set of notes that he is short he must run off a second edition copy at a penalty of \$1.

(a) Let x and y be numbers between 200 and 300—integers if you want a strict interpretation. If the printer produces a first edition of x sets of notes, and if the enrollment turns out to be y students, what will be the printer's corresponding loss— call it $L(x, y)$?

(b) For a fixed x, draw the graph of L as a function of y with domain $[200, 300]$. Record the maximum loss possible for that fixed x—call it $M(x)$.

(c) State a clear rule for $M(x)$ as a function with inputs x in the domain $[200, 300]$. Graph $M(x)$. Find the x_0 for which M is a minimum—if there is one.

Such an x_0, if it exists, has been called a "mini-max" solution of the printer's loss problem: it represents the best move he can make to minimize his maximum possible loss due to perverse action of his "opponent"—class enrollment.

21. Show that if $P''(x) > 0$ on $[0, 1]$ and if $P(1) = 1$ and $P'(1) \leq 1$, then there exists no "fixed point" q with $0 \leq q < 1$ such that $P(q) = q$.

(Suggestion: If such a q did exist, then for some x_0 with $q < x_0 < 1$ we would have

$$P'(x_0) = \frac{P(1) - P(q)}{1 - q} = 1,$$

by the mean value theorem. Apply the same theorem once more to the function P'.)

*22. Suppose that f is a function with the property that

$$-\frac{1}{2} \leq f'(x) \leq \frac{1}{2}$$

for all $x \geq 0$ and $f(0)$ is positive.
(a) Use the mean value theorem to show that $f(x) \leq f(0) + \frac{1}{2}x$ for all $x \geq 0$.
(b) Show that $f(x) - x$ is negative for sufficiently large values of x.
(c) Show that f has exactly one fixed point.
(d) Show that the fixed point x_0 is the limit of sequence

$$0, f(0), f(f(0)), f(f(f(0))), \ldots.$$

*23. Check through the proof of the mean value theorem which I gave in Sec. 15.1 and show that information about $f'(x)$ at the elements of $[a, b]$ really isn't necessary. That is, prove this slightly more general version of the theorem: *If a function f is continuous on $[a, b]$ and has derivatives $f'(x)$ at all x with $a < x < b$, then there must be some input c with $a < c < b$ such that*

$$f(b) - f(a) = f'(c)(b - a).$$

*24. (a) Using the result of Problem 22, show that information about $f'(x)$ at the end points of $[a, b]$ really isn't necessary for the claims of Theorem C ("derivative sign controls increase") in Sec. 15.2. That is, prove this slightly more general version of the theorem: *Suppose that f is continuous on $[a, b]$ and differentiable at all x with $a < x < b$.*
   If $f'(x) = 0$ for all x in $\langle a, b \rangle$, then f is constant on $[a, b]$.
   If $f'(x) \geq 0$ (> 0) for all x in $\langle a, b \rangle$, then f is (strictly) increasing on $[a, b]$.
   If $f'(x) \leq 0$ (< 0) for all x in $\langle a, b \rangle$, then f is (strictly) decreasing on $[a, b]$.
   (b) To which parts of Problems 6 and 13 does the version in (a) apply particularly well?

*25. Write out the proofs of statements (ii) and (iii) in Theorem D ("at the sign of the second derivative"), analogous to those I gave for parts (i) and (iv), in Sec. 15.4.

*26. I invite you to complete the proof of Theorem E (on "convexity"), in Sec. 15.4. Specifically:
   (a) Show that the linear function L whose graph passes through the points $(x_1, f(x_1))$ and $(x_2, f(x_2))$ can be described by the formula

$$L(x) = f(x_2) + f'(c)(x - x_2)$$

   for some input c of f with $x_1 < c < x_2$.
   (b) Show that if x is any input of f with $c \leq x \leq x_2$ and $f''(x) \geq 0$ for all x in the interval $[a, b]$, then $f(x) \leq L(x)$.

27. Here is an alternate definition of "convexity" for a function f defined on an interval $[a, b]$: *for any two inputs x and y in $[a, b]$, the "average" (the midpoint) of their outputs should be greater than the output of their average*, that is,

$$\frac{f(x) + f(y)}{2} \geqslant f\left(\frac{x + y}{2}\right). \tag{*}$$

(a) Illustrate this relationship in terms of a graph, and show that it is implied by the definition of convexity (Definition I) which I gave in Sec. 15.3.

*(b) Does the alternate definition imply Definition I, conversely?

*28. In the spirit of the definition in Problem 27(a), call a region $\mathscr{R}$ in the plane "*convex*" if, for any two points P and Q in $\mathscr{R}$, the straight line segment PQ also lies in $\mathscr{R}$.

Can you generalize Example 1 in Chap. 1 by giving arguments to show that, among all regions having a smooth perimeter of given length c, the one which will provide maximum area *must be convex* (if it exists at all)?

29. Suppose that an object moves around in an xy plane and that its coordinates are describable by functions $x = f(t)$ and $y = g(t)$ for time t in some interval $[a, b]$, with $f(a) \neq f(b)$. And suppose also that f and g are each continuous on $[a, b]$; and are differentiable for $a < t < b$, with the rates $f'(t)$ and $g'(t)$ never 0 simultaneously. We might picture the *path* of the object as in the accompanying Figure (a). Shouldn't there be some time t_0 *between* a and b at which the "instantaneous direction" of the object should be the *same* as the straight line direction between the starting point $(f(a), g(a))$ and the terminal point $(f(b), g(b))$? Looking at Figure (b), a blowup of Figure (a), might we not expect

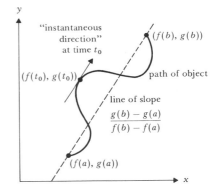

FIGURE (a)

$$\frac{g(b) - g(a)}{f(b) - f(a)} = \lim_{t \to t_0}\left[\frac{g(t) - g(t_0)}{f(t) - f(t_0)}\right] = \lim_{t \to t_0}\frac{\{[g(t) - g(t_0)]/(t - t_0)\}}{\{[f(t) - f(t_0)]/(t - t_0)\}}$$

$$= \frac{\lim\limits_{t \to t_0}\{[g(t) - g(t_0)]/(t - t_0)\}}{\lim\limits_{t \to t_0}\{[f(t) - f(t_0)]/(t - t_0)\}} = \frac{g'(t_0)}{f'(t_0)}, \tag{*}$$

for some t_0 with $a < t_0 < b$? I invite you to show that (*) does indeed hold, by applying the mean value theorem (say, as stated in Problem 23) to the auxiliary function

$$h(t) = g(t) - \left[\frac{g(b) - g(a)}{f(b) - f(a)}\right]f(t) \qquad \text{for } a \leqslant t \leqslant b.$$

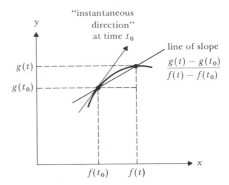

FIGURE (b)

*30. Use the result of Problem 27 to establish the following result (named after the Marquis de l'Hospital (1690+)). Suppose that f and g are continuous on $[a, b]$ and differentiable on $\langle a, b], with

$f(a) = g(a) = 0$ and $f'(t) \neq 0$ for all inputs $t > a$. If

$$\lim_{t \to a} \frac{g'(t)}{f'(t)} = A,$$

then $\lim_{t \to a} g(t)/f(t) = A$, also.

(Suggestion: For any fixed t in $\langle a, b]$,

$$\frac{g(t) - g(a)}{f(t) - f(a)} = \frac{g'(t_0)}{f'(t_0)}$$

for some t_0 with $a < t_0 < t$.)

31. Use the result of Problem 30 to evaluate the following limits:
    (a) $\lim_{t \to 1} h(t)$, where

    $$h(t) = \frac{t - 1}{\log_e t} \qquad \text{for } t > 1.$$

    Sample reasoning: Let $g(t) = t - 1$ and $f(t) = \log_e (t)$ on, say, $[1, 2]$. Then $g(1) = f(1) = 0$, and

    $$\lim_{t \to 1} \frac{g'(t)}{f'(t)} = \lim_{t \to 1} \frac{1}{1/t} = \lim_{t \to 1} t = 1.$$

    Hence

    $$1 = \lim_{t \to 1} \frac{g(t)}{f(t)} = \lim_{t \to 1} h(t)$$

    (since limits are determined "locally," Property $\hat{C}$ in Sec. 11.7.)

    (b) $\lim_{x \to 0} h(x)$, where $h(x) = \dfrac{x^2}{e^x - 1}$, $\qquad$ for $0 < x \leqslant 1$.

    (c) $\lim_{x \to 0} h(x)$, where $h(x) = \dfrac{x}{e^{2x} - e^x}$, $\qquad$ for $0 < x \leqslant 1$.

    (d) $\lim_{x \to 1} h(x)$ where $h(x) = x^{1/(x-1)}$, $\qquad$ for $1 < x \leqslant 2$.

    (Suggestion: Write $x^{1/(x-1)} = e^{[1/(x-1)] \log_e x}$.)

15.7 HOW TO APPROXIMATE IF YOU MUST

Excluding simple additions and multiplications of integers and the like — most calculations people make involve *approximations*. In previous decades mathematicians and their helpers toiled wearily to accumulate tables of "values" for functions such as $\sqrt{x}$, e^x, $\log_e x$, and so on. What were these values — on which most of physical science and technology depended? Approximations. Nowadays people instruct computers to recalculate such values whenever they are needed. How — when computers are essentially just very fast adding and multiplying machines? Again, by approximations.

On what ideas is this enormous human and mechanical effort based? Here is one of the simplest:

Suppose that we have a function f whose output $f(x_0)$ and derivative $f'(x_0)$ we can calculate exactly at some input x_0. As I noted in Sec. 14.4, we might hope to "approximate" the graph of f *near* the point $P_0 = (x_0, f(x_0))$ by a line through that point and having slope $f'(x_0)$. See Fig. 15-11.

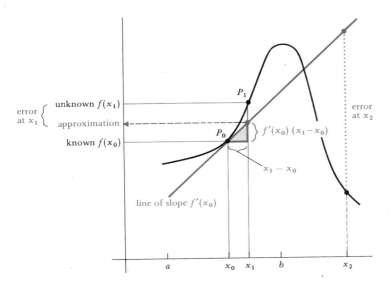

FIGURE 15-11

That is, we might hope to approximate f by the *linear function*

$$L(x) = f(x_0) + f'(x_0)(x - x_0). \tag{1}$$

Recall: as we move horizontally away from the input x_0 to another input x_1, the altitude of the line changes from $f(x_0)$ by the amount $f'(x_0)(x_1 - x_0)$. If x_1 is "close enough" to x_0, we might accept the linear output

$$L(x_1) = f(x_0) + f'(x_0)(x_1 - x_0) \tag{2}$$

as an "approximation" to the true but unknown output $f(x_1)$. The "approximation" will be "good" if the

$$\text{\textit{Error at }} x_1 = f(x_1) - L(x_1)$$

$$= f(x_1) - f(x_0) - f'(x_0)(x_1 - x_0) \tag{3}$$

is "small." How small should "small" be? And when will x_1 be "close enough" to x_0? Note in Fig. 15-11 that this scheme can produce an error $f(x_2) - L(x_2)$ at an input x_2 which (in magnitude) far exceeds the unknown output $f(x_2)$ itself. A possible disaster!—because x_2 wasn't "close enough" to x_0.

Now, how "small" an error should be depends on us, or on whoever does the calculating. We should choose an allowable error amount—call it ϵ—and then should not accept any approximation $L(x_1)$ where the error has magnitude $|f(x_1) - L(x_1)| > \epsilon$. The main trouble is this: we may never know the error $f(x_1) - L(x_1)$ *exactly*. (If we did, we could compute $f(x_1) = L(x_1) + [f(x_1) - L(x_1)]$ exactly.) So how can we tell whether x_1 is "close enough" to x_0 to make the error $|f(x_1) - L(x_1)| \leq \epsilon$? What *guarantee* can we ever have on error magnitude?

The mean value theorem to the rescue: Note that the error expression (3) involves the difference $f(x_1) - f(x_0)$. Although we don't know $f(x_1)$, we can write

$$f(x_1) - f(x_0) = f'(c)(x_1 - x_0) \qquad \text{for some } c \text{ between } x_0 \text{ and } x_1, \qquad (4)$$

provided derivatives $f'(x)$ exist between x_0 and x_1. Then the error must be of the form

$$\begin{aligned} f(x_1) - L(x_1) &= f(x_1) - f(x_0) - f'(x_0)(x_1 - x_0) \\ &= f'(c)(x_1 - x_0) - f'(x_0)(x_1 - x_0) \\ &= [f'(c) - f'(x_0)](x_1 - x_0). \end{aligned} \qquad (5)$$

What about the difference $f'(c) - f'(x_0)$? Let's use the "mean value" result again to write

$$f'(c) - f'(x_0) = f''(d)(c - x_0) \qquad \text{for some } d \text{ between } x_0 \text{ and } c, \qquad (6)$$

provided second derivatives $f''(x)$ exist, say, between x_0 and x_1. Putting the results (5) and (6) together, we can get an *upper estimate* for the magnitude of the error:

$$\begin{aligned} |f(x_1) - L(x_1)| &= |f''(d)(c - x_0)(x_1 - x_0)| \\ &= |f''(d)| \cdot |c - x_0| \cdot |x_1 - x_0| \\ &< |f''(d)|(x_1 - x_0)^2 \end{aligned} \qquad (7)$$

($|c - x_0| < |x_1 - x_0|$ since c lies between x_0 and x_1). When can such an inequality be of use? In cases where we can guess an upper bound B for $|f''(d)|$. I'll summarize and give an example.

Theorem F (on "guaranteed error estimates"): Suppose that a function f has $|f''(x)| \leq B$ for all x in some interval $[a, b]$. If x_0 and x_1 are in $[a, b]$, then the "linear approximation"

$$L(x_1) = f(x_0) + f'(x_0)(x_1 - x_0)$$

for the output $f(x_1)$ has error magnitude

$$|f(x_1) - L(x_1)| \leq B(x_1 - x_0)^2. \qquad (8)$$

EXAMPLE 1. Let's try to approximate $\sqrt{4.12}$—say, with an error of no more than $\epsilon = 0.001$. We can consider $f(x) = \sqrt{x}$, say, on the interval $4 \leq x \leq 5$. It's easy to calculate $f(x_0) = x_0^{1/2}$ and $f'(x_0) = \frac{1}{2}x_0^{-1/2}$ at $x_0 = 4$. Namely,

$$f(4) = 2 \quad \text{and} \quad f'(4) = \frac{1}{2}\frac{1}{\sqrt{4}} = \frac{1}{4}.$$

The "linear approximation" scheme of Fig. 15-11 then offers the value

$$L(4.12) = f(4) + f'(4)(4.12-4)$$
$$= 2 + \tfrac{1}{4}(0.12) = 2.03$$

as an approximation to $\sqrt{4.12}$. How large is the *error* $\sqrt{4.12} - 2.03$? According to Theorem F above, we'll have

$$|\sqrt{4.12} - 2.03| \leqslant B(0.12)^2 = B(0.0144)$$

if B is an upper estimate for $|f''(x)|$ on the interval $[4, 5]$. Note that

$$f''(x) = \left(\tfrac{1}{2}x^{-1/2}\right)' = -\tfrac{1}{2}\tfrac{1}{2}x^{-3/2} = -\tfrac{1}{4}\frac{1}{x^{3/2}}, \tag{9}$$

and that

$$|f''(x)| = \tfrac{1}{4}\frac{1}{x^{3/2}} \tag{10}$$

is a *decreasing* function on $[4, 5]$. It must take its largest value at $x = 4$. Thus

$$|f''(x)| = \tfrac{1}{4}\frac{1}{x^{3/2}} \leqslant \tfrac{1}{4}\frac{1}{4^{3/2}} = \tfrac{1}{4}\frac{1}{2^3} = \frac{1}{32} \qquad \text{for } x \text{ in } [4, 5].$$

Whatever the true error may be, we have a guarantee that

$$|\sqrt{4.12} - 2.03| \leqslant \tfrac{1}{32}(0.0144) = 0.00045.$$

In this case, the "linear approximation" scheme got us well within the allowable error amount $\epsilon = 0.001$.

But what if—say, for some delicate calculation in astronomy, where small angular errors contribute large deviations at great distances—what if we needed to know $\sqrt{4.12}$ with an error no greater than $\epsilon' = 0.00001$? The "linear approximation" scheme can deliver nothing better than 2.03. What shall we do?

Why not try to approximate f near x_0 by a *quadratic polynomial* $Q(x) = ax^2 + bx + c$. We might try to adjust the constants a, b, and c so that $Q(x_0) = f(x_0)$, $Q'(x_0) = f'(x_0)$, and moreover $Q''(x_0) = f''(x_0)$. We might then accept the quadratic output $Q(x_1)$ as an approximation for $f(x_1)$. Can we get a guaranteed upper bound for the error magnitude $|f(x_1) - Q(x_1)|$? And will it be no greater than $\epsilon' = 0.00001$? If yes—good. If not—how about trying to approximate f near x_0 by a polynomial of even higher degree?

In a later section I'll discuss how to get error bounds for such approximations with polynomials. Meanwhile, to suggest how approximation can improve with higher-degree polynomials, I've superimposed a quadratic in Fig. 15-12 upon the linear approximation of Fig. 15-11.

Isaac Newton had a different way to approximate $r_0 = \sqrt{4.12}$. He noted that r_0 must be a root of the polynomial $g(x) = x^2 - 4.12$. He made a first guess at a root—call it r_1, and then traced along approximating lines to generate a whole sequence r_n of what he *hoped* were

FIGURE 15-12

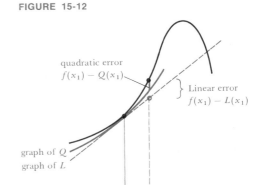

quadratic error
$f(x_1) - Q(x_1)$

Linear error
$f(x_1) - L(x_1)$

graph of Q
graph of L

$x_0 \qquad x_1$

FIGURE 15-13

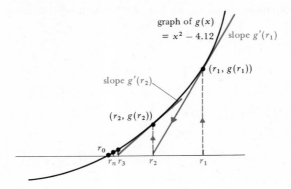

better and better approximations converging to r_0—as in Fig. 15-13. Can we have a guarantee that Newton's method will in fact lead to approximations of whatever accuracy we might wish?

I invite you to consider such questions, and to try your own hand at making a few approximations and error estimates in doing the problems of the next section.

15.8 PROBLEMS ON APPROXIMATION

°1. Use the technique of "linear approximation" to approximate each of the following numbers. Estimate the size of the error. In each case sketch a graph of the function whose output you are trying to calculate, and draw the approximating line.

(a) $\sqrt{3.98}$ (b) $\sqrt[3]{27.2}$

(c) $\sqrt[5]{1.15}$ (d) $\dfrac{1}{(0.99)^3}$

(e) $\sqrt{49.9}$ (f) $\sqrt[4]{15.4}$

(g) $\dfrac{1}{(3.01)^2}$ (h) $(64.3)^{5/6}$

°2. If $f(x) = 1/(x+3)$, find an approximation for $f(2.92)$.
°3. If $f(x) = \sqrt{x-2}$, find an approximation for $f(38.4)$.
°4. Find an approximate value for $(1.97)\sqrt[3]{(1.97)^2+4}$.
5. Suppose you try to approximate a function f near an input x_0 by a quadratic polynomial $Q(x) = ax^2 + bx + c$ in such a way that

$$Q(x_0) = f(x_0), \quad Q'(x_0) = f'(x_0), \quad \text{and} \quad Q''(x_0) = f''(x_0).$$

(a) How should you choose the values of a, b, and c?
(b) Find a quadratic polynomial that approximates $f(x) = \sqrt{x}$ at $x_0 = 4$. Use this polynomial to approximate the value of $\sqrt{4.12}$.
6. An illustration of Newton's Method. Let $g(x) = x^2 - 4.12$ and let r_1 be a first guess at a root of g.
(a) Show that the straight line through $(r_1, g(r_1))$ with slope $g'(r_1)$ is given by the linear function

$$L(x) = g'(r_1)x + g(r_1) - g'(r_1)r_1.$$

(b) Show that $L(r_2) = 0$ if r_2 is the input

$$r_2 = \frac{g'(r_1)r_1 - g(r_1)}{g'(r_1)}.$$

(c) Repeat steps (a) and (b) to find

$$r_3 = \frac{g'(r_2)r_2 - g(r_2)}{g'(r_2)}.$$

(d) To find r_{n+1} once r_n is known, Newton suggested drawing a straight line through $P = (r_n, g(r_n))$ with slope $g'(r_n)$, and letting r_{n+1} be the x coordinate of the point where that line intersects the x axis.

Show that r_{n+1} is given by

$$r_{n+1} = \frac{g'(r_n)r_n - g(r_n)}{g'(r_n)}.$$

(e) Let $r_1 = 1$ and calculate r_2, r_3, and r_4.
(f) Does the sequence $\{r_n\}$ seem to approach $\sqrt{4.12}$?
(g) What happens in the case where you guess $r_1 = 0$?
7. Repeat the steps of Problem 6 for $g(x) = x^3 - 8.2$.

15.9 THE "NECK-AND-NECK RACE ARGUMENT"

The key to the methods of Chap. 7, was that if two functions f and g shared the same "starting values" $f(a) = g(a)$ and had identical derivatives $f'(x) = g'(x)$ for all x in an interval $[a, b]$, then they must be identical on $[a, b]$: $f(x) = g(x)$ for all x in $[a, b]$. Thanks to results flowing from the mean value theorem, we can validate the argument completely: we need merely note that the difference function $h(x) = g(x) - f(x)$ has the properties

$$h(a) = g(a) - f(a) = 0 \tag{1}$$

and

$$h'(x) = [g(x) - f(x)]' = g'(x) - f'(x) = 0 \qquad \text{for all } x \text{ in } [a, b]. \tag{2}$$

Thus h must be constant on $[a, b]$—namely,

$$h(x) = g(x) - f(x) = h(a) = 0, \qquad \text{for all } x \text{ in } [a, b] \tag{3}$$

(by Theorem C, "derivative sign controls increase," in Sec. 15.2). Conclusion:

Theorem G (the "neck-and-neck race argument"): If $f(a) = g(a)$ and $f'(x) = g'(x)$ for all x in $[a, b]$, then $f(x) = g(x)$ for all x in $[a, b]$.

Here are two further examples of how we can use this result.

EXAMPLE 1. A bacterium of the kind E. Coli (which I discussed in Secs. 6.5 and 13.3), with an average lifetime of one hour, will eat approximately its own weight in sugar per hour. If we start out at noon with a colony of E. Coli weighing 2 g, and let the colony grow and eat its way along until 3 p.m., how many grams of sugar will it have consumed by 3 p.m.?

To answer, let's use the limiting results in Sec. 13.3 and suppose that the bacterial population size—and therefore its weight—changes exponentially with time: The colony should weigh $W(t) = 2e^t$ grams at t hours after noon. ($W(0) = 2e^0 = 2$ g.) Let's suppose also that during any subinterval $[t_0, t_1]$ of an hour of life, an individual bacterium will consume $(t_1 - t_0)$ times its weight in sugar—an amount proportional to the length of the subinterval. Finally, let's let $A(t)$ denote the total amount of sugar consumed by the colony during the first t hours after noon. We should have $A(0) = 0$.

The problem is to find the single output $A(3)$. But again, one of the easiest ways to find the number $A(3)$ is to ask about the entire picture of how $A(t)$ increases during the interval $[0, 3]$. Pick any two instants t_0 and t in $[0, 3]$—say, with $t_0 < t$. How much sugar will the colony consume during the subinterval $[t_0, t]$? The amount $A(t) - A(t_0)$. How can we estimate $A(t) - A(t_0)$? There will be *at least* $W(t_0) = 2e^{t_0}$ grams worth of bacteria alive and eating during that interval. If $t - t_0$ is very small, then most of the bacteria would eat approximately $(t - t_0)$ times their weight in sugar. So we might consider the quantity $2e^{t_0}(t - t_0)$ as a *lower bound* for the true amount of consumption during $[t_0, t]$. Similarly, there will be *at most* $W(t) = 2e^t$ grams of bacteria alive during $[t_0, t_1]$. So we might consider $2e^t(t - t_0)$ as an *upper bound*:

$$2e^{t_0}(t - t_0) \leqslant A(t) - A(t_0) \leqslant 2e^t(t - t_0). \tag{4}$$

To get an *average rate of consumption*, divide through by $(t - t_0)$:

$$2e^{t_0} \leqslant \frac{A(t) - A(t_0)}{t - t_0} \leqslant 2e^t. \tag{5}$$

Similarly, if $t < t_0$,

$$2e^t \leqslant \frac{A(t_0) - A(t)}{t_0 - t} = \frac{A(t) - A(t_0)}{t - t_0} \leqslant 2e^{t_0}. \tag{6}$$

If we hold t_0 fixed and let t converge to t_0, we can arrive at an *instantaneous* rate of change $A'(t_0) = 2e^{t_0}$—as in Fig. 15-14.

FIGURE 15-14

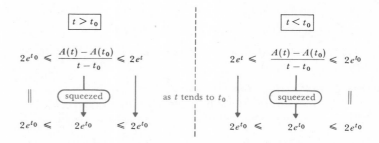

(Here I've used the continuity of e^t; the "squeezing" property of limits, $\hat{P}$ in Chap. 11; and the "interlacing" property of derivatives, D' in Chap. 14.)

Here then is what we know about the consumption function A:

$$A(0) = 0 \quad \text{and} \quad A'(t) = 2e^t \qquad \text{for } 0 \leq t \leq 3 \text{ hours.} \tag{7}$$

How can we find A itself? Recall that $(e^t)' = e^t$, and

$$(2e^t + c)' = 2(e^t)' + 0 = 2e^t \tag{8}$$

for any constant c. Why not let $c = -2$, so that the function

$$F(t) = 2e^t - 2$$

will have properties

$$F(0) = 2e^0 - 2 = 0 \quad \text{and} \quad F'(t) = 2e^t \qquad \text{for } 0 \leq t \leq 3 \text{ hours} \tag{9}$$

identical to those for the unknown A in (7)? By the neck-and-neck race argument, there can be no more doubts: the unknown $A(t)$ and our constructed $F(t) = 2e^t - 2$ must be *identical*. In particular, $A(3) = 2e^3 - 2 = 38$ g, approximately.

EXAMPLE 2: *Gravity again.* You may recall from Chap. 7 my discussion of straight vertical fall (from a cliff) due to "gravity." How will gravity affect a *nonvertical* trajectory? Suppose that you throw a ball. Say that it leaves your hand at a height of 6 ft above ground with an initial velocity of 80 ft/sec in a direction 45° from the horizontal. What *horizontal* distance will it cover before hitting the ground? How long will the trip take? And what shape will the trajectory have?

Let's try to answer these questions in terms of a slightly simplified mathematical model where we might suppose that air resistance doesn't retard the ball in any way. How might "gravity" affect the motion? Let's suppose—as physical experiments suggest—that the attraction between the ball and the earth primarily affects the *vertical* aspects of the ball's motion—not the horizontal. If so, then we should keep track of the ball's horizontal and vertical positions (in its plane of flight) by *separate* functions of time, $H(t)$ and $V(t)$—as in Fig. 15-15.

FIGURE 15-15

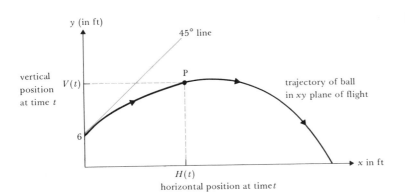

FIGURE 15-16

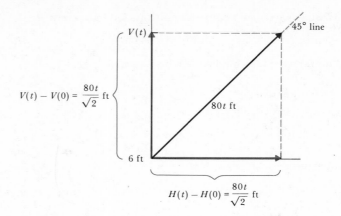

At the instant of thrust, $t = 0$, these position functions have "initial values"

$$H(0) = 0 \text{ ft} \quad \text{and} \quad V(0) = 6 \text{ ft}. \tag{10}$$

How about their initial velocities? Let's suppose that for *very small* times t' after the instant of thrust, the ball still flies very close to the 45° line. With an initial velocity of 80 ft/sec along that line the ball should advance approximately $80t$ ft along that line in t sec — again, for *very small* t. See Fig. 15-16. Since the (black) hypotenuse in Fig. 15-16 is related to the (green) sides by a factor of $\sqrt{2}$, we should expect a purely horizontal position change and a purely vertical position change of approximately

$$H(t) - H(0) = \frac{80t}{\sqrt{2}} \text{ ft} \quad \text{and} \quad V(t) - V(0) = \frac{80t}{\sqrt{2}} \text{ ft} \tag{11}$$

during the short time t after thrust. If we divide the position changes in (11) by the time lapse t, and then think of letting t tend to zero, we can conclude that

$$H'(0) = \frac{80}{\sqrt{2}} \text{ ft/sec} \quad \text{and} \quad V'(0) = \frac{80}{\sqrt{2}} \text{ ft/sec}. \tag{12}$$

What else can we say about $H(t)$ and $V(t)$? Since "gravity" doesn't affect the horizontal aspects of motion — then shouldn't the *horizontal velocity* $H'(t)$ remain constant $(= 80/\sqrt{2}$ ft/sec$)$ — at least until the ball hits the ground? Suppose so. (Isaac Newton did too.) Then by the "neck-and-neck race argument," we must have

$$H(t) = \frac{80}{\sqrt{2}}t \qquad \text{for } 0 \leqslant t \leqslant T \text{ (impact time)} \tag{13}$$

— because the function $(80/\sqrt{2})t$ has the same output 0 at $t = 0$ as does H, and shares the same constant derivative value $80/\sqrt{2}$.

Matters are different for the vertical position function $V(t)$: As I argued in Sec. 7.5, V should have an acceleration due to "gravity" of approximately

$$V''(t) = -32 \text{ ft/sec}^2. \tag{14}$$

(I've included a negative sign because the attraction between earth and ball *retards* the ball's positive upward velocity.) What can we conclude about the *vertical velocity* function $V'(t)$? Note that the function $f(t) = -32t + 80/\sqrt{2}$ shares the same output $80/\sqrt{2}$ with $V'(t)$ at $t = 0$, and shares the same constant derivative value -32 for $t > 0$. Hence by the "neck-and-neck race argument," V' and f must be identical:

$$V'(t) = -32t + \frac{80}{\sqrt{2}} \text{ ft/sec} \qquad \text{for } 0 \leq t \leq T. \tag{15}$$

And $V(t)$ itself? What function will share with V the initial value $V(0) = 6$ and the derivative values in (15)? How about

$$g(t) = -16t^2 + \frac{80}{\sqrt{2}} t + 6?$$

Check that it does. Hence V and g are identical:

$$V(t) = -16t^2 + \frac{80}{\sqrt{2}} t + 6 \qquad \text{for } 0 \leq t \leq T. \tag{16}$$

We've arrived at explicit formulas for H and V!

When will the ball hit the ground? At the time $T > 0$ for which $V(T) = 0$. Namely,

$$V(T) = -16T^2 + \frac{80}{\sqrt{2}} T + 6 = 0.$$

Check via the quadratic formula that T must be

$$T = \frac{1}{16}\left(\frac{1}{\sqrt{2}} + \sqrt{896}\right) = 3.64 \text{ sec (approximately)}.$$

The horizontal distance which the ball covers in the T seconds until it hits the ground must be

$$H(T) = \frac{80}{\sqrt{2}} T = 206 \text{ ft (approximately)}.$$

Finally what about the shape of the ball's trajectory? At any time $t \leq T$, the coordinates of the ball in its xy plane of flight are just

$$x = H(t) = \frac{80}{\sqrt{2}} t \quad \text{and} \quad y = V(t) = -16t^2 + \frac{80}{\sqrt{2}} t + 6. \tag{17}$$

If we write $t = \sqrt{2}x/80$ and substitute that expression into the formula for y, we can get the equation

$$y = -\frac{x^2}{200} + x + 6. \tag{18}$$

All points (x, y) on the trajectory *must* satisfy this equation. (I invite you to investigate its geometric aspects further in doing Problem 7 of Sec. 15-11.)

If you had wanted the ball to land, say, 100 ft away, how should you have modified your angle or speed of throw? (Do Problem 8 of Sec. 15.11.)

15.10 ANTIDERIVATIVES

What were the main technical tasks in the food consumption and ball throwing examples just above? To find a function $F(t)$ whose derivative $F'(t)$ would equal a given function $f(t)$, such as $f(t) = 2e^t$ or $f(t) = -32t + 80/\sqrt{2}$. For convenience, people have given a name to a function whose derivative is a given function f:

Definition II: Suppose that a function f is defined on some interval $[a, b]$. If F is some other function with the property that

$$F'(x) = f(x) \qquad \text{for all } x \text{ in } [a, b], \tag{1}$$

then let's call F an *antiderivative of f (on $[a, b]$)*.

Note that if a given function f does have an antiderivative F, then it must have *infinitely many* antiderivatives: For any constant C, the function $G(x) = F(x) + C$ must also be an antiderivative:

$$G'(x) = (F(x) + C)' = F'(x) + 0 = f(x). \tag{2}$$

Can there still be other antiderivatives G for f, not of the form $F(x) + C$? No! The same reasoning as for the "neck-and-neck race argument" shows that any two antiderivatives F and G for the same function f can differ *only* by a constant: Their difference $H(x) = G(x) - F(x)$ must have derivative

$$H'(x) = G'(x) - F'(x) = f(x) - f(x) = 0 \qquad \text{on } [a, b]. \tag{3}$$

Hence

$$H(x) = G(x) - F(x) = G(a) - F(a) = \text{a constant } C$$

or

$$G(x) = F(x) + C \qquad \text{for all } x \text{ in } [a, b]. \tag{4}$$

Theorem H (on "antiderivatives"): If F and G are antiderivatives for the same function f on an interval $[a, b]$—that is, if

$$F'(x) = G'(x) \qquad \text{on } [a, b],$$

then $G(x) = F(x) + C$ for all x in $[a, b]$, for some constant C.

This result still leaves a question: *need a given function f*—say, one with a nice smooth graph—*necessarily have even* ONE *antiderivative?* For example, need there be a function $F(x)$ whose derivative will be $f(x) = 1/(1 + \log_e x)$ on the interval $[1, 2]$?

I'll return to this question in a later section. Meanwhile, in connection with a particular problem—such as the one on food consumption just above—you might have hopes that an antiderivative F *does* exist for a given function f, and that finding it will help solve the problem. How in practice, should you search for F? What other way is there but to try to use the properties of derivatives *backward*?

The very name "antiderivative" was designed to suggest a reverse procedure. I've indicated backward versions of the main derivative rules in the following

Table of rules for finding antiderivatives

A function h of the form	will have an antiderivative H of the form	
Particular functions:		
$(p+1)x^p \quad (p \neq -1)$	x^{p+1}	
or		
$x^p \quad (p \neq -1)$	$\dfrac{1}{p+1}x^{p+1}$	
e^x	e^x	
$e^{ax} \quad (a \neq 0)$	$\dfrac{1}{a}e^{ax}$	
$\dfrac{1}{x}$	$\log_e x$	
General functions:		
$cF'(x)$	$cF(x)$	
$F'+G'$	$F+G$	
$F'G+FG'$	$F \cdot G$	("Leibnitz's product rule" backward)
$-\dfrac{G'}{G^2}$	$\dfrac{1}{G}$	
$\dfrac{F'G-G'F}{G^2}$	$\dfrac{F}{G}$	
$G'(F(x)) \cdot F'(x)$	$G(F(x))$	(the "chain rule" backward)
Special applications of the "chain rule":		
$cG'(cx)$	$G(cx)$	(the "chain rule" with $F(x) \equiv cx$)
$[F(x)]^p F'(x)(p \neq -1)$	$\dfrac{1}{p+1}[F(x)]^{p+1}$	(the "chain rule" with $G'(y) = y^p$)
$e^{F(x)}F'(x)$	$e^{F(x)}$	(the "chain rule" with $G'(y) = e^y$)
$\dfrac{1}{F(x)}F'(x)$	$\log_e F(x)$	$\left(\text{the "chain rule" with } G'(y) = \dfrac{1}{y}\right)$

In a particular problem, the main practical task in finding antiderivatives is to *recognize* parts of a given function h as having a usable form "$F'(x)$," "$G(x)$," or the like. Here are examples:

EXAMPLE 1. Write $h(x) = 5x^3$ as $h(x) = (5/4)(4x^3)$ to recognize an antiderivative $H(x) = (5/4)x^4$. As a check, differentiate:

$$H'(x) = (5/4)(x^4)' = (5/4)(4x^3) = 5x^3.$$

EXAMPLE 2. Write $h(x) = 5/x - 7x^2$ as $h(x) = 5(1/x) - (7/3)(3x^2)$ to recognize an antiderivative $H(x) = 5\log_e x - (7/3)x^3$.

EXAMPLE 3. One possible way to find an antiderivative for $h(x) = 2x(x^2+2)^{27}$ would be to write h out as a polynomial of degree 55 and treat each of its terms separately—which might take half a day. Far less tedious would be to recognize the inside expression $F(x) = x^2 + 2$ as an antiderivative of the factor $F'(x) = 2x$. F itself appears as being fed into a power function $G'(y) = y^{27}$, which in turn has an antiderivative $G(y) = (1/28)y^{28}$.

So h has the form

$$h(x) = G'(F(x)) \cdot F'(x). \tag{5}$$

Using the "chain rule" backward, we can conclude that

$$H(x) = G(F(x)) = \frac{1}{28}(x^2+2)^{28}$$

is an antiderivative for h.

How about $k(x) = 5x(3x^2+2)^{27}$? Here the inside expression $F(x)$ has $F'(x) = 6x$. So let's just write

$$k(x) = \left(\frac{5}{6}\right)(6x)(3x^2+2)^{27}$$

to recognize as antiderivative the function

$$K(x) = \left(\frac{5}{6}\right)\frac{1}{28}(3x^2+2)^{28}.$$

EXAMPLE 4. $h(x) = 2xe^{3x} + 3x^2e^{3x}$ has the form

$$h(x) = F'(x)G(x) + F(x)G'(x),$$

where $F(x) = x^2$, $F'(x) = 2x$, $G(x) = e^{3x}$, and $G'(x) = 3e^{3x}$. Hence, using "Leibnitz's product rule" backward, we can recognize

$$H(x) = F(x)G(x) = x^2e^{3x}$$

as an antiderivative for $h(x)$.

Antidifferentiation "by parts": Long ago someone thought of using "Leibnitz's product rule"

$$(FG)' = F'G + FG' \tag{6}$$

not only backward but *sideways*—in the rearranged form

$$F'G = (FG)' - FG'. \tag{7}$$

Suppose that you can recognize a given function h as a product $h(x) = F'(x)G(x)$. Following the addition rule for derivatives *backward*, we can conclude from (7) that

an antiderivative of $F'G$
= an antiderivative of $(FG)'$ — an antiderivative of FG'. (8)

Now the function FG is an antiderivative for its own derivative $(FG)'$. Hence we can simplify (8), and write what has been called

A RULE FOR ANTIDIFFERENTIATION "BY PARTS":

> an antiderivative of $F'G$
> = $F \cdot G$ — an antiderivative for FG' (9)

What good is such a rule? Sometimes it's just easier to succeed in finding an antiderivative for FG' than for an originally given $F'G$ — as in the following

EXAMPLE 5. $h(x) = e^{ax}x$, where $a \neq 0$. If we think of the factor e^{ax} as $F'(x)$, it will have antiderivative $F(x) = (1/a)e^{ax}$. The remaining factor $G(x) = x$ has the easy derivative $G'(x) = 1$. Hence an antiderivative of h will be

$F \cdot G$ — an antiderivative of FG'

$$= \left(\frac{1}{a}e^{ax}\right)(x) - \text{an antiderivative of } \left(\frac{1}{a}e^{ax}\right)(1).$$ (10)

The product $FG' = (1/a)(e^{ax})(1) = (1/a^2)(ae^{ax})$ has antiderivative $(1/a^2)e^{ax}$. So finally, the function

$$H(x) = \frac{1}{a}e^{ax}x - \frac{1}{a^2}e^{ax}$$
$$= \frac{1}{a}e^{ax}\left(x - \frac{1}{a}\right)$$ (11)

is an antiderivative of $h(x) = e^{ax}x$. Would you have guessed it?

Note that if I had chosen in the other order, taking x as $F'(x)$ and e^{ax} as $G(x)$, I would have been faced with finding an antiderivative for $FG' = (1/2)x^2(ae^{ax}) = (a/2)x^2e^{ax}$ — a more complicated function than the original h. So success with the procedure of antidifferentiation "by parts" — if possible at all — depends on making a wise choice.

Some people find such searching for antiderivatives a challenge to their ingenuity and to their powers of pattern recognition and free association. Some view it as a game. I invite you to try your hand at it in doing the problems of the next section.

I'll record here an unfortunately confusing notation for antiderivatives which however has long been in use and which you may see elsewhere. People often use the symbol

$$\int f(x)\,dx$$ (12)

to denote an antiderivative function $F(x)$ of a given function $f(x)$. The symbols $\int$ and dx which appear fore and aft of the $f(x)$ in (12) are *nothing but symbols*; and an expression such as

$$\int (x^3 + 5)\,dx = \frac{1}{4}x^4 + 5x$$

means nothing more nor less than the statement: "the function $\frac{1}{4}x^4 + 5x$ is an antiderivative of the function $x^3 + 5$." (And the latter statement, again, means nothing more nor less than that

$$(\tfrac{1}{4}x^4 + 5x)' = x^3 + 5.)$$

Here is how several backward differentiation rules look in terms of the $\int dx$ symbolism:

The addition rule:

$$\int (f + g)\, dx = \int f\, dx + \int g\, dx$$

or

$$\int (F' + G')\, dx = \int F'\, dx + \int G'\, dx$$
$$= F + G$$

The "chain rule":

$$\int G'(F(x))F'(x)\, dx = G(F(x))$$

The rule on antidifferentiation "by parts":

$$\int F'G\, dx = FG - \int FG'\, dx.$$

15.11 PROBLEMS ON ANTIDERIVATIVES

°1. Find antiderivatives for the following functions. (Consider the domains as consisting of all values x for which the formulas make sense.)

(a) $f(x) = 4x^3 + 2x^{-1/2}$

   Sample reasoning: $\int f(x)\, dx = 4\int x^3\, dx + 2\int x^{-1/2}\, dx = 4\int x^3\, dx + 4\int \tfrac{1}{2}x^{-1/2}\, dx = 4(x^4/4) + 4x^{1/2} = x^4 + 4x^{1/2}.$

(b) $f(x) = 2x^{-3}$ (c) $f(x) = x^{-3} + x^{-1/2}$

(d) $f(x) = \left(x - \dfrac{1}{x}\right)^2$ (e) $f(x) = \dfrac{1 - x^2}{x^2}$

(f) $f(x) = \dfrac{8}{x^5}$ (g) $f(x) = \dfrac{1}{\sqrt{x + 4}}$

(h) $f(x) = \dfrac{x^2}{2} - \dfrac{2}{x^2}$ (i) $f(x) = x^2(x^2 + 1)^3$ $2x\left(x^2 + 1\right)^3$

(j) $f(x) = \dfrac{x^2}{\sqrt{x^3 + 8}}$

   Sample reasoning: Note that $g(x) = x^3 + 8$ has $g'(x) = 3x^2$ and $h(y) = \sqrt{y}$ has $h'(y) = 1/2\sqrt{y}$.
   Write

$$f(x) = \frac{2}{3}\left(\frac{1}{2\sqrt{x^3 + 8}}\right)(3x^2),$$

then

$$\int f(x)\, dx = \frac{2}{3} \int h'(g(x))g'(x)\, dx$$

$$= \frac{2}{3} \int \frac{1}{2\sqrt{x^3+8}} (3x^2)\, dx$$

$$= \frac{2}{3} \sqrt{x^3+8},$$

by the "chain rule" for antidifferentiation.

(k) $f(x) = x^2 + 1 + 2x(x+3)$.

Sample reasoning: Note that $(x^2+1)' = 2x$ and $(x+3)' = 1$, and recall that $(gh)' = g'h + gh'$. Hence

$$\int [1 \cdot (x^2+1) + (x+3) \cdot 2x]\, dx = (x+3)(x^2+1).$$

(l) $f(x) = (x^3+1)6x^2$ (m) $f(x) = \dfrac{1}{(x+2)^2}$

(n) $f(x) = \dfrac{x}{\sqrt{x^2+1}}$ (o) $f(x) = \dfrac{6x(x^2+1) - (3x^2+2)(2x)}{(x^2+1)^2}$

(p) $f(x) = \dfrac{4x^2}{\sqrt{x^3+8}}$ (q) $f(x) = \dfrac{e^x}{(e^x+1)^3}$

(r) $f(x) = \dfrac{2}{x}(\log_e x)^7$ (s) $f(x) = \dfrac{x^2 - 2x + 1}{(x-1)^4}$

(t) $f(x) = \dfrac{x^3}{\sqrt{a^4+x^4}}$ (u) $f(x) = \dfrac{x^2 - 2x + 2}{(x-1)^4}$

(v) $f(x) = \dfrac{x^2+1}{\sqrt{x^3+3x}}$ (w) $f(x) = \dfrac{2x+3}{\sqrt{x^2+3x}}$

(x) $f(x) = x(a+bx^3)^2$ (y) $f(x) = \dfrac{x^{n-1}}{\sqrt{a+bx^n}}$

(z) $f(x) = 3xe^{x^2}$

°2. Find the indicated antiderivatives (assuming domains for which the formulas make sense).

(a) $\int (x^{-1/2} + x^{3/2})\, dx$ (b) $\int (x^{3/2} + 5\sqrt{x} - 3)\, dx$

(c) $\int (x+a)^{3/2}\, dx$ (d) $\int \sqrt{x}(3x-2)\, dx$

(e) $\int x^2\sqrt{3x^3+9}\, dx$ (f) $\int \dfrac{x^2+2x+1}{\sqrt{x}}\, dx$

(g) $\int (\sqrt{a} - \sqrt{x})^2\, dx$ (h) $\int \dfrac{(\sqrt{a} - \sqrt{x})^2}{\sqrt{x}}\, dx$

(i) $\int x^{n-1}\sqrt{a+bx^n}\, dx$ (j) $\int \sqrt{2-x}\, dx$

(k) $\int (2x+1)\sqrt{x^2+x+1}\, dx$

°3. Use the rule on antidifferentiation "by parts" to find antiderivatives for each of the following functions. (Consider the domains to consist of all values x for which the formulas make sense.)

(a) $h(x) = x^2 e^x$

Sample reasoning: $h(x) = F'(x)G(x)$ where $F'(x) = e^x$ and $G(x) = x^2$. Hence

$$\int h(x)\, dx = \int F'(x)G(x)\, dx$$

$$= F(x)G(x) - \int F(x)G'(x)\, dx = x^2 e^x - \int e^x 2x\, dx$$

$$= x^2 e^x - 2 \int e^x x\, dx = x^2 e^x - 2[e^x(x-1)]$$

(See Example 5 of Sec. 15.10.)

$$= x^2 e^x - 2e^x x + 2e^x = e^x(x^2 - 2x + 2).$$

(b) $h(x) = 4xe^{5x}$

(c) $h(x) = (3x-2)e^{-x}$

(d) $h(x) = (2x^2 - 4x + 3)e^{2x}$

(e) $h(x) = x \log_e x$

(f) $h(x) = \log_e x \;(= (\log_e x) \cdot 1)$

(g) $h(x) = x \log_e (x+1)$

(h) $h(x) = x^3 \log_e x$

(i) $h(x) = (ax + b)\log_e x,$ a and b are constants

(j) $h(x) = x^2 \log_e (x+1)$

(k) $h(x) = \log_e (x^2 + 2)$

(l) $h(x) = x^2 e^x$

*(m) $h(x) = x^n e^x$

4. Show that $\int (af + bg)\, dx = a \int f\, dx + b \int g\, dx$ if a and b are constants.

5. Can you find an antiderivative for the function $f(x) = |x|$ on the domain $[-1, 1]$? On the domain $[0, 1]$?

6. Suppose that we start out at noon with a colony of bacteria weighing 5 g. Suppose that a bacterium has an average lifetime of 45 minutes before splitting, and that during its lifetime the bacterium will eat approximately twice its own weight in sugar. How much sugar will the colony consume by 6 p.m.?

7. Investigate the graph of the function

$$f(x) = -\frac{x^2}{200} + x + 6$$

which relates the x and y coordinates (at a given instant) of a ball thrown from a height of 6 ft above ground with an initial velocity of 80 ft/sec in a direction 45° from the horizontal—such as I discussed in Example 2 of Sec. 15.9. Find the intervals on the x axis for which the function is increasing and for which it is decreasing. Also determine the convexity or concavity of the function. In what sense does the graph of this function picture the actual flight of the ball?

8. Suppose that I throw a ball from a height of 6 feet above ground with an initial velocity of c ft/sec in a direction 45° from the horizontal.

(a) Show that the horizontal and vertical distances are given by

$$H(t) = \frac{ct}{\sqrt{2}} \text{ and } V(t) = -16t^2 + \frac{ct}{\sqrt{2}} + 6.$$

(b) Use the quadratic formula to find the time $T > 0$ when the ball will hit the ground.

(c) Find the horizontal distance $H(T)$ which the ball covers in the T seconds until it hits the ground.

(d) For what value of c will $H(T) = 100$?

(e) For a given value of c, does the ball spend more time going up or going down?

(f) How does the velocity at impact time T compare with the initial velocity c?

(g) If I change my angle of throw to 30° from the horizontal and if I throw it with initial velocity 80 ft/sec, how far away will the ball land?

(h) Can I make the ball land 100 ft away if I throw it with initial velocity of 80 ft/sec at an angle of 45° but I change the height from which I release the ball?

9. Suppose that during a time interval $[t_1, t_2]$, the thrust of a rocket ship tapers off in such a way that the acceleration of the ship along a straight line is of the form $f''(t) = ae^{-bt}$ ft/sec², where a and b are constants. Write an expression for the position $f(t)$ of the ship along the line at times t in $[t_1, t_2]$, in terms of the position $f(t_1)$ and velocity $f'(t_1)$ of the ship at time t_1 and the constants a and b.

10. Suppose that you want to shoot an arrow to the sun. At what speed should it leave the bowstring?

The arrow must overcome gravity and air resistance. The latter is not a negligible factor—but let's neglect it in this problem and consider a model wherein only gravity acts. Think of the arrow as moving outward along a straight line directed from the center of the earth, and let $f(t)$ denote its position along that line at t seconds after launch. Take $f(0) = 4000 \times 5280$ ft, the approximate radius of the earth. At any instant t the arrow will have velocity $v(t) = f'(t)$. We have to find an appropriate value for $v(0)$. You may recall that in Example 1 of Sec. 7.5, I discussed a physical model for the gravitational attraction between the earth and a body falling off a cliff. If we adopt the same kind of model here, then we can suppose that at each instant of its flight the arrow's acceleration will be inversely proportional to the square of its distance from the center of the earth. That is,

$$v'(t) = -\frac{K}{[f(t)]^2}. \qquad (*)$$

(Since the direction of motion is outward from the earth, I've used a minus sign in (*) to indicate the decelerating effect of gravity.) We can evaluate the positive constant K by noting that acceleration is approximately -32 ft/sec² at the surface of the earth; that is, when $f(0) = 4000 \times 5280$ ft. Thus

$$K = 32(4000)^2(5280)^2 \qquad \text{(in units of ft}^3\text{/sec}^2\text{)}.$$

Since the sun is so very far away we might approximate the original problem of getting the arrow there by seeking an initial velocity which will guarantee that the arrow *must keep on going* no matter at what distance r it may be from the center of the earth. That is, for any $r > r_0 = 4000 \times 5280$ ft, the arrow's velocity at that distance — call it $V(r)$ — must be *positive*. How can we learn about velocity $V(r)$ as a function of distances r from the relationship (*) involving velocity $v(t)$ as a function of times t? Recall that distance $r = f(t)$ for $t \geq 0$. Let $[0, T\rangle$ be an interval during which the arrow keeps moving outward: that is, during which $v(t) = f'(t) > 0$. (We'll try to pick an initial velocity so that we can have $T = \text{``}\infty\text{''}$.)

(a) Say why $f(t)$ on $[0, T\rangle$ must have an inverse function — call it $g(r)$ — which announces the time $t = g(r)$ at which the arrow will reach distance r.

(b) Say why for any t_1 in $[0, T\rangle$, and corresponding $r_1 = f(t_1)$, we must have

$$\frac{dg}{dr}(r_1) = \frac{1}{v(t_1)}. \tag{†}$$

(c) Say why

$$V(r_1) = v(g(r_1))$$

and

$$\frac{dV}{dr}(r_1) = v'(t_1)\frac{1}{v(t_1)} = v'(t_1)\frac{1}{V(r_1)}. \tag{‡}$$

(d) Substitute (‡) into (*) to get

$$V(r)\frac{dV}{dr} = \frac{1}{2}\frac{dV^2}{dr} = -\frac{K}{r^2}, \tag{**}$$

for all distances r corresponding to times t in $[0, T\rangle$; that is, for all r in $[r_0, r_T\rangle$, where $r_0 = f(0) = 4000 \times 5280$ ft, and $r_T = f(T)$. Show why part (d) implies that

$$V^2(r) = \frac{2K}{r} + \left[V^2(r_0) - \frac{2K}{r_0}\right], \tag{***}$$

for any r in $[r_0, r_T\rangle$. (Compare the values at $r = r_0$, and the derivatives of both sides of (***), and apply the "neck-and-neck argument.")

(e) Show why $v(0) = V(r_0) = \sqrt{\dfrac{2K}{r_0}}$

$$= \sqrt{\frac{2 \cdot 32\,(4000)^2(5280)^2}{(4000)(5280)}}$$

$$= 36{,}700 \text{ ft/sec (approx.)}$$

$$= \text{almost 7 miles/sec}$$

is the *smallest* possible value for the arrow's initial velocity in order that its velocity $V(r)$ be positive at *all* distances $r > 0$ from the earth. Note that this result is independent of the weight of the arrow.

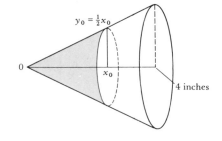

11. Calculate the volume of the ice cream cone indicated in the figure—using the method of Sec. 7.6 involving the *rate of change* of the volume of a (shaded) cap.

12. Use the method of Sec. 7.6 (and Problems 5 and 6 in Sec. 7.7) to calculate the area lying under the graph of $f(x) = e^x$ and above the interval $[0, 1]$.

**13. In Fig. 7-15 and Sec. 7.8, I partially described a strange function —call it $C(x)$—invented by Georg Cantor. At $x = 0$, $C(0) = 0$; and $C'(x) = 0$ over each of infinitely many open (green) subintervals of $[0, 1]$ *whose lengths added to 1, the length of the entire domain* $[0, 1]$. The same properties hold for the simplest of functions, the constant function $D(x) \equiv 0$. Yet I claimed that $C(1) = 1$; whereas $D(1) = 0$. Thus if $C(x)$ can be defined precisely on $[0, 1]$, it will provide an example to show that the "neck-and-neck race argument" of Sec. 15.9 *need not apply* if $C'(x) = D'(x)$ for "almost all" inputs x (in the sense of length), but requires a stronger hypothesis, such as the one (in Sec. 15.9) that $C'(x) = D'(x)$ for *all* x.

Here is a complete definition of the function $C(x)$:

Express each input x in $[0, 1]$ as an "infinite series"

$$x = \frac{a_1}{3^1} + \frac{a_2}{3^2} + \frac{a_3}{3^3} + \frac{a_4}{3^4} + \cdots + \frac{a_n}{3^n} + \cdots, \tag{*}$$

where each $a_i = 0$ or 1 or 2. (See Sec. 10.6 for the meaning of such a "series.") Then define

$$C(x) = \frac{(\frac{1}{2}a_1)}{2^1} + \frac{(\frac{1}{2}a_2)}{2^2} + \frac{(\frac{1}{2}a_3)}{2^3} + \frac{(\frac{1}{2}a_4)}{2^4} + \cdots + \frac{(\frac{1}{2}a_n)}{2^n} + \cdots \tag{**}$$

if all the $a_2 = 0$ or 2 (no 1's). Otherwise define

$$C(x) = \frac{(\frac{1}{2}a_1)}{2^1} + \frac{(\frac{1}{2}a_2)}{2^2} + \cdots + \frac{(\frac{1}{2}a_{N-1})}{2^{N-1}} + \frac{a_N}{2^N} \tag{***}$$

if a_N is the first $a_i = 1$.

(a) Check that (***) defines $C(x)$ just as in Fig. 7-15 for inputs in the infinitely many open green subintervals. Thus (**) defines C for inputs x *not* in any green subinterval— including end points of the subintervals.

(b) Check that end points of the subintervals are precisely those x which can be expressed in (*) either with $a_i \neq 1$ for all i and $a_i = 2$ for all $i \geqslant$ some N; or with $a_i \neq 1$ for all $i <$ some N, $a_N = 1$, and $a_i = 0$ for all $i > N$. Check that (**) and (***) give the same value for $C(x)$ if x is such an end point.

(c) Check that C is continuous at each x in $[0, 1]$.

(d) Check that $C'(x) = 0$ at each x inside an open (green) subinterval.

(e) Does $C'(x)$ exist for x which are not inside open subintervals or end points of them?

(f) Set up a one-to-one correspondence between $[0, 1]$ and the set T of all x in $[0, 1]$ which can be expressed in (*) with $a_i \neq 1$ for all i. What does such a correspondence say about the "size" of T? What can we conclude from Sec. 7.8 about the length of T?

15.12   SUMMARY OF CHAPTER 15

THE MEAN VALUE THEOREM: If a function f has derivatives $f'(x)$ at all inputs in an interval $[a, b]$, then there must be some input c with $a < c < b$ such that $f'(c) = [f(b) - f(a)]/(b - a)$, or equivalently, $f(b) - f(a) = f'(c)(b - a)$.
(Sec. 15.1)

THEOREM ("INCREASE CONTROLS DERIVATIVE SIGN"): Suppose that f is a differentiable function on the interval $[a, b]$.

If f is constant on $[a, b]$, then $f'(x) = 0$, for all x in $[a, b]$.

If f is increasing on $[a, b]$, then $f'(x) \geq 0$, for all x in $[a, b]$.

If f is decreasing on $[a, b]$, then $f'(x) \leq 0$, for all x in $[a, b]$.
(Sec. 15.2)

THEOREM ("DERIVATIVE SIGN CONTROLS INCREASE"): Suppose that f is a differentiable function on the interval $[a, b]$.

If $f'(x) = 0$ for all x in $[a, b]$, then f is constant on $[a, b]$.

If $f'(x) \geq 0$ for all x in $[a, b]$, then f is increasing on $[a, b]$. Moreover, if $f'(x) > 0$ for all x in the open interval $\langle a, b \rangle$, then f is *strictly* increasing on $[a, b]$.

If $f'(x) \leq 0$ for all x in $[a, b]$, then f is decreasing on $[a, b]$. Moreover, if $f'(x) < 0$ for all x in the open interval $\langle a, b \rangle$, then f is *strictly* decreasing on $[a, b]$.
(Sec. 15.2)

THEOREM ("AT THE SIGN OF THE SECOND DERIVATIVE"): Suppose that f is differentiable on $[a, b]$, that $f'(x_0) = 0$ at some input x_0 with $a < x_0 < b$, and that $f''(x_0)$ exists.

If $f(x_0)$ is a relative maximum, then $f''(x_0) \leq 0$;   and
if $f(x_0)$ is a relative minimum, then $f''(x_0) \geq 0$.
Conversely,
if $f''(x_0) < 0$, then $f(x_0)$ is a relative maximum; and
if $f''(x_0) > 0$, then $f(x_0)$ is a relative minimum.
(Sec. 15.3)

DEFINITIONS: Let's call a function f *convex* on an interval $[a, b]$ if, given any two inputs $x_1 < x_2$ in $[a, b]$, we have

$$f(x) \leq L(x) \qquad \text{for all } x \text{ in the subinterval } [x_1, x_2],$$

where $L(x)$ is the unique linear function with outputs $L(x_1) = f(x_1)$

and $L(x_2) = f(x_2)$. Let's call f *concave* if the above inequality is always reversed: $f(x) \geqslant L(x)$.
(Sec. 15.3)

THEOREM (ON "CONVEXITY"): If $f''(x) \geqslant 0$ for all x in an interval $[a, b]$, then f is convex there. If $f''(x) \leqslant 0$ for all x in $[a, b]$, then f is concave there.
(Sec. 15.3)

For a program for sketching graphs and finding maxima and minima, see Sec. 15.5.

THEOREM (ON "GUARANTEED ERROR ESTIMATES"): Suppose that a function f has $|f''(x)| \leqslant B$ for all x in some interval $[a, b]$. If x_0 and x_1 are in $[a, b]$, then the "linear approximation"

$$L(x_1) = f(x_0) + f'(x_0)(x_1 - x_0)$$

for the output $f(x_1)$ has error magnitude

$$|f(x_1) - L(x_1)| \leqslant B(x_1 - x_0)^2.$$

(Sec. 15.7)

THEOREM (THE "NECK-AND-NECK RACE ARGUMENT"): If $f(a) = g(a)$ and $f'(x) = g'(x)$ for all x in $[a, b]$, then $f(x) = g(x)$ for all x in $[a, b]$.
(Sec. 15.9)

DEFINITION: Suppose that a function f is defined on some interval $[a, b]$. If F is some other function with the property that

$$F'(x) = f(x) \qquad \text{for all } x \text{ in } [a, b],$$

then let's call F an *antiderivative of f* (on $[a, b]$).
(Optional notation: $F(x) = \int f(x)\, dx$.)
(Sec. 15.10)

REMARK: if a given function f has an antiderivative F, then any function $G(x) = F(x) + C$, where C is a constant, must also be an antiderivative for f.

THEOREM (ON "ANTIDERIVATIVES"): If F and G are antiderivatives for the same function f on an interval $[a, b]$—that is, if $F'(x) = G'(x)$ on $[a, b]$, then $G(x) = F(x) + C$ for all x in $[a, b]$, for some constant C.
(Sec. 15.10)

For guidelines in recognizing antiderivatives, see the Table in Sec. 15.10. For the particular method of *antidifferentiation by parts*,

an antiderivative of $F'G$
$= FG -$ an antiderivative of FG',

see (9) in Sec. 15.10.

differential equations
and trig functions

In this chapter I'll discuss several examples of how to find functions which are related to their own derivatives—by equations such as $f' = cf$ and $f'' = cf$. Such functions can describe quantities which grow, decay, or oscillate as time goes on.

To help solve the equations, I'll extend our catalog of differentiable functions to include trigonometric functions and their inverses.

16.1 THE PROBABILITY THAT YOU WON'T BE STRUCK DEAD BY A METEORITE WHILE WALKING ON THE MOON

Suppose that by checking sunspots and other indicators, you can arrange your visit to avoid major meteorite showers. Nevertheless, meteorites of various sizes may still arrive to the surface of the moon at "random" times. If one of them strikes your space suit with sufficient momentum, it will penetrate and be lethal. Suppose that you step onto the moon's surface at noon. What can we say about the probability $p(t)$ that you will *not* be hit by a lethal meteorite during the first t hours of your visit? For a stay of zero length we can suppose $p(0) = 1$. But how will $p(t)$ decrease as time t goes on?

To answer such questions, let's try to capture—in a mathematical model—what we might mean by the lethal meteorites arriving "at random" to a given surface, such as a space suit.

First, let's think of any two nonoverlapping intervals of time— even adjacent intervals as in Fig. 16-1. Intuitively, shouldn't we mean by "randomness" of arrival that *the number of lethal meteor arrivals in either one of the time intervals is* INDEPENDENT *of the number of arrivals in the other*? In Chap. 3, I suggested that we might think of a result such as "i arrivals during a certain time interval" as represented by a subset—call it A_i—of some large total list of possible outcomes.

FIGURE 16-1

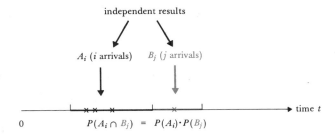

independent results

A_i (*i* arrivals) B_j (*j* arrivals)

time *t*

0        $P(A_i \cap B_j) \ = \ P(A_i) \cdot P(B_j)$

Although such a list might well be infinitely large for the present model, let's suppose that we can assign probability numbers $P(A)$ to its subsets such as A_i, and that these numbers will satisfy the standard rules which I developed for probabilities in Chapter 3. In particular, subsets A_i and B_j representing *independent* results — as in Fig. 16-1 — should have

$$P(A_i \cap B_j) = P(A_i) \cdot P(B_j). \tag{1}$$

As a second basic feature for a model of lethal meteorite arrival, how about supposing that *the number of arrivals in a time interval depends only on its* LENGTH — not on when it begins? See Fig. 16-2.

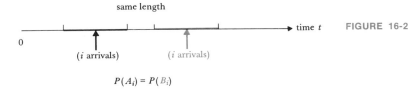

same length

time *t*

0

(*i* arrivals)   (*i* arrivals)

$P(A_i) = P(B_i)$

FIGURE 16-2

More specifically, for *very short* intervals, does your intuitive feeling of "randomness" suggest that the probability of *exactly one* arrival during an interval should be approximately *proportional* to the length of the interval? Shouldn't an arrival during 2 milliseconds be about twice as likely as an arrival during 1 millisecond? If so, let's suppose that, for some positive constant of proportionality λ,

$$\left. \begin{array}{l} \text{the probability of} \\ \text{\small EXACTLY ONE}\text{ arrival} \\ \text{during an interval} \\ \text{of length } T \end{array} \right\} = \lambda T + e(T), \tag{2}$$

where $e(T)$ represents approximation error. We might suppose that for shorter and shorter intervals, the error gets smaller and smaller relative to the main term in (2), namely

$$\lim_{T \to 0} \frac{e(T)}{\lambda T} = 0. \tag{3}$$

Finally, how about supposing that the probability of *more than one* arrival during an interval of length T — call it $m(T)$ — gets smaller and smaller for shorter and shorter intervals even as compared with the probability of exactly one arrival? That is,

$$\lim_{T \to 0} \frac{m(T)}{\lambda T} = 0. \tag{4}$$

Since the probabilities of mutually exclusive results *add* (recall Sec. 3.1), note that the expressions (2) and (4) together yield

$$\left.\begin{array}{l} \text{the probability of} \\ \text{ONE or MORE arrivals} \\ \text{during an interval} \\ \text{of length } T \end{array}\right\} = [\lambda T + e(T)] + m(T). \tag{5}$$

Now, what can we deduce from such assumptions as to the behavior of the function $p(t)$, the probability that you will not be lethally hit before t hours ellapse? Why not ask how $p(t)$ changes between some instant s and an instant t very shortly later? I've analyzed the possibilities in Fig. 16-3.

FIGURE 16-3

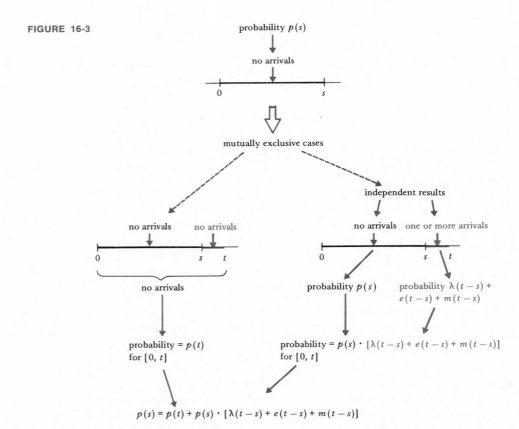

In Fig. 16-3, the mutually exclusive results,

"no arrivals at all during the (half-open) interval $[0, t\rangle$,"   (6)

and

"no arrivals during $[0, s\rangle$, then *some* arrival during $[s, t\rangle$—that is, a *first* arrival during $[s, t\rangle$,"

have probabilities which *add* to $p(s)$—the probability of no arrivals during the shorter interval $[0, s\rangle$. To explore the change in p over the interval $[s, t\rangle$, let's rearrange the sum (6) to display the difference

$$p(s) - p(t) = \lambda p(s)(t-s) + p(s)e(t-s) + p(s)m(t-s).$$ (7)

Note that this difference is just the *probability of a first meteorite arrival during* $[s, t\rangle$.

As a minor consequence of the model, we can now conclude that the survival probability $p(t)$ must be a *continuous* function of the time t. This is because $p(s) \leqslant 1$ for any s; and in each of the terms on the right-hand side of (7), $p(s)$ is multiplied by a quantity which tends to zero as $t-s$ gets smaller and smaller. Hence the left-hand difference, $p(t) - p(s)$ must tend to zero too.
(*More in detail:* $\lim\limits_{n\to\infty} p(s_n) = p(t)$ for any sequence $\{s_n < t\}$ with $\lim\limits_{n\to\infty} s_n = t$; and similarly for sequences $\{t_n > s\}$ with $\lim\limits_{n\to\infty} t_n = s$.)

Better yet, why not determine the *rate* of change of the function p over an interval $[s, t]$? Let's divide equation (7) through by $-(t-s)$ to get the difference ratio

$$\frac{p(t) - p(s)}{t-s} = -\lambda p(s) - p(s)\left[\frac{e(t-s)}{t-s}\right] - p(s)\left[\frac{m(t-s)}{t-s}\right].$$ (8)

If we hold, say, s fixed at a value t_0 and consider the function p only on the domain $t \geqslant t_0$, we can take limits to get

$$\lim_{t\to t_0} \frac{p(t) - p(t_0)}{t-t_0} = -\lambda p(t_0) - p(t_0)\lim_{t\to t_0}\left[\frac{e(t-t_0)}{(t-t_0)}\right]$$

$$- p(t_0)\lim_{t\to t_0}\left[\frac{m(t-t_0)}{t-t_0}\right]$$

$$= -\lambda p(t_0) - p(t_0) \cdot 0 - p(t_0) \cdot 0$$

$$= -\lambda p(t_0).$$ (9)

The last two limits in (9) are zero since

$$\lim_{t\to t_0}\left[\frac{e(t-t_0)}{t-t_0}\right] = \lambda \lim_{t\to t_0}\left[\frac{e(t-t_0)}{\lambda(t-t_0)}\right]$$

$$= \lambda \lim_{T\to 0}\left[\frac{e(T)}{\lambda T}\right] = 0$$ (10)

in view of (3), when we set $T = t - t_0$. Likewise for $[m(t-t_0)]/(t-t_0)$.

Next, let's hold $t = t_0$, and consider the function p only on the domain $0 \leqslant s \leqslant t_0$. Then

$$\lim_{s \to t_0} \frac{p(s) - p(t_0)}{s - t_0} = \lim_{s \to t_0} \frac{p(t_0) - p(s)}{t_0 - s}$$

$$= -\lambda \lim_{s \to t_0} p(s) - (\lim_{s \to t_0} p(s)) \lim_{s \to t_0} \left[\frac{e(t_0 - s)}{t_0 - s} \right]$$

$$- (\lim_{s \to t_0} p(s)) \lim_{s \to t_0} \left[\frac{m(t_0 - s)}{t_0 - s} \right]$$

$$= -\lambda p(t_0) - p(t_0) \cdot 0 - p(t_0) \cdot 0$$

$$= -\lambda p(t_0). \tag{11}$$

(Here the continuity of $p(s)$ at t_0 came in handy.)

Conclusion: There exists a derivative

$$p'(t_0) = -\lambda p(t_0) \qquad \text{at any } t_0 \geqslant 0 \tag{12}$$

(by the "interlacing" property of derivatives, D' in Chap. 14).

Thus the still unknown survival probability function $p(t)$ has a relationship to its own derivative function $p'(t)$ which is very similar to that which you might recall for bacterial population size. Namely — and in general symbols:

$$f'(t) = af(t) \qquad \text{for } t \geqslant 0, \tag{13}$$

where a is a fixed constant. In the present case $a = -\lambda$ and is negative. For the population size function — the exponential form $\hat{S}(t) = Ne^{(1/H)t}$ of Sec. 13.3 (Example 2) and Sec. 14.10 (Example 3), I argued that $\hat{S}'(t) = (1/H)\hat{S}(t)$. There $a = 1/H$, the reciprocal of the average lifetime H of an individual bacterium.

In fact, remembering the general result on derivatives of exponentials,

$$(e^{at})' = a(e^{at}) \qquad \text{at any } t, \tag{14}$$

we can see that the *specific* exponential function

$$g(t) = e^{at}$$

satisfies the relationship (13) with its own derivative. In particular, if we choose $a = -\lambda$, then g *has exactly the same relationship to its own derivative g' as does the unknown probability survival function p to its derivative p'*. Moreover, g even satisfies the *same initial condition* as does p: $p(0) = 1$, and

$$g(0) = e^{a \cdot 0} = e^0 = 1. \tag{15}$$

Can we conclude that $p(t)$ and $g(t)$ must be identical? Why should they be? Might not the true probability function $p(t)$ be some highly nonexponential function which just *happens* to satisfy the same relationship (13) and the same initial condition (15) as the exponential function $g(t) = e^{-\lambda t}$? Or is g the *unique function* — from among the infinite host of possibilities — which satisfies (13) and (15) together?

If we could show that g is the *only* function satisfying (13) and (15) together—then, since the unknown function p satisfies (13) and (15) also, we'll have forced the conclusion that p and q are identical. And, except for knowing the constant λ explicitly, we'll have evaluated

$$p(t) = e^{-\lambda t} \qquad \text{for all } t \geq 0.$$

In a later section, I'll discuss how we might interpret and evaluate the constant λ itself, and how we might further use the result (16). Meanwhile, note what the form $e^{-\lambda t}$ implies: No matter what the probability $p(t_0)$ may be for your surviving during a visit of length t_0, the probability for your surviving n times as long goes down as a power:

$$p(nt_0) = e^{-\lambda n t_0} = [e^{-\lambda t_0}]^n = p(t_0)^n. \tag{16}$$

For example, if you estimate your probability of surviving for one day ($t_0 = 24$ hours) as, say, 0.9; then your survival probability for a week will be

$$p(7 \times 24) = [p(24)]^7 = (0.9)^7 = 0.478 \text{ approximately.} \tag{17}$$

The matter is analogous to your getting 7 heads *in a row* while tossing a coin loaded 9 to 1 in favor of heads. Even though the odds are favorable for any one toss, the independence of results on separate tosses forces a *product* of probabilities—which can get uncomfortably small when the number of factors gets large.

16.2   THE "GROWTH" DIFFERENTIAL EQUATION AND ITS SOLUTION

People have long used the term:

Definition I: *differential equation* to describe an equality relating various derivatives of a function, the function itself, and perhaps other known functions.

EXAMPLE 1. One of the simplest cases:

$$f'(x) = x \qquad \text{for } 0 \leq x \leq 1. \tag{1}$$

Here the output values of the function f itself don't appear, merely those of a known function $h(x) = x$. The sought-for $f(x)$ must be one of the antiderivatives of $h(x) = x$; namely, $f(x) = \frac{1}{2}x^2 + C$, for some constant C.

EXAMPLE 2. The position function $p(t)$ for falling down a cliff. In Sec. 7.5, I argued that Newton's "axioms" about the "gravitational" attraction between the earth and a falling body could be approximated by the statement about "acceleration":

$$p''(t) = 32 \text{ ft/sec}^2 \qquad \text{for } 0 \leq t \leq T, \text{ the time of impact.} \tag{2}$$

Here is another differential equation. In fact, most "laws" about motion—involving velocities p' and accelerations p''—naturally constitute differential equations.

In (2), the sought-for function p and even its first derivative p' don't appear. But I used the "neck-and-neck race argument" (in Secs. 7.5 and 15.9) to identify p with the function $g(t) = 16t^2$ which had the same initial values $g(0) = 0$ and $g'(0) = 0$ as required for p.

In further keeping with old usage,

Definition II: Let's call any particular function a _solution_ of an indicated differential equation if—together with its derivatives—it satisfies the required relationship.

EXAMPLE 3. The function $\frac{1}{2}x^2 + C$ is a "solution" of the equation (1), $f'(x) = x$, for any choice of the constant C. And there can be no solutions of any other form—since all antiderivatives of $h(x) = x$ can differ only by a constant.

EXAMPLE 4. $16t^2$ is a "solution" of equation (2), $p''(t) = 32$ for $0 \leqslant t \leqslant T$.

Now, in the last section we were faced with a differential equation

$$f'(t) = af(t) \qquad \text{for } t \geqslant 0 \tag{3}$$

which did involve outputs $f(t)$ as well as derivatives. In a sense, such an equation is harder to "solve" than the equation (1) $f'(x) = x$, since in (3) the derivatives f' are related to _unknown_ quantities f, rather than to known quantities x.

In the last section I argued that an unknown probability of survival function $p(t)$ must constitute a _solution_ for the differential equation (3) with $a = -\lambda$, a given constant. And I checked that the specific exponential function $g(t) = e^{at}$ was also a solution of (3). In fact, _any multiple_ be^{at} must be a solution, too, since

$$(be^{at})' = b(e^{at})' = bae^{at} = a(be^{at}) \qquad \text{for all } t. \tag{4}$$

But the unknown probability function $p(t)$ and the specific exponential $g(t) = e^{at}$ also satisfy the same _initial condition_—which we can write in general form as

$$f(0) = 1. \tag{5}$$

The question was: could we identify the functions p and g just because they were both solutions of the same differential equation (3), $f' = af$, and both satisfied the same initial condition (5), $f(0) = 1$?

We could say yes immediately if we could apply the "neck-and-neck race argument." But for that result we would have to know that $p'(t) = g'(t)$ for all $t \geqslant 0$. As matters stand, all we know is that each of the functions p and g has a certain relationship with its _own_ derivative, $p' = -\lambda p$ and $g' = -\lambda g$. But we have no connection between the derivatives p' and g' themselves.

To identify p and g, what we need is an analog of the "neck-and-neck race argument"—a "uniqueness" result for solutions of the differential equation (3). Here is such a claim:

Theorem A ("_unique solution of the growth equation_"): For a given interval $[0, T]$ and given constants a and b, the differential equation

$$f'(t) = af(t) \qquad \text{for all } t \text{ in } [0, T] \tag{6}$$

can have only *one* solution satisfying the initial condition

$$f(0) = b; \qquad (7)$$

namely, $g(t) = be^{at}$.

Why should such a claim be valid? Let's suppose that $G(t)$ is some other solution of (6) which also satisfies the initial condition (7), $G(0) = b$. As with the "neck-and-neck race argument," we might consider the *difference* function $h(t) = G(t) - be^{at}$ and try to show that $h \equiv 0$ identically. That would mean that any such other G must coincide with $g(t) = be^{at}$.

Because of the special differentiation property of exponentials, $(e^{at})' = ae^{at}$, it will be easier for a

Proof of Theorem A (on the "unique solution of the growth equation") to consider the ratio function

$$r(t) = \frac{G(t)}{e^{at}} = G(t)e^{-at} \qquad \text{for } t \text{ in } [0, T], \qquad (8)$$

and to show that $r(t) \equiv b$ for t in $[0, T]$. If $r \equiv b$, then $G \equiv be^{at}$.

To see whether r is such a constant function, why not differentiate? By "Leibnitz's product rule,"

$$r'(t) = G'(t)e^{-at} + G(t)(e^{-at})'$$
$$= G'(t)e^{-at} + G(t)(-ae^{-at})$$
$$= e^{-at}[G'(t) - aG(t)] \qquad \text{for } t \text{ in } [0, T]. \qquad (9)$$

But the last factor $[G' - aG]$ must be 0 for t in $[0, T]$, because we supposed that G satisfies the differential equation (6); that is, that $G'(t) = aG(t)$ on $[0, T]$. Hence, $r' \equiv 0$ on $[0, T]$, and $r(t) \equiv r(0)$ on $[0, T]$. What value is $r(0)$?

$$r(0) = \frac{G(0)}{e^{a \cdot 0}} = b.$$

So $r(t) \equiv b$ on $[0, T]$; and $G(t) \equiv be^{at}$ is the *unique* solution satisfying the differential equation (6) and initial condition (7).   End of the proof.

I've called the relationship $f' = af$ the "growth equation," since it arises whenever the rate of change of a quantity is proportional—at every instant—to the amount of the quantity itself. For other applications, including that of radioactive decay, I invite you to look at the problems of the next section.

16.3   PROBLEMS INVOLVING THE GROWTH EQUATION

°1. Find $f(1)$, $f(5)$, and $f(10)$ if $f'(t) = af(t)$ for $0 \leqslant t \leqslant 10$ and
   (a) $a = -3$ and $f(0) = 5$
   (b) $a = 0.002$ and $f(0) = 30$
   (c) $a = 0.75$ and $f(0) = 10^6$

°2. Suppose that $f'(t) = af(t)$ for all $t \geq 0$. Find a if
   (a) $f(0) = 10^6$ and $f(3) = 10^{10}$
   (b) $f(0) = 2$ and $f(5000) = 1$
   (c) $f(5570) = \frac{1}{2}f(0)$

3. Living plant and animal tissues contain two forms of the element carbon, nonradioactive "C-12" and a radioactive "isotope" "C-14" — almost invariably in the ratio 10^{12} to 1. But when an organism dies, its tissues receive no new carbon of either kind. Their C-12 then remains more or less intact, and their C-14 radiates away. (You might recall Problem 7 of Sec. 13.5 for a model of such decrease.) Laboratory experiments indicate that C-14 has a rate of decrease (due to radiation) which is proportional at any instant to the amount of C-14 present at that instant; and that it would take an ounce of C-14 about 5750 years until it would be reduced to $\frac{1}{2}$ ounce by radiation.

   (a) Suppose that archeologists unearth ruins of an ancient building, and examine wood samples for their amounts of C-12 and C-14. (A geiger counter can measure even a trace of C-14 via the intensity of its radiation.) And suppose the wood samples show the ratio of C-12 to C-14 as 10^{12} to $\frac{3}{4}$. How old would you estimate the building to be?

   (Suggestion: If $f(t)$ denotes the amount of C-14 in the wood t years after it was chopped, for what t will $f(t) = \frac{3}{4}f(0)$?)

   (b) If the ratio of C-12 to C-14 were 10^{12} to $\frac{1}{4}$, how old would the building be?

4. Would you expect telephone call arrivals at a central exchange during a weekday morning to exhibit properties of randomness such as I discussed for meteorites in Sec. 16.1? Suppose they do, and suppose that a counting device in your exchange has reported the one-minute interval from 9:30 to 9:31 a.m. to be free of arriving calls on 27 weekdays out of 100.

   (a) What probability can you assign to the result that no calls arrive between 9:30 and 9:45 a.m. on a given weekday?

   (b) If you wanted to make a small repair during a weekday morning, what is the longest interval during which you can plan to work with at least 80% chances of being undisturbed by an incoming call?

5. Suppose that the population in a certain country has a birthrate of 2% per year and a death rate of 1% per year, and that we can represent the population size approximately by a differentiable function $f(t)$.

   (a) Write a differential equation describing the growth of $f(t)$.

   (b) How long will it take the population to double?

   (c) How long will it take the population to double if medical advances reduce the death rate to $\frac{1}{2}$%?

6. If three equal sized populations have growth rates of 1%, 2%, and 4%, what will be the ratios of the population sizes 100 years from now?

7. Suppose that the death rate in a population is 1% and that a group of idealists agree to have no children while the rest of the population has a birth rate of 1.5%. How large a fraction of the total population must the group of idealists be to achieve the objective of zero population growth?

8. Think of particles of ragweed pollen blown by the winds and arriving by chance on a given surface.

   (a) Can you transpose the probabilistic assumptions of Sec. 16.1 from time intervals to surface regions—using "area" instead of "length"? And would those principles then seem to apply to pollen arrivals?

   (b) Suppose so, and suppose that on a given day you examine 10 different 1-sq in. samples of surface and find 3 of them free of pollen. What are the chances that 40 sq in. on the surface of your head be free of pollen likewise?

9. A "*difference equation*" for prices. The current *demand* for a commodity depends on its current *price*, and also on buyers' expectations about future prices. In an "open market," the current price of a commodity depends in turn on the balance between the current demand and the current *supply* of the commodity. And the current *supply* of the commodity often depends on the price at which it sold—on the rewards which it brought to its suppliers—in the previous season. Thus demand, price, and supply are interrelated; and it may be difficult to predict what values they will take in the future. Moreover, *expectations* about future prices add a further complicating relationship. For example, if buyers expect prices to rise in the future, they may hurry to stockpile a commodity at today's prices. This extra current demand, pitted against a limited potential to increase the supply, can itself drive up prices and thus fulfill the gloomy expectations which started the demand. Inflation. Before considering the added complications of future expectations, economists have tried to understand the simpler relations between current demand, price, and supply, and past prices. Here is a simple model: Let $n = 0, 1, 2, 3, \ldots$ denote successive years. And suppose that in each year the current demand D_n is a linear function of the current price p_n.

$$D_n = a + b p_n \qquad \text{for } n = 0, 1, 2, \ldots, \qquad (*)$$

where a and b are coefficients which (ideally) don't change from year to year. ($a > 0$ and $b < 0$ so that demand decreases with increasing price.) Suppose that current supply S_n is a linear function of the commodity price p_{n-1} in the past year,

$$S_n = c + d p_{n-1} \qquad \text{for } n = 1, 2, 3, \ldots. \qquad (**)$$

(Here $c > 0$ and $d > 0$.) Finally, suppose that the current price p_n is that which equalizes current demand and supply,

$$D_n = S_n \qquad \text{for } n = 1, 2, 3, \ldots. \qquad (***)$$

The relationships (*), (**), and (***) together yield a relationship between prices for successive years

$$a + bp_n = c + dp_{n-1}$$

or

$$p_n = \left(\frac{d}{b}\right)p_{n-1} + \left(\frac{c-a}{b}\right) \qquad \text{for } n = 1, 2, 3, \ldots. \tag{†}$$

In terms of yearly increments in price, we could write (†) as

$$P_n - p_{n-1} = \left(\frac{d-b}{b}\right)p_{n-1} + \left(\frac{c-a}{b}\right) \qquad \text{for } n = 1, 2, 3, \ldots. \tag{‡}$$

Except for the constant term, note the similarity between the relation (‡) and the "growth" differential equation of Sec. 16.1. The main distinctions are that in (‡) we have a function p_n (or $p(n)$) with integer inputs rather than $f(t)$, and on the left-hand side of (‡) we have a *difference* $p_n - p_{n-1}$ rather than a derivative $f'(t)$. Equations such as (‡) or (†) are called "difference equations."

(a) Use (†) to get a formula for p_n for $n = 1, 2, 3, \ldots$, in terms of p_0 and the constants $A = d/b$ and $B = (c-a)/b$.

(b) Say why the formula of part (a) represents the *unique* "solution" of (†) — or of (‡) — having the "initial" value p_0.

(c) Find what relationships between the constants a, b, c, and d will force prices (i) to rise from year to year, (ii) to fall, and (iii) to remain steady.

(d) Sketch graphs of $\{p_n\}$ for the cases in part (c).

(e) What similarity does your solution in part (a) bear to the exponential solution of the growth differential equation?

16.4 SOUNDS, HEARTBEATS, AND THE HARMONY OF THE UNIVERSE

What happens when you speak or sing? Your throat muscles set up vibrations in the walls of your air pipes. If you could watch a cell on such a wall, you might see it being displaced from one side to another. The farther it is moved from its original neutral position the more distended are the elastic muscles in the throat wall and the more "force" they exert to restore the wall to its original position. The same for the action of heart muscles. People have considered this action to be similar to what you might observe if you had a small object fastened between two springs or rubber bands, as in Fig. 16-4. If you pull the object from its neutral position (say, $x = 0$) to some starting position x_0, and then let go, the springs will pull and push the object back and forth — *reversing their action* each time the object overshoots the neutral position.

If you could attach a pen to the object and pass a roll of paper underneath, you could record the object's position as a function of time (as in Fig. 7-9). With axes pointing in the usual directions such a record might look like the curve in Fig. 16-5. Such a curve would

FIGURE 16-4

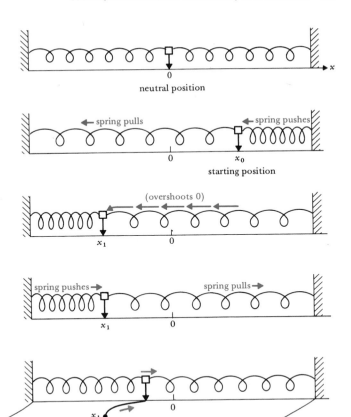

FIGURE 16-5

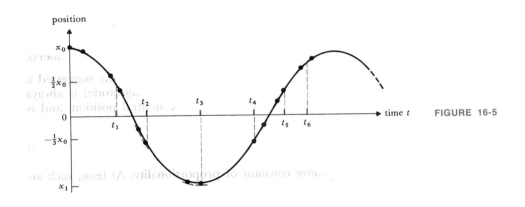

be an *experimental approximation* to the graph of the object's true position function $p(t)$. Recall that the *slope* at a graph point $(t_0, p(t_0))$ displays the object's *velocity* $p'(t_0)$ at time t_0. (I've indicated several slopes in green in Fig. 16-5.) And the *rate of change of slopes* at any graph point $(t_0, p(t_0))$ is the object's *acceleration* $p''(t_0)$ at time t_0.

Long ago (around 1700) Robert Hooke wondered how to "explain" the action of springs in some fundamental way. He experimented with many different kinds of springs and objects, recorded position data, and even made approximate calculations of velocities and accelerations. Among all those numbers he noted a *pattern*: if an object is twice as far to the right of the neutral position at some time T_2 as it was at some other time T_1, then the springs seem to cause it to *DEcelerate* (and go leftward) twice as much at T_2 as at T_1.

Here is how such a pattern appears in Fig. 16-5, where position $p(t)$ always corresponds to displacement from the neutral position $x = 0$. If you made approximate calculations for various $p''(t)$ values, you would find that

$$p(t_1) = \tfrac{1}{2}p(0) \qquad\qquad \text{(positive numbers)}$$

and

$$p''(t_1) = \tfrac{1}{2}p''(0) \text{ approximately} \qquad\qquad \text{(negative numbers).}$$

Similarly,

$$p(t_5) = \tfrac{1}{2}p(t_6) \qquad\qquad \text{(positive numbers)}$$

and

$$p''(t_5) = \tfrac{1}{2}p''(t_6) \text{ approximately} \qquad\qquad \text{(negative numbers).}$$

Moreover,

$$p(t_4) = -p(t_5) \qquad\qquad \text{(negative numbers)}$$

and

$$p''(t_4) = -p''(t_5) \text{ approximately} \qquad\qquad \text{(positive numbers).}$$

Similarly,

$$p(t_2) = -\tfrac{1}{3}p(0) \qquad\qquad \text{(negative numbers)}$$

and

$$p''(t_2) = -\tfrac{1}{3}p''(0) \text{ approximately} \qquad\qquad \text{(positive numbers).}$$

To Hooke, such approximate experimental results suggested a basic relationship: that the acceleration (in magnitude) is always *proportional* to the displacement from the neutral position, and is always opposite in sign. In symbols

$$p''(t) = -\lambda p(t), \tag{1}$$

where λ is a *positive* constant of proportionality. At least, such an equation might describe the motion until it was significantly affected by "friction."

You might recall (from Sec. 7.5) that Isaac Newton conceived of the product $mp''(t)$ of the mass and the acceleration of an object as measuring the "force" "acting on" the object. If we multiply equation (1) through by the mass m, we can get the statement

$$\text{"force"} = mp''(t) = -Lp(t), \tag{2}$$

where $L = m\lambda > 0$. Hooke and others interpreted this relationship as a "law" describing the action of idealized (or "frictionless") springs: "the force exerted by springs is always proportional to displacement from the neutral position, and opposite in direction."

What equation (1) says is that the position function $p(t)$ of the object connected to springs satisfies the *differential equation*

$$f''(t) = -\lambda f(t) \qquad \text{for } t \text{ in some interval.} \tag{3}$$

For convenience, let's call it the "oscillator equation." This equation has been used for more or less accurate description of vibrating guitar strings, tuning forks, vocal muscles, and heart muscles. But the quantity f in (3) needn't refer to a physical displacement. Suppose we were to study the growth of a herd of deer living in some closed-off area free of predators and blithely eating grass. We could try to approximate the size of the herd at time t by a function $h(t)$. And for a simplified theory we might suppose $h'(t)$ and $h''(t)$ to exist, so that we could talk of the "rate of increase or decrease" of the herd size and of corresponding "acceleration." Now if $h(t)$ grows very large, the limited food supply will be felt by all of the deer, and may well act as a "force" to decelerate the growth of the herd. Many animals may die for lack of sufficient nourishment, and the herd size may well begin to fall. But then, if there are few deer to compete for the next crop of food, the reproduction will act as a "restoring force" to push $h(t)$ up again. If A is some "average size" for the herd, it may well be that the "displacement" $f(t) = h(t) - A$ (which has $f'(t) = h'(t)$ and $f''(t) = h''(t)$) satisfies an equation such as (3). Actual observations of herds have shown oscillations in size just as in Fig. 16-5.

Because the "oscillator equation," $f'' = -\lambda f$, seems to apply to many diverse situations, people have tried to identify its possible *solutions*. Now the oscillator equation may somewhat resemble the "growth" equation $f' = -\lambda f$ of Secs. 16.1 and 16.2 (with $a = -\lambda$). But there is a big difference: in the oscillator equation, it's the *acceleration* $f''(t)$, not the velocity $f'(t)$, which is negatively proportional to position. So it shouldn't come as a surprise that the exponential solution $e^{-\lambda t}$ of the "growth equation" is *not* a solution of the "oscillator equation":

$$(e^{-\lambda t})'' = (-\lambda e^{-\lambda t})' = -\lambda (e^{-\lambda t})' = (-\lambda)^2 e^{-\lambda t}$$

$$\neq -\lambda (e^{-\lambda t}). \tag{4}$$

[handwritten note in right margin:] $\varsigma'' = $ acceleration
$\varsigma' = $ velocity

(An exponential position function $e^{-\lambda t}$ would always have *positive* acceleration $(-\lambda)^2 e^{-\lambda t}$.)

How then can we find solutions of the "oscillator equation"? Long ago, people noticed that one can get a tracing such as that in Fig. 16-5 by attaching a pen to a point P on the rim of a rotating wheel — as in Fig. 16-6.

FIGURE 16-6

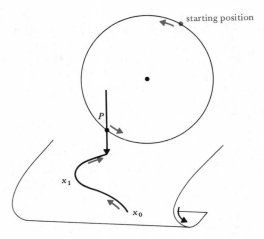

For concreteness, we might think of a wheel of radius one inch, and we might start rotating the point P from a rightward horizontal position — as in Fig. 16-7.

FIGURE 16-7

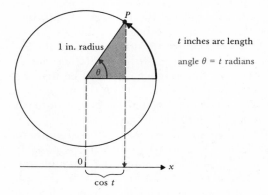

Let's rotate P through an arc of length t inches. You might possibly recall from high-school trigonometry that the (green) angle θ corresponding to this arc is called "t radians" in size, and that the base of the shaded triangle in which it appears has a length "cosine t" inches — just the displacement of the penpoint from the neutral position $x = 0$.

These thoughts suggest that to find solutions of the "oscillator equation" we might well review properties of "trigonometric functions."

16.5 SINES, COSINES, ARCLENGTH, AND "RADIANS"

You'll find a review of "trigonometric" results in Appendix A. But for those whose recollections are dim, I'll restate the main ideas here: in terms of an "angle" θ drawn at the center of a circle of *unit* radius — as in Fig. 16-8.

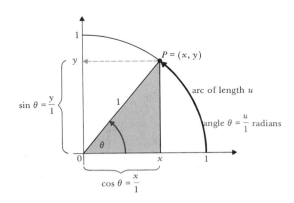

FIGURE 16-8

Following ancient procedure, we might consider the (shaded) right triangle determined by θ, and *assign* to θ the quantities

$$\text{``}\sin \theta\text{''} = \frac{\text{length of side opposite } \theta}{\text{length of hypotenuse}} = \frac{y \text{ units}}{1 \text{ unit}} = y \qquad (1)$$

and

$$\text{``}\cos \theta\text{''} = \frac{\text{length of side adjacent to } \theta}{\text{length of hypotenuse}} = \frac{x \text{ units}}{1 \text{ unit}} = x. \qquad (2)$$

(For a given angle, the $\sin \theta$ and $\cos \theta$ ratios don't depend on what particular unit we might use for measuring length — inch, foot, or any other.)

Note that if we stay with a circle of radius ONE unit, then — in terms of that unit — *the quantities $x = \cos \theta$ and $y = \sin \theta$ are just the coordinates of the point P at the end of the arc corresponding to θ, as in Fig.* 16-8:

$$P = (\cos \theta, \sin \theta), \qquad (3)$$

and $(\cos \theta)^2 + (\sin \theta)^2 = 1$.

Do you believe that for every real number θ between 0 and 90 there exists an "angle" of that many "degrees"? How about for $\theta > 90$, or $\theta < 0$? Traditionally, people have *supposed* that every real number θ does correspond to some "angle" (in degrees). And they've essentially used the coordinate idea $P = (\cos \theta, \sin \theta)$ in (3) to extend the definition of "$\sin \theta$" and "$\cos \theta$" for all real θ. See Fig. 16-9.

FIGURE 16-9

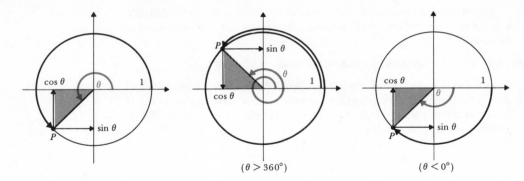

$(\theta > 360°)$ $(\theta < 0°)$

The assignments to (inputs) θ of (outputs) "sin θ" and "cos θ" constitute the two basic "trigonometric functions." With some checking, or by some remembering, you might guess their graphs to look like the sketches in Fig. 16-10.

FIGURE 16-10

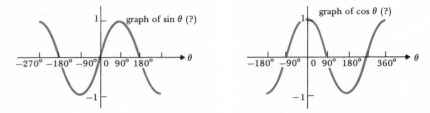

Now, how can we discover whether derivatives (sin θ)′ and (cos θ)′ truly exist; and if so, what their values might be? (We need such information if these functions are to yield exact solutions of the "oscillator equation.") To get answers, we'll have to consider difference ratios of the form

$$R(\theta) = \frac{\sin \theta - \sin \theta_0}{\theta - \theta_0}. \tag{4}$$

Note that the numbers sin θ and sin θ_0 in the numerator of R refer to *lengths* (of sides of triangles, as in Fig. 16-8). What relationship do such lengths have with the angles θ and θ_0 in the denominator measured, say, in "degrees"? It's not clear. Why not try to avoid this question altogether by somehow measuring θ and θ_0 themselves in terms of *lengths*?

Such was the motivation for a system called "radian" measure — which I'll adopt for the remainder of the chapter. Let's look at the (black) arc of length u which corresponds to the (green) angle θ in Fig. 16-8. And let's quote the size of θ as

$$\frac{\text{the length of } \theta\text{'s arc}}{\text{the radius of the circle}} = \frac{u \text{ units}}{1 \text{ unit}} = u \text{ "radians."} \tag{5}$$

(For example, the angle 0° is the same as the angle "0 radians." The angle "90°" corresponds to an arc which is $\frac{1}{4}$ of the entire circumference, so the angle measures $\frac{1}{4}(2\pi) = $ "$\frac{1}{2}\pi$ radians.")

To be consistent, let's write the *inputs* of the trigonometric functions in terms of radians also: "sin u" and "cos u." Then the key lengths in Fig. 16-8 will all appear in terms of u, as in Fig. 16-11.

Just as for angles θ in Fig. 16-9, we can think of arcs which wind more than once around the circle, or which are "negative" in that they wind in an opposite (a clockwise) direction. Here's a question about arcs similar to one about "angles": Do you believe that for every real number u there is a unique arc exactly u units in length? (Such an assumption corresponds to one above for angles.) If so, we can think of the functions sin u and cos u as defined for all reals. Their graphs should be identical to the curves in Fig. 16-10 except with inputs changed from θ (in degrees) to u (in radians). See Fig. 16-12.

FIGURE 16-11

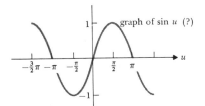 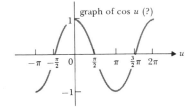

FIGURE 16-12

To calculate the derivative of, say, sin u at an input u_0, we can now consider a ratio of differences of lengths,

$$R(u) = \frac{\sin u - \sin u_0}{u - u_0}.$$

In the denominator, the difference $u - u_0$ appears as the length of an arc $P_0 P$ as in Fig. 16-13.

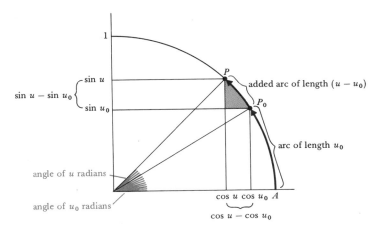

FIGURE 16-13

But, you might ask, what do we really know about the "length" of an arc? How can we estimate it to compute derivatives?

Perhaps you recall from Sec. 10.1 that I defined the length of the entire circumference of a circle as *a limit (or least upper bound) of lengths of inscribed approximating polygons.* (For even more details, look back to Problem 14 in Sec. 10.5 and Problem 6 in Sec. 12.4.)

Let's suppose that we can assign a "length" to any *sub*arc of the circle in the very same way. See Fig. 16-14, where I've indicated an approximating "polygonal line" in green.

FIGURE 16-14

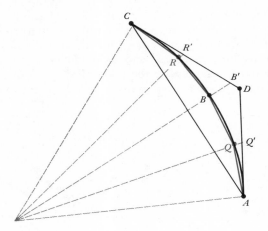

What properties can we expect of such "length"? Perhaps the most intuitive one is just the

"Additive property of arc length": the sum of the lengths of two adjacent arcs *AB* and *BC* should be the length of their "union" *AC.*

Besides being intuitive, this result follows from the definition of arclength for $\widehat{AC}$ via "polygonal approximations," because each approximation for $\widehat{AC}$ can be split into two adjacent parts—one approximating $\widehat{AB}$, the other $\widehat{BC}$. For more details, see Problem 14 of Sec. 10.5.

Note that I've already applied the "additive property" in Fig. 16-13, by assigning length $t-t_0$ to the arc P_0P.

Now here is a second result, whereby we can bound the length of a given arc between simpler lengths of segments:

"A sandwich property of arc length": The length of any arc *AC* must always exceed the chord length $|AC|$ between the end points. On the other hand, if an arc $\widehat{AC}$ is less than a quarter circle, then *its length can never exceed the length of the exterior route along segments AD and DC tangent to the circle at A and C,* as in Fig. 16-14:

$$|AC| < \text{arclength } \widehat{AC} \leqslant |AD| + |DC|. \tag{6}$$

Why? Note in Fig. 16-14 that $|AQ| < |AQ'|$, $|QB| < |Q'D| + |DB'|$, and so on. We could add such inequalities for *any* (green) approximating polygon, to find that its total length "$L(AC)$" $< |AD| + |DC|$. For a sequence of finer and finer approximations with lengths $L_n(AC)$, we would get

$$\text{Arclength } AC = \lim_{n \to \infty} L_n(AC) \leqslant |AD| + |DC|.$$

(Recall Problem 14 of Sec. 10.5.)

Let's note one more result—which you may recall from elementary geometry, and which will help for computing derivatives: any two angles whose corresponding sides are perpendicular—as in Fig. 16-15—must be equal; and (the shaded) right triangles containing them are *similar*.

FIGURE 16-15

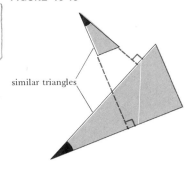

similar triangles

16.6   CONTINUITY AND DERIVATIVES OF TRIG FUNCTIONS

We might expect $\sin u$ and $\cos u$ to be continuous functions at any input u_0—since a small change of arclength u should cause only a small change in the coordinates of the point $P = (\cos u, \sin u)$ at the end of the arc. See Fig. 16-11. For the record:

Theorem B (on "continuity of sin and cos"): the functions $\sin u$ and $\cos u$ are continuous at any input u_0.

For a more precise argument in support of Theorem B look at the shaded triangle in Fig. 16–13. Each of its sides is shorter than the hypotenuse $|P_0P|$. So by the "sandwich argument" for arcs we must have

$$|\sin u - \sin u_0| < |P_0P| \leq |u - u_0| \tag{1}$$

and

$$|\cos u - \cos u_0| < |P_0P| \leq |u - u_0|, \tag{2}$$

at least when $|u - u_0| < \pi/2$. Thus $\lim_{u \to u_0} (\sin u - \sin u_0) = 0$ and $\lim_{u \to u_0} (\cos u - \cos u_0) = 0$.

Here now is an intuitive view of what we can expect for the *derivatives* of $\sin u$ and $\cos u$ at some input u_0. Look at the darkly shaded region P_0PQ in Fig. 16-16. Except for the curvature of the

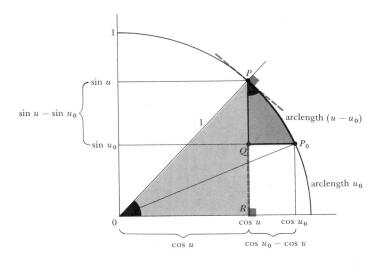

arclength $(u - u_0)$ **FIGURE 16-16**

arc P_0P, the region is *almost* a triangle—with hypotenuse of length approximately $u - u_0$. If the region were a true triangle, then—by the geometric principle of Fig. 16-15—it would be similar to the larger (lightly) shaded triangle POR. And ratios of corresponding sides would be equal. Namely, we would have

$$\frac{\text{side adjacent}}{\text{hypotenuse}} = \frac{\sin u - \sin u_0}{u - u_0} = \frac{\cos u}{1} = \cos u \tag{3}$$

and

$$\frac{\text{side opposite}}{\text{hypotenuse}} = \frac{\cos u_0 - \cos u}{u - u_0} = \frac{\sin u}{1} = \sin u. \tag{4}$$

Since the region P_0PQ is not a true triangle, the ratios in (3) and (4) may only be approximately equal—even when P_0 and P are very close. However, since $\cos u$ and $\sin u$ are continuous functions, the approximations suggest that at u_0 we might expect limits

$$(\sin u)' = \lim_{u \to u_0}\left[\frac{\sin u - \sin u_0}{u - u_0}\right] = \lim_{u \to u_0} \cos u = \cos u_0 \tag{5}$$

and

$$(\cos u)' = \lim_{u \to u_0}\left[\frac{\cos u - \cos u_0}{u - u_0}\right] = -\lim_{u \to u_0}\left[\frac{\cos u_0 - \cos u}{u - u_0}\right]$$
$$= -\lim_{u \to u_0} \sin u = -\sin u_0. \tag{6}$$

And we might conjecture

Theorem C ("derivatives of sin and cos"): At any u,

$$(\sin u)' = \cos u, \quad \text{and} \quad (\cos u)' = -\sin u.$$

EXAMPLE 1. If Theorem C is true, we've just found two solutions of the "oscillator equation" $f''(u) = -\lambda f(u)$ for the case $\lambda = 1$. Namely, $\sin u$ and $\cos u$. Just check

$$(\sin u)'' = [(\sin u)']' = [\cos u]'$$
$$= -\sin u \quad \text{for all } u \tag{7}$$

and

$$(\cos u)'' = [(\cos u)'] = [-\sin u]' = -[\sin u]'$$
$$= -\cos u \quad \text{for all } u. \tag{8}$$

EXAMPLE 2. Earlier in Fig. 16-6, I started with the idea of a *rotating* wheel, of radius 1 inch. To explore that idea further, let's suppose that the point P in Fig. 16-8 is on the rim of such a wheel. And let's turn the wheel at a *constant rate*, so that the arc of length u inches (traced out by P)—and its corresponding angle of u *radians*—will be proportional to time t. If we start off with an angle of 0 radians at time 0 seconds, the angle should read

$$u = Mt \quad \text{(radians)} \tag{9}$$

after t seconds—where M represents the constant rate, "M radians per second."

With $u = Mt$ in Fig. 16-8, the vertical displacement of the point P will be

$$y = q(t) = \sin Mt \qquad \text{(inches)} \qquad \text{after } t \text{ seconds,} \tag{10}$$

and the horizontal displacement will be

$$x = p(t) = \cos Mt \qquad \text{(inches)} \qquad \text{after } t \text{ seconds.} \tag{11}$$

Let's use the "chain rule" to check whether these displacements satisfy an "oscillator equation":

$$q'(t) = (\sin Mt)' = (\cos Mt)(Mt)' = M \cos Mt$$

and

$$\begin{aligned} q''(t) &= M(\cos Mt)' = M(-\sin Mt)(Mt)' \\ &= M(-\sin Mt)M = -M^2(\sin Mt) \\ &= -M^2 q(t). \end{aligned} \tag{12}$$

Similarly,

$$p'(t) = (\cos Mt)' = (-\sin Mt)(Mt)' = -M \sin Mt$$

and

$$\begin{aligned} p''(t) &= -M(\sin Mt)' = -M(\cos Mt)(Mt)' = -M^2 \cos Mt \\ &= -M^2 p(t). \end{aligned} \tag{13}$$

Thus the functions $\sin Mt$ and $\cos Mt$ *are* solutions of the oscillator equation

$$f''(t) = -M^2 f(t) \qquad \text{for all } t. \tag{14}$$

But we can turn matters around: Given any $\lambda > 0$, we can choose $M = \sqrt{\lambda}$ in (14). And we now know that *the oscillator equation*

$$f''(t) = -\lambda f(t) \qquad \text{for } 0 \leqslant t \leqslant T \tag{15}$$

has at least two solutions: $\sin(\sqrt{\lambda}\, t)$ *and* $\cos(\sqrt{\lambda}\, t)$.

You might note in equation (13) that the units of $p''(t)$ on the left-hand side are those of acceleration, "inches per second per second." On the right-hand side, the units of $p(t)$ are those of position, "inches." It's the quantity M^2 which makes up the difference in time units, "per second per second." This is consistent with the fact that in (9) the rate M itself reads in "radians *per second*" —and "radian measure" mentions no specific unit of length.

EXAMPLE 3. Traditionally, the function $\tan u = (\sin u)/(\cos u)$, for u's where $\cos u \neq 0$. If Theorem C is true, we can use an old property for derivatives of quotients to get

$$(\tan u)' = \frac{(\sin u)'(\cos u) - (\sin u)(\cos u)'}{(\cos u)^2}$$

$$= \frac{(\cos u)(\cos u) - (\sin u)(-\sin u)}{(\cos u)^2}$$

$$= \frac{(\cos u)^2 + (\sin u)^2}{(\cos u)^2} = \frac{1}{(\cos u)^2} = (\text{``secant } u\text{''})^2. \qquad \textbf{(16)}$$

We could go on finding derivatives for a whole mountain of functions built up from the basic $\sin t$ and $\cos t$. I invite you to try your hand at evaluating a few of these in doing the problems of Sec. 16.8.

But first, you might note how the "sandwich property" for arc length can yield a precise

Proof of theorem C (that (sin u)′ = cos u and (cos u)′ = − sin u): Recall the "almost triangular" (darkly shaded) region P_0PQ in Fig. 16-16. It was *almost* similar to a (lightly shaded) triangle POR which had sides $\sin u$, $\cos u$, and 1. Now note in Fig. 16-17 how we can add on to the region P_0PQ to get a *true* triangle (SPQ) which really is similar to the triangle POR with sides $\sin u$, $\cos u$, and 1.

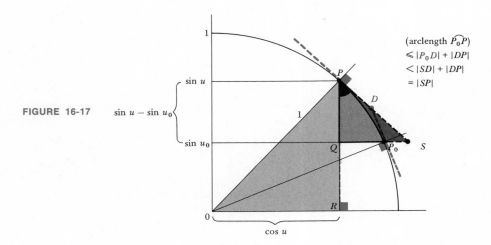

$$\begin{aligned}(\text{arclength } \widehat{P_0P}) \\ \leqslant |P_0D| + |DP| \\ < |SD| + |DP| \\ = |SP|\end{aligned}$$

FIGURE 16-17

(The similarity of triangles SPQ and POR follows again by the geometric principle of Fig. 16-15.) Now we have a true equality between ratios of corresponding sides:

$$\frac{\text{side adjacent}}{\text{hypotenuse}} = \frac{\sin u - \sin u_0}{|SP|} = \frac{\cos u}{1} = \cos u. \qquad \textbf{(17)}$$

Moreover, we can relate the hypotenuse length $|SP|$ to $u - u_0$, the arclength of P_0P. By the "sandwich property,"

$$u - u_0 \leqslant |P_0D| + |DP|. \qquad \textbf{(18)}$$

But in the small triangle P_0DS, the side length $|P_0D| < |SD|$. Hence

$$u - u_0 \leqslant |P_0D| + |DP| < |SD| + |DP| = |SP|. \tag{19}$$

Let's substitute the inequality $(u - u_0) < |SP|$ into the similarity statement (17) to get a *lower bound* for the difference ratio

$$R(u) = \frac{\sin u - \sin u_0}{u - u_0};$$

namely,

$$\frac{\sin u - \sin u_0}{u - u_0} \geqslant \frac{\sin u - \sin u_0}{|SP|} = \cos u. \tag{20}$$

If we could get a corresponding *upper bound* for $R(u)$ we might see how to squeeze it to a limit $(\sin u)'$ as we let u approach u_0. For this purpose, drop a perpendicular from the point P to the radius OP_0, as in Fig. 16–18, and look at the triangle TPQ which it cuts out of the (previously darkly shaded) region P_0PQ.

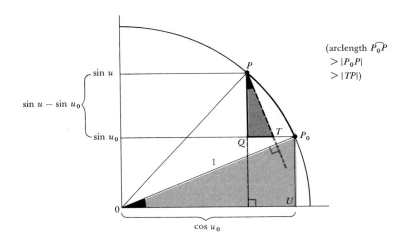

(arclength $\overset{\frown}{P_0P}$
$> |P_0P|$
$> |TP|$)

FIGURE 16-18

By the same geometric principle of Fig. 16-15, the new triangle TPQ is similar to the (lightly shaded) triangle P_0OU. So corresponding sides have the equal ratios

$$\frac{\text{side adjacent}}{\text{hypotenuse}} = \frac{\sin u - \sin u_0}{|TP|} = \frac{\cos u_0}{1} = \cos u_0. \tag{21}$$

But note that

$$|TP| < |P_0P| < u - u_0, \qquad \text{the arclength of } P_0P, \tag{22}$$

again by the "sandwich property." Together with (21), this inequality gives an upper bound for the difference ratio $R(u)$:

$$\frac{\sin u - \sin u_0}{u - u_0} \leqslant \frac{\sin u - \sin u_0}{|TP|} = \cos u_0. \tag{23}$$

The final "sandwich" is

$$\cos u < \frac{\sin u - \sin u_0}{u - u_0} \leq \cos u_0. \tag{24}$$

Now keeping u_0 fixed, and $u > u_0$ (as in all the figures above), let's let u tend to u_0. We'll force the *squeeze* in Fig. 16-19.

FIGURE 16-19

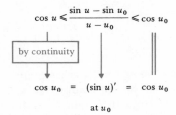

By interchanging the roles for u_0 and u, we could find, similarly, that

$$\lim_{u \to u_0} \frac{\sin u - \sin u_0}{u - u_0} = \cos u_0$$

where u is restricted to the domain $\{u < u_0\}$. *Conclusion:* at least for all u_0 between 0 and $\pi/2$,

$$(\sin u)' = \cos u_0 \tag{25}$$

(—by the "interlacing property" of limits").

I invite you to check that, although the above figures portray only the case $0 < u_0 < \pi/2$, nevertheless the result $(\sin u)' = \cos u$ is true at *any* real u. Do Problem 11 of Sec. 16.8. Check also (in the same problem) that the result $(\cos u)' = -\sin u$ can be obtained precisely by the same geometric methods.

These results also follow from traditional trigonometric identities, as you can see in Problem 12 of Sec. 16.8. In particular, note that we can derive the $\cos u$ result from the $\sin u$ result if we use the relationships

$$\cos u = \sin\left(\frac{\pi}{2} - u\right) \quad \text{and} \quad \sin u = \cos\left(\frac{\pi}{2} - u\right). \tag{26}$$

Just view $\cos u$ as a *composition* of the sine function with the linear function $\pi/2 - u$. And apply the "chain rule":

$$(\cos u)' = \left[\sin\left(\frac{\pi}{2} - u\right)\right]'$$

$$= \left[\cos\left(\frac{\pi}{2} - u\right)\right]\left(\frac{\pi}{2} - u\right)'$$

$$= (\sin u)(-1) = -\sin u. \tag{27}$$

16.7 SOLUTIONS OF THE "OSCILLATOR EQUATION"

$$f''(t) = -\lambda f(t) \qquad \text{(say, for } 0 \leqslant t \leqslant T), \tag{1}$$

where λ is a given positive constant. We've just found two solutions —in Example 2 of the last section: $\underline{\sin(\sqrt{\lambda}t)}$, and $\underline{\cos(\sqrt{\lambda}t)}$. Can there be any others?

As with the "growth equation," so also here: *if a function $f(t)$ is a solution, and if b is any constant, then the scaled function $bf(t)$ is also a solution.* This is because a scaling constant "passes through" the process of several differentiations:

$$[bf(t)]'' = [(bf(t))']' = [bf'(t)]' = b[f'(t)]' = bf''(t). \tag{2}$$

So if

$$f''(t) = -\lambda f(t),$$

we can multiply through by b to get

$$bf''(t) = b[-\lambda f(t)] = -\lambda[bf(t)]. \tag{3}$$

Together, (2) and (3) say that

$$[bf(t)]'' = -\lambda[bf(t)]. \tag{4}$$

Moreover, *any two solutions of the "oscillator equation"* (1) *add up to still another solution.* This is because the operation of addition also "passes through" the process of several differentiations:

$$[f(t) + g(t)]'' = [(f(t) + g(t)']' = [f'(t) + g'(t)]' = f''(t) + g''(t). \tag{5}$$

So if

$$f''(t) = -\lambda f(t) \quad \text{and} \quad g''(t) = -\lambda g(t),$$

we can add to get

$$f''(t) + g''(t) = -\lambda f(t) - \lambda g(t) = -\lambda[f(t) + g(t)]. \tag{6}$$

Together, (5) and (6) say that

$$[f(t) + g(t)]'' = -\lambda[f(t) + g(t)]. \tag{7}$$

From these notes, we can conclude what I'll call

Theorem D (solutions of the "oscillator equation"): For any two real numbers A and B, the function

$$\underline{f(t) = A \sin(\sqrt{\lambda}t) + B \cos(\sqrt{\lambda}t)} \tag{8}$$

is a solution of the "oscillator equation"

$$f''(t) = -\lambda f(t) \qquad \text{for } 0 \leqslant t \leqslant T \tag{9}$$

(where λ and T are given positive constants).

EXAMPLE 1. Suppose $\lambda = 4$. Find a solution which has *initial value* $f(0) = 3$, and *initial rate* $f'(0) = -2$. Let's try for a solution of the

[margin note, handwritten:]

solutions to
$$f''(t) = -\lambda f(t)$$
are
$$f(t) = \sin\sqrt{\lambda} \cdot t$$
$$f(t) = \cos\sqrt{\lambda} \cdot t$$
$$f(t) = A \sin(\sqrt{\lambda} t) + B \cos(\sqrt{\lambda} t)$$

form (8) above. At any t, it must have derivative

$$f'(t) = A\sqrt{\lambda} \cos{(\sqrt{\lambda}t)} - B\sqrt{\lambda} \sin{(\sqrt{\lambda}t)}. \tag{10}$$

(I've used the "chain rule" again, for each term.) In particular (since $\sin 0 = 0$ and $\cos 0 = 1$) we can evaluate $f(0)$ in (8) and $f'(0)$ in (10) as

$$f(0) = A \cdot 0 + B \cdot 1 = 3 \tag{11}$$

and

$$f'(0) = A \cdot \sqrt{\lambda} - B \cdot 0 = -2. \tag{12}$$

With $\sqrt{\lambda} = \sqrt{4} = 2$, solve to get $A = -1$ and $B = 3$. So

$$f(t) = -\sin 2t + 3 \cos 2t \qquad \text{(for all } t\text{)}$$

satisfies the "oscillator equation" $f'' = -4f$, with *initial conditions* $f(0) = 3$ and $f'(0) = -2$.

Can there be any other solution — call it $g(t)$ — of the same "oscillator equation" which shares the same *initial conditions*, $g(0) = f(0)$ and $g'(0) = f'(0)$, but which is *different* from f? In other words,

> **Question:** *does a "uniqueness result" hold for the "oscillator equation" analogous to that* in Theorem A (Sec. 16.2) *for the "growth equation"?*

I invite you to explore this question in doing Problem 15 of Sec. 16.8.

EXAMPLE 2. Suppose that we're looking at an object whose motion we suspect is (ideally) describable by an "oscillator equation,"

$$p'' = -\lambda p;$$

but that we have no idea of the value of the positive constant of proportionality λ. Is there any way to find λ — and to chart future positions $p(t)$ of the object — without actually measuring accelerations p'' and comparing them with positions p.

Yes, if it's true that solutions of the "oscillator equation" can be *only* of the form

$$f(t) = A \sin{(\sqrt{\lambda}t)} + B \cos{(\sqrt{\lambda}\ t)} \tag{8}$$

in Theorem D. For concreteness, let's return to the object connected to springs in Fig. 16-4. Here's how to find λ with one easy measurement of time: Start the object off at position $p(0) = x_0 =$ say, 3 inches. In letting it go, make sure you impart no initial velocity, so that $p'(0) = 0$. All you have to do is to note the length of time T which the object takes until it *first* reaches the neutral position $x = 0$. (Disregard the "overshoot.") Suppose $T = \frac{1}{2}$ second.

Now let's feed our information into the expressions

$$p(t) = A \sin{(\sqrt{\lambda}t)} + B \cos{(\sqrt{\lambda}t)} \tag{13}$$

and

$$p'(t) = \sqrt{\lambda}A \cos{(\sqrt{\lambda}t)} - B\sqrt{\lambda} \sin{(\sqrt{\lambda}t)}, \tag{14}$$

just as in Example 1:

$$p(0) = A \cdot 0 + B \cdot 1 = 3 \text{ inches} \qquad (13')$$

and

$$p'(0) = \sqrt{\lambda} A \cdot 1 - B\sqrt{\lambda} \cdot 0 = 0 \text{ in./sec.} \qquad (14')$$

Hence $A = 0$ and $B = 3$ inches. So the formula for position, in (13), *must* be simply

$$p(t) = 3 \cos(\sqrt{\lambda} t) \qquad \text{inches} \qquad (\text{for } t \text{ in seconds}). \qquad (15)$$

Except for the scaling constant 3, we can get an idea of the graph of $p(t)$ by looking at the $\cos u$ graph in Fig. 16-12, with the interpretation $u = \sqrt{\lambda} t$. When will the $\cos u$ graph *first* hit zero altitude? Answer: when

$$u = \sqrt{\lambda} t = \frac{\pi}{2}. \qquad (16)$$

Hence $p(t) = 3 \cos(\sqrt{\lambda} t) = 0$ first at the input

$$t = \frac{1}{\sqrt{\lambda}} \frac{\pi}{2}. \qquad (17)$$

For the case I described above, we can identify the input t in (17) experimentally as $T = \frac{1}{2}$ sec. That is,

$$\frac{1}{2} = \frac{1}{\sqrt{\lambda}} \frac{\pi}{2} \text{ (seconds)} \qquad (18)$$

—which we can solve for $\sqrt{\lambda} = \pi$ (radians per second).

Conclusion: As long as "friction" doesn't significantly alter the effect of the springs, the displacement of the object from its neutral position should be predictable as

$$p(t) = 3 \cos(\pi t) \qquad \text{inches} \qquad \text{for } t \text{ in seconds.} \qquad (19)$$

Looking still at sums of the form

$$f(t) = A \sin(\sqrt{\lambda} t) + B \cos(\sqrt{\lambda} t), \qquad (8)$$

we might also ask whether their graphs *always* have the same wave-like shape as those of sines and cosines individually—a shape as in Figs. 16-4 and 16-5.

I invite you to recall a little trigonometry in Problems 3 and 5 of Sec. 16.8, and show that a sum $f(t)$ as in (8) must always have the *alternate form*

$$f(t) = R \cos[\sqrt{\lambda}(t - \tau)] \qquad (\text{for all } t), \qquad (20)$$

where $R = \sqrt{A^2 + B^2}$, and τ is some fixed number such that

$$A = \sin(\sqrt{\lambda}\tau) \quad \text{and} \quad B = \cos(\sqrt{\lambda}\tau).$$

The number R governs the height of the waves in the graph of f— and is usually called the "amplitude." The number τ represents a *shift* in inputs from the simpler function $R \cos \sqrt{\lambda} t$. We might interpret this as a change in starting time (say, from $t = 0$ to $t = \tau$). τ is usually called the "phase" of the function f. The remaining constant, $\sqrt{\lambda}$, determines how fast the graph oscillates. I invite you to check (in Problem 7 of Sec. 16.8) that the graph of f *"repeats itself"* after every $2\pi/\sqrt{\lambda}$ units of time — and no sooner. That is,

$$f\left(t + \frac{2\pi}{\sqrt{\lambda}}\right) = f(t) \qquad \text{for any } t. \tag{21}$$

$2\pi/\sqrt{\lambda}$ is usually called the "period" of f. Its reciprocal, $\sqrt{\lambda}/2\pi$, measures the "number of oscillations per unit time" — and is usually called the "frequency" of f.

See Figs. 16-20 and 16-21 for the graphs of $R\cos[\sqrt{\lambda}(t-\tau)]$ in several cases. (In drawing all these figures, I used the basic relations $(\cos t)' = -\sin t$, and $(\cos at)' = -a\sin at$, to help me get accurate slopes at key inputs.)

FIGURE 16-20

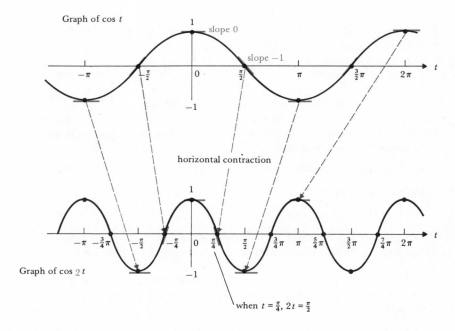

FIGURE 16-21

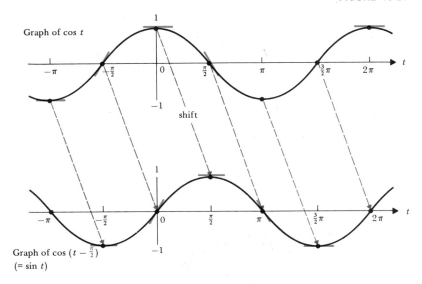

Graph of cos t

shift

Graph of $\cos\left(t - \frac{\pi}{2}\right)$
$(= \sin t)$

In summary: *If* the "oscillator equation" can have solutions only of the form $f(t) = A \sin(\sqrt{\lambda}t) + B \cos(\sqrt{\lambda}t)$ (and you should find this *true*, as in Problem 15 of Sec. 16.8), then *any phenomenon governed mainly by "restoring forces" proportional to deviations from some neutral value must exhibit an oscillatory behavior.*

In many instances—such as heartbeat records and voltages transmitting the human voice—the actual function presented is a *sum* of wavelike components contributed by many different sources (for example, muscles), each vibrating with its own frequency and intensity:

$$f(t) = [A_1 \sin(\sqrt{\lambda_1}t) + B_1 \cos(\sqrt{\lambda_1}t)] + [A_2 \sin(\sqrt{\lambda_2}t) + B_2 \cos(\sqrt{\lambda_2}t)]$$

$$+ \cdots + [A_n \sin(\sqrt{\lambda_n}t) + B_n \cos(\sqrt{\lambda_n}t)]. \tag{22}$$

See Fig. 16-22 for the graph of a mere two-term sum, and Fig. 16-23 for the voltage representing a human voice pronouncing the sound "*ae*."

If one wants to detect a voice or other specific signal from among a total sum of oscillations such as $f(t)$ in (22), then certain terms in the sum may be more important than others. Terms with very high frequencies (high values of $\sqrt{\lambda}$) may merely represent "static," and terms with very low frequencies may merely represent "rumble." If we were given only the total sum $f(t)$, could we isolate a particular group of terms, and "filter out" the others? (That's what the circuitry in expensive radios is claimed to do.) A more specific example:

FIGURE 16-22

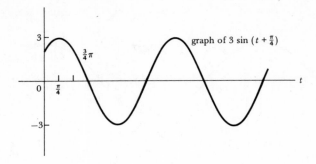

graph of $3 \sin\left(t + \frac{\pi}{4}\right)$

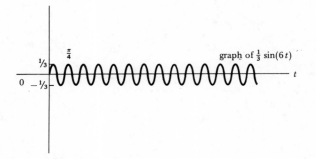

graph of $\frac{1}{3} \sin(6t)$

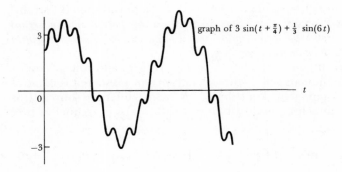

graph of $3 \sin\left(t + \frac{\pi}{4}\right) + \frac{1}{3} \sin(6t)$

FIGURE 16-23

could we pick out and *evaluate* the constants A_2 and B_2 from among all the others in the sum (22)?

I'll return to this question in a later section. Meanwhile, try your own hand at a few trigonometric expressions in the problems of the next section.

And you might ask this: What is the universe made of? Of "atoms" — at least such has been the popular conception for some time. And what is an "atom" made of? Of electrons whirling in circular orbits around a "nucleus" composed of other whirling objects — so the current theories hold. But then must not every observable motion be the sum total of a vast number of oscillations which arise from circular motions? So thought Hermann Helmholtz, a physicist, long ago (1850+); and he *conjectured* that the graph of any continuous function (representing some motion) can be approximated as closely as one pleases by a "sum of oscillations" as in (22). You might think of any one term in the sum as describing the vibration of an appropriately tuned guitar string. So if you could hear all the strings corresponding to the terms in (22) playing together, you would hear an immense chord. In his inner ear Helmholtz heard the symphony of chords of all the motions of the universe.

I invite you to explore Helmholtz's conjecture in Problem 19 of Sec. 16.8.

$$\sin'(x) = \cos(x)$$
$$\cos'(x) = -\sin(x)$$
$$\tan'(x) = \frac{1}{\cos^2 u} = \sec^2 u$$
$$\sec'(x) = \tan(x) \cdot \sec(x)$$

16.8 PROBLEMS ON TRIG FUNCTIONS AND OSCILLATIONS

°1. (a) Draw a circle of radius 1 and locate angles of
$30°$, $30° \pm 90°$, $30° \pm 180°$, $30° \pm 360°$, $30° \pm 720°$.
$45°$, $45° \pm 90°$, $45° \pm 180°$, $45° \pm 360°$, $45° \pm 720°$.

(b) Translate the angles of part (a) into "radians."

(c) Compute $\sin u$, $\cos u$, and $\tan u$ for the angles in part (b).

°2. For each of the following trigonometric functions $f(u)$, defined for radian inputs u with $-4\pi \leq u \leq 4\pi$, calculate f' and f''. (Apply the chain rule if necessary.) Then use information from these derivatives to make a careful ~~sketch of the graph of~~ f.

(a) $\sin u$ (b) $\cos u$ (c) $\sin 2u$

(d) $\cos 2u$ (e) $\sin \frac{1}{2} u$ (f) $\cos \frac{1}{2} u$

(g) $\sin\left(u - \frac{\pi}{4}\right)$ (h) $\cos\left(u - \frac{\pi}{4}\right)$ (i) $\sin\left(u + \frac{\pi}{4}\right)$

(j) $\cos\left(u + \frac{\pi}{4}\right)$ (k) $\sin 2\left(u + \frac{\pi}{4}\right)$ (l) $\cos(3u - 1)$

3. Here's how to recast an expression of the form

$$A \sin u + B \cos u \qquad (*)$$

into a form involving only a cosine. Recall the identity

$$\cos(u - v) = \cos u \cos v + \sin u \sin v \qquad (\dagger)$$

(from Appendix A). How can we make the constants A and B in (*) play the roles of $\sin v$ and $\cos v$ in (†)? Recall that $(\sin v)^2 + (\cos v)^2 = 1$ always. So write (*) as

$$\sqrt{A^2+B^2}\left\{\left(\frac{B}{\sqrt{A^2+B^2}}\right)\cos u + \left(\frac{A}{\sqrt{A^2+B^2}}\right)\sin u\right\}. \qquad (**)$$

(a) Now draw a circle of radius $\sqrt{A^2+B^2}$ and locate an angle v such that

$$\cos v = \frac{B}{\sqrt{A^2+B^2}} \quad \text{and} \quad \sin v = \frac{A}{\sqrt{A^2+B^2}}.$$

(b) Show why $v = \arctan(A/B)$.

(c) Once you've found v, put (**), (†), and (*) together to show that

$$A \sin u + b \cos u = \sqrt{A^2+B^2}\,\cos(u-v) \qquad (***)$$

°4. Write each of the following expressions in the form (***) of Problem 3, for a specific value of v:

(a) $\sin u + 4 \cos u$

  Sample:

  $$v = \arctan\frac{1}{4}$$

  and

  $$\sin u + 4 \cos u = \sqrt{17}\cos\left(u - \arctan\frac{1}{4}\right)$$

(b) $\sin u - \dfrac{1}{3}\cos u$

(c) $2 \sin u - 5 \cos u$.

5. Use the results of Problem 3 to show that any function of the form

$$f(t) = A \sin \omega t + B \cos \omega t$$

can be rewritten in the form

$$f(t) = R \cos[\omega(t-\lambda)],$$

where $R > 0$ and $\omega > 0$. As I noted in Sec. 16.7, the constant R is usually called the *amplitude* of f; τ, the *phase* of f; $\omega/2\pi$, the *frequency* of f; and $2\pi/\omega$, the *period* of f.

°6. Write each of the following functions in the form (*) of Problem 5, identifying its amplitude, phase, frequency, and period; and sketch a graph. In each case, note how the phase τ shifts the graph from a similar graph with $\tau = 0$.

(a) $\sin 2t + 4 \cos 2t$

(b) $\sin 2t - \frac{1}{3}\cos 2t$

(c) $2 \sin 3t - 5 \cos 3t$

(d) $\sin(4t+2)$.

7. In Fig. 16-12, I indicated how sin u and cos u are usually defined for all real inputs in terms of their definition for u's in $[-\pi, \pi]$ or $[0, 2\pi]$. Via formulas:

$$\sin(u+2\pi n) = \sin u \qquad \text{for all } u \text{ in } [-\pi, \pi] \text{ and } n = 0, \pm 1, \pm 2, ...,$$

and

$$\cos(u + 2\pi n) = \cos u \qquad \text{for all } u \text{ in } [0, 2\pi] \text{ and } n = 0, \pm 1, \pm 2, ...$$

(a) Use these definitions to show that the graph of

$$f(t) = A \cos [\omega(t-\tau)]$$

must "repeat itself" after every $2\pi/\omega$ units of time; that is, that

$$f\left(t+\frac{2\pi}{\omega}\right) = f(t) \qquad \text{for all } t.$$

(b) Show that we can't have

$$f(t+T') = f(t) \qquad \text{for all } t,$$

if T' is any time length *shorter* than $T = 2\pi/\omega$, the "period" of f.

(c) If ω is a positive integer, how many times must the graph of $f(t) = A \cos[\omega(t-\tau)]$ repeat itself during the interval $[0, 2\pi]$?

(d) Check your answer in part (c) against the functions (a)–(d) in Problem 6.

8. (a) Recall that

$$\tan u = \frac{\sin u}{\cos u}, \qquad \text{for all } u \neq \frac{\pi}{2}(2k+1)$$

for some integer k. Calculate $(\tan u)'$ and $(\tan u)''$ at all inputs where these derivatives exist; and use information from these derivatives to graph tan u carefully.

(b) Do the same for

$$\text{secant } u = \frac{1}{\cos u} \qquad \text{for all } u \neq \frac{\pi}{2}(2k+1).$$

°9. Find f' for the following functions, at all inputs where f and f' make sense.

(a) $f(x) = \log_e \sqrt{3 \cos 4x}$.

Sample reasoning: Apply the chain rule several times to get

$$f'(x) = \frac{1}{\sqrt{3 \cos 4x}} (\sqrt{3 \cos 4x})'$$

$$= \frac{1}{\sqrt{3 \cos 4x}} \left[\frac{1}{2} (3 \cos 4x)^{-1/2}\right] (3 \cos 4x)'$$

$$= \frac{1}{2} \frac{1}{3 \cos 4x} 3 \cdot 4(-\sin 4x) = -2\frac{\sin 4x}{\cos 4x} = -2 \tan 4x.$$

(b) $f(t) = \tan 3t$

(c) $f(v) = 2 \cot \dfrac{v}{2}$ $\quad \left(\text{recall cot } u = \dfrac{1}{\tan u}\right)$

$\tan = \dfrac{\sin}{\cos}$

$\sec = \dfrac{1}{\cos}$

$\cot = \dfrac{\cos}{\sin}$

$\csc = \dfrac{1}{\sin}$

(d) $f(x) = \sec x = \dfrac{1}{\cos x}$

(e) $f(x) = \dfrac{1}{2} \sin^2 x$ (f) $f(t) = \sqrt{\cos 2t}$

(g) $f(u) = (\tan 3u)^{1/3}$ (h) $f(x) = x \cos x$

(i) $f(u) = \dfrac{\sin u}{u}$ (j) $f(x) = \sin 2x \cos x$

(k) $f(x) = \log_e (\sin ax)$ (l) $f(x) = e^{ax} \sin bx$

(m) $f(x) = \log_e \left(\tan \dfrac{x}{2} \right)$ (n) $f(x) = \sin^2(\pi - x)$

*(o) $f(x) = x^{\sin x}$ *(p) $f(x) = (\cos x)^x$

10. Find f'' for several of the functions in Problem 8, at inputs where f'' exists.

*11. In Sec. 16.6 I proved part of Theorem C by showing that

$$(\sin u)'_{\text{at } u_0} = \cos u_0$$

for all u_0 with $0 < u_0 < \pi/2$. Now help complete the proof of Theorem C:

(a) Use similar geometric arguments to show that

$$(\sin u)'_{\text{at } 0} = \cos 0 = 1 \quad \text{and} \quad (\sin u)'_{\text{at } \pi/2} = \cos \frac{\pi}{2} = 0.$$

(b) Use geometric arguments to show that $(\cos u)'_{\text{at } u_0} = -\sin u_0$ for all u_0 with $0 < u_0 < \pi/2$.

(c) An alternative to (b): use the relation $\cos u = \sin(\pi/2 - u)$ and the chain rule to show that $(\cos u)' = -\sin u$ for $0 < u < \pi/2$.

(d) Check the identities and definitions

$$\sin(u) = \sin(\pi - u) = -\sin(\pi + u) = -\sin(-u)$$
$$= \sin(u \pm 2\pi) = \text{etc.} \quad \text{for all } u,$$

and

$$\cos(u) = -\cos(\pi - u) = -\cos(\pi + u) = \cos(-u)$$
$$= \cos(u \pm 2\pi) = \text{etc.} \quad \text{for all } u;$$

and use them together with the chain rule and the previous cases, to show that

$$(\sin u)' = \cos u \quad \text{and} \quad (\cos u)' = -\sin u \quad \text{for all } u.$$

12. (a) Use the result of Problem 10(a) to show that

$$\lim_{u \to 0} \left[\frac{\sin u}{u} \right] = 1.$$

(b) If you knew that $\lim_{u \to 0} [(\sin u)/u] = 1$ independently of Problem 10, show how you could use this result together with the trigonometric identity

$$\sin x - \sin y = 2 \cos\left(\frac{x+y}{2}\right) \cos\left(\frac{x-y}{2}\right)$$

(from Appendix A) to prove that $(\sin u)' = \cos u$ for all u.
(c) Do the same for $(\cos u)' = -\sin u$ via the identity

$$\cos x - \cos y = -2 \sin\left(\frac{x+y}{2}\right) \sin\left(\frac{x-y}{2}\right).$$

13. Show that if angles θ are measured in degrees, then

$$\frac{d \sin \theta}{d\theta} = \frac{\pi}{180} \cos \theta \quad \text{and} \quad \frac{d \cos \theta}{d\theta} = -\frac{\pi}{180} \sin \theta.$$

(Suggestion: Let θ degrees correspond to u radians. Then $\sin \theta = \sin u$, whereas $\theta = (180/\pi)u$. Examine the ratio

$$\frac{\sin \theta - \sin \theta_0}{\theta - \theta_0} = \frac{\sin u - \sin u_0}{[(180/\pi)u] - [(180/\pi)u_0]}.)$$

°14. In Sec. 16.7 (Theorem D), I indicated that any function of the form $f(t) = A \sin(\sqrt{\lambda} t) + B \cos(\sqrt{\lambda} t)$ provided a solution for the "oscillator equation" $f''(t) = -f(t)$; where $\lambda > 0$, and inputs t could be any real numbers. In each of the following cases, determine values for A and B so that f will satisfy the conditions indicated.
(a) $\lambda = 4; f(0) = 3, f'(0) = -5$
(b) $\lambda = 4; f(0) = 3, f'(0) = 5$
(c) $\lambda = 4; f(0) = 3, f\left(\frac{\pi}{8}\right) = 2$
(d) $\lambda = 4; f'(0) = 0, f'\left(\frac{\pi}{8}\right) = -1$
(e) $\lambda = 9; f(1) = 3, f'(1) = 5$
(f) $\lambda = 9; f(0) = 3, f'(1) = 5$
Do there exist values for A and B such that f will satisfy the following conditions?
(g) $\lambda = 4; f(0) = 3, f(\pi) = 2$
(h) $\lambda = 4; f'(0) = 0, f'(\pi) = -1$

15. Help prove a UNIQUENESS RESULT FOR THE OSCILLATOR EQUATION: *For a given interval $[0, T]$ and given constants $\lambda > 0$, a, and b, the differential equation*

$$f''(t) = -\lambda f(t) \qquad \text{for all } t \text{ in } [0, T] \tag{*}$$

can have only one solution satisfying the initial conditions

$$f(0) = a \quad \text{and} \quad f'(0) = b; \tag{**}$$

namely

$$g(t) = \left(\frac{b}{\sqrt{\lambda}}\right) \sin(\sqrt{\lambda} t) + a \cos(\sqrt{\lambda} t). \tag{†}$$

(a) First check that $g(0) = a$ and $g'(0) = b$, for g as given in (†). Next, suppose that $h(t)$ is some other function satisfying (*) and (**); that is, that

$$h''(t) = -\lambda h(t) \text{ on } [0, T], \quad \text{and } h(0) = a \quad \text{and} \quad h'(0) = b.$$

Form the *difference* function $D(t) = g(t) - h(t)$, and try to show that $D(t) = 0$ on $[0, T]$.

(b) Check that

$$D''(t) = -\lambda D(t) \text{ on } [0, T], \text{ and } D(0) = 0 \quad \text{and } D'(0) = 0 \quad (\ddagger)$$

because both g and h satisfy (*) and (**).

Here's a clever auxiliary function that someone cooked up to do the rest of the job: Let

$$K(t) = \lambda [D(t)]^2 + [D'(t)]^2.$$

(The squares are there to avoid misleading cancellations.)

(c) In view of (‡), show that $K'(t) = 0$ on $[0, T]$; hence $K(t) = 0$ on $[0, T]$; hence $D(t) = 0$ on $[0, T]$; hence $h(t) = g(t)$ on $[0, T]$.

16. Suppose that an object moves back and forth in a straight line under springlike influence such as I discussed in Sec. 16.4. If it takes 3 seconds to move from dead center to its maximum displacement, how long must it take to go half of the way?

(Suggestion: The displacement from dead center must be of the form $f(t) = A \sin(\sqrt{\lambda} t) + B \cos(\sqrt{\lambda} t)$. If we start counting time when the object is exactly at dead center, we'll have $f(0) = 0$, hence $B = 0$. What's given is that $f(2) = A$, the maximum value of $A \sin(\sqrt{\lambda} t)$. Solve for λ, and then find the smallest t for which $f(t) = \frac{1}{2}A$.)

17. Suppose that an object oscillates along a straight line, as in Sec. 16.4, with a maximum displacement of $\frac{1}{2}$ ft. And suppose we observe its velocity to be 5 ft/sec as it passes dead center. How long will it take to reach its maximum displacement?

*18. One vibrating string will give a tone that sounds "an octave higher" than that of a second string if it is vibrating twice as fast as the second string. Suppose that at a given instant both strings have equal displacements from dead center. How much more "force" will there be on the first string than on the second? (Suppose that the "force" is proportional in each case to the acceleration at that instant.)

19. Explore Helmholtz's conjecture (which I mentioned at the end of the last section) for the following cases of a continuous function f. For some choice of allowable error, say, $\epsilon = 1/10$, see whether you can find constants $A_1, B_1, A_2, B_2, \ldots, A_n, B_n,$ and $\lambda_1, \lambda_2, \ldots, \lambda_n$ — as many as you need — so that $|f(t) - [A_1 \sin(\lambda_1 t) + B_1 \cos(\lambda_1 t) + \cdots + A_n \sin(\lambda_n t) + B_n \cos(\lambda_n t)]| < \epsilon$ for $0 \le t \le 1$.

(a) $f(t) \equiv 1$ (b) $f(t) \equiv t$ (c) $f(t) \equiv t^2$

Sketch graphs of the approximating sums of trig functions.

16.9 INVERSE TRIG FUNCTIONS

Whenever we learn how to differentiate new functions—such as sin u, cos u, and tan u in Sec. 16.6, then we can possibly add *still more* to the list of differentiable functions by looking at the *inverses* of the new functions (if they have any).

To even dream of inverses, we'll have to restrict the domains of sin u, cos u, and tan u to sets where the functions are one-to-one. There are many ways to do so. I've pictured the traditional choices (in black) in Figs. 16-24, 16-25, and 16-26, together with the corresponding inverse functions (in green).

Graph of sin u

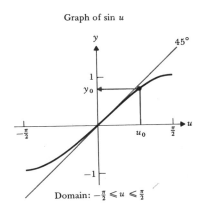

Domain: $-\frac{\pi}{2} \leqslant u \leqslant \frac{\pi}{2}$

Graph of inverse, "arcsin y"

Domain: $-1 \leqslant y \leqslant 1$

FIGURE 16-24

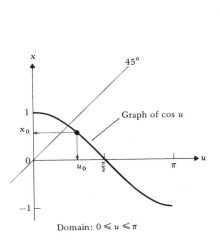

Domain: $0 \leqslant u \leqslant \pi$

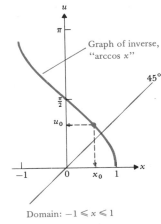

Domain: $-1 \leqslant x \leqslant 1$

FIGURE 16-25

FIGURE 16-26   Graph of tan u Graph of inverse, "arctan u"

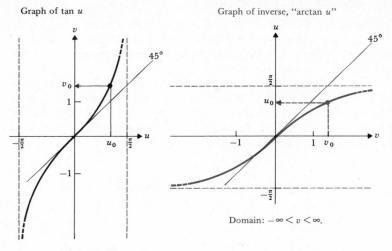

Domain: $-\frac{\pi}{2} < u < \frac{\pi}{2}$

Domain: $-\infty < v < \infty$.

For $f(u) = \sin u$ as in Fig. 16-24, the inverse function $g(y)$ is often called "arcsin y." To calculate $g'(y_0)$ at an input $y_0 = f(u_0) = \sin u_0$, we need merely take *reciprocals*:

$$g'(y_0) = \frac{1}{f'(u_0)}, \tag{1}$$

provided $f'(u_0) \neq 0$. Such was the message of Theorem A (on "derivatives of inverses") in Sec. 14.10. But

$$f'(u_0) = (\sin u)' \text{ at } u_0 = \cos u_0 \tag{2}$$

—the key result (Theorem C) of Sec. 16.6. You might recall (say, from Fig. 16-12) that $\cos u > 0$ for all inputs u with $-\pi/2 < u < \pi/2$. Such u's—via the relation $y = \sin u$ in Fig. 16-24—correspond to y's in the open interval $-1 < y < 1$. Together these facts yield

$$g'(y_0) = \frac{1}{\cos u_0} \qquad \text{at any } y_0 \text{ with } -1 < y_0 < 1. \tag{3}$$

If we could only express the right-hand side of (3) solely in terms of y_0, we'd have an effective formula for $g'(y_0)$. But recall: $y_0 = \sin u_0$. Hence

$$y_0{}^2 + (\cos u_0)^2 = (\sin u_0)^2 + (\cos u_0)^2 = 1, \tag{4}$$

and we can solve for

$$\cos u_0 = \sqrt{1 - y_0{}^2} \tag{5}$$

(using the positive root, since $\cos u > 0$ for $-\pi/2 < u < \pi/2$). Conclusion:

$$\boxed{(\arcsin y)' = \frac{1}{\sqrt{1-y^2}} \qquad \text{at all } y \text{ with } -1 < y < 1.} \tag{6}$$

Next case: The inverse function of cos u, pictured in Fig. 16-25, is often called "arccos x." At $x_0 = \cos u_0$, we'll have

$$(\text{arccos } x)' = \frac{1}{(\cos u)'} = \frac{1}{-\sin u_0}, \tag{7}$$

provided $\sin u_0 \neq 0$. You might recall (again from Fig. 16-12) that $\sin u > 0$ for all inputs u with $0 < u < \pi$. Such u's—via the relation $x = \cos u$ in Fig. 16-25—correspond to x's in the open interval $-1 < x < 1$. As before, we can also solve the equation

$$(\sin u_0)^2 + x_0{}^2 = (\sin u_0)^2 + (\cos u_0)^2 = 1$$

for

$$\sin u_0 = \sqrt{1 - x_0{}^2}. \tag{8}$$

Conclusion:

$$\boxed{(\text{arccos } x)' = -\frac{1}{\sqrt{1-x^2}} \qquad \text{at all } x \text{ with} -1 < x < 1.} \tag{9}$$

Similarly: At any $v_0 = \tan u_0$

$$(\text{arctan } v)' = \frac{1}{(\tan u)'} = \frac{1}{(1/\cos u_0)^2} = (\cos u_0)^2. \tag{10}$$

(I calculated $(\tan u)'$ in Example 3 of Sec. 16.6.) To solve for $(\cos u_0)^2$ in terms of $v_0 = \tan u_0$, let's divide the identity $1 = (\sin u_0)^2 + (\cos u_0)^2$ through by $(\cos u_0)^2$, to get

$$\frac{1}{(\cos u_0)^2} = \left(\frac{\sin u_0}{\cos u_0}\right)^2 + 1 = (\tan u_0)^2 + 1$$

$$= v_0{}^2 + 1. \tag{11}$$

Conclusion:

$$\boxed{(\text{arctan } v)' = \frac{1}{v^2+1} \qquad \text{at any } v.} \tag{12}$$

I'll summarize the results with a uniform notation for inputs:

Theorem (on "derivatives of inverse trig functions"): At any input x with $-1 < x < 1$:

$$(\text{arcsin } x)' = \frac{1}{\sqrt{1-x^2}} \quad \text{and} \quad (\text{arccos } x)' = -\frac{1}{\sqrt{1-x^2}}.$$

At any input x whatsoever:

$$(\text{arctan } x)' = \frac{1}{x^2+1}.$$

$$\text{arc sec}' y = \frac{1}{y\sqrt{y^2-1}}$$

EXAMPLE 1. If $f(x) = \text{arcsin } ax$, then by the "chain rule"

$$f'(x) = \frac{1}{\sqrt{1-(ax)^2}}(ax)' = \frac{a}{\sqrt{1-a^2x^2}}.$$

EXAMPLE 2. If $f(x) = \arctan ax$, then

$$f'(x) = \frac{1}{(ax)^2 + 1}(ax)' = \frac{a}{a^2x^2 + 1}.$$

EXAMPLE 3. If $f(x) = \arctan x^2$, then by the "chain rule"

$$f'(x) = \frac{1}{(x^2)^2 + 1}(x^2)' = \frac{2x}{x^4 + 1}.$$

EXAMPLE 4. If $f(x) = \log_e \cos x$, then by the "chain rule"

$$f'(x) = \frac{1}{\cos x}(\cos x)' = \frac{1}{\cos x}(-\sin x) = -\tan x.$$

16.10 ANTIDERIVATIVES OF TRIG FUNCTIONS

Read backward, each new formula we've found for the derivative of a trig or an inverse trig function provides a new possibility for recognizing antiderivatives. So we can extend (from Sec. 15.10) the

Table of rules for finding antiderivatives

A function h of the form	will have an antiderivative H of the form
$a \cos ax$	$\sin ax$
$a \sin ax$	$-\cos ax$
$\dfrac{a}{(\cos ax)^2}$	$\tan ax$
$\dfrac{a}{\sqrt{1 - a^2x^2}} \quad (\lvert ax \rvert < 1)$	$\arcsin ax$
$-\dfrac{a}{\sqrt{1 - a^2x^2}} \quad (\lvert ax \rvert < 1)$	$\arccos ax$
$\dfrac{a}{a^2x^2 + 1}$	$\arctan ax$
$-\tan x = \dfrac{1}{\cos x}(-\sin x)$	$\log_e \cos x$ (by the "backward chain rule")

EXAMPLE 1. The function $h(u) = (\sin u)^2(\cos u)$ has the form $G'(F(u))F'(u)$, where $F(u) = \sin u$, $G'(y) = y^2$ and $G(y) = \frac{1}{3}y^3$. By the "backward chain rule" (recall Sec. 15.10), $h(u)$ has an antiderivative

$$H(u) = G(F(u)) = \frac{1}{3}(\sin u)^3. \tag{1}$$

EXAMPLE 2. If we write $k(x) = (\cos x)^3$ as

$$k(x) = (\cos x)^2 \cos x = [1 - (\sin x)^2](\cos x)$$

$$= \cos x - (\sin x)^2(\cos x) \tag{2}$$

we can use the result in Example 1 to write an antiderivative

$$K(x) = \sin x - \frac{1}{3}(\sin x)^3. \tag{3}$$

EXAMPLE 3. If we write the function $h(x) = 1/(x^2 + 4)$ as

$$h(x) = \frac{1}{4(\frac{1}{2}x)^2 + 4} = \frac{1}{4}\frac{1}{(\frac{1}{2}x)^2 + 1} = \frac{1}{2}\frac{\frac{1}{2}}{(\frac{1}{2}x)^2 + 1} \tag{4}$$

we might — as in the above table — recognize an antiderivative for h:

$$H(x) = \frac{1}{2}\arctan\frac{1}{2}x. \tag{5}$$

If you care to try your own hand at recognizing more anti-derivatives, look at several of the problems in the next section.

16.11 PROBLEMS ON TRIG FUNCTIONS OF ALL SORTS

°1. Find f' at all possible inputs:

(a) $f(x) = (\sin x)^5$

(b) $f(x) = \dfrac{1}{(\sin x)^2 + 1}$

(c) $f(x) = \sin(\arccos x)$

(d) $f(x) = \sin(3x^2 + 2)$

(e) $f(x) = \cos\sqrt{1 - x^2}$

(f) $f(x) = \sin x^2 \cos x^3$

(g) $f(x) = \log_e \cos x$

(h) $f(x) = \tan 5x^2$

(i) $f(x) = \tan\left(\dfrac{x+1}{x-1}\right)$

(j) $f(x) = \sec x = \dfrac{1}{\cos x}$

(k) $f(x) = \cot 3x = \dfrac{1}{\tan 3x}$

(l) $f(x) = \arcsin(3x + 2)$

(m) $f(x) = \arccos\sqrt{1 - x^2}$

(n) $f(x) = \arctan\left(\dfrac{x+1}{x-1}\right)$

(o) $f(x) = e^{\arcsin 2x}$

(p) $f(x) = \dfrac{\arcsin x}{\arccos x}$

(q) $f(x) = \cos(\arcsin x)$

°2. Find antiderivatives for the following functions. (Assume the domains to be such that the formulas make sense.)

(a) $h(x) = 3x^2 \sin x^3$

(b) $h(x) = 6x^2(\sin x^3)^4$

(c) $h(x) = (\sec x)^2 = \dfrac{1}{(\cos x)^2}$ (Recall Example 3 of Sec. 16.6.)

(d) $h(x) = (\sin x)^2 \cos x$

(e) $h(x) = (\tan x)^3 \sec^2 x$ (Recall that $(\tan x)' = \dfrac{1}{(\cos x)^2} = (\sec x)^2$.)

(f) $h(x) = \dfrac{\cos x}{\sin x}$ (Suggestion: use the chain rule backward.)

(g) $h(x) = 3x^2 (\sec x^3)^2$

(h) $h(x) = \dfrac{1}{1+4x^2}$

(i) $h(x) = \dfrac{x}{1-4x^2}$

(j) $h(x) = \dfrac{1}{x^2+9}$

(k) $h(x) = \dfrac{1}{(x-2)^2+1}$

(Suggestion: Recall an antiderivative for $1/(y^2+1)$, and modify it.)

(l) $h(x) = \dfrac{1}{x^2+2x+2}$ (m) $h(x) = \dfrac{1}{x^2+2x+5}$

(n) $h(x) = \dfrac{2x+3}{x^2+2x+5}$

(Can you write h as a sum of easier functions?)

(o) $h(x) = \dfrac{1}{\sqrt{25-x^2}}$ (p) $h(x) = \dfrac{1}{\sqrt{16-9x^2}}$

(q) $h(x) = \dfrac{1}{\sqrt{2x-x^2}}$

(Suggestion: Write $2x-x^2 = 1-(1-2x+x^2) = 1-(x-1)^2$.)

(r) $h(x) = \dfrac{3-2x}{\sqrt{2x-x^2}}$

(Can you write h as a sum of easier functions?)

(s) $h(x) = \dfrac{e^x}{e^{2x}+1}$

(t) $h(x) = \dfrac{1}{(\log_e x)^2+1}\left(\dfrac{1}{x}\right)$

(u) $h(x) = \dfrac{e^x}{\sqrt{1-e^{2x}}}$ (for $x < 0$)

(v) $h(x) = \dfrac{\cos x}{4-\sin^2 x}$

3. Use the "antidifferentiation by parts" method of Sec. 15.10 to find the indicated antiderivatives:

(a) $\int \arctan x\, dx$.

Sample reasoning: Write $\arctan x = F'(x)G(x)$ where $F'(x) = 1$, $F(x) = x$, $G(x) = \arctan x$ and $G'(x) = 1/(x^2 + 1)$. Then

$$\int F'G\, dx = FG - \int G'F\, dx$$

$$= x \arctan x - \int \left(\frac{1}{x^2 + 1}\right) x\, dx$$

$$= x \arctan x - \frac{1}{2} \int \frac{1}{x^2 + 1}\, 2x\, dx.$$

Note that $[\log_e (x^2 + 1)]' = [1/(x^2 + 1)](2x)$. Hence

$$\int \arctan x\, dx = x \arctan x - \frac{1}{2} \log_e (x^2 + 1).$$

(b) $\int x \arctan x\, dx$

(c) $\int \arcsin x\, dx$

(d) $\int x\left(\frac{1}{\cos x}\right)^2 dx$

*16.12 A "BACKWARD APPROACH" TO TRIG FUNCTIONS

In defining $\sin \theta$, $\cos \theta$, $\sin u$, and $\cos u$ above, I always *supposed* that for any real number θ there existed an "angle" of that many "degrees." I supposed that for any real number u there was a unique arc that many units in length, on the circumference of unit circle. Can such intuitive assumptions be supported with any precision? (If not, sailors' compasses would have phantom directions.)

Now the very notion of "angle" is itself as difficult to define — without going in *logical* circles — as were the geometric notions of "point" and "line" in Chap. 4. So let's avoid "angles," and focus on "arclength" u. If you're willing, moreover, to reverse our path and to define (say) arccos x *before* trying to define cos u—then doubts about the existence of arcs of all lengths u will disappear.

Here's how: Pick any x in the interval $[-1, 1]$. There will correspond to it a unique point $P = (x, \sqrt{1-x^2})$ on the upper half of the unit circle, as in Fig. 16-27. By the limiting methods I recalled before (Sec. 10.1, Problem 14 of Sec. 10.5 and Problem 6 of Sec. 12.4), the arc AP will have a unique length u $(0 \leq u \leq \pi)$. Let's assign this value (as output) to the number x as input, and call the function "arccos x." I invite you to check — using the "sandwich inequalities" for arclength in Sec. 16.5 — that (so defined) arccos x is a *continuous* function at all x in $[-1, 1]$, and is *strictly decreasing*. Let's call its inverse function "cos u." The graphs for $u = $ arccos x and $x = \cos u$

FIGURE 16-27

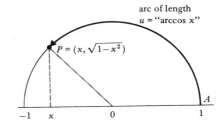

arc of length
$u = $ "arccos x"

$P = (x, \sqrt{1-x^2})$

$-1 \quad x \qquad 0 \qquad\qquad 1$

are just as pictured before in Fig. 16-25; only now *think of the black function as the inverse of the green.*

The clinching argument: since arccos x is *continuous*, its outputs u must take on *all* values between its minimum $0 = $ arccos 1 and $\pi = $ arccos (-1). (Recall the result on "intermediate values" in Sec. 13.1.) Put otherwise, cos u is defined for *all* inputs u in $[0, \pi]$.

I invite you to explore how we might extend the definition of cos u to all other real u, in terms of the outputs I just defined on $[0, \pi]$.

16.13 SUMMARY OF CHAPTER 16

DEFINITIONS: A *differential equation* is an equality relating various derivatives of a function, the function itself, and perhaps other known functions. Any particular function which—together with its derivatives—does satisfy the indicated relationship is called a *solution* of the given differential equation.
(Sec. 16.2)

THEOREM (UNIQUE SOLUTION OF THE "GROWTH EQUATION"): For a given interval $[0, T]$ and given constants a and b, the differential equation

$$f'(t) = af(t) \qquad \text{for all } t \text{ in } [0, T]$$

can have only *one* solution satisfying the *"initial condition,"*

$$f(0) = b;$$

namely, $g(t) = be^{at}$.
(Sec. 16.2)

For a discussion of "sines," "cosines," "arclength," and "radians," see Sec. 16.5. (All results below for such "trigonometric functions" refer to inputs measured in "radians.")

THEOREM: The functions sin u and cos u are continuous at any real input u_0.
(Sec. 16.6)

THEOREM: $(\sin u)' = \cos u$, and $(\cos u)' = -\sin u$ at any real input u.
(Sec. 16.6)

COROLLARY:

$$(\tan u)' = \left(\frac{\sin u}{\cos u}\right)' = \frac{1}{(\cos u)^2} = (\sec u)^2$$

at any input u such that cos $u \neq 0$.
(Sec. 16.6, Example 3)

THEOREM (SOLUTIONS OF THE "OSCILLATOR EQUATION"): For any two real numbers A and B, the function

$$f(t) = A \sin (\sqrt{\lambda} t) + B \cos (\sqrt{\lambda} t)$$

is a solution of the *"oscillator equation"*

$$f''(t) = -\lambda f(t) \qquad \text{for } 0 \leqslant t \leqslant T$$

(where λ and T are given positive constants).
(Sec. 16.7)

THEOREM: Functions of the form $A \sin (\sqrt{\lambda}t) + B \cos (\sqrt{\lambda}t)$ are the *only* possible solutions of the equation $f''(t) = -\lambda f(t)$ for $0 \leqslant t \leqslant T$ and $\lambda > 0$. The constants A and B are *uniquely* determined by given "initial conditions" $f(0) = b$ and $f'(0) = c$.
(Problem 15 of Sec. 16.8)

THEOREM: A function $f(t) = A \sin (\sqrt{\lambda}t) + B \cos (\sqrt{\lambda}t)$ has the alternate form

$$f(t) = R \cos [\sqrt{\lambda}(t-\tau)].$$

Here R is called the *amplitude* of f, τ the *phase* of f, $\sqrt{\lambda}/2\pi$ the *frequency* of f, and $2\pi/\sqrt{\lambda}$ the *period* of f. And

$$f\left(t + \frac{2\pi}{\sqrt{\lambda}}\right) = f(t) \qquad \text{for any } t.$$

(Problem 5 of Sec. 16.8)

For definitions of the "inverse trig functions" "arcsin," "arccos," and "arctan," see Sec. 16.9.

THEOREM (ON "DERIVATIVES OF INVERSE TRIG FUNCTIONS"): At any input x with $-1 < x < 1$:

$$(\arcsin x)' = \frac{1}{\sqrt{1-x^2}} \quad \text{and} \quad (\arccos x)' = -\frac{1}{\sqrt{1-x^2}}.$$

At any input x whatsoever: $(\arctan x)' = 1/(x^2+1)$.
(Sec. 16.9)

For a table of antiderivatives involving trig functions, see Sec. 16.10.

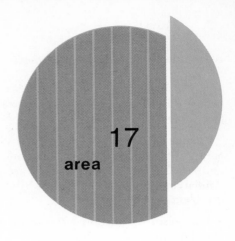

area

17

In this chapter and the next, I'll discuss how we can define and calculate a number of quantities—areas, volumes, savings, averages, probabilities, and so on—by taking limits of "approximating sums." I'll devote this chapter mostly to the topic of "area"—where approximation ideas first arose.

17.1 DO REGIONS ALWAYS HAVE VOLUMES OR AREAS?

You might recall from Sec. 7.6 how I calculated the volume of a "mountain": by studying the rate at which the volume of a "cap" of the mountain changed with respect to its height. Even to begin that calculation, I had to *assume* that all the "caps" could have a "volume" measure reasonably assigned to them. And I used other intuitive properties of "volume," such as that of "addition":

volume of $S \cup T$ = volume of S + volume of T (1)

for nonoverlapping regions S and T in three-dimensional space.

Now, the mountain "cap" I drew in Fig. 7-13 had so simple a shape that it would be hard to believe in its not having a reasonable "volume" too. But what if the mountain had a far less regular shape? Can there be regions in three-dimensional space to which it's impossible to assign "volumes" in some reasonable way—in particular, so that the "addition" property (1) would hold? If there is one such, then we should beware. In that case, valid calculations for "volume"—such as in Sec. 7.6—might lead to *in*valid results. (Recall that the formula $M = 1$ followed *validly* from the unreasonable assumption that a largest integer M existed—Sec. 7.2.)

Similarly, can there be regions in the two-dimensional plane to which it's impossible to assign "areas" in a reasonable way? How about the (grey) set of points in Fig. 17-1, which results if we extract from the unit square *all* vertical line segments whose feet are rational numbers? We can also think of this set as the *union* of all vertical line segments in the square whose feet are irrational numbers. Either way, do you believe that this set "has area"?

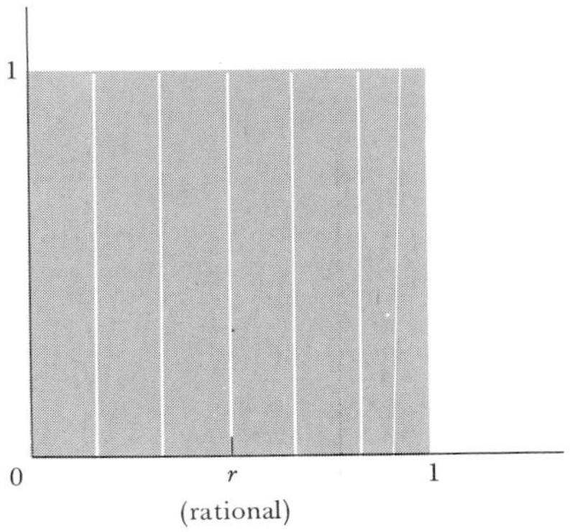

There need be no mystery about "volume" and "area." Let's merely see how the notions are commonly defined for the simplest regions, and then *extend* the definitions—in a precise way—to more complicated sets.

Note that, like "probability" (in Chap. 3) and "length" (in Sec. 10.1), we can think of "volume" and "area" as further examples of *functions*: to certain sets S (as inputs), we assign "volumes" $V(S)$ (or "areas" $A(S)$) as outputs. Let's just be clear about the assignment rules.

Because it's easier to draw pictures in two dimensions than in three, I'll start with "area."

FIGURE 17-1

17.2 HOW WE MIGHT DEFINE "AREA"

For that most basic of sets, a rectangle R with sides of length a and b, what should "area" $A(R)$ mean other than the product $A(R) = ab$? Next, how shall we assign "area" to a union

$$W = R_1 \cup R_2 \cup \cdots \cup R_n \qquad (2)$$

of nonoverlapping rectangles, as in Fig. 17-2 (where $n = 5$)?

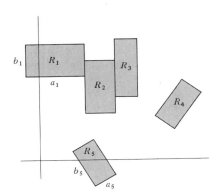

FIGURE 17-2

If we want "areas" to be nonnegative numbers which satisfy the intuitively reasonable "addition" rule

$$A(S \cup T) = A(S) + A(T) \qquad (3)$$

for nonoverlapping sets S and T, then let's assign area

$$A(W) = A(R_1) + A(R_2) + \cdots + A(R_n) \qquad (4)$$

to the union W of rectangles in (2).

Thus, if $S = R_1 \cup R_2 \cup R_3$ and $T = R_4 \cup R_5$ in Fig. 17-2, we would have

$$
\begin{aligned}
A(S \cup T) &= A(R_1) + A(R_2) + A(R_3) + A(R_4) + A(R_5) \\
&= \underbrace{[A(R_1) + A(R_2) + A(R_3)]}_{} + \underbrace{[A(R_4) + A(R_5)]}_{} \\
&= \underbrace{\qquad\qquad}_{A(S)} \quad + \quad \underbrace{\qquad\qquad}_{A(T)}.
\end{aligned}
\tag{5}
$$

But now, how shall we assign "area" to a set with a curved boundary, such as Q in Fig. 17-3?

FIGURE 17-3

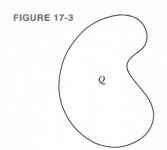

FIGURE 17-4

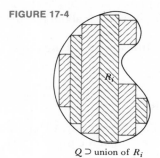

$Q \supset$ union of R_i

FIGURE 17-5

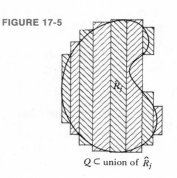

$Q \subset$ union of $\hat{R}_j$

Do you recall meeting a similar problem before? What about that of defining the "length" of the circumference of a circle, in Sec. 10.1? I argued there that we might define such a "length" as a limit (or least upper bound) of the lengths of *inscribed* "approximating polygons," or as a limit (or greatest lower bound) of the lengths of *circumscribed* "approximating polygons"—provided such limits existed and always gave the same value.

Why not try a similar procedure here? We might guide ourselves by another intuitively reasonable property for area—which even follows from the "addition" rule (3)—namely that

$$
A(S) \leqslant A(T) \qquad \text{when } S \subset T.
\tag{6}
$$

Thus, if the set Q in Fig. 17-3 *deserves* an area assignment "$A(Q)$" at all, we might hope to approximate $A(Q)$ from below—as in Fig. 17-4—by a sum of areas of rectangles R_i whose union lies *inside* Q. (Such a union would play a role analogous to an *inscribed* polygon in the "length of arc" definition.) We might also hope to approximate $A(Q)$ from above—as in Fig. 17-5—by a sum of areas of rectangles $\hat{R}_j$ whose union *contains* Q. (Analogous to a polygon *circumscribed* about a circle.)

The question is: for which sets Q can we necessarily find a sequence of better and better "inside area" approximations, and a corresponding sequence of "outside area" approximations—with both sequences tending to a *common* limit? And will that limiting value be the same for all similar approximating sequences? If so, we could then *define* the common limiting value as the "area" $A(Q)$.

To explore the idea of "area" even further, you might ask whether *rectangles* need be the basic "building blocks." Why not squares or triangles? Would the limiting value $A(Q)$ be changed with these? (See Problems 4 of Sec. 17.4, and 18 of Sec. 17.8.)

Suppose we know, somehow, that a set Q does have an area value $A(Q)$ assignable to it. How can we *evaluate* $A(Q)$? Need we actually calculate "approximating areas" and find their limit? Many a set Q can be cut into parts of a special, simpler form such as I've pictured in Fig. 17-6: *a set sitting beneath the graph of some nonnegative function.*

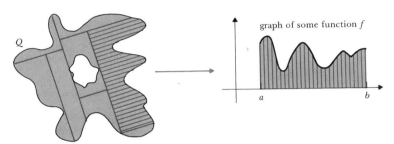

graph of some function f

FIGURE 17-6

And we might hope to find the area of Q if we knew how to evaluate the areas of such simpler sets *determined by graphs*.

Just as I checked the *rate* at which the cap of a mountain changed its volume with increasing height (in Sec. 7.6), so we might check the *rate* at which a subset under a graph changes its area with increasing base. See Fig. 17-7 (and recall Problems 5 and 6 of Sec. 7.7). If we can find the rate $F'(x)$, then (by antidifferentiation) we might find $F(x)$; and in particular, $F(b)$ — the total shaded area.

To answer such questions of existence and evaluation of areas, I'll focus now on sets that do sit beneath graphs. And for simplicity, I'll use as basic regions only rectangles with vertical sides.

FIGURE 17-7

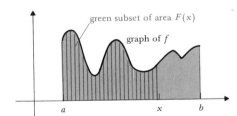

green subset of area $F(x)$

graph of f

17.3 AREAS UNDER GRAPHS

Note that even the green shaded set in Fig. 17-1 (the unit square minus various vertical segments) is a set which "sits under a graph." In that case, the graph is of the function

$$f(x) = \begin{cases} 0 & \text{for rational } x \text{ in } [0, 1], \text{ and} \\ 1 & \text{for irrational } x \text{ in } [0, 1]. \end{cases}$$

But that set gives troubles: How can we get *inside* it with even a single rectangle of nonzero area?

To avoid such troubles, let's look at sets with smoother boundaries — say, sitting under graphs of *continuous* functions. And with finite intervals $[a, b]$ as "bases" (as in Fig. 17-7).

Here is one systematic way to generate approximating "inside" and "outside" rectangles for a region—call it Q—sitting beneath the graph of a continuous nonnegative function f and above an interval $[a, b]$: Divide the base $[a, b]$ into subintervals by numbers x_i, as in Fig. 17-8.

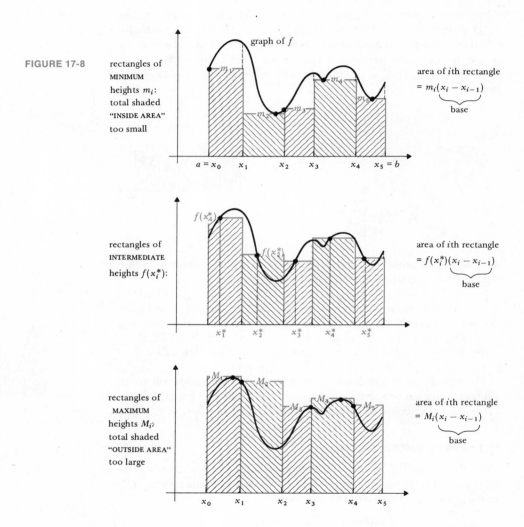

FIGURE 17-8

rectangles of **MINIMUM** heights m_i: total shaded "INSIDE AREA" too small

area of ith rectangle $= m_i(\underbrace{x_i - x_{i-1}}_{\text{base}})$

rectangles of **INTERMEDIATE** heights $f(x_i^*)$:

area of ith rectangle $= f(x_i^*)(\underbrace{x_i - x_{i-1}}_{\text{base}})$

rectangles of **MAXIMUM** heights M_i: total shaded "OUTSIDE AREA" too large

area of ith rectangle $= M_i(\underbrace{x_i - x_{i-1}}_{\text{base}})$

Over any particular one of the closed subintervals, say $[x_{i-1}, x_i]$, the function f, being *continuous*, must have a minimum output— call it m_i, and a maximum output—call it M_i. We can construct an "inside" rectangle with base $[x_{i-1}, x_i]$ and height m_i, which will sit under the graph and will have area $m_i(x_i - x_{i-1})$. Similarly, we can construct an "outside" rectangle with the same base

$[x_{i-1}, x_i]$ but with height M_i. It will tower above the graph and will have area $M_i(x_i - x_{i-1})$.

The union of all the "inside" rectangles will lie inside the region Q, and its area

$$\text{``}A^{\text{in}}\text{''} = m_1(x_1 - x_0) + m_2(x_2 - x_1) + m_3(x_3 - x_2) + \cdots \qquad (1)$$

will provide a *lower approximation* for the quantity we seek to establish, "$A(Q)$."

The union of all the "outside" rectangles will contain Q, and its area

$$\text{``}A^{\text{out}}\text{''} = M_1(x_1 - x_0) + M_2(x_2 - x_1) + M_3(x_3 - x_2) + \cdots \qquad (2)$$

will provide an *upper approximation* for "$A(Q)$."

If you wished, you could also consider rectangles of intermediate height: From each subinterval $[x_{i-1}, x_i]$ you might select some input—call it x_i^*—whose output $f(x_i^*)$ you viewed as fairly "representative" of the other ouputs above $[x_{i-1}, x_i]$. And you could construct a rectangle with base $[x_{i-1}, x_i]$, height $f(x_i^*)$, and area $f(x_i^*)(x_i - x_{i-1})$. What could we say about the sum of such areas,

$$S = f(x_1^*)(x_1 - x_0) + f(x_2^*)(x_2 - x_1) + f(x_3^*)(x_3 - x_2) + \cdots? \qquad (3)$$

It should represent some sort of *intermediate approximation* to that quantity "$A(Q)$" which still awaits a precise definition. So far, all we can say is that

$$A^{\text{in}} \leq S \leq A^{\text{out}}, \qquad (4)$$

since the sums defining these three quantities have corresponding terms in the same relation:

$$m_i(x_i - x_{i-1}) \leq f(x_i^*)(x_i - x_{i-1}) \leq M_i(x_i - x_{i-1}) \qquad \text{for each } i. \qquad (5)$$

How close are the approximating areas A^{in}, S, and A^{out} to an ultimate "$A(Q)$"? The answer certainly depends on the particular choice of subintervals $[x_{i-1}, x_i]$. For example, note in Fig. 17-9 how the total "inside area" increases when I add new (green) subdivision points—thus creating more and thinner "inside" rectangles.

FIGURE 17-9

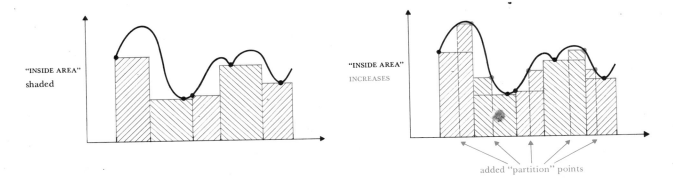

"INSIDE AREA"
shaded

"INSIDE AREA"
INCREASES

added "partition" points

For convenience, a

Definition: Let's use the term *partition* (of an interval $[a, b]$) for any finite set of numbers $\{x_i\}$ with

$$a = x_0 < x_1 < x_2 < \cdots < x_n = b; \tag{6}$$

and let's denote partitions by symbols such as $\sigma = \{x_i\}$ and $\tau = \{x'_j\}$.

Henceforth, when I indicate "inside," "intermediate," and "outside" areas according to a particular partition σ, I'll denote the dependence of these quantities upon σ by subscripts. Thus, I'll write

$$A_\sigma^{\text{in}} \le S_\sigma \le A_\sigma^{\text{out}} \qquad \text{(for any } \sigma\text{)} \tag{7}$$

as a more precise version of the inequalities (4). (Note that the "intermediate" area S_σ depends on still another item: a particular choice of "representative" inputs x_i^* from the subintervals $[x_{i-1}, x_i]$ of σ.)

Just as for stockings and fish nets, it will be handy to have some measure of how large the subintervals $[x_{i-1}, x_i]$ are for a specific partition σ:

Definition: Let's use the term *mesh* of a partition σ to stand for the largest of all the lengths $(x_i - x_{i-1})$ of subintervals corresponding to σ. (Notation: "mesh (σ).")

For example, the partition $\sigma = \{0, \frac{1}{4}, \frac{3}{4}, 1\}$ of the interval $[0, 1]$ has mesh $(\sigma) = \frac{1}{2}$.

By adding (green) points in Fig. 17-9, I created a partition with smaller mesh. And the resulting thinner rectangles appear to yield an *improved* (increased) lower approximation for the quantity we seek—a suitable "area" value for the region Q beneath the graph of f. Similarly, the smaller mesh in Fig. 17-10 appears to yield an *improved* (decreased) upper approximation for "$A(Q)$."

FIGURE 17-10

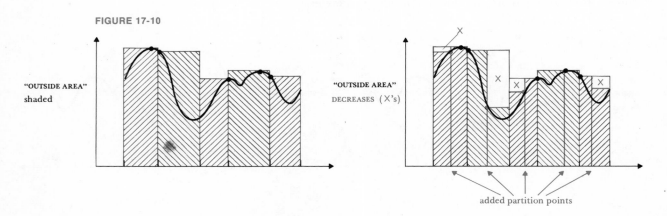

"OUTSIDE AREA"
shaded

"OUTSIDE AREA"
DECREASES (X's)

added partition points

To continue the analogy with "arclength," we might ask:

If we pick a *sequence* of partitions $\sigma_1, \sigma_2, \ldots, \sigma_n, \ldots$, with meshes tending to 0, will the corresponding "inside" and "outside" area approximations necessarily tend to some *common limit A*, as in Fig. 17-11?

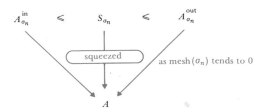

$$A_{\sigma_n}^{\text{in}} \quad \leqslant \quad S_{\sigma_n} \quad \leqslant \quad A_{\sigma_n}^{\text{out}}$$

squeezed   as mesh (σ_n) tends to 0

$$A$$

FIGURE 17-11

And would that value A be the same as someone else might get choosing some *other* sequence of partitions $\tau_1, \tau_2, \tau_3, \ldots \lim_{n \to \infty} \text{mesh}$ $(\tau_n) = 0$? If so, it would seem reasonable to define A as "$A(Q)$," the "area" of the region Q.

Recall that for any partition subinterval $[x_{i-1}, x_i]$ the minimum and maximum values, m_i and M_i, are themselves *outputs* — say

$$m_i = f(x_i^{\min}) \quad \text{and} \quad M_i = f(x_i^{\max}), \tag{8}$$

where the inputs $x_i^{\min}$ and $x_i^{\max}$ lie in $[x_{i-1}, x_i]$. So both the two flanking area approximations in Fig. 17-11,

$$A_\sigma^{\text{in}} = \underset{f(x_1^{\min})}{m_1}(x_1 - x_0) + \underset{f(x_2^{\min})}{m_2}(x_2 - x_1) + \underset{f(x_3^{\min})}{m_3}(x_3 - x_2) + \cdots \tag{9}$$

and

$$A_\sigma^{\text{out}} = \underset{f(x_1^{\max})}{M_1}(x_1 - x_0) + \underset{f(x_2^{\max})}{M_2}(x_2 - x_1) + \underset{f(x_3^{\max})}{M_3}(x_3 - x_2) + \cdots \tag{10}$$

really have the *same form* as the "intermediate" approximation

$$S_\sigma = f(x_1^*)(x_1 - x_0) + f(x_2^*)(x_2 - x_1) + f(x_3^*)(x_3 - x_2) + \cdots \tag{11}$$

And we might record the conjecture pictured in Fig. 17-11 as

Theorem A (on "the existence of area under graphs"): Suppose that f is a continuous nonnegative function on an interval of finite length, $[a, b]$. Then there exists a *unique number* — label it, say, "$A_a^b(f)$" to indicate its dependence on a, b, and f — with the following properties:

Suppose that $\sigma_1, \sigma_2, \ldots, \sigma_n, \ldots$ is *any* sequence of partitions of $[a, b]$ whose *meshes tend to zero*. For every σ_n: choose some input x_i^* from each subinterval $[x_{i-1}, x_i]$ of σ_n, and form the sum

$$S_{\sigma_n} = f(x_1^*)(x_1 - x_0) + f(x_2^*)(x_2 - x_1) + f(x_3^*)(x_3 - x_2) + \cdots \tag{12}$$

(the inputs x_i and x_i^* all depend on n). Then

$$\lim_{n\to\infty} S_{\sigma_n} = A_a^b(f).\tag{13}$$

In particular, for *any* fixed partition $\sigma = \{x_i\}$ of $[a, b]$: if we let m_i and M_i be the minimum and maximum values of f on the subinterval $[x_{i-1}, x_i]$, and if we form the sums

$$A_\sigma^{\text{in}} = m_1(x_1 - x_0) + m_2(x_2 - x_1) + m_3(x_3 - x_2) + \cdots$$

and

$$A_\sigma^{\text{out}} = M_1(x_1 - x_0) + M_2(x_2 - x_1) + M_3(x_3 - x_2) + \cdots,$$

then

$$A_\sigma^{\text{in}} \leq A_a^b(f) \leq A_\sigma^{\text{out}}.\tag{14}$$

Still more specifically: for a *constant function* $f \equiv C$ on $[a, b]$, then

$$A_\sigma^{\text{in}} = A_a^b(f) = A_\sigma^{\text{out}} = C(b - a).\tag{15}$$

If this theorem is true, why not *interpret* the quantity $A_a^b(f)$ as the "area" beneath the graph of f and above $[a, b]$? In very simple cases we might even hope to compute S_{σ_n} and evaluate the limit as n increases:

EXAMPLE 1: $f(x) = x^2$ on $[0, 1]$. Let's choose σ_n so as to divide $[0, 1]$ into n subintervals of equal length $1/n$. That is, let $\sigma_n = \{x_i = i/n,\ \text{for}\ i = 0, 1, 2, \ldots, n\}$. And from the ith interval $[(i-1)/n,\ i/n]$ let's choose x_i^* as the right-hand end point, $x_i^* = i/n$. Then

$$S_{\sigma_n} = \left(\frac{1}{n}\right)^2\left(\frac{1}{n} - \frac{0}{n}\right) + \left(\frac{2}{n}\right)^2\left(\frac{2}{n} - \frac{1}{n}\right) + \left(\frac{3}{n}\right)^2\left(\frac{3}{n} - \frac{2}{n}\right) + \cdots$$

$$+ \left(\frac{n}{n}\right)^2\left(\frac{n}{n} - \frac{n-1}{n}\right)$$

$$= \left(\frac{1}{n}\right)^2\left(\frac{1}{n}\right) + \left(\frac{2}{n}\right)^2\left(\frac{1}{n}\right) + \left(\frac{3}{n}\right)^2\left(\frac{1}{n}\right) + \cdots + \left(\frac{n}{n}\right)^2\left(\frac{1}{n}\right)$$

$$= \frac{1}{n^3}\left[1^2 + 2^2 + 3^2 + \cdots + n^2\right].\tag{16}$$

Just by chance, you might recall that I used "induction" to develop a formula for the [ ] sum in (16): back in Sec. 6.7 (Problem 1(a)) I showed that

$$1^2 + 2^2 + 3^2 + \cdots + n^2 = \tfrac{1}{6}n(n+1)(2n+1) \qquad \text{for any } n.\tag{17}$$

With such aid, we can write

$$S_{\sigma_n} = \frac{\tfrac{1}{6}n(n+1)(2n+1)}{n\cdot n\cdot n} = \frac{1}{6}\left(\frac{n+1}{n}\right)\left(\frac{2n+1}{n}\right)$$

$$= \frac{1}{6}\left(1 + \frac{1}{n}\right)\left(2 + \frac{1}{n}\right).\tag{18}$$

Hence

$$\lim_{n\to\infty} S_{\sigma_n} = \frac{1}{6}\lim_{n\to\infty}\left(1+\frac{1}{n}\right)\lim_{n\to\infty}\left(2+\frac{1}{n}\right) = \frac{1}{6}\cdot 1\cdot 2 = \frac{1}{3}.$$

For a more complicated function f — which appears hard to handle in any other way — one might consider having a computer calculate a long sum S_σ as an approximation to $A_a{}^b(f)$. But the question then becomes: how large will the error $|S_\sigma - A_a{}^b(f)|$ be? Here's how to answer such a question in case f is either *increasing* on $[a,b]$ or *decreasing* on $[a,b]$:

EXAMPLE 2: $f(x) = 1/(1+x^4)$ on $[0,1]$. Let's choose the same σ_n, with n equal subintervals, as in Example 1. Note in Fig. 17-12 that — because f is *decreasing* — each "inside rectangle" is of the same height (and area) as the "outside rectangle" next on its right. So if we subtract the "inside" rectangle sum $A_{\sigma_n}^{\text{in}}$ from the "outside" rectangle sum $A_{\sigma_n}^{\text{out}}$, such "paired" rectangle areas will cancel each other leaving only two:

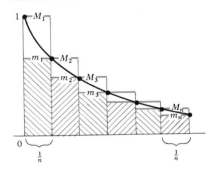

FIGURE 17-12

$$A_{\sigma_n}^{\text{out}} - A_{\sigma_n}^{\text{in}} = M_1\frac{1}{n} - m_n\frac{1}{n}$$

$$= [f(0) - f(1)]\frac{1}{n}$$

$$= \left[1 - \frac{1}{2}\right]\frac{1}{n} = \frac{1}{2n}. \tag{19}$$

If Theorem A is valid, then the "true area" $A_0{}^1(f)$ must lie somewhere in between $A_{\sigma_n}^{\text{in}}$ and $A_{\sigma_n}^{\text{out}}$ — as must any "intermediate" approximation S_{σ_n} based on the partition σ_n. See Fig. 17-13.
Conclusion: The error $|S_{\sigma_n} - A_0{}^1(f)| < 1/2n$ if we divide $[0,1]$ into intervals of length $1/n$.

Put another way: Suppose that you want to compute $A_0{}^1(1/1+x^4)$ with an error of no more than $\epsilon = 0.01$, using subintervals of length $1/n$. How small can n be? Answer: $n = 1/\epsilon = 100$ will be sufficient. Then, for any choice of x_i^* from $[x_{i-1}, x_i]$, you'll have

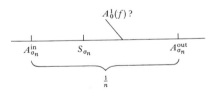

FIGURE 17-13

$$\left|S_{\sigma_n} - A_0{}^1\left(\frac{1}{1+x^4}\right)\right| < \frac{1}{n} = \epsilon.$$

In Sec. 17.9, I'll give more arguments in support of Theorem A (asserting the existence of a reasonable quantity $A_a{}^b(f)$). Meanwhile, you might get the flavor of approximating areas via rectangle sums — by doing problems in the next section.

17.4 PROBLEMS ON APPROXIMATING AREAS

1. (a) Think of area as a function which assigns (output) numbers $A(S)$ to (input) regions S, and make a precise list of all the properties you expect of this function.

(b) Compare your list with that for probabilities in Chapter 3.

2. In the accompanying figure, I've represented a region W in three different ways as the union of nonoverlapping rectangles.

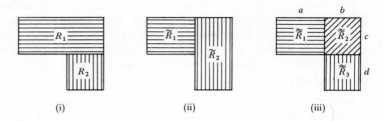

(i)   (ii)   (iii)

Write out the areas $A(R_i)$, $A(\tilde{R}_j)$, and $A(\tilde{\tilde{R}}_k)$ of the various rectangles, in terms of a, b, c, and d; and check that all three sums

$$(i)\ A(R_1)+A(R_2),\quad (ii)\ A(\tilde{R}_1)+A(\tilde{R}_2),\quad (iii)\ A(\tilde{\tilde{R}}_1)+A(\tilde{\tilde{R}}_2)+A(\tilde{\tilde{R}}_3)$$

give the *same* value for $A(W)$ according to the definition in Sec. 17.2. (Note the special relationship that the representation (iii) has to the other two: we can get the $\tilde{\tilde{R}}_k$'s by "intersecting" the various R_i's with $\tilde{R}_j$'s; and each $\tilde{\tilde{R}}_k$ is a *subrectangle* of an R_i and an $\tilde{R}_j$.)

*3. Try to generalize the results in Problem 2, to show that whenever a region W can be represented in two different ways as a union of nonoverlapping rectangles, $W = R_1 \cup R_2 \cup \cdots \cup R_m$ and $W = \tilde{R}_1 \cup \tilde{R}_2 \cup \cdots \cup \tilde{R}_n$, then

$$A(R_1)+A(R_2)+\cdots+A(R_m) = A(\tilde{R}_1)+A(\tilde{R}_2)+\cdots+A(\tilde{R}_n)$$

$$(*)$$

—so that we can assign the quantity in (*) as the *unique* area "$A(W)$."

(Suggestion: Intersect the R_i's and $\tilde{R}_j$'s to form $\tilde{\tilde{R}}_k$'s, and compare each sum in (*) with the sum $A(\tilde{\tilde{R}}_1)+A(\tilde{\tilde{R}}_2)+\cdots$.)

4. What possibilities are there for using other shapes than rectangles as the basic "building blocks" for defining and measuring "area"? How would it be if we used only squares, or only triangles? Compare the separate use of rectangles, squares, and triangles in defining the area of a given circle.

°5. Determine the "mesh" (the length of the largest subinterval) of each of the following partitions of the interval $[0, 1]$.

(a) $\sigma = \{0, 1\}$ (b) $\sigma = \left\{0, \dfrac{1}{2}, 1\right\}$

(c) $\sigma = \left\{0, \dfrac{1}{4}, \dfrac{1}{2}, \dfrac{3}{4}, 1\right\}$ (d) $\sigma = \left\{0, \dfrac{1}{3}, \dfrac{2}{3}, 1\right\}$

(e) $\sigma = \left\{0, \dfrac{1}{4}, \dfrac{1}{3}, \dfrac{1}{2}, \dfrac{2}{3}, \dfrac{3}{4}, 1\right\}$ (f) $\sigma = \left\{\dfrac{i}{n}; i = 0, 1, 2, \ldots, n\right\}$

Which of these partitions arises from one (or more) of the others by "adding points"?

°6. Here is some concrete work in approximating areas:

(a) Draw three identical copies of the graph of $f(x) = 2 - x^2$ for x in $[0, 1]$, one below the other as in Fig. 17-8, on a thin sheet of paper; and on each copy divide $[0, 1]$ into subintervals according to the partition $\sigma = \{0, \frac{1}{2}, 1\}$ — partition (b) in Problem 5.

(b) On the top copy of the graph of f, sketch and shade rectangles which will yield an "inside area" approximation A_σ^{in}, as in Fig. 17-8; and *compute* A_σ^{in} numerically.

(c) On the bottom copy of the graph of f, sketch and shade rectangles which will yield an "outside area" approximation A_σ^{out}, as in Fig. 17-8; and compute A_σ^{out} numerically.

(d) On the middle copy of the graph of f, choose representative points x_i^* from the intervals $[x_{i-1}, x_i]$ of σ; sketch and shade corresponding rectangles which will yield an "intermediate" area approximation

$$S = f(x_1^*)(x_1 - x_0) + f(x_2^*)(x_2 - x_1),$$

as in Fig. 17-8; and compute S numerically.

(e) Compare the total shaded regions and the numerical values in parts (b), (c) and (d). Is $A_\sigma^{in} \leq S \leq A_\sigma^{out}$?

(f) Repeat parts (a)–(e) for the same f and for each of the other partitions σ listed in (a)–(e) of Problem 5. By superposing sheets of paper and holding them up to the light, compare shaded regions corresponding to A_σ^{in} and A_τ^{in} for different partitions σ and τ. Do the same for A_σ^{out} and A_τ^{out}.

(g) Check whether

$$A_\sigma^{in} \leq A_\tau^{in} \quad \text{and} \quad A_\sigma^{out} \geq A_\tau^{out}$$

in all cases where the partition τ arises from the partition σ by "adding points."

7. Let $f(x) = 2 - x^2$ on $[0, 1]$ as in Problem 6, and choose a partition σ_n so as to divide $[0, 1]$ into n subintervals of equal length $1/n$ (see part (f) of Problem 5).

(a) Let x_i^* be the right-hand end point of the ith subinterval, $[x_{i-1}, x_i]$, and write out a specific expression for the sum

$$S_{\sigma_n} = f(x_1^*)(x_1 - x_0) + f(x_2^*)(x_2 - x_1) + \cdots. \qquad (*)$$

(b) Try to find $\lim\limits_{n \to \infty} S_{\sigma_n}$ as in Example 1 of Sec. 17.3, using the formula (17) of that example.

(c) Repeat parts (a) and (b) with x_i^* now the *left-hand* end point of $[x_{i-1}, x_i]$. Are the limits the same?

°8. Repeat Problem 6 for the function $g(x) = x^3$ on $[0, 1]$.

9. Repeat Problem 7 for the function $g(x) = x^3$ on $[0, 1]$. (This time, you might use the formula

$$1^3 + 2^3 + 3^3 + \cdots + n^3 = \frac{n^2(n+1)^2}{4}.$$

10. For each of the following functions f—which are strictly increasing or strictly decreasing on $[0, 1]$, and for the partition $\sigma_n = \{i/n; i = 0, 1, 2, \ldots, n\}$ having subintervals of equal length $1/n$, calculate the difference $A_{\sigma_n}^{\text{out}} - A_{\sigma_n}^{\text{in}}$ between "outside" and "inside" area approximations. (See Example 2 of Sec. 17.3.)

(a) $f(x) = \dfrac{2}{1+x^2}$ (b) $f(x) = x^3$

(c) $f(x) = e^x$ (d) $f(x) = \cos\dfrac{\pi}{2}x$

11. Recall that according to Theorem A of the last section, the "true area" $A_0^1(f)$ beneath the graph of any of the functions f in Problem 10 must lie somewhere *between* the inside approximation $A_{\sigma_n}^{\text{in}}$ and the outside approximation $A_{\sigma_n}^{\text{out}}$. Thus we can approximate $A_0^1(f)$ by either $A_{\sigma_n}^{\text{in}}$ or $A_{\sigma_n}^{\text{out}}$ and incur an *error* of no more than $A_{\sigma_n}^{\text{out}} - A_{\sigma_n}^{\text{in}}$.

(a) For each of the functions in Problem 10, say what value of n will guarantee an approximation error of no more than $\epsilon = 0.01$. In each case, quote the smallest value of n which you know will provide the guarantee—the smaller the n the less the computation to get an approximation.

(b) Repeat part (a) for $\epsilon = 0.001$.

12. (a) Show that if we approximate a "true area" $A_0^1(f)$ by the *average* between inside and outside areas, $\frac{1}{2}(A_{\sigma_n}^{\text{in}} + A_{\sigma_n}^{\text{out}})$, then the approximation error

$$\left| A_0^1(f) - \frac{1}{2}(A_{\sigma_n}^{\text{in}} + A_{\sigma_n}^{\text{out}}) \right| \qquad (*)$$

will be no greater than $\frac{1}{2}(A_{\sigma_n}^{\text{out}} - A_{\sigma_n}^{\text{in}})$. (Indicate all the relevant quantities on a coordinate line.)

(b) For each of the functions in Problem 10, find a value of n—as small as you can get—which will render the error in (*) less than $\epsilon = 0.01$. Compare these values of n with those in Problem 11(a).

(c) Repeat part (b) for $\epsilon = 0.001$, and compare with the results of Problem 11(b).

13. Recall the function $f(x) = 2 - x^2$ on $[0, 1]$, in Problem 7. Should the area beneath the graph of f and above $[0, 1]$ be the *sum* of the corresponding areas above the subintervals $[0, \frac{1}{2}]$ and $[\frac{1}{2}, 1]$?

(a) Draw a graph of f and illustrate the regions in question.

(b) Consider f as restricted to $[0, \frac{1}{2}]$, and let

$$\sigma_n = \left\{ \frac{i}{2n}; \ i = 0, 1, 2, \ldots, n \right\}$$

be a partition of $[0, \frac{1}{2}]$ into n equal subintervals. Repeat the steps of Problem 7 and evaluate $\lim_{n \to \infty} S_{\sigma_n}$ in this new case.

(c) Now consider f as restricted to $[\frac{1}{2}, 1]$ and let

$$\sigma_n = \left\{ \frac{1}{2} + \frac{i}{2n}; \ i = 0, 1, 2, \ldots, n \right\}$$

be a partition of $[\frac{1}{2}, 1]$ into n equal subintervals. Repeat the steps of Problem 7 and evaluate $\lim_{n \to \infty} S_{\sigma_n}$ in this case.

(d) Compare the results of parts (b) and (c) with the old $\lim_{n \to \infty} S_{\sigma_n}$ for f on $[0, 1]$ in Problem 7.

14. If the graph of one function sits above that of another, what should be true about corresponding areas under the graphs? Compare the results of Problems 7 and 8.

15. What will happen to the area under the graph of $f(x) = 2 - x^2$ in Problem 7 if we *triple* the height of the graph—that is, if we replace $f(x)$ by $h(x) = 3f(x) = 3(2 - x^2)$ on $[0, 1]$? Draw the graphs of f and h above the same axis; and then repeat the steps of Problem 7 for the new function h. Compare the new $\lim_{n \to \infty} S_{\sigma_n}$ for h with the old ones for f in Problem 7.

16. Should the areas under the graphs of $f(x) = 2 - x^2$ in Problem 7 and $g(x) = x^3$ in Problem 8 add up to the area under the graph of the sum function $k(x) = (2 - x^2) + x^3$ on $[0, 1]$? Draw the graphs of f, g, and k above a common axis; and then repeat the steps of Problem 7 for the new function k. Compare the new $\lim_{n \to \infty} S_{\sigma_n}$ for k with the old ones for f in Problem 7 and for g in Problem 8.

17.5 PROPERTIES OF AREA

If the quantity $A_a^b(f)$ does exist—as asserted by Theorem A (in Sec. 17.3)—we might still ask whether it satisfies properties we intuitively expect of "area."

For example: do areas assigned to adjacent regions add up to give the area of the union? In answer:

Theorem B (on "adding adjacent areas"): if $a < c < b$, and if f is continuous and nonnegative on $[a, b]$, then

$$A_a^b(f) = A_a^c(f) + A_c^b(f). \tag{1}$$

Why? The reasons should lie in the approximating sums S_{σ_n} whose limits define the $A(f)$'s. For a

Proof of Theorem B, let's choose a sequence $\sigma_1, \sigma_2, \sigma_3, \ldots$ of partitions whose meshes tend to zero, and moreover *let's include the input c*

FIGURE 17-14

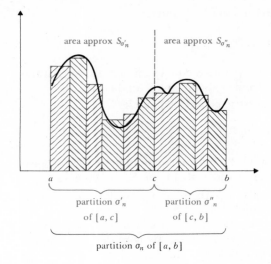

area approx $S_{\sigma'_n}$ | area approx $S_{\sigma''_n}$

a c b

partition σ'_n
of $[a, c]$

partition σ''_n
of $[c, b]$

partition σ_n of $[a, b]$

*as one of the x_i's in each partition σ_n—*as in Fig. 17-14. Any such partition σ_n will then always "split" into a partition—call it σ'_n—of $[a, c]$, and a partition—call it σ''_n—of $[c, b]$. And any approximating sum of rectangle areas over all of $[a, b]$ will split correspondingly:

$$S_{\sigma_n} = S_{\sigma'_n} + S_{\sigma''_n}. \tag{2}$$

Note also that meshes of σ'_n and σ''_n can't exceed that of σ_n, and so must tend to zero as n increases. Hence, according to Theorem A, and the old "addition property" of limits,

$$
\begin{aligned}
A_a{}^b(f) = \lim_{n \to \infty} S_{\sigma_n} &= \lim_{n \to \infty} [S_{\sigma'_n} + S_{\sigma''_n}] \\
&= \lim_{n \to \infty} S_{\sigma'_n} + \lim_{n \to \infty} S_{\sigma''_n} \\
&= A_a{}^c(f) + A_c{}^b(f).
\end{aligned} \tag{3}
$$

End of the proof.

Next question: does $A_a{}^b(f)$ satisfy the inequality we might expect for regions $S \subset T$; namely, $A(S) \leq A(T)$? In answer:

Theorem C (on "comparing areas"): If f and g are continuous non-negative functions with

$$f(x) \leq g(x)$$

for all x in $[a, b]$, then

$$A_a{}^b(f) \leq A_a{}^b(g). \tag{4}$$

In particular, if h is a continuous nonnegative function on $[a, b]$ with absolute maximum M and absolute minimum m, then

$$m(b-a) \leq A_a{}^b(f) \leq M(b-a). \tag{5}$$

Why? The reasons again should lie with the approximating sums for f and g. See Fig. 17-15 (and also Fig. 17-16).

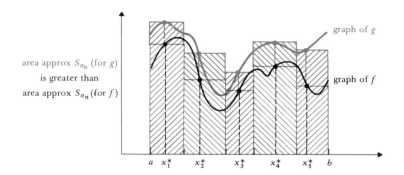

FIGURE 17-15

area approx S_{σ_n} (for g)
is greater than
area approx S_{σ_n} (for f)

graph of g

graph of f

a x_1^* x_2^* x_3^* x_4^* x_5^* b

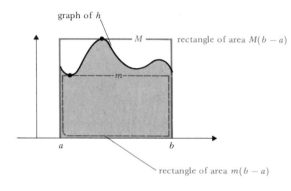

graph of h

M — rectangle of area $M(b-a)$

m

FIGURE 17-16

a b

rectangle of area $m(b-a)$

Here's how a

***Proof of Theorem C follows from the old "comparison property" of
limits:*** Note that for *any* partition $\sigma_n = \{x_i\}$ and any choice of inputs
x_i^* from subintervals $[x_{i-1}, x_i]$, we must always have $f(x_i^*) \leq g(x_i^*)$.
Hence

$$S_{\sigma_n}(\text{for } f) = f(x_1^*)(x_1 - x_0) + f(x_2^*)(x_2 - x_1) + f(x_3^*)(x_3 - x_2) + \cdots$$
$$\leq g(x_1^*)(x_1 - x_0) + g(x_2^*)(x_2 - x_1) + g(x_3^*)(x_3 - x_2) + \cdots$$
$$= S_{\sigma_n}(\text{for } g). \tag{6}$$

Now let's choose a sequence of partitions $\sigma_1, \sigma_2, \sigma_3, \ldots$ with meshes
tending to zero. Then according to Theorem A, we must have

$$A_a^b(f) = \lim_{n \to \infty} S_{\sigma_n}(\text{for } f) \leq \lim_{n \to \infty} S_{\sigma_n}(\text{for } g) = A_a^b(g). \tag{7}$$

The particular inequalities

$$m(b-a) \leq A_a^b(h) \leq M(b-a) \tag{8}$$

capture the situation in Fig. 17-16.

One way to derive these inequalities is to let the functions f and g
above play the roles

$$f(x) \equiv h(x) \quad \text{and} \quad g(x) = M \quad \text{for all } x \text{ in } [a, b]. \tag{9}$$

Then

$$A_a^b(h) = A_a^b(f) \leq A_a^b(g) = M(b-a), \tag{10}$$

since a function of constant output C has "area" $C(b-a)$ over $[a, b]$ (recall (15) above). Here $C = M$. Then, switch roles: let

$$f(x) = m \quad \text{and} \quad g(x) = h(x) \qquad \text{for all } x \text{ in } [a, b]. \tag{11}$$

So

$$A_a{}^b(f) = m(b-a) \leq A_a{}^b(g) = A_a{}^b(h). \tag{12}$$

(Here $C = m$.)   End of the proof.

Do you believe that doubling the height of all vertical line segments in a region will necessarily double the area — at least for a region such as I've indicated in Fig. 17-17?

FIGURE 17-17

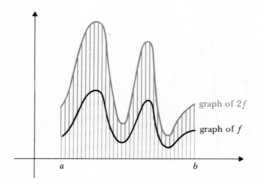

More generally: Suppose we start with one such region (shaded grey) in Fig. 17-18, and then shift each of its vertical segments upward by *different amounts* — according to the heights of some *unrelated (green) function g*. Will the shifted grey region necessarily have the same area as the original one?

FIGURE 17-18

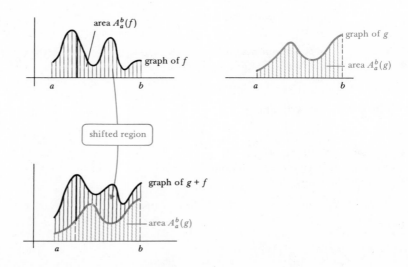

"Yes" was the guess of Francesco Cavalieri, who thought about such matters in 1600+. We can answer such questions without guesswork — on the basis of the simplest limit properties:

Theorem D (on "scaling and adding areas"): if f is a continuous nonnegative function on $[a, b]$ and c is a constant $\geqslant 0$, then

$$A_a^b(cf) = cA_a^b(f). \qquad (13)$$

If g is another continuous nonnegative function on $[a, b]$, then

$$A_a^b(f + g) = A_a^b(f) + A_a^b(g). \qquad (14)$$

(With this last equality, we can argue that the shifted grey region in Fig. 17-18 deserves area

$$A_a^b(f + g) - A_a^b(g) = A_a^b(f),$$

the same as that of the original region.)

For

A proof of Theorem D, just note that any approximating sum for the scaled function cf must have the form

$$
\begin{aligned}
S_{\sigma_n}&(\text{for } cf) \\
&= [cf(x_1^*)](x_1 - x_0) + [cf(x_2^*)](x_2 - x_1) + [cf(x_3^*)](x_3 - x_2) + \cdots \\
&= c[f(x_1^*)(x_1 - x_0) + f(x_2^*)(x_2 - x_1) + f(x_3^*)(x_3 - x_2) + \cdots] \\
&= c \cdot S_{\sigma_n}(\text{for } f). \qquad (15)
\end{aligned}
$$

Hence, for partitions $\sigma_1, \sigma_2, \sigma_3, \ldots$ with meshes tending to zero, we must have

$$
\begin{aligned}
A_a^b(cf) &= \lim_{n \to \infty} S_{\sigma_n}(\text{for } cf) = \lim_{n \to \infty} c \cdot S_{\sigma_n}(\text{for } f) = c \lim_{n \to \infty} S_{\sigma_n}(\text{for } f) \quad (16) \\
&= cA_a^b(f).
\end{aligned}
$$

Similarly, any approximating sum for the function $f + g$ must have the form

$$
\begin{aligned}
S_{\sigma_n}(\text{for } f + g) &= [f(x_1^*) + g(x_1^*)](x_1 - x_0) + [f(x_2^*) + g(x_2^*)](x_2 - x_1) + \cdots \\
&= [f(x_1^*)(x_1 - x_0) + f(x_2^*)(x_2 - x_1) + \cdots] \\
&\quad + [g(x_1^*)(x_1 - x_0) + g(x_2^*)(x_2 - x_1) + \cdots] \\
&= S_{\sigma_n}(\text{for } f) + S_{\sigma_n}(\text{for } g). \qquad (17)
\end{aligned}
$$

And

$$
\begin{aligned}
A_a^b(f + g) &= \lim_{n \to \infty} S_{\sigma_n}(\text{for } f + g) = \lim_{n \to \infty} [S_{\sigma_n}(\text{for } f) + S_{\sigma_n}(\text{for } g)] \\
&= \lim_{n \to \infty} S_{\sigma_n}(\text{for } f) + \lim_{n \to \infty} S_{\sigma_n}(\text{for } g) \\
&= A_a^b(f) + A_a^b(g). \qquad (18)
\end{aligned}
$$

End of the proof.

The reasoning in this section still depends on the validity of Theorem A — which asserts that $A_a^b(f)$ does exist as the unique limit of suitable approximating sums. And I'll argue for Theorem A in Sec. 17.9. But first, let's see how we might use the "adding" and "comparing" properties of $A_a^b(f)$ — tentatively established in Theorems B and C — to bypass approximating sums for the job of actually *evaluating* $A_a^b(f)$.

17.6 HOW TO CALCULATE AREA UNDER A GRAPH

Do you recall the method involving rates which I used in Sec. 7.6 to find the volume of a mountain? In the same spirit, and for *any* positive continuous function f, let's try to establish the *rate* at which the area under the graph of f changes over intervals of increasing length. See Fig. 17-19.

FIGURE 17-19

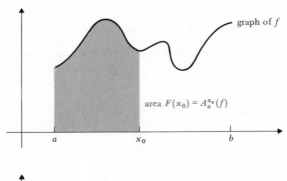

area $F(x_0) = A_a^{x_0}(f)$

graph of f

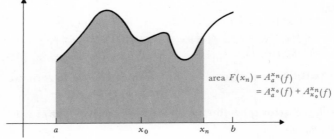

area $F(x_n) = A_a^{x_n}(f)$
$= A_a^{x_0}(f) + A_{x_0}^{x_n}(f)$

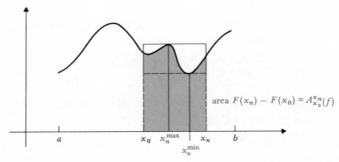

area $F(x_n) - F(x_0) = A_{x_0}^{x_n}(f)$

$$f(x_n^{\min})(x_n - x_0) \leqslant F(x_n) - F(x_0) \leqslant f(x_n^{\max})(x_n - x_0)$$

For every x in the interval $[a, b]$, let's denote the area beneath the graph of f and above the subinterval $[a, x]$ by the symbol

$$F(x) = A_a^x(f). \tag{19}$$

To include the extreme case $x = a$, let's define the area above a single point as zero:

Definition: $A_a{}^a(f) = 0$ for any a and f.

The expression (19) assigns to each x (as input) a unique number $F(x)$ (as output), and thus defines a new *function F* on $[a, b]$. We might call F the "cumulative area function." At what rate does it increase?

To answer let's pick inputs x_0 and x_n in $[a, b]$ with $x_0 < x_n$. By the "adding property" (of Theorem B) we must have the difference $F(x_n) - F(x_0) = A_{x_0}^{x_n}(f)$, as I've indicated in Fig. 17-19. Now, on the closed interval $[x_0, x_n]$, the continuous function f must assume an absolute maximum—say, at an input "$x_n{}^{\max}$", and an absolute minimum—say, at an input "$x_n{}^{\min}$". Why not apply the "comparison" inequalities of Theorem C $(m(b-a) \leqslant A_a^b(h) \leqslant M(b-a))$ to the subinterval $[x_0, x_n]$ itself? If we do, we get

$$f(x_n{}^{\min})(x_n - x_0) \leqslant F(x_n) - F(x_0) \leqslant f(x_n{}^{\max})(x_n - x_0). \tag{20}$$

To form a difference ratio for F, divide (20) through by $(x_n - x_0)$; and get

$$f(x_n{}^{\min}) \leqslant \frac{F(x_n) - F(x_0)}{x_n - x_0} \leqslant f(x_n{}^{\max}). \tag{21}$$

To find $F'(x_0)$, let's pick a sequence of inputs $x_n > x_0$ with $\lim_{n \to \infty} x_n = x_0$. Note that for each n, the inputs $x_n{}^{\min}$ and $x_n{}^{\max}$ lie *between* x_0 and x_n. Hence $x_n{}^{\min}$ and $x_n{}^{\max}$ will be squeezed toward x_0 as n increases:

$$\lim_{n \to \infty} x_n{}^{\min} = x_0 \quad \text{and} \quad \lim_{n \to \infty} x_n{}^{\max} = x_0.$$

Since f is continuous at x_0, these "input" limits imply corresponding "output" limits:

$$\lim_{n \to \infty} f(x_n{}^{\min}) = f(x_0)$$

and

$$\lim_{n \to \infty} f(x_n{}^{\max}) = f(x_0).$$

These in turn put the squeeze on the difference ratios

$$\frac{F(x_n) - F(x_0)}{x_n - x_0},$$

as in Fig. 17-20.

Conclusion: If we restrict $F(x)$ to the interval $[x_0, b]$, then $F'(x_0)$ exists and has value none other than $f(x_0)$ itself. If we can treat $F(x)$ similarly on the interval $[a, x_0]$, we could "interlace" the results and have:

Theorem E (on "the derivative of the cumulative area function"): Suppose that f is any continuous nonnegative function on an interval $[a, b]$. Let $F(x) = A_a{}^x(f)$ for each x in $[a, b]$. Then

$$F'(x_0) = f(x_0) \qquad \text{at each } x_0 \text{ in } [a, b].$$

FIGURE 17-20

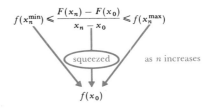

In other words, the "cumulative area function" F is an *antiderivative* of the original function f on the interval $[a, b]$. It has the special properties that

$$F(a) = A_a{}^a(f) = 0, \qquad (22)$$

and that

$$F(b) = A_a{}^b(f)$$

is the total area beneath the graph of f and above the full interval $[a, b]$.

You may recall that any other antiderivative G for the same function f can differ from F only by some constant

$$G(x) = F(x) + C \qquad \text{for all } x \text{ in } [a, b] \qquad (23)$$

(such was the message of Theorem H in Sec. 15.10). Hence, if Theorem E is true, here is a

Method for finding area via antiderivatives: *Find any antiderivative G for the given function f. Then simply form the difference*

$$
\begin{aligned}
G(b) - G(a) &= [F(b) + C] - [F(a) + C] \\
&= F(b) - F(a) \\
&= A_a{}^b(f) - A_a{}^a(f) \\
&= A_a{}^b(f). \qquad (24)
\end{aligned}
$$

FIGURE 17-21

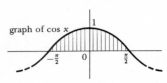

graph of cos x

EXAMPLE 1: How much area lies between the x axis and one loop of the cos x graph? See Figs. 17-21 and 17-22. $G(x) = \sin x$ is an antiderivative of $\cos x$; that is, $(\sin x)' = \cos x$. Hence the shaded area $A_{-\pi/2}^{\pi/2}(\cos x)$ in Fig. 17-21 equals

$$G\left(\frac{\pi}{2}\right) - G\left(-\frac{\pi}{2}\right) = \sin\frac{\pi}{2} - \sin\left(-\frac{\pi}{2}\right)$$

$$= 1 - (-1) = 2 \text{ sq units.}$$

Would you have guessed it?

FIGURE 17-22

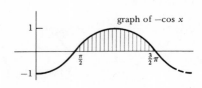

graph of $-\cos x$

Similarly, $H(x) = -\sin x$ is an antiderivative of $-\cos x$, so the shaded area $A_{\pi/2}^{3\pi/2}(-\cos x)$ in Fig. 17-22 equals

$$H\left(\frac{3}{2}\pi\right) - H\left(\frac{1}{2}\pi\right) = \left(-\sin\frac{3}{2}\pi\right) - \left(-\sin\frac{1}{2}\pi\right) = (-1) - (-1)$$

$$= 2 \text{ sq units.}$$

EXAMPLE 2: How much area lies beneath the graph of $f(x) = 1/x$ for $a \leqslant x \leqslant b$, as in Fig. 17-23? Do you recall (from Sec. 14.10, Theorem B) that $G(x) = \log_e x$ is an antiderivative of $f(x) = 1/x$? Since it is, the shaded area

$$A_a{}^b\left(\frac{1}{x}\right) = G(b) - G(a) = \log_e b - \log_e a = \log_e\left(\frac{b}{a}\right),$$

for any $b > a > 0$. (If $a = 1/100$ and $b = 1$, then $\log_e(b/a) = \log_e 100 = 2\log_e 10 = 4.605$, approximately.)

FIGURE 17-23

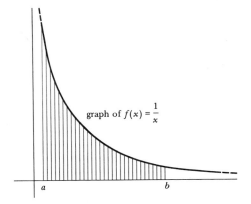

graph of $f(x) = \dfrac{1}{x}$

To complete a

Proof of Theorem E: Let's consider the case where $x_0 > 0$ and $a \leq x_n < x_0$. Then

$$F(x_0) = A_a{}^{x_0}(f) = A_a{}^{x_n}(f) + A_{x_n}^{x_0}(f) \qquad \text{(by Theorem A again)}$$
$$= F(x_n) + A_{x_n}^{x_0}(f). \tag{25}$$

So $F(x_0) - F(x_n) = A_{x_n}^{x_0}(f)$, and inequalities hold as before:

$$f(x_n{}^{\min})(x_0 - x_n) \leq F(x_0) - F(x_n) \leq f(x_n{}^{\max})(x_0 - x_n), \tag{26}$$

where $x_n{}^{\min}$ and $x_n{}^{\max}$ now lie in the interval $[x_n, x_0]$. This time divide the inequalities through by the positive quantity $x_0 - x_n$, to get

$$f(x_n{}^{\min}) \leq \frac{F(x_0) - F(x_n)}{x_0 - x_n} = \frac{F(x_n) - F(x_0)}{x_n - x_0} \leq f(x_n{}^{\max}). \tag{27}$$

As before, the extreme terms both tend to $f(x_0)$ as n increases, and squeeze the difference ratio $[F(x_n) - F(x_0)]/(x_n - x_0)$ to the same limit. Thus, restricted to the interval $[a, x_0]$, the function F has derivative $F'(x_0) = f(x_0)$.

Finally, by the "interlacing property" of derivatives (Property D' in Chap. 14), we can say that F considered on the full interval $[a, b]$ has derivative $F'(x_0) = f(x_0)$—at any x_0 in $[a, b]$.   End of the proof.

17.7 THE PROBABILITY THAT A NEEDLE WILL HIT A CRACK IN THE FLOOR—AND HOW TO APPROXIMATE π

Suppose that you are in the middle of a large room whose floor is made of parallel boards—each of width, say, d inches. Think of tossing a needle at random onto the floor—a needle of length L inches, where $L < d$. What's the probability that the needle will touch one of the cracks between the floor boards?

In order not to worry about the width of the needle and the chances of its falling against a wall, let's look at a slightly idealized

FIGURE 17-24

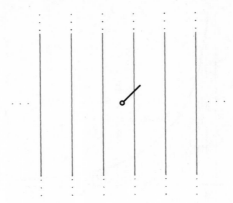

model: of a line segment falling at random on an infinite grid of parallel lines, as in Fig. 17-24. How can we describe all the *essentially distinct* possible outcomes of such an experiment? One way is to assume that the altitude of the needle and the particular crack on which it might fall are irrelevant matters. We could then describe the remaining features of a possible needle position by a pair of numbers: the *angle* θ which the needle makes with a horizontal direction, and the *distance x* of the needle's *head* from, say, the nearest crack on its left—as in Figs. 17-25 and 17-26.

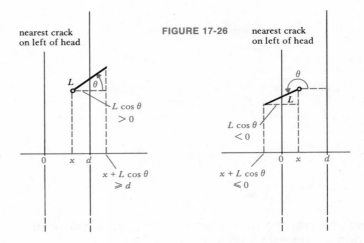

FIGURE 17-25

FIGURE 17-26

According to this scheme, we could describe the collection Ω of all distinct possible outcomes of the experiment by the set of all ordered pairs (θ, x) where $0 \leq \theta < 2\pi$ and $0 \leq x < d$. And we can picture Ω as a rectangle in a θ, x plane. See Fig. 17-27. Which of the points in Ω represent positions where the needle touches a crack? Check in Fig. 17-25 that for the needle to touch the crack on the right of its head

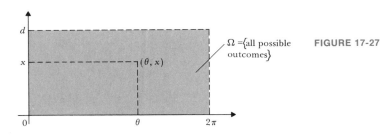

FIGURE 17-27

we must have

$$x + L \cos \theta \geqslant d, \qquad \text{that is, } x \geqslant d - L \cos \theta. \tag{1}$$

Alternatively, the needle can touch the crack on the left of its head (as in Fig. 17-26), and for this we must have

$$x + L \cos \theta \geqslant 0, \qquad \text{that is, } x \geqslant -L \cos \theta. \tag{2}$$

Thus, we can picture the compound result "the needle touches a crack" as the subset—call it T—of all points (θ, x) in Ω whose coordinates satisfy one or the other of these inequalities (1) and (2). I've colored this subset green in Fig. 17-28.

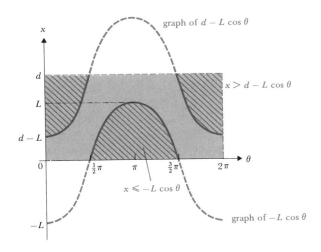

FIGURE 17-28

    What probability should we assign to T? If we feel intuitively that all possible outcomes (θ, x) are "equally likely," then we might well assign probability

$$P(T) = \frac{\text{area of } T}{\text{area of } \Omega} \tag{3}$$

by analogy with the finite cases of Chap. 3, and as I argued in Sec. 4.9 (Example 2). The area of the rectangle Ω is just the base $\times$ height product $2\pi \cdot d$ sq units. And the area of T is twice the area

$A_{\pi/2}^{3\pi/2}(-L\cos\theta)$ under one loop of the graph of $-L\cos\theta$. But that area

$$A_{\pi/2}^{3\pi/2}(-L\cos\theta) = L \cdot A_{\pi/2}^{3\pi/2}(-\cos\theta)$$

$$= L \cdot 2 \text{ sq units}, \tag{4}$$

by the "scaling" result (Theorem D) and the calculation in Example 1 of the last section. Hence

$$P(T) = \frac{2\cdot 2\cdot L}{2\pi\cdot d} = \frac{2}{\pi}\left(\frac{L}{d}\right). \tag{5}$$

Note that the lengths L and d appear only via their ratio, so that we'd get the same result for a needle twice as long in a room with floor boards twice as wide—as you might expect.

Now go ahead and toss your needle a large number of times—say, n; and denote by M_n the number of times that the needle actually touches a crack. Do you believe that the "frequency ratio"

$$\frac{M_n}{n} = \frac{\text{number of successes}}{\text{total number of trials}} \tag{6}$$

should provide a good approximation to the probability $P(T)$ of successfully touching a crack on any *one* trial? If so—and if my assumptions for Ω and $P(T)$ were wise—then we should also have a good approximation for the value of π:

$$\frac{2}{\pi}\left(\frac{L}{d}\right) = P(T) = \frac{M_n}{n} \text{ (approximately)} \tag{7}$$

yields

$$\pi = 2\left(\frac{L}{d}\right)\frac{n}{M_n} \text{ (approximately)}. \tag{8}$$

I invite you to make 25 or 50 tosses of an actual needle (or toothpick), and to see how near the right-hand quantity in (8) comes to 3.14, a commonly used approximation for π.

17.8 MORE AREA PROBLEMS

°1. For each of the following functions, sketch a graph, and then find the area of the region lying beneath the graph and above the x axis.

(a) $f(x) = e^{-x}$ for x in $[1, 2]$

(b) $f(x) = e^{-x}$ for x in $[-2, 2]$

(c) $f(x) = 2x^{-3}$ for x in $[1, 2]$

(d) $f(x) = \dfrac{1}{\sqrt{x+4}}$ for x in $[-2, 2]$

(e) $f(x) = \dfrac{x^2}{\sqrt{x^3+8}}$ for x in $[-1, 1]$

(f) $f(x) = xe^{x^2} + 3e^x$ for x in $[-2, 2]$

(g) $f(x) = \dfrac{x^2 - 2x + 2}{(x-1)^4}$ for x in $[2, 4]$

(h) $f(x) = \begin{cases} x^2 & \text{for } x \text{ in } [0, 1] \\ 4 - x^2 & \text{for } x \text{ in } [1, 2] \end{cases}$

    (Suggestion: first find the areas above $[0, 1]$ and $[1, 2]$ separately, then add the results.)

(i) $f(x) = \begin{cases} e^x & \text{for } x \text{ in } [0, 1] \\ xe^{x^2} & \text{for } x \text{ in } [1, 2] \end{cases}$

(j) $f(x) = e^{|x|}$ for x in $[-1, 2]$

    (Suggestion: Calculate areas separately over $[-1, 0]$ and $[0, 2]$.)

(k) $f(x) = |x^3 + 1|$ for x in $[-1, 2]$

°2. Each of the following functions has discontinuities. Sketch a graph, and then find the area of the region beneath the graph and above the x axis by calculating areas over separate subintervals of continuity.

(a) $f(x) = \begin{cases} e^x & \text{for } x \text{ in } [0, 1] \\ e^{2x} & \text{for } x \text{ in } \langle 1, 2] \end{cases}$

(b) $f(x) = \begin{cases} x^2 & \text{for } x \text{ in } [0, 1] \\ x^2 - 1 & \text{for } x \text{ in } \langle 1, 2] \\ x^2 - 4 & \text{for } x \text{ in } \langle 2, 3] \end{cases}$

(c) $f(x) = \begin{cases} 0 & \text{for } |x| < 1 \\ e^{-|x|} & \text{for } 1 \leq |x| \leq 2 \end{cases}$

°3. In each of the following cases, the graph of f lies both above and below the x axis. Sketch and shade the region lying between the graph and the x axis; and find the *total shaded area* by adding the areas for f over subintervals where $f \geq 0$ together with the areas for $-f$ over subintervals where $f \leq 0$.

(a) $f(x) = x^2 - 1$ for x in $[0, 2]$.
    Sample: $f(x) \leq 0$ on $[0, 1]$ and ≥ 0 on $[1, 2]$. See the accompanying figures.

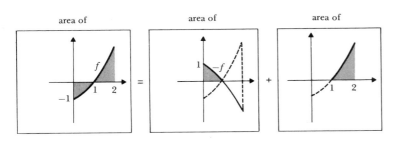

An antiderivative of f for all x is $F(x) = \frac{1}{3}x^3 - x$. Hence

$$F(2) - F(1) = \left(\frac{1}{3}2^3 - 2\right) - \left(\frac{1}{3}1^3 - 1\right) = \frac{4}{3}$$

is the area over $[1, 2]$. Also, $-F$ is an antiderivative of $-f$. Hence

$$[-F(1)] - [-F(0)] = \left(1 - \frac{1}{3}1^3\right) - \left(0 - \frac{1}{3}0^3\right) = \frac{2}{3}$$

is the area under $[0, 1]$. Total area $= \frac{4}{3} + \frac{2}{3} = 2$.

(b) $f(x) = \cos x$ for x in $[0, \pi]$

(c) $f(x) = x^2 + x - 2$ for x in $[-3, 3]$

(d) $f(x) = e^{2x} - e^x$ for x in $[-1, 1]$

(e) $f(x) = (\log_e x)\dfrac{1}{x}$ for x in $\left[\dfrac{1}{e}, e\right]$

4. For each part of Problem 3, suppose now that those subregions lying below the x axis have "*negative area*" and add together the areas of all subregions letting positive and negative amounts possibly cancel each other—to get a "NET *signed area.*" How does this "net signed area" compare with the number $F(b) - F(a)$, where $[a, b]$ is the entire domain of f and F is any antiderivative of f? b ε C

5. For each function f, with domain $[a, b]$, given in Problem 3, see whether the following alternate procedure gives the same "net signed area" as I discussed in Problem 4. Pick a constant c such that the function $g(x) = f(x) + c > 0$ on all of $[a, b]$. Then find the area beneath the graph of g and above $[a, b]$, and subtract from it the rectangular area $c(b - a)$. Draw pictures to illustrate this method.   b ε C

°6. Each of the following parts describes the boundaries of a region. Sketch the region, and then divide it into subregions each of which you can picture as lying under the graph of an appropriate function (as in Fig. 17-6). Then find the areas of the individual subregions and add them together to get the area of the original region.

(a) The region between the graphs of $f(x) = \cos (\pi/2)x$ and $g(x) = 2x^2 - 2$ for x in $[-1, 1]$.
Sample: See the figure.
Since

$$F(x) = \frac{2}{\pi} \sin \frac{\pi}{2}x$$

is an antiderivative of $f(x)$, the subregion above the x axis has area

$$F(1) - F(-1) = \frac{2}{\pi} \sin \frac{\pi}{2} - \frac{2}{\pi} \sin \left(-\frac{\pi}{2}\right) = \frac{4}{\pi}.$$

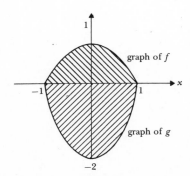

graph of f

graph of g

Since $-G(x) = -(\frac{2}{3}x^3 - 2x)$ is an antiderivative of $-g(x)$, the subregion below the x axis has area

$$[-G(1)] - [-G(-1)] = -\left(\frac{2}{3}1^3 - 2\right) - \left[-\frac{2}{3}(-1)^3 + 2(-1)\right]$$
$$= \frac{8}{3}.$$

So the total area is $4/\pi + 8/3$.

  (b) The region between the graphs of $f(x) = x^2$ and $g(x) = x^4$ for x in $[0, 1]$.

  (c) The region between the graphs of $f(x) = x^2 - x$ and $g(x) = x - x^3$ for x in $[0, 1]$.

  (d) The region bounded by the y axis and by the graphs of $f(x) = \sin x$ and $g(x) = \cos x$ for x in $[0, \pi/4]$.

7. (a) Take any of the functions f in Problem 1 and create a single discontinuity by redefining $f(1)$ as 100, all other outputs $f(x)$ remaining the same. Would you still be willing to assign the same area as before to the region beneath the altered graph of f?

  (b) What if you redefined f at any *finite* number of inputs?

 *(c) What if you redefined f at all rational inputs x?

8. Look back at the problem of a needle hitting a crack in the floor which I discussed in the last section. Let's now describe the position of the needle in a different way, paying no attention to its "head": Let y denote the distance between the *midpoint* of the needle and the nearest crack on its left $(0 \le y < d)$. And measure the angle ϕ $(-\pi/2 < \phi \le \pi/2)$, as in the figure. Sketch the set Ω of pairs (ϕ, y), in a ϕy plane, representing all possible outcomes for a toss of the needle, and describe the subregion of outcomes corresponding to the needle's touching a crack. Will the probability of touching be the same as what I calculated in the last section?

9. What are the chances that a (pipelike) capillary tube, one millimeter long and of radius r millimeters—where r is some random value between 1/10 and 2/10 millimeters, will be able to hold completely the contents of a spherical droplet of fluid, of radius R—where R is some random value between 0 and 4/10 millimeters?

   (Suggestion: Describe the set of all possible outcomes (r, R), and find the probability of the subregion where $4\pi R^3/3 \le \pi r^2$.)

10. Suppose that a ship founders somewhere between 10 and 18 miles offshore, and that it sends out a lifeboat with only enough fuel to travel 20 miles. Suppose further that the lifeboat heads in a more or less straight line making an angle θ with the perpendicular to the shore, where θ is some random angle between 0 and $\pi/4$. See the figure. What are the chances that the lifeboat will reach shore before its fuel is exhausted? (Sketch the set of all possible outcomes (θ, x), and determine the subregion corresponding to successful landing.)

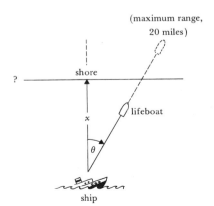

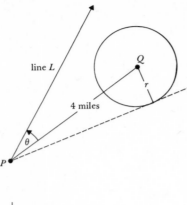

line L

4 miles

Q

r

θ

P

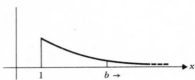

1

$b \rightarrow$

x

11. Another encounter problem: Suppose that you start from a point P and go along a straight line L looking for a colony of creatures occupying a roughly circular area about a point Q, as in the figure. Suppose that the colony has radius r somewhere between 1/8 and 1/4 miles, and that the angle θ between L and the best path PQ may be anywhere between $-60°$ and $60°$. What are the chances of your encountering the colony?

12. How can we define and calculate areas for "unbounded" regions, such as that beneath the graph of $f(x) = 1/x^2$ and above the "half-line" $[1, \infty)$? See the figure. Why not find the area above a subinterval $[1, b]$ and then see what happens if we pick b larger and larger? Since $F(x) = -1/x$ is an antiderivative for $f(x)$, the area above $[1, b]$ — call it $A(b)$, to show its dependence on b — is

$$A(b) = F(b) - F(1) = \left(-\frac{1}{b}\right) - \left(-\frac{1}{1}\right) = 1 - \frac{1}{b}$$

for all $b > 1$. Hence for any sequence $\{b_n\}$ where $\lim_{n \to \infty} b_n = \infty$ (and $b_n > 1$ for all n), we should have

$$\lim_{n \to \infty} A(b_n) = \lim_{n \to \infty} \left(1 - \frac{1}{b_n}\right) = 1 - \lim_{n \to \infty} \frac{1}{b_n} = 1 - 0 = 1. \qquad (*)$$

Recall Problem 12 of Sec. 11.3 where I described such a situation by the symbol "$\lim_{b \to \infty} A(b)$" = 1. Why not *define* the area of the total region as this limit?

Here are several other functions defined over half-lines. In each case see whether "$\lim_{b \to \infty} A(b)$" makes sense as the "area" of the region beneath the graph.

(a) $f(x) = e^{-x}$ for all $x \geq 0$

(b) $f(x) = e^x$ for all $x \geq 0$

(c) $f(x) = \frac{x-1}{x^3}$ for all $x \geq 2$

(d) $f(x) = \frac{1}{x}$ for all $x \geq 1$

(e) $f(x) = \frac{x^2}{(x^3 - 1)^4}$ for all $x \geq 1$

(f) $f(x) = \cos x$ for all $x \geq 0$

(g) $f(x) = \frac{1}{x^2 + 1}$ for all $x \geq 0$

(h) $f(x) = e^{-|x|}$ for all real x
    (Suggestion: find the limit of areas over $[-b, b]$ as b increases.)

(i) $f(x) = \frac{1}{x^2 + 1}$ for all real x.

13. (a) How can we define and calculate areas for regions whose horizontal base is bounded but which are unbounded *vertically*, such as that beneath the graph of $g(x) = 1/\sqrt{x}$ for $0 \leq x \leq 1$? See Fig. (i).

FIGURE (i)

g

$0 \leftarrow a$ 1

FIGURE (ii)

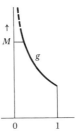

How about as a limit, as _a_ tends to zero, of the area above $[a, 1]$? Since $G(x) = 2\sqrt{x}$ is an antiderivative of g, the area above $[a, 1]$ must be

$$A(a) = G(1) - G(a) = 2\sqrt{1} - 2\sqrt{a} = 2 - 2\sqrt{a}$$

for all _a_ with $0 < a < 1$, and

$$\lim_{a \to 0} A(a) = \lim_{a \to 0} (2 - 2\sqrt{a}) = 2 - 2 \lim_{a \to 0} \sqrt{a} = 2.$$

(b) How is the function $g(x) = 1/\sqrt{x}$ for $0 < x \leqslant 1$ related to the function $f(x) = 1/x^2$ for $x \geqslant 1$ in Problem 12? And what can you conclude about the corresponding areas?

(c) For a fixed $M > 1$ find the area of the shaded region in Fig. (ii). Do these values have a limit as M increases? How does it compare with the limit in part (a)?

14. Sketch graphs for each of the following functions and see whether the procedure of Problem 13(a) gives a reasonable area assignment for the region beneath the graph.

(a) $f(x) = x^{-2/3}$ for $0 < x \leqslant 2$

(b) $f(x) = \dfrac{1}{x}$ for $0 < x \leqslant 1$

(c) $f(x) = \dfrac{1}{\sqrt{|x|}}$ for $x \neq 0$ in $[-1, 1]$

(Find areas over $[-1, 0\rangle$ and $\langle 0, 1]$ separately.)

(d) $f(x) = \dfrac{1}{\sqrt{|x-3|}}$ for $0 < x < 3$ and $3 < x < 6$

15. I've been defining "area" for a region beneath the graph of a function _f_ as a limit of areas of unions of thin _vertical_ rectangles, as in Fig. (i). Would we get the same value if we used unions of thin _horizontal_ rectangles, as in Fig. (ii)?

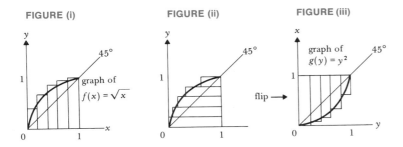

FIGURE (i)   **FIGURE (ii)**   **FIGURE (iii)**

Note in Fig. (iii) that this second method corresponds to working with the function $g(y)$ which is the inverse of $f(x)$ (in the specific case, to subtracting the area under the graph of _g_ from that of the unit square). Check whether the two methods give the same result in each of the following cases. Make sketches similar to

Figs. (i)–(iii).

(a) $f(x) = \dfrac{1}{x}$ on $[1, 2]$ (b) $f(x) = \sqrt{x}$ on $[0, 1]$

(c) $f(x) = x^3$ on $[0, 1]$ (d) $f(x) = x^3$ on $[1, 2]$

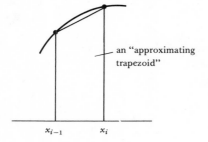

an "approximating trapezoid"

16. (a) For each of the functions f in Problem 15, divide the given interval into four subintervals of equal length, and calculate "inside" and "outside" areas for the region under the graph—as you did in Problem 6 of Sec. 17.4. Compare these results with the limiting values you calculated in Problem 15.

(b) Repeat part (a), except this time use "approximating trapezoids," as in the accompanying figure, rather than "inside" or "outside" rectangles; and compare your results with those in part (a) and in Problem 15.

(Such trapezoids are often used in actual numerical approximations to areas, done by computers.)

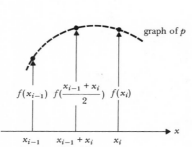

graph of p

$f(x_{i-1})\ f\left(\dfrac{x_{i-1}+x_i}{2}\right)\ f(x_i)$

$x_{i-1}\qquad \dfrac{x_{i-1}+x_i}{2}\qquad x_i$

*17. (a) Given three heights, $f(x_{i-1})$, $f((x_{i-1}+x_i)/2)$, and $f(x_i)$, as in the accompanying figure, find constants A, B, and C (in terms of $x_{i-1}, x_i, f(x_{i-1}), f((x_{i-1}+x_i)/2)$, and $f(x_i)$) so that the quadratic polynomial $p(x) = Ax^2 + Bx + C$ will have outputs

$$p(x_{i-1}) = f(x_{i-1}),\ p\left(\frac{x_{i-1}+x_i}{2}\right) = f\left(\frac{x_{i-1}+x_i}{2}\right),\ \text{and } p(x_i) = f(x_i)$$

—that is, so that the "parabolic" graph of p will pass through the three points given in the figure.

(b) Find the area of the region beneath the graph of the quadratic $p(x)$ which you found in part (a), and above the interval $[x_{i-1}, x_i]$.

(c) Repeat part (b) of Problem 16, except this time use a "parabolically fitted region," as in the present problem, in place of each trapezoidal region. Compare your results with those in Problems 15 and 16. (Such parabolic fitting—called "Simpson's method"—is another scheme used in some numerical approximations.)

18. Suppose that $B_a{}^b(f)$ denotes an assignment of "area" to the same regions as $A_a{}^b(f)$, via some other scheme—say, based on triangles. If $B_a{}^b(f)$ assigns the same areas to rectangles as does $A_a{}^b(f)$, and if $B_a{}^b(f)$ also shares the "adding" and "comparing" properties of Theorems B and C in Sec. 17.5, must $B_a{}^b(f)$ be *identical* to $A_a{}^b(f)$?

(Suggestion: Show that Theorem E of Sec. 17.6 holds for $B_a{}^b(f)$, and use the neck-and-neck race argument of Sec. 15.9.)

*17.9 WHY UNIQUE AREAS DO EXIST BENEATH CONTINUOUS GRAPHS

Theorem A of Sec. 17.3 asserted that, given any continuous non-negative function f on an interval $[a, b]$, there exists a unique number $A_a^b(f)$ serving as the limit of *any* sequence of approximating sums

$$S_{\sigma_n} = f(x_1^*)(x_1 - x_0) + f(x_2^*)(x_2 - x_1) + f(x_3^*)(x_3 - x_2) + \cdots \qquad (1)$$

based on partitions σ_n whose meshes tend to zero as n increases. For a

Proof of Theorem A, let's first try to locate a suitable candidate for the quantity $A_a^b(f)$ — one which won't depend on particular partitions. Afterwards we can see why

$$\lim_{n \to \infty} \text{mesh}(\sigma_n) = 0 \text{ should imply } \lim_{n \to \infty} S_{\sigma_n} = A_a^b(f). \qquad (2)$$

You may recall from Figs. 17-9 and 17-10 how inside and outside areas improve when we add more points to a partition. To help describe such operations here are two

Definitions: For a given interval $[a, b]$, let's say that a partition τ is a *refinement* of another partition σ if τ includes all the points of σ and (possibly) some others. Notation: $\sigma \subset \tau$.

Given two partitions σ and τ of $[a, b]$, let's denote by "$\sigma \cup \tau$" the partition consisting of all points appearing in σ or in τ (or in both); and let's call $\sigma \cup \tau$ the *common refinement* of the partitions σ and τ.

(The reason for the name is that both $\sigma \subset \sigma \cup \tau$ and $\tau \subset \sigma \cup \tau$.)

EXAMPLE 1. If $\sigma = \{0, \frac{1}{2}, 1\}$ and $\tau = \{0, \frac{1}{4}, \frac{1}{2}, \frac{3}{4}, 1\}$, then $\sigma \subset \tau$.

EXAMPLE 2. If $\sigma = \{0, \frac{1}{2}, 1\}$ and $\tau = \{0, \frac{1}{3}, \frac{2}{3}, 1\}$, then

$\sigma \cup \tau = \{0, \frac{1}{3}, \frac{1}{2}, \frac{2}{3}, 1\}$.

For a given partition $\sigma = \{x_i\}$, recall the definitions of Sec. 17.3:

$$A_\sigma^{\text{in}} = m_1(x_1 - x_0) + m_2(x_2 - x_:) + m_3(x_3 - x_2) + \cdots \qquad (3)$$

and

$$A_\sigma^{\text{out}} = M_1(x_1 - x_0) + M_2(x_2 - x_1) + M_3(x_3 - x_2) + \cdots, \qquad (4)$$

where m_i and M_i denote the minimum and maximum values of f on a subinterval $[x_{i-1}, x_i]$. In that section, I noted a

First fact:

$$A_\sigma^{\text{in}} \leq A_\sigma^{\text{out}} \quad \text{for any partition } \sigma. \qquad (5)$$

Then, Figs. 17-9 and 17-10 *suggested* a

Second fact:

$$A_\sigma^{\text{in}} \leq A_\tau^{\text{in}} \quad \text{and} \quad A_\tau^{\text{out}} \leq A_\sigma^{\text{out}} \quad \text{whenever } \sigma \subset \tau. \qquad (6)$$

How can we verify these inequalities for *any* partitions σ and τ, where τ is a refinement of σ? Now, τ may contain many extra points not in σ — say, m; but we can think of getting from σ to τ by adding in *one such extra point at a time*. This procedure would yield a chain of "intermediate partitions"

$$\sigma \subset \tau_1 \subset \tau_2 \subset \cdots \subset \tau_{m-1} \subset \tau \tag{7}$$

each differing from the one before by *one* extra point. If we can prove that the inequalities (6) hold for partitions differing by just one point, then we would have

$$A_\sigma^{\text{in}} \leq A_{\tau_1}^{\text{in}} \leq A_{\tau_2}^{\text{in}} \leq \cdots \leq A_\tau^{\text{in}} \text{ and } A_\tau^{\text{out}} \leq \cdots A_{\tau_2}^{\text{out}} \leq A_{\tau_1}^{\text{out}} \leq A_\sigma^{\text{out}} \tag{8}$$

—a proof of (6) for general $\sigma \subset \tau$.

Why then should

$$A_\sigma^{\text{in}} \leq A_\tau^{\text{in}} \text{ and } A_\tau^{\text{out}} \leq A_\sigma^{\text{out}}$$

when τ has just one more point than σ? Note that the sums (such as (3)) defining A_σ^{in} and A_τ^{in} differ at *just one place*: Suppose that τ's extra point—call it x'—lies in the interval $[x_{i-1}, x_i]$ of σ. See Fig. 17-29.

FIGURE 17-29

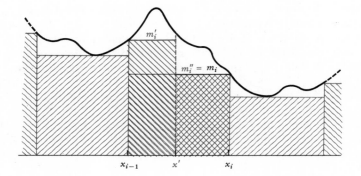

Then the term $m_i(x_i - x_{i-1})$ in A_σ^{in} gets replaced in A_τ^{in} by two terms of the form

$$m_i'(x' - x_{i-1}) + m_i''(x_i - x'), \tag{9}$$

where m_i' is the minimum of f on the smaller subinterval $[x_{i-1}, x']$ and m_i'' is the minimum of f on $[x', x_i]$. Now for any function: *the larger the set over which we seek a minimum, the smaller that minimum will be.* Thus, even without Fig. 17-29, we should know that

$$m_i \leq m_i' \quad \text{and} \quad m_i \leq m_i''. \tag{10}$$

Hence the two terms (9) in A_τ^{in},

$$m_i'(x' - x_{i-1}) + m_i''(x_i - x') \geq m_i(x' - x_{i-1}) + m_i(x_i - x')$$
$$= m_i[(x' - x_{i-1}) + (x_i - x')]$$
$$= m_i(x_i - x_{i-1}), \tag{11}$$

exceed the corresponding single term in A_σ^{in}. So $A_\sigma^{\text{in}} \leq A_\tau^{\text{in}}$.

Similarly, the sums A_σ^{out} and A_τ^{out} differ at just one place. See Fig. 17-30. The maxima M_i' and M_i'' of f on the new smaller intervals $[x_{i-1}, x']$ and $[x', x_i]$ can't exceed the maximum M_i over all of

FIGURE 17-30

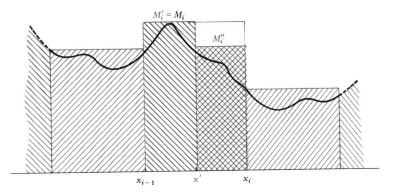

$[x_{i-1}, x_i]$. Hence the two terms in A_τ^{out},

$$M_i'(x' - x_{i-1}) + M_i''(x_i - x') \leq M_i(x' - x_{i-1}) + M_i(x_i - x')$$
$$= M_i[(x' - x_{i-1}) + (x_i - x')]$$
$$= M_i(x_i - x_{i-1}), \qquad \text{(12)}$$

amount to less than the corresponding single term in A_σ^{out}. So $A_\tau^{\text{out}} \leq A_\sigma^{\text{out}}$. And we've completely proved the inequalities (6)—the "SECOND FACT."

If we knew that $A_a^b(f)$ existed, we might expect the inequalities

$$A_\sigma^{\text{in}} \leq A_a^b(f) \leq A_\tau^{\text{out}} \qquad \text{(13)}$$

for any partitions σ and τ. But the problem at hand is to show that $A_a^b(f)$ *does* exist—to squeeze our area approximations toward a suitable candidate value for $A_a^b(f)$. For this purpose, we might ask how the quantities A_σ^{in} and A_τ^{out} compare when neither σ nor τ is necessarily a refinement of the other. Why not try relating A_σ^{in} and A_τ^{out} via the "common refinement" $\sigma \cup \tau$? By the "SECOND FACT,"

$$A_\sigma^{\text{in}} \leq A_{\sigma \cup \tau}^{\text{in}} \quad \text{and} \quad A_{\sigma \cup \tau}^{\text{out}} \leq A_\tau^{\text{out}}. \qquad \text{(14)}$$

And by the "FIRST FACT," $A_{\sigma \cup \tau}^{\text{in}} \leq A_{\sigma \cup \tau}^{\text{out}}$. Putting these inequalities together, we'll have

$$A_\sigma^{\text{in}} \leq A_{\sigma \cup \tau}^{\text{in}} \leq A_{\sigma \cup \tau}^{\text{out}} \leq A_\tau^{\text{out}}, \qquad \text{(15)}$$

or a ***Third fact:***

$$A_\sigma^{\text{in}} \leq A_\tau^{\text{out}} \qquad \text{for } any \text{ partitions } \sigma \text{ and } \tau. \qquad \text{(16)}$$

To locate candidates for $A_a^b(f)$, let's examine the set of values A_σ^{in} for *all* possible partitions σ of $[a, b]$—I've pictured it in black on a coordinate line in Fig. 17-31. And likewise let's examine the set of all possible values A_τ^{out}—I've pictured it in green in Fig. 17-31.

FIGURE 17-31

(Note that the outermost values $m(b-a)$ and $M(b-a)$ correspond to the simplest partition of all, $\sigma = \{a, b\}$.)

What does the "THIRD FACT" say? It says that any green value A_τ^{out} is an upper bound for the entire black set of values A_σ^{in}. Hence the black set must have a *least* upper bound $L \leq A_\tau^{\text{out}}$. On the other hand, since $L \leq$ any green A_τ^{out}, the green set must have a *greatest* lower bound $G \geq L$.

If $L < G$, what reasonable choice could we make for $A_a^b(f)$? Is any one value in the interval $[L, G]$ more worthy than another? Such is the case for the region in Fig. 17-1, lying beneath a *discontinuous* graph. (You might check that case to find $L = 0$ and $G = 1$.)

When can we conclude that $L = G$? For any partition $\sigma = \{x_i\}$, we have the inequalities

$$A_\sigma^{\text{in}} \leq L \leq G \leq A_\sigma^{\text{out}}. \tag{17}$$

Hence the difference $G - L$ can't exceed the difference

$$
\begin{aligned}
A_\sigma^{\text{out}} - A_\sigma^{\text{in}} &= [M_1(x_1 - x_0) + M_2(x_2 - x_1) + M_3(x_3 - x_2) + \cdots] \\
&\quad - [m_1(x_1 - x_0) + m_2(x_2 - x_1) + m_3(x_3 - x_2) + \cdots] \\
&= [M_1 - m_1](x_1 - x_0) + [M_2 - m_2](x_2 - x_1) \\
&\quad + [M_3 - m_3](x_3 - x_2) + \cdots.
\end{aligned} \tag{18}
$$

Each term $[M_i - m_i](x_i - x_{i-1})$ in the last sum is the area of a "difference rectangle" between outside and inside rectangles constructed above the interval $[x_{i-1}, x_i]$. See Fig. 17-32, where I've colored such "difference rectangles" green.

FIGURE 17-32

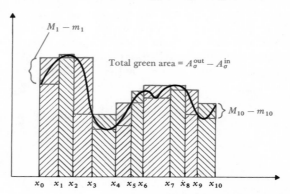

If f is *continuous*, can we choose partitions σ_n with subinterval lengths $x_i - x_{i-1}$ so small and corresponding difference rectangle heights $M_i - m_i$ so small, that the *total* (green) area $A_{\sigma_n}^{\text{out}} - A_{\sigma_n}^{\text{in}}$ will be as small as we please? If so, we could force the difference $G - L$ to be zero—and at the same time approximate the common value

$$G = L = \text{``}A_a^b(f)\text{''}$$

by $A_{\sigma_n}^{\text{in}}$, by $A_{\sigma_n}^{\text{out}}$, and by any intermediate area S_{σ_n}.

The answer lies in the property of "uniform continuity" of a continuous function on a closed interval $[a, b]$. I discussed that property in Sec. 12.9 (Theorem F), and I'll recall it here as a

Fourth fact. Given any $\epsilon > 0$, there exists a positive number δ_ϵ such that $|f(x) - f(x')| < \epsilon$ whenever x and x' are two inputs in $[a, b]$ with $|x - x'| < \delta_\epsilon$.

In particular, consider *any* partition $\sigma = \{x_i\}$ with mesh $< \delta_\epsilon$. Then any two inputs x and x' from the same subinterval $[x_{i-1}, x_i]$ must have outputs with $|f(x) - f(x')| < \epsilon$. If we choose $x = x_i{}^{\max}$ and $x' = x_i{}^{\min}$, we'll have

$$M_i - m_i = |f(x_i{}^{\max}) - f(x_i{}^{\min})| < \epsilon \text{ for every subinterval } [x_{i-1}, x_i].$$
$$\text{(19)}$$

Let's apply these inequalities to the last sum in (18), to get

$$0 \leq A_\sigma{}^{\text{out}} - A_\sigma{}^{\text{in}} = (M_1 - m_1)(x_1 - x_0) + (M_2 - m_2)(x_2 - x_1)$$

$$+ (M_3 - m_3)(x_3 - x_2) + \cdots$$

$$< \epsilon(x_1 - x_0) + \epsilon(x_2 - x_1) + \epsilon(x_3 - x_2) + \cdots$$

$$= \epsilon[(x_1 - x_0) + (x_2 - x_1) + (x_3 - x_2) + \cdots]$$

$$= \epsilon(b - a).$$
$$\text{(20)}$$

Or, a

Key inequality:

$$|A_\sigma{}^{\text{out}} - A_\sigma{}^{\text{in}}| < \epsilon(b - a) \qquad \text{whenever mesh } (\sigma) < \delta_\epsilon, \qquad \text{(21)}$$

where δ_ϵ is related to ϵ as in the "FOURTH FACT."

As a first consequence of this "KEY INEQUALITY," we *can* conclude that $G = L$. Otherwise, if $G > L$, we could choose an ϵ such that $\epsilon(b - a) < G - L$, get a corresponding δ_ϵ, and choose a partition σ with mesh $(\sigma) < \delta_\epsilon$—to arrive at the impossible inequalities

$$G - L \leq A_\sigma{}^{\text{out}} - A_\sigma{}^{\text{in}} < \epsilon(b - a) < G - L.$$

So we've come to a unique candidate for area:

Definitions: Let $A_a{}^b(f)$ denote the common value $G = L$.

Note then that

$$A_\sigma^{\text{in}} \leq A_a{}^b(f) \leq A_\sigma{}^{\text{out}} \qquad \text{for any } \sigma \qquad \text{(22)}$$

—one of the assertions of Theorem A.

As a second consequence of the "KEY INEQUALITY," let's show that for a sequence $\sigma_1, \sigma_2, \sigma_3, \ldots$ of partitions of $[a, b]$:

$$\lim_{n \to \infty} \text{mesh} (\sigma_n) = 0 \qquad \text{(23)}$$

implies that

$$\lim_{n \to \infty} |A_{\sigma_n}^{\text{out}} - A_{\sigma_n}^{\text{in}}| = 0. \qquad \text{(24)}$$

The latter limit means that given any positive quantity—call it ϵ', we must have

$$|A_{\sigma_n}^{\text{out}} - A_{\sigma_n}^{\text{in}}| < \epsilon' \qquad \text{for } all \ n \geq \text{some index } N_{\epsilon'} \qquad \text{(25)}$$

(where $N_{\epsilon'}$ may depend on the choice of ϵ'). Note how closely these required inequalities resemble the "key inequality" (21) in form. To use (21) let's choose ϵ so that $\epsilon' = \epsilon(b-a)$. That is, given ϵ', let's feed $\epsilon = \epsilon'/(b-a)$ into the "FOURTH FACT," and get a corresponding positive quantity δ_ϵ. Since $\lim_{n\to\infty}$ mesh $(\sigma_n) = 0$, we can claim that

$$\text{mesh } (\sigma_n) < \delta_\epsilon \qquad \text{for all } n \geq \text{ some index } N. \tag{26}$$

This is the index "$N_{\epsilon'}$" we need in (25). Via the "KEY INEQUALITY," we must have

$$|A_{\sigma_n}^{\text{out}} - A_{\sigma_n}^{\text{in}}| < \epsilon(b-a) = \epsilon' \qquad \text{when mesh } (\sigma_n) < \delta_n,$$
$$\text{and mesh } (\sigma_n) < \delta_n \qquad \text{for all } n \geq N_{\epsilon'}. \tag{27}$$

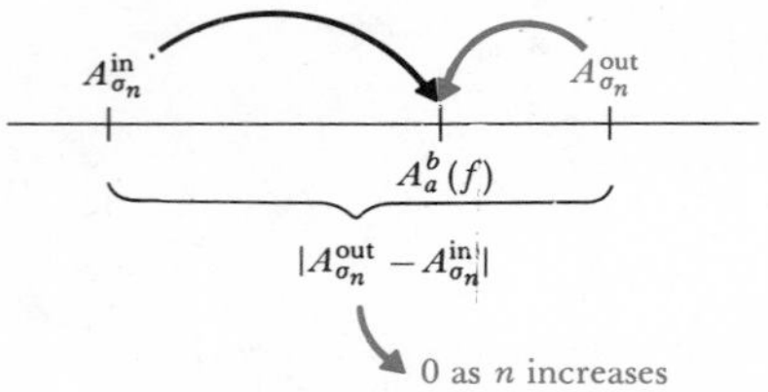

So $\lim_{n\to\infty}$ mesh $(\sigma_n) = 0$ *does* imply that $\lim_{n\to\infty} |A_{\sigma_n}^{\text{out}} - A_{\sigma_n}^{\text{in}}| = 0$.

Moreover, since

$$A_{\sigma n}^{\text{in}} \leq A_a^{\ b}(f) \leq A_{\sigma n}^{\text{out}} \qquad \text{for all } \sigma_n,$$

the flanking values $A_{\sigma n}^{\text{in}}$ and $A_{\sigma n}^{\text{out}}$ themselves are squeezed toward the middle one, $A_a^{\ b}(f)$, when the differences $|A_{\sigma_n}^{\text{out}} - A_{\sigma_n}^{\text{in}}|$ approach zero. See Fig. 17-33. And any "intermediate approximations" based on σ_n,

$$S_{\sigma_n} = f(x_1^*)(x_1 - x_0) + f(x_2^*)(x_2 - x_1) + f(x_3^*)(x_3 - x_2) + \cdots$$

(which lie between the corresponding $A_{\sigma_n}^{\text{in}}$ and $A_{\sigma_n}^{\text{out}}$) must also be forced to the limit $A_a^{\ b}(f)$, as in Fig. 17-34.

FIGURE 17-33

$A_{\sigma_n}^{\text{in}}$ $A_{\sigma_n}^{\text{out}}$

$A_a^b(f)$

$|A_{\sigma_n}^{\text{out}} - A_{\sigma_n}^{\text{in}}|$

↘ 0 as n increases

FIGURE 17-34

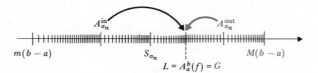

That is,

$$\lim_{n\to\infty} S_{\sigma n} = A_a^{\ b}(f) \qquad \text{when } \lim_{n\to\infty} \text{mesh } (\sigma_n) = 0.$$

End of a proof for Theorem A.

17.10 SUMMARY OF CHAPTER 17

In Secs. 17.1 and 17.2, general considerations: whether areas always exist, areas of simple regions.

From Sec. 17.3 on, a special case: the area of a region beneath the graph of a continuous function and above an interval $[a, b]$. The main idea: approximate the region by a union of thin vertical rectangles (see Fig. 17-8). Then show that when such rectangles get finer and finer, the corresponding sums of the areas of the rectangles converge to a unique limit—the area of the region. The following definitions and results carry out the idea.

DEFINITIONS: Call any finite set of numbers $\sigma = \{x_i\}$, labeled in left-to-right order

$$a = x_0 < x_1 < x_2 < \cdots < x_n = b, \tag{28}$$

a *partition* of the interval $[a, b]$. (σ divides $[a, b]$ into subintervals $[x_{i-1}, x_i]$ which we can use as bases of approximating rectangles.) Let's use the term *mesh of σ* (or "mesh (σ)") to denote the largest of the lengths $x_i - x_{i-1}$ of the subintervals of σ. (The mesh will measure how thin the approximating rectangles are (Sec. 17.3).)

THEOREM (ON "THE EXISTENCE OF AREA UNDER GRAPHS"): Suppose that f is a continuous nonnegative function on an interval $[a, b]$. Then there exists a unique number $A_a{}^b(f)$ which we can interpret as the area of the region beneath the graph of f and above the interval $[a, b]$. This area value may be approximated as follows:

Suppose that $\sigma_1, \sigma_2, \ldots, \sigma_n, \ldots$ is *any* sequence of partitions of $[a, b]$ whose *meshes tend to zero*. For every σ_n, choose some input x_i^* from each subinterval $[x_{i-1}, x_i]$ of σ_n, and form the sum of areas of rectangles (with base $x_i - x_{i-1}$ and height $f(x_i^*)$):

$$S_{\sigma_n}(f) = f(x_1^*)(x_1 - x_0) + f(x_2^*)(x_2 - x_1) + f(x_3^*)(x_3 - x_2) + \cdots$$

(the inputs x_i and x_i^* all depending on n). Then

$$\lim_{n \to \infty} S_{\sigma_n}(f) = A_a{}^b(f).$$

In particular, for *any* fixed partition $\sigma = \{x_i\}$ of $[a, b]$: if we let m_i and M_i be the minimum and maximum values of f on the subinterval $[x_{i-1}, x_i]$, and if we form the sums

$$A_\sigma{}^{\text{in}}(f) = m_1(x_1 - x_0) + m_2(x_2 - x_1) + m_3(x_3 - x_2) + \cdots$$

(an "inside area"), and

$$A_\sigma{}^{\text{out}}(f) = M_1(x_1 - x_0) + M_2(x_2 - x_1) + M_3(x_3 - x_2) + \cdots$$

(an "outside area"), then

$$A_\sigma{}^{\text{in}}(f) \le A_a{}^b(f) \le A_\sigma{}^{\text{out}}(f).$$

(See Fig. 17-8.) For a constant function $f \equiv C$ on $[a, b]$,

$$A_\sigma{}^{\text{in}}(f) = A_a{}^b(f) = A_\sigma{}^{\text{out}}(f) = C(b - a)$$

for any σ. (Sec. 17.3 and 17.9.) For a proof of this result, and for related definitions, see Sec. 17.9.

Further properties of $A_a{}^b(f)$:

THEOREM (ON "ADDING ADJACENT AREAS"): If $a < c < b$ and if f is continuous and nonnegative on $[a, b]$, then

$$A_a{}^b(f) = A_a{}^c(f) + A_c{}^b(f).$$

(Sec. 17.5.)

THEOREM (ON "COMPARING AREAS"): If f and g are continuous nonnegative functions with $f(x) \leqslant g(x)$ for all x in $[a, b]$, then

$$A_a{}^b(f) \leqslant A_a{}^b(g).$$

(Sec. 17.5.)

THEOREM (ON "SCALING AND ADDING AREAS"): If f is a continuous nonnegative function on $[a, b]$ and c is a constant $\geqslant 0$, then

$$A_a{}^b(cf) = cA_a{}^b(f).$$

If g is another continuous nonnegative function on $[a, b]$, then

$$A_a{}^b(f+g) = A_a{}^b(f) + A_a{}^b(g).$$

(Sec. 17.5.)

DEFINITION: $A_a{}^a(f) = 0$ for any a and f.
(Sec. 17.6)

THEOREM (ON "THE DERIVATIVE OF THE CUMULATIVE AREA FUNCTION"): Suppose that f is any continuous nonnegative function on an interval $[a, b]$. Let $F(x) = A_a{}^x(f)$ for each x in $[a, b]$. Then

$$F'(x_0) = f(x_0) \qquad \text{for each } x_0 \text{ in } [a, b].$$

(That is, the *cumulative area* from a to x, as a function of x, provides an antiderivative for f.)
(Sec. 17.6.)

METHOD FOR FINDING AREA VIA ANTIDERIVATIVES: Find *any* antiderivative G for the given function f. Then

$$G(b) - G(a) = A_a{}^b(f).$$

(Sec. 17.6.)

See Sec. 17.7 for the probability that a needle will hit a crack in a floor.

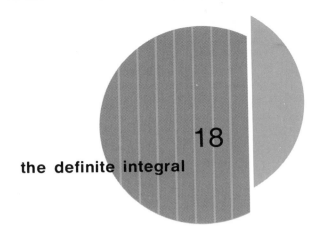

18

the definite integral

In this chapter I'll show how the approximation ideas for defining and calculating "area"—which I explored in the last chapter—lead to a very general method. I'll use this method for finding volumes, determining the worth of an investment, finding average waiting times between telephone calls, and "tuning" radio signals.

18.1 THE "DEFINITE INTEGRAL"

All the steps I took in the last chapter were to show how "area" could be *defined* precisely—and *evaluated*—for various irregular regions. Must one again trudge a similar route to deal with "volume" and its properties—or with other notions involving "approximating sums"?

No. In Secs. 17.3 through 17.7, I drew graphs of nonnegative functions f and spoke of "areas" beneath them. But if you'll look back at all the actual inequalities and other algebraic and limit statements in those sections, you'll see that NONE *of them depends on the nonnegativity of the functions f, and* NONE *depends for its validity on our interpreting various sums as "areas."* Though historically deduced for a specific goal (area), the results tell a *general story* about the existence of a unique limit for certain approximating sums.

Traditionally, this unique limit has been called

Definition: The *definite integral (of f from a to b)*, and has been denoted by the symbol

$$\int_a^b f(x)\,dx. \tag{*}$$

Henceforth, I'll use this symbol instead of the "$A_a{}^b(f)$" which I associated with area. We can then give $\int_a^b f(x)\,dx$ various interpretations depending on the application.

Another name for the quantity in (*) is the "Riemann integral," after Bernhard Riemann who helped clarify the notion. The $\int$ sign in (*), an old fashioned S, is supposed to recall "sums" such as S_{σ_n}. The "$f(x)\ dx$" is supposed to recall the ith term, $f(x_i^*)(x_i - x_{i-1})$, of such a sum (Leibnitz denoted small differences such as $x_i - x_{i-1}$ by "dx"). And the a and b recall the end points of the given interval $[a, b]$. If we choose to label inputs by some other letter such as t, then the expression $\int_a^b f(t)\ dt$ has the same meaning as $\int_a^b f(x)\ dx$.

(You'll have to distinguish the sign $\int_a^b$ *with* end points from the sign $\int$ without end points, which I noted in Sec. 15.10 as a traditional symbol for antiderivatives. The two are related in Theorem G below.)

Here now is a summary of the main results (Theorems A–E) of the last chapter — avoiding the unnecessary hypothesis that $f \geqslant 0$ and the "area" interpretation. I'll state it as two theorems:

> **Theorem F (on the existence of the "definite integral"):** Suppose that f is a continuous function on an interval $a \leqslant x \leqslant b$. Then there exists a *unique number* — label it $\int_a^b f(x)\ dx$ — with the following properties.

I. *The extreme case $a = b$:* $\int_a^a f(x)\ dx = 0$.

II. *Approximating sums*: Given a partition $\sigma = \{x_i\}$ of the interval $[a, b]$, choose some input x_i^* from each subinterval $[x_{i-1}, x_i]$ of σ and form the sum

$$S_\sigma = f(x_1^*)(x_1 - x_0) + f(x_2^*)(x_2 - x_1) + f(x_3^*)(x_3 - x_2) + \cdots, \tag{1}$$

one term corresponding to each subinterval $[x_{i-1}, x_i]$. If $\sigma_1, \sigma_2, \sigma_3, \ldots$ is a sequence of such partitions *with meshes tending to zero*, and if S_{σ_n} are corresponding sums as in (1) (where the x_i's and x_i^*'s depend on n), then

$$\lim_{n \to \infty} S_{\sigma_n} = \int_a^b f(x)\ dx. \tag{2}$$

III. *Lower and upper bounds*: Given any partition $\sigma = \{x_i\}$, let $S_\sigma{}^{\min}$ denote the sum in (1) when $f(x_i^*)$ = the minimum output of f on $[x_{i-1}, x_i]$ for each i, and let $S_\sigma{}^{\max}$ denote the sum in (1) when $f(x_i^*)$ = the maximum output of f on $[x_{i-1}, x_i]$ for each i. Then

$$S_\sigma{}^{\min} \leqslant \int_a^b f(x)\ dx \leqslant S_\sigma{}^{\max}. \tag{3}$$

In particular,

$$m(b-a) \leqslant \int_a^b f(x)\ dx \leqslant M(b-a), \tag{4}$$

where m denotes the absolute minimum of f on $[a, b]$ and M denotes its absolute maximum.

IV. *Adjacent intervals:* If $a \leqslant c \leqslant b$, then

$$\int_a^b f(x)\ dx = \int_a^c f(x)\ dx + \int_c^b f(x)\ dx. \tag{5}$$

V. *Scaling:* If c is any constant, then

$$\int_a^b [cf(x)]\ dx = c\left[\int_a^b f(x)\ dx\right]. \tag{6}$$

VI. *Adding functions:* If g is another continuous function on $[a, b]$, then

$$\int_a^b [f(x) + g(x)] \, dx = \int_a^b f(x) \, dx + \int_a^b g(x) \, dx. \qquad (7)$$

VII. *Comparing functions:* If g is continuous on $[a, b]$ and $f(x) \leq g(x)$ for all x in $[a, b]$, then

$$\int_a^b f(x) \, dx \leq \int_a^b g(x) \, dx. \qquad (8)$$

VIII. *A constant function:* If $f(x) = C$ for all x in $[a, b]$, then

$$\int_a^b f(x) \, dx = C(b - a). \qquad (9)$$

The process of forming definite integrals is called *integration*. And the next result has been called the "fundamental theorem of the integral calculus" because it relates the two key operations of calculus, integration and differentiation.

Theorem G (the "fundamental theorem"): Suppose that $a < b$ and that f is any continuous function on the interval $[a, b]$. Define a new function F on $[a, b]$ by forming

$$F(x) = \int_a^x f(t) \, dt, \qquad (10)$$

the definite integral of f from a to x, for *each* x in $[a, b]$. Then

$$F'(x_0) = f(x_0) \qquad \text{at each } x_0 \text{ in } [a, b]. \qquad (11)$$

That is, F is an antiderivative of f, with

$$F(a) = 0 \quad \text{and} \quad F(b) = \int_a^b f(t) \, dt.$$

More generally, if G is *any* antiderivative of f on $[a, b]$, then

$$\boxed{G(b) - G(a) = \int_a^b f(t) \, dt.} \qquad (12)$$

More specifically: if a given function $g(x)$ has a continuous derivative $g'(x)$ on $[a, b]$, then

$$g(b) - g(a) = \int_a^b g'(t) \, dt, \qquad (13)$$

since g is an antiderivative of g'.

These results show that integration and differentiation are essentially "opposite" operations. The relation $F'(x) = f(x)$ in (11) says that differentiation *undoes* the cumulative work of integration. And the expression (13) shows how integration recovers a difference $g(b) - g(a)$ from the values of all instantaneous rates $g'(t)$ got by differentiation.

You might recall that the "mean value theorem" of Chap. 15 expresses the overall difference of outputs

$$g(b) - g(a) = g'(c)(b - a) \qquad (14)$$

in terms of the rate $g'(c)$ at one *unknown* input c somewhere between a and b. In (13) we can now view the same difference $g(b) - g(a)$ also as a limit of sums of many similar differences over tiny subintervals $[x_{i-1}, x_i]$ of $[a, b]$. When a partition $\sigma = \{x_i\}$ has very small mesh, *each term in a corresponding sum*

$$S_{\sigma_n} = g'(x_1^*)(x_1 - x_0) + g'(x_2^*)(x_2 - x_1) + g'(x_3^*)(x_3 - x_2) + \cdots \qquad (15)$$

—being a product of a rate $g'(x_i^*)$ times an input change $(x_i - x_{i-1})$— *should approximate the output change* $g(x_i) - g(x_{i-1})$. In fact, by the "mean value theorem," there must be some x_i^* in each subinterval $[x_{i-1}, x_i]$ such that

$$g(x_i) - g(x_{i-1}) = g'(x_i^*)(x_i - x_{i-1}) \textit{ exactly.} \qquad (16)$$

Being continuous, the rates $g'(x)$ shouldn't differ by much over any tiny interval $[x_{i-1}, x_i]$. So for whichever x_i^* we choose in each $[x_{i-1}, x_i]$, we might expect the approximations $g'(x_i^*)(x_i - x_{i-1})$ to add up to a good approximation S_{σ_n} for the overall difference $g(b) - g(a)$. And (13) says that they do: they approach $g(b) - g(a)$ as a limit, for smaller and smaller mesh sizes.

One further note on the result $F'(x) = f(x)$ in (11). It answers the question I pointed out in Sec. 15.10: Does every continuous function f necessarily have even one antiderivative? Yes; namely

$$F(x) = \int_a^x f(t)\, dt.$$

The result $G(b) - G(a) = \int_a^b f(x)\, dx$ in (12) shows how we might hope to evaluate an integral of a given function exactly— by searching for some antiderivative G of f.

Let's see now how we can apply the "definite integral" to concepts other than area.

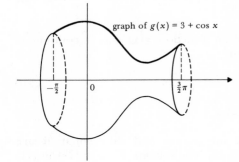

graph of $g(x) = 3 + \cos x$

FIGURE 18-1

EXAMPLE 1. Imagine the potlike region we could cut out in three-dimensional space by rotating the graph g in Fig. 18-1 about the horizontal axis. Let's establish the existence of a volume V for that region, and calculate V exactly. We might think first of approximating a true volume for the pot by adding the volumes of the circular slabs, as in Fig. 18-2.

FIGURE 18-2

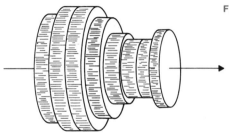

FIGURE 18-3

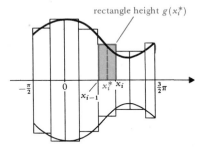

I got these slabs by picking a partition $\sigma = \{x_i\}$ of the interval $[-\pi/2, 3\pi/2]$, as in Fig. 18-3. From each subinterval $[x_{i-1}, x_i]$ I picked an input x_i^* and rotated the rectangle of "representative" height $g(x_i^*)$ about the horizontal axis to get a corresponding slab. Note that the "slab" is a "right circular cylinder." (I've redrawn it in Fig. 18-4.)

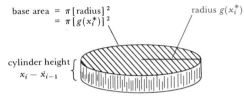

FIGURE 18-4

Will you accept the volume of the cylinder as the product of its base area and its own height – that is,

$$\pi[g(x_i^*)]^2(x_i - x_{i-1}), \tag{17}$$

for each i? If so, then the total approximating volume of the slabs in Fig. 18-2 is the sum

$$S_\sigma = \pi[g(x_1^*)]^2(x_1 - x_0) + \pi[g(x_2^*)]^2(x_2 - x_1)$$
$$+ \pi[g(x_3^*)]^2(x_3 - x_2) + \cdots. \tag{18}$$

We can write S_σ in the more familiar form

$$S_\sigma = f(x_1^*)(x_1 - x_0) + f(x_2^*)(x_2 - x_1) + f(x_3^*)(x_3 - x_2) + \cdots \tag{19}$$

by defining

$$f(x) = \pi[g(x)]^2 = \pi(3 + \cos x)^2 \qquad \text{for} -\frac{\pi}{2} \le x \le \frac{3}{2}\pi. \tag{20}$$

Note that f is continuous on $[-\pi/2, 3\pi/2]$. *Conclusion:* if we form approximating volumes as in Fig. 18-2, corresponding to any sequence $\sigma_1, \sigma_2, \sigma_3, \ldots$ of partitions of $[-\pi/2, 3\pi/2]$ whose meshes tend to zero, then these approximations must converge to the unique number

$$\int_{-\pi/2}^{3\pi/2} f(x)\, dx = \int_{-\pi/2}^{3\pi/2} \pi(3 + \cos x)^2\, dx. \tag{21}$$

If we wish, we can choose x_i^*'s so that for each σ_n the union of slabs in Fig. 18-2 will fit *inside* the pot and provide a "lower approximation" to the pot's "volume." Or we can adjust the x_i^*'s so that the union of slabs will *contain* the pot and provide an "upper approximation" to its "volume." Whatever the x_i^*'s, the limit will be the same — the integral in (21). Do you feel it's reasonable to assign this quantity as *the volume V* of the potlike region?

Now how can we evaluate V? Since

$$f(x) = \pi(3 + \cos x)^2 = 9\pi + 6\pi \cos x + \pi \cos^2 x,$$

let's use the addition and scaling properties of the definite integral to write

$$
\begin{aligned}
V &= \int_{-\pi/2}^{3\pi/2} f(x)\, dx \\
&= \int_{-\pi/2}^{3\pi/2} 9\pi\, dx + 6\pi \int_{-\pi/2}^{3\pi/2} \cos x\, dx + \pi \int_{-\pi/2}^{3\pi/2} \cos^2 x\, dx.
\end{aligned}
\tag{22}
$$

The first integral on the right-hand side has value

$$\int_{-\pi/2}^{3\pi/2} 9\pi\, dx = 9\pi \left[\frac{3}{2}\pi - \left(-\frac{\pi}{2}\right) \right] = 18\pi^2 \tag{23}$$

since $\int_a^b C\, dx = C(b-a)$ always. The second integral has value

$$
\begin{aligned}
\int_{-\pi/2}^{3\pi/2} \cos x\, dx &= \sin\left(\frac{3}{2}\pi\right) - \sin\left(-\frac{\pi}{2}\right) \\
&= (-1) - (-1) = 0,
\end{aligned}
\tag{24}
$$

since $G(x) = \sin x$ is an antiderivative of $\cos x$, and

$$\int_a^b \cos x\, dx = G(b) - G(a).$$

For the third integral,

$$\int_{-\pi/2}^{3\pi/2} \cos^2 x\, dx,$$

you may not know an antiderivative for $\cos^2 x$. But you could forge ahead anyway if you recalled from "trigonometry" that

$$\cos^2 x = \frac{1 + \cos 2x}{2} \qquad \text{for any } x$$

(see Appendix A). Then, by the addition and scaling properties of integrals again, we could write

$$
\begin{aligned}
\int_{-\pi/2}^{3\pi/2} \cos^2 x\, dx &= \int_{-\pi/2}^{3\pi/2} \frac{1}{2} + \frac{1}{2} \int_{-\pi/2}^{3\pi/2} \cos 2x\, dx \\
&= \frac{1}{2}\left[\left(\frac{3}{2}\pi\right) - \left(-\frac{\pi}{2}\right) \right] + \frac{1}{2} \int_{-\pi/2}^{3\pi/2} \cos 2x\, dx.
\end{aligned}
\tag{25}
$$

Since $(\sin 2x)' = 2\cos 2x$, the function $H(x) = \frac{1}{2}\sin 2x$ is an antiderivative for $\cos 2x$. Hence the last integral has value

$$\int_{-\pi/2}^{3\pi/2} \cos 2x\, dx = H\left(\frac{3}{2}\pi\right) - H\left(-\frac{\pi}{2}\right) = \left[\frac{1}{2}\sin 2\left(\frac{3}{2}\pi\right)\right] - \left[\frac{1}{2}\sin 2\left(-\frac{\pi}{2}\right)\right]$$

$$= \frac{1}{2}\sin 3\pi - \frac{1}{2}\sin(-\pi) = 0 - 0 = 0. \qquad (26)$$

If you substitute values from (23)–(26) back into (22) you'll find

$$V = \underbrace{\int_{-\pi/2}^{3\pi/2} 9\pi\, dx}_{18\pi^2} + \underbrace{6\pi \int_{-\pi/2}^{3\pi/2} \cos x\, dx}_{6\pi \cdot 0} + \underbrace{\pi \int_{-\pi/2}^{3\pi/2} \cos^2 x\, dx}_{\pi \cdot (\pi + 0)}$$

$$= 19\pi^2 \quad \text{(cubic units).} \qquad (27)$$

EXAMPLE 2: *Should you "invest" a dollar or keep it in a bank?* If you put a dollar into a bank which gives, say, 5% interest annually, but which compounds the interest very frequently — say, daily — then at the end of one year you should have approximately $e^{0.05}$ dollars in the bank. Such was my conclusion in Sec. 10.2 (Example 3). By the end of a second year you should have $(e^{0.05})(e^{0.05}) = e^{(0.05)2}$ dollars, and by the end of a 10th year you should have $(e^{0.05})^{10} = e^{(0.05)10} = \$1.64$ approximately. By similar reasoning, an initial bank account of \$1 should increase in size by a factor of approximately $e^{0.05L}$ over any period of length L (years) — provided the 5% interest rate remains unchanged.

Now suppose that someone who needs money for an enterprise asks you to give him your dollar, and tells you that in return he hopes to pay you "dividends" of increasing size at monthly intervals during a ten-year period. In Fig. 18-5 I've indicated how the proposed payments might be displayed, and in Fig. 18-6 I've

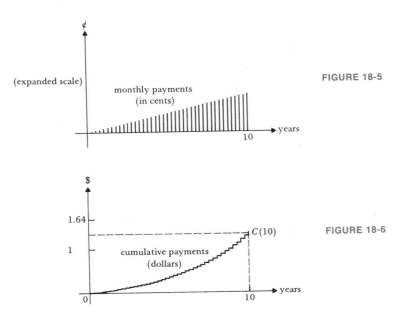

FIGURE 18-5

FIGURE 18-6

sketched a corresponding *cumulative* dividend graph. Assuming that the enterprise will prove successful and that the dividends will be paid to you over the ten-year period as proposed, will you have more money after 10 years via the investment or by keeping your dollar in the bank at 5%?

If the cumulative amount of dividends after 10 years, which I've labeled $C(10)$ in Fig. 18-6, exceeds the value $e^{(0.05)10} = \$1.64$ which the dollar will earn in a bank, then clearly the investment is better. But suppose $C(10) < e^{(0.05)10}$; say, $C(10) = \$1.50$. The investment might still be better. Why? Because having invested your dollar, you could then deposit each payment of Fig. 18-5 in the bank, and let it accumulate its own interest from the time it was received until the end of the ten-year period. It's the sum total of all such interest accumulations which we should compare with the single value $\$e^{(0.05)10}$ in order to see whether the investment is worthwhile.

To avoid actually doing such a tedious summation of 120 terms, let's approximate the steplike cumulative payment graph in Fig. 18-6 by a smoother one—as if payments would flow to you in a continuous fashion. The function

$$C(t) = \frac{1.50}{10^2} t^2 \qquad \text{(dollars after } t \text{ years)} \tag{28}$$

will have the final output $C(10) = \$1.50$, and its rate of change per unit time,

$$C'(t) = \frac{1.50}{10^2} 2t \tag{29}$$

increases linearly with time, just as the monthly payments appear to do in Fig. 18-5.

If we do accept $C(t) = (1.50/10^2)t^2$ as an idealized description of cumulative payments, then in any small subinterval $[t_{i-1}, t_i]$ of the ten-year period, we should receive

$$C(t_i) - C(t_{i-1}) = C'(t_i^*)(t_i - t_{i-1})$$

$$= \frac{1.50}{10^2} 2t_i^* (t_i - t_{i-1}) \quad \text{dollars,} \tag{30}$$

where t_i^* is some time between t_{i-1} and t_i. (So says the mean value theorem of Chap. 15.) If you put this payment in the bank for a remaining period of approximately $10 - t_i^*$ years, it will increase by a factor of approximately $e^{0.05(10 - t_i^*)}$—and will thus contribute approximately

$$D_i = e^{0.05(10 - t_i^*)} \cdot \left\{ \frac{1.50}{10^2} 2t_i^* (t_i - t_{i-1}) \right\}$$

$$= [(0.03e^{0.5})t_i^* e^{-(0.05)t_i^*}](t_i - t_{i-1}) \quad \text{dollars} \tag{31}$$

to your total money after 10 years. See Fig. 18-7.

FIGURE 18-7

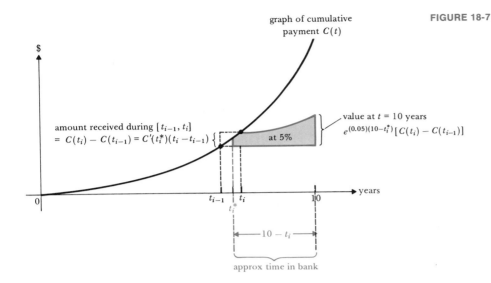

graph of cumulative
payment $C(t)$

amount received during $[t_{i-1}, t_i]$
$= C(t_i) - C(t_{i-1}) = C'(t_i^*)(t_i - t_{i-1})$

at 5%

value at $t = 10$ years
$e^{(0.05)(10-t_i^*)}[C(t_i) - C(t_{i-1})]$

years

$10 - t_i$

approx time in bank

If we choose a partition $\sigma = \{t_i\}$ of the ten-year period $[0, 10]$ with tiny subintervals $[t_{i-1}, t_i]$, then the sum total of all such contributions D_i from the different subintervals will be

$$S_\sigma = [(0.03e^{0.5})t_1^* e^{-(0.05)t_1^*}](t_1 - t_0) + [(0.03e^{0.5})t_2^* e^{-(0.05)t_2^*}](t_2 - t_1) + \cdots,$$

(32)

which we can write in the form

$$S_\sigma = h(t_1^*)(t_1 - t_0) + h(t_2^*)(t_2 - t_1) + \cdots$$

by defining

$$f(t) = (0.03e^{0.5})te^{-(0.05)t} \qquad \text{for } 0 \leqslant t \leqslant 10.$$

(33)

As a product of a linear and an exponential function, each continuous, h itself must be continuous too. What can we conclude, therefore, from the result on the existence of a definite integral (Theorem F)? For any sequence of partitions $\sigma_1, \sigma_2, \sigma_3, \ldots$ of $[0, 10]$ whose meshes tend to zero, the corresponding total contributions S_{σ_n} must converge to

$$\int_0^{10} f(t)\, dt = \int_0^{10} (0.03e^{0.5})te^{-(0.05)t}\, dt$$

$$= (0.03e^{0.5}) \int_0^{10} te^{-(0.05)t}\, dt$$

(34)

—a quantity which we might interpret as *the total money after 10 years from all payments received (and deposited at 5% interest) in a continuous stream during the ten-year period.*

How can we evaluate the last integral in (34)? By finding an antiderivative $H(t)$ for the function $h(t) = te^{-(0.05)t}$. Then $\int_0^{10} h(t)\, dt = H(10) - H(0)$, according to Theorem G. You might recall that I handled just such a function h via the procedure of "antidifferentiation by parts," in Sec. 15.10 (Example 5). We can write h as a product $F'G$, where

$$F(t) = \left(-\frac{1}{0.05}\right)e^{-(0.05)t}, \quad G(t) = t, \quad \text{and} \quad G'(t) = 1 \qquad \text{for all } t. \quad \text{(35)}$$

Then ("by parts"),

an antiderivative H of $F'G$
$$= FG - \text{an antiderivative for } G'F$$
$$= \left(-\frac{1}{0.05}\right)e^{-(0.05)t}t - \text{an antiderivative of } (1)\left(-\frac{1}{0.05}\right)e^{-(0.05)t}.$$

The product

$$G'F = (1)\left(-\frac{1}{0.05}\right)e^{-(0.05)t}$$

has antiderivative

$$\left(-\frac{1}{0.05}\right)^2 e^{-(0.05)t},$$

since $(e^{at})' = ae^{at}$ for any a. Hence

$$H(t) = \left(-\frac{1}{0.05}\right)e^{-(0.05)t}t - \left(-\frac{1}{0.05}\right)^2 e^{-(0.05)t}$$
$$= (-20)e^{-(0.05)t}[t - (-20)]. \qquad \text{(36)}$$

And

$$H(10) - H(0) = [(-20)e^{-0.5}30] - [(-20)e^0(20)]$$
$$= 400 - 600(0.606) = 37 \quad \text{(approx).} \qquad \text{(37)}$$

Finally,

$$\int_0^{10} f(t)\, dt = 0.03e^{0.5} \int_0^{10} h(t)\, dt$$

$$= (0.03)(1.65)(37) = \$1.83 \text{ approx.} \qquad \text{(38)}$$

Conclusion: The (idealized) continuous cumulative payment scheme in Fig. 18-7, together with 5% interest on the payments, offers *more* return on your original dollar after 10 years than does simply keeping the $1 in the bank for that period: $1.83 as against $1.64. For an investment of $1000 the difference would be $190. Might not the original monthly payment scheme of Figs. 18-5 and 18-6 offer approximately the same advantages? I invite you to estimate the difference in Problem 9 of the next section.

What was my approach in both of these examples? First, I tried to *approximate* a sought-for quantity (volume or total dollar returns) *by a sum of small contributions* corresponding to subintervals $[x_{i-1}, x_i]$ of a basic input interval $[a, b]$. Then I tried to *recognize* that sum as having the form

$$f(x_1^*)(x_1 - x_0) + f(x_2^*)(x_2 - x_1) + f(x_3^*)(x_3 - x_2) + \cdots$$

for a *suitable continuous function* f. The sought-for quantity would be the limit of such approximations for partitions $\sigma = \{x_i\}$ of smaller and smaller mesh — the definite integral $\int_a^b f(x)\, dx$. Finally, I tried to *evaluate $\int_a^b f(x)\, dx$ — or its simpler component integrals — by finding an antiderivative $G(x)$ for $f(x)$* and calculating the difference

$$G(b) - G(a) = \int_a^b f(x)\, dx.$$

Note this difference in goals between Examples 1 and 2: In Example 1, *the definite integral was the goal,* the precise volume of a region — and sums S_σ were approximations. In Example 2, however, the definite integral was *itself an approximation,* easier to calculate than the original messy sum of interest accumulations.

For specific functions, it will sometimes be convenient to use the

Notation:

$[G(x)]_a^b$ *to denote* $G(b) - G(a)$. (39)

Thus, for the function $h(t) = te^{-(0.05)t}$, with antiderivative $H(t) = (-20)e^{-(0.05)t}(t+20)$ as in (37) above, we could express $\int_0^{10} h(t)\, dt = H(10) - H(0)$ in detail, but compactly, as

$$\int_0^{10} te^{-(0.05)t}\, dt = [(-20)e^{-(0.05)t}(t+20)]_0^{10}. \qquad (40)$$

Before I continue with further applications of the definite integral, I invite you to try your own hand at setting up and evaluating several integrals — in doing the problems of the next section.

18.2   PROBLEMS ON THE DEFINITE INTEGRAL

°1. For each of the following cases, evaluate the indicated definite integral $\int_a^b f(x)\, dx$ by finding some antiderivative $G(x)$ for $f(x)$ and using the result $\int_a^b f(x)\, dx = G(b) - G(a)$, of Theorem G (the "fundamental theorem") in Sec. 18.1.

(a) $\int_0^{1/2} \cos \pi x\, dx$

    Sample reasoning: since $(1/\pi \sin \pi x)' = \cos \pi x$,

$$\int_0^{1/2} \cos \pi x\, dx = \left[\frac{1}{\pi} \sin \pi x\right]_0^{1/2} = \frac{1}{\pi} \sin \frac{\pi}{2} - \frac{1}{\pi} \sin 0 = \frac{1}{\pi}.$$

(b) $\int_2^3 x^5\, dx$ (c) $\int_2^3 x^{-5}\, dx$ (d) $\int_0^1 e^x\, dx$

(e) $\int_0^1 e^{2x}\, dx$ (f) $\int_1^2 \frac{1}{x}\, dx$ (g) $\int_0^1 (2x+1)^3\, dx$

    Sample reasoning: By the chain rule,

$$[(2x+1)^4]' = 4(2x+1)^3(2x)' = 4(2x+1)^3 2.$$

Hence $[\frac{1}{8}(2x+1)^4]' = (2x+1)^3$; and

$$\int_0^1 (2x+1)^3\, dx = \left[\frac{1}{8}(2x+1)^4\right]_0^1 = \frac{1}{8}3^4 - \frac{1}{8}1^4 = \frac{1}{8}(9^4 - 1).$$

(h) $\int_0^2 \sqrt{4x+1}\, dx$ (i) $\int_{-1}^1 (2x+4)^{-3}\, dx$

(j) $\int_0^1 \dfrac{1}{3x+7}\, dx$ (k) $\int_0^1 e^{3x}\, dx$

(l) $\int_0^2 \dfrac{2x+1}{\sqrt{x^2+x+1}}\, dx$ (Suggestion: recall the chain rule again.)

(m) $\int_{\pi 4}^{\pi/2} \dfrac{\cos x}{\sin^2 x}\, dx$

°2. Use the "scaling" and "adding" properties of the definite integral (as described in Theorem F of Sec. 18.1) to evaluate the following integrals.

(a) $\int_1^3 (x^2 - 4x + 5)\, dx$

Sample reasoning:

$$\int_1^3 (x^2 - 4x + 5)\, dx = \int_1^3 x^2\, dx + (-4)\int_1^3 x\, dx + 5\int_1^3 1\, dx$$

$$= \left[\frac{x^3}{3}\right]_1^3 - 4\left[\frac{x^2}{2}\right]_1^3 + 5[x]_1^3$$

$$= \frac{3^3 - 1^3}{3} - 4\frac{3^2 - 1^2}{2} + 5(3 - 1).$$

(b) $\int_{-1}^4 (x^3 - 17x^2 + 4x + 5)\, dx$ (c) $\int_1^2 \left(\sqrt{x} + \dfrac{1}{\sqrt{x}}\right) dx$

(d) $\int_1^2 \left(x + \dfrac{1}{x}\right) dx$ (e) $\int_0^{\pi/2} (3\sin x - 2\cos x)\, dx$

(f) $\int_0^1 (e^{2x} - 2e^x)\, dx$

(g) $\int_{-1}^1 (|x|^3 - 2|x|)\, dx$

Sample reasoning:

$$f(x) = |x|^3 - 2|x| = \begin{cases} x^3 - 2x & \text{for } 0 \leqslant x \leqslant 1 \\ \\ (-x)^3 - 2(-x) = -x^3 + 2x & \\ & \text{for } -1 \leqslant x \leqslant 0 \end{cases}$$

Hence $\int_{-1}^1 f(x)\, dx = \int_{-1}^0 f(x)\, dx + \int_0^1 f(x)\, dx$

$$= \int_{-1}^0 (x^3 - 2x)\, dx + \int_0^1 (-x^3 + 2x)\, dx$$

(h) $\int_{-1}^{2} e^{|x|}\, dx$

(i) $\int_{-1}^{2} f(x)\, dx$, where $f(x) = \begin{cases} x^2 & \text{for } -1 \leqslant x \leqslant 1 \\ x^3 & \text{for } 1 < x \leqslant 2 \end{cases}$

(j) $\int_{0}^{\pi} |\cos x|\, dx$

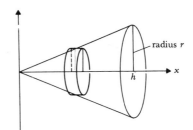

radius r

3. Find the volume of the cone in the accompanying figure, as a limit of sums of volumes of thin disks. That is, represent the volume as a definite integral—as I did in Example 1 of the last section—and evaluate the integral.

°4. Now approximate the volume of the cone in Problem 3 in a different way—by sums of volumes of thin cylindrical shells, as in the accompanying figure.
Represent the limit of these approximations as a definite integral. Then evaluate the integral and see whether it has the same value as that in Problem 3.

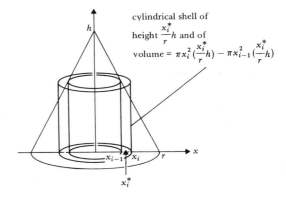

cylindrical shell of

height $\dfrac{x_i^*}{r} h$ and of

volume $= \pi x_i^2 \left(\dfrac{x_i^*}{r} h\right) - \pi x_{i-1}^2 \left(\dfrac{x_i^*}{r} h\right)$

5. Think of cutting a sphere of radius r out of three-dimensional space by rotating the (semicircular) graph of the function $\sqrt{r^2 - x^2}$ for $|x| \leqslant r$ about the x axis. Then show pictorially how to approximate the volume of the sphere by a sum of volumes of thin disks. Formulate the limit of such approximations as a definite integral, and evaluate the integral to see whether it agrees with the value $(4/3)\pi r^3$ that you may have been taught long ago.

6. Suppose that you bore a cylindrical hole along the diameter of a solid metal sphere, from one pole to the other, leaving a tire-like solid shape. And suppose that, after you've cut away the polar caps, the hole measures 2 inches in *length*. What volume of metal must be left? See three possible cross sections in Fig. (i).

(a) Can it be that the volume V of remaining metal is independent of the radius r of the original sphere (for all $r \geqslant 1$ inch)? On the assumption that V *is* independent of r, try to conclude what value V must have—without doing any calculations.

(b) Verify the assumption and your conclusion in part (a) by finding V as a limit of sums of volumes of thin disks each having a hole through its middle of radius $\sqrt{r^2 - 1}$ inches. See Fig. (ii).

FIGURE (i)

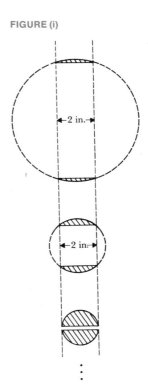

2 in.

2 in.

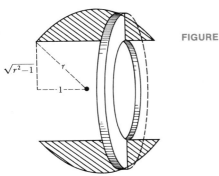

FIGURE (ii)

$\sqrt{r^2-1}$

r

1

7. For each of the following functions g, sketch the graph of g and sketch the region in three-dimensional space which you could cut out by rotating the graph of g about the x axis—as in Fig. 18-1. Show how you might approximate the volume of this region by circular disks, and represent the volume precisely as a definite integral. Then evaluate the integral.

(a) $g(x) = 1 - x^4$ for x in $[-1, 1]$

(b) $g(x) = e^{-|x|}$ for x in $[-1, 1]$

(Suggestion: consider volumes corresponding to the separate intervals $[-1, 0]$ and $[0, 1]$.)

(c) $g(x) = \dfrac{1}{1 + x^2}$ for x in $[-1, 1]$

(d) $g(x) = \cos x$ for x in $\left[-\dfrac{\pi}{2}, \dfrac{\pi}{2} \right]$.

°**8.** Recall the idealized investment scheme of Example 2, in the last section. Suppose now that the cumulative payments could be described by the function $\tilde{C}(t) = (1.5/10^2 e) e^{(0.1)t}$, instead of the function $C(t) = (1.5/10^2) t^2$ in Example 2. (Note that both functions yield the same total payment after 10 years

$$\tilde{C}(10) = C(10) = \$1.50,$$

for each dollar invested.)

(a) Draw a graph of $\tilde{C}$. What qualitative difference would you expect in the total amount of money you would have after 10 years, if you get paid according to $\tilde{C}$ rather than C?

(b) Now check the difference by retracing the steps in Example 2 for the new function $\tilde{C}$, and calculating the total amount of money accrued during 10 years by investing $1.

9. How far off was the idealized integral in Example 2 (on investment) from the original messy sum which it was supposed to approximate? Suppose that the monthly payments which I sketched crudely in Fig. 18-5 could be described more precisely as having the form $\$bi$ after the ith month (for $1 \leqslant i \leqslant 120$, the equivalent of 10 years).

(a) Check that, in order to have a cumulative payment of $1.50 after 10 years, the constant b should equal $(1.5)/[(120 \cdot 121)/2]$. (You might use the summation result of Problem 1(b) in Sec. 6.7.)

(b) Show that the exact total earnings from one invested dollar are given by the sum

$$(b1) e^{0.05[10 - (1/12)]} + (b2) e^{0.05[10 - (2/12)]}$$

$$+ \cdots + (bi) e^{0.05[10 - (i/12)]} + \cdots \qquad (*)$$

where $1 \leqslant k \leqslant 120$.

(c) Convert from months to fractions of a year by letting $t_i = i/12$ for $1 \leqslant i \leqslant 120$. Then $0 \leqslant t_i \leqslant 10$, and the sum (*) reads

$$(12b)\,t_1 e^{0.05(10-t_1)} + (12b)\,t_2 e^{0.05(10-t_2)} + \cdots$$
$$+ (12b)\,t_i e^{0.05(10-t_i)} + \cdots \qquad\qquad (**)$$

Show that the sum (**) has the form

$$f(t_1)\,(t_1 - t_0) + f(t_2)\,(t_2 - t_1) + \cdots + f(t_i)\,(t_i - t_{i-1}) + \cdots (***)$$

where

$$f(t) = (144b)\,t e^{t[0.05(10-t)]} \qquad \text{for } 0 \leqslant t \leqslant 10, \qquad (\dagger)$$

$t_0 = 0$, and $t_i - t_{i-1} = 1/12$ for $1 \leqslant i \leqslant 120$.

(d) Check that $144b = 0.03$ (rounded off), so that the function f in $(\dagger)$ is essentially the same as that I considered in Example 2.

(e) Show that f is strictly increasing in the interval $[0, 10]$, and hence that the sum (***) is an "outside area" approximation to the area beneath the graph of f and above $[0, 10]$. (Recall Fig. 17-12.)

(f) Show that the error between the sum (***) and the integral $\int_0^{10} f(t)\,dt$ (the idealized result in Example 2) is no greater than

$$\frac{1}{12}[f(10) - f(0)] = \frac{1}{12}[(0.03)\,10 - 0] = \$0.025.$$

(Recall the method of Example 2 in Sec. 17.4.)

10. Let's reformulate the idealized investment scheme of Example 2, in the last section, in more general terms. Suppose that banks compound interest continuously at an annual rate p, so that after L years in a bank \$1 will be worth \$$e^{pL}$. And suppose that a particular enterprise offers for each \$1 invested a "continuous flow" of repayments accumulating to $C(t)$ dollars after t years. Suppose further that $C(t)$ has a derivative $g(t) = C'(t)$, which we can interpret as the *rate of payment per unit time* after t years. Now invest D dollars in the enterprise and pick some future cutoff time T. Think of each bit of repayment money, arriving at a time $t < T$, as immediately transferred to a bank, there to remain until time T.

(a) Retrace the arguments in Example 2 and show why the definite integral $\int_0^T Dg(t)e^{p(T-t)}\,dt$ should represent an idealized version of how much money you will have in the bank at time T.

(b) Check that in Example 2, $g(t) = (0.03)t$ dollars per year after t years.

(c) For the general case where the rate of payment increases *linearly* with time—that is, where $g(t) = mt$ dollars per year after t years—evaluate the integral $\int_0^T Dg(t)e^{p(T-t)}\,dt$ in terms of the constants $m, D, p,$ and T.

(d) In Example 2, where $p = 0.05$, the investment scheme appeared as more profitable at the end of $T = 10$ years than merely keeping money in the bank for that period. Will it still be more profitable if banks offer 8% interest per annum? (Then $p = 0.08$; and as before, $m = 0.03$, $D = \$1$, and $T = 10$ years.)

(e) What if banks offer 4% per annum, the other constants being the same as in part (d)?

(f) What effect does the length of time T have on the relative advantages of investing a dollar as in Example 2 versus keeping it solely in a bank? On a common axis, make careful sketches of the graphs of the two functions

$$A(T) = \int_0^T Dmte^{p(t-T)} \, dt \qquad \text{for } 0 \leqslant T \leqslant 15$$

and

$$B(T) = De^{pT} \qquad \text{for } 0 \leqslant T \leqslant 15.$$

(Choose $\$D = 1$, $m = 0.03$, and $p = 0.05$, as in Example 2.) For what values of T is $A(T) > B(T)$? $A(T) < B(T)$?

11. *Work.* Physicists have defined "work" technically in a strange but successful way. It involves the notion of "force," which I discussed in Example 1 of Sec. 7.5. If an object moves through a distance d (feet) while acted upon by a constant "force" F (lb), then physicists say that "work" has been done in the amount dF (ft-lb). And the total amount of "work" done during an object's journey is to be the sum of the amounts in separate parts. One strange consequence of this definition is that if you lift a 200-lb weight 4 ft into the air and then put it down again, then, although personally exhausted, you will have presided over a total of *zero* "work." This is because the amount of "work" (4×200 ft-lb done) "against gravity" exactly cancels the amount ($4 \times (-200)$ ft-lb) done "with the aid of gravity." On the other hand, this technical definition of work successfully underpins much of the physicists' theories of motion and of electricity.

You might expect that the definition wouldn't be very useful unless it could be adapted to many situations where the "force" acting upon an object *changes* its magnitude (and perhaps also its sign) during the course of the motion. More particularly, suppose that an object moves in a straight line, and that it's acted upon by a force of size $F(x)$ lb when at a distance of x ft from the starting point—where $F(x)$ varies continuously with x. How can we *define* and calculate the "total work" done through a distance of b ft, in the spirit of the original technical definition? Why not divide the interval $[0, b]$ into small subintervals $[x_{i-1}, x_i]$ by a partition $\sigma = \{x_i\}$, and *approximate the force $F(x)$ acting on the object through a subinterval $[x_{i-1}, x_i]$ by a constant force $F(x_i^*)$*, where x_i^* is a representative position in $[x_{i-1}, x_i]$? The "work" done by this approximating constant force through the distance $x_i - x_{i-1}$

would be the product $F(x_i^*)(x_i - x_{i-1})$, according to the original technical definition. And the total work done through $[0, b]$ by these approximating forces would then be the sum

$$S_\sigma = F(x_1^*)(x_1 - x_0) + F(x_2^*)(x_2 - x_1) + \cdots. \qquad (*)$$

If the concept of "total work" is to make sense at all, shouldn't approximations such as in (*) tend to a unique value as we choose partitions σ with smaller and smaller meshes? They do, according to Theorem F of Sec. 18.1. They tend to the definite integral $\int_a^b F(x)\,dx$ — and it's this quantity which physicists have accepted as the *definition* of "work," in generalization of the constant force case.

Here is a specific situation: Find the amount of work it would take to move a 200-lb man in a straight line all the way to the moon (a distance of approximately 240,000 miles), against the earth's gravity (and neglecting the moon's gravity).

You might recall (from Example 1 of Sec. 7.5) my discussing Newton's assumption about the "gravitational force" F exerted by the earth (a body of mass M) upon the man (a body of mass m) when the man is at distance D from the earth's center — namely, that it should be of the form $F = C(mM/D^2)$, where the constant C depends on units of measurement. Now, when a man standing on the surface of the earth (4000 miles from its center) is said to "weigh" 200 lb, the precise physical interpretation is that his "mass m" is such that the earth exerts 200 lb of "force" upon him — that is, $C[mM/(4000)^2] = 200$ lb (and $CmM = 200(4000)^2$). When the man is at some other distance $x > 4000$ miles from the earth's center, shouldn't the gravitational force upon him be $F(x) = [200(4000)^2/x^2]$ lb? Evaluate:

$$\int_{4000}^{240,000} \frac{200(4000)^2}{x^2}\,dx$$

12. Will it take more work against the earth's gravity to move one 200-lb man *all* the way to the moon, or two 200-lb men *halfway* to the moon?

13. Do you recall the objects attached to springs which I discussed in Sec. 16.4? (See Fig. 16.4.) In that section I pointed out Robert Hooke's conclusion that the force acting on any such object, aside from being proportional to its mass (m), was always negatively proportional to its displacement (x) from a "dead center" position: $F(x) = -m\lambda x$, where $\lambda > 0$.

   (a) Suppose two such objects (of identical mass) are displaced from their "dead centers," one twice as far as the other. How many times more work is involved in moving the first than the second?

   (b) Which takes more work: to displace one such object of mass m by a distance d from its dead center, or to displace a similar object of mass $2m$ by a distance $\frac{1}{2}d$?

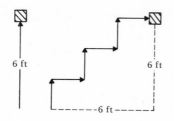

6 ft

6 ft

6 ft

14. How much more work (according to the technical definition) should it take to raise a lb object against gravity to a height of 6 ft along a "staircase" path, as in the figure, rather than straight up?

15. In Problems 12 and 13 of Sec. 17.8, in order to calculate the area of "unbounded" regions, I considered the limit of integrals as one end point converged either to "∞" or to 0. Here is a common

> **Definition:** the limits
>
> $$\int_a^\infty f(x)\, dx = \lim_{b \to \infty} \int_a^b f(x)\, dx;$$
>
> $$\int_{-\infty}^b f(x)\, dx = \lim_{a \to -\infty} \int_a^b f(x)\, dx;$$
>
> $$\int_{-\infty}^\infty f(x)\, dx = \lim_{c \to \infty} \int_{-c}^c f(x)\, dx;$$
>
> $$\int_a^b f(x)\, dx = \lim_{c \to b} \int_a^c f(x)\, dx, \text{ where } f \text{ is defined on } [a, b\rangle \text{ and}$$
>
> unbounded near b;
>
> $$\int_a^b f(x)\, dx = \lim_{c \to a} \int_c^b f(x)\, dx, \text{ where } f \text{ is defined on } \langle a, b] \text{ and}$$
>
> unbounded near a;

—if they exist—are called *improper integrals*. Each has meaning in terms of sequences of end points; for example,

$$\lim_{b \to \infty} \int_a^b f(x)\, dx$$

should be a number L such that

$$\lim_{n \to \infty} \int_a^{b_n} f(x)\, dx = L$$

for all sequences $\{b_n > a\}$ with $\lim_{n \to \infty} b_n = \infty$.

   Use such an improper integral to express the amount of work it would take to move a 200-lb object (as in Problem 11, except this time not a man) in a straight line out from the surface of the earth to the "farthest reaches of space."

16. *The length of a curve.* So far, I've discussed the notion of "length" only for straight-line segments, polygons, and arcs of circles. (Recall Sec. 10.1 and Problems 11–14 of Sec. 10.5, and Problem 6 of Sec. 12.4.)

   Do other, more wiggly, curves necessarily have definable "lengths," and if so, how can we calculate them? As a first step in extending the notion of "length," let's look at curves which don't wiggle too wildly—say, at graphs of differentiable functions, whose "slopes" always exist. How can we define "length" for the graph of such a function f defined on an interval $[a, b]$? Why not lean on the only method we know so far—that used to define arclength for circles? Let's try to approximate the graph better and better by a sequence of polygons, and see whether their lengths tend to a unique limit. To do this in an orderly fashion, let's pick a partition $\sigma = \{x_i\}$ of the interval $[a, b]$ and draw line segments between successive points $P_i = (x_i, f(x_i))$ on the graph of the function—as in the figure.

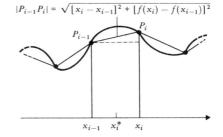

(a) Check that the length of the ith segment is

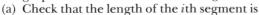

$$|P_{i-1}P_i| = \sqrt{[x_i - x_{i-1}]^2 + [f(x_i) - f(x_{i-1})]^2}.$$

(b) Why can we also write

$$|P_{i-1}P_i| = \sqrt{1 + [f'(x_i^*)]^2}\,(x_i - x_{i-1}),$$

where x_i^* is an input in $[x_{i-1}, x_i]$, for each i?
(Recall the mean value theorem of Chap. 15.)

(c) Suppose that $f'(x)$ is itself *continuous on* $[a, b]$. Why does the definite integral $\int_a^b \sqrt{1 + [f'(x)]^2}\, dx$ merit assignment as the "length" of the graph of f?

(d) Would the conclusion in (c) still hold if $f'(x)$ were discontinuous at finitely many inputs of $[a, b]$?

(e) Represent the length of the graph of $f(x) = x^2$ for x in $[0, 1]$ as a definite integral.

17. (a) Sketch the graph of $f(x) = x^3$ for x in $[0, 1]$; and for any positive number $b \leq 1$, represent the length—call it $L(b)$—of the graph between the points $(0, 0)$ and (b, b^3) via a definite integral, as in Problem 16.

(b) Suppose now that an object moves along the graph from $(0, 0)$ to $(1, 1)$, and that at each point (x, x^3) the object is acted upon by a force equal to the altitude of the graph at that point: $f(x) = x^3$ lb (for x measured in feet). How much work will be done during the journey?

Note: Above any small subinterval $[x_{i-1}, x_i]$ of $[0, 1]$, the length of the curve is

$$L(x_i) - L(x_{i-1}) = L'(x_i^*)(x_i - x_{i-1}), \qquad (*)$$

where $L(x)$ is the cumulative length function in part (a), x_i^* is some input in $[x_{i-1}, x_i]$, and (*) holds thanks to the mean value theorem. Over the same small subinterval $[x_{i-1}, x_i]$, the force acting upon the object is approximately $F(x_i^*) = (x_i^*)^3$. Approximate the work done over $[x_{i-1}, x_i]$, then approximate the total work done over all such subintervals—just as in Problem 11.

18. (a) Sketch the graph of $f(x) = \log_e \cos x$ for x in $[\pi/3, 1]$.

(b) Show why the definition of "length" in Problem 16 leads to the definite integral $\int_{\pi/3}^1 (1/\cos x)\, dx$ as the length of the graph in part (a).

(c) Evaluate the integral in part (b). (Suggestion: note that

$$\frac{1}{\cos x} = \frac{\cos x}{\cos^2 x} = \frac{\cos x}{1 - \sin^2 x} = \frac{\cos x}{(1 - \sin x)(1 + \sin x)}$$

$$= \frac{1}{2} \frac{\cos x}{1 - \sin x} + \frac{1}{2} \frac{\cos x}{1 + \sin x}.$$

Can you write each of the last terms in the form $G(F(x))F'(x)$?)

19. How will the "length" notion work for other graphs of continuous — but not necessarily differentiable — functions?

(a) Would you expect the graph indicated in Fig. (i) to have a unique finite number assignable as its length?

(b) How about the graph in Fig. (ii)?

FIGURE (i)

FIGURE (ii)

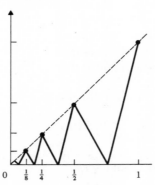

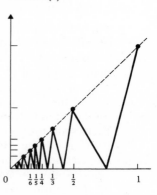

*(c) How about the graph of Cantor's function, which I discussed in Sec. 7.8 and in Problem 13 of Sec. 15.11?

*20. (a) Think of rotating the graph of a continuous nonnegative function $f(x)$, for x in $[a, b]$, about the x axis and "sweeping out" a "surface" in 3-dimensional space. Say how you would go about assigning an "area" value to such a surface.

FIGURE (i)

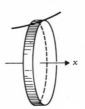

In particular, if you think of making approximations, which basic shape would be more appropriate to use: a right circular "hoop" as in Fig. (i), or a (possibly) "slanted hoop" as in Fig. (ii)? (You might recall from geometry that the area of a trapezoid such as in Fig. (iii) is $\frac{1}{2}(b + B)l$. Hence the surface area of a "slanted hoop" such as the slice

FIGURE (ii)

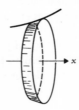

FIGURE (iii)

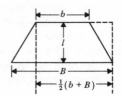

of cone in Fig. (iv) is $\frac{1}{2}(2\pi r + 2\pi R)l = \pi(r+R)l$—got by adding the areas of approximating trapezoids.)

(b) Test your definition in part (a) by calculating the surface area of the full cone in Fig. (iv), the case where $r=0$ and l is the entire "slant height." Is your value πRl?

(c) Let $f(x) = x^3$ for x in $[0, 1]$, as in Problem 17, and find the area of the surface obtained by rotating the graph of f about the x axis.

21. Here's another strange but successful technical notion: physicists define *pressure* as "force per unit area." If force is constant over a flat surface, the definition may present no difficulties. But what does it even *mean* in the case of forces which vary from point to point on a surface? Here physicists invoke the notion of "instantaneous" rate—essentially the idea of a derivative. They define "pressure *at* a point P" as a limit of ratios F_n/A_n where F_n is the total force acting upon a region R_n surrounding the point P and A_n is the area of R_n, and the regions are shrunk so that $\lim_{n\to\infty} A_n = 0$. The concept of "pressure" is especially useful in the case of fluids, concerning which Blaise Pascal noted this property: The amount of "pressure" acting on a tiny flat surface centered at a point P anywhere in a container of fluid is independent of the orientation of the surface—whether it's vertical, horizontal, or at an angle. For a container of liquid of any shape—with some open surface on top—the amount of pressure at a point P depends only on its distance down from the top, not on its horizontal location—whether P is at the side of the container or somewhere in the interior. See Fig. (i). In fact, the pressure at P is approximately the weight of a vertical column of the liquid, of unit cross-sectional area, as it would rise from P to the top surface. See Fig. (i).

In particular, *water* weighs about 62.5 lb/ft³. What total force, then, would be exerted upon the vertical backface of a dam such as pictured in Figs. (ii) and (iii), by water backed up behind the dam to a height of 30 ft? Note that the pressure at all points of the dam in the thin shaded strip in Fig. (ii), at depths between x_{i-1} and x_i feet, should be approximately $62.5x_i^*$ lb/ft²—corresponding to the weight of a column of water x_i^* ft high and 1 sq ft in cross-sectional area—as in Fig. (iii).

FIGURE (iv)

FIGURE (i)

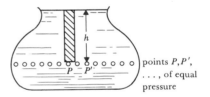

points P, P', ..., of equal pressure

FIGURE (ii)

rear view of dam

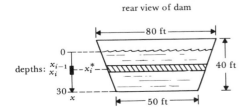

FIGURE (iii)

side view of dam

column of water x_i^* ft high

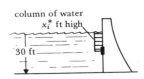

30 ft

(a) Show that the shaded strip in Fig. (ii) can be approximated by a rectangle of area

$$\left[80 - 2 \cdot \frac{15}{40}(10 + x_i^*)\right](x_i - x_{i-1}) \text{ sq ft}$$

(b) Why can we approximate the total force acting on the shaded strip in Fig. (ii) by the product $(62.5x_i^*)(x_i - x_{i-1})$ lb?

(c) Represent the total force on the dam as a definite integral—the limit of sums over thin strips as in Fig. (ii). And evaluate the integral.

(d) Suppose that the rear face of a dam has a slope of 45°, as in Fig. (iv), with other dimensions as in Fig. (ii).
What area should be assigned in this case to the region of points on the backface of the dam lying between depths of x_{i-1} and x_i feet? And what total force acts upon this dam?

22. Suppose that a dam has a vertical backface which is roughly parabolic in shape, as in Fig. (v).

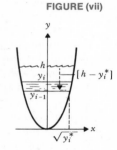

FIGURE (iv)

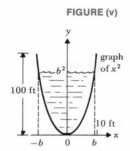

FIGURE (v)

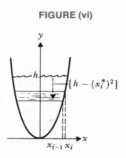

FIGURE (vi)   **FIGURE (vii)**

(a) For any b in $[0, 10]$, find the area $A(b)$ of the backface which is under water when the water is at height $h = b^2$ ft. (Subtract the area beneath the graph in Fig. (v) and above the interval $[-b, b]$ from the rectangle area $2b \times b^2 = 2b^3$ sq ft.)

(b) Show that the region in Fig. (vi) between altitudes x_{i-1}^2 ft and x_i^2 ft has area $2(x_i^*)(x_i - x_{i-1})$ sq ft, for some x_i^* in $[x_{i-1}, x_i]$. (You might apply the mean value theorem to the cumulative area function $A(b)$ in part (a), or you might approximate the shaded region directly by a rectangle.)

(c) Using thin regions as in Fig. (vi), approximate the total force upon the dam when the water is $h = b^2$ ft high, for a fixed b in $[0, 10]$; then represent the limit of finer and finer approximations by a definite integral and evaluate it.

(d) For fixed $h \le 100$ ft, divide the interval $[0, h]$ on the y axis into small subintervals $[y_{i-1}, y_i]$ as in Fig. (vii), and use these to approximate the total force on the dam. Does the limit of such approximations have the same value as that in part (c)?

23. Compare the total area of water pressing against the "trapezoidal" dam of Figs. (ii) and (iii) in Problem 21, with that pressing

against the "parabolic" dam in Problem 22 at maximum capacity ($h = 100$ ft). Which is greater? Which dam must withstand a greater total force?

°24. Any function whose rule is given by an integral with a "varying right-hand end point,"

$$h(t) = \int_a^{f(t)} g(x)\, dx \qquad \text{for } \alpha \leqslant t \leqslant \beta, \qquad (*)$$

is really a *composition* of the form $h(t) = G(f(t))$, where $G(y) = \int_a^y g(x)\, dx$ for $y \geqslant a$. (Let's suppose here that f is differentiable on some interval $[\alpha, \beta]$ and that g is continuous on some interval $[a, b]$ which contains the range of f.) Hence, if we take the "fundamental theorem" (Theorem G) of Sec. 18.1 — which says that $G'(y_0) = g(y_0)$ — and put it together with the "chain rule" for differentiation of compositions, we'll have

$$h'(t_0) = G'(f(t_0))f'(t_0)$$
$$= g(f(t_0))f'(t_0) \qquad (**)$$

for any t_0 in $[\alpha, \beta]$.

Use the relationship (**) to differentiate the following functions:

(a) $h(t) = \int_0^{t^2} x^3\, dx \qquad$ for $t \geqslant 0$

(b) $h(t) = \int_0^{t^2} \sin x\, dx \qquad$ for t in $[0, \sqrt{\pi}]$

(c) $h(t) = \int_0^{\log e\, t} e^{2x}\, dx \qquad$ for $t \geqslant 1$

(d) $h(t) = \int_t^1 x^3\, dx \qquad$ for t in $[0, 1]$

   (Suggestion: $h(t) = \int_0^1 x^3\, dx - \int_0^t x^3\, dx$.)

(e) $h(t) = \int_{t^2}^1 x^3\, dx \qquad$ for t in $[0, 1]$

25. (a) Try to formulate a result similar to that of the fundamental theorem of Sec. 18.1 concerning a "varying left-hand end point." How can you express the derivative $H'(x_0)$ of the function

$$H(x) = \int_x^b f(t)\, dt \qquad \text{for } x \text{ in } [a, b]$$

in terms of f?

(b) Try to get a result analogous to that in Problem 22 concerning the derivative of the function

$$k(t) = \int_{f(t)}^b g(x)\, dx \qquad \text{for } \alpha \leqslant t \leqslant \beta.$$

(c) Differentiate $k(t) = \int_{t^2}^1 \sin x\, dx \qquad$ for t in $[0, \sqrt{\pi}]$.

°26. Think of the cone in Problem 1 (with dimensions r and h in feet) as standing on its vertex and as being filled with water more and more rapidly, so that the water level is t^2 ft after t seconds. Denote by $V(t)$ the accumulated volume of water (in cu ft) in the cone after t seconds; and find the rate $V'(t)$ (in cu ft per sec) of accumulation at any $t \leqslant \sqrt{h}$.

27. In Problem 11 a 200-lb man was journeying toward the moon, against the earth's gravitational force. Suppose that his distance (in miles) from the center of earth, after t seconds of travel, could be described by a function $f(t)$.

(a) Indicate, in terms of f, the cumulative amount of "work" done in moving the man during the first t seconds of the journey.

(b) Suppose that the man was traveling at 4 miles per second when he was at a distance of 1000 miles from the earth's surface (5000 miles from its center). At what *rate* (in miles-lb per sec.) was he then accumulating "work"? (This is the rate at which "energy" was being spent in moving him.)

28. Suppose that water is at the 80-ft level behind the parabolic dam of Problem 22, and rising at that instant at a rate of 2 ft per hour. At what rate is the total force on the dam increasing at the same instant?

29. Suppose that fluid for intravenous feeding is contained in a flask as pictured in Figs. (i) and (ii), and that the fluid will be drained through a tube from the bottom of the flask at a constant rate of $\frac{1}{2}$ cubic centimeters (cc) per minute.

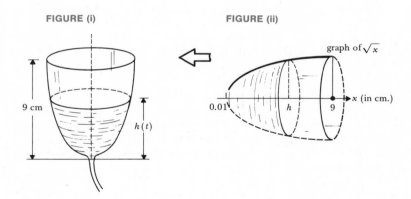

FIGURE (i)   FIGURE (ii)

(a) How long will it take to empty a full flask in this manner? (Divide the total volume by the drainage rate.)

(b) So that we can be alert to possible malfunction, predict at what level the fluid should ideally stand after t minutes of drainage.

Suggestion: Denote the fluid level (plus 0.01 cm), at time t, by $h(t)$ — as in Fig. (i); and show that the corresponding volume must be

$$V(t) = \int_{0.01}^{h(t)} \pi x \, dx.$$

Then express $V'(t)$ according to the result in Problem 24, and (for "ideal" operation) set $V'(t) = \frac{1}{2}\,\mathrm{cc}$ per min. This procedure should yield a relation between $h(t)$ and $h'(t)$ — a "differential equation." See what function h provides a unique solution to this equation, with the "initial condition" that $h(0) = 9$ cm. (Recall that $h(t)h'(t) = \frac{1}{2}\,[h(t)^2]'$.)

30. The following cases involve definite integrals of functions for which you may not know how to find antiderivatives — so that you couldn't evaluate the integrals via the "fundamental theorem" of Sec. 18.1. In these cases, use the method of Example 2 in Sec. 17.3, and in Problems 6 and 10–12 of Sec. 17.4, to *approximate* the integrals — by "inside" or "outside" sums — with an error no greater than 0.01.
   (a) The length of the graph of $f(x) = x^2$ for x in $[0, 1]$ (Problem 14(e)).
   (b) The surface area swept out by rotating the graph of $g(x) = 1 - x^4$ for x in $[-1, 1]$ about the x axis (see Problem 5(a)).
   *(c) The total work required to move the 200-lb man of Problem 9 on a *semicircular* path from the earth to the moon.

*31. Use the properties of the definite integral listed in Theorem F of Sec. 18.1 to show that $\int_a^b g(x)\,dx$ must be 0 if g is a continuous nonnegative function which is not identically 0 on $[a, b]$.
   Suggestion: Suppose that $g(x_0) = A > 0$, so that the continuous function $g(x) - \frac{1}{2}A$ will be positive at $x = x_0$. Recall the result on "nearby signs" (Theorem B) in Sec. 13.1; and show that $g(x) - \frac{1}{2}A > 0$ on some subinterval $[c, d]$ of $[a, b]$. Hence $g(x) > \frac{1}{2}A$ on $[c, d]$. What can you then conclude about $\int_c^d g(x)\,dx$? And how will its value compare with that of $\int_a^b g(x)\,dx$?

32. Suppose that f and g are continuous functions on an interval $[a, b]$, and furthermore that g is nonnegative but not identically 0 in $[a, b]$. Show that there must exist some input c between a and b such that

$$\frac{\int_a^b f(x)g(x)\,dx}{\int_a^b g(x)\,dx?} = f(c). \tag{*}$$

This result is often called a "mean value theorem for integrals."
   Suggestion: Use the properties of the definite integral listed in Theorem F of Sec. 18.1 to show that the ratios on the left-hand side of (*) must lie between the absolute minimum and the absolute maximum values of f on $[a, b]$. What can you then conclude from the result on "intermediate values" (Theorem A) of Sec. 13.1?

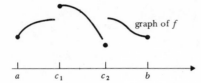

graph of f

33. Suppose that a function f is continuous on an interval $[a, b]$ except possibly at finitely many inputs — say, $c_1 < c_2 < \cdots < c_m$. Suppose further that for each fixed subinterval of the form $[c_{i-1}, c_i]$ or $[a, c_1]$ or $[c_m, b]$ f could be redefined if necessary at the end points so as to be continuous there, too. See the graph in the accompanying figure.

*(a) Check that all the results of Theorem F (on the existence of the "definite integral") in Sec. 18.1 still hold for such an f (provided you replace maxima over subintervals by least upper bounds, and minima by greatest lower bounds, in part III of Theorem F).

(b) On the basis of part (a), show that

$$\int_a^b f(x)\, dx = \int_a^{c_1} f(x)\, dx + \int_{c_1}^{c_2} f(x)\, dx + \cdots + \int_{c_{m-1}}^{c_m} f(x)\, dx$$
$$+ \int_{c_m}^b f(x)\, dx,$$

where for each integral on the right-hand side f is suitably redefined at the end points (if necessary) so as to be continuous on the corresponding closed interval.

(c) Sketch a graph of

$$f(x) = \begin{cases} x^2 - 1 & \text{for } -1 \leqslant x < 0 \\ 1 & \text{for } x = 0 \\ x + 1 & \text{for } 0 < x < 2 \\ e^x & \text{for } 2 \leqslant x \leqslant 3, \end{cases}$$

and evaluate $\int_{-1}^3 f(x)\, dx$.

18.3 "AVERAGES"

If f is a continuous function on an interval $[a, b]$, and if we divide $[a, b]$ into a sufficiently large number n of subintervals $[x_{i-1}, x_i]$ of *equal* length $x_i - x_{i-1} = (b - a)/n$, then a sum such as

$$S = f(x_1^*)\left(\frac{b-a}{n}\right) + f(x_2^*)\left(\frac{b-a}{n}\right) + \cdots + f(x_n^*)\left(\frac{b-a}{n}\right) \tag{1}$$

will be close to the value of the definite integral $\int_a^b f(x)\, dx$ — for any choice of "representative" inputs x_i^* in $[x_{i-1}, x_i]$. So says the basic result (Theorem F of Sec. 18.9) on the definite integral. If we divide (1) through by $(b - a)$, we can conclude that the sum

$$\frac{1}{b-a} S = f(x_1^*)\frac{1}{n} + f(x_2^*)\frac{1}{n} + \cdots + f(x_n^*)\frac{1}{n} \tag{2}$$

or

$$\frac{1}{b-a} S = \frac{f(x_1^*) + f(x_2^*) + \cdots + f(x_n^*)}{n}, \tag{3}$$

will be close to the value

$$\frac{1}{b-a}\int_a^b f(x)\,dx$$

for sufficiently large n. Note how the expressions (2) and (3) display the quantity $[1/(b-a)]S$ as an "average" of the n *output* values $f(x_i^*)$ — each accorded an equal "weight" $(1/n)$. For this reason people sometimes interpret the limiting value

$$\frac{1}{b-a}\int_a^b f(x)\,dx \qquad (4)$$

as a kind of *average output value* for the function f over its entire domain $[a,b]$ — with the understanding that input values are accorded "equal weights."

EXAMPLE 1: *The average output value of* $\cos mx$ *for* x *in* $[0,2\pi]$, *and* m *an integer* $\neq 0$. Recalling that $(\sin mx/m)' = \cos mx$, we can write

$$\frac{1}{2\pi}\int_0^{2\pi}\cos mx = \frac{1}{2\pi}\left[\left(\frac{\sin m\cdot 2\pi}{m}\right)-\left(\frac{\sin 0\cdot 2\pi}{m}\right)\right]$$

$$= \frac{1}{2\pi}(0-0) = 0 \qquad (5)$$

— just what we might expect as an average value, since the positive heights in the graph of $\cos mx$ seem *equally* counterbalanced by negative ones. (See Fig. 18-8, where $m = 3$.)

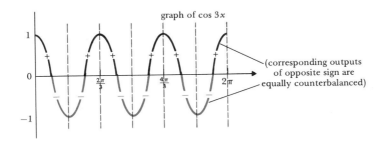

graph of cos 3x

(corresponding outputs of opposite sign are equally counterbalanced)

FIGURE 18-8

You might recall that on several occasions I've used a sum similar to the

$$f(x_1^*)\frac{1}{n}+f(x_2^*)\frac{1}{n}+\cdots+f(x_n^*)\frac{1}{n}$$

in (2), to represent an "average." Thus in Sec. 3.1, I considered the sum $(\$4)(2/6) + (-\$3)(4/6)$ as an "average payoff per trial" for a game yielding \$4 with probability 2/6 and $-\$3$ with probability 4/6. And in the population growth examples of Sec. 5.8 and Sec.

13.8, where an organism could contribute k offspring with probability p_k $(0 \leqslant k \leqslant n)$, I interpreted the sum

$$0 \cdot p_0 + 1 \cdot p_1 + 2 \cdot p_2 + \cdots + n \cdot p_n$$

as the "average number of offspring per parent." More generally: suppose that a situation involving chance can produce any one of *finitely many* numerical outcomes $f(1)$, $f(2), \ldots, f(n)$ —each $f(i)$ with a corresponding probability p_i, where $p_1 + p_2 + \cdots + p_n = 1$. I've argued that we can interpret the sum

$$f(1)p_1 + f(2)p_2 + \cdots + f(n)p_n \tag{6}$$

as an "average value" for the $f(i)$'s.

Such recollections suggest a further insight into the role of the definite integral $[1/(b-a)] \int_a^b f(x)\, dx$ as an "average": Think of selecting an input x "at random" from among the infinitely many points in the interval $[a, b]$, and of my paying you an amount $f(x)$ depending on which x you choose. What "average payment" can you expect?

$$\frac{1}{b-a} \int_a^b f(x)\, dx?$$

Here is a specific case of random choice of input:

EXAMPLE 2. Suppose that at some random time within the last 5 hours a human victim receives a dose of 10^6 dangerous bacteria, of a kind which split into two after an (average) lifetime of $\frac{1}{2}$ hour. What "average number" of bacteria can we expect the victim to have *now*?

In Sec. 13.3 (Example 1) I argued that such a bacterial population, if unchecked, would have approximate size $f(t) = 10^6 e^{2t}$ after a known incubation time of t hours. How can we interpret the "randomness" of the actual (but *unknown*) incubation time—call it $\tilde{t}$? The set of all possible outcomes for $\tilde{t}$ is the interval $[0, 5]$. If you will accept the same formulation as I gave for "random" arrival at a bus stop in Sec. 4.9 (Fig. 4-22), then we can assign to any subinterval $[r, s]$ of $[0, 5]$ the ratio

$$\frac{\text{length of } [r, s]}{\text{length of } [0, 5]} = \frac{s - r}{5} \tag{7}$$

as the *probability that $[r, s]$ contains the actual incubation time $\tilde{t}$.* The *half-open* interval $[r, s) = \{$all t with $r \leqslant t < s\}$ merits the probability $(s - r)/5$ just as well—if you believe that the single end point s has 0 probability for being the actual incubation time $\tilde{t}$. (To support this belief, note that if we close down on s with smaller and smaller intervals $[r_n, s]$, then $\lim_{n \to \infty} (s - r_n)/5 = 0$.)

With such probability assignments in mind, let's divide $[0, 5]$ into $n - 1$ small half-open subintervals $[t_{i-1}, t_i)$ and one small closed subinterval $[t_{n-1}, t_n]$ by a partition $\sigma = \{t_0, t_1, t_2, \ldots, t_n\}$. See Fig. 18-9.

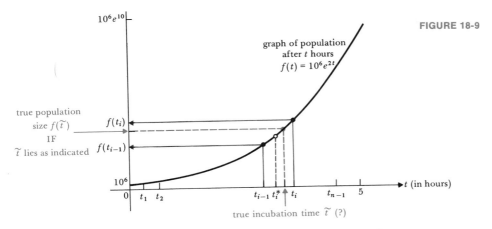

FIGURE 18-9

The true incubation time $\tilde{t}$ lies in *one* of these subintervals—we don't know which. The probability that it lies in, say, the ith is $p_i = (t_i - t_{i-1})/5$. And if $\tilde{t}$ does lie somewhere between t_{i-1} and t_i, then the population size now (after $\tilde{t}$ hours of incubation) should be somewhere between $f(t_{i-1})$ and $f(t_i)$. How can we "average" the population size over the n possible subintervals, in the spirit of expression (6),

$$f(1)p_1 + f(2)p_2 + \cdots + f(n)p_n?$$

If we represent each interval $[t_{i-1}, t_i\rangle$ by its *maximum* population output $f(t_i)$, then we can view the sum

$$\bar{S}(\sigma) = f(t_1)p_1 + f(t_2)p_2 + f(t_3)p_3 + \cdots + f(t_n)p_n \qquad (8)$$

as an upper approximation for a "reasonable population average" — provided one exists. If we represent $[t_{i-1}, t_i\rangle$ by its *minimum* population output $f(t_{i-1})$, then we can view the sum

$$\underline{S}(\sigma) = f(t_0)p_1 + f(t_1)p_2 + f(t_2)p_3 + \cdots + f(t_{n-1})p_n \qquad (9)$$

as a lower approximation for a "reasonable population average." If we choose intermediate inputs t_i^* in $[t_{i-1}, t_i\rangle$, then the sum

$$\begin{aligned}
S(\sigma) &= f(t_1^*)p_1 + f(t_2^*)p_2 + f(t_3^*)p_3 + \cdots + f(t_n^*)p_n \\
&= f(t_1^*)\left(\frac{t_1 - t_0}{5}\right) + f(t_2^*)\left(\frac{t_2 - t_1}{5}\right) + f(t_3^*)\left(\frac{t_3 - t_2}{5}\right) + \cdots \\
&\qquad\qquad + f(t_n^*)\left(\frac{t_n - t_{n-1}}{5}\right) \\
&= \left[\frac{1}{5}f(t_1^*)\right](t_1 - t_0) + \left[\frac{1}{5}f(t_2^*)\right](t_2 - t_1) + \cdots + \left[\frac{1}{5}f(t_n^*)\right](t_n - t_{n-1})
\end{aligned} \qquad (10)$$

might well serve as a better approximation to a reasonable average. Does a "reasonable average" really exist? By Theorem F on the existence of the definite integral, all the three sums (8), (9), and (10) will get closer and closer to a common number

$$\int_0^5 \frac{1}{5}f(t)\,dt = \frac{1}{5}\int_0^5 f(t)\,dt \qquad (11)$$

if we choose a sequence of partitions $\sigma_1, \sigma_2, \sigma_3, \ldots$ with meshes tending to 0. Thus again we're led to the expression $1/(b-a) \int_a^b f(x)\, dx$ as an "average value"—in this case, for the disease population size in a victim after a random incubation time between 0 and 5 hours.

Since e^{2t} has antiderivative $\frac{1}{2}e^{2t}$ we can calculate the "average value"

$$\frac{1}{5}\int_0^5 f(t)\, dt = \frac{1}{5}\int_0^5 10^6 e^{2t}\, dt = \frac{10^6}{5}\int_0^5 e^{2t}\, dt = \frac{1}{5}\left[\frac{1}{2}e^{2t}\right]_0^5$$

$$= \frac{10^6}{5}\left[\frac{1}{2}e^{2\cdot 5} - \frac{1}{2}e^{2\cdot 0}\right] = 10^5(e^{10}-1)$$

$$= 3.15 \times 10^9 \text{ approximately} \tag{12}$$

—an increase by a factor of about 3,000 from the size at the instant of first infection.

Note how this "average of output values" $f(t)$ compares with the output value at the single input $t_0 = 2\frac{1}{2}$ hours—we might view t_0 as the "average input time." $f(2\frac{1}{2}) = \frac{1}{5}10^6 e^{2\cdot(5/2)} = 3.56 \times 10^7$ approximately. So the output for the *average input* is about 1/100th the size of the *average output*. Why? Because the population size $f(t)$ increases so rapidly ("exponentially") *after* time t_0.

Can the definite integral be of service in formulating averages over infinitely many outputs $f(x)$ when the inputs x are not "equally likely" to be chosen? I'll discuss such a case in the next section.

18.4 THE AVERAGE TIME BETWEEN TELEPHONE CALLS

Viewed from a central switchboard, the times at which individual telephone calls arrive are matters of chance. Now, if you wanted to plan a central telephone exchange so as to minimize people's frustration in waiting for free trunk lines, you would do well to examine some aspects of this "random" telephone traffic. For example, can one reasonably speak of and measure an "average time between incoming calls"? And if so, how is such an "average" related to the probability that the exchange will be free of incoming calls for a given length of time?

Although the intensity of telephone traffic varies among different parts of the day, let's try to set up a model for the traffic in a period during which people's behavior is fairly uniform—for example, during morning work hours (excluding coffee breaks). Now, how can we interpret "randomness" of arrival for telephone calls? I urge you to review my discussion in Sec. 16.1 regarding randomness of arrival of lethal meteorites to the surface of a space suit. I based a model for meteorite arrival on three main assumptions:

(1) that arrivals during nonoverlapping intervals of time should be *independent* of each other;

(2) that the probability of *exactly one* arrival during a short time interval should be approximately *proportional* (with some constant λ) *to the length of the interval*; and

(3) that the probability for *more than one* arrival during a time interval should *tend to zero compared to the length of that interval* as we make that length shorter and shorter.

Do you feel that these assumptions might reasonably apply to incoming telephone calls during subintervals of the morning work hours? If so, then from Sec. 16.1 we immediately have a form for the probability that there be no incoming calls during a subinterval of length L, namely $p(L) = e^{-\lambda L}$ — where λ is an as yet unknown constant.

How can we relate $e^{-\lambda L}$ to an "average time" between incoming calls? Suppose that a call arrives at some instant during the morning work hours. Let's represent that instant as $t = 0$ on a coordinate line, and look at a subsequent (say, half-open) interval $[0, T\rangle$ of morning time. When will the *next* call arrive? With probability $p(T) = e^{-\lambda T}$ there will be *no* arrivals during $[0, T\rangle$, and the next call will arrive later than T. But the next call might arrive somewhere within $[0, T\rangle$. To analyze the possibilities, let's proceed as in Example 2 and divide $[0, T\rangle$ into n small (half-open) subintervals $[t_{i-1}, t_i\rangle$, by a partition $\sigma = \{0 = t_0 < t_1 < t_2 < \cdots < t_n = T\}$. What's the probability that the next call will arrive during a particular one of these subintervals $[t_{i-1}, t_i\rangle$, and not before? If we reason exactly as I did, following Fig. 16-3, regarding a first meteorite arrival, we can conclude that *the next call will arrive during $[t_{i-1}, t_i\rangle$ with probability*

$$p(t_{i-1}) - p(t_i) = e^{-\lambda t_{i-1}} - e^{-\lambda t_i}. \tag{1}$$

Now how can we get at an "average time" between the call that arrived at $t = 0$ and the *next* call? From each subinterval $[t_{i-1}, t_i\rangle$ of $[0, T\rangle$, let's pick some input t_i^* to approximate the infinitely many possible arrival times in $[t_{i-1}, t_i\rangle$ for the next call. Then let's weight (multiply) this "representative" t_i^* with the corresponding probability in (1) that the next call *will* arrive during $[t_{i-1}, t_i\rangle$, and let's sum over the possibilities:

$$S(\sigma) = t_1^*[p(t_0) - p(t_1)] + t_2^*[p(t_1) - p(t_2)] + \cdots + t_n^*[p(t_{n-1}) - p(t_n)]. \tag{2}$$

Such a sum is in the general form $f(1)p_1 + f(2)p_2 + \cdots + f(1)p_n$ for "averages" — and corresponds to the intermediate approximation (10) of Example 2 in the last section. Although it neglects possible arrivals of the next call after $[0, T\rangle$, let's see whether $S(\sigma)$ must tend to some *unique* limit as we let the mesh of σ tend to zero. (The smaller the intervals $[t_{i-1}, t_i\rangle$ are, the better each should be represented by any one of its inputs t_i^*.)

If only $S(\sigma)$ were of the form

$$g(t_1^*)(t_1 - t_0) + g(t_2^*)(t_2 - t_1) + \cdots + g(t_n^*)(t_n - t_{n-1}) \tag{3}$$

for some continuous function g, we would then know that the $S(\sigma)$ tend to $\int_0^T g(t)\, dt$ — by the basic Theorem F on definite integrals. Can you write the output difference $p(t_{i-1}) - p(t_i)$ in a form involving input differences $(t_i - t_{i-1})$?

Free associate.

And you might remember the mean value theorem (of Sec. 15.1), which says that

$$p(t_i) - p(t_{i-1}) = p'(t_i^*)(t_i - t_{i-1}) \tag{4}$$

for some t_i^* between t_{i-1} and t_i. And for subscripts in the opposite order,

$$p(t_{i-1}) - p(t_i) = -p'(t_i^*)(t_i - t_{i-1}).$$

More specifically, since $p(t) = e^{-\lambda t}$,

$$
\begin{aligned}
e^{-\lambda t_{i-1}} - e^{-\lambda t_i} &= -(e^{-\lambda t})'_{\text{at } t_i^*}(t_i - t_{i-1}) \\
&= -[-\lambda e^{-\lambda t_i}](t_i - t_{i-1}) \\
&= \lambda e^{-\lambda t_i}(t_i - t_{i-1}) \\
&\qquad \text{for some } t_i^* \text{ in } [t_{i-1}, t_i\rangle. \tag{5}
\end{aligned}
$$

If we choose these very same t_i^* to define $S(\sigma)$ in (2) we can write

$$
\begin{aligned}
S(\sigma) &= t_1^* \lambda e^{-\lambda t_1^*}(t_1 - t_0) + t_2^* \lambda e^{-\lambda t_2^*}(t_2 - t_1) + \cdots \\
&\quad + t_n^* \lambda e^{-\lambda t_n^*}(t_n - t_{n-1}) \\
&= g(t_1^*)(t_1 - t_0) + g(t_2^*)(t_2 - t_1) + \cdots + g(t_n^*)(t_n - t_{n-1}), \tag{6}
\end{aligned}
$$

where $g(t) = \lambda t e^{-\lambda t}$, a continuous function for all t. *Conclusion:* If we let the mesh size of σ tend to zero, then $S(\sigma)$ — the approximate "average time," neglecting arrivals later than $[0, T\rangle$ — must tend to

$$\int_0^T \lambda t e^{-\lambda t}\, dt. \tag{7}$$

In Example 5 of Sec. 15.10 I used the method of "antidifferentiation by parts" to show that for any constant $a \neq 0$, the function xe^{ax} has as antiderivative

$$\frac{1}{a}e^{ax}\left(x - \frac{1}{a}\right).$$

Letting $a = -\lambda$ in (7), we can therefore write

$$
\begin{aligned}
\int_0^T \lambda t e^{-\lambda t}\, dt &= \lambda \int_0^T t e^{-\lambda t}\, dt = \lambda\left[\frac{1}{-\lambda}e^{-\lambda t}\left(t - \frac{1}{-\lambda}\right)\right]_0^T \\
&= \left[-e^{-\lambda T}\left(T + \frac{1}{\lambda}\right)\right] - \left[-e^{-\lambda \cdot 0}\left(0 + \frac{1}{\lambda}\right)\right] \\
&= \frac{1}{\lambda} - e^{-\lambda T}\left(T + \frac{1}{\lambda}\right) \\
&= \frac{1}{\lambda} - \frac{1}{\lambda}e^{-\lambda T} - \frac{1}{\lambda}e^{-\lambda T}(\lambda T). \tag{8}
\end{aligned}
$$

But what if the next call arrives after the interval $[0, T\rangle$ — as it can do with probability $e^{-\lambda T}$? We could eliminate such a possibility by further idealizing the model of telephone traffic and assuming "uniform" conditions to hold for all time — not just for morning working hours. Then we could examine larger and larger intervals $[0, T_n)$ where $\{T_n\}$ is any sequence with $\lim\limits_{n\to\infty} T_n = \infty$. Check that the probabilities $e^{-\lambda T_n} = (e^{-\lambda})^{T_n}$ for the next call to arrive after $[0, T_n)$ will tend to 0, since $e^{-\lambda} < 1$ (see Problem 8 of Sec. 6.9). Shouldn't the corresponding integrals $\int_0^{T_n} \lambda t e^{-\lambda t}\, dt$ therefore provide better and better representations of an *overall average time* between the call at $t = 0$ and the next call? If so, then from (8) we can calculate that average as

$$\lim_{n\to\infty} \int_0^{T_n} \lambda t e^{-\lambda t}\, dt = \lim_{n\to\infty} \left[\frac{1}{\lambda} - \frac{1}{\lambda} e^{-\lambda T_n} - \frac{1}{\lambda} e^{-\lambda T_n}(\lambda T_n) \right]$$

$$= \frac{1}{\lambda} - \frac{1}{\lambda} \lim_{n\to\infty} e^{-\lambda T_n} - \frac{1}{\lambda} \lim_{n\to\infty} e^{-\lambda T_n}(\lambda T_n). \qquad (9)$$

Here $\lim\limits_{n\to\infty} e^{-\lambda T_n} = 0$, and

$$\lim_{n\to\infty} e^{-\lambda T_n}(\lambda T_n) = 0 \qquad (10)$$

also.

To see why (10) holds, note that $x < e^x$ for all $x \geqslant 0$ (from Example 2 of Sec. 15.2). Hence $\frac{1}{2}x < e^{x/2}$, and $x < 2e^{x/2}$; and in particular, $\lambda T_n < 2e^{(1/2)\lambda T_n}$. Thus

$$e^{-\lambda T_n}(\lambda T_n) < 2e^{-\lambda T_n} e^{(1/2)\lambda T_n} = 2e^{-(1/2)\lambda T_n}; \qquad (11)$$

and $\lim\limits_{n\to\infty} e^{-\lambda T_n}(\lambda T_n) = 0$ because

$$\lim_{n\to\infty} e^{-(1/2)\lambda T_n} = \lim_{n\to\infty} \left[e^{-\lambda/2} \right]^{T_n} = 0.$$

(The result is general: any positively divergent sequence $\{x_n\}$ will be overpowered by the "negative exponential" sequence $\{e^{-x_n}\}$.)

Final conclusion: for any sequence of positive values $\{T_n\}$ with $\lim\limits_{n\to\infty} T_n = \infty$, we must have

$$\lim_{n\to\infty} \int_0^{T_n} \lambda t e^{-\lambda t}\, dt = \frac{1}{\lambda}. \qquad (12)$$

(Such a result is often denoted

$$\text{``} \int_0^\infty \lambda t e^{-\lambda t}\, dt = \frac{1}{\lambda}. \text{''}$$

See Problem 13 of the Sec. 18.2 for a general discussion.) Are you willing to accept $1/\lambda$ as the average waiting time between two incoming calls in an arbitrarily long "uniform" period of traffic? If so, then we have a new interpretation for the constant λ: *the reciprocal of the average waiting time.* And we can hope to measure λ, or $1/\lambda$, approximately: For example, record the lengths of time between 100 distinct pairs of adjacent incoming calls. Add these lengths and divide by 100. Will the result approximate $1/\lambda$? Suppose that such an experiment leads to an approximate value for $1/\lambda$ of, say, $\frac{1}{2}$ minute. Then $\lambda = 2$ approximately, in "1/minute" units. And now we can calculate the probability that the central exchange will be free of incoming calls for a period of, say, $L = 1$ minute: namely,

$$p(L) = e^{-\lambda L} = e^{-[2(1/\text{minutes})](1 \text{ minute})} = e^{-2}$$

$$= \frac{1}{(2.718+)^2} = 0.135 \text{ approximately.} \tag{13}$$

Note that the probability for no call during a period of length $T = 60$ minutes is $p(60) = e^{-2 \cdot 60} = e^{-120}$, a very small number. Moreover, for these values of λ and T, the quantity $(1/\lambda)e^{-\lambda T}(\lambda T)$ appearing in (8) has value $\frac{1}{2}e^{-120}(120)$ — which is also very small. Thus even if we restricted ourselves to looking at next call arrival times within a one-hour period $[0, T\rangle = [0, 60\rangle$, the integral $\int_0^{60} \lambda t e^{-\lambda t}\, dt$ in (8) would already agree very closely with the idealized waiting time $1/\lambda$.

18.5 "A DENSITY FUNCTION"

In the last section I explored a model wherein the probability for waiting at least t minutes between arriving telephone calls was of the form $e^{-\lambda t}$. ($1/\lambda$ was the "average" number of minutes between calls.) Correspondingly, we can describe *the probability of waiting* LESS *than t minutes* by the function

$$G(t) = 1 - e^{-\lambda t} \qquad \text{for all } t \geq 0 \tag{1}$$

(since $P(A') = 1 - P(A)$ for any complementary sets A and A' representing some result and its negative). Note that the function $G(t)$ is increasing: It represents the *cumulative amount of probability* for an actual waiting time to be a number in the interval $[0, t\rangle$ — and the larger the interval, the more likely it is to contain the actual waiting time. In the last section I repeatedly used the *difference* $e^{-\lambda a} - e^{-\lambda b} = (1 - e^{-\lambda b}) - (1 - e^{-\lambda a}) = G(b) - G(a)$ as the probability for a waiting time to be in an interval $[a, b)$. This meaning for the difference depended not so much on the specific formula $G(t) = 1 - e^{-\lambda t}$ as on the basic addition rule for probabilities of mutually exclusive results:

$$G(b) = \left\{ \begin{array}{l} \text{probability of a} \\ \text{waiting time in} \\ [0, b\rangle = \\ [0, a\rangle \ \cup \ [a, b\rangle \end{array} \right\} = \underbrace{\left\{ \begin{array}{l} \text{probability of a} \\ \text{waiting time in} \\ [0, a\rangle \end{array} \right\}}_{G(a)} + \left\{ \begin{array}{l} \text{probability of a} \\ \text{waiting time in} \\ [a, b\rangle \end{array} \right\} \tag{2}$$

or

$$G(b) - G(a) = \left\{ \begin{array}{l} \text{probability of a} \\ \text{waiting time in} \\ [a, b\rangle \end{array} \right\}. \tag{3}$$

In the last section I applied the mean value theorem to differences, and wrote $G(t_i) - G(t_{i-1}) = G'(t_i^*)(t_i - t_{i-1})$. But we also have another result which speaks about differences, the "fundamental theorem" in Sec. 18.1. It says in this case that, since G has a continuous derivative

$$g(t) = G'(t) = (1 - e^{-\lambda t})' = -(\lambda)e^{-\lambda t} = \lambda e^{-\lambda t} \qquad \text{all } t \geq 0, \qquad (4)$$

we can write

$$\begin{Bmatrix} \text{probability of a} \\ \text{waiting time in} \\ [a, b\rangle \end{Bmatrix} = G(b) - G(a) = \int_a^b g(t)\,dt \qquad \text{for } 0 \leq a < b. \qquad (5)$$

Thus we can visualize the probability assigned to any interval $[a, b\rangle$ as the area above $[a, b]$ and beneath the graph of g—as in Fig. 18-10.

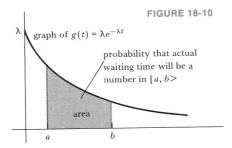

FIGURE 18-10

graph of $g(t) = \lambda e^{-\lambda t}$

probability that actual waiting time will be a number in $[a, b>$

area

a　b

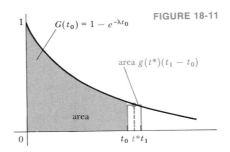

FIGURE 18-11

$G(t_0) = 1 - e^{-\lambda t_0}$

area $g(t^*)(t_1 - t_0)$

area

t_0 $t^* t_1$

In particular, the *cumulative probability* $G(t_0)$ from 0 to any $t_0 > 0$ corresponds to the cumulative area $\int_0^{t_0} g(t)\,dt$. At t_0, $G'(t_0) = g(t_0)$ tells the *rate of increase* of that cumulative probability, per unit time. And for a very short interval $[t_0, t_1]$ as in Fig. 18-11, the product

$$g(t^*)(t_1 - t_0) \qquad \text{for any } t^* \text{ in } [t_0, t_1] \qquad (6)$$

approximates the probability assigned to $[t_0, t_1\rangle$. In view of such services, some people interpret $g(t)$ as describing a "density" with which probability is distributed at inputs t. And they call g the *"probability density function"* corresponding to the cumulative probability function G.

The density function appeared in the last section in connection with "averages." Via approximations such as (6), I argued that we could regard the definite integral

$$\int_0^T t g(t)\,dt \qquad (7)$$

as representing an "average" among all the possible waiting times t in a long interval $[0, T]$—wherein each such t got a "weight" proportional to its corresponding density $g(t)$.

Note also these further properties of the density function g:

$$g(t) \geq 0 \qquad \text{at all inputs } t, \qquad (8)$$

since G is increasing. And for any sequence $\{T_n\}$ with $\lim_{n\to\infty} T_n = \infty$,

$$\lim_{n\to\infty} \int_0^{T_n} g(t)\, dt = \lim_{n\to\infty} [G(T_n) - G(0)] = 1; \tag{9}$$

that is, we get closer and closer to the total amount of probability, 1, as we look at larger and larger intervals $[0, T_n)$.

Here is how we can use density functions to visualize the essentials of a statistical problem.

EXAMPLE 1: *How to judge whether a typist is ill.* Suppose that you have a job proofreading material from a typist who normally produces a serious misprint on the average of once in 50 pages—but who produces misprints about 10 times as often when she is ill. Suppose that you've just received a page with a bad misprint. Since correcting extensive mistakes is troublesome, you might like to suggest to the typist that she take time off if she really isn't feeling well. But you might not want to offend her by making such a suggestion if she's not ill. How can you judge?

You might decide to check how soon the next misprint appears. You might even try to figure out a "cutoff" number N to test matters as follows: *if the next bad misprint appears in less than N pages, you could conclude that the typist is ill; and if later than N pages, that she's working normally.* If you do consider such a test, you should be aware that whatever conclusion it leads you to *may* be wrong. The most embarrassing error on your part would be to conclude that the typist is ill when she's really well. The other kind of error would be to conclude that she's well when she's really ill. If you choose the cutoff number N too large, then even "normal" misprints would be likely to appear with the next N pages—and you might well make an error of the first kind (the embarrassing kind). If N is too small, then even misprints made in illness might tend to come after N pages—and you might make an error of the second kind. Is it possible to choose an N which will hold your chances for an embarrassing error to, say, one in ten, while still *minimizing* your chances for an error of the second kind? (See Fig. 18-12.)

To answer such a question, let's ask what assumptions you're willing to make about the typist's misprints. Think of the typist's

FIGURE 18-12

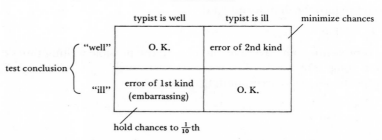

output as recorded on one long moving tape. Do you believe that the misprints "arrive" on that tape more or less "at random" — in the fashion of meteorites (Sec. 16.1) and telephone calls (Sec. 18.4)? If so, then we should compare the following two probabilistic models. If the typist is well:

$$\left.\begin{array}{l}\text{the probability of}\\ \text{waiting less than } t \text{ pages}\\ \text{between misprints}\end{array}\right\} = G(t) = 1 - e^{-\lambda t} \text{ for } t \geqslant 0, \tag{10}$$

where $\dfrac{1}{\lambda} = 50$ pages.

If the typist is ill:

$$\left.\begin{array}{l}\text{the probability of}\\ \text{waiting less than } t \text{ pages}\\ \text{between misprints}\end{array}\right\} = H(t) = 1 - e^{-\mu t} \text{ for } t \geqslant 0, \tag{11}$$

where $\dfrac{1}{\mu} = \dfrac{50}{10} = 5$ pages.

I've sketched corresponding density functions in Fig. 18-13.

Model for NORMAL typist:

probability of next misprint *before N* pages (leading to embarrassing error)

$$= \int_0^N g(t)\, dt = 1 - e^{-(0.02)N}$$

FIGURE 18-13

graph of density function
$g(t) = (0.02)e^{-(0.02)t}$

$\lambda = \frac{1}{50}$
$= 0.02$

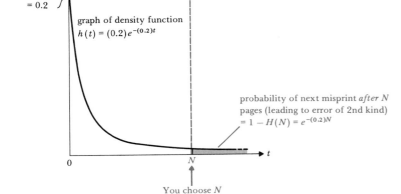

Model for ILL typist:

$\lambda = \frac{1}{5}$
$= 0.2$

graph of density function
$h(t) = (0.2)e^{-(0.2)t}$

probability of next misprint *after N* pages (leading to error of 2nd kind)
$= 1 - H(N) = e^{-(0.2)N}$

You choose N

You don't know which model in Fig. 18-13 describes the true situation. Nevertheless, for a given "cutoff" N, you can calculate the probability of making an embarrassing judgment *if* the typist is working normally. It's the probability that she will produce a misprint *before* N pages — and equals the (green) area under the *top* graph in Fig. 18-13, $\int_0^N g(t)\,dt = 1 - e^{-(0.02)N}$. If you want to hold this probability to 1/10th, choose N so that

$$1 - e^{-(0.02)N} = 0.1,$$

or

$$e^{-(0.02)N} = 0.9,$$

or

$$e^{(0.02)N} = 1.1 \text{ (approx)},$$

or

$$(0.02)N = \log_e 1.1 \text{ (approx)} = 0.095 \text{ (approx)},$$

or

$$N = \frac{0.095}{0.02} = 4.8 \text{ pages (approx).} \tag{12}$$

Any larger value for N would give chances for embarrassment greater than one in ten.

Here then is the "test": *If the next misprint comes before* 4.8 *pages, conclude that the typist is "ill"; if after, conclude that she's well.*

But what if the typist is really ill? Then the *bottom* graph of Fig. 18-13 describes her behavior. Beneath that graph, the (green) area to the right of N is the probability that she will produce a misprint after N pages, and fool you into thinking that she's well (an error of the "second kind"). You've already chosen N as large as you can, $N = 4.8$ pages approximately — so you can't minimize this kind of error any farther, with the present "test." You should expect it to occur with a probability of $1 - H(4.8) = e^{-(0.2)(4.8)} = e^{-0.96} = \frac{1}{2}$ (approximately). Thus you'll have 50–50 chances for error in judgment *if* the typist really is ill. Is such a test worthwhile? With different values for allowable error probability it's used extensively in manufacturing "quality control."

18.6 CENTERS OF GRAVITY

When will a see-saw balance? In Fig. 18-14 I've sketched one with three children's weights on it. Let's suppose that the board itself weighs a negligible amount in comparison with the children. Generations of children and physicists have found that in order for such weights to balance they must be so positioned with respect to the "fulcrum" (the balancing point) as to provide for an equality of the form

$$r_1 m_1 = r_2 m_2 + r_3 m_3. \tag{1}$$

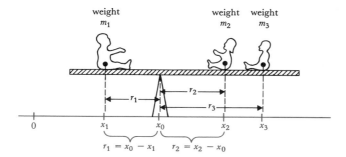

FIGURE 18-14

Here r_i denotes an approximate distance between the ith weight and the fulcrum. If we choose any x coordinate system parallel to the board, and label positions as I've done in green in Fig. 18-14, then we can write the condition (1) for balancing as

$$(x_0 - x_1) m_1 = (x_2 - x_0) m_2 + (x_3 - x_0) m_3$$

— or with all terms on one side, as

$$(x_1 - x_0) m_1 + (x_2 - x_0) m_2 + (x_3 - x_0) m_3 = 0. \qquad (2)$$

In turn, we can separate out terms involving the fulcrum position x_0 to get equivalent equations

$$x_0 (m_1 + m_2 + m_3) = x_1 m_1 + x_2 m_2 + x_3 m_3, \qquad (3)$$

or

$$x_0 = \frac{x_1 m_1 + x_2 m_2 + x_3 m_3}{m_1 + m_2 + m_3}, \qquad (4)$$

or

$$x_0 = x_1 \left[\frac{m_1}{m_1 + m_2 + m_3} \right] + x_2 \left[\frac{m_2}{m_1 + m_2 + m_3} \right] + x_3 \left[\frac{m_3}{m_1 + m_2 + m_3} \right]. \qquad (5)$$

Note that the positive [ ] quantities in (5) add up to 1, just as elementary probabilities do. And (5) displays the necessary fulcrum position for balance as an *average* of the positions x_i, each x_i appearing with corresponding "probability"

$$p_i = \frac{m_i}{m_1 + m_2 + m_3}$$

proportional to m_i, the same form as the sum

$$f(1) p_1 + f(2) p_2 + \cdots + f(n) p_n$$

in Sec. 18.3.

The position x_0 is usually called the *center of gravity* of the system of weights (in the x direction).

With these thoughts in mind, let's see how we might determine the balancing point for, say, a vertical triangle which is a inches long, b inches high and is cut out of a thin uniform piece of material c inches thick and weighing w ounces per cubic inch. See Fig. 18-15. We might introduce a (green) coordinate system and a partition $\sigma = \{x_i\}$ of the interval $[0, a]$; and we might approximate the triangular slab by the union of thin vertical rectangular slabs, as in Fig. 18-15.

FIGURE 18-15

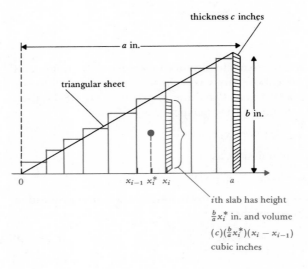

thickness c inches

a in.

triangular sheet

b in.

0

x_{i-1} x_i^* x_i

a

ith slab has height
$\frac{b}{a}x_i^*$ in. and volume
$(c)(\frac{b}{a}x_i^*)(x_i - x_{i-1})$
cubic inches

The ith of these will have weight equal to w ounces per cubic inch times its volume in cubic inches; namely,

$$m_i = w\left[c \cdot \frac{b}{a}x_i^* \cdot (x_i - x_{i-1}) \right]$$

$$= \left(\frac{wcb}{2}x_i^* \right)(x_i - x_{i-1}) \text{ ounces} \tag{6}$$

and this weight will be located approximately x_i^* inches from $x = 0$.

If we can generalize from equation (4) involving an array of three weights, the union of the small green rectangles should balance about a fulcrum located at

$$x_0(\sigma) = \frac{x_1^* m_1 + x_2^* m_2 + x_3^* m_3 + \cdots + x_n^* m_n}{m_1 + m_2 + m_3 + \cdots + m_n}. \tag{7}$$

Let's use the expressions $m_i = [(wcb/a)x_i^*](x_i - x_{i-1})$ of (6) to write the numerator in (7) as a sum of the form

$$S(\sigma) = x_1^*\left(\frac{wcb}{a}x_1^* \right)(x_1 - x_0) + x_2^*\left(\frac{wcb}{a}x_2^* \right)(x_2 - x_1) + \cdots . \tag{8}$$

If we pick partitions with smaller and smaller meshes, such sums must converge to the integral

$$\int_0^a x\left(\frac{wcb}{a}x\right) dx = \left(\frac{wcb}{a}\right) \int_0^a x^2\, dx$$

$$= \left(\frac{wcb}{a}\right)\left[\frac{x^3}{3}\right]_0^a = \left(\frac{wcb}{a}\right)\left(\frac{a^3}{3}-\frac{0^3}{3}\right) = \frac{1}{3}wcba^2 \text{ ounce-} \qquad \text{(9)}$$
$$\text{inches.}$$

Similarly, the denominator sum in (7) has the form

$$\frac{wcb}{a}x_1^*(x_1-x_0) + \frac{wcb}{a}x_2^*(x_2-x_1) + \cdots + \frac{wcb}{a}x_n^*(x_n - x_{n-1}), \qquad \text{(10)}$$

and must converge to

$$\int_a^b \left(\frac{wcb}{a}x\right) dx = \frac{wcb}{a}\left[\frac{x^2}{2}\right]_0^a = \frac{wcb}{a}\left(\frac{a^2}{2}-\frac{0^2}{2}\right) = wabc \text{ ounces} \qquad \text{(11)}$$

—just the total weight of the triangle, $(w \text{ oz/in.}^3)[\frac{1}{2}(a \text{ in.}) \cdot (b \text{ in.}) \cdot (c \text{ in.})]$. Thus for partitions σ of smaller and smaller mesh, the approximate fulcrum positions $x_0(\sigma)$ in (7) tend to a ratio of limits

$$\frac{\int_0^a x[(wcb/a)x]\, dx}{\int_0^a [(wcb/a)x]\, dx} = \frac{\frac{1}{3}wcba^2 \text{ ounce-inches}}{\frac{1}{2}wabc \text{ ounces}} = \frac{2}{3}a \text{ inches.} \qquad \text{(12)}$$

Note how the influence of the density w, the thickness c, and even the height b of the triangle disappear. Do you believe that any such triangle should balance above a point $\frac{2}{3}$ of the way along its base? Cut one out of wood or cardboard and see.

Note also, from (6) and (11), how the function $(wcb/a)x$ (ounces per inch) plays the role of a "weight density function"—describing how weight is distributed at different positions x from the origin. In the numerator of (12) each distance x is multiplied ("weighted") in proportion to its corresponding density $(wcb/a)x$. You might recall from the last section that a "probability density function" performs the same services in the formation of "averages."

18.7 "TUNING"

As I noted in Sec. 16.7, a voice or music can be transmitted electronically as a voltage function—which will be a sum of many scaled sine or cosine functions, each representing a vibration of a particular frequency and intensity. Usually the original message becomes corrupted by "noise" vibrations of too high or too low frequencies. How can a radio set receiving a total corrupted sum $f(t)$ of vibrations isolate or "tune in" on one or more particular frequencies and discover their contributions to the total sound? Equivalently: how can the set "filter out" all the other frequencies?

Let's look at a simple case. Suppose we know the received voltage $f(t)$ to be of the form

$$f(t) = a_1 \cos t + a_2 \cos 2t + a_3 \cos 3t + \cdots + a_{100} \cos 100t, \qquad \text{(1)}$$

but we don't know the values of the a_i's (the "amplitudes" corresponding to the various frequencies). How can we treat the function $f(t)$ to find a particular a_i—say, a_3? Here is one approach: if we multiply the sum in (1) through by cos $3t$, we'll have

$$f(t) \cos 3t = a_1[\cos t \cos 3t] + a_2[\cos 2t \cos 3t] + a_3(\cos 3t)^2$$

$$+ \cdots + a_{100}[\cos 100t \cos 3t]; \tag{2}$$

an expression wherein the quantity a_3 appears together with a *nonnegative* function $(\cos 3t)^2$, whereas all other a_i's appear with products $[\cos it \cos 3t]$ of cosines of *unlike* frequencies. I've sketched the graph of $(\cos 3t)^2$ in Fig. 18-16, and the graph of an unlike product cos $2t$ cos $3t$ in Fig. 18-17.

FIGURE 18-16

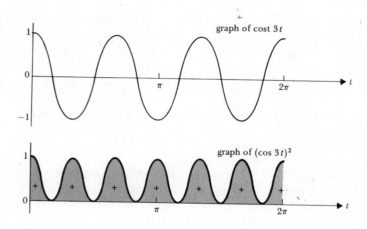

graph of cost $3t$

graph of $(\cos 3t)^2$

FIGURE 18-17

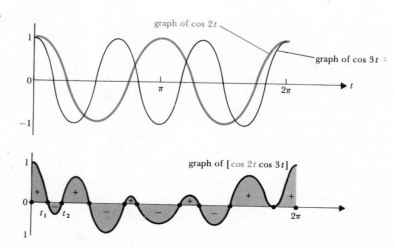

graph of cos $2t$

graph of cos $3t$

graph of $[\cos 2t \cos 3t]$

What might an "average output" be for the function $\cos 2t \cos 3t$ in Fig. 18-17? Will the positive outputs cancel the negative ones to give an average of 0? And can we expect the same to be true for any product $\cos it \cos 3t$ of cosines of *unlike* frequencies? If so, then this single fact might usefully serve to distinguish the behavior of the functions $\cos it \cos 3t$ when $i \neq 3$ from the behavior of the non-negative function $(\cos 3t)^2$—and might help us to sort a_3 out from all the other a_i's in the sum (2). To follow such a program, let's use the definite integral

$$\frac{1}{(b-a)} \int_a^b \cdots dt$$

to provide an "average output" value, as in Sec. 18.5. What values can we find for

$$\frac{1}{2\pi} \int_0^{2\pi} (\cos 3t)^2 \, dt \quad \text{and} \quad \frac{1}{2\pi} \int_0^{2\pi} \cos it \cos 3t \, dt \qquad (i \neq 3)?$$

For use with such products of cosines, here is an old trigonometric relationship:

$$\cos u \cos v = \frac{1}{2} \cos (u+v) + \frac{1}{2} \cos (u-v)$$

$$\text{for all real numbers } u \text{ and } v. \qquad (3)$$

(See Appendix A and Problem 12 of Sec. 16.8.) In particular, if we let $u = mt$ and $v = nt$, we'll have

$$\cos mt \cos nt = \frac{1}{2} \cos (m+n)t + \frac{1}{2} \cos (m-n)t \qquad \text{for any } m, n, \text{ and } t,$$

$$(4)$$

and

$$\int_0^{2\pi} [\cos mt \cos nt] \, dt = \frac{1}{2} \int_0^{2\pi} \cos (m+n)t \, dt + \frac{1}{2} \int_0^{2\pi} \cos (m-n)t \, dt. \qquad (5)$$

Since $H(t) = \sin (m+n)/(m+n)$ is an antiderivative of $\cos (m+n)t$ when $m+n \neq 0$ we can evaluate

$$\int_0^{2\pi} \cos (m+n)t \, dt = H(2\pi) - H(0) = \frac{\sin (m+n)2\pi}{m+n} - \frac{\sin (m+n)0}{m+n}$$

$$= 0 - 0 = 0. \qquad (6)$$

Similarly,

$$\int_0^{2\pi} \cos (m-n)t \, dt = \frac{\sin (m-n)2\pi}{m-n} - \frac{\sin (m-n)0}{m-n} = 0 - 0 = 0, \qquad (7)$$

when $m \neq n$. When $m = n$, then $\cos (m-n)t = \cos 0 = 1$ for all t, and

$$\int_0^{2\pi} \cos (m-n)t \, dt = \int_0^{2\pi} 1 \, dt = 2\pi. \qquad (8)$$

Substitute (6), (7), and (8) into (5) to get

$$\int_0^{2\pi} \cos mt \cos nt \, dt = \begin{cases} 0 & \text{when } m \neq n, \\ \pi & \text{when } m = n \neq 0. \end{cases} \tag{9}$$

Thus we have averages

$$\frac{1}{2\pi} \int_0^{2\pi} (\cos 3t)^2 \, dt = \frac{1}{2\pi}\pi = \frac{1}{2}, \tag{10}$$

and

$$\frac{1}{2\pi} \int_0^{2\pi} \cos it \cos 3t \, dt = \frac{1}{2\pi}0 = 0 \qquad \text{for all } i \neq 3. \tag{11}$$

All the cosine products with unlike frequencies *do* have 0 output averages.

Finally, how can we operate upon the given function $f(t)$ in order actually to distinguish the amplitude a_3 from all the rest? Why not average the product $f(t) \cos 3t$ — or its representation in (2) as a sum? Since the integral of a sum of functions is the sum of their separate integrals, we'll have

$$\frac{1}{2\pi} \int_0^{2\pi} f(t) \cos 3t \, dt = a_1 \frac{1}{2\pi} \int_0^{2\pi} [\cos t \cos 3t] \, dt$$

$$+ a_2 \frac{1}{2\pi} \int_0^{2\pi} [\cos 2t \cos 3t] \, dt$$

$$+ a_3 \frac{1}{2\pi} \int_0^{2\pi} (\cos 3t)^2 \, dt + \cdots$$

$$+ a_{100} \frac{1}{2\pi} \int_0^{2\pi} [\cos 100t \cos 3t] \, dt. \tag{12}$$

And wonders of wonders, all the averages on the right-hand side of (12) are 0 except that for $(\cos 3t)^2$, which is $\frac{1}{2}$. Thus

$$\frac{1}{2\pi} \int_0^{2\pi} f(t) \cos 3t \, dt = a_3 \frac{1}{2}$$

or

$$a_3 = \frac{1}{\pi} \int_0^{2\pi} f(t) \cos 3t \, dt. \tag{13}$$

Similarly, knowing $f(t)$ we can calculate any a_i simply as

$$a_i = \frac{1}{\pi} \int_0^{2\pi} f(t) \cos it \, dt. \tag{14}$$

Via such operations of integration, electronic circuitry is designed for "tuning in" preferred frequencies and "filtering out" others.

18.8 PROBLEMS ON AVERAGES

°1. In Sec. 18.3, I argued that we might interpret the quantity

$$\frac{1}{b-a} \int_a^b f(x)\, dx$$

as the "average output" of a continuous function defined on an interval $[a, b]$ if we consider all inputs x in $[a, b]$ as "equally likely." Find such average outputs for the following functions:
(a) $f(x) = x$ on $[a, b]$
(b) $f(x) = x^n$ on $[a, b]$ for $n = 2, 3, \ldots$
(c) $f(x) = \sin mx$ for x in $[a, a+2\pi]$, where $m = 0, \pm 1, \pm 2, \ldots$, and a is any fixed real number.
(d) $f(x) = e^x$ on $[a, b]$.

2. Review Example 2 in Sec. 18.3, on a random incubation time for a bacterial population, and calculate what "average number" of bacteria we can expect (now) if the bacteria have (average) lifetimes of 1 hour.

3. Here is an excerpt from the 1969 federal tax rate schedule for single persons:

Taxable Income (x)		Tax (T(x))
Over—	but not over—	
$6000	$8,000	$1,130 + 25% of excess over $6000
$8000	$10,000	$1,630 + 28% of excess over $8000

Suppose that within the $6000–$8000 category persons' taxable incomes are spread more or less uniformly. If you were to pick a person at random from that category, what would you "expect" his tax to be? Are you willing to interpret this "expected tax value" as the *average* of outputs $T(x)$? If so, describe $T(x)$ algebraically in terms of x, and calculate the average output.

4. Sometimes disk-like platelets in a blood sample are oriented at random angles to viewing light in a microscope—so that they appear oval in shape with deceptively foreshortened dimensions. I've sketched a 2-dimensional version of such a situation in the accompanying figure.

If all values between 0 and π are equally likely for the angle θ, what "average" platelet dimension will the viewer record?

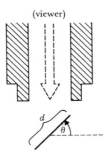
(viewer)

5. With reference to the incoming telephone calls in Sec. 18.4, suppose that there are successive arrivals at 9:02, 9:03, 9:07, 9:12, 9:20, 9:21, 9:25, 9:35, 9:37, and 9:41 a.m. What are the chances that the next call won't arrive until after 10 a.m.?

6. Here are dates of major auto accidents on a 100-mile stretch of highway during January, 1970: Jan. 3, Jan. 7, Jan. 8, Jan. 11, Jan. 17, Jan. 20, Jan. 23, Jan. 30. Do you believe that such accidents might satisfy the same general probabilistic properties

as I discussed for arrivals of meteorites (in Sec. 16.1) and of telephone calls (in Sec. 18.4)? If so, and if weather and other conditions would be comparable, what are the chances of having *no* major accidents on the same stretch of highway during the entire second week of January, 1971?

7. Suppose that an urban university is located at the center of a city which is roughly circular, with a radius of 10 miles; and that the students' homes are distributed more or less uniformly throughout the city.

   (a) For any fixed positive $r \leq 10$, what is the probability—call it $G(r)$—that a randomly chosen student will live no further than r miles from the university?

   (b) Find the "probability density" $g(r) = G'(r)$, the rate at which the probability $G(r)$ accumulates at distance r.

   (c) What is the average student commuting distance from home to school?

   (d) What is the average time it would take a student to go from home to school on a more or less straight route, riding a local bus which itself averages 10 mph?

   (e) Suppose that students who live more than 5 miles from the center of town could transfer from local to express buses when they reach the 5 mile radius, and thereafter travel nonstop to the center at an average of 20 mph. By how much would such an option reduce the average commuting time from its value in part (d)?

8. The two (dotted) regions pictured in the accompanying figure have approximately equal area. Think of a fisherman casting his nets uniformly throughout either region. In which will his average distance from land be the smallest?

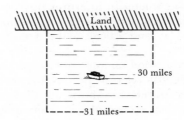

*9. Suppose that a water reservoir has just been filled to its capacity of 100 million cubic feet by a rainstorm; and that water is drawn from it by nearby towns at the fairly constant rate of 1 million cubic feet daily. At this rate the reservoir would be exhausted in 100 days. But the average period between rainstorms is only 30 days. What "average" amount of water can we therefore expect to find left in the reservoir just prior to the next rainstorm?

Suggestions: Suppose that arrivals of rainstorms have the

same general probabilistic properties as those of meteorites (Sec. 16.1) and telephone calls (Sec. 18.4). Then

(a) Describe the cumulative probability—call it $G(t)$—that the next storm will occur in a time interval $[0, t)$, for any $t > 0$.

(b) Find the "probability density" $g(t) = G'(t)$. You might recall my arguments in Sec. 18.5 to the effect that the product $g(t^*)(t_1 - t_0)$, where $t_0 \leqslant t^* \leqslant t_1$, approximates the probability for the next rainstorm to occur during a short subinterval $[t_0, t_1]$.

(c) Note that if the next rainstorm occurs at some time t^*, the water remaining in the reservoir just prior to the storm will be

$$f(t^*) = \begin{cases} 10^8 - 10^6 t^* & \text{if } 0 \leqslant t^* \leqslant 100, \\ 0 & \text{if } t^* \geqslant 100. \end{cases}$$

What "average output" can you assign for the function f relative to the "density" $g(t)$—and in the spirit of the integral (7) of Sec. 18.5?

*10. Factories often use the same kind of "statistical test" for the proper functioning of machines which I described in Example 1 of Sec. 18.5 in connection with a typist's misprints—because occurrences of machine errors often seem to have the same probabilistic properties as occurrences of misprints, telephone calls, and meteorites. Suppose, for example, that while functioning normally a machine produces only one faulty unit per hour, on the average; but that when the machine's adjustment screws loosen up, it tends to produce an average of 10 defectives per hour. Suppose that an inspector samples the stream of units coming from the machine and notices a defective.

(a) For what minimal time T should he continue to check the machine's output, and find it free of defectives, before he can conclude that the machine is in fact working normally— and can leave the scene with the "confidence" that the chances of his being in error are only 0.05?

Suggestion: If he is in error, and the machine is working *abnormally*, what is the probability that the next defective will appear after a time t? And for what value $t = T$ will that probability be reduced to 0.05?

(b) Suppose that the inspector decides upon an inspection period of length T as in part (a), and that during the period another defective unit does appear. He'll have to call technicians to examine the machine's adjustments, perhaps disrupting the production. What are the chances that the machine is working normally anyway?

**11. With reference to the accident data in Problem 6, what are the chances of having *exactly one* major accident on the given stretch of highway during the second week of January, 1971?

On the basis of several probabilistic assumptions about meteorite arrivals, I found (in Sec. 16.1) a differential equation for the probability—call it now $p_0(t)$—that there be *no* occurrences in an interval $[0, t)$. And I argued that $p_0(t) = e^{-\lambda t}$ was the only "solution" of that equation which also satisfied the reasonable "initial condition" $p_0(0) = 1$. In Sec. 18.4 I argued that we could interpret $1/\lambda$ as the average number of occurrences per unit time. Now I invite you to examine the probability of *exactly one* occurrence during $[0, t)$—call it $p_1(t)$—in a similar fashion:

(a) For $s < t$ and $t - s$ small, give probabilistic reasons why

$$p_1(t) = p_1(s) \cdot [1 - \lambda(t-s) - e(t-s) - m(t-s)] + p_0(s) \cdot [\lambda(t-s) + e(t-s)], \qquad (*)$$

where the functions $e(x)$ and $m(x)$ are as in Sec. 16.1.

(b) Show why (*) leads to the relationship

$$p_1'(t_0) = -\lambda p_1(t_0) + \lambda p_0(t_0) \qquad \text{at all } t_0 \geqslant 0. \qquad (**)$$

(c) Try to show that the differential equation

$$f'(t) = -\lambda f(t) + \lambda e^{-\lambda t} \qquad \text{for } t \geqslant 0, \qquad (***)$$

together with the *initial condition* $f(0) = 0$, must have a unique solution. Recall that $p_0(t) = e^{-\lambda t}$.

(d) Check that the product $e^{-\lambda t}\lambda t$ satisfies both (***) and the initial condition in part (c); hence that $p_1(t) = e^{-\lambda t}\lambda t$ for all $t \geqslant 0$.

12. As in Sec. 18.6, compute the balancing point ("center of gravity") for the system of weights indicated in the accompanying figure.

13. Compute the balancing point ("center of gravity" in the x direction) for a thin uniform vertical sheet of wood weighing $\frac{1}{4}$ ounce per square inch, and cut out as in the figure.

14. Suppose that you cut a vertical slice off a uniform solid ball, weighing w ounces per cubic inch, as in Fig. (i). Above what point on the axis can you suspend the remaining object so that it won't tip?

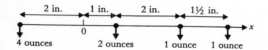

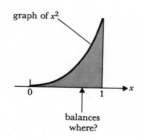

graph of x^2

balances where?

FIGURE (i)

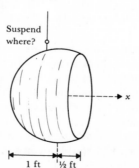

Suspend where?

1 ft   ½ ft

FIGURE (ii)

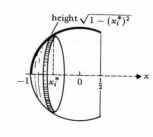

height $\sqrt{1 - (x_i^*)^2}$

Suggestion: Approximate the ball by thin vertical slabs, as in Fig. (ii), corresponding to small subintervals $[x_{i-1}, x_i]$ on the x axis. Calculate the weight m_i of each slab and think of it as located approximately x_i^* feet from $x = 0$. Find the center of gravity of such a system of weights, and then pick partitions $\{x_i\}$ with smaller and smaller meshes. To what limit do the corresponding centers of gravity tend?

15. Show that the operation of finding an "average output" of a function has the familiar properties of "scaling" and "addition"

$$[\text{av of } (cf)] = c[\text{av of } f], \tag{*}$$

and

$$[\text{av of } (f_1 + f_2)] = [\text{av of } f_1] + [\text{av of } f_2] \tag{**}$$

—in each of these three cases:

(a) The f's have finitely many inputs $x_1, x_2, \ldots, x_n$, each x_i having probability p_i, so that

$$\text{av } (f) = f(x_1)p_1 + f(x_2)p_2 + \cdots + f(x_n)p_n.$$

(b) The f's are defined (and continuous) on an interval $[a, b]$ all of whose inputs x are equally likely, so that

$$\text{av}(f) = \frac{1}{(b-a)} \int_a^b f(x)\, dx.$$

(c) The f's are defined (and continuous) on an interval $[a, b]$ where the total probability distribution can be described by a (continuous) density function $g(x)$, so that we might define

$$\text{av}(f) = \int_a^b f(x)g(x)\, dx. \text{ (Here } \int_a^b g(x)\, dx = 1.\text{)}$$

16. Can you build an arching tower of dominos that will lean horizontally *as far as you please?*

Suggestions: Using dominos of weight w and length L, build the tower from the *top down*, as in the figure. Let c_n denote the center of gravity of the first n dominos together.

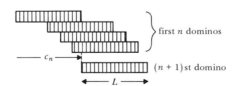

(a) Show that ideally you can place an $(n+1)$st domino beneath the first n so as to have

$$c_{n+1} = \frac{(nw)c_n + w(c_n + \tfrac{1}{2}L)}{(n+1)w}.$$

(To be safe, you might actually place the domino slightly to the left.)

(b) Show that

$$c_n = \frac{1}{2}L\left(1 + \frac{1}{2} + \frac{1}{3} + \cdots + \frac{1}{n}\right).$$

(c) Do the numbers c_n increase without bound? Compare

$$1 + \tfrac{1}{2} + \tfrac{1}{3} + \tfrac{1}{4} + \tfrac{1}{5} + \tfrac{1}{6} + \tfrac{1}{7} + \tfrac{1}{8} + \tfrac{1}{9} + \tfrac{1}{10} + \tfrac{1}{11} + \tfrac{1}{12} + \tfrac{1}{13} + \tfrac{1}{14} + \tfrac{1}{15} + \tfrac{1}{16}$$

with

$$1 + \tfrac{1}{2} + (\tfrac{1}{4} + \tfrac{1}{4}) + (\tfrac{1}{8} + \tfrac{1}{8} + \tfrac{1}{8} + \tfrac{1}{8}) + (\tfrac{1}{16} + \tfrac{1}{16} + \tfrac{1}{16} + \tfrac{1}{16} + \tfrac{1}{16} + \tfrac{1}{16} + \tfrac{1}{16} + \tfrac{1}{16})$$

and so on.

18.9 CHANGE OF VARIABLES

For help in evaluating definite integrals let's ask how they behave with respect to *composition* of functions, $h(x) = g(f(x))$. In Fig. 18-18 I've sketched one of the simplest cases: $f(x) = mx + s$ is an increasing *linear* function on an interval $[a, b]$; and $g(y)$ is a positive *constant* function on the range of f, the interval $[A, B]$ where $A = f(a) = ma + s$ and $B = f(b) = mb + s$. The composition $h(x) = g(f(x))$ will be constant on the original x interval $[a, b]$. You can think of the composition $g(f(x))$ as the result of a *"change or substitution of input variables"*, $f(x)$ replacing y as an input for g.

FIGURE 18-18

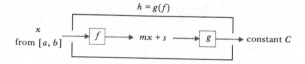

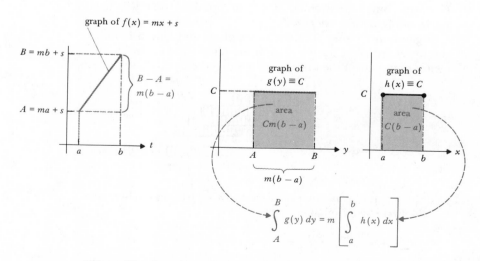

What this change accomplishes in Fig. 18-18 is a change of scale between the x interval $[a, b]$ and the y interval $[A, B]$—by an

amount m which is just the slope (or "magnification factor") of the linear substitution function $f(x)$, $m \equiv f'(x)$. The result is a magnification of areas by the same amount m:

$$\int_A^B g(y)\,dy = m \int_a^b h(x)\,dx. \tag{1}$$

In this simple case we can also write the relationship (1) completely in terms of f and g, as

$$\int_{f(a)}^{f(b)} g(y)\,dy = m \int_a^b g(f(x))\,dx = \int_a^b g(f(x)m\,dx,$$

or

$$\boxed{\int_{f(a)}^{f(b)} g(y)\,dy = \int_a^b g(f(x))f'(x)\,dx.} \tag{2}$$

Need some relationship such as (2) hold for more general functions, where $f'(x)$ and $g(y)$ are not constant? Look at the f and g of Fig. 18-19.

FIGURE 18-19

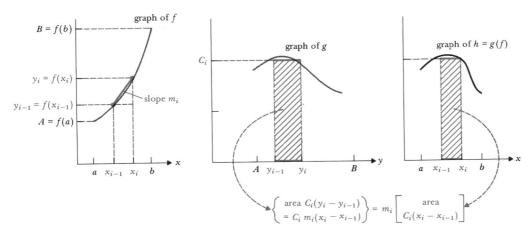

If f is smooth enough, shouldn't we be able to approximate its graph over a tiny subinterval $[x_{i-1}, x_i]$ by the graph of a linear function with some slope m_i? And if g is smooth enough, shouldn't we be able to approximate its graph over the corresponding inverval between $y_{i-1} = f(x_{i-1})$ and $y_i = f(x_i)$ by a constant height C_i? And won't the composition $h(x) = g(f(x))$ then be approximately equal to C_i for x in $[x_{i-1}, x_i]$? If so, might we not again expect corresponding areas to have the relation

$$\int_{y_{i-1}}^{y_i} g(y)\,dy = m_i \int_{x_{i-1}}^{x_i} h(x)\,dx \quad \text{(approximately)}$$

$$= \int_{x_{i-1}}^{x_i} g(f(x))f'(x)\,dx \quad \text{(approximately)?} \tag{3}$$

And provided approximation errors don't accumulate too much, couldn't we add equalities such as (3) over many adjacent subintervals to get

$$\int_A^B g(y)\,ay = \int_{y_0}^{y_1} g(y)\,dy + \int_{y_1}^{y_2} g(y)\,dy + \int_{y_2}^{y_3} g(y)\,dy + \cdots$$

$$\overset{\text{(approx)}}{=} \int_{x_0}^{x_1} g(f(x))f'(x)\,dx + \int_{x_1}^{x_2} g(f(x))f'(x)\,dx$$

$$+ \int_{x_2}^{x_3} g(f(x))f'(x)\,dx + \cdots$$

$$= \int_a^b g(f(x))f'(x)\,dx? \qquad (4)$$

Thus, a

Conjecture: the relationship

$$\int_{f(a)}^{f(b)} g(y)\,dy = \int_a^b g(f(x))f'(x)\,dx \qquad (2)$$

might hold for very general functions f and g—as long as $f(x)$, $f'(x)$, and $g(y)$ are all continuous, so that the integrals do exist.

If the conjecture is correct, here is how we can use it:

EXAMPLE 1. To evaluate $\int_0^3 e^{x^2/2} \cdot x\,dx$, let's make the substitution $y = f(x) = \frac{1}{2}x^2$. f is an increasing function on $[0,3]$ with $f(0) = 0$, $f(3) = \frac{1}{2}3^2 = \frac{9}{2}$, and $f'(x) = x$. Thus

$$e^{x^2/2} \cdot x = e^{f(x)}f'(x) = g(f(x))f'(x), \qquad (5)$$

where $g(y) = e^y$. By (2) we should have

$$\int_0^{9/2} e^y\,dy = \int_0^3 e^{x^2/2}x\,dx \qquad (6)$$

since $(e^y)' = e^y$. We can conclude that

$$\int_0^3 e^{x^2/2}x\,dx = \int_0^{9/2} e^y\,dy = [e^y]_0^{9/2} = e^{9/2} - e^0 = e^{9/2} - 1.$$

In (6) the _left-hand_ integral was easier to calculate than the right-hand one. In some cases it's the other way around:

EXAMPLE 2. Let's check to see whether the area of a circle of unit radius is indeed $\pi 1^2 = \pi$ when calculated by definite integrals. As I've indicated in Fig. 18-20 we can approximate $\frac{1}{4}$th the area of the circle by a sum of areas of approximating rectangles:

$$S(\sigma) = \sqrt{1 - (x_1^*)^2}(x_1 - x_0) + \sqrt{1 - (x_2^*)^2}(x_2 - x_1)$$
$$+ \sqrt{1 - (x_3^*)^2}(x_3 - x_2) + \cdots \qquad (7)$$

Since the function $g(x) = \sqrt{1 - x^2}$ is continuous for x in $[0,1]$, this sum $S(\sigma)$ should converge to $\int_0^1 \sqrt{1 - x^2}\,dx$ as we pick partitions $\sigma = \{x_i\}$ with smaller and smaller mesh. The problem remains to evaluate $\int_0^1 \sqrt{1 - x^2}\,dx$. If we knew an antiderivative for $g(x) = \sqrt{1 - x^2}$ we could settle the matter directly. But we haven't met

FIGURE 18-20

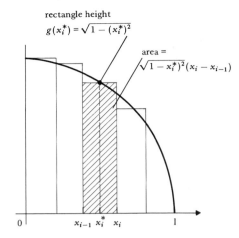

rectangle height
$$g(x_i^*) = \sqrt{1 - (x_i^*)^2}$$

area =
$$\sqrt{1 - x_i^*)^2}(x_i - x_{i-1})$$

0 x_{i-1} x_i^* x_i 1

one before—although you may recall that the reciprocal expression $1/\sqrt{1-x^2}$ has arcsin x as an antiderivative. Where else might you have seen the form $\sqrt{1-x^2}$?

Free associate.

How about among trigonometric functions? $\cos u = \sqrt{1 - \sin^2 u}$. With just this bit of a hunch to go by, let's define $f(u) = \sin u$ for u in $[0, \pi/2]$. Then we'll have $f(0) = \sin 0 = 0, f(\pi/2) = \sin \pi/2 = 1$, and $f'(u) = (\sin u)' = \cos u$. And we'll be able to write

$$g(f(u))f'(u) = \sqrt{1 - (\sin u)^2}\, \cos u$$

$$= (\cos u)^2. \tag{8}$$

If the conjecture (2) is true, with the roles of y and x now played by x and u, we can conclude that

$$\int_0^1 \sqrt{1-x^2}\, dx = \int_0^1 g(x)\, dx = \int_0^{\pi/2} g(f(u))f'(u)\, du$$

$$= \int_0^{\pi/2} (\cos u)^2\, du. \tag{9}$$

This time, the *rightmost* integral is easiest to evaluate: if we write $(\cos u)^2 = \frac{1}{2} + \frac{1}{2}\cos 2u$, as I did in Example 1 of Sec. 18.9, we can get

$$\int_0^{\pi/2} (\cos u)^2\, du = \int_0^{\pi/2} \frac{1}{2}\, du + \frac{1}{2}\int_0^{\pi/2} \cos 2u\, du$$

$$= \frac{1}{2}\frac{\pi}{2} + \frac{1}{2}\left[\frac{\sin 2u}{2}\right]_0^{\pi/2} = \frac{\pi}{4} + \frac{\sin 2\,(\pi/2)}{4} - \frac{\sin 0}{4}$$

$$= \frac{\pi}{4} + \frac{\sin \pi}{4} - 0 = \frac{\pi}{4} + 0 - 0 = \frac{\pi}{4}. \tag{10}$$

Thus the area of $\frac{1}{4}$th of the circle is $\pi/4$, and that of the whole is π—as it should be.

In all the cases of the substitution formula

$$\int_{f(a)}^{f(b)} g(y)\,dy = \int_a^b g(f(x))f'(x)\,dx \tag{11}$$

which I've discussed so far, the function f defining the change of variables has been increasing. But what if it were not? What if $f(b)$ $< f(a)$? What meaning could we then assign to the left-hand symbol in (11), with its upper end point $B = f(b)$ *less* than its lower $A = f(a)$?

Let's look again at a simple case: say, $f(x) = -x$ on $[-1, 1]$, and $g(y) = C$ (some positive constant) for all y. Then $f(-1) = 1, f(1) = -1, f'(x) \equiv -1$ on $[-1, 1]$ and $g(f(x)) \equiv C$ on $[-1, 1]$. So if (2) *were to hold in this case*, we would have to have

$$\int_1^{-1} C\,dy = \int_{f(a)}^{f(b)} g(y)\,dy = \int_a^b g(f(x))f'(x)\,dx$$

$$= \int_{-1}^1 C(-1)\,dx$$

$$= -\int_{-1}^1 C\,dx. \tag{12}$$

Here $\int_{-1}^1 C\,dx$ is the area of a rectangle with $[-1, 1]$ as base and of height C. Since approximating rectangles figured so strongly in the definition of the definite integral, would you be willing to extend (12) to a general definition regarding end points $B < A$?

Definition I: If $F(x)$ is given on an interval $[B, A]$, where $B < A$, and if $\int_B^A F(x)\,dx$ exists, then define the symbol

$$\int_A^B F(x)\,dx \quad \text{to mean} \quad -\int_B^A F(x)\,dx. \tag{13}$$

We might further interpret this definition by forming approximating sums for $\int_A^B F(x)\,dx$ with partitions labeled in *right-to-left order*, $\tilde{\sigma} = \{B = x_n < x_{n-1} < \cdots < x_1 < x_0 = A\}$, as in Fig. 18-21. For a continuous F, such sums will converge to $-\int_B^A F(x)\,dx$.

FIGURE 18-21(a)

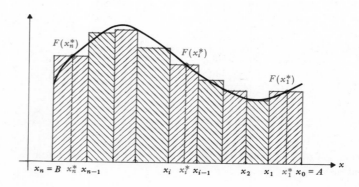

FIGURE 18-21(b)

$$S(\widetilde{\sigma}) = \quad F(x_1^*)(x_1 - x_0) + F(x_2^*)(x_2 - x_1) + \cdots + F(x_n^*)(x_n - x_{n-1})$$
$$= \quad -[F(x_n^*)(x_{n-1} - x_n) + \cdots + F(x_2^*)(x_1 - x_2) + F(x_1^*)(x_0 - x_1)]$$

as mesh of $\widetilde{\sigma}$
tends to zero

$$\int_A^B F(x)\, dx = -\int_B^A F(x)\, dx$$

Note that with the notion of $\int_a^b F\, dx$ extended as in Definition A, we'll have

$$\int_a^b F\, dx + \int_b^a F\, dx = 0 = \int_a^a F\, dx \tag{14}$$

for any a and b, a relationship which fits in nicely with the "extreme case $(a = b)$" and with the "adjacent intervals" properties (I and IV) of the basic Theorem F on definite integrals in Sec. 18.1. In fact, *all* the properties in that theorem still hold for the extended notion $\int_a^b F\, dx$ (with reversed inequality signs in III and VII if $b < a$). I invite you to check this claim, in doing Problem 4 of the next section. Moreover, the "fundamental theorem" G of Sec. 18.1 still holds: $[\int_a^x f(t)\, dt]' = f(t)$. This is because Definition I merely introduces a minus sign—which will cancel suitably when we form difference ratios. For example, if $x_1 < x_2 \le a$, then

$$\frac{\int_a^{x_2} f(t)\, dt - \int_a^{x_1} f(t)\, dt}{x_2 - x_1} = \frac{-\int_{x_2}^a f(t)\, dt - \left[-\int_{x_1}^a f(t)\, dt\right]}{x_2 - x_1}$$

$$= \frac{\int_{x_1}^a f(t) - \int_{x_2}^a f(t)\, dt}{x_2 - x_1}$$

$$= \frac{\int_{x_1}^{x_2} f(t)\, dt + \int_{x_2}^a f(t)\, dt - \int_{x_2}^a f(t)\, dt}{x_2 - x_1}$$

$$= \frac{\int_{x_1}^{x_2} f(t)\, dt}{x_2 - x_1} \quad = f'(t) \tag{15}$$

just as before, in the proof of the "fundamental theorem." (Do Problem 5 of the next section.)

With $\int_A^B g(y)\, dy$ now definable for $B < A$ as well as for $B \geqslant A$, here's a precise version of the previous conjecture:

Theorem H (on "change of variables"): Suppose that f is any function which is defined, and which has a continuous derivative function f', on an interval $[a, b]$. And suppose that $g(y)$ is a function continuous on the range of f. Then

$$\int_{f(a)}^{f(b)} g(y)\, dy = \int_a^b g(f(x))f'(x)\, dx. \tag{16}$$

We might follow alternate approaches to

A proof of theorem H: In Fig. 18-22 I've outlined an argument involving approximating sums for both integrals in (16): it carries forward the ideas of Fig. 18-19 for a *strictly increasing* function f.

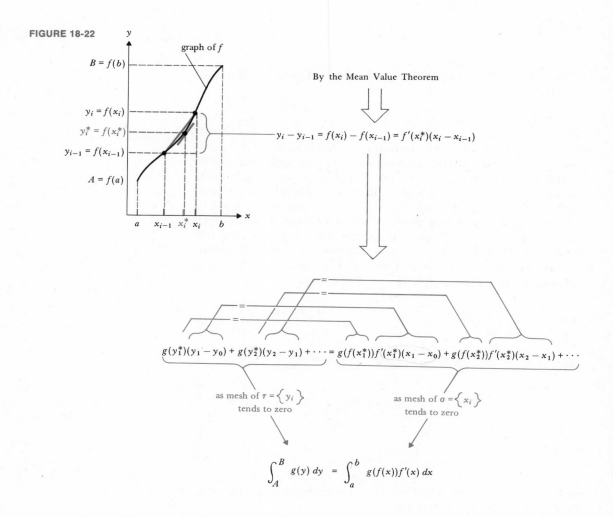

FIGURE 18-22

(Why must the mesh of $\{y_i\}$ tend to zero as the mesh of $\{x_i\}$ does? Because for any i,

$$|y_i - y_{i-1}| = |f'(x_i^*)||x_i - x_{i-1}|$$

$$\leq M|x_i - x_{i-1}|, \tag{17}$$

where M is the maximum of the continuous function $|f'(x)|$ on $[a, b]$.)

Now here's a second argument which doesn't require f to be increasing. It depends instead on the "chain rule" for derivatives — which is the key result so far on composition of functions, and on the "fundamental theorem" G of Sec. 18.1 — which relates derivatives to integrals. The idea is to replace the right-hand end point b in (16) by a "variable" input u, and to show that

$$\int_{f(a)}^{f(u)} g(y)\,dy = \int_a^u g(f(x))f'(x)\,dx \qquad \text{for all } u \text{ in } [a,b]. \tag{18}$$

The assertion in (16) will then appear for the special case $u = b$.

Regarding the left-hand side of (18), we're supposing that f' is continuous on $[a,b]$. Hence f will be also; and its range must contain every number y between m and M, the absolute minimum and the absolute maximum of f on $[a,b]$ — by the "intermediate value theorem" (Theorem A) of Sec. 13.1. Thus we can rephrase our hypothesis on g to say that g is defined and continuous on the interval $[m,M]$. And for any number z in $[m,M]$, it makes sense to talk about the quantity $G(z) = \int_{f(a)}^z g(y)\,dy$ (using Definition A if $z < f(a)$). Note that we can write the left-hand side of (18) as a composition $G(f(u))$. By the chain rule it must have derivative

$$G'(f(u_0))f'(u_0) \qquad \text{at any } u_0 \text{ in } [a,b]. \tag{19}$$

Here

$$G'(f(u_0)) = \left[\int_{f(a)}^z g(y)\,dy\right]'_{\text{at } z_0 \,=\, f(u_0)} = g(f(u_0)), \tag{20}$$

by the "fundamental theorem" G. But by the same Theorem G, the right-hand side of (18) has derivative

$$\left[\int_a^x g(f(x))f'(x)\,dx\right]'_{\text{at } u_0} = g(f(u_0))f'(u_0). \tag{21}$$

Compare (19) and (20) against (21) to see that *both sides of* (18) *have the same derivative at each* u_0 *in* $[a,b]$. Note further that both sides of (18) have the same value 0 when $u = a$. *Conclusion:* both sides of (18) are identical for all u in $[a,b]$ — by the "neck-and-neck race argument" of Sec. 15.9.   End of the proof.

Now try your hand at using the substitution idea to simplify and evaluate some of the integrals in the next section.

18.10 PROBLEMS ON CHANGE OF VARIABLES

°1. Use the "change of variables" method of Sec. 18.9 to evaluate the following definite integrals.

(a) $\displaystyle\int_1^e (\log_e x)^3 \frac{1}{x}\,dx.$

Sample reasoning: Note that if we let $y = f(x) = \log_e x$, then $f(1) = 0, f(e) = 1$, and $f'(x) = 1/x$. Hence, letting $g(y) = y^3$ we can write

$$\int_1^e (\log_e x)^3 \frac{1}{x} \, dx = \int_1^e g(f(x)) f'(x) \, dx = \int_{f(1)}^{f(e)} g(y) \, dy$$

$$= \int_0^1 y^3 \, dy = \left[\frac{y^4}{4} \right]_0^1 = \frac{1^4}{4} - \frac{0^4}{4} = \frac{1}{4}.$$

(b) $\displaystyle\int_0^1 \frac{3x^2}{\sqrt{x^3+1}} \, dx$

(c) $\displaystyle\int_0^1 \frac{5x^2}{\sqrt{x^3+1}} \, dx$ (d) $\displaystyle\int_1^2 \frac{1}{(1+\log_e x)^2} \frac{1}{x} \, dx$

(e) $\displaystyle\int_1^2 \frac{1}{1+(\log_e x)^2} \frac{1}{x} \, dx$ (Suggestion: recall arctan y.)

(f) $\displaystyle\int_{\pi/4}^{\pi/2} \frac{\cos x}{(1+\sin x)^2} \, dx$ (g) $\displaystyle\int_{\pi/4}^{\pi/2} \frac{\cos x}{1+(\sin x)^2} \, dx$

(h) $\displaystyle\int_0^1 \frac{e^x}{(1+e^x)^2} \, dx$ (i) $\displaystyle\int_0^1 \frac{e^x}{1+e^{2x}} \, dx$

(j) $\displaystyle\int_0^1 \frac{x}{x^2+2x+2} \, dx$

Sample reasoning: Let's try to transform the numerator algebraically so that it will have the form $f'(x) = 2x+2$ where $f(x) = x^2+2x+2$, the denominator term. Write $x = \frac{1}{2}(2x) = \frac{1}{2}(2x+2-2) = \frac{1}{2}(2x+2) - 1$.

Then

$$\int_0^1 \frac{x}{x^2+2x+2} \, dx = \frac{1}{2} \int_0^1 \frac{2x+2}{x^2+2x+1} \, dx - \int_0^1 \frac{1}{(x+1)^2+1} \, dx.$$

In the first integral on the right-hand side, let

$$y = f(x) = x^2+2x+1 \quad \text{and} \quad g(y) = \frac{1}{y}$$

as planned; in the second, let $y = f(x) = x+1$ and $g(y) = 1/(y^2+1)$.

(k) $\displaystyle\int_0^1 \frac{x-1}{x+1} \, dx$

(l) $\displaystyle\int_1^5 \frac{-x+2}{x^2+3x+10} \, dx$

(m) $\displaystyle\int_0^1 \frac{2x+1}{3x^2+6x+5} \, dx$

°2. Evaluate the following integrals

(a) $\int_0^1 \sqrt{4-x^2}\,dx$

(Suggestion: let $x = f(u) = 2\sin u$, and proceed as in Example 3 of Sec. 18.9.)

(b) $\int_0^1 \sqrt{2x-x^2}\,dx$

(Suggestion: write $2x - x^2 = 1 - (1 - 2x + x^2)$.)

(c) $\int_0^1 (x^2+1)^{-3/2}\,dx$.

Sample reasoning: Let $x = f(u) = \tan u$. Then $x^2 + 1 = (\tan u)^2 + 1 = (\sec u)^2 = [1/(\cos u)]^2$; and also $f(0) = 0$, $f(\pi/4) = 1$, and $f'(u) = (\sec u)^2 = 1/(\cos u)^2$. Thus

$$\int_0^1 (x^2+1)^{-3/2}\,dx = \int_0^{\pi/4} [f(u)^2 + 1]^{-3/2} f'(u)\,du$$

$$= \int_0^{\pi/4} [(\sec u)^2]^{-3/2} (\sec u)^2\,du$$

$$= \int_0^{\pi/4} \cos u\,du$$

$$= [\sin u]_0^{\pi/4} = \sin\frac{\pi}{4} - 0 = \frac{\sqrt{2}}{2}.$$

(d) $\int_{-1}^0 (x^2+2x+2)^{-3/2}\,dx$

(e) $\int_1^e (x^2+2x+2)^{-3/2}\,dx$

(f) $\int_0^1 (e^{2x} + 2e^x + 2)^{-3/2} e^x\,dx$

3. You might recall from doing Problem 16(e) of Sec. 18.2 that we can represent the length of the graph of x^2 for x in $[0, 1]$ by the integral $\int_0^1 \sqrt{1+4x^2}\,dx$. In Problem 30(a) of the same section I suggested that you try to approximate the quantity. Now let's try to evaluate it precisely.

(a) Let $x = f(u) = \frac{1}{2}\tan u$ for $0 \le u \le u_0 = \arctan 2$. Recall that

$$1 + (\tan u)^2 = (\sec u)^2 = \frac{1}{(\cos u)^2}$$

and that $(\tan u)' = (\sec u)^2$; and show that

$$\int_0^1 \sqrt{1+4x^2}\,dx = \frac{1}{2}\int_0^{u_0} \frac{1}{(\cos u)^3}\,du$$

$$= \frac{1}{2}\int_0^{u_0} \frac{\cos u}{(\cos u)^4}\,du$$

$$= \frac{1}{2}\int_0^{u_0} \frac{\cos u}{(1-\sin^2 u)^2}\,du.$$

(b) Make a further change of variables to show that

$$\frac{1}{2} \int_0^{u_0} \frac{\cos u}{(1 - \sin^2 u)^2} \, du = \frac{1}{2} \int_0^{2/\sqrt{5}} \frac{1}{(1 - v^2)^2} \, dv. \qquad (*)$$

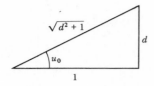

(Note from the figure that if $\tan u_0 = d$, then $\sin u_0 = d/\sqrt{d^2 + 1}$.)

(c) Check that

$$\frac{1}{(1 - v^2)^2} = \frac{1}{4}\left[\frac{1}{(1 - v)^2} + \frac{1}{1 - v} + \frac{1}{(1 + v)^2} + \frac{1}{1 + v}\right] \qquad (**)$$

for all $v \neq \pm 1$. (In the next chapter you'll find a standard method for arriving at such identities.)

(d) Substitute (**) into the right-hand integral of (*) and complete the evaluation.

4. Check that all the properties of the definite integral listed in Theorem F of Sec. 18.1 still hold with the definition extended to mean $\int_a^b f(x) \, dx = -\int_b^a f(x) \, dx$ when $b < a$ (—provided we reverse the inequality signs in parts III and VII of Theorem F when $b < a$).

*5. Check that the "fundamental theorem" (Theorem G) of Sec. 18.2 still holds when the definition of integral is extended to mean

$$\int_a^b f(x) \, dx = -\int_b^a f(x) \, dx \quad \text{if } b < a.$$

18.11 SUMMARY OF CHAPTER 18

All the results in Chapter 17 on areas under graphs of nonnegative continuous functions extend more generally to arbitrary continuous functions—yielding a new quantity, the "definite integral":

Theorem (on the existence of the "definite integral"): Suppose that f is a continuous function on an interval $[a, b]$. Then there exists a *unique number*—label it $\int_a^b f(x) \, dx$ and call it the *definite integral of f from a to b*—with the following properties:

I. *The extreme case $a = b$:* $\int_a^a f(x) \, dx = 0$.

II. *Approximating sums:* Given a partition $\sigma = \{x_i\}$ of the interval $[a, b]$, choose some input x_i^* from each subinterval $[x_{i-1}, x_i]$ of σ and form the sum

$$S_\sigma(f) = f(x_1^*)(x_1 - x_0) + f(x_2^*)(x_2 - x_1) + f(x_3^*)(x_3 - x_2) + \cdots, \qquad (1)$$

one term corresponding to each subinterval $[x_{i-1}, x_i]$. If $\sigma_1, \sigma_2, \sigma_3, \ldots$ is a sequence of such partitions *with meshes tending to zero*, and if S_{σ_n} are corresponding sums as in (1) (where the x_i's and x_i^*'s depend on n), then

$$\lim_{n \to \infty} S_{\sigma_n}(f) = \int_a^b f(x) \, dx. \qquad (2)$$

III. *Lower and upper bounds.* Given any partition $\sigma = \{x_i\}$, let $S_\sigma^{min}(f)$ denote the sum in (1) when $f(x_i^*) =$ the minimum output of f on $[x_{i-1}, x_i]$ for each i, and let $S_\sigma^{max}(f)$ denote the sum in (1) when $f(x_i^*) =$ the maximum output of f on $[x_{i-1}, x_i]$ for each i. Then

$$S_\sigma^{min}(f) \le \int_a^b f(x)\, dx \le S_\sigma^{max}(f). \tag{3}$$

In particular,

$$m(b-a) \le \int_a^b f(x)\, dx \le M(b-a), \tag{4}$$

where m denotes the absolute minimum of f on $[a, b]$ and M denotes its absolute maximum.

IV. *Adjacent intervals:* If $a \le c \le b$, then

$$\int_a^b f(x)\, dx = \int_a^c f(x)\, dx + \int_c^b f(x)\, dx. \tag{5}$$

V. *Scaling:* If c is any constant, then

$$\int_a^b cf(x)\, dx = c \int_a^b f(x)\, dx. \tag{6}$$

VI. *Adding functions:* If g is another continuous function on $[a, b]$, then

$$\int_a^b [f(x) + g(x)]\, dx = \int_a^b f(x)\, dx + \int_a^b g(x)\, dx. \tag{7}$$

VII. *Comparing functions:* If g is continuous on $[a, b]$ and $f(x) \le g(x)$ for all x in $[a, b]$, then

$$\int_a^b f(x)\, dx \le \int_a^b g(x)\, dx. \tag{8}$$

VIII. *A constant function:* If $f(x) = C$ for all x in $[a, b]$ then

$$\int_a^b f(x)\, dx = C(b-a). \tag{9}$$

(Sec. 18.1)

Definition: If $f(x)$ is given on an interval $[b, a]$ where $b < a$, and if $\int_b^a f(x)\, dx$ exists, then define

$$\int_a^b f(x)\, dx = - \int_b^a f(x)\, dx.$$

(Sec. 18.9)

Remark. With $\int_a^b f$ extended as in this definition all the results (1)–(9) above still hold, except with reversed signs in (3) and (8) when $b < a$. (Sec. 18.9 and Problem 4 of Sec. 18.10)

Theorem (the "fundamental theorem of the integral calculus"): Suppose that $a < b$ and that f is any continuous function on the interval $[a, b]$. Define a new function F on $[a, b]$ by forming

$$F(x) = \int_a^x f(t)\, dt, \qquad \text{for each } x \text{ in } [a, b]. \tag{10}$$

Then

$$F'(x_0) = f(x_0) \qquad \text{at each } x_0 \text{ in } [a, b]. \tag{11}$$

That is, F is an antiderivative of f—with $F(a) = 0$ and $F(b) = \int_a^b f(t)\,dt$. More generally, if G is *any* antiderivative of f on $[a, b]$, then

$$G(b) - G(a) = \int_a^b f(t)\,dt. \tag{12}$$

More specifically: if a given function $g(x)$ has a continuous derivative $g'(x)$ on $[a, b]$, then

$$g(b) - g(a) = \int_a^b g'(t)\,dt. \tag{13}$$

(Sec. 18.1)

For an extension to functions with some discontinuities, see Sec. 18.2, Problem 33.

Remark. The results (10)–(13) hold also for the case $b < a$ and intervals $[b, a]$. See Sec. 18.9 and Problem 5 of Sec. 18.10.

A corollary: Every continuous function has an antiderivative.
(Sec. 18.1)

For the derivative of a function of the form $h(t) = \int_a^{f(t)} g(x)\,dx$, see Sec. 18.2, Problem 22.

For a "mean value theorem for integrals," see Sec. 18.2, Problem 32.

Theorem (on "change of variables"): Suppose that f is any function which is defined, and which has a continuous derivative f', on an interval $[a, b]$. And suppose that g is a function continuous on the range of f. Then

$$\int_{f(a)}^{f(b)} g(y)\,dy = \int_a^b g(f(x))f'(x)\,dx.$$

(Sec. 18.9)

Applications of the definite integral

To volumes: Sec. 18.1 and Sec. 18.2, Problems 3–7.
To total investment earnings: Sec. 18.1 and Sec. 18.2, Problems 8–10.
To "work": Sec. 18.2, Problems 11–14, 17.
To "length" of curves: Sec. 18.2, Problems 16–18.
To "surface area": Sec. 18.2, Problem 20.
To "pressure": Sec. 18.2, Problems 21–23.
To averages of functions; and in particular, growth of organisms: Sec. 18.3.
To average time between telephone calls: Sec. 18.4.
To "density functions": Sec. 18.5 and Sec. 18.6.
To a statistical "decision problem": Sec. 18.5.
To "centers of gravity": Sec. 18.6.
To "tuning" of signals: Sec. 18.7.

Regarding "improper integrals" of the form

$$\text{"}\int_a^\infty f(x)\,dx\text{"} = \lim_{b \to \infty} \int_a^b f(x)\,dx,$$

see Problem 15 of Sec. 18.2.

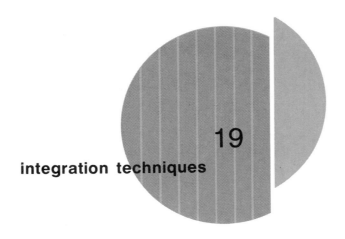

19

integration techniques

Nowadays electronic computers are often used to calculate an approximating sum for a definite integral that would otherwise be difficult to evaluate exactly. But such computers are expensive to use, and still not widely available. Moreover, they require specific values for all constants in a given problem; and they don't *directly* expose the relationship between these values and the calculated approximating sum. For these reasons people still find themselves trying to evaluate certain definite integrals exactly. To aid in such calculations, long tables have been compiled, some giving explicit formulas for many integrals $\int_\alpha^\beta f(x)\, dx$ in terms of the constants defining f and the interval end points α and β, some giving antiderivatives of f's—from which the integrals can be derived. But even such tables can't be all-inclusive. One may have to manipulate a given integral into a simpler form—or break it into simpler parts—which one can then find treated in the tables. In the following sections I've collected together a number of such manipulations—they can't handle all cases. I invite you to examine some of the items in the list, especially in conjunction with the several concrete examples. Even when not faced with practical needs, some people view the simplification and evaluation of definite integrals as a sort of challenging game—like doing crossword puzzles.

In Sec. 19.15, I'll show how one of these techniques leads to a common method, "Taylor's formula," for approximating the values of many functions.

19.1 BASIS OF PRINCIPLES FOR EVALUATING INTEGRALS

In all cases, the integration is to be performed only over intervals $[\alpha, \beta]$ where the functions involved make sense.

First, here are four key principles:

I. *The basic properties regarding scaling and addition* (from Sec. 18.1):

$$\int_\alpha^\beta cf(x)\, dx = c\int_\alpha^\beta f(x)\, dx,$$
$$\int_\alpha^\beta (f+g)\, dx = \int_\alpha^\beta f\, dx + \int_\alpha^\beta g\, dx.$$

II. *The "fundamental theorem"* (of Sec. 18.1): if F is any antiderivative of f, then

$$\int_\alpha^\beta f(x)\, dx = [F(x)]_\alpha^\beta = F(\beta) - F(\alpha).$$

III. *"Change of variables"* (from Sec. 18.9):

$$\int_{f(\alpha)}^{f(\beta)} g(y)\, dy = \int_\alpha^\beta g(f(x))f'(x)\, dx.$$

Try "change of variables," letting $y = f(x)$, in specific cases when you have to evaluate the left-hand integral and the right-hand integral promises to be simpler. To aid the memory, note that in going from left to right

y *becomes* $f(x)$,

$g(y)$ *becomes* $g(f(x))$,

and symbolically

dy *becomes* $f'(x)\, dx$.

Go from *right to left* when you can recognize a given integral as having the right-hand form and when the left-hand integral promises to be simpler.

IV. *"Integration by parts"*: In Sec. 15.10 I discussed the ("anti-differentiation by parts") relationship:

an antiderivative of $f'g = fg - $ an antiderivative of fg'.

Via principles II and I this equation leads to the following relation between definite integrals—called "integration by parts":

$$\int_\alpha^\beta f'(x)g(x)\, dx = [f(x)g(x)]_\alpha^\beta - \int_\alpha^\beta f(x)g'(x)\, dx.$$

Use this method whenever you can recognize a given integral as having the form on the left-hand side and when the integral on the right promises to be simpler.

EXAMPLE 1. $\int_0^{\pi/2} x \cos x \, dx$. If we think of $\cos x$ as $f'(x)$, where $f(x) = \sin x$; and if we let $g(x) = x$, so that $g'(x) = 1$; then we'll have

$$\int_0^{\pi/2} (\cos x) x \, dx = [(\sin x)x]_0^{\pi/2} - \int_0^{\pi/2} (\sin x) 1 \, dx$$

$$= \left(\sin \frac{\pi}{2}\right)\frac{\pi}{2} - 0 - [-\cos x]_0^{\pi/2}$$

$$= \frac{\pi}{2} - 1.$$

Next, here are

V. *Specific results from earlier work with antiderivatives* (from Secs. 15.10 and 16.10):

(a) $\displaystyle\int_a^\beta x^p \, dx = \left[\frac{1}{p+1}x^{p+1}\right]_\alpha^\beta$ $(p \neq -1)$

(b) $\displaystyle\int_a^\beta \frac{1}{x} \, dx = [\log_e x]_\alpha^\beta$ $(\beta \geqslant \alpha > 0)$

(c) $\displaystyle\int_\alpha^\beta e^{ax} \, dx = \left[\frac{1}{a}e^{ax}\right]_\alpha^\beta$ $(a \neq 0)$

(d) $\displaystyle\int_\alpha^\beta \cos ax \, dx = \left[\frac{1}{a}\sin ax\right]_\alpha^\beta$ $(a \neq 0)$

$\displaystyle\int_\alpha^\beta \sin ax \, dx = -\left[\frac{1}{a}\cos ax\right]_\alpha^\beta$ $(a \neq 0)$

(e) $\displaystyle\int_\alpha^\beta \tan ax \, dx = \left[\frac{1}{a}\log \cos ax\right]_\alpha^\beta$ $(a \neq 0)$

(f) $\displaystyle\int_\alpha^\beta \frac{1}{(\cos ax)^2} \, dx = \left[\frac{1}{a}\tan ax\right]_\alpha^\beta$ $(a \neq 0)$

(g) $\displaystyle\int_\alpha^\beta \frac{1}{\sqrt{1-a^2x^2}} \, dx = \left[\frac{1}{a}\arcsin ax\right]_\alpha^\beta$ $(\alpha, \beta$ and a such that $a > 0$, $|a\alpha| < 1$, and $|a\beta| < 1)$

also $= -\left[\frac{1}{a}\arccos ax\right]_\alpha^\beta$

(h) $\displaystyle\int_\alpha^\beta \frac{1}{a^2x^2+1} \, dx = \left[\frac{1}{a}\arctan ax\right]_\alpha^\beta$ $(a \neq 0)$

(In this chapter, consider all logs as $\log_e$.)

The techniques in the rest of the chapter depend basically on the previous items I–V. The general procedure is to manipulate a given function *algebraically*, if necessary, so as to get it into a form whereby we can apply one or more of the basic principles I–IV—then to complete the evaluation via some already established results, such as in V. But first try your hand at the problems in the next section.

19.2 PROBLEMS

°1. Evaluate the following integrals (mainly via "change of variables," part III in Sec. 19.1):

(a) $\displaystyle\int_0^{1/4} \frac{dx}{\sqrt[3]{1-2x}}\,dx$ (b) $\displaystyle\int_1^2 \frac{\sec^2 2x}{\sqrt{\tan 2x}}\,dx$

(Recall that $(\tan u)' = (\sec u)^2$)

(c) $\displaystyle\int_{(\pi/4)^2}^{(\pi/2)^2} \frac{\sin\sqrt{x}}{\sqrt{x}}\,dx$

(d) $\displaystyle\int_{-1}^1 \frac{dy}{y^2+16}$

(Suggestion: let $y=f(x)=4x$, so that the denominator will become x^2+1 after factoring 16.)

(e) $\displaystyle\int_0^{\pi/4} (\cos 5x)^{-7}\tan 5x\,dx$

(f) $\displaystyle\int_0^{1/2} \frac{3\arcsin x}{\sqrt{1-x^2}}$ (g) $\displaystyle\int_1^3 \frac{(\log_e x)^3}{x}\,dx$

(h) $\displaystyle\int_0^{1/\sqrt{2}} \frac{x}{\sqrt{1-x^4}}\,dx$

(Suggestion: consider $y=f(x)=x^2$.)

(i) $\displaystyle\int_0^{\sqrt{2}} \frac{3x}{x^4+4}\,dx$

(j) $\displaystyle\int_0^{\pi/6} \sin^2 x\cos x\,dx$

*(k) $\displaystyle\int_{-1}^0 \frac{1}{\sqrt{-4x(x+2)}}\,dx$

°2. Evaluate the following integrals. (Where convenient, use "integration by parts," part IV of Sec. 19.1.)

(a) $\displaystyle\int_0^1 \arctan x\,dx$
(Suggestion: Let $f'(x)=1$ and $g(x)=\arctan x$.)

(b) $\displaystyle\int_{1/\sqrt{2}}^1 \arcsin x\,dx$

(c) $\displaystyle\int_1^e \cos(\log_e x)\,dx$

(d) $\displaystyle\int_0^{10} x\arctan x\,dx$

(e) $\displaystyle\int_0^1 \frac{x^3}{\sqrt{1+x^2}}\, dx$ (f) $\displaystyle\int_0^1 x^3\sqrt{1-x^2}\, dx$

19.3   TECHNIQUES FOR HANDLING POLYNOMIALS AND THEIR RECIPROCALS AND RATIOS

(a) Integrate any *polynomial* by integrating each term (via V(a) in Sec. 19.1) and adding (I).

(b) *The reciprocal of a power of a linear function,*

$$\int_\alpha^\beta \frac{1}{(ax+b)^n}\, dx.$$

It would be much easier to evaluate an integral of the form $\int_\alpha^\beta (1/y^n)\, dy$. To arrive at this form, let $g(y) = 1/y^n$, and consider the "change of variables" $y = f(x) = ax+b$. Then $f'(x) = a$. To get the form $g(f(x))f'(x)$ in III of Sec. 19.1, write

$$\frac{1}{(ax+b)^n} = \frac{1}{a}\frac{a}{(ax+b)^n} \qquad \text{(when } a \neq 0, n = 1, 2, 3, \ldots\text{)}.$$

Then

$$\int_\alpha^\beta \frac{1}{(ax+b)^n}\, dx = \frac{1}{a}\int_\alpha^\beta \frac{a}{(ax+b)^n}\, dx = \frac{1}{a}\int_\alpha^\beta g(f(x))f'(x)\, dx$$

$$= \frac{1}{a}\int_{f(\alpha)}^{f(\beta)} g(y)\, dy = \frac{1}{a}\int_{a\alpha+b}^{a\beta+b} \frac{1}{y^n}\, dy.$$

Continue via V(a) or V(b) of Sec. 19.1.

(c) *The reciprocal of a product of two unlike linear factors.* When $r_1 \neq r_2$, write

$$\frac{1}{(x-r_1)(x-r_2)} = \frac{A}{x-r_1} + \frac{B}{x-r_2} \tag{1}$$

and calculate values for the constants A and B so that (1) will hold as an identity for all $x \neq r_1$ or r_2. To find A and B, multiply (1) through by $(x-r_1)(x-r_2)$, and get

$$1 = A(x-r_2) + B(x-r_1)$$

or

$$1 = (A+B)x - (r_2 A + r_1 B). \tag{2}$$

In order for (2) to hold as an identity for *all* values of x, the constants terms must be equal on both sides of (2), and similarly the coefficients of x. These requirements lead to two equations involving A and B:

$$A + B = 0, \tag{3}$$

$$r_2 A + r_1 B = 1.$$

Since $r_1 \neq r_2$, this system of simultaneous equations can be solved for a unique pair of values for A and B,

$$A = \frac{1}{r_2 - r_1}, \qquad B = \frac{-1}{r_2 - r_1}.$$

(See Appendix A.) Also see Problem 1 of Sec. 19.4 for an alternate method for finding A and B. Finally,

$$\int_\alpha^\beta \frac{1}{(x - r_1)(x - r_2)}\, dx = A \int_\alpha^\beta \frac{1}{(x - r_1)}\, dx + B \int_\alpha^\beta \frac{1}{(x - r_2)}\, dx.$$

Continue via part (a).

EXAMPLE 1. To evaluate $\int_0^1 [1/(x + 2)(x - 3)]\, dx$, let's write

$$\frac{1}{(x + 2)(x - 3)} = \frac{A}{x + 2} + \frac{B}{x - 3}$$

or, multiplying through by $(x + 2)(x - 3)$,

$$1 = A(x - 3) + B(x + 2)$$

$$= (A + B)x - 3A + 2B.$$

To have an identity, set

$$A + B = 0,$$

$$-3A + 2B = 1.$$

Multiply the first of these equations by -2 and add it to the second to get $A = -\frac{1}{5}$, and then $B = \frac{1}{5}$. Hence

$$\int_0^1 \frac{1}{(x + 2)(x - 3)}\, dx = \int_0^1 \left[-\frac{1}{5}\left(\frac{1}{x + 2}\right) + \frac{1}{5}\left(\frac{1}{x - 3}\right) \right] dx$$

$$= -\frac{1}{5} \int_0^1 \frac{1}{x + 2}\, dx + \frac{1}{5} \int_0^1 \frac{1}{x - 3}\, dx. \qquad (4)$$

To simplify the first integral in (4), let $f(x) = x + 2$, and $g(y) = 1/y$, so that $f'(x) = 1$:

$$\int_0^1 \frac{1}{x + 2}\, dx = \int_0^1 g(f(x))f'(x)\, dx = \int_2^3 g(y)\, dy = \int_2^3 \frac{1}{y}\, dy$$

$$= [\log_e y]_2^3 = \log_e 3 - \log_e 2 = \log_e \frac{3}{2}. \qquad (5)$$

Similarly, to handle the second integral in (4), let $f(x) = x - 3$ and get

$$\int_0^1 \frac{1}{x - 3}\, dx = \int_{-3}^{-2} \frac{1}{y}\, dy. \qquad (6)$$

Now although the function $\log_e y$ is an antiderivative for y, it has meaning only for $y > 0$—whereas the y inputs in (6) are in the interval $[-3, -2]$. To remedy this situation, make a further substitution $z = f(y) = -y$, and check that

$$\int_{-3}^{-2} \frac{1}{y} \, dy = -\int_{2}^{3} \frac{1}{z} \, dz$$

$$= -[\log_e z]_{2}^{3} = -\log_e \frac{3}{2}. \tag{7}$$

Finally, put (6) and (7) in (4) to get

$$\int_{0}^{1} \frac{1}{(x+2)(x-3)} \, dx = -\frac{1}{5} \log_e \frac{3}{2} + \frac{1}{5}\left(-\log_e \frac{3}{2}\right) = -\frac{2}{5} \log_e \frac{3}{2}.$$

(d) *A generalization of (c): mixed powers of linear factors.* When r_1, r_2, and r_3 are all unequal, write

$$\frac{1}{(x-r_1)^k (x-r_2)^m (x-r_3)^n} = \frac{A_1}{x-r_1} + \frac{A_2}{(x-r_1)^2} + \cdots + \frac{A_k}{(x-r_1)^k}$$

$$+ \frac{B_1}{x-r_2} + \frac{B_2}{(x-r_2)^2} + \cdots + \frac{B_m}{(x-r_2)^m}$$

$$+ \frac{C_1}{x-r_3} + \frac{C_2}{(x-r_3)^2} + \cdots + \frac{C_n}{(x-r_3)^n}. \tag{8}$$

Multiply (8) through by $(x-r_1)^k (x-r_2)^m (x-r_3)^n$ to get an equation similar to (2). Then equate coefficients of all powers of x to get a system of $k+m+n$ simultaneous equations for the unknown constants A_i, B_i, and C_i. Once you solve for these constants, you can write

$$\int_{\alpha}^{\beta} \frac{1}{(x-r_1)^k (x-r_2)^m (x-r_3)^n} \, dx$$

$$= A_1 \int_{\alpha}^{\beta} \frac{1}{x-r_1} \, dx + \cdots + A_k \int_{\alpha}^{\beta} \frac{1}{(x-r_1)^k} \, dx$$

$$+ B_1 \int_{\alpha}^{\beta} \frac{1}{x-r_2} \, dx + \cdots + B_m \int_{\alpha}^{\beta} \frac{1}{(x-r_2)^m} \, dx$$

$$+ C_1 \int_{\alpha}^{\beta} \frac{1}{x-r_3} \, dx + \cdots + C_n \int_{\alpha}^{\beta} \frac{1}{(x-r_3)^n} \, dx \tag{9}$$

and continue via part (b). Proceed similarly in case there are more than three distinct kinds of linear factors.

(e) *How to calculate*

$$\int_{\alpha}^{\beta} \frac{1}{(x^2+1)^{n+1}} \, dx \text{ in terms of } \int_{\alpha}^{\beta} \frac{1}{(x^2+1)^n} \, dx.$$

Write

$$\int_{\alpha}^{\beta} \frac{1}{(x^2+1)^n} \, dx \quad \text{as} \quad \int_{\alpha}^{\beta} f'(x) g(x) \, dx,$$

where $f(x) = x$, $g(x) = [1/(x^2+1)^n]$, and

$$g'(x) = \left[\frac{-2nx}{(x^2+1)^{n+1}}\right].$$

Then "integrate by parts" (IV) to get

$$\int_\alpha^\beta \frac{1}{(x^2+1)^n}\,dx = \left[x\frac{1}{(x^2+1)^n}\right]_\alpha^\beta - \int_\alpha^\beta x\frac{-2nx}{(x^2+1)^{n+1}}\,dx$$

$$= \left[\frac{x}{(x^2+1)^n}\right]_\alpha^\beta + 2n\int_\alpha^\beta \frac{x^2+1-1}{(x^2+1)^{n+1}}\,dx$$

$$= \left[\frac{x}{(x^2+1)^n}\right]_\alpha^\beta + 2n\int_\alpha^\beta \frac{1}{(x^2+1)^n}\,dx$$

$$- 2n\int_\alpha^\beta \frac{1}{(x^2+1)^{n+1}}\,dx. \tag{10}$$

Solve for the last integral

$$\int_\alpha^\beta \frac{1}{(x^2+1)^{n+1}}\,dx = \frac{1}{2n}\left[\frac{x}{(x^2+1)^n}\right]_\alpha^\beta + \left(1-\frac{1}{2n}\right)\int_\alpha^\beta \frac{1}{(x^2+1)^n}\,dx. \tag{11}$$

Apply the relationship (11) repeatedly — going from $n+1$, to n, to $n-1$, and so on — until you are left with the $\int_\alpha^\beta [1/(x^2+1)]\,dx$, which you can evaluate via V(h).

EXAMPLE 2.

$$\int_0^1 \frac{1}{(x^2+1)^3}\,dx = \frac{1}{2\cdot 2}\left[\frac{x}{(x^2+1)^3}\right]_0^1 + \left(1-\frac{1}{2\cdot 2}\right)\int_0^1 \frac{1}{(x^2+1)^2}\,dx$$

$$= \frac{1}{4}\left\{\frac{1}{(1^2+1)^3} - \frac{0}{(0^2+1)^3}\right\} + \frac{3}{4}\left\{\frac{1}{2}\left[\frac{x}{(x^2+1)}\right]_0^1\right.$$

$$+ \left.\left(1-\frac{1}{2\cdot 1}\right)\int_0^1 \frac{1}{(x^2+1)}\,dx\right\}$$

$$= \frac{1}{4}\cdot\frac{1}{8} + \frac{3}{4}\left\{\frac{1}{2}\left[\frac{1}{1^2+1} - \frac{1}{0^2+1}\right]\right.$$

$$- \left.\frac{1}{2}[\arctan 1 - \arctan 0]\right\}$$

$$= \frac{1}{32} + \frac{3}{4}\cdot\left\{\frac{1}{2}\cdot\frac{1}{2} - \frac{1}{2}\arctan 1\right\}$$

$$= \frac{1}{32} + \frac{3}{16} - \frac{3}{8}\frac{\pi}{4}.$$

(f) *The reciprocal of a power of a quadratic*

$$\int_\alpha^\beta \frac{1}{(ax^2+bx+c)^n}\,dx \qquad (a\neq 0, n=1,2,3,\ldots).$$

If $b^2-4ac>0$, then $ax^2+bx+c=a(x-r_1)(x-r_2)$ where r_1 and r_2 are the "roots" $[(-b\pm\sqrt{b^2-4ac})/2a]$. In this case continue via Sec. 19.3 (c) or (d). If $b^2-4ac=0$, then $ax^2+bx+c=a(x-r)^2$ where $r=-b/2a$. In this case continue via Sec. 19.3 (b). There remains the case $b^2-4ac<0$ (a "negative discriminant"): "Complete the square" and write

$$ax^2 + bx + c = a\left\{ x^2 + \frac{b}{a}x + \left(\frac{b}{2a}\right)^2 - \left(\frac{b}{2a}\right)^2 + \frac{c}{a} \right\}$$

$$= a\left\{ \left(x + \frac{b}{2a}\right)^2 + A^2 \right\} = aA^2\left\{ \left(\frac{x}{A} + \frac{b}{2aA}\right)^2 + 1 \right\}, \quad \text{(12)}$$

where

$$A = \sqrt{\frac{c}{a} - \left(\frac{b}{2a}\right)^2} = \sqrt{\frac{4ac - b^2}{4a^2}}.$$

Hence

$$\frac{1}{(ax^2 + bx + c)^n} = \frac{1}{a^n A^{2n}} \frac{1}{\{(x/A + b/2aA)^2 + 1\}^n}$$

$$= \frac{1}{a^n A^{2n-1}} \frac{(1/A)}{\{(x/A + b/2aA)^2 + 1\}^n},$$

and

$$\int_\alpha^\beta \frac{1}{(ax^2 + bx + c)^n} dx = \frac{1}{a^n A^{2n-1}} \int_\alpha^\beta g(f(x))f'(x)\, dx,$$

where $f(x) = x/A + b/2aA$ and $g(y) = 1/(y^2 + 1)^n$. Apply "change of variables" (III) and then V(h) or part (e) of this section.

EXAMPLE 3. $\int_0^1 [1/(2x^2 + x + 1)^3]\, dx$. Here $b^2 - 4ac = 1 - 8 = -7 < 0$ and

$$A = \sqrt{\frac{4ac - b^2}{4a^2}} = \sqrt{\frac{7}{16}}.$$

Let

$$f(x) = \frac{x}{\sqrt{7/16}} + \frac{1}{\sqrt{7}} \quad \text{and} \quad g(y) = \frac{1}{[y^2 + 1]^3}$$

and write

$$\int_0^1 \frac{1}{(2x^2 + x + 1)^3}\, dx$$

$$= \frac{1}{2^3 (7/16)^{5/2}} \int_0^1 \frac{1}{\{[(x/\sqrt{7/16}) + (1/\sqrt{7})]^2 + 1\}^3} \left(\frac{1}{\sqrt{7/16}}\right) dx$$

$$= \frac{2^9}{7^3} \int_{4 \cdot 0/\sqrt{7} + 1/\sqrt{7}}^{4 \cdot 1/\sqrt{7} + 1/\sqrt{7}} \frac{1}{[y^2 + 1]^3}\, dy,$$

letting

$$f(x) = \frac{x}{\sqrt{7/16}} + \frac{1}{\sqrt{7}} \quad \text{and} \quad g(y) = \frac{1}{[y^2 + 1]^3}.$$

For a complete answer, let $\alpha = 1/\sqrt{7}$ and $\beta = 5/\sqrt{7}$ and continue exactly as in Example 2.

(g) *The ratio of a linear function and a power of a quadratic function,*

$$\int_\alpha^\beta \frac{dx+e}{(ax^2+bx+c)^n}\, dx.$$

When $a \neq 0$ and $d \neq 0$, let's try to get the integral into the form

$$\int_\alpha^\beta g(f(x))f'(x)\, dx,$$

where

$$g(y) = \frac{1}{y^n} \quad \text{and} \quad y = f(x) = ax^2 + bx + c.$$

Then $f'(x) = 2ax + b$. To get the ratio into the form $g(f(x))f'(x)$, write

$$\frac{dx+e}{(ax^2+bx+c)^n} = \frac{(d/2a)(2ax+b)+e-(bd/2a)}{(ax^2+bx+c)^n}$$

$$= \left(\frac{d}{2a}\right)\frac{2ax+b}{(ax^2+bx+c)^n} + \left(e - \frac{bd}{2a}\right)\frac{1}{(ax^2+bx+c)^n}.$$

Then $\tag{13}$

$$\int_\alpha^\beta \frac{dx+e}{(ax^2+bx+c)^n}\, dx = \frac{d}{2a}\int_\alpha^\beta \frac{2ax+b}{(ax^2+bx+c)^n}\, dx$$

$$+ \left(e - \frac{bd}{2a}\right)\int_\alpha^\beta \frac{1}{(ax^2+bx+c)^n}\, dx. \tag{14}$$

The first integral on the right-hand side of (14) is in the proposed form. The second integral is a kind of "remainder" — not of the same form. But we can handle it via part (f).

(h) *A mixture of (d) and (g):* the ratio

$$\frac{P(x)}{(x-r)^m(ax^2+bx+c)^n}, \tag{15}$$

where $a \neq 0$, $b^2 - 4ac < 0$, m and $n = 1, 2, 3, \ldots$, and $P(x)$ is a polynomial *of degree* $< m + 2n$, *the degree of the denominator.* Write

$$\frac{P(x)}{(x-r)^m(ax^2+bx+c)^n} = \frac{A_1}{x-r} + \frac{A_2}{(x-r)^2} + \cdots + \frac{A_m}{(x-r)^m}$$

$$+ \frac{D_1x+E_1}{ax^2+bx+c} + \frac{D_2x+E_2}{(ax^2+bx+c)^2}$$

$$+ \cdots + \frac{D_nx+E_n}{(ax^2+bx+c)^n}. \tag{16}$$

Then multiply (16) through by $(x-r)^m(ax^2+bx+c)^n$ and equate coefficients of the various powers of x to get $m + 2n$

simultaneous equations in the unknown constants A_i, D_i, and E_i. Once you solve for these quantities, you can integrate each of the terms on the right-hand side of (16) via parts (a), (f), and (g) of this section. Follow a similar procedure if the denominator includes more than one distinct linear factor or quadratic factor — allowing an additional set of terms in (16) for each such factor (as in (d)). An identity of the form (16) is commonly called a *partial fractions expansion*.

EXAMPLE 4. Let's evaluate

$$\int_2^5 \frac{P(x)}{Q(x)}\,dx$$

where

$$\frac{P(x)}{Q(x)} = \frac{x^2 + 2x + 3}{(x-1)(x^2+1)}.$$

To use the method of Sec. 19.3 (h), write

$$\frac{x^2 + 2x + 3}{(x-1)(x^2+1)} = \frac{A}{x-1} + \frac{Dx+E}{x^2+1}, \tag{17}$$

$$x^2 + 2x + 3 = A(x^2+1) + (Dx+E)(x-1)$$
$$= (A+D)x^2 + (E-D)x + (A-E). \tag{18}$$

For (18) to be an identity, we must have

$$\left.\begin{array}{ll} A+D & =1 \\ -D+E & =2 \\ A \quad -E & =3 \end{array}\right\}, \tag{19}$$

from which $A = 3$, $E = 0$, and $D = -2$. So

$$\frac{P(x)}{Q(x)} = 3\frac{1}{x-1} - \frac{2x}{x^2+1}. \tag{20}$$

Hence

$$\int_2^5 \frac{P(x)}{Q(x)}\,dx = 3\int_2^5 \frac{1}{x-1}\,dx - \int_2^5 \frac{2x}{x^2+1}\,dx$$

$$= 3\,[\log y]_{2-1}^{5-1} - [\log u]_{2^2+1}^{5^2+1}$$

$$= 3\log 4 - \log\frac{26}{5}. \tag{21}$$

(i) *The general "rational function" — that is, ratio of polynomials* $P(x)/Q(x)$: Try to express $Q(x)$ as a product of powers of linear and quadratic factors, as in part (h). If the degree of $P(x)$ is less than that of $Q(x)$, apply part (h) directly. Otherwise, divide P by Q to get an identity

$$\frac{P(x)}{Q(x)} = T(x) + \frac{P_1(x)}{Q(x)}, \tag{22}$$

where $T(x)$ and $P_1(x)$ are polynomials, the degree of P_1 being strictly less than that of Q. Then integrate T via part (a) and P_1/Q via part (h).

EXAMPLE 5. Let's evaluate

$$\int_2^5 \frac{P(x)}{Q(x)}\,dx,$$

where

$$\frac{P(x)}{Q(x)} = \frac{x^3 + 2x^2 + 5x + 2}{x^2 - 1}.$$

The numerator has higher degree than the denominator. So divide

$$
\begin{array}{r}
x+2 \\
x^2-1\ \overline{\big)\ x^3 + 2x^2 + 5x + 2} \\
\underline{x^3 \qquad\ -\ x} \\
2x^2 + 6x \\
\underline{2x^2 \qquad -2} \\
6x + 4
\end{array}
$$

and write

$$\frac{P(x)}{Q(x)} = (x+2) + \frac{6x+4}{x^2-1}$$

$$= (x+2) + 3\frac{2x}{x^2-1} + 4\frac{1}{(x-1)(x+1)}. \tag{23}$$

To handle the last term (as in part (c)), write

$$\frac{1}{(x-1)(x+1)} = \frac{A}{x-1} + \frac{B}{x+1} \tag{24}$$

or

$$1 = A(x+1) + B(x-1) = (A+B)x + (A-B). \tag{25}$$

To make (25) an identity in x, we need

$$A+B=0 \quad \text{and} \quad A-B=1 \tag{26}$$

or $A = \frac{1}{2}$ and $B = -\frac{1}{2}$. Then

$$\int_2^5 \frac{P(x)}{Q(x)}\,dx = \int_2^5 x\,dx + \int_2^5 2\,dx + 3\int_2^5 \frac{2x}{x^2-1}\,dx$$

$$+ 4\frac{1}{2}\int_2^5 \frac{1}{x-1}\,dx + 4\frac{1}{2}\int_2^5 \frac{1}{x+1}\,dx$$

$$= \left[\frac{x^2}{2}\right]_2^5 + 2(5-2) + 3\int_{2^2-1}^{5^2-1} \frac{1}{y}\,dy + 2\int_{2-1}^{5-1} \frac{1}{u}\,du$$

$$+ 2\int_{2+1}^{5+1} \frac{1}{v}\,dv. \tag{27}$$

To get the last three integrals in (27), I made these changes of variables: in the 1st, $y = f(x) = x^2 - 1$ with $f'(x) = 2x$; in the 2nd, $u = f(x) = x - 1$; in the 3rd, $v = f(x) = x + 1$. Finally,

$$\int_2^5 \frac{P(x)}{Q(x)} \, dx = \frac{1}{2}(5^2 - 2^2) + 2(5 - 2) + 3[\log y]_{2^2-1}^{5^2-1} + 2[\log u]_{2-1}^{5-1}$$

$$+ 2[\log v]_{2+1}^{5+1}$$

$$= \frac{21}{2} - 6 + 3\log\frac{24}{3} + 2\log\frac{4}{1} + 2\log\frac{6}{3} = \frac{9}{2} + 15\log 2. \quad \textbf{(28)}$$

19.4 PROBLEMS ON POLYNOMIALS AND "RATIONAL FUNCTIONS"

°1. In part (c) of Sec. 19.3, I presented one way of finding constants A and B so that we could write

$$\frac{1}{(x - r_1)(x - r_2)} = \frac{A}{x - r_1} + \frac{B}{x - r_2} \qquad \text{for all } x \neq r_1 \text{ or } r_2, \qquad (*)$$

where $r_1 \neq r_2$. Here is another way. Multiply (*) through by $(x - r_1)(x - r_2)$, as before, to get

$$1 = A(x - r_2) + B(x - r_1). \qquad (**)$$

Then substitute two *convenient* values for x into (**)—such as $x = r_1$ and $x = r_2$—to get two equations for the as yet unknown constants A and B.
   Find such A and B for the case $1/(x - 2)(x + 5)$.

2. Use the method of Problem 1 and the scheme in part (d) of Sec. 19.3 to write

$$\frac{1}{(x - 2)^2(x + 5)} = \frac{A_1}{x - 2} + \frac{A_2}{(x - 2)^2} + \frac{B_1}{x + 5}$$

with specific A_1, A_2, and B_1.

°3. Evaluate the following integrals (as in (i) and other parts of Sec. 19.3).

(a) $\displaystyle\int_3^4 \frac{x^2 + 3x + 4}{x - 2} \, dx$

(b) $\displaystyle\int_3^4 \frac{x^2 - 2x - 1}{x^2 - 4x + 4} \, dx$

(c) $\displaystyle\int_{-1}^1 \frac{x - 3}{(x - 2)^2(x + 5)} \, dx$

(d) $\displaystyle\int_0^1 \frac{3x + 33}{(x + 1)(x^2 + 9)} \, dx$

(e) $\displaystyle\int_{-1}^1 \frac{x^2}{(x^2 + 4)^2} \, dx$

(f) $\displaystyle\int_2^3 \frac{3x}{(x - 1)^2(x^2 + x + 1)} \, dx$

19.5 EXPRESSIONS INVOLVING ROOTS OF LINEAR FUNCTIONS

(a) Here's how to integrate a product

$$h(x) = R(x)S((ax + b)^{1/n}),$$

where R and S are "rational functions" (ratios of polynomials), $a \neq 0$, and $n = 2, 3, 4, \ldots$. Let

$$f(x) = (ax+b)^{1/n},$$

so that

$$f'(x) = \frac{1}{n}(ax+b)^{(1/n)-1}a = \frac{a}{n}\frac{(ax+b)^{1/n}}{ax+b}, \qquad (1)$$

$$ax+b = f(x)^n, \quad \text{and} \quad x = \frac{f(x)^n - b}{a}. \qquad (2)$$

To get $h(x)$ in the form $g(f(x))f'(x)$, write

$$h(x) = \frac{R(x)S((ax+b)^{1/n})f'(x)}{f'(x)}.$$

Then substitute from (1) and (2) to get

$$h(x) = \frac{R\{[f(x)^n-b]/a\}S(f(x))}{(a/n)[f(x)/f(x)^n]}f'(x)$$

$$= g(f(x))f'(x), \qquad (3)$$

where

$$g(y) = \frac{n}{a}R\left(\frac{y^n - b}{a}\right)S(y)y^{n-1} \qquad (4)$$

will be a rational function of y. Continue via "change of variables" (III) and then Sec. 19.3 (i).

EXAMPLE 1. $\int_0^1 h(x)\,dx$, where $h(x) = x\sqrt{2x+5}$. To remove the root, try the change of variables $f(x) = \sqrt{2x+5}$. Then

$$x = \frac{1}{2}f(x)^2 - \frac{5}{2} \quad \text{and} \quad f'(x) = \frac{1}{2}(2x+5)^{-1/2}2 = \frac{1}{\sqrt{2x+5}} = \frac{1}{f(x)}.$$

Hence

$$h(x) = \left[\frac{1}{2}f(x)^2 - \frac{5}{2}\right]f(x) = \left[\frac{1}{2}f(x)^2 - \frac{5}{2}\right]f^2(x)f'(x)$$

$$= \left[\frac{1}{2}f(x)^4 - \frac{5}{2}f(x)^2\right]f'(x)$$

and

$$\int_0^1 h(x)\,dx = \int_{\sqrt{2\cdot 0+5}}^{\sqrt{2\cdot 1+5}} \left[\frac{1}{2}y^4 - \frac{5}{2}y^2\right]dy$$

$$= \frac{1}{2}\frac{1}{5}[y^5]_{\sqrt{5}}^{\sqrt{7}} - \frac{5}{2}\frac{1}{3}[y^3]_{\sqrt{5}}^{\sqrt{7}}$$

$$= \frac{1}{10}[7^{5/2} - 5^{5/2}] - \frac{5}{6}[7^{3/2} - 5^{3/2}].$$

(b) Follow a similar procedure for more complicated algebraic combinations of functions of x and $(ax+b)^{1/n}$, such as

$$\frac{R(x)S((ax+b)^{1/n})}{T(x)U((ax+b)^{1/n})+V(x)W((ax+b)^{1/n})},$$

where R, S, T, U, V, and W are rational functions.

(c) Follow a similar procedure when the role of $(ax+b)^{1/n}$ is played by the root of a *ratio* of linear functions,

$$\left(\frac{ax+b}{cx+d}\right)^{1/n}.$$

In this case, let

$$f(x)=\left(\frac{ax+b}{cx+d}\right)^{1/n}.$$

19.6   EXPRESSIONS INVOLVING SQUARE ROOTS OF QUADRATIC FUNCTIONS

(a) Suppose we're given an algebraic combination of rational functions of x and of $\sqrt{x^2-r^2}$, such as

$$h(x)=R(x)S(\sqrt{x^2-r^2}) \qquad (r\neq 0).$$

We might write

$$\sqrt{x^2-r^2}=\sqrt{x-r}\sqrt{x+r}=(x-r)\sqrt{\frac{x+r}{x-r}}. \tag{1}$$

Then

$$h(x)=R(x)S\left((x-r)\left(\frac{x+r}{x-r}\right)^{1/2}\right)$$

will be of the form considered in Sec. 19.5 (c) with $n=2$. But for a frequently useful and easier method involving a change to trigonometric functions, see Sec. 19.12.

(b) The same goes for

$$\sqrt{r^2-x^2}=\sqrt{r-x}\sqrt{r+x}=(r-x)\sqrt{\frac{r+x}{r-x}}.$$

(c) For the case $\sqrt{x^2+r^2}$, see part (c) of Sec. 19.12, where trigonometric functions again provide a solution.

(d) *The square root of a general quadratic.* When $a\neq 0$, "complete the square" and write

$$ax^2+bx+c=a\left\{\left(x+\frac{b}{2a}\right)^2+\left(\frac{4ac-b^2}{4a^2}\right)\right\}.$$

Assuming this quantity to be nonnegative — so that its square root makes sense — there are four possible cases:

(i) $a>0$ and $b^2-4ac>0$: then

$$\sqrt{ax^2+bx+c}=\sqrt{a}\sqrt{y^2-r^2}, \tag{2}$$

where

$$y = x + \frac{b}{2a} \quad \text{and} \quad r = \sqrt{\frac{b^2 - 4ac}{4a^2}}.$$

(ii) $a < 0$ and $b^2 - 4ac > 0$: then

$$\sqrt{ax^2 + bx + c} = \sqrt{-a}\sqrt{r^2 - y^2} \qquad (3)$$

where, again,

$$y = x + \frac{b}{2a} \quad \text{and} \quad r = \sqrt{\frac{b^2 - 4ac}{4a^2}}.$$

(iii) $a > 0$ and $b^2 - 4ac < 0$: then

$$\sqrt{ax^2 + bx + c} = \sqrt{a}\sqrt{y^2 + r^2} \qquad (4)$$

where

$$y = x + \frac{b}{2a} \quad \text{and here} \quad r = \sqrt{\frac{4ac - b^2}{4a^2}}.$$

(iv) $a > 0$ and $b^2 - 4ac = 0$: then

$$\sqrt{ax^2 + bx + c} = \sqrt{a}\left(x + \frac{b}{2a}\right).$$

After a change of variables via the function $f(x) = x + b/2a$, cases (i)–(iii) will correspond respectively to parts (a)–(c) in this section. In case (iv) the root has disappeared.

19.7 PROBLEMS INVOLVING ROOTS

°1. Evaluate the following integrals (making "changes of variables" where suitable).

(a) $\displaystyle\int_1^2 \frac{x^{1/2}}{1 + x^{1/4}}\, dx$ (b) $\displaystyle\int_1^2 \frac{1 - \sqrt{x}}{1 + \sqrt{x}}\, dx$ (c) $\displaystyle\int_0^3 \frac{\sqrt{x+1} - 1}{\sqrt{x+1} + 1}\, dx$

(d) $\displaystyle\int_2^3 \frac{\sqrt{t^3 - 1}}{t}\, dt$ (e) $\displaystyle\int_{-1/2}^{1/2} \sqrt{\frac{1+y}{1-y}}\, dy$ (f) $\displaystyle\int_1^2 \frac{1}{x^{1/2} + x^{1/3}}\, dx$

(g) $\displaystyle\int_0^1 5x\sqrt{3x + 1}\, dx$ (h) $\displaystyle\int_2^3 \frac{\sqrt{3x+2} - 1}{\sqrt{3x+2} + 1}\, dx$

°2. For each of the following integrals, make a change of variables so as to transform the integral into one of the categories (i)–(iv) discussed in Sec. 19.6. Then evaluate the integral, if possible.

(a) $\displaystyle\int_0^1 \frac{1}{\sqrt{4 - 2x - x^2}}\, dx$ (b) $\displaystyle\int_0^1 \sqrt{2x^2 + 3x + 15}\, dx$

(c) $\displaystyle\int_0^1 \sqrt{2x^2 + 3x + 1}\, dx$ (d) $\displaystyle\int_0^1 \frac{1}{\sqrt{x^2 + 6x + 9}}\, dx$

19.8 SOME EXPRESSIONS INVOLVING EXPONENTIALS AND LOGS

(a) When $a \neq 0$, and $n = 1, 2, 3, \ldots$, the integral

$$\int_{\alpha}^{\beta} e^{ax} x^n \, dx \quad \text{has the form} \quad \int_{\alpha}^{\beta} f'(x) g(x) \, dx,$$

where

$$f'(x) = e^{ax}, \quad f(x) = \frac{1}{a} e^{ax}, \quad \text{and} \quad g(x) = x^n.$$

Hence, via "integration by parts" (IV),

$$\int_{\alpha}^{\beta} e^{ax} x^n \, dx = \left[\frac{1}{a} e^{ax} x^n \right]_{\alpha}^{\beta} - \int_{\alpha}^{\beta} \left(\frac{1}{a} e^{ax} \right) (n x^{n-1}) \, dx$$

$$= \frac{1}{a} \left[e^{ax} x^n \right]_{\alpha}^{\beta} - \frac{n}{a} \int_{\alpha}^{\beta} e^{ax} x^{n-1} \, dx. \tag{1}$$

The relationship (1) shows how to evaluate the left-hand integral, involving n, in terms of an almost identical integral on the far right, involving $n-1$. By applying (1) n times, with decreasing exponents, we can arrive at $\int_{\alpha}^{\beta} e^{ax} x^0 \, dx$ — which is evaluated in V(c) of Sec. 19.1.

EXAMPLE 1.

$$\int_{0}^{2} e^{3x} x^2 \, dx = \frac{1}{3} \left[e^{3x} x^2 \right]_{0}^{2} - \frac{2}{3} \int_{0}^{2} e^{3x} x \, dx$$

$$= \frac{1}{3} \left[e^{3 \cdot 2} 2^2 - e^{3 \cdot 0} \cdot 0^2 \right] - \frac{2}{3} \left\{ \frac{1}{3} \left[e^{3x} x \right]_{0}^{2} - \frac{1}{3} \int_{0}^{2} e^{3x} \, dx \right\}$$

$$= \frac{4}{3} e^6 - \frac{2}{3^2} \left[e^{3 \cdot 2} 2 - e^{3 \cdot 0} 0 \right] + \frac{2}{3^3} \left[e^{3 \cdot 2} - e^{3 \cdot 0} \right]$$

$$= \frac{4}{3} e^6 - \frac{4}{9} e^6 + \frac{2}{27} (e^6 - 1).$$

(b) For purposes of integration, convert an expression c^x into the form e^{ax} by letting $a = \log_e c$.

(c) For $n = \pm 1, \pm 2, \pm 3, \ldots$,

$$\int_{\alpha}^{\beta} \frac{(\log_e x)^n}{x} \, dx = \int_{\alpha}^{\beta} g(f(x)) f'(x) \, dx,$$

where

$$f(x) = \log_e x \quad \text{and} \quad g(y) = y^n.$$

Continue via III and V(a) of Sec. 19.1.

(d) For $p \neq -1$, and $n = \pm 1, \pm 2, \pm 3, \ldots$, the integral

$$\int_{\alpha}^{\beta} x^p (\log_e x)^n \, dx \quad \text{has the form} \quad \int_{\alpha}^{\beta} f'(x) g(x) \, dx$$

where

$$f'(x) = x^p, \quad f(x) = \frac{x^{p+1}}{p+1}, \quad \text{and} \quad g(x) = (\log_e x)^n.$$

Hence, via integration by parts,

$$\int_\alpha^\beta x^p (\log_e x)^n \, dx = \left[\frac{x^{p+1}}{p+1} (\log_e x)^n \right]_\alpha^\beta$$

$$- \int_\alpha^\beta \frac{x^{p+1}}{p+1} \left[n(\log_e x)^{n-1} \frac{1}{x} \right] dx$$

$$= \frac{1}{p+1} \left[x^{p+1} (\log_e x)^n \right]_\alpha^\beta$$

$$- \frac{n}{p+1} \int_\alpha^\beta x^p (\log_e x)^{n-1} \, dx.$$

This equation relates integrals involving exponents n and $n-1$, and we can use it repeatedly in one direction or the other to arrive at $\int_\alpha^\beta x^p (\log_e x)^0 \, dx$ of V(a) of Sec. 19.1.

19.9 PROBLEMS ON EXPONENTIALS AND LOGS

°1. Evaluate the following integrals (as in Sec. 19.8):

(a) $\int_0^1 e^{3x} x^3 \, dx$

(b) $\int_1^2 (\log_e x)^3 x^3 \, dx$

(c) $\int_1^2 (\log_e x)^3 \frac{1}{x} \, dx$

(d) $\int_{-1}^1 \left(\frac{e^x + e^{-x}}{2} \right) x^n \, dx$

19.10 EXPRESSIONS INVOLVING TRIGONOMETRIC FUNCTIONS

Here it's helpful to have various trigonometric identities at hand, such as

(i) $\sin u = \cos \left(\frac{\pi}{2} - u \right) = \sqrt{1 - \cos^2 u}$,

(ii) $\sec u = \frac{1}{\cos u} = \sqrt{1 + \tan^2 u}$,

(iii) $\sin (u + v) = \sin u \cos v + \cos u \sin v$,

(iv) $\sin 2u = 2 \sin u \cos u$,

(v) $\sin^2 u = \frac{1 - \cos 2u}{2}$ and $\cos^2 u = \frac{1 + \cos 2u}{2}$,

(vi) $\sin u + \sin v = 2 \sin \left(\frac{u+v}{2} \right) \sin \left(\frac{u-v}{2} \right)$.

(For others, see Appendix A.)

(a) *A product* $(\sin x)^m (\cos x)^{2k+1}$, *where m and $k = 0, \pm 1, \pm 2, \ldots$.*
Write

$$(\cos x)^{2k+1} = (\cos^2 x)^k \cos x = (1 - \sin^2 x)^k \cos x.$$

Since $\cos x = (\sin x)'$, we can let $f(x) = \sin x$ and $g(y) = y^m(1-y^2)^k$, and get

$$\int_\alpha^\beta (\sin x)^m (\cos x)^{2k+1}\, dx = \int_\alpha^\beta (\sin x)^m (1-\sin^2 x)^k \cos x\, dx$$

$$= \int_\alpha^\beta g(f(x))f'(x)\, dx, \qquad (1)$$

where $f(x) = \sin x$ and $g(y) = y^m(1-y^2)^k$, a rational function. Continue via III and Sec. 19.3.

Proceed similarly for a product $(\cos x)^m(\sin x)^{2k+1}$ letting $f(x) = \cos x$.

For an alternate method involving "integration by parts," see Problem 1 of Sec. 19.11.

(b) *An even power* $(\sin x)^{2k} = (\sin^2 x)^k$, *where* $n = 1, 2, 3, \ldots$. Write $\sin^2 x = \frac{1}{2} - \frac{1}{2}\cos 2x$ (identity (v)). Hence

$$(\sin x)^{2k} = \left(\frac{1}{2}\right)^k (1-\cos 2x)^k$$

$$= \left(\frac{1}{2}\right)^k \left\{ 1 - k\cos 2x + \frac{k(k-1)}{2}\cos^2 2x - \cdots \right\}. \qquad (2)$$

Each term in the $\{\ \}$ expression is of the form $c(\cos 2x)^j$. If j is odd, integrate that term via a "change of variables" with $f(x) = 2x$, followed by (a). If j is even, use the identities (v) again — as many times as necessary.
(See also Problem 2 of Sec. 19.11.)

EXAMPLE 1.

$$\int_0^{\pi/2} \sin^4 x\, dx = \int_0^{\pi/2} \left(\frac{1}{2} - \frac{1}{2}\cos 2x\right)^2 dx$$

$$= \frac{1}{4}\int_0^{\pi/2} 1\, dx - \frac{1}{4}\int_0^{\pi/2} (\cos 2x)2\, dx + \frac{1}{4}\int_0^{\pi/2} (\cos 2x)^2\, dx$$

$$= \frac{1}{4}\left(\frac{\pi}{2} - 0\right) - \frac{1}{4}[\sin 2x]_{2\cdot 0}^{2\cdot\pi/2} + \frac{1}{4}\int_0^{\pi/2} \left(\frac{1}{2} + \frac{1}{2}\cos 4x\right) dx$$

$$= \frac{\pi}{8} - \frac{1}{4}[\sin 2\pi - \sin 0]$$

$$+ \frac{1}{8}\int_0^{\pi/2} 1\, dx + \frac{1}{8}\frac{1}{4}\int_0^{\pi/2} (\cos 4x)4\, dx$$

$$= \frac{\pi}{8} - 0 + \frac{1}{8}\left(\frac{\pi}{2} - 0\right) + \frac{1}{32}[\sin 4x]_{4\cdot 0}^{4\cdot\pi/2}$$

$$= \frac{3\pi}{16} + \frac{1}{32}\left(\sin 16 \cdot \frac{\pi}{2} - \sin 16 \cdot 0\right) = \frac{3}{16}\pi.$$

(Here I used the identity $\cos^2 u = \frac{1}{2} + \frac{1}{2}\cos 2u$.)

(c) Try to transform more complicated trigonometric expressions into sums of products as in (a) and (b) via identities such as (i)–(vi). Then apply parts (a) and (b).

(d) *A general method for handling expressions h involving $\sin x$ and $\cos x$ through products sums and ratios:* From identities such as (i), (ii), and (v) there follow the further identities

$$\sin x = \frac{2 \tan (x/2)}{1 + \tan^2 (x/2)} \quad \text{and} \quad \cos x = \frac{1 - \tan^2 (x/2)}{1 + \tan^2 (x/2)}. \tag{3}$$

Note also that if $f(x) = \tan x/2$, then

$$f'(x) = \frac{1}{2} \sec^2 \frac{x}{2} = \frac{1}{2}\left(1 + \tan^2 \frac{x}{2}\right). \tag{4}$$

Substitute (3) and (4) into a given expression h to get h in the form $h(x) = g(f(x))f'(x)$, where g is a rational function. Then apply III and Sec. 19.3.

(e) How can we handle $\int_\alpha^\beta (\sin ax)x^n \, dx$, where $a \neq 0$, and $n = 1, 2, 3, \ldots$? Note that the separate factors $\sin ax$ and x^n are easy to integrate and differentiate. In particular, differentiating x^n would reduce the exponent and make for a simplification. In such a situation, try "integration by parts" (IV). The integral

$$\int_\alpha^\beta (\sin ax)x^n \, dx \quad \text{has the form} \quad \int_\alpha^\beta f'(x)g(x) \, dx,$$

where

$$f'(x) = \sin ax, \quad f(x) = -\frac{1}{a} \cos ax, \quad \text{and} \quad g(x) = x^n.$$

Hence, via "integration by parts,"

$$\int_\alpha^\beta (\sin ax)x^n \, dx = \left[-\frac{1}{a}(\cos ax)x^n\right]_\alpha^\beta - \int_\alpha^\beta \left(-\frac{1}{a} \cos ax\right)(nx^{n-1}) \, dx$$

$$= -\frac{1}{a}[(\cos ax)x^n]_\alpha^\beta + \frac{n}{a} \int_\alpha^\beta (\cos ax)x^{n-1} \, dx. \tag{5}$$

Similarly,

$$\int_\alpha^\beta (\cos ax)x^n \, dx = \left[\left(\frac{1}{a} \sin ax\right)x^n\right]_\alpha^\beta - \int_\alpha^\beta \left(\frac{1}{a} \sin ax\right)(nx^{n-1}) \, dx$$

$$= \frac{1}{a}[(\sin ax)x^n]_\alpha^\beta - \frac{n}{a} \int_\alpha^\beta (\sin ax)x^{n-1} \, dx. \tag{6}$$

If we apply the last two relations repeatedly and alternately, we can arrive at integrals of the form $\int_\alpha^\beta (\sin ax)x^0 \, dx$ and $\int_\alpha^\beta (\cos ax)x^0 \, dx$, evaluated in V(d).

EXAMPLE 2. $\int_0^{\pi/2} e^{2x} \sin 3x\, dx$. Integrate by parts, letting $e^{2x} = f'(x)$ and $\sin 3x = g(x)$. Then

$$\int_0^{\pi/2} e^{2x} \sin 3x\, dx = \left[\frac{1}{2}e^{2x}\sin 3x\right]_0^{\pi/2} - \int_0^{\pi/2}\left(\frac{1}{2}e^{2x}\right)(3\cos 3x)\,dx$$

$$= \frac{1}{2}\left(e^{2\cdot\pi/2}\sin 3\cdot\frac{\pi}{2} - e^{2\cdot 0}\sin 3\cdot 0\right)$$

$$- \frac{3}{2}\int_0^{\pi/2} e^{2x}\cos 3x\, dx. \tag{7}$$

Although the right-hand integral in (7) is no simpler than the original one, it has almost the same form—with $\cos 3x$ replacing $\sin 3x$. Since $(\cos 3x)' = -3\sin 3x$, let's integrate by parts once more to get an equation involving the *original* integral on both sides. Then perhaps we can solve for it.

$$\int_0^{\pi/2} e^{2x}\cos 3x\, dx = \left[\frac{1}{2}e^{2x}\cos 3x\right]_0^{\pi/2} + \frac{3}{2}\int_0^{\pi/2} e^{2x}\sin 3x\, dx. \tag{8}$$

Substitute (8) into the right-hand side of (7) to get

$$\int_0^{\pi/2} e^{2x}\sin 3x\, dx = \frac{1}{2}\left(e^{2(\pi/2)}\sin 3\frac{\pi}{2} - e^0\sin 0\right)$$

$$- \frac{3}{2^2}\left(e^{2(\pi/2)}\cos 3\frac{\pi}{2} - e^0\cos 0\right)$$

$$- \left(\frac{3}{2}\right)^2\int_0^{\pi/2} e^{2x}\sin 3x\, dx, \tag{9}$$

or

$$\int_0^{\pi/2} e^{2x}\sin 3x\, dx = \frac{1}{1+(3/2)^2}\left\{\frac{1}{2}e^\pi\sin\frac{3}{2}\pi - \frac{3}{2^2}\left(e^\pi\cos\frac{3}{2}\pi - 1\right)\right\}$$

$$= \frac{4}{13}\left\{-\frac{1}{2}e^\pi + \frac{3}{4}\right\}. \tag{10}$$

19.11 PROBLEMS INVOLVING TRIGONOMETRIC FUNCTIONS

1. (a) Here is an alternate method to the one I discussed in part (a) of Sec. 19.10 for evaluating $\int_\alpha^\beta (\cos x)^m(\sin x)^{2k+1}\, dx$. Write

$$(\cos x)^m(\sin x)^{2k+1} = -[(\cos x)^m(-\sin x)](\sin x)^{2k} = f'(x)g(x),$$

and use integration by parts to express the original integral in terms of an integral $\int_\alpha^\beta (\cos x)^{m+2}(\sin x)^{2k-1}\, dx$.

(b) Repeat the procedure of part (a) several times to evaluate

$$\int_0^{\pi/2} (\cos x)^5(\sin x)^5\, dx.$$

°2. Here is an alternate method to the one I discussed in part (b) of Sec. 19.10 for evaluating $\int_\alpha^\beta (\sin x)^{2n} dx$.

(a) For $m \geq 2$, write

$$(\sin x)^m = (\sin x)(\sin x)^{m-1} = f'(x)g(x),$$

and use integration by parts to get

$$\int_\alpha^\beta (\sin x)^m \, dx$$

$$= [-(\cos x)(\sin x)^{m-1}]_\alpha^\beta + (m-1) \int_\alpha^\beta (\cos x)^2 (\sin x)^{m-2} \, dx$$

$$= [-(\cos x)(\sin x)^{m-1}]_\alpha^\beta$$

$$+ (m-1) \int_\alpha^\beta [1 - (\sin x)^2](\sin x)^{m-2} \, dx. \qquad (*)$$

(b) Solve (*) for $\int_\alpha^\beta (\sin x)^m \, dx$ in terms of [ ] quantities and the integral $\int_\alpha^\beta (\sin x)^{m-2} \, dx$.

(c) Use the result of part (b) to evaluate $\int_0^{\pi/2} (\sin x)^5 \, dx$.

°3. Evaluate the following integrals:

(a) $\int_{-\pi/2}^\pi (\sin x)^3 \, dx$

(b) $\int_0^\pi (\sin x)^m \cos x \, dx$

(c) $\int_0^\pi \sin x \, (\cos x)^m \, dx$

(d) $\int_0^{\pi/2} (\cos x)^{2/3}(\sin x)^3 \, dx$

(e) $\int_0^\pi (\sin u)^2(\cos u)^2 \, du$

(f) $\int_0^{\pi/4} \frac{(\sin x)^3}{(\cos x)^2} \, dx$

(g) $\int_{\pi/4}^{\pi/2} \frac{(\cos x)^3}{\sin x} \, dx$

(h) $\int_0^{\pi/2} \sin 2x(\cos x)^2 \, dx$

(i) $\int_0^{1/3} \frac{(\sec 3x)^2}{1 + \tan 3x} \, dx$

(j) $\int_0^{10} (\tan u)^2 \, du$

(k) $\int_{-\pi/40}^{\pi/40} \frac{1}{\cos 10x} \, dx$

(l) $\int_0^1 x \sin (x^2) \cos (x^2) \, dx$

(m) $\int_0^{\pi/4} \frac{(\sin t)^2}{(\cos t)^4} \, dt$

(n) $\int_0^1 (\tan u)^5 \, du$

°4. Evaluate:

(a) $\int_0^{\pi/2} x^2 \sin x \, dx$

(b) $\int_0^{\pi/2} x^3 \cos x \, dx$

(c) $\int_{-\pi/2}^{\pi/2} e^{3x} \cos 5x \, dx$

(d) $\int_0^\pi (\cos x)^4 \, dx$

(e) $\int_0^\pi (\sin x)^6 \, dx$

19.12 USING TRIGONOMETRIC FUNCTIONS TO SIMPLIFY SQUARE ROOTS OF QUADRATICS

(a) To handle $\sqrt{r^2 - x^2}$, where $r > 0$, consider the substitution $x = f(u) = r \sin u$. Then

$$\sqrt{r^2 - x^2} = \sqrt{r^2 - f^2(u)} = \sqrt{r^2 - r^2 \sin^2 u}$$

$$= r\sqrt{1 - \sin^2 u} = r \cos u \tag{1}$$

and

$$f'(u) = r \cos u.$$

Suppose that S is a rational function, and that $\alpha = f(u_0) = r \sin u_0$ and $\beta = f(u_1) = r \sin u_1$. Then, via "change of variables" (III),

$$\int_\alpha^\beta S(\sqrt{r^2 - x^2}) \, dx = \int_{u_0}^{u_1} S(\sqrt{r^2 - f^2(u)}) f'(u) \, du$$

$$= \int_{u_0}^{u_1} S(r \cos u) \, r \cos u \, du$$

$$= \int_{u_0}^{u_1} h(\cos u) \, du, \tag{2}$$

where h is a rational function. Integrate the last integral in (2) via the methods of Sec. 19.10.

EXAMPLE 1. To evaluate $\int_0^1 (9 - x^2)^{3/2} \, dx$, let $x = f(u) = 3 \sin u$ for $0 \leq u \leq \pi/2$. Then $(9 - x^2)^{1/2} = (9 - 9 \sin^2 u)^{1/2} = 3\sqrt{1 - \sin^2 u} = 3 \cos u$, and $f'(u) = 3 \cos u$; and

$$\int_0^1 [(9 - x^2)^{1/2}]^3 \, dx = \int_0^{\pi/2} [3 \cos u]^3 \, 3 \cos u \, du$$

$$= 3^4 \int_0^{\pi/2} \cos^4 u \, du. \tag{3}$$

We could treat the last integral in (3) just as I did the integral $\int_0^{\pi/2} \sin^4 x \, dx$ in Example 1 of Sec. 19.10. More simply, you might check that via a further change of variables $u = f(x) = \pi/2 - x$, we can get

$$\int_0^{\pi/2} \cos^4 u \, du = \int_0^{\pi/2} \sin^4 x \, dx. \tag{4}$$

Hence borrowing from the result of Example 1 in Sec. 19.10,

$$\int_0^1 (9 - x)^{3/2} \, dx = 3^4 \int_0^{\pi/2} \sin^4 x \, dx = 3^4 \left(\frac{3}{8} \frac{\pi}{2} \right).$$

(b) Similarly, to handle $\sqrt{x^2 - r^2}$ where $r > 0$, let

$$x = f(u) = r \sec u = \frac{r}{\cos u}.$$

Then

$$\sqrt{x^2 - r^2} = \sqrt{f^2(u) - r^2} = \sqrt{r^2 \sec^2 u - r^2}$$

$$= r\sqrt{\sec^2 u - 1} = r \tan u = r \frac{\sin u}{\cos u} \qquad (5)$$

and

$$f'(u) = r \left(\frac{1}{\cos u} \right)' = -\frac{r \sin u}{\cos^2 u}.$$

Thus, if S is a rational function and $\alpha = r \sec u_0$ and $\beta = r \sec u_1$,

$$\int_\alpha^\beta S(\sqrt{x^2 - r^2})\, dx = \int_{u_0}^{u_1} S(\sqrt{f^2(u) - r^2}) f'(u)\, du$$

$$= \int_{u_0}^{u_1} S\left(r \frac{\sin u}{\cos u}\right)\left(-\frac{r \sin u}{\cos^2 u}\right) du \qquad (6)$$

and the last integral should yield to the methods of Sec. 19.10.

(c) To handle $\sqrt{x^2 + r^2}$, where $r > 0$, let $x = f(u) = r \tan u$. Then

$$\sqrt{x^2 + r^2} = \sqrt{f^2(u) + r^2} = \sqrt{r^2 \tan^2 u + r^2}$$

$$= r\sqrt{\tan^2 u + 1} = r \sec u = \frac{r}{\cos u} \qquad (7)$$

and

$$f'(u) = r(\tan u)' = r \sec^2 u = \frac{r}{\cos^2 u}. \qquad (8)$$

If S is a rational function and $\alpha = r \sec u_0$, and $\beta = r \sec u_1$, then

$$\int_\alpha^\beta S(\sqrt{x^2 + r^2})\, dx = \int_{u_0}^{u_1} S(\sqrt{f^2(u) + r^2}) f'(u)\, du$$

$$= \int_{u_0}^{u_1} S\left(\frac{r}{\cos u}\right)\left(\frac{r}{\cos^2 u}\right) du, \qquad (9)$$

and the last integral should yield to the methods of Sec. 19.10.

EXAMPLE 2. $\int_0^{3/2} \sqrt{4x^2 + 9}\, dx$. To use part (c), write

$$\sqrt{4x^2 + 9} = 2\sqrt{x^2 + \left(\frac{3}{2}\right)^2},$$

and let $x = f'(u) = (3/2) \tan u$. Then

$$\sqrt{4x^2 + 9} = \sqrt{4f(u)^2 + 9} = 2\frac{3}{2}\sqrt{\tan^2 u + 1} = \frac{3}{\cos u} \qquad (10)$$

and

$$f'(u) = \frac{3}{2}\frac{1}{\cos^2 u}. \qquad (11)$$

Now $0 = (3/2)\tan 0$, and let $3/2 = (3/2)\tan u_1$; that is, choose

$$u_0 = \arctan 0 = 0 \quad \text{and} \quad u_1 = \arctan 1 = \frac{\pi}{4}.$$

Then

$$\int_0^{3/2} \sqrt{4x^2 + 9}\, dx = \int_0^{\pi/4} \sqrt{4f(u)^2 + 9}\, f'(u)\, du$$

$$= \int_0^{\pi/4} \left(\frac{3}{\cos u}\right)\left(\frac{3}{2}\frac{1}{\cos^2 u}\right) du = \frac{9}{2}\int_0^{\pi/4} \frac{1}{\cos^3 u}\, du. \quad (12)$$

To evaluate the last integral in (12), let's use the method of Sec. 19.10. Write

$$\frac{1}{\cos^3 u} = \frac{\cos u}{\cos^4 u} = \frac{\cos u}{(1 - \sin^2 u)^2},$$

and make a second "change of variables" $F(u) = \sin u$. Then $F'(u) = \cos u$. Check that $\sin 0 = 0$ and $\sin(\pi/4) = 1/\sqrt{2}$. Hence

$$\int_0^{\pi/4} \frac{1}{(1 - \sin^2 u)^2}\cos u\, du = \int_0^{1/\sqrt{2}} \frac{1}{(1 - y^2)^2}\, dy. \quad (13)$$

To evaluate the last integral in (13) by the method of Sec. 19.3, let's suppose that constants A_i and B_i exist such that

$$\frac{1}{(y-1)^2(y+1)^2} = \frac{A_1}{y-1} + \frac{A_2}{(y-1)^2} + \frac{B_1}{y+1} + \frac{B_2}{(y+1)^2} \quad \text{for all } y \neq \pm 1. \quad (14)$$

Then let's multiply (14) through by $(y-1)^2(y+1)^2$, to get

$$1 = A_1(y-1)(y+1)^2 + A_2(y+1)^2 + B_1(y+1)(y-1)^2 + B_2(y-1)^2. \quad (15)$$

Rather than equate coefficients to find the constants A_i and B_i, let's substitute four different values $y = 0$, $y = 1$, $y = -1$, and $y = 2$ into (15) to get four simultaneous equations (recall Problem 1 of Sec. 19.3):

$$\left.\begin{array}{l} 1 = -A_1 + A_2 + B_1 + B_2, \\[2mm] 1 = \quad\ 4A_2, \\[2mm] 1 = \qquad\qquad 4B_2, \\[2mm] 1 = 9A_1 + 9A_2 + 3B_1 + B_2. \end{array}\right\} \quad (16)$$

Since $A_2 = \frac{1}{4}$ and $B_2 = \frac{1}{4}$, the equations reduce to two:

$$\left.\begin{array}{l} \dfrac{1}{2} = -A_1 + B_1, \\[4mm] -\dfrac{3}{2} = 9A_1 + 3B_1. \end{array}\right\} \quad (17)$$

—for which we can calculate a simultaneous solution $A_1 = -\frac{1}{4}$ and $B_1 = \frac{1}{4}$. Thus

$$\int_0^{1/\sqrt{2}} \frac{1}{(y-1)^2(y+1)^2}\,dy = \frac{1}{4}\int_0^{1/\sqrt{2}} \frac{1}{1-y}\,dy + \frac{1}{4}\int_0^{1/\sqrt{2}} \frac{1}{(y-1)^2}\,dy$$

$$+ \frac{1}{4}\int_0^{1/\sqrt{2}} \frac{1}{y+1}\,dy + \frac{1}{4}\int_0^{1/\sqrt{2}} \frac{1}{(y+1)^2}\,dy$$

$$= -\frac{1}{4}\left[\log(1-y)\right]_0^{1/\sqrt{2}} + \frac{1}{4}(-1)\left[\frac{1}{y-1}\right]_0^{1/\sqrt{2}}$$

$$+ \frac{1}{4}\left[\log(y+1)\right]_0^{1/\sqrt{2}} + \frac{1}{4}(-1)\left[\frac{1}{y+1}\right]_0^{1/\sqrt{2}}. \tag{18}$$

(In the 1st integral of (18), I made the change of variables $f(y) = 1-y$ rather than $y-1$, so that the resulting expression $\log(1-y)$ would make sense. $1-y > 0$ when $y < 1/\sqrt{2}$.) Finally, put the results (12), (13), and (18) together to get

$$\int^{3/2} \sqrt{4x^2+9}\,dx = \frac{9}{2}\left\{-\frac{1}{4}\log\left(\frac{1-1/\sqrt{2}}{1-0}\right) - \frac{1}{4}\left[\left(\frac{-\sqrt{2}}{\sqrt{2}-1}\right) - \left(\frac{1}{0-1}\right)\right]\right.$$

$$\left. + \frac{1}{4}\log\left(\frac{1/\sqrt{2}+1}{0+1}\right) - \frac{1}{4}\left[\frac{\sqrt{2}}{\sqrt{2}+1} - \frac{1}{0+1}\right]\right\}$$

$$= \frac{9}{8}\log\left(\frac{\sqrt{2}}{\sqrt{2}-1}\right) + \frac{9}{8}\log\left(\frac{\sqrt{2}+1}{\sqrt{2}}\right) - \frac{1}{4}(9\sqrt{2}). \tag{19}$$

19.13 PROBLEMS ON SQUARE ROOTS OF QUADRATICS AND ON "HYPERBOLIC" FUNCTIONS

°1. Evaluate the following integrals (using change of variables via trigonometric functions, as in Sec. 19.12, where convenient):

(a) $\int_0^1 \sqrt{4-x^2}\,dx$

(b) $\int_0^2 \frac{1}{\sqrt{x^2+4}}\,dx$

(c) $\int_{-1}^1 \frac{x^3}{\sqrt{x^2+25}}$

(d) $\int_{-1}^1 \frac{x^2}{\sqrt{2-x^2}}\,dx$

(e) $\int_0^1 \frac{1}{\sqrt{2t-t^2}}\,dt$

(f) $\int_{\sqrt{3}}^{3\sqrt{3}} \frac{1}{x^2\sqrt{x^2+9}}\,dx$

(g) $\int_0^{\sqrt{5}} x^2\sqrt{5-x^2}\,dx$

(h) $\int_3^6 \frac{\sqrt{x^2-9}}{x}\,dx$

(i) $\int_0^1 \frac{x}{\sqrt{x^2+4x+13}}\,dx$

(j) $\int_1^3 \frac{1}{t^2-2t+5}\,dt$

2. Here are definitions of the so-called "hyperbolic" functions:

$$\sinh x = \frac{e^x - e^{-x}}{2} \quad \text{for all } x \qquad \cosh x = \frac{e^x + e^{-x}}{2} \quad \text{for all } x$$

$$\tanh x = \frac{\sinh x}{\cosh x} \quad \text{for all } x \qquad \text{sech } x = \frac{1}{\cosh x} \quad \text{for all } x$$

Graph the functions, and then check these properties analogous to those for corresponding trig functions:

(a) $(\cosh x)^2 - (\sinh x)^2 = 1$ for all x
(b) $\sinh (-x) = -\sinh x$ and $\cosh (-x) = \cosh x$ for all x
(c) $1 - (\tanh x)^2 = (\text{sech } x)^2$ for all x
(d) $(\sinh x)' = \cosh x$ at all x
(e) $(\cosh x)' = \sinh x$ at all x
(f) $(\tanh x)' = (\text{sech } x)^2$ at all x

3. Evaluate the following integrals, using change of variables via the "hyperbolic" functions of Problem 2.

(a) $\int_2^4 \sqrt{x^2 - 1}\, dx$

   (Suggestion: Let $x = f(t) = \cosh t$.)

(b) $\int_1^{\sqrt{2}} \frac{1}{x^2 \sqrt{x^2 - 1}}\, dx$

(c) $\int_0^1 \sqrt{x^2 + 1}\, dx$ (d) $\int_0^1 \sqrt{1 - x^2}\, dx$

19.14 MIXED PROBLEMS ON EVALUATING DEFINITE INTEGRALS

1. Find the length of the graph of each of the following functions. (Recall Problem 16 of Sec. 18.2.)
   (a) $f(x) = x^{3/2}$ for $0 \leqslant x \leqslant 4$
   (b) $f(x) = \log_e (\cos x)$ for $0 \leqslant x \leqslant \pi/3$
   (c) $f(x) = 4 - x^2$ for $-2 \leqslant x \leqslant 2$
   (d) $f(x) = \log_e x$ for $1 \leqslant x \leqslant e$

2. Here is a miscellaneous collection of integrals to evaluate — in terms of end points a and b. Assume in each case that the interval $[a, b]$ is one on which the given function is continuous.

(a) $\int_a^b 2x^3\, e^2\, dx$ (b) $\int_a^b \frac{x^4 + 1}{x^2 - x}\, dx$

(c) $\int_a^b \frac{3x - 2}{(x + 2)(x + 1)(x - 1)}\, dx$ (d) $\int_a^b \frac{x^5 + 2x^3}{\sqrt{x^2 + 4}}\, dx$

(e) $\int_a^b \sqrt{2 + \sqrt{x}}\, dx$ (f) $\int_a^b \frac{\cos x\, dx}{\sqrt{1 + \tan x}}$

(g) $\int_a^b \frac{\tan x}{\cos^2 x}\, dx$ (h) $\int_a^b \sqrt{x^2 + 1}\, dx$

(i) $\displaystyle\int_a^b \frac{dx}{e^x + e^{-x}}$

(j) $\displaystyle\int_a^b \frac{dx}{\sqrt{1 + \sqrt{x}}}$

(k) $\displaystyle\int_a^b \frac{\cot x}{\log (\sin x)}\, dx$

(l) $\displaystyle\int_a^b \frac{\sin x\, e^{\sec x}}{\cos^2 x}\, dx$

(m) $\displaystyle\int_a^b \frac{dx}{\sqrt{2x - x^2}}$

(n) $\displaystyle\int_a^b \frac{\sin x}{1 + \cos^2 x}\, dx$

(o) $\displaystyle\int_a^b \frac{dx}{\sin x \cos x}$

(p) $\displaystyle\int_a^b \sqrt{1 - \sin x}\, dx$

(q) $\displaystyle\int_a^b \frac{dx}{\sqrt{(a^2 + x^2)^3}}$

(r) $\displaystyle\int_a^b \frac{dx}{x^6 - 1}$

(s) $\displaystyle\int_a^b \frac{x\, dx}{1 + \sqrt{x}}$

(t) $\displaystyle\int_a^b \log (\sqrt{x - 1})\, dx$

(u) $\displaystyle\int_a^b \frac{dx}{1 - \tan^2 x}$

(v) $\displaystyle\int_a^b \frac{x\, dx}{x^2 + 4x + 3}$

(w) $\displaystyle\int_a^b \frac{dx}{x(1 + \sqrt[3]{x})}$

(x) $\displaystyle\int_a^b \frac{(2e^{2x} - e^x)\, dx}{\sqrt{3e^{2x} - 6e^x - 1}}$

(y) $\displaystyle\int_a^b \frac{(x + 1)\, dx}{(x^2 + 2x - 3)^{2/3}}$

(z) $\displaystyle\int_a^b \log (x + \sqrt{1 + x^2})\, dx$

(aa) $\displaystyle\int_a^b \frac{\tan^{-1} x}{x^2}\, dx$

(bb) $\displaystyle\int_a^b (x + 1)^2 e^x\, dx$

(cc) $\displaystyle\int_a^b \frac{8\, dx}{x^4 + 2x^3}$

(dd) $\displaystyle\int_a^b \frac{\cos x\, dx}{\sin^3 x - \sin x}$

(ee) $\displaystyle\int_a^b \frac{x\, dx}{1 + \sqrt{x} + x}$

(ff) $\displaystyle\int_a^b \frac{\sec^2 x\, dx}{\sec^2 x - 3\tan x + 1}$

(gg) $\displaystyle\int_a^b e^{2t} \cos (e^t)\, dt$

(hh) $\displaystyle\int_a^b x \log (x^3 + x)\, dx$

(ii) $\displaystyle\int_a^b \frac{\sec^2 x}{\sqrt{4 - \sec^2 x}}\, dx$

(jj) $\displaystyle\int_a^b \frac{dx}{1 + 2\sin x}$

(kk) $\displaystyle\int_a^b \frac{dx}{\cot^3 x}$

(ll) $\displaystyle\int_a^b (\arcsin x)^2\, dx$

(mm) $\displaystyle\int_a^b \frac{x^3\, dx}{(x^2 + 1)^2}$

(nn) $\displaystyle\int_a^b x\sqrt{2x + 1}\, dx$

(oo) $\displaystyle\int_a^b e^{-x} \arctan (e^x)\, dx$

(pp) $\displaystyle\int_a^b \frac{\tan x\, dx}{\tan x + \sec x}$

(qq) $\displaystyle\int_a^b \cos\sqrt{x}\,dx$

(rr) $\displaystyle\int_a^b x\sin^2(2x)\,dx$

(ss) $\displaystyle\int_a^b \frac{x^3+x^2}{x^2+x-2}\,dx$

(tt) $\displaystyle\int_a^b \frac{dx}{e^{4x}+4e^{2x}+3}$

(uu) $\displaystyle\int_a^b \frac{\cos 2x-1}{\cos 2x+1}\,dx$

(vv) $\displaystyle\int_a^b \frac{dx}{(\cos^2 x+4\sin x-5)\cos x}$

(ww) $\displaystyle\int_a^b \sqrt{1-x^2}\,\arcsin x\,dx$

19.15 AN APPLICATION OF INTEGRATION BY PARTS: TAYLOR'S FORMULA FOR APPROXIMATING BY POLYNOMIALS

How can actual values be calculated — or approximated — for outputs of functions such as e^x, $\log x$, $\sin x$, $\sqrt{1+x}$, and so on? What schemes were used to compile all the existing "tables" of values for these functions? And what corresponding "subroutines" do high speed computers use to produce the same values each time one is needed? Here is a leading method. You might consider it as a refinement of the mean value theorem,

$$f(x)=f(a)+f'(c)(x-a)\qquad (c\text{ between }a\text{ and }x),\qquad(1)$$

or of the "fundamental theorem" of Sec. 18.1,

$$f(x)=f(a)+\int_a^x f'(t)\,dt.\qquad(2)$$

Both (1) and (2) express an output $f(x)$ in terms of some other — perhaps more easily computable — output $f(a)$, plus an "error term." You might consider the relations (1) and (2) as approximations of f — over some interval of x's surrounding a — by the simplest of functions, the constant function $\equiv f(a)$. Hopefully we could improve the approximation by using more complicated — but still computable — functions, such as *polynomials* of various degrees.

The scheme bearing the name of Brooks Taylor $(1700+)$ is to choose *polynomials whose outputs and whose various derivatives* MATCH *those of f at some fixed input a, where $f(a), f'(a), f''(a)$, and so on, are easily computable*. I invite you to check that if a function f is n times differentiable at an input a, then the *unique* polynomial $P(x)$ *of degree n* whose output and whose first n derivative values match those of f at a,

$$
\begin{aligned}
P(a)&=f(a),\\
P'(a)&=f'(a),\\
P''(a)&=f''(a),\\
&\ \ \vdots\qquad\quad\vdots\\
P^{(n)}(a)&=f^{(n)}(a),
\end{aligned}\qquad(3)
$$

is the polynomial

$$P_{n,a}(x) = f(a) + \frac{f'(a)}{1!}(x-a) + \frac{f''(a)}{2!}(x-a)^2$$

$$+ \cdots + \frac{f^{(k)}(a)}{h!}(x-a)^k + \cdots + \frac{f^{(n)}(a)}{n!}(x-a)^n. \qquad (4)$$

(See Problem 7 of the next section.) As I indicated in an earlier discussion of approximation (Sec. 15.7), the main question is how to estimate the size of the *error* $|f(x) - P_{n,a}(x)|$. For polynomials of degree $n \geq 1$, what corresponds to the expression $\int_a^x f'(t)\, dt$ in (2)?

To get an answer, let's suppose that f is as many times differentiable as necessary; and let's work through successive cases of approximation by $P_{n,a}(x)$, first with $n = 0$ (the case in (2)), then $n = 1$, then $n = 2, 3, \ldots$. To get from the $n = 0$ to the $n = 1$ case, let's try to split the expression $[f'(a)/1!](x-a)$ (which appears in $P_{1,a}(x)$) off from the error term $\int_a^x f'(t)\, dt$ in (2) and see what new error term is left. That is, for fixed x let's write

$$\int_a^x f'(t)\, dt = f'(a)(x-a) + ? \qquad (5)$$

How can we fill in the "?" in (5)? Note that the left-hand integral has the form $\int_a^x F'(t)G(t)\, dt$, where

$$F'(t) = 1, \quad F(t) = t - x, \quad \text{and} \quad G(t) = f'(t). \qquad (6)$$

Hence, applying integration by parts, we can write

$$\int_a^x f'(t)\, dt = [F(t)G(t)]_a^x - \int_a^x F(t)G'(t)\, dt$$

$$= [(t-x)f'(t)]_a^x - \int_a^x (t-x)f''(t)\, dt$$

$$= (x-x)f'(x) - (a-x)f'(a) - \int_a^x (t-x)f''(t)\, dt$$

$$= f'(a)(x-a) + \int_a^x f''(t)(x-t)\, dt. \qquad (7)$$

Together, (2) and (7) give

$$f(x) = f(a) + f'(a)(x-a) + \int_a^x f''(t)(x-t)\, dt$$

$$= P_{1,a}(x) + \int_a^x f''(t)(x-t)\, dt. \qquad (8)$$

And we have an error term in the form

$$f(x) - P_{1,a}(x) = \int_a^x f''(t)(x-t)\, dt. \qquad (9)$$

If we knew that $|f''(t)| \leq$ some constant M for all t between a and x, we could say that

$$|f(x) - P_{1,a}(x)| \leq M \int_a^x |x-t|\, dt = M \int_a^x (x-t)\, dt$$

$$= M\left\{ x(x-a) - \left[\frac{t^2}{2}\right]_a^x \right\} = M \frac{(x-a)^2}{2}. \qquad (10)$$

Now how can we pass from the case $n = 1$ to $n = 2$? By the same procedure. Write the error term in (8) in the form

$$\int_a^x f''(t)(x-t)\,dt = \int_a^x F'(t)G(t)\,dt,$$

where now

$$F'(t) = (x-t), \quad F(t) = -\frac{(x-t)^2}{2}, \quad \text{and} \quad G(t) = f''(t). \qquad (11)$$

Then

$$\int_a^x f''(t)(x-t)\,dt = [F(t)G(t)]_a^x - \int_a^x F(t)G'(t)\,dt$$

$$= \left[-\frac{(x-t)^2}{2} f''(t) \right]_a^x - \int_a^x \left[-\frac{(x-t)^2}{2} \right] f^{(3)}(t)\,dt$$

$$= \left[-\frac{(x-x)^2}{2} f''(x) \right] - \left[-\frac{(x-a)^2}{2} f''(a) \right]$$

$$\quad - \int_a^x \left[-\frac{(x-t)^2}{2} \right] f^{(3)}(t)\,dt$$

$$= \frac{f''(a)}{1}(x-a)^2 + \int_a^x f^{(3)}(t)\frac{(x-t)^2}{2}\,dt. \qquad (12)$$

Together (8) and (12) yield

$$f(x) = f(a) + f'(a)(x-a) + f''(a)\frac{(x-a)^2}{2} + \int_a^x f^{(3)}(t)\frac{(x-t)^2}{2}\,dt$$

$$= \bar{P}_{2,a}(x) + \int_a^x f^{(3)}(t)\frac{(x-t)^2}{2}\,dt. \qquad (13)$$

I invite you (in Problem 8 of the next section) to show (by induction) that the procedure can be carried on and on, to yield the result

Theorem ("Taylor's formula"): Suppose that $f(x)$ is $n+1$ times differentiable, and that $f^{n+1}(x)$ is a continuous function, on an interval $[\alpha, \beta]$. Then for any two inputs a and x in $[\alpha, \beta]$,

$$f(x) = f(a) + \frac{f'(a)}{1!}(x-a) + \frac{f''(a)}{2!}(x-a)^2 + \cdots + \frac{f^k(a)}{k!}(x-a)^k$$

$$+ \cdots + \frac{f^{(n)}(a)}{n!}(x-a)^n + \int_a^x f^{(n+1)}(t)\frac{(x-t)^n}{n!}\,dt. \qquad (14)$$

EXAMPLE 1. $f(x) = e^x$ for all x. Here $f'(x) = e^x$, $f''(x) = e^x$, and in fact $f^{(k)}(x) = e^x$ for all $k = 1, 2, 3, \ldots$ and at all x. Thus, for $a = 0$, for any x and for any $n = 1, 2, 3, \ldots$, Taylor's formula becomes

$$e^x = e^0 + \frac{e^0}{1!}(x-0) + \frac{e^0}{2!}(x-0)^2 + \cdots + \frac{e^0}{n!}(x-0)^n + \int_0^x e^t\frac{(x-t)^n}{n!}\,dt$$

$$= 1 + x + \frac{x^2}{2!} + \frac{x^3}{3!} + \cdots + \frac{x^n}{n!} + \int_0^x e^t\frac{(x-t)^n}{n!}\,dt. \qquad (15)$$

In particular, if x is any input in $[0, 1]$, then $e^t \leqslant e^1 \leqslant 3$ for all t with $0 \leqslant t \leqslant x$. And if $n = $ say, 7, then $n! = 7 \cdot 6 \cdot 5 \cdot 4 \cdot 3 \cdot 2 \cdot 1 = 5040$. Hence we can estimate the error term as

$$\left| \int_0^x e^t \frac{(x-t)^7}{7!} \, dt \right| \leqslant \frac{1}{5040} \int_0^x e^t (x-t)^7 \, dt \leqslant \frac{3}{7!} \int_0^x (x-t)^7 \, dt$$

$$= \frac{3}{7!} \left[-\frac{(x-t)^8}{8} \right]_0^x = \frac{3}{8!} x^8 \leqslant \frac{3}{8!}. \tag{16}$$

So, with less error than 0.00008 we can approximate e^x by

$$1 + x + \frac{x^2}{2!} + \frac{x^3}{3!} + \frac{x^4}{4!} + \frac{x^5}{5!} + \frac{x^6}{6!} + \frac{x^7}{7!}.$$

EXAMPLE 2. $f(x) = \sin x$ for all x. Hence $f'(x) = \cos x$, $f''(x) = -\sin x$, $f^{(3)}(x) = -\cos x$, and so on, at each input x. For $a = 0$, $f(0) = \sin 0 = 0$, $f'(0) = \cos 0 = 1$, $f''(0) = -\sin 0 = 0$, $f^{(3)}(0) = -\cos 0 = -1$, and so on. Thus for any x and any $n = 1, 2, 3, \ldots$, Taylor's formula becomes

$$\sin x = 0 + \frac{1}{1!}(x-0) + \frac{0}{2!}(x-0)^2 + \frac{(-1)}{3!}(x-0)^3 + \frac{0}{4!}(x-0)^4$$

$$+ \frac{1}{5!}(x-0)^5 + \cdots + \frac{\sin^{(n)} 0}{n!}(x-0)^n + \int_0^x [\sin^{(n+1)} t] \frac{(x-t)^n}{n!} \, dt. \tag{17}$$

Now, the $(n+1)$st derivative $\sin^{(n+1)} u = \pm \sin u$ or $\pm \cos u$ for any u and any n. Hence $|\sin^{(n+1)} t| \leqslant 1$ for all t and n. If $0 \leqslant x \leqslant \pi/4$, then for $n = 6$, we can estimate the error term as

$$\left| \int_0^x [\sin^{(6+1)} t] \frac{(x-t)^6}{6!} \, dt \right| \leqslant \frac{1}{6!} \int_0^x |\sin^{(7)} t| (x-t)^6 \, dt = \frac{1}{6!} \int_0^x (x-t)^6 \, dt$$

$$= \frac{1}{6!} \left[-\frac{(x-t)^7}{7!} \right]_0^x = \frac{1}{7!} x^7 < \frac{1}{7!} < 0.0002. \tag{18}$$

And to within 0.0002, we can approximate $\sin x$ by $x - x^3/3 + x^5/5!$. (Recall that $\sin^{(6)}(0) = 0$.)

19.16 PROBLEMS ON APPROXIMATION VIA TAYLOR'S FORMULA

°1. (a) With reference to Example 1 of Sec. 19.15, where I approximated e^x at inputs in $[0, 1]$ by

$$1 + x + \frac{x^2}{2!} + \frac{x^3}{3!} + \cdots + \frac{x^n}{n!},$$

what n (the smaller the better) would be sufficient to use if we wanted an error of no more than 0.01? Of no more than 10^{-7}?

(b) Repeat part (a) replacing the interval $[0, 1]$ by $[-2, 2]$.

°2. (a) With reference to Example 2 of Sec. 19.15, where I approximated sin x, at any x, by

$$x - \frac{x^3}{3!} + \frac{x^5}{5!} - \cdots + (-1)^m \frac{x^{2m+1}}{(2m+1)!} \qquad (m = 1, 2, 3, \ldots),$$

what m (the smaller the better) would be sufficient to use if we wanted an error of no more than 0.01? Of no more than 10^{-7}?

(b) Repeat part (a) by restricting x to the interval $[-\frac{1}{10}, \frac{1}{10}]$.

3. Show how to approximate $\cos x$ for all x with an error of no more than 0.005.

4. Show how to approximate $\log_e x$ for x in the interval $[0.9, 1.1]$, with an error of no more than 0.005.

5. Show how to approximate $\sqrt{x}$ for x in the interval $[0.9, 1.1]$, with an error of no more than 0.005.

6. Check by differentiation that the polynomial

$$P_{n,a}(x)$$
$$= f(a) + \frac{f'(a)}{1!}(x-a) + \frac{f''(a)}{2!}(x-a)^2 + \cdots + \frac{f^{(n)}(a)}{n!}(x-a)^n$$

of Sec. 19.15 does indeed have the property that

$$P_{n,a}(a) = f(a), \; P'_{n,a}(a) = f'(a), \; P''_{n,a}(a) = f''(a), \ldots, \text{ and}$$

$$P^{(n)}_{n,a}(a) = f^{(n)}(a), \qquad\qquad (**)$$

where f is a given function n times differentiable at $x = a$.

7. (a) Check that any polynomial of the form

$$D(x) = d_0 + d_1(x-a) + d_2(x-a)^2 + \cdots + d_n(x-a)^n \qquad (*)$$

for which

$$D(a) = 0, D'(a) = 0, D''(a) = 0, \ldots, \text{and } D^{(n)}(a) = 0$$

must be identically zero — that is, $d_i = 0$ for $0 \le i \le n$.

(b) Check that any two polynomials $P(x)$ and $Q(x)$ of the form (*) for which

$$P(a) = Q(a), P'(a) = Q'(a), P''(a) = Q''(a), \ldots, \text{ and}$$

$$P^{(n)}(a) = Q^{(n)}(a)$$

must be identical. (Suggestion: Consider the difference $D(x) = P(x) - Q(x)$.)

*(c) Check that, for a fixed a, any nth degree polynomial can be written in the form (*) with uniquely determined coefficient d_i $(0 \le i \le n)$.

(d) Use parts (a)–(c) to show that the polynomial $P_{n,a}$ in Problem 6 is the *unique* nth degree polynomial having property (**) of that problem.

*8. Suppose that $f(x)$ is $n+1$ times differentiable, and that $f^{n+1}(x)$ is a continuous function on an interval $[\alpha, \beta]$. Use induction and "integration by parts" (as in (12) of Sec. 19.15) to show that

$$f(x) = f(a) + \frac{f'(a)}{1!}(x-a) + \frac{f''(a)}{2!}(x-a)^2 + \cdots$$

$$+ \frac{f^k(a)}{k!}(x-a)^k + \cdots + \frac{f^{(n)}(a)}{n!}(x-a)^n$$

$$+ \int_a^x f^{(n+1)}(t)\frac{(x-t)^n}{n!}\,dt$$

for any two inputs a and x in $[\alpha, \beta]$.

19.17 SUMMARY OF CHAPTER 19

See Sec. 19.1–19.14 for a list of techniques for evaluating definite integrals.

In Sec. 19.15 is "Taylor's approximation formula":

$$f(x) = f(a) + \frac{f'(a)}{1!}(x-a) + \frac{f''(a)}{2!}(x-a)^2 + \cdots + \frac{f^{(n)}(a)}{n!}(x-a)^n$$

$$+ \int_a^x f^{(n+1)}(t)\frac{(x-t)^n}{n!}\,t,$$

valid for a function f which is $n+1$ times continuously differentiable on an interval containing a and x.

For applications to approximations of e^x, $\log_e x$, $\sin x$, and $\cos x$, see Sec. 19.15, and the problems of Sec. 19.16.

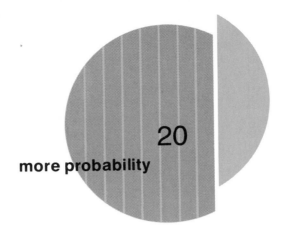

20

more probability

In this chapter I'll try to review and bring together the various strands of reasoning about probability that I've followed earlier. I'll also discuss the notion of "conditional probability," and a number of its applications — some involving limits and integration, and some not.

20.1 A REVIEW

What I attempted to do in each of the examples involving "randomness" — from that in Sec. 1.2 on clinical evidence to that in Sec. 4.9 on a meeting at a bus stop, to that in Sec. 18.4 on the arrival of telephone calls — was to set up a little "*model*." I hoped that each model would capture the important aspects of the "real-life" experiments in question. Here are the basic steps which I found convenient to take in building each model:

(a) First, I *decided upon a set Ω representing all possible outcomes for the experiment.*

In the clinical evidence example, Ω was a list of eight symbols, $\Omega = \{sss, ssd, sds, dss, sdd, dsd, dds, ddd\}$. For the meeting at a bus stop, I let Ω be a square in the plane, a set of all pairs (x, y) representing possible arrival times of two people. In the case of telephone calls, I took Ω to be the set of all real numbers $t > 0$ — each t being a possible arrival time for the next call after that at time 0.

The set Ω describing "possible outcomes" of an experiment need not be unique. For example, someone else considering arriving telephone calls might want to describe an individual possible outcome in far more detail — say, as an infinite sequence $\omega = (t_1 < t_2 < t_3 \cdots)$, where t_i is the possible arrival time of the ith call after time 0, for $i = 1, 2, 3, \ldots$. There is nothing wrong with using such ω's, except that they are bulkier than mere real numbers t and they may contain far more information than one really needs.

(b) Secondly, I *paid particular attention to various* SUBSETS *of* Ω, *each of which seemed to represent some "compound result."* For any two or more such subsets $A_1, A_2, \ldots, A_n$, their *union* $A_1 \cup A_2 \cup \cdots \cup A_n$, their intersection $A_1 \cap A_2 \cap \cdots \cap A_n$, and their individual complements $A_1', A_2', \ldots, A_n'$ again represented "compound results."

For the clinical evidence experiment, the subset $\{ssd, sds, dss\}$ meant "exactly 2 victims survive." For the meeting at a bus stop I considered subsets of the square Ω in the plane — subsets which had "area." And for the telephone call experiment, I let the interval $[t_{i-1}, t_i)$ represent the result that "the next call arrives between times t_{i-1} (inclusive) and t_i."

(c) Thirdly, to make a model quantitative, I *decided upon some* RULE — *that is, upon some function — which would assign a probability number $P(S)$ to each subset S representing a "compound result."* The main idea of the assignment was this: the relative magnitudes of any two outputs $P(S)$ and $P(T)$ should express our feelings as to the relative chances for the actual outcome of the experiment to appear in S as against T. Specifically, the probability function was to have these properties:

$$P(\Omega) = 1 \quad \text{and} \quad P\text{ (empty set)} = 0, \tag{1}$$

$$0 \leqslant P(S) \leqslant 1 \qquad \text{for any subset } S, \tag{2}$$

$$P(S) \leqslant P(T) \qquad \text{if } S \subset T, \tag{3}$$

$$P(S_1 \cup S_2 \cup \cdots \cup S_n) = P(S_1) + P(S_2) + \cdots + P(S_n)$$

$$\text{for } \textit{mutually exclusive} \text{ sets } S_i, \tag{4}$$

and

$$P(S') = 1 - P(S) \text{ for } \textit{complementary} \text{ sets } S \text{ and } S'. \tag{5}$$

(You might recall my extending property (4) by induction from the special case $n = 2$, in Sec. 6.6.)

Why these particular properties? People came to them via several approaches. One was that of the "frequency theorists": If you toss a die a large number of times, n, and if a "1" appears M_n of these times, why not *define* the probability of a "1" as the "frequency" of its appearance, the ratio M_n/n? And if a "2" appears N_n of the times, why not define its probability as the ratio N_n/n? The result "1 or 2" would have occurred $M_n + N_n$ times out of n, and its frequency would be

$$\frac{M_n + N_n}{n} = \frac{M_n}{n} + \frac{N_n}{n}. \tag{6}$$

Equation (6) exposes property (4) — as well as (2) and (3). In fact, all the properties follow from such frequency definitions. The main objection to using particular observed frequencies as the very *definition* probabilities was this: What if we redid the tosses, or increased the number of tosses? The ratios might well change. How can we tell what is really an appropriate value for the probability of a "1"? To this, some frequency theorists replied: let's define the probability of a "1" as the $\lim_{n \to \infty} M_n/n$. But then the objection was: How can we ever be sure that a limit exists? And if it does, how can we be sure what its value is? No *finite* sequence of numbers can ever really determine a "limit." To this, some frequency theorists replied: If (finitely) many observed ratios

$$\frac{M_1}{1}, \frac{M_2}{2}, \frac{M_3}{3}, \ldots, \frac{M_n}{n}$$

seem to tend to some value p, let's just *assume* that p is their limit. So it came to an assumption in the end.

When considering dice, Pierre de Laplace and others were willing to *start* with an assumption: In the *absence of any information* favoring one side of the die over the others, one may *assign "equal likelihood"* to all of the six possible outcomes for a single toss. Laplace then felt it "reasonable" to *define* the probability of a compound result such as "1 or 2" as the relative number of outcomes favoring the result. Since the number i of sides showing a "1" and the number j of sides showing a "2" are both one, the relative number of outcomes favoring "1 or 2" is

$$\frac{2}{6} = \frac{i+j}{6} = \frac{i}{6} + \frac{j}{6} \tag{7}$$

—again an equation suggesting properties (4), (3), and (2). And, again, all the properties (1)–(5) follow from such definitions.

The currently popular scheme—which I've outlined in items (a), (b), and (c) above—is to adopt the properties suggested by the "frequency" and "equal likelihood" approaches as *reasonable requirements* for almost any model of a real-life experiment involving chance. You can assign numbers $P(S)$ *in any way relevant to the experiment*, as long as they are consistent with the properties. For example, if you are trying to construct a model corresponding to a real coin which you've seen fall "heads" 605 times during 1000 tosses, feel free to assign a probability of 0.6 for "heads" and 0.4 for "tails," if you like. The proof of a particular model will be in its usefulness. If you can decide, say, how to bet successfully with the coin on the basis of the numbers 0.6 and 0.4, then keep the model. If not, throw it away and construct another. (Perhaps you should toss the coin 100,000 times before deciding on a probability for "heads.") Finally, if honoring the properties (1)–(5) brings only frustration, throw *them* away. But then the burden lies upon *you* to find better guidelines.

Here are a few of the methods I used earlier in assigning probabilities $P(S)$. For the clinical evidence examples of Secs. 1.2 and 3.2, I defined $P(S)$ in terms of more basic quantities. Namely, I first assigned an "elementary probability" $p(\omega)$ to each possible outcome "ω" in the set $\Omega = \{sss, ssd, sds, \ldots\}$. Recall Fig. 3-3 where the $p(\omega)$'s were all equal to $\frac{1}{8}$, and Fig. 3-6 where they differed for different ω's. In each case I followed a standardization suggested by both the "frequency" and the "equal likelihood" approaches, and chose $p(\omega)$ values with

$$p(\omega) \geq 0 \qquad \text{for all } \omega \text{ in } \Omega \tag{8}$$

and

$$\text{the sum of all } p(\omega)\text{'s} = 1. \tag{9}$$

Then to assign probabilities $P(S)$ to subsets I added the elementary weights: I *defined*

$$P(S) = \begin{cases} \text{the sum of the } p(\omega)\text{'s} \\ \text{for all } \omega\text{'s in } S \end{cases} \tag{10}$$

All the desired properties (1)–(5) flow from this definition and from the standardizations (8) and (9)—as you may have checked in Problem 20 of Sec. 3.4.

For the meeting at a bus stop—with Ω the set of points in a 5×5 square—I argued by analogy with the "equal likelihood" approach for experiments with finitely many outcomes, and I assigned probabilities to subsets in proportion to their areas. More explicitly, I *defined*

$$P(S) = \frac{\text{area of } S}{\text{area of } \Omega} \qquad \text{for all subsets } S \text{ of } \Omega \text{ having area.} \tag{11}$$

(I argued also that such a definition embodied the notion of two persons arriving at the bus stop "independently" of each other.) The purpose of having the area of Ω in the denominator of (11) was to guarantee property (1), that $P(\Omega) = 1$. All the other properties (2)–(5) then follow from the basic addition and nonnegativity properties of areas.

Finally, in constructing models from the arrivals of meteorites and telephone calls, my procedure was essentially this: I *supposed* that there was a reasonable assignment of probabilities to various subsets of $\Omega = \{\text{all } t \geq 0\}$—an assignment which did satisfy properties (1)–(5). I supposed also that the probabilities satisfied further requirements--specially tailored to the experiment at hand, such as "independence of arrivals in nonoverlapping time intervals." Then I asked to what form of $P(S)$ all these requirements led. The answer, for intervals $S = [0, t\rangle$ and $S = [a, b\rangle$, was

$$P([0, t\rangle) = 1 - e^{-\lambda t} \quad \text{and} \quad P([a, b\rangle) = e^{-\lambda a} - e^{-\lambda b}. \tag{12}$$

(You might check in doing Problem 10 of Sec. 20.4 that a probability function $P(S)$, satisfying (12) and all the other requirements, really *does* exist.)

20.2 MORE REVIEW: "RANDOM VARIABLES" AND "AVERAGES"

In some probability problems, the "possible outcomes" of an experiment serve mainly as a groundwork. Other related quantities may be of greater interest. Thus the tossing of a die which I discussed in Sec. 3.1 was the basis for a bet which promised "payoffs," as in Fig. 20-1. The "payoff" schedule of Fig. 20-1 defines a function f. And if you are trying to decide whether to accept the bet, the outputs of f may concern you more than its inputs.

Similarly, for the set $\Omega = [0, 5]$ of possible lengths t for the incubation period of a disease — which I considered in Example 2 of Sec. 18.3. A length t was less important than the *size* of the infection after t hours, $f(t) = 10^6 \, e^{2t}$.

In case you meet the term elsewhere, you should know that lately some people have given the name *"random variable"* to any such function f whose domain is the set Ω of possible outcomes of some experiment.

The main question I asked so far about the "random variables" f which I just reviewed was this: What number can we take as an "average" output value? The meaning of "average" which I suggested in Secs. 3.1 and 18.3 was this: *If numbers $f(1)$, $f(2)$, $f(3)$, . . . have corresponding probabilities $p_1, p_2, p_3, \ldots$, where the p_i's add to 1, then we can regard the sum*

$$f(1)p_1 + f(2)p_2 + f(3)p_3 + \cdots \tag{1}$$

as an "average" of the f_i's.

In particular, if an experiment has finitely many possible outcomes $\Omega = \{\omega_1, \omega_2, \ldots, \omega_n\}$, and to each outcome ω_i we assign an elementary probability $p(\omega_i)$ and a payoff $f(\omega_i)$, we can say that the "average payoff" is the sum

$$f(\omega_1)p(\omega_1) + f(\omega_2)p(\omega_2) + \cdots + f(\omega_n)p(\omega_n). \tag{2}$$

Thus for a "true" die, where each outcome $\omega = 1, 2, \ldots, 6$ can appear with probability $p(\omega) = \frac{1}{6}$, the "average payoff" of the function f in Fig. 20-1 will be the sum

$$(\$4)\frac{1}{6} + (\$-3)\frac{1}{6} + (\$-3)\frac{1}{6} + (\$-3)\frac{1}{6} + (\$-3)\frac{1}{6} + (\$4)\frac{1}{6}. \tag{3}$$

Note that by *grouping together* the elementary probabilities of outcomes which share the same payoff, we can write the average *equivalently* as

$$(\$4)\left[\frac{1}{6} + \frac{1}{6}\right] + (\$-3)\left[\frac{1}{6} + \frac{1}{6} + \frac{1}{6} + \frac{1}{6}\right] = (\$4)\frac{2}{6} + (\$-3)\frac{4}{6}. \tag{4}$$

In its own way, the last sum has the same general form (1) for "averages" as does (3). The special feature of the alternate sum (4) is that it displays only *distinct* output values, $\$4$ and $\$-3$, and shows how each is allotted its full amount of probability for occurring. (The probabilities again add to 1: $\frac{2}{6} + \frac{4}{6} = 1$.)

In Secs. 18.3, 18.4, and 18.5 I discussed how we might extend the averaging principle (1) to experiments with infinitely many possible outcomes. Thus, for the case of possible incubation times t distributed "with equal likelihood" throughout an interval $\Omega = [0, 5]$, I argued that we might use an *integral* to represent an "average

FIGURE 20-1

possible outcomes (inputs ω)		corresponding payoffs (outputs $f(\omega)$)
1	$\longrightarrow$	$\$4$
2	$\longrightarrow$	-3
3	$\longrightarrow$	-3
4	$\longrightarrow$	-3
5	$\longrightarrow$	-3
6	$\longrightarrow$	4

value" for the bacterial population size function $f(t) = 10^6\, e^{2t}$, namely,

$$\frac{1}{5} \int_0^5 f(t)\, dt = \frac{1}{5} \int_0^5 10^6\, e^{2t}\, dt \qquad (5)$$

—the "analog" of the finite sum (3) with equal $p(\omega)$'s.

In the case of possible waiting times t until the arrival of a telephone call (in Secs. 18.4 and 18.5) I found that probability was *not* distributed with equal likelihood throughout $\Omega = [0, \infty)$. It decreased for larger and larger times t. However, I was able to describe its distribution via a "cumulative probability function" $G(t) = 1 - e^{-\lambda t}$ and a "probability density function" $g(t) = G'(t) = \lambda e^{\lambda t}$. As an "average value" for the waiting times t, I argued for a limit of integrals

$$\lim_{n \to \infty} \int_0^{t_n} t g(t)\, dt = \lim_{n \to \infty} \int_0^{t_n} t \lambda e^{\lambda t}\, dt, \qquad (6)$$

where $\lim_{n \to \infty} t_n = \infty$. In the integrals, each distinct time t is weighted (multiplied) by the density $g(t)$ of probability at t—again in the spirit of the sums (1) and (2).

Note a convenience resulting from the definition of "average" in terms of sums or integrals: *If we can write a payoff function $f(\omega)$ for some experiment as a sum $f(\omega) = h(\omega) + k(\omega)$ of simpler payoff functions $h(\omega)$ and $k(\omega)$ connected with the same experiment, then we can calculate the average of f as the sum of the averages of h and k.*

Why? For an experiment with finitely many possible outcomes, $\Omega = \{\omega_1, \omega_2, \ldots, \omega_n\}$, we'll have

$$
\begin{aligned}
\text{Average of } f &= f(\omega_1)p(\omega_1) + f(\omega_2)p(\omega_2) + \cdots \\
&= [h(\omega_1) + k(\omega_1)]p(\omega_1) + [h(\omega_2) + k(\omega_2)]p(\omega_2) + \cdots \\
&= [h(\omega_1)p(\omega_1) + h(\omega_2)p(\omega_2) + \cdots] + [k(\omega_1)p(\omega_1) \\
&\quad + k(\omega_2)p(\omega_2) + \cdots] \\
&= [\text{average of } h] + [\text{average of } k]. \qquad (7)
\end{aligned}
$$

Similarly, for scaling a function by a constant c:

$$
\begin{aligned}
\text{Average of } [cf] &= [cf(\omega_1)]p(\omega_1) + [cf(\omega_2)]p(\omega_2) + \cdots \\
&= cf(\omega_1)p(\omega_1) + cf(\omega_2)p(\omega_2) + \cdots \\
&= c[f(\omega_1)p(\omega_1) + f(\omega_2)p(\omega_2) + \cdots] \\
&= c[\text{average of } f]. \qquad (8)
\end{aligned}
$$

And when we define averages by integrals, we get the same results— via the properties of the definite integral:

$$\frac{1}{b-a} \int_a^b [h(t) + k(t)]\, dt = \frac{1}{b-a} \int_a^b h(t)\, dt + \frac{1}{b-a} \int_a^b k(t)\, dt \qquad (9)$$

for the case of "equal likelihood" among all t's in $[a, b]$. And also

$$\int_a^b [h(t) + k(t)]g(t)\,dt = \int_a^b h(t)g(t)\,dt + \int_a^b k(t)g(t)\,dt \qquad \text{(10)}$$

for the case of probabilities distributed throughout $[a, b]$ according to some density function g. Similarly for scaling by a constant c.

I've already used the "addition property" of averages in discussing the "tuning" of signals, in Sec. 18.7. Here is another application:

EXAMPLE 1. Imagine a situation where there are n distinct jobs to be done and n people to do them, and where each job can be done best by a unique one of the n people. Suppose, however, that each day a "work roster" is made up by assigning people to jobs "at random." You might then expect a *given* person to have 1 in n chances of getting the job for which he's best suited — or equivalently, you might expect a *given* job to receive a "correct placement" with probability $1/n$. Now on a given work roster there may be several such "correct placements," or many, or none. What's the *average number of correct placements* that we can expect per day? Make a guess before reading on.

To answer, let's first describe the possible work rosters — the possible outcomes "ω." One way is to represent the jobs as numbered boxes from left to right (see Fig. 20-2) and to give each person a (green) number corresponding to the job he does *best*.

FIGURE 20-2

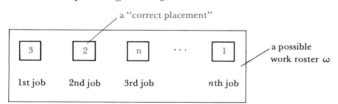

a "correct placement"

| 3 | 2 | n | ⋯ | 1 |

1st job   2nd job   3rd job nth job

a possible work roster ω

Then we can picture a particular roster ω by recording the number of the person in the box corresponding to the job he was given. And we can visualize all possible rosters ω as corresponding to all permutations of the n green integers among the boxes. Let's interpret the "randomness" of roster assignments by saying that all ω's should be *equally likely*.

For a given roster ω we can recognize a "correct placement" as a box labeled i which receives the same (green) integer i — for example, $i = 2$ in Fig. 20-2. How can we find the average number of such placements? In order to simplify bookkeeping, why not give to each box — without regard to the others — a bonus of \$1 if (and only if) it receives a correct placement? Then, except for the dollar sign, the number of correct placements will be the sum of the bonuses paid out. *And the average number of correct placements will be the sum of the average bonuses for the individual boxes.* In symbols, let's define for each fixed integer $i \leq n$ an auxiliary "bonus" payoff function

$$f_i(\omega) = \begin{cases} 1 & \text{if box } i \text{ receives a correct placement, in } \omega; \\ 0 & \text{otherwise.} \end{cases} \qquad \text{(11)}$$

Then the total number of correct placements in a roster ω will be the sum

$$f(\omega) = f_1(\omega) + f_2(\omega) + f_3(\omega) + \cdots + f_n(\omega), \tag{12}$$

and corresponding averages will have the relationship

$$\text{av of } f = \text{av of } f_1 + \text{av of } f_2 + \text{av of } f_3 + \cdots + \text{av of } f_n. \tag{13}$$

All that remains is to calculate the average of an individual bonus payoff function f_i. Now, that function will have output 1 precisely for those rosters ω wherein the ith job gets a correct placement—a result which I suggested should have probability $1/n$. And f_i will have output 0 with the remaining probability $1 - 1/n$. So the average output of f_i should be

$$1 \cdot \frac{1}{n} + 0 \cdot \left(1 - \frac{1}{n}\right) = \frac{1}{n} \tag{14}$$

—and this for each i. Thus the right-hand side of (13) is the sum of n $(1/n)$'s, and the average of $f = n \cdot 1/n = 1$.

Conclusion: No matter how large the number n of jobs and people, if people are assigned *randomly* to the jobs, then the average number of correct placements will be exactly *one*. Strange?

Here's how to check according to the old assignment rules that the probability for a correct placement in the ith box is $1/n$: Let's let Ω denote the set of all distinct rosters ω, and B_i denote the subset of ω's which have an i fixed in the ith box. Since all ω's are equally likely, we should have probability

$$P(B_i) = \frac{\text{size of } B_i}{\text{size of } \Omega} \tag{15}$$

as I argued in Sec. 3.1. There are as many ω's in Ω as there are distinct permutations of the integers $1, 2, \ldots, n$—namely $n! = n(n-1)(n-2) \cdots 2 \cdot 1$ (a result in Sec. 6.8). For the ω's in B_i—where the integer i is fixed in the ith box—there remain $n-1$ integers to be permuted among the remaining $n-1$ boxes, in $(n-1)!$ distinct ways. So the size of B_i is $(n-1)!$, and

$$P(B_i) = \frac{(n-1)!}{n!} = \frac{(n-1)(n-2) \cdots 2 \cdot 1}{n(n-1)(n-2) \cdots 2 \cdot 1} = \frac{1}{n}. \tag{16}$$

*20.3   MODELS VS. REALITY

Suppose we witness someone tossing a coin 1000 times, winning \$1 for "head" and losing \$1 for each tail. And suppose his "net win" after the 1000th toss is very small, say \$2—giving him an OBSERVED *net win* of \$2/1000 = \$0.002 *per toss*. We might decide that the coin is rather "true." And if we had to build a *model* for an arbitrary number n of tosses of the coin, we might well decide to assign *equal likelihood* to all of the possible outcomes—that is, to all patterns of wins and losses of the form

$$\omega = (\$1, \$-1, \$-1, \$1, \dots, \$-1).$$ (1)

n entries
(one for each trial)

Now for each such theoretically possible pattern ω, we can calculate a THEORETICAL *net win per toss*; namely,

$$T(\omega) = \frac{\text{the sum of the entries in } \omega}{n}.$$ (2)

For some ω's this quantity will be far from the observed value of $\$0.002$ per toss. For example, the unlikely but possible case of n successive heads, with corresponding $\omega_0 = (\$1, \$1, \$1, \$1, \dots, \$1)$, yields a value

$$T(\omega_0) = \frac{\$1 + \$1 + \$1 + \cdots + \$1}{n} = \$1 \text{ } per \text{ } toss.$$

A basic question concerning the connection between the model and the observed data is this: How much probability is allotted *within the model itself* to those patterns ω whose theoretical net win per toss $T(\omega)$ is very close to the observed value $\$0.002$—or to the *ideal* value of $\$0$, from which the observed $\$0.002$ differs very little? In other words: *Does the model itself say that the chances are great for observing in a future experiment a quantity ("net win per toss") close to the quantity we already observed in the past?* If so, we can have hopes that our model is a good one—the basic hopes of anyone trying to predict something in the future from past data. (Note well, however, that by some quirk the actual coin may have fooled us during the 1000 trials we witnessed, and we have *no* way of knowing this in advance of future trials.)

When n is small it may be impossible to get a good model. For example, here are the 8 possible patterns in a model for $n = 3$ tosses—together with their theoretical net wins per toss.

Pattern ω	Theoretical net win per toss $T(\omega)$
($\$1, \$1, \$1$)	$\$1$ per toss
($\$1, \$1, \$-1$)	$\$\frac{1}{3}$ per toss
($\$1, \$-1, \$1$)	$\$\frac{1}{3}$ per toss
($\$1, \$-1, \$-1$)	$\$-\frac{1}{3}$ per toss
($\$-1, \$1, \$1$)	$\$\frac{1}{3}$ per toss
($\$-1, \$1, \$-1$)	$\$-\frac{1}{3}$ per toss
($\$-1, \$-1, \$1$)	$\$-\frac{1}{3}$ per toss
($\$-1, \$-1, \$-1$)	$\$-1$ per toss

None of these $T(\omega)$ values are anywhere near being within, say, $\$0.01$ of the ideal value $\$0$ per toss—as was the *observed* number $\$0.002$. Why? Because $n = 3$ is too small a number of entries to permit suitable canceling of $1's and $—1's. If we're to guarantee high probability for finding ω's with corresponding $T(\omega)$ close to $0 per toss, let's look to models with *large n*'s. Here is a result which has comforted statisticians throughout the years.

Theorem A ("a law of large numbers"): Suppose that for each positive integer n we form a model where Ω_n is the set of all 2^n patterns of 1's and -1's, of the form $\omega = (1, -1, -1, 1, \ldots, -1)$, and that we assign equal elementary probabilities $p(\omega) = 1/2^n$ to all the patterns ω. Let's also define for each ω its "theoretical net win per toss,"

$$T_n(\omega) = \frac{\text{the sum of the 1's and } -1\text{'s in } \omega}{n}. \tag{3}$$

Finally, let's pick an allowable error bound $\delta > 0$ and form the subset

$$B_{n,\delta} = \{\text{all } \omega\text{'s in } \Omega_n \text{ for which } |T_n(\omega)| \le \delta\}. \tag{4}$$

$B_{n,\delta}$ will have probability

$$P(B_{n,\delta}) = \frac{\text{size of } B_{n,\delta}}{2^n};$$

and as we choose models with larger and larger n, we'll find that

$$\lim_{n \to \infty} P(B_{n,\delta}) = 1. \tag{5}$$

Here's how we can establish such a result with the aid of "auxiliary payoff functions"–in the spirit of the person-job matching example of the last section:

A sketch of a proof of the theorem A (a "law of large numbers"): Let's look at a model for a fixed n; and to simplify bookkeeping let's define a payoff function f_i for each $i \le n$ by the rule

$$f_i(\omega) = \text{the } i\text{th entry in } \omega; \text{ that is, the amount } (\$\pm 1) \text{ won}$$
$$\text{on the } i\text{th toss of the pattern } \omega. \tag{6}$$

Then we can write

$$T_n(\omega) = \frac{f_1(\omega) + f_2(\omega) + f_3(\omega) + \cdots + f_n(\omega)}{n}.$$

And we can write the condition $|T_n(\omega)| \le \delta$, for closeness to the ideal net win of $0 per toss, as

$$\left| \frac{f_1(\omega) + f_2(\omega) + f_3(\omega) + \cdots + f_n(\omega)}{n} \right| \le \delta; \tag{7}$$

or as

$$|f_1(\omega) + f_2(\omega) + f_3(\omega) + \cdots + f_n(\omega)| \le n\delta;$$

or as

$$[f_1(\omega) + f_2(\omega) + f_3(\omega) + \cdots + f_n(\omega)]^2 \le n^2\delta^2. \tag{8}$$

(It's often easier to work with squares than with absolute values.)

Note that the complement of the set $B_{n,\delta}$ is precisely the set

$$B'_{n,\delta} = \left\{ \begin{array}{l} \text{all } \omega\text{'s in } \Omega_n \text{ for which} \\[1em] [f_1(\omega) + f_2(\omega) + f_3(\omega) + \cdots + f_n(\omega)]^2 > n^2\delta^2 \end{array} \right\}. \tag{9}$$

And since $P(B_{n,\delta}) = 1 - P(B'_{n,\delta})$ we could prove the theorem just as well by showing that

$$\lim_{n \to \infty} P(B'_{n,\delta}) = 0. \tag{10}$$

Here is how we can use the "addition" and "scaling" properties of averages to prove (10): Since

$$\begin{aligned}[f_1 + f_2 + f_3 + \cdots + f_n]^2 = {} & f_1{}^2 + f_2{}^2 + f_3{}^2 + \cdots + f_n{}^2 \\ & + 2(f_1 f_2) + 2(f_1 f_3) + \cdots + 2(f_2 f_3) + \cdots \\ & + 2(f_{n-1} f_n), \end{aligned}$$

we must have

the average of $[f_1 + f_2 + f_3 + \cdots + f_n]^2$

$$\begin{aligned} = {} & \text{av of } f_1{}^2 + \text{av of } f_2{}^2 + \text{av of } f_3{}^2 + \cdots + \text{av of } f_n{}^2 \\ & + \text{av of } (f_1 f_2) + 2 \text{ av of } (f_1 f_3) + \cdots + 2 \text{ av of } (f_2 f_3) + \cdots \\ & + 2 \text{ av of } (f_{n-1} f_n). \end{aligned} \tag{11}$$

Since each f_i has only ± 1 as outputs, $f_i{}^2(\omega) = 1$ for all ω. Check that the average of $f_i{}^2$ must therefore be 1 for each i. But what about the products $f_i f_j$ of payoff functions for different tosses $i \neq j$? I invite you to check this key point: that since all patterns of \$1's and \$—1's are equally likely for the two tosses i and j,

the average of $(f_i f_j) = 0$. \tag{12}

(Do Problem 6 in the next section.) If so, then all terms on the right-hand side of (11) are 0 except for the n averages of squares, which are 1. And we can conclude that

the average of $[f_1 + f_2 + f_3 + \cdots + f_n]^2 = n$. \tag{13}

On the other hand,

$$[f_1(\omega) + f_2(\omega) + f_3(\omega) + \cdots + f_n(\omega)]^2 > n^2\delta^2$$

for all ω's in the set $B'_{n,\delta}$—by the very definition (9) of $B'_{n,\delta}$. Shouldn't the average of $[f_1 + f_2 + f_3 + \cdots + f_n]^2$ therefore be at least as great as the product $n^2\delta^2 P(B'_{n,\delta})$? (Check this key point in doing Problem 7 of the next section.) If so, then from (13) we get the inequality

$$n \geqslant n^2\delta^2 P(B'_{n,\delta}); \tag{14}$$

which we can divide by $n^2\delta^2$ and write as

$$P(B'_{n,\delta}) \leqslant \frac{1}{n\delta^2}. \tag{15}$$

All these arguments were for a model with fixed, but arbitrary n.

If we now step from model to model and choose n larger and larger, the probability $P(B'_{n,\delta})$ must tend to zero. *And the probability for picking a pattern ω with theoretical net win per toss within δ of \$0 per toss, the probability $P(B_{n,\delta})$ must approach* 1.   End of the proof.

20.4 PROBLEMS ON "RANDOM VARIABLES" AND "AVERAGES"

First, you might review several problems in Sec. 3.4, and also Problems 1–11 on "averages" in Sec. 18.8.

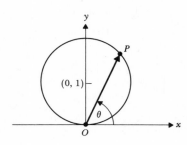

1. People have considered models for the passage of light rays through media which contain randomly situated spheres of some substance. The attenuation suffered by a ray in its passage through any one of these spheres may be proportional to the length of the chord traversed by the light in that sphere. Here is a 2-dimensional version of part of the problem: Suppose that a light ray going in a random direction θ $(-\pi/2 \leqslant \theta \leqslant \pi/2)$ enters a unit disk at a point O and exists at a point P, as in the accompanying figure.

    What is the average length of the chord OP?

    (a) Check that for a fixed θ, P lies on the line with equation $y = (\tan\theta)x$ and on the circle with equation $x^2 + (y-1)^2 = 1$. Solve these two equations simultaneously for the coordinates of P in terms of θ. (Recall that $1 + (\tan\theta)^2 = (\sec\theta)^2 = (\cos\theta)^{-2}$.)

    (b) Write the length $|OP|$ as a function $L(\theta)$.

    (c) If all θ's $[0, \pi]$ are equally likely, what is the "average output" of the "random variable" $L(\theta)$?

2. In Sec. 17.7, I discussed the probability that a randomly tossed needle would hit a crack between parallel floor boards. I represented possible outcomes by pairs (θ, x), where θ described the angle at which the needle falls $(0 \leqslant \theta < 2\pi)$, and x denoted the distance between the needle's head and the nearest crack on the left $(0 \leqslant x < d)$. See Figs. 17-25, 17-26, and 17-27. Now, for each possible outcome (θ, x), suppose that we are interested only in the distance — call it $D(\theta, x)$ — between the needle's head and whichever crack is nearest. What "average value" can we expect for this distance?

    (a) Check that

$$D(\theta, x) = \begin{cases} x & \text{if } 0 \leqslant x \leqslant \frac{1}{2}d \\ d-x & \text{if } \frac{1}{2}d \leqslant x \leqslant d \end{cases} = f(x)$$

regardless of θ. (Here I've added the possibility that $x = d$, a result of 0 probability. This addition completes the definition of $f(x)$ as a continuous function on the closed interval $[0, d]$.)

    (b) For the model in Sec. 17.4, I assumed all possible (θ, x) pairs to be equally likely. Disregarding θ now, shouldn't all the x values in $[0, d]$ be equally likely? If so, will you accept

$(1/d) \int_0^d f(x)\, dx$ as representing the "average distance" in question? Evaluate the integral.

(c) How does the *theoretical* "average value" which you calculated in part (b) for a model of *one* toss of the needle compare with an *observed* "average value" for several actual experiments? Toss a needle 10 times, each time recording the distance from its head to the nearest crack. Add the distances and divide by 10. Check this ratio against the value in part (b). Make a similar check for 20 tosses.

3. Suppose that a machine which produces a batch of 100 units each day is out of adjustment, so that in fact there are about 8 defective units in each day's batch. Suppose further that, after receiving some complaints, a team of 5 inspectors decides to examine a number of batches to determine the extent of malfunctioning. From a given batch the inspectors propose to draw simultaneously one unit apiece. Then each man will examine his unit for faults. How many defective units will the team find "on the average" per batch?

   If there were only *one* inspector—picking one unit from each batch—you might expect him to find approximately 8/100 defectives, averaging over many batches. Will the increased manpower of 5 inspectors yield an even better discovery rate (per man)—that is, will the team find *more* than 5(8/100) defectives averaging over many batches? Or, will they find *less*? (The inspectors do compete with each other in the sense that any defective picked by one of them can't be in the hands of any of the others.)

   Here are steps by which you might arrive at a detailed answer:

(a) Suppose that we could write down some list Ω of possible outcomes ω for the experiment of the five inspectors (on a given day) each picking a unit from the batch. For each fixed $i = 1, 2, \ldots, 5$, think of an "inspector's success function f_i" defined as follows:

   $f_i(\omega) = 1$ if the ith inspector finds a defective according to the outcome ω—*regardless of what the other inspectors find.*

   $f_i(\omega) = 0$ if the ith inspector fails to find a defective.

   Would you agree that, looking *only* at the ith inspector, his probability for success in finding a defective is 8/100; and for failure, $1 - 8/100$—so that the sum

$$1\left(\frac{8}{100}\right) + 0\left(1 - \frac{8}{100}\right) = \frac{8}{100} \qquad (*)$$

   should represent the "average output" of his success function? Note that the quantity in (*) doesn't depend on i.

(b) Check that, in terms of the f_i's of part (a), we can represent the total number of defectives found according to the outcome ω by the sum

$$f(\omega) = f_1(\omega) + f_2(\omega) + \cdots + f_5(\omega). \tag{**}$$

(c) Why do (*) and (**) together imply that the average output of f must be $5 \times (8/100)$?

(d) For an actual description of the ω's which I suggested in part (a), suppose that the units in a given batch are numbered from 1 through 100, and that those with numbers 1–8 are defective. (This labeling is merely for our convenience in setting up a model, and needn't correspond in any way to the order in which the units were manufactured.) Then we can represent each possible outcome by a "5-tuple" of integers, such as

$$(38, 5, 27, 99, 50)$$
$$\nwarrow i\text{th slot}$$

—the integer in the ith slot representing the unit picked by the ith inspector. Check that there are $100 \cdot 99 \cdot 98 \cdot 97 \cdot 96$ distinct such ω's (you might recall Sec. 6.8). All of these are equally likely. Check moreover that there are exactly $8(99 \cdot 98 \cdot 97 \cdot 96)$ ω's which definitely display one of the integers 1–8 in the ith slot, for a fixed i. What then must be the probability that $f_i(\omega) = 1$?

*(e) If the 5-man team will find the same number $(8/100)$ of defectives per batch *per man*, averaging over many batches, what advantage might there be to having a team of 5 inspectors, rather than merely one?

4. Now let's examine a model for the experiment of tossing a "true" coin 3 times, to see what the model itself may have to say about an "average number of heads" and an "average *frequency* for heads." Write a vertical list Ω of the $2^3 = 8$ possible ("equally likely") patterns ω of "heads" (H) and "tails" (T) for the experiment of three tosses. And to each ω (as input) assign two outputs,

$h(\omega)$ = the number of H's in ω

and

$F(\omega)$ = the "frequency" of H's in ω, $= \dfrac{h(\omega)}{3}$,

as in the following table:

Possible pattern ω	Elementary probability $p(\omega)$	Head count $h(\omega)$	Head frequency $F(\omega)$
HHH	$\dfrac{1}{8}$	3	$\dfrac{3}{3} = 1$
HHT	$\dfrac{1}{8}$	2	$\dfrac{2}{3}$
$\vdots$	$\vdots$	$\vdots$	$\vdots$

(a) Determine the "average outputs" of the functions h and F, by sums

$$h(\omega_1)p(\omega_1) + h(\omega_2)p(\omega_2) + \cdots \qquad (*)$$

and

$$F(\omega_1)p(\omega_1) + F(\omega_2)p(\omega_2) + \cdots . \qquad (**)$$

(b) For each $k = 0, 1, 2, 3$ in the range of h, indicate the subset — call it A_k — of all those ω's for which $h(\omega) = k$; and record the probability $P(A_k)$. Then check whether the sum

$$0 \cdot P(A_0) + 1P(A_1) + 2P(A_2) + 3P(A_3) \qquad (\dagger)$$

gives you the same average value for h as you got in (*). (Note that the sum ($\dagger$) can be got from (*) by "grouping" the ω's together in the sets A_k.)

(c) Check that the range of F consists of the fractions $k/3$ for $k = 0, 1, 2, 3$; and that each subset A_k in part (b) consists of exactly those ω's for which $F(\omega) = k/3$. Check whether the sum

$$\frac{0}{3} \cdot P(A_0) + \frac{1}{3}P(A_1) + \frac{2}{3}P(A_2) + \frac{3}{3}P(A_3) \qquad (\dagger\dagger)$$

has the same value as that in (**) — namely, $\frac{1}{2}$, as you might have guessed.

(d) The "average frequency" value $\frac{1}{2}$ in (**) and ($\dagger\dagger$) is a number based on the theoretical model in the table. How close to this theoretical average value $\frac{1}{2}$ does the *model itself* say that we're likely to find the *observed* head frequency in an actual experiment of three tosses — which must result in one of the patterns ω? More particularly: let's choose an allowable error amount — say, $\delta = 0.1$. Indicate the set — call it B_δ — of all ω's in the table for which

$$\left| F(\omega) - \frac{1}{2} \right| = \left| \frac{h(\omega)}{3} - \frac{1}{2} \right| < 0.1.$$

How large is the probability $P(B_\delta)$?

5. (a) Repeat the steps of Problem 4 for the experiment of tossing a coin four times.

(b) Do the same for 5 tosses.

(c) Do the probabilities $P(B_\delta)$, for finding an observed head frequency within $\delta = 0.1$ of the theoretical average value $\frac{1}{2}$, increase appreciably when you increase the number of tosses from 3 to 4 to 5?

(d) Toss an *actual coin* 5 times. Record the pattern of heads and tails, and the head frequency. Is that *observed* frequency within 0.1 of $\frac{1}{2}$?

(e) Toss an actual coin 50 times and display the results in groups of 5. Calculate the observed head frequency in each one of these 10 groups separately. For what *fraction* of the groups is this "observed head frequency" within 0.1 of $\frac{1}{2}$? How does that fraction compare with the probability $P(B_\delta)$ calculated via a model for 5 tosses?

6. Look again at the three tosses of a true coin in Problem 4. Suppose now that for each "head" we win \$1 and for each "tail" we lose \$1. In the discussion of the "law of large numbers" in Sec. 20.3, I used "payoff functions f_i" to keep track of such wins and losses. Here is their definition in the present setting: for each fixed toss number $i = 1$, 2, or 3, and for each possible outcome ω in the table of Problem 4, let

$$f_i(\omega) = \begin{cases} +1 & \text{if the } i\text{th toss in } \omega \text{ yields a head } (H), \\ -1 & \text{if the } i\text{th toss in } \omega \text{ yields a tail } (T). \end{cases}$$

(a) Check that the average output of $f_i(\omega)$ is 0, for each i.

(b) Check that the average output of $[f_i(\omega)]^2$ is 1 for each i.

(c) Pick any two different toss numbers, $i \neq j$, and show that the average output of the product $f_i(\omega)f_j(\omega)$ is 0.

*(d) Extend the results of parts (a), (b), and (c) to the cases of n tosses of a coin — as needed for the proof of the "law of large numbers" which I sketched in Sec. 20.3.

7. Here is another property of averages which I needed in Sec. 20.3: Suppose that f is a function (a "random variable") defined on a list of outcomes $\Omega = \{\omega_i\}$ having elementary probabilities $p(\omega_i)$. Suppose further that $f(\omega_i) \geq 0$ for all ω_i's; and that $f(\omega_i) \geq$ some given constant b for all ω_i's in a given subset $B \subset \Omega$. Then the average output of f must be $\geq bP(B)$.

(a) Show that this property must hold.

(b) Suppose that $f(x)$ is a continuous nonnegative function defined on an interval $\Omega = [a, b]$, where all inputs x are equally likely, and that $f(x) \geq b$ for some subinterval $B = [c, d]$. Show that the average output of f must be $\geq bP(B)$.

(c) Repeat part (b) for the case where probabilities are definable on $[a, b]$ via a continuous "probability density" function $g(x)$.

8. Two "random variables" f_1 and f_2 can have widely different output values and yet share the same "average output value," or *mean* value as it's often called. For example, two different kinds of payoff for a single toss of a true coin:

$$\begin{cases} f_1(H) = \$1 \\ f_1(T) = \$-1 \end{cases} \quad \text{and} \quad \begin{cases} f_2(H) = \$10 \\ f_2(T) = \$-10 \end{cases}. \tag{*}$$

Both have mean values equal to zero. Similarly two probability density functions, which "distribute" probabilities in widely different ways, can lead to the same "average." For example:

$$g_1(x) = \begin{cases} 1 & \text{for } x \text{ in } \left[-\frac{1}{2}, \frac{1}{2}\right] \\ 0 & \text{for all other } x \end{cases}$$

and

$$g_2(x) = \begin{cases} \dfrac{1}{10} & \text{for } x \text{ in } [-5,5] \\ 0 & \text{for all other } x \end{cases}.$$ (**)

Both these g_i's yield averages equal to zero. (Similarly two widely different positionings of weights can lead to the same "center of gravity," as in the accompanying figure.)

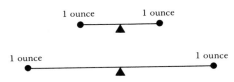

1 ounce   1 ounce

1 ounce   1 ounce

To distinguish between such different situations, people often consider the so-called *variance* "σ^2" of a random variable $f(\omega)$ — namely, the average output of the function $h(\omega) = [f(\omega) - \mu]^2$, where μ is the mean or average output of f itself. For each input ω, h displays the *difference* between the actual output $f(\omega)$ and the average output μ — squared so as to prohibit cancellation of $h(\omega)$ values for different ω's when the average of h is computed. (The square root of the variance, σ, is usually called the "standard deviation" of f.)

(a) Compute and compare the variances of the functions f_1 and f_2 in (*).

(b) Compute the variances of the three "payoff" functions f_i in Problem 6, and compare these with the variances of their sum $f_1(\omega) + f_2(\omega) + f_3(\omega)$.

(c) For a continuous probability density $g(x)$, defined for all x — one for which

$$\mu = \int_{-\infty}^{\infty} xg(x)\, dx$$ (†)

represents an "average x" — the variance is usually defined as the integral

$$\sigma^2 = \int_{-\infty}^{\infty} (x - \mu)^2 g(x)\, dx.$$ (††)

(You might recall Problem 15 of Sec. 18.2 regarding the definition of such "improper integrals" as limits of definite integrals.) Compute and compare the variances for the densities g_1 and g_2 in (**).

(d) You might recall from Secs. 18.4 and 18.5 that the possible waiting times t between telephone calls at an exchange have a probability density $g(t) = \lambda e^{-\lambda t}$, where the "average waiting time" is

$$\mu = \int_0^{\infty} t(\lambda e^{-\lambda t})\, dt = \frac{1}{\lambda},$$

say, in minutes. What average discrepancy might we expect between actual waiting times and the theoretical average $1/\lambda$? Compute the variance σ^2 of g, as in part (c). Note that σ^2 will read in units of "(minutes)^2." How large is the standard deviation σ—which reads in "minutes"—say, as compared with the average $1/\lambda$?

9. In Problem 8(d), the density function $g(t) = \lambda e^{-\lambda t}$ for possible waiting times t between telephone arrivals was based on *uniform* conditions of telephone traffic. (You might recall my discussion in Sec. 18.4.) Other conditions might lead to other forms for an appropriate density function. Although g itself may be unknown, suppose that actual records of calls arriving at an exchange lead to an estimate of, say, $\mu = 0.4$ minutes between calls on the average and $\sigma = 0.4$ minutes also. On the basis of this scant information, can we form *any* idea whatsoever about the probability for a future waiting time to be some relatively large value—say greater than 2 minutes? More particularly, how small must the probability be for a future waiting time t to differ from $\mu = 0.4$ minutes by 2 minutes? —in symbols, the probability

$$P(\text{all } t \text{ such that } |t - 0.4| > 2). \tag{*}$$

(a) Suppose that $g(t)$ is a continuous probability density function defined for all t, and that $b > 0$. Show that

$$P(\text{all } t \text{ such that } |t - \mu| > b) \leq \frac{\sigma^2}{b^2}, \tag{†}$$

that is, show that

$$\sigma^2 \geq b^2 \left\{ \int_{-\infty}^{\mu-b} g(t)\, dt + \int_{\mu+b}^{\infty} g(t)\, dt \right\}. \tag{††}$$

(Recall Problem 7.) The inequality (†) is named after P. L. Chebychev.

(b) Use (†) to estimate the probability in (*).

10. In Sec. 18.4, I argued that we might assign probability $P([a, b\rangle) = \int_a^b \lambda e^{-\lambda t}\, dt = e^{-\lambda a} - e^{-\lambda b}$ to the interval $[a, b\rangle$ of possible waiting times t between telephone call arrivals. (Here $1/\lambda$ is the average waiting time.) Are you willing to extend this probability assignment to subsets of $[0, \infty\rangle$ of the form

$$A = [a_1, b_1\rangle \cup [a_2, b_2\rangle \cup \cdots \cup [a_n, b_n\rangle, \tag{*}$$

where the $[a_i, b_i]$'s are *nonoverlapping* (half-open) intervals—via the definition

$$P(A) = P([a_1, b_1\rangle) + P([a_2, b_2\rangle) + \cdots + P([a_n, b_n\rangle)$$
$$= (e^{-a_1\lambda} - e^{-b_1\lambda}) + (e^{-a_2\lambda} - e^{-b_2\lambda}) + \cdots + (e^{-a_n\lambda} - e^{-b_n\lambda}). \tag{**}$$

Check that the assignment rule in (**) satisfies properties (1)–(5) in Sec. 20.1.

20.5 CONDITIONAL PROBABILITY

If someone gives you partial information about the outcome of an experiment, how should that alter your calculation of probabilities? I touched upon this question in Sec. 3.5 regarding "independence" of results from a coin and a die. Let's look at it again in a different setting.

EXAMPLE 1. Suppose that an object has been lost somewhere in a rectangular field. What's the probability that it lies in a region S? If we feel that all locations in the field are equally likely for the lost object, then we might assign to any region S a probability *proportional to its area*. To picture such proportionalities, I've sketched in Fig. 20-3 a scale model of the field—say, as cut out of wood of thickness h.

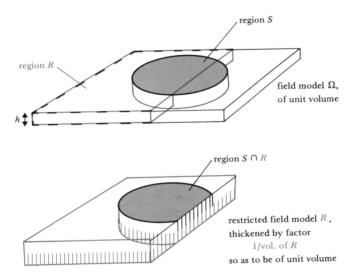

region S

region R

field model Ω, of unit volume

h

region $S \cap R$

restricted field model R, thickened by factor

1/vol. of R

so as to be of unit volume

FIGURE 20-3

Let's think of each region S as *solid*, of uniform thickness h—so the area of its top face will be proportional to its volume. And let's choose h so that the entire field Ω will have *unit* volume. Then we can write the probability of a region S simply as

$$P(S) = \text{the volume of } S. \tag{1}$$

Now what if someone tells us he's sure that the object lies in a region R—say, the left-hand $\frac{2}{3}$ of the field. What new assignment of probabilities should we make in light of this new information? If we trust our informant, then certainly we should restrict the set of possible locations of the object to the region R itself; and within any given region S we should look only at the intersection $S \cap R$. And since we've received no information to the contrary, shouldn't subregions *within R* still have probabilities of the same relative sizes as before—that is, *proportional to their volumes*? If so, then we need merely adjust the constant of proportionality so that the new probability for R itself will be 1. I've pictured such an adjustment in the lower part of Fig. 20-3 as a thickening of the wood. If R has volume $\frac{2}{3}$ in the original field Ω, then we can achieve unit volume for R by thickening the wood by a factor of $\frac{3}{2}$—the reciprocal of $\frac{2}{3}$. More generally, *whenever we know that the object definitely lies on some region R with nonzero volume, we can incorporate that information by assigning to any other region S of Ω, a* NEW PROBABILITY *for containing the object,*

$$P_R(S) = \left(\frac{1}{\text{volume of } R}\right) \text{volume of } S \cap R \qquad (2)$$

—proportional to the old probability of $S \cap R$. The new rule (2) will assign 0 probability to any subset S of Ω not overlapping R. And we'll have

$$P_R(R) = \frac{\text{volume of } R \cap R}{\text{volume of } R} = 1. \qquad (3)$$

I've used a subscript "R" for the new assignment P_R to emphasize its basic dependence on the given, fixed, region R. (And in (2), let's consider only regions S which themselves have volume.)

Shouldn't the new assignment P_R, *in its own right*, have the usual properties of probability functions? Here's a check that it adds properly for mutually exclusive subsets S and T, as in Fig. 20-4.

FIGURE 20-4

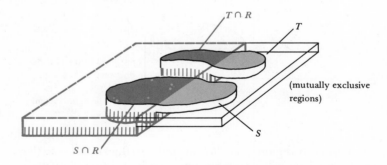

The parts of S and T that lie in R—namely, $S \cap R$ and $T \cap R$—must also be mutually exclusive. Hence their volumes must add to yield the volume of $[S \cup T] \cap R$. And

$$P_R(S \cup T) = \frac{\text{volume of } [S \cup T] \cap R}{\text{volume of } R}$$

$$= \frac{\text{volume of } S \cap R + \text{volume of } T \cap R}{\text{volume of } R}$$

$$= \frac{\text{volume of } S \cap R}{\text{volume of } R} + \frac{\text{volume of } T \cap R}{\text{volume of } R}$$

$$= P_R(S) + P_R(T). \qquad (4)$$

Will the other usual properties hold similarly? And what can we learn from this example about the general question of assigning new probabilities in the light of new information?

You may already have noticed that the new probabilities $P_R(S)$ in (2) were merely ratios of old probabilities,

$$P_R(S) = \frac{P(S \cap R)}{P(R)}, \tag{5}$$

for all subsets S of Ω, representing compound results. And you may also have noticed that *none of the arguments I gave in Example 1* — for restricting Ω to R and for using the proportionality factor $1/P(R)$ — *depended in any way on the particulars of that example.* Even the calculation (4) to check the "addition property" for mutually exclusive sets holds more generally: Suppose that we start with *any* probability function P and define P_R in terms of P via (5). If S and T are mutually exclusive subsets in Ω, then just as in (4) we can write

$$P_R(S \cup T) = \frac{P([S \cup T] \cap R)}{P(R)} = \frac{P(S \cap R) + P(T \cap R)}{P(R)}$$

$$= \frac{P(S \cap R)}{P(R)} + \frac{P(T \cap R)}{P(R)}$$

$$= P_R(S) + P_R(T). \tag{6}$$

I invite you to show in Problem 8 of Sec. 20.7 that the other usual properties of probability functions hold for P_R, in just the same way.

For all these reasons, people have adopted the ratios in (5) as a general

Definition I: If we have an original assignment of probabilities $P(S)$ to subsets of some list Ω of possible outcomes, and if we receive information that the actual result lies in a particular subset R (with $P(R) > 0$), let's assign to each S the value

$$P_R(S) = \frac{P(S \cap R)}{P(R)} \tag{7}$$

as the *conditional probability* (that the actual outcome lies in S) *given* R.

Once we hear that an actual outcome lies in a subset R of an original set Ω of possibilities, why keep the rest of Ω outside R? Why still define new probabilities $P_R(S)$ for subsets S of Ω instead of merely for subsets of R? One reason is that we might get reports — or be asked hypothetical questions — about the actual outcome being in any one of several regions $R_1, R_2, R_3, \ldots$. It's nice to be able to compare corresponding "new probabilities" $P_{R_1}(S), P_{R_2}(S), P_{R_3}(S), \ldots$, for the same subset S of Ω. Here are several instances.

EXAMPLE 2. The U.S. Census reported 5267 families as living below "poverty level" in 1967 — and classified these families further according to occupation and to sex of family head, as in the following table.

	Nonfarm	Farm	(Row totals)
Male head	3178	366	3544
Female head	1687	36	1723
(Column totals)	4865	402	5267

Suppose we hear that an interview is planned with a family chosen at random from the 5267. What's the probability that the family will be in a given one of the four categories of the table? If we consider the 5267 families as constituting a set Ω of equally *likely* outcomes for selection, then the four categories describe subsets of Ω—whose probabilities should be proportional to their sizes, as in Fig. 20-5.

FIGURE 20-5

	nonfarm (subset R_1)	farm (subset R_2)	(row totals)
male head (subset M)	$P(M \cap R_1) = \dfrac{3178}{5267}$	$P(M \cap R_2) = \dfrac{366}{5267}$	$P(M) = \dfrac{3544}{5267}$
female head (subset F)	$P(F \cap R_1) = \dfrac{1687}{5267}$	$P(F \cap R_2) = \dfrac{36}{5267}$	$P(F) = \dfrac{1723}{5267}$
(column totals)	$P(R_1) = \dfrac{4865}{5267}$	$P(R_2) = \dfrac{402}{5267}$	$P(\Omega) = \dfrac{5267}{5267} = 1$

Now suppose we hear that the interview will take place in a city. What are the chances (the conditional probability) that the family head will be a woman? And how would these chances differ if we knew that the interview would take place on a farm? Can we expect the two answers to differ by a factor of $1687/36 =$ approximately 47, the ratio of nonfarm "female" families to farm "female" families? No. Because the questions ask about *conditional* probabilities, where the amounts of "new information" in the sets R_1 and R_2 *narrow the original list Ω down in very different ways.* Specifically

$$P_{R_1}(F) = \frac{P(F \cap R_1)}{P(R_1)} = \frac{1687/5267}{4865/5267} = \frac{1687}{4865} = 0.36 \text{ approx}$$

and

$$P_{R_2}(F) = \frac{P(F \cap R_2)}{P(R_2)} = \frac{36/5267}{402/5267} = \frac{36}{402} = 0.09 \text{ approx}$$

—values which differ by a factor of 4.

EXAMPLE 3. Perhaps you recall my asking (in Problem 9 of Sec. 3.4) whether information about the *color* of an unseen card can alter the chances that a second unseen card be an ace. Here again are the two versions of a game, both involving a deck of four cards—a red ace (*ra*), a red king (*rk*), a black ace (*ba*), and a black king (*bk*): Your friend mixes the deck and simultaneously extracts two cards from it, which he keeps hidden from you.

Version 1. Your friend says: "One of my cards is an ace. What are the chances that I have two aces?"

Version 2. Your friend says: "One of my cards is a *red* ace. What are the chances that I have two aces?"

The questions ask for *conditional* probabilities. Should the answers differ, or is the redness of the ace in the second version irrelevant? Think again—before looking at Fig. 20-6, where I've listed the six equally likely patterns for your friend's two cards. (The order in each pattern is immaterial, since the two cards are to be drawn *simultaneously*.)

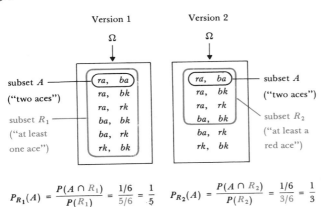

FIGURE 20-6

$$P_{R_1}(A) = \frac{P(A \cap R_1)}{P(R_1)} = \frac{1/6}{5/6} = \frac{1}{5} \qquad P_{R_2}(A) = \frac{P(A \cap R_2)}{P(R_2)} = \frac{1/6}{3/6} = \frac{1}{3}$$

20.6 RECONSTRUCTION VIA CONDITIONAL PROBABILITIES

Sometimes data for constructing a model arrive from the "real world" in the *form* of conditional probabilities. In such cases one might have to work *backwards to assign "original" probabilities to some subsets. Thus, if you think that you know reasonable values for an original probability $P(R)$ and for a conditional probability $P_R(S)$, you might note that

$$P(R \cap S) = P(S \cap R) = \cancel{P(R)}\left[\frac{P(S \cap R)}{\cancel{P(R)}}\right], \tag{1}$$

and you might assign to $R \cap S$ as its "original probability" the product of known values

$$\boxed{P(R \cap S) = P(R)P_R(S).} \tag{2}$$

EXAMPLE 1. Suppose that you had received some of the poverty data of Fig. 20-5 via a statement of this form:

"Approximately 92.3% of the families living below the poverty level have nonfarm occupations; and of these, approximately 36% are headed by females." (3)

How could you compute the chances that a randomly chosen poor family will turn out to live in the city and have a woman as its head?

Imagine again, as in the last section, a model with set Ω of all poor families listed in the census, and with subsets as labeled in Fig. 20-5. Then you might interpret the percentages in the statement (3) as

$$P(R_1) = 0.923 \quad \text{and} \quad P_{R_1}(F) = 0.360 \tag{4}$$

(R_1 for nonfarm occupation, and F for female head). If so, then the "original" probability for $R_1 \cap F$ should be

$$P(R_1 \cap F) = P(R_1)P_{R_1}(F)$$
$$= (0.923)(0.360) = 0.332 \text{ approx.} \tag{5}$$

Note: In making such a probability assignment to the set $R_1 \cap F$ you would be assuming that the given data is basically *consistent* with some probability function $P(S)$. Suppose, for example, that the statement (3) had included the additional sentence: "Overall, females head only 29.7% of the families below the poverty level." We would then have a probability for F, $P(F) = 0.297$, which is *less* than the probability in (5) for a subset $R_1 \cap F$ of F—in violation of a basic "property" of probability functions. What should you do in such a case? Before giving up the property, you might go to the source of the data and look for errors.

Sometimes we can reconstruct the probability for a set S from the probabilities of many pieces—as I've indicated schematically in Fig. 20-7.

FIGURE 20-7

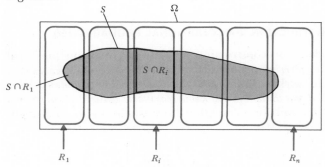

$$P(S \cap R_i) = P(R_i)P_{R_i}(S)$$
$$P(S) = P(S \cap R_1) + P(S \cap R_2) + \cdots + P(S \cap R_i) + \cdots + P(S \cap R_n)$$
$$= P(R_1)P_{R_1}(S) + P(R_2)P_{R_2}(S) + \cdots + P(R_i)P_{R_i}(S) + \cdots + P(R_n)P_{R_n}(S)$$

(6)

The relation (6) will hold if the R_i's are mutually exclusive, and have Ω as their union. Then the actual result of an experiment must lie in *one* of them—in the ith with probability $P(R_i)$. And if we knew that the result did lie in R_i, we could say that it had probability $P_{R_i}(S)$ for lying in S. Note how equation (6) expresses the original probability $P(S)$ as an *average* of these conditional probabilities $\{P_{Ri}(S)\}$. Here are several instances.

EXAMPLE 2. Doctors estimate that about 30% of ulcer sufferers vomit blood at some time, as do 20% of patients with cirrhosis of the liver, and 10% of patients with stomach inflammation—other causes being relatively rare. Regarding the prevalence of the three diseases, one guess for the population of Wisconsin is that about 2% of the people do have ulcers, 0.5% have cirrhosis, and 0.7% have stomach inflammation—and persons with more than one of these are rare. What are the chances that a randomly chosen Wisconsinite will have the blood symptom?

Think of the entire Wisconsin population (Ω) as divided into four mutually exclusive subsets:

U = those who have ulcers, C = those who have cirrhosis,
I = those who have inflammation,   and R = all the rest.

And denote by B the subset of those who vomit blood. Are you willing to interpret the given data via the probabilities

$$P(U) = 0.02, \quad P(C) = 0.005, \quad P(I) = 0.007,$$

and   (7)

$$P(R) = 1 - [P(U) + P(C) + P(I)] = 0.968,$$

and via the conditional probabilities

$$P_U(B) = 0.30, \quad P_C(B) = 0.20,$$
$$P_I(B) = 0.10 \quad \text{and} \quad P_R(B) = 0.\tag{8}$$

If so, then we can reconstruct probabilities for intersections:

$$P(U \cap B) = P(U)P_U(B) = (0.02)(0.30) = 0.006,$$
$$P(C \cap B) = P(C)P_C(B) = (0.005)(0.20) = 0.001,$$
$$P(I \cap B) = P(I)P_I(B) = (0.007)(0.10) = 0.0007,\tag{9}$$

and

$$P(R \cap B) = P(R)P_R(B) = (0.968)0 = 0.$$

And we can add these together to get

$$P(B) = P(U)P_U(B) + P(C)P_C(B) + P(I)P_I(B) + P(R)P_R(B)$$
$$= 0.006 + 0.001 + 0.0007$$
$$= 0.0077\tag{10}$$

(just as in Fig. 20-7).

EXAMPLE 3. Now suppose you are a Wisconsin doctor, and you hear that someone has just walked in through your door vomiting blood. Before you learn another fact about him, your thoughts might turn to the three common causes which I discussed in Example 2—ulcers, cirrhosis of the liver, and stomach inflammation. How much more likely is one than another? The answer might help decide what measures you should take first. In (7) I listed the probabilities of these causes for a random Wisconsinite. But the patient who just arrived is no longer completely random: you know about him that he is in the subset "B" of those with a blood symptom. How should this information change your estimates of the three causes? We need the conditional probabilities

$$P_B(U) = \frac{P(U \cap B)}{P(B)}, P_B(C) = \frac{P(C \cap B)}{P(B)}, \text{and} P_B(I) = \frac{P(I \cap B)}{P(B)}.$$

I've already calculated the numerators and denominators for these ratios in (9) and (10). Thus

$$P_B(U) = \frac{P(U)P_U(B)}{P(U)P_U(B) + P(C)P_C(B) + P(I)P_I(B) + P(R)P_R(B)}$$

$$= \frac{(0.02)(0.30)}{(0.02)(0.30) + (0.005)(0.20) + (0.007)(0.10) + (0.968)0}$$

$$= \frac{0.006}{0.0077} = 0.78 \text{ (approx)}. \tag{11}$$

Similarly,

$$P_B(C) = \frac{0.001}{0.0077} = 0.13 \text{ (approx)} \tag{12}$$

and

$$P_B(I) = \frac{0.0007}{0.0077} = 0.09 \text{ (approx)}. \tag{13}$$

Note from (12) and (13) that for a patient vomiting blood, cirrhosis of the liver is *more probable* than stomach inflammation—whereas it's less probable for a person selected at random.

Equation (11) shows how to calculate the conditional probability $P_B(U)$ of a "cause" (U) given an "effect" (B) in terms of conditional probabilities in the other direction—of the effect (B) given causes (U, C, and so on). It's an instance of what's called "Bayes' formula":

$$P_S(R_i) = \frac{P(R_i)P_{R_i}(S)}{P(R_1)P_{R_1}(S) + P(R_2)P_{R_2}(S) + \cdots + P(R_n)P_{R_n}(S)}. \tag{14}$$

Many people currently view (14) as a tool for replacing old estimates of chances, the $P(R_i)$'s, by new ones, the $P_S(R_i)$'s—once a result described by S has been observed.

So far I've discussed how to represent the probability of a subset $P(S)$ as an average of conditional probabilities $\{P_{R_i}(S)\}$ corresponding to *finitely* many "basic" sets $\{R_i\}$ in which the actual result of an experiment might lie. But what if the total set of possibilities Ω seems to split most conveniently into *infinitely* many basic sets R_i? Here are two cases.

EXAMPLE 4. Fix a point P on a circle of unit length. Then choose at random a second point X on the circle, and similarly a third point Y independent of X. Except in the highly unlikely case that X and Y turn out to be end points of a diameter, they will divide the circle into a longer arc and a shorter arc. What are the chances that the fixed point P will be contained in the *longer* arc—as I've indicated in Fig. 20-8? Would you say 50–50? By analogy, which of two nets is more likely to catch a goldfish (P), a larger one or a smaller one?

Let's analyze matters more precisely. The first point X will lie at some distance x units measured clockwise around the circle from P—call this possible result "R_x," for $0 \leqslant x < 1$. Once we know the position of X, where must Y fall in order to insure the result—call it "S"—that P lies in the longer arc? I've indicated the possible positions for Y in green in Fig. 20-9.

FIGURE 20-8

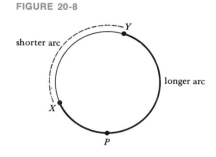

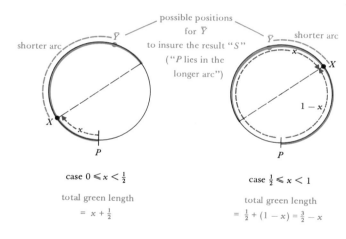

FIGURE 20-9

Given a distance x of X, do you believe it's reasonable to assign a new probability $P_{R_x}(S)$ for the result S, equal to the *length* of the green arc of possible (equally likely) positions for Y? If so, we'll have

$$P_{R_x}(S) = \begin{cases} \dfrac{1}{2}+x & \text{for } 0 \leqslant x < \dfrac{1}{2}, \\[2mm] \dfrac{3}{2}-x & \text{for } \dfrac{1}{2} \leqslant x < 1. \end{cases} \tag{15}$$

Don't the assignments (15) make sense even though the probability of X having any *particular* distance x—of the result R_x—is 0? Since all the x's in $[0, 1]$ are equally likely, we might represent an *average* of the quantities $P_{R_x}(S)$ for $0 \leqslant x < 1$ by the definite integral

$$\int_0^1 P_{R_x}(S) \, dx = \int_0^{1/2} \left(\frac{1}{2}+x\right) dx + \int_{1/2}^1 \left(\frac{3}{2}-x\right) dx$$

$$= \left[\frac{x}{2}+\frac{x^2}{2}\right]_0^{1/2} + \left[\frac{3}{2}x-\frac{x^2}{2}\right]_{1/2}^1$$

$$= \left[\frac{1}{2}\left(\frac{1}{2}+\frac{1}{4}\right)-0\right] + \left[\frac{1}{2}(3-1)-\frac{1}{2}\left(\frac{3}{2}-\frac{1}{4}\right)\right] = \frac{3}{4}, \quad \text{(16)}$$

as I argued in Sec. 18.3. The integral stands in analogy to the finite sum $P_{R_1}(S)P(R_1) + P_{R_2}(S)P(R_2) + \cdots + P_{R_n}(S)P(R_n)$ in (6). Should we accept its value, 3/4, as $P(S)$? (In the next section, I'll give a different calculation for $P(S)$.)

In the next example, the basic R's turn out not to be equally likely.

EXAMPLE 5. *Are two cheap batteries (one in reserve) more trustworthy than one expensive battery?* Suppose that individual expensive batteries are rated as lasting *twice* as long as individual cheap batteries, on the average. Are the following two results equally probable?

(A) A single expensive battery will serve for at least T hours.

(B) Either the first of two cheap batteries will itself serve for at least T hours, or it will fail at some time $t < T$ and the second cheap battery will serve at least for the remaining $T-t$ hours.

To answer, we should know more about how batteries fail. Imagine test records for a given kind of battery, wherein each tested unit is replaced upon failure by another unit, and the successive instants of failure are marked off on a continuous tape. Would you expect the failures to arrive in a chance manner similar to the meteorites which I discussed in Sec. 16.1 and the telephone calls I discussed in Sec. 18.4? Some actual tests seem to support such expectations. Let's form models for expensive and for cheap batteries analogous to those for meteorites and telephone calls, and let's see to what conclusions they lead. If we do, we'll immediately have

$$\left.\begin{array}{l}\text{the probability that an expensive}\\ \text{battery fails } after \text{ time } t\end{array}\right\} = e^{-\lambda t} \quad \text{for any } t > 0, \quad \text{(17)}$$

where

$$\frac{1}{\lambda} = \left\{\begin{array}{l}\text{the average lifetime of}\\ \text{an expensive battery}\end{array}\right\}; \quad \text{(18)}$$

and

$$\left\{\begin{array}{l}\text{the probability that a cheap}\\ \text{battery fails } after \text{ time } t\end{array}\right\} = e^{-\mu t} \quad \text{for any } t > 0, \quad \text{(19)}$$

where

$$\frac{1}{\mu} = \left\{\begin{array}{l}\text{the average lifetime of}\\ \text{a cheap battery}\end{array}\right\}. \quad \text{(20)}$$

So I argued in Sec. 18.4. In particular, the probability for an expensive battery to fail after at least T hours (result "A") will be

$$P(A) = e^{-\lambda T}. \tag{21}$$

How can we analyze the result "B" involving two successive batteries? The first cheap battery could *itself* serve for at least T hours. Let's call the result "R." It's a subcase of B having probability

$$P(R) = e^{-\mu T}. \tag{22}$$

And if we know that R describes the actual result, then we can assign to B a conditional probability

$$P_R(B) = 1. \tag{23}$$

Alternatively, the first cheap battery could fail at one of the infinitely many instants $t < T$. Why not handle these probabilities in the same way as I did the infinitely many different dividend arrival times of Sec. 18.1 (Example 2) or the possible telephone call arrival times in Sec. 18.4? Namely, let's divide $[0, T\rangle$ by a partition $\sigma = \{t_0 < t_1 < \cdots < t_n\}$ into many small (half-open) intervals $[t_{i-1}, t_i\rangle$. And let's denote by R_i the result that the first cheap battery fails during $[t_{i-1}, t_i\rangle$. See Fig. 20-10, where I've indicated the mutually exclusive results R and $R_1, R_2, \ldots, R_n$ in green.

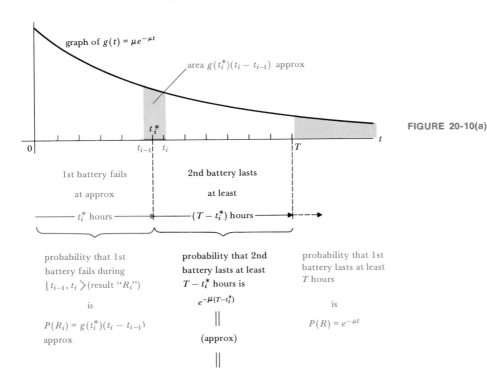

FIGURE 20-10(a)

FIGURE 20-10(b) $P(B) = P(R_1)P_{R_1}(B) + \cdots + P(R_i)P_{R_i}(B) + \cdots + P(R_n)P_{R_n}(B) + P(R)P_R(B)$

(approx)
$$= \cdots + g(t_i^*)(t_i - t_{i-1})e^{-\mu(T-t_i^*)} + \cdots + e^{-\mu t} \cdot 1. \tag{24}$$

Borrowing again from results on telephone calls in Sec. 18.4 we can write the probability of each R_i as

$$P(R_i) = e^{-\mu t_{i-1}} - e^{-\mu t_i} = g(t_i^*)(t_i - t_{i-1}), \tag{25}$$

where t_i^* is some input in $[t_{i-1}, t_i\rangle$ and $g(t) = \mu e^{-\mu t}$ (g is a "probability density" function such as I discussed in Sec. 18.5. It's the derivative of the "cumulative probability function" $G(t) = 1 - e^{-\mu t}$, and describes the relative amounts of probability near different inputs t.)

Now, suppose we hear that the first cheap battery has failed at some instant in the short interval $[t_{i-1}, t_i\rangle$ — the result "R_i." Doesn't it seem reasonable to approximate a new probability $P_{R_i}(B)$ for success of the *team* of two cheap batteries by $e^{-\mu(T-t_i^*)}$, the probability that the *second* battery *on its own* will last a remaining $T - t_i^*$ hours — where t_i^* is any representative input in $[t_{i-1}, t_i\rangle$, say, the one in (25)? If so, then we can put together a probability $P(B)$ as I've indicated in (24) in Fig. 20-10. If we pick new partitions σ with smaller and smaller meshes, might not the approximations for $P_{R_i}(B)$ by $e^{-\mu(T-t_i^*)}$ get better and better? Anyhow, what we can conclude by the key result of Chap. 18 is that the right-hand sum in (24) will tend to the limiting value

$$\int_0^T g(t)e^{-\mu(T-t)}\,dt + e^{-\mu T} \cdot 1$$

— which has the form

$$\int_0^T g(t)P_{R_t}(B)\,dt + P(R)P_R(B), \tag{26}$$

if we denote by "R_t" the result that the first battery fails exactly at t. This form is again an *average* of conditional probabilities weighted proportionally to corresponding original probabilities, just as in Fig. 20-7. Shall we accept the quantity in (26) as $P(B)$? If we do, we can evaluate it as

$$P(B) = \int_0^T (\mu e^{-\mu t})(e^{-\mu T + \mu t})\,dt + e^{-\mu T} \cdot 1$$
$$= \mu e^{-\mu T} \int_0^T 1\,dt + e^{-\mu T} \cdot 1$$
$$= e^{-\mu T}(\mu T + 1). \tag{27}$$

Finally, let's compare the "success" probabilities $P(A) = e^{-\lambda T}$ for the single expensive battery and $P(B) = e^{-\mu T}(\mu T + 1)$ for the team of cheap batteries. To do so, let's recall that

$$\frac{1}{\mu} = \left\{ \begin{array}{l} \text{the average} \\ \text{lifetime of a} \\ \text{cheap battery} \end{array} \right\} = \frac{1}{2}\left\{ \begin{array}{l} \text{the average} \\ \text{lifetime of an} \\ \text{expensive battery} \end{array} \right\} = \frac{1}{2}\frac{1}{\lambda}, \tag{28}$$

or $\mu = 2\lambda$. Hence

$$\frac{P(B)}{P(A)} = \frac{e^{-\mu T}(\mu T + 1)}{e^{-\lambda T}} = \frac{e^{-2\lambda T}(2\lambda T + 1)}{e^{-\lambda T}} = \frac{2\lambda T + 1}{e^{\lambda T}}. \tag{29}$$

Which is larger, the numerator or the denominator in (29)? Note in Fig. 20-11 how the linear function $2x + 1$ and the exponential e^x compare. If $x = \lambda T < 1.2$ (approx), then the numerator in (29) is larger than the denominator; if $x = \lambda T > 1.2$ (approx), then the opposite must be true. Equivalently,

$$\frac{P(B)}{P(A)} > 1 \quad \text{if } T < (1.2)\,\frac{1}{\lambda}$$

and

$$\frac{P(B)}{P(A)} < 1 \quad \text{if } T > (1.2)\,\frac{1}{\lambda}.$$

Conclusion: If you're interested in a short period of time T (less than 1.2 times the average lifetime of an expensive battery) use two cheap batteries. Otherwise, choose one expensive battery. Similar results hold for many other kinds of equipment and materials.

FIGURE 20-11

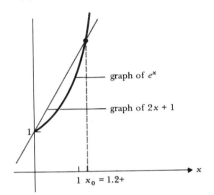

graph of e^x

graph of $2x + 1$

$1\ x_0 = 1.2+$

20.7 PROBLEMS ON CONDITIONAL PROBABILITY

1. A "prime" integer is one which is not divisible by any integer other than itself or 1—for example, 7. Suppose that someone chose an integer between 1 and 20, at random.
   (a) What are the chances that it was a "prime"?
   (b) If you hear that the chosen integer was greater than 10, what are the chances that it was a prime?
2. Suppose that someone tossed two dice, say, one red and one green.
   (a) What are the chances that the sum of the numbers on the dice was even?
   (b) How should you change your answer in part (a) if you hear that at least one of the dice read "3"?
3. Suppose that a ship is lost somewhere in a square region 30 miles wide, as in the figures.
   (a) What are the chances that the ship is in the southern half of the region?
   (b) If you were given information that the ship is in the north-eastern half of the region, how would such news change the chances that the ship is in the southern half of the region?

   (Suggestion: Relative to suitably placed axes, find the coordinates of the point of intersection P_0 in the figure. To compute area, recall Example 2 of Sec. 18.9.)

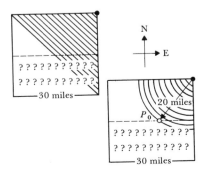

(c) If you were given information that a station on the northeast corner of the region received a distress signal from the ship, which could have originated no further than 20 miles from that station, how would such news change the chances that the ship is in the southern half of the region?

4. Recall the table of census figures in Example 2 of Sec. 20.5. Suppose that, a family head is chosen at random and interviewed. If that person turns out to be a female, what are the chances that she works in a nonfarm occupation?

5. Here are data concerning the U.S. farm population in 1960:

	White	Nonwhite
Under 14 years	2,526,000	491,000
14 years and over	7,137,000	721,000

(a) If we hear that a farm occupant has been chosen at random, what are the chances that he is under 14 years of age?
(b) If we hear in addition that he is nonwhite, how does this information change the chances that he is under 14 years of age?
(c) What if we hear that he is white?

6. Here is a table describing smoking habits in a small town:

	Smokers	Nonsmokers
Males	213	405
Females	152	269

(a) If we hear that an inhabitant is selected at random and is a male, what are the chances that he's a smoker?
(b) If we hear that an inhabitant is selected at random and is a smoker, what are the chances that the person is a male?

Note on interpretations: You might think of sex as determining temperament to some extent — either biologically or culturally — and thus as influencing a person's partiality to smoking. And you might consider the conditional probability of part (a) as measuring the extent of such influence in the town. But would you consider the conditional probability in part (b) as measuring the extent to which smokerhood determines sex?

Moral: Don't try to read out of a model any deeper meanings than you put into it. And watch out for others who do.

7. Look again at the two versions of a game in Example 3 of Sec. 20.5. Suppose now that your friend picks two cards from the same 4-card deck, not simultaneously as before, but first one,

then the other. Here are modified versions of his questions:

Version 1: Your friend says: "My *first* card is an ace. What are the chances that I have two aces?"

Version 2: Your friend says: "My *first* card is a red ace. What are the chances that I have two aces?"

Does this mention of the order in picking change the answers from those I indicated in Fig. 20-6?

8. Suppose that probabilities $P(S)$ have been assigned to subsets S of some list Ω and that R is a particular subset with $P(R) > 0$. In Sec. 20.5 I argued that we could assign new, "conditional," probabilities to subsets S by the formula

$$P_R(S) = \frac{P(S \cap R)}{P(R)} \tag{*}$$

—reflecting information that an actual outcome is known to be in R. Check that the probabilities $P_R(S)$ in (*) satisfy all of the properties (1)–(5) which I noted for probabilities in Sec. 20.1.

9. Give an example of a probability model with mutually exclusive subsets R_1 and R_2, and a third subset S, such that

$$P_{R_1 \cup R_2}(S) \neq P_{R_1}(S) + P_{R_2}(S).$$

In other words, *for fixed S*, the quantity $P_R(S)$ as a function of R does NOT have the additive property of probabilities (4) in Sec. 20.1.

10. Regarding the medical Example 4 of Sec. 20.6, suppose that a patient appears *not* spitting blood. Based on this information, compute the probabilities that he has (i) ulcers, (ii) cirrhosis, or (iii) stomach inflammation—and compare these with the corresponding probabilities for these illnesses which I computed for a patient who did have the blood symptom.

11. Suppose newspapers report that, prior to an election in a certain state, 65% of the male voters and 35% of the female voters favor candidate X, and that 53% of the electorate are male.

   (a) Express these data as probabilities and conditional probabilities.

   (b) Find the probability that a randomly selected voter would favor candidate X.

12. Here are some U.S. data from 1963–1964:

Family income	Percent of children (6–16 years) receiving a routine medical checkup
Under $2000	12.0%
$2000–3999	18.4%
$4000–6999	28.0%
$7000–9999	36.8%
$10,000 and over	49.7%

(a) Are the data in the table sufficient for you to calculate the probability that a randomly selected child in the 6–16 year age group would have received a routine checkup?

(b) Suppose you were given estimates that families of children in the stated age group were distributed among the several income categories in 1963–1964 according to these percentages: 12% (under $2000), 27% ($2000–3999), 39% ($4000–6999), 14% ($7000–9999) and 8% ($10,000 and over). Would such additional data enable you to find the probability mentioned in part (a)? If so, compute it.

(c) Suppose that a randomly chosen child in the 6–16 year group of 1963–1964 turned out to have had a routine medical checkup. What's the probability that his family's income was in the $4000–6999 category?

(d) Find the probability in part (c) if the child had turned out *not* to have had a routine checkup.

13. Suppose that a small mail-order firm employs two clerks, A and B, and that the chances for A to make a mistake in a particular business letter are 1 in 20 and that corresponding chances for B are 1 in 15. Suppose that accounts are assigned to the clerks at random; but that once an account is assigned to a clerk, he keeps it through successive correspondence:

(a) If you've had just one letter from the firm, and if it contained an error, what are the chances that you're dealing with A? with B? Which is the "most likely"?

*(b) If you've had just one letter from the firm and it contained an error, what are the chances that your next letter will contain an error? will be free of error?

14. Suppose that buses pass a certain station every 5 minutes (as in Sec. 4.9), and that *you* arrived there at some random time. If you've already been waiting 2 minutes for a bus, what are the chances that you won't have to wait more than 1 additional minute?

(Suggestion: determine the subset R of your possible arrival times corresponding to which you would have to wait at least 2 minutes for the next bus.)

15. Suppose that both you and your neighbor have 8-ft long cars and have only a 20-ft length of curb for parallel parking for the two cars. Suppose also that your neighbor is inconsiderate and parks at random along the curb.

(a) If your neighbor always gets home before you, what's the probability that you'll be able to park your car on a given day?

(Suggestion: consider the possible results $R_x (0 \leqslant x \leqslant 12)$ that your neighbor parks his car with its nose x ft from the front end of the available space, and the corresponding conditional probabilities *given* R_x.)

(b) If you have 50–50 chances of getting home before your neighbor, what's the probability that you'll be able to park on a given day?

16. In Example 5 of Sec. 20.6, I discussed a model for a battery, arguing that possible outcomes for its lifetime t might be assigned probabilities via a probability density function $g(t) = \lambda e^{-\lambda t}$, where $\lambda =$ the "average lifetime" (say, in hours). Suppose that you have such a battery, with an average lifetime rating of 20 hours, and must rely on it to search for a lost object: if the battery fails before the object is found, then the entire mission is hopeless. Suppose you feel that success will be certain if you'll have 12 hours to search; and that if your search is restricted to a shorter period, then the chances for success will go down proportionally. What is the probability that your mission will succeed?

   (Suggestion: consider the possible results R_t ($0 \leqslant t < \infty$) that the battery will last t hours. What are the corresponding conditional probabilities for success?)

17. Which plan is more reliable for a 48-h period of use? (i) Two batteries (one a spare), each with a 20-h average lifetime; or (ii) one battery with a 35-h average lifetime?

*18. Just as new information can lead us to consider new conditional probabilities $P_R(S)$ in place of original probabilities $P(S)$, it should also lead us to recompute "average values" corresponding to the new probabilities $P_R(S)$. You may recall the problem of a needle hitting a crack between floor boards, which I discussed in Sec. 17.7. There x denoted the distance between the needle's head and the nearest crack on its left.

   (a) Compute the "average value" of x.
   (b) Compute the "average value" of x given information that the needle *did* touch a crack.

      (Suggestion: Find the average value of x for a given θ in Fig. 17-28. Then integrate over θ.)

   (c) Toss an actual needle 20 times and average the x distances for those cases where the needle does touch a crack. How does this observed value compare with the theoretical one in part (b)?

19. Suppose that you are interested in buying a batch of 10 objects from a factory, and that the batch contains n defectives — a fixed number ($0 \leqslant n \leqslant 10$) unknown to you. Here are two possible sampling plans which you might use to decide whether to accept the batch:

   (i) Pick two objects at random from the batch. If *both* are satisfactory, buy; otherwise reject the batch.
   (ii) Pick two objects at random from the batch. If both are satisfactory, buy; if both are defective, reject; if one is satisfactory and one defective, then select a third object, and buy or reject the batch according to whether that third object is OK or not.

(a) In terms of n, calculate the probability—call it $A_1(n)$—that you will accept the batch after sampling and deciding according to plan (i).

(Suggestion: You might think of the objects as numbered 1–10, the first n of them being defective; and represent possible sampling outcomes as $\omega = (i, j)$.)

(b) In terms of n, calculate the probability—call it $A_2(n)$—that you will accept the batch after sampling and deciding according to plan (ii).

(Suggestion: You might represent possible sampling outcomes as triples $\omega = (i, j, k)$, where the third entry (k) is irrelevant if i and j *both* refer to satisfactory objects (a result R_1) or both refer to unsatisfactory objects (a result R_2). The third entry would be relevant if the first two refer to a mixture of nondefective and defective (a result R_3). Then you might consider conditional probabilities of acceptance relative to R_1, R_2, and R_3.)

(c) On a common n axis, plot the functions $A_1(n)$ and $A_2(n)$ from parts (a) and (b). Which sampling plan offers more protection to you?

20.8   INDEPENDENCE AGAIN

The notion of conditional probability is a key ingredient in the idea of "independence" between two results. You may recall (from Sec. 3.5) my phrasing an intuitive criterion for such independence— namely: *knowledge that one of the results has taken place should not change our feelings about the chances for the other to take place.* Suppose that we can represent the results in question by subsets A and B of some set Ω for which we've already assigned probabilities $P(S)$. And suppose that A and B have original probabilities $P(A)$ and $P(B)$—where $P(A) > 0$. If we get new information that the actual outcome lies in A, then we can represent our changed feelings about B precisely by the conditional probability $P_A(B)$—so I've argued in the last few sections. Now if the new information about A really didn't change our feelings about B, and if the probability numbers do reflect this "independence," shouldn't we have

$$P_A(B) = P(B)? \tag{1}$$

By the very definition of $P_A(B)$, equation (1) means that

$$\frac{P(B \cap A)}{P(A)} = P(B). \tag{2}$$

Many people have adopted a rearranged version of (2) as a quantitative

Definition II: Suppose that we've already assigned probabilities $P(S)$ to subsets S of a set Ω of possible outcomes of an experiment.

Call two particular subsets A and B *independent* if

$$P(A \cap B) = P(A)P(B). \tag{3}$$

This is the relation for which I argued in Sec. 3.5, from a special case, and which I used in later examples to formulate assumptions about independence. It has the advantages of being "symmetric" in A and B, and of making sense even if $P(A)$ or $P(B) = 0$. (If $P(A) > 0$, we can divide (3) by $P(A)$ to arrive at (2) and (1) again.) The relation (3) is a special case of the more general

$$P(A \cap B) = P(A)P_A(B) \tag{4}$$

of Sec. 20.6, when $P(A) > 0$ and there is independence, $P_A(B) = P(B)$.

In order even to state Definition II for independence, we must already have an assignment of original probabilities $P(S)$ to subsets S of Ω. But what about going in the other direction? In building a model, how should we assign probabilities $P(S)$ to subsets S of a list Ω of possible outcomes *in order to* GUARANTEE *that certain subsets (or results) A and B will be independent?* Here are two old examples:

EXAMPLE 1. How shall we assign probabilities for the experiment of simultaneously tossing a "loaded" coin and a "loaded" die? You might recall (from Fig. 3-13) the list Ω of 8 possible joint outcomes for such an experiment. I've recorded Ω again in the upper left frame of Fig. 20-12. (H denotes "heads," T, "tails.")

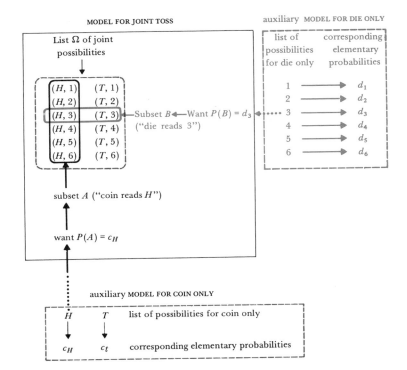

MODEL FOR JOINT TOSS   auxiliary MODEL FOR DIE ONLY   FIGURE 20-12

In Fig. 20-12, the subset A outlined in black represents the result, *"the coin reads heads."* Note how it cuts vertically across rows since it doesn't restrict what the die should read. The subset B outlined in green represents the result, *"the die reads 3."* And it cuts horizontally across columns since it doesn't restrict what the coin should read. Can we assign elementary probabilities $p(\omega)$ to the possible joint outcomes ω in Ω so that the joint model will have the following two reasonable features?

(i) The result A should have the same probability value $P(A)$ in Ω as the probability for getting a "head" in a model describing *only* the coin. Similarly, the result B should have the same probability $P(B)$ in Ω as for a corresponding result in a model describing *only* the die.

(ii) The results A and B should appear as *independent.*

In Fig. 20-12, I've indicated in black an auxiliary model for tossing only the coin—with elementary probabilities c_H and c_T for "heads" and "tails"; and in green, an auxiliary model for tossing only the die—with elementary probabilities d_1, d_2, ..., d_6. Whatever the ultimate probability assignments $P(S)$ may be for subsets S of the *joint* list Ω, we'll have to have

$$P(A) = c_H \quad \text{and} \quad P(B) = d_3 \tag{5}$$

for the first feature (i). And we'll have to have

$$P(A \cap B) = P(A)P(B) \tag{6}$$

for the second feature (ii). Note finally that the intersection $A \cap B$ contains the *single* joint outcome $(H, 3)$. Hence the "compound" probability $P(A \cap B)$ should be nothing other than the *elementary probability* $p(H, 3)$ which we have yet to assign to $(H, 3)$—at least according to the prescriptions I reviewed in Sec. 20.1. Together with (5) and (6) this last note forces upon us the elementary probability assignment

$$p(H, 3) = P(A \cap B) = P(A)P(B) = c_H d_3. \tag{7}$$

If we demand similar features for other parts of subsets describing the coin only and the die only, we'll be *forced* to the "product scheme" which I've recorded in Fig. 20-13 for assigning joint elementary probabilities.

FIGURE 20-13

Joint elementary probabilities		Row totals
$p(H, 1) = c_H d_1$	$p(T, 1) = c_T d_1$	$1d_1$
$p(H, 2) = c_H d_2$	$p(T, 2) = c_T d_2$	$1d_2$
$p(H, 3) = c_H d_3$	$p(T, 3) = c_T d_3$	$1d_3$
$p(H, 4) = c_H d_4$	$p(T, 4) = c_T d_4$	$1d_4$
$p(H, 5) = c_H d_5$	$p(T, 5) = c_T d_5$	$1d_5$
$p(H, 6) = c_H d_6$	$p(T, 6) = c_T d_6$	$1d_6$
column totals: $\quad c_H 1$	$c_T 1$	1
		(grand total)

$(c_H + c_T = 1) \qquad (d_1 + d_2 + d_3 + d_4 + d_5 + d_6 = 1)$

Note that the p's are nonnegative and sum to 1 (since the c's and d's have these properties separately), and that the first-column subset "A" and the third-row subset "B" do have probabilities $P(A)$ and $P(B)$ which satisfy (5) and (6). I invite you to check in similar but more general models that *any* subset $\tilde{A}$ which is a union of columns and *any* subset $\tilde{B}$ which is a union of rows will be independent, with $P(\tilde{A} \cap \tilde{B}) = P(\tilde{A})P(\tilde{B})$, when probabilities $P(S)$ are calculated via a "product scheme" such as in Fig. 20-13. Do Problem 3 of Sec. 20.10.

EXAMPLE 2. Another look at the longer-arc vs. shorter-arc problem of Fig. 20-8 (Example 4) in the last section. Let's record the clockwise distances of the randomly chosen points X and Y from the fixed point P by x and y as in Fig. 20-14. Then we can represent a possible choice for both X and Y via a single (ordered) pair of numbers (x, y) lying in a unit square Ω, as in Fig. 20-15. (I recorded the arrivals of two persons at a bus stop in just the same way, in Fig. 4-23.)

FIGURE 20-14　　　　　　　　　　　　　　　　　　　　　　**FIGURE 20-15**

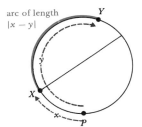

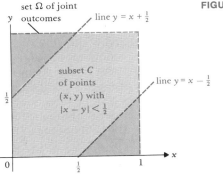

Check that the arc between X and Y which does *not* contain P (the green arc in Fig. 20-14) must have length $|x-y|$. For which outcomes (x, y) will that arc be the *shorter* one? Precisely when x and y satisfy the inequality

$$|x-y| < \frac{1}{2}, \tag{8}$$

or equivalently

$$-\frac{1}{2} < x-y < \frac{1}{2}, \tag{9}$$

—or, equivalently, the joint inequalities

$$y < x+\frac{1}{2} \quad \text{and} \quad y > x-\frac{1}{2}. \tag{10}$$

I've indicated such outcomes as constituting the green subset C in Fig. 20-15. C represents the result that the fixed point P will be in the *longer* arc between X and Y. What probability $P(C)$ shall we assign to C? Its area? If so, then since each grey triangle in Fig. 20-15 has area $\frac{1}{2}\frac{1}{2}\frac{1}{2} = \frac{1}{8}$, C should have probability

$$P(C) = 1 - \frac{1}{8} - \frac{1}{8} = \frac{3}{4} \tag{11}$$

—the same value as I got via conditional probabilities in the last section. You may recall my arguing once (after Fig. 4-24) that such an "area" assignment of probabilities would yield independence between subsets restricting only x values and subsets restricting only y values. Now, by reasoning as in Example 1, we can conclude that the "area" assignment is *forced* upon us if we require two features for the model of jointly choosing X and Y:

(i) The probability for x to lie in a subinterval $[a, b]$ of $[0, 1]$ should be the same in the joint model as in a model for choosing only X at random—namely, $b - a$. Similarly the probability for y to lie in a subinterval $[c, d]$ of $[0, 1]$ should be the same in the joint model as in a model for choosing only Y at random—namely, $d - c$.

(ii) In the joint model, any result A describing only the outcome for X should be independent of any result B describing only the outcome for Y.

A subset A restricting only x must cut vertically across all y levels, and a subset B restricting only y must cut horizontally across all x values—as in Fig. 20-16. In Fig. 20-16, features (i) and (ii) force the "area" assignment (12) for all rectangles of the form $A \cap B$. And using the addition property of probabilities for unions of mutually exclusive subsets we could conclude that the "area" assignment must extend to subsets such as C in Fig. 20-15 and even to any subset S of Ω which has area. (I invite you to examine this point in Problem 4 of Sec. 20.10.) Thus the conclusion $P(C) = \frac{3}{4}$ in (11) is inescapable if X and Y are chosen randomly and independently.

FIGURE 20-16

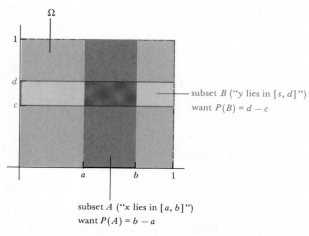

subset B ("y lies in $[s, d]$")
want $P(B) = d - c$

subset A ("x lies in $[a, b]$")
want $P(A) = b - a$

want $P(A \cap B) = P(A)P(B) = (b - a)(d - c)$
$= $ area of $A \cap B$ (12)

EXAMPLE 3: POPULATION EXTINCTION REVISITED. If you read my discussion in Sec. 5.8 about a model for *extinction of dynasties*, you might recall that it involved a special mixture of independence and dependence. Let's return to that model briefly and analyze its key points using the idea of conditional probability. I had three sets, R_1, R_2, and R_3:

R_1 represented the production by an original organism "A" of two viable offspring, "C" and "D."

R_2 represented the extinction, within $n-1$ hours, of "C" and its entire "dynasty" of successors.

R_3 represented the extinction, within $n-1$ hours, of "D" and its entire dynasty.

And I needed the probability $P(R_1 \cap R_2 \cap R_3)$. One of my assumptions for the model was that *once offspring such as "C" and "D" were born*, their separate dynasties would have *independent* fates. Why not express such independence via a new probability function based on knowing the result R_1? Namely,

$$P_{R_1}(R_2 \cap R_3) = P_{R_1}(R_2)P_{R_1}(R_3). \tag{13}$$

Even so, how can we bring the quantity in (13) to bear on the desired $P(R_1 \cap R_2 \cap R_3)$? Why not apply the general relationship $P(R \cap S) = P(R)P_R(S)$, with $R = R_1$ and $S = R_2 \cap R_3$, to write $P(R_1 \cap R_2 \cap R_3)$ as

$$P(R_1 \cap [R_2 \cap R_3]) = P(R_1)P_{R_1}(R_2 \cap R_3). \tag{14}$$

Then together (13) and (14) give

$$P(R_1 \cap R_2 \cap R_3) = P(R_1)P_{R_1}(R_2)P_{R_1}(R_3). \tag{15}$$

The expression (15) is a more accurate version of the three-factor product I used in Sec. 5.8. It leads to the same calculations, however, in view of the other key assumption for the model. I supposed that once a new organism is born its dynasty lives *independently of the circumstances of the birth*, and moreover *behaves probabilistically in exactly the same way as the dynasty of the original parent "A."* Thus both the quantities $P_{R_1}(R_2)$ and $P_{R_1}(R_3)$ don't depend essentially on R_1 or on the names "C" or "D"—merely on the number of hours, $n-1$, allowed for extinction. I let x_{n-1} denote the common value of $P_{R_1}(R_2)$ and $P_{R_1}(R_3)$, and went on in Fig. 5-18 to get a relationship between x_{n-1} and x_n.

20.9 THE PROBABILITY OF ULTIMATE VICTORY

Suppose that you are pitted against strong forces; but, undaunted, you propose to go on winning or losing individual encounters with them until either you or they are completely exhausted. What's the probability that you will exhaust them before they can exhaust you?

To answer, let's consider a model for the repeated trials. Here is one, phrased in terms of a "game" wherein you toss a "loaded" coin again and again, winning $1 from your opponent each time the coin falls "heads" and losing $1 to him for each "tail." Suppose that the coin has probability p of falling "heads" at any trial, and that you enter the game with initial resources of, say, k dollars, while your opponent starts with $M - k$ dollars. Throughout the game the total amount of money divided between you and your opponent will remain the same, M. The question is: What's the probability that your cumulative winnings will rise to the level of M—leaving your opponent exhausted—without first falling to $0? How will this probability for your "ultimate victory" depend on the size k of your initial resources relative to the total resources M? Let's think of M as a fixed quantity and denote your "ultimate victory" probability by $v(k)$ to display its dependence on k. In the extreme case that you start with $k = M$ dollars, we might say that you've "won" already, without a battle, and we could let $v(M) = 1$. In the other extreme that you start with $k = 0$ dollars, we might say that you've "lost" already; and let $v(0) = 0$. What about $v(k)$ for intermediate k? If the coin is "true," so that $p = \frac{1}{2}$ and wins of $+\$1$ and $-\$1$ are equally likely at each trial, would you guess that your victory probability should be *proportional* to your initial resources

$$v(k) = \frac{k}{M}, \quad \text{for } k = 0, 1, 2, \ldots, M? \tag{1}$$

And what if the coin is "loaded," $p \neq \frac{1}{2}$?

For greater precision, let's visualize the collection "Ω" of all possible ways in which the game could be played out. We can picture any one of them via a graph ω (or "path") showing cumulative winnings—as in Fig. 20-17.

FIGURE 20-17 Ω = (all possible paths)

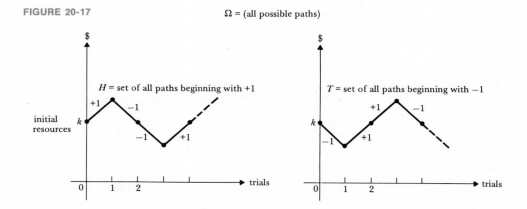

The goal is to calculate a probability $v(k)$ for the subset—call it "V_k"—of "victorious paths," those which start at level k and at some trial hit level M without first hitting 0, as I've pictured in Fig. 20-18.

FIGURE 20-18

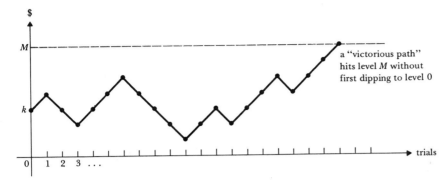

a "victorious path" hits level M without first dipping to level 0

Let's suppose that suitable probabilities $P(S)$ can be assigned to subsets S of paths. What's the main feature of the game which we might expect them to capture? How about this one: Because tosses are "independent" of each other, *the game essentially will start over again after the first toss*—the only difference being that *your resources will then be either $\$k+1$ or $\$k-1$ dollars* instead of $\$k$, depending on whether you get a "head" or a "tail" on the first toss. In Fig. 20-19 I've indicated how each old "victorious path" of Fig. 20-18 will lead again to victory (with one trial less) in a "new (green) game" starting after the first toss.

FIGURE 20-19

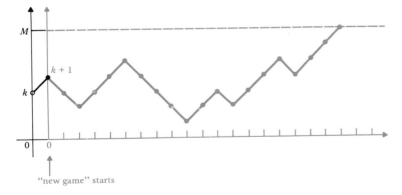

"new game" starts

Without looking any further into the details of the probability assignment $P(S)$, let's see more precisely what we can conclude from the "starting afresh" feature of the game: The original victory set V_k splits into two parts—one lying in the subset H of all paths starting with $+\$1$ and one lying in the subset T of all paths starting with $-\$1$ (see Fig. 20-17). And we can relate the original probability $v(k) = P(V_k)$ to new probabilities based on information about the first toss, via the equation

$$P(V_k) = P(H)P_H(V_k) + P(T)P_T(V_k) \qquad (2)$$

(just as in Fig. 20-7). If you get a "head" on your first toss and you then really start the game afresh with resources of $k+1$ dollars, shouldn't your new victory probability $P_H(V_k)$ be exactly the same as an original $P(V_{k+1})$? That is, shouldn't we have

$$P_H(V_k) = P(V_{k+1}) = v(k+1), \tag{3}$$

and similarly

$$P_T(V_k) = P(V_{k-1}) = v(k-1)? \tag{4}$$

If so, then the relationship (2) becomes

$$v(k) = P(H)v(k+1) + P(T)v(k-1). \tag{5}$$

Moreover, to incorporate the hypothesis, we should have as probabilities for "heads" and "tails" on any one toss the values

$$P(H) = p \quad \text{and} \quad P(T) = 1 - p. \tag{6}$$

Thus (5) becomes

$$v(k) = pv(k+1) + (1-p)v(k-1) \qquad \text{for } k = 1, 2, \ldots, M-1. \tag{7}$$

Conclusion: We can think of your victory probability as given by a *specific* function v which assigns to each initial resource value $k = 0, 1, 2, \ldots, M$ (as input) the victory probability $v(k)$ (as output). *And this function v must satisfy the following equation* (which I've phrased in more general functional notation using "f")

$$f(k) = pf(k+1) + (1-p)f(k-1) \qquad \text{for } k = 1, 2, \ldots, M, \tag{8}$$

together with "*boundary conditions*"

$$f(0) = 0 \quad \text{and} \quad f(M) = 1. \tag{9}$$

How can we determine the specific function v from (8) and (9)? Where have you seen a similar situation? Do you recall the "differential equations" of Chap. 16 and their "boundary conditions"? To paraphrase the methods of Chap. 16, we might try to guess at some specific function which satisfies (8) and (9), and then identify it with the sought-for v by showing that (8) and (9) together can have *only one* solution. I invite you to verify such "uniqueness" in doing Problem 8 of Sec. 20.10. (Also look back at Problem 9 of Sec. 16.3, where I considered another (so-called) "difference equation.") Here, let's try to guess at specific "solutions" for (8) and (9).

I conjectured that for a "true" coin we might expect victory probabilities proportional to initial resources. With $p = 1 - p = \frac{1}{2}$, equation (8) reads

$$f(k) = \frac{1}{2}f(k+1) + \frac{1}{2}f(k-1). \tag{10}$$

And the function $g(k) = k/M$, with outputs proportional to inputs, *does* satisfy (10) and (9):

$$g(k) = \frac{k}{M} = \frac{1}{2}\left(\frac{k+1}{M}\right) + \frac{1}{2}\left(\frac{k-1}{M}\right) = \frac{1}{2}g(k+1) + \frac{1}{2}g(k-1) \tag{11}$$

and

$$g(0) = \frac{0}{M} = 0 \quad \text{and} \quad g(M) = \frac{M}{M} = 1. \tag{12}$$

So *if* (8) and (9) have a unique solution, we can identify

$$v(k) = g(k) = \frac{k}{M} \qquad \text{for } k = 0, 1, 2, \ldots, M. \tag{13}$$

Note that we could have rearranged (10) in the forms

$$f(k+1) = 2f(k) + f(k-1) = 0 \tag{14}$$

or

$$[f(k+1) - f(k)] - [f(k) - f(k-1)] = 0. \tag{15}$$

The last equation displays a *difference of differences* of outputs. By a leap of the imagination, does it remind you of a differential equation with a *derivative of derivatives*,

$$f''(t) = 0? \tag{16}$$

Note also that the only solution of (16) with $f(0) = 0$ and $f(M) = 1$ is the linear function $g(t) = t/M$, analogous to the $g(k)$ in (13).

But what about a "loaded" coin; for example, with $p = \frac{1}{3}$? Then equation (8) becomes

$$f(k) = \frac{1}{3}f(k+1) + \frac{2}{3}f(k-1). \tag{17}$$

I invite you to rewrite equation (17) displaying $f(k+1)$ in terms of $f(k)$ and $f(k-1)$, and to solve for successive values $f(k+1)$ for $k = 2, 3, \ldots$ (Do Problem 8 in the next section.) But first, let's explore an analogy with (15): Rearrange (17) as

$$f(k+1) \quad -3f(k) = 2f(k-1) = 0 \tag{18}$$

or

$$[f(k+1) - f(k)] - [f(k) - f(k-1)] = f(k) - f(k-1). \tag{19}$$

Does the last form remind you of a differential equation

$$f''(t) = f'(t)? \tag{20}$$

Note that the exponential function e^t provides a solution for (20). Why not let our imagination leap again, and see whether equation (17) will be satisfied by a specific function of the form

$$g(k) = c^k \qquad \text{for } k = 0, 1, 2, \ldots, M, \tag{21}$$

where c is some positive base, and inputs k appear as *exponents*, just as in e^t? In order for $g(k) = c^k$ to satisfy (17) we must have

$$c^k = \frac{1}{3}c^{k+1} + \frac{2}{3}c^{k-1},$$

or (dividing by c^{k-1}),

$$c = \frac{1}{3}c^2 + \frac{2}{3} \tag{22}$$

—a condition on c. More generally, for a coin loaded with probability p for "heads" ($p \neq \frac{1}{2}$), we'll need c to satisfy the equation

$$c^k = pc^{k+1} + (1-p)c^{k-1}, \qquad \text{or} \qquad c = pc^2 + (1-p),$$

or

$$pc^2 - c + (1-p) = 0. \tag{23}$$

In Problem 8(c) of Sec. 20.10, I invite you to check the following: The quadratic $Q(c) = pc^2 - c + (1-p)$ in (23) has two roots, $c_1 = 1$ and $c_2 = (1-p)/p$. Moreover, each of the "exponential" functions

$$g_1(k) \equiv 1^k \equiv 1 \quad \text{and} \quad g_2(k) = \left(\frac{1-p}{p}\right)^k \tag{24}$$

satisfies (8), and so does any combination of the form

$$g(k) = Ag_1(k) + Bg_2(k), \tag{25}$$

where A and B are any constants. In particular, if we choose

$$A = \frac{1}{1 - [(1-p)/p]^M} \quad \text{and} \quad B = \frac{-1}{1 - [(1-p)/p]^M} \tag{26}$$

we'll have a specific function

$$g_3(k) = \frac{1 - [(1-p)/p]^k}{1 - [(1-p)/p]^M} \qquad \text{for } k = 1, 2, \ldots, M \tag{27}$$

which satisfies not only (8), but also the "boundary conditions" (9), $g_3(0) = 0$ and $g_3(M) = 1$. If (8) and (9) together have a *unique* solution, then we can identify the values $g_3(k)$ in (27) as the long sought victory probabilities $v(k)$. (See also Problem 9 of Sec. 20.10 for another method of arriving at the values in (27).)

For a concrete instance, suppose again that your chances for success in any one trial are 1 in 3 — so that

$$p = \frac{1}{3} \quad \text{and} \quad \frac{(1-p)}{p} = \frac{2/3}{1/3} = 2.$$

Suppose that you start with $k = 995$ dollars, and your opponent with only 5 dollars—so that $M = 1000$. Still your chances for ultimate victory are *only*

$$v(995) = \frac{1 - 2^{995}}{1 - 2^{1000}} = \frac{2^{995} - 1}{2^{1000} - 1} = \frac{2^{995}}{2^{1000}} \text{(approx)} = \frac{1}{2^5} = 0.03 \text{ (approx)}.$$

Why so small? Apparently a repeated number of "tails"—which are more likely than "heads"—can pull down your huge initial lead before it does you much good.

20.10   PROBLEMS ON CONDITIONAL PROBABILITY
AND INDEPENDENCE

First, you might review some of the problems on independence in Sec. 3.6.

°1. Suppose that we have a coin loaded 2 to 1 in favor of "heads," and a die all of whose faces are equally likely except for "3," which is twice as likely to turn up as any of the others.

    (a) Describe the possible outcomes for the "experiment" of tossing the coin and the die—and assign elementary probabilities according to the product scheme of Example 1 in Sec. 20.8.

    (b) Check that these two results are "independent":

        (i) "the coin shows heads," and

        (ii) "the die shows an even number."

    (c) Check that these two results are "independent":

        (i) "the coin shows heads," and

        (ii) "the die shows an odd number."

°2. Set up a model for the tossing of two dice, say, one red and one green—each loaded as for the die in Problem 1.

    (a) Check that these two results are independent:

        (i) "the red die shows an even number," and

        (ii) "the green die shows an odd number."

    (b) Are the following two results independent?

        (i) "the sum of the numbers on the dice is even," and

        (ii) "the green die shows an odd number."

*3. Help generalize the results of Problems 1 and 2 and Example 1 of Sec. 20.8: Suppose that one experiment (such as tossing a coin) can have outcomes $\Omega_a = \{a_1, a_2, a_3, \ldots, a_m\}$ with corresponding elementary probabilities $q(a_i)$. ($q(a_i) \geq 0$ for $i = 1, 2, \ldots, m$, and $q(a_1) + q(a_2) + \cdots + q(a_m) = 1$.) And suppose that a second experiment (such as tossing a die) can have outcomes $\Omega_b = \{b_1, b_2, b_3, \ldots, b_n\}$ with corresponding elementary probabilities $r(b_j)$. ($r(b_i) \geq 0$ for $j = 1, 2, \ldots, n$, and $r(b_1) + r(b_2) + \cdots + r(b_n) = 1$.) Now think of a new experiment consisting of the *joint* performance of the two original experiments—"type a" and "type b". Let's describe its possible outcomes as ordered pairs $\omega = (a_i, b_j)$ and assign corresponding "elementary probabilities"

$$p(\omega) = q(a_i)r(b_j) \tag{*}$$

for each $i = 1, 2, \ldots, m$, and $j = 1, 2, \ldots, n$.

    (a) Make a table picturing the list Ω of all joint outcomes ω, as in Fig. 20-12, with rows corresponding to different a_i's and columns corresponding to different b_j's. Near each ω record its elementary probability $p(\omega)$.

    (b) Note that $p(\omega) \geq 0$ for all ω's. What is the sum of the $p(\omega)$'s in the ith row of the table in part (a)? What is the sum of the $p(\omega)$'s in the jth column? Show that the sum of *all* the $p(\omega)$'s is 1.

(c) Now pick any subsets $S \subset \Omega_a$ and $T \subset \Omega_b$ and consider these *corresponding* subsets of Ω:

$$\tilde{S} = \{\text{all } \omega = (a_i, b_j) \text{ with } a_i \text{ in } S \text{ and } b_j \text{ unrestricted}\}$$

and

$$\tilde{T} = \{\text{all } \omega = (a_i, b_j) \text{ with } a_i \text{ unrestricted and } b_j \text{ in } T\}.$$

$\tilde{S}$ represents the result in the *joint* experiment that the subexperiment of "type a" had some outcome in the set S, and $\tilde{T}$ represents the result in the *joint* experiment that the subexperiment of "type b" had some outcome in the set T. Show that $\tilde{S}$ must correspond to a *union of rows* in the table of part (a), and that $\tilde{T}$ must correspond to a *union of columns*.

(d) Show why any union of rows $\tilde{S}$ and union of columns T as in part (c) must be independent — that is, why

$$\left\{\begin{array}{l}\text{the sum of } p(\omega) \text{ for} \\ \text{all } \omega\text{'s in } \tilde{S} \cap \tilde{T}\end{array}\right\}$$

$$= \left\{\begin{array}{l}\text{the sum of } p(\omega) \text{ for} \\ \text{all } \omega\text{'s in } \tilde{S}\end{array}\right\} \cdot \left\{\begin{array}{l}\text{the sum of } p(\omega) \\ \text{for all } \omega\text{'s in } \tilde{T}\end{array}\right\}. \qquad (**)$$

4. Suppose that we can represent a list Ω of outcomes Ω of an experiment as a rectangle in the plane — as I did in Example 2 of Sec. 4.9 and Example 2 of Sec. 20.8. Recall that for mutually exclusive subsets S_i in Ω, a probability function $P(S)$ must share the same addition property (4) of Sec. 20.1 as the function $A(S) = (\text{area of } S)/(\text{area of } \Omega)$.

(a) Suppose that we can argue — as I did in Example 2 of Sec. 20.8 — that $P(S) = A(S)$ whenever S is a rectangle with horizontal and vertical sides. Show then that $P(S)$ must $= A(S)$ whenever S is a union of any finite number of such rectangles all mutually exclusive.

(b) Try to extend the result $P(S) = A(S)$ to all sorts of other subsets of Ω for which you know how to compute areas. In particular, consider any triangle, and any finite union of mutually exclusive triangles and rectangles (such as the subset C in Fig. 20-15). Can you use results on the definite integral from Chapters 17 and 18 to extend the equality $P(S) = A(S)$ to still more complicated S?

5. Do you recall Example 2 of Sec. 4.9, regarding your arrival time (x) and the arrival time (y) of an enemy, during a 5-minute period? I pictured the list of all joint outcomes, $\Omega = \{(x, y)\}$, as a 5×5 square in Fig. 4-23.

(a) Now pick some subset of your possible arrival times — say, a union of subintervals $S = [1, 2] \cup [3, 4]$. And pick some subset of possible arrival times for your enemy — say, $T = [0, 1] \cup [2.5, 3.5]$. Consider corresponding subsets in the joint list Ω:

$\tilde{S} = \{$all (x, y) with x in S and $0 \leqslant y \leqslant 5\}$

and

$\tilde{T} = \{$all (x, y) with $0 \leqslant x \leqslant 5$ and y in $T\}$.

In Ω, the subset $\tilde{S}$ represents your arriving at some time in S, regardless of when your enemy arrives; and the subset $\tilde{T}$ represents your enemy's arriving at some time T regardless of when you arrive. Indicate Ω, $\tilde{S}$, and $\tilde{T}$ on a picture. Show that $\tilde{S}$ must be a *union of vertical strips*, each stretching across the square Ω; and that T must be a *union of horizontal strips*, each stretching across the square Ω.

(b) Show that the intersection $\tilde{S} \cap \tilde{T}$ must be a union of mutually exclusive rectangles.

(c) In Example 2 of Sec. 20.8, I argued essentially that if we want subsets such as $\tilde{S}$ and $\tilde{T}$ to be "independent" we are forced to assign probabilities to subrectangles of Ω which are proportional to their areas.

$$P(\text{rectangle}) = \frac{\text{area of rectangle}}{\text{area of } \Omega}. \qquad (*)$$

Using (*), calculate the probabilities of the sets $\tilde{S}$, $\tilde{T}$, and of the intersection $\tilde{S} \cap \tilde{T}$ in part (b), and show that $\tilde{S}$ and $\tilde{T}$ are indeed independent.

* (d) Repeat parts (a)–(c) for more general unions

$$S = [a_1, b_1] \cup [a_2, b_2] \cup \cdots \cup [a_m, b_m],$$

where the $[a_i, b_i]$ are mutually exclusive subintervals of some interval $a \leqslant x \leqslant b$, and

$$T = [c_1, d_1] \cup [c_2, d_2] \cup \cdots \cup [c_n, d_n],$$

where the $[c_j, d_j]$ are mutually exclusive subintervals of some interval $c \leqslant y \leqslant d$.

6. (a) Suppose that you have $15 and an opponent has $20, and that you agree to toss a "true" coin—"heads" you give him $1, "tails" he gives you $1—until one of you is broke. What are your chances for winning? (See Sec. 20.9.)

(b) Would your chances for winning be altered if $\pm$$5 were exchanged each time rather than $\pm$$1?

(c) Answer parts (a) and (b) for the case of a coin loaded 4 to 3 in favor of heads. Does the *size* of the "stakes" ($1 or $5) make a difference in this case?

7. An English botanist, Robert Brown, discovered that a very small particle suspended in a jar of fluid will move around in a jerky fashion. Later observers tried to explain this motion in terms of random collisions between the particle and molecules of the fluid. Here is a simplified model to describe the changes in *one*

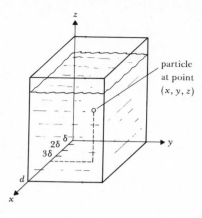

coordinate of the particle relative to axes placed as in the figure. To approximate the motion, let's pick a very small number $\delta > 0$ and mark off off the locations $\delta, 2\delta, 3\delta, \ldots$, in the interval $[0, d]$ on the x axis. Imagine that on each of its collisions with a molecule of the fluid, the particle (that is, its x coordinate) is pushed through a distance δ from one of these locations to a neighboring one, with 50–50 chances of going in either direction.

What predictions can we make, on the basis of this model, which we could then check against observations to see whether the model has any use at all?

(a) If we start the particle in the model at a position roughly $\frac{2}{3}$ of the way from 0 to d, what are the chances that in its successive movements the particle will arrive at d before it gets to 0? (Suggestion: See Sec. 20.9.)

(b) Suppose that we observe a large number of actual particles in actual jars, and start recording the motion of each particle at some time when it is $\frac{2}{3}$ of the way between opposite walls. In what fraction of the cases could you expect the particle to reach the nearer of the two walls first?

(c) Suppose that the walls of the jar are membranes through which a slight but steady current of fluid flows, so that at any stage the particle has 4 to 3 odds for going in the direction of the current rather than against it. If we start observing the particle when it's halfway between walls, what are the chances for its reaching the wall *upstream* of the current before reaching the downstream wall? Try the case $d = 2$ in. and $\delta = 0.1$ in.

$\Big($Note that

$$\frac{1-r^k}{1-r^{2k}} = \frac{1-r^k}{(1-r^k)(1+r^k)} = \frac{1}{1+r^k}.\Big)$$

*8. (a) Show that the *sum* of any two solutions of the difference equation

$$f(k) = pf(k+1) + (1-p)f(k-1) \qquad \text{for } k = 1, 2, \ldots, m$$

$$(*)$$

must again be a solution. (I considered this equation in Sec. 20.9.)

(b) Help show that there can be only one function $f(k)$ which satisfies (*) (with $0 < p < 1$) together with the boundary conditions:

$$f(0) = 0 \quad \text{and} \quad f(m) = 1. \tag{**}$$

Suppose $g(k)$ is such a solution. Rewrite (*) in terms of g as

$$g(k+1) = \Big(\frac{1}{p}\Big)g(k) - \Big(\frac{1-p}{p}\Big)g(k-1). \tag{***}$$

From (**) we know already that $g(0) = 0$. Let b denote $g(1)$.

Then (***) implies that $g(2) = (1/p)b$, and that

$$g(3) = \left(\frac{1}{p}\right)g(2) - \left(\frac{1-p}{p}\right)g(1) = \frac{1}{p^2}b - \frac{1-p}{p}b$$

$$= \frac{1-p+p^2}{p}b;$$

and so on. Write a specific formula for $g(k)$ in terms of b and k, for all $k = 2, 3, \ldots, M$; and show that there is a *unique* value of b which will permit $g(M) = 1$ as in (*). Will your formula for $g(k)$ not then display the unique form which any solution g of (*) and (**) must have?

(c) To complete the method for getting a solution g which I discussed in (21)–(24) of Sec. 20.9, check that the quadratic $Q(x) = px^2 - x + (1-p)$ has the numbers 1 and $(1-p)/p$ as its two roots. (Here $0 < p < 1$.)

*9. Here is another way to find a solution for the difference equation (*) in Problem (8):

(a) Write the left-hand side as $(p + 1 - p)f(k)$. Then rearrange terms to get (*) in the form

$$f(k) - f(k+1) = \left(\frac{1-p}{p}\right)[f(k-1) - f(k)].$$

(b) Let $r = (1-p)/p$ and let $a_k = f(k) - f(k+1)$ for $k = 0, 1, \ldots, m-1$. Then use the first boundary condition (**) in Problem 8, and results about "geometric" series (recall Example 3 of Sec. 10.6) to show that, for $1 \leqslant k \leqslant M$,

$$0 - f(k) = [f(0) - f(1)] + [f(1) - f(2)] + \cdots$$
$$+ [f(k-1) - f(k)]$$

$$= a_1 + a_2 + \cdots + a_{k-1} = a_1 \frac{1-r^k}{1-r} = -f(1)\frac{1-r^k}{1-r}.$$

(c) Find the value of $f(1)$ which will yield $f(M) = 1$ in part (b).

20.11 RELATING MANY SETS

How can we capture the notion of "independence" among *many* subsets, $S_1, S_2, S_3, \ldots, S_n$? Should we expect more relationships between probabilities than merely equalities of the form $P(R \cup S) = P(R)P(S)$ holding for different pairs $R = S_i$ and $S = S_j$? You might recall my suggesting in Sec. 6.6 that an equation of the form

$$P(S_1 \cap S_2 \cap \cdots \cap S_n) = P(S_1)P(S_2) \cdots \cdots P(S_n)$$

should hold too. More generally, suppose the sets $S_1, S_2, S_3, \ldots, S_n$ aren't necessarily independent. We can still relate their original and conditional probabilities by two-by-two via the basic formula

$$P(R \cap S) = P(R)P_R(S) \qquad (1)$$

of Sec. 20.6. But what relations connect all the sets *simultaneously*? As one approach to an answer, why not apply the equality $P(R \cap S) = P(R)P_R(S)$ repeatedly to different groups of sets—as I've indicated in Fig. 20-20, with green sets playing the role of R and black sets playing the role of S?

FIGURE 20-20

$$
\begin{aligned}
P(S_1 \cap \cdots \cap S_{n-1} \cap S_n) &= P(s_1 \cap \cdots \cap S_{n-1})P_{s_1 \cap \cdots \cap S_{n-1}}(S_n) \\
&= P(S_1 \cap \cdots \cap S_{n-2} \cap S_{n-1})P_{S_1 \cap \cdots \cap S_{n-1}}(S_n) \\
&= P(S_1 \cap \cdots \cap S_{n-2})P_{S_1 \cap \cdots \cap S_{n-2}}(S_{n-1})P_{S_1 \cap \cdots \cap S_{n-1}}(S_n) \\
&= P(S_1 \cap \cdots \cap S_{n-3} \cap S_{n-2})P_{S_1 \cap \cdots \cap S_{n-2}}(S_{n-1})P_{S_1 \cap \cdots S_{n-1}}(S_n) \\
&= P(S_1 \cap \cdots \cap S_{n-3})P_{S_1 \cap \cdots \cap S_{n-3}}(S_{n-2})P_{S_1 \cap \cdots \cap S_{n-2}}(S_{n-1})P_{S_1 \cap \cdots \cap S_{n-1}}(S_n) \\
&\;\;\vdots \\
&= P(S_1)P_{S_1}(S_2)P_{S_1 \cap S_2}(S_3) \cdot \cdots\cdots \cdot P_{S_1 \cap \cdots \cap S_{n-1}}(S_n).
\end{aligned}
$$

The result—call it a "PROBABILITY CHAIN"—

$$
\begin{aligned}
&P(S_1 \cap S_2 \cap \cdots \cap S_n) \\
&= P(S_1)P_{S_1}(S_2)P_{S_1 \cap S_2}(S_3) \cdot \cdots \cdot P_{S_1 \cap S_2 \cap \cdots \cap S_{n-1}}(S_n),
\end{aligned} \tag{2}
$$

displays the original probability of $S_1 \cap S_2 \cap \cdots \cap S_n$ as an orderly product of the original probability for S_1 and successive conditional probabilities. It's valid as long as all of the intersections have nonzero probabilities, so that the conditional probabilities make sense. Now, let's apply the equality.

If the $S_1, S_2, \ldots, S_n$ represent intuitively "independent" results—with original probability $P(S_i)$ of an S_i unchanged by information about the other S_j's, then shouldn't we have

$$P_{S_1 \cap S_2 \cap \cdots \cap S_{i-1}}(S_i) = P(S_i) \tag{3}$$

for each of the factors in (3)? If so, we immediately get the expected product form

$$P(S_1 \cap S_2 \cap \cdots \cap S_n) = P(S_1)P(S_2) \cdot \cdots \cdot P(S_n). \tag{4}$$

Nowadays, people **DEFINE** an entire family of subsets as being *independent* if *every finite collection of the sets satisfies* (4). Thus for three subsets R, S, T, independence means that *all* of the equalities

$$P(R \cap S) = P(R)P(S), \quad P(S \cap T) = P(S)P(T),$$
$$P(T \cap R) = P(T)P(R),$$

and

$$P(R \cap S \cap T) = P(R)P(S)P(T) \tag{5}$$

must hold. (There are cases where the first three hold but the last doesn't, as I invite you to check in Problem 7 of Sec. 20.14.)

EXAMPLE 1: *Seven independent disease victims revisited.* In Sec. 1.2, I calculated the probability that 6 out of the seven survive on the assumption that each had an *individual survival probability* of $\frac{1}{2}$. But what if we were dealing with a disease for which the individual survival probability is some other value—call it p? Imagine again the list Ω of all 2^r possible survival patterns ω for the seven victims, of the form

$$\omega_0 = (s, s, d, s, d, d, s) \tag{6}$$

ith entry refers to ith victim

($s =$ survives, $d =$ dies). How should we now assign elementary probabilities $p(\omega)$ to the ω's, and what will be the "compound" probability $P(C)$ of the subset C representing the result that "exactly 6 victims survive"?

Let's consider first the fate of a single victim—say the ith—without regard to the others. We can represent his survival by the subset—call it "S_i"—of all patterns ω which have an "s" as their ith entry. And we can represent his death by the complementary subset $D_i = S_i'$. Whatever the ultimate assignment of elementary probabilities $p(\omega)$ will be, we'll want to have

$$P(S_i) = p \quad \text{and} \quad P(D_i) = 1 - p \tag{7}$$

as individual survival and death probabilities—and this for each $i \leq 7$.

Next, let's turn to a particular survival pattern for all the victims together, such as $\omega_0 = (s, s, d, s, d, d, s)$. The first entry "$s$" tells us that the first victim survived: ω_0 lies in the subset S_1. The second entry "s" tells us that ω_0 lies in the subset S_2. The third entry "d" tells us that ω_0 lies in D_3. Check that ω_0 is the *single* pattern which lies in the 7-fold intersection

$$S_1 \cap S_2 \cap D_3 \cap S_4 \cap D_5 \cap D_6 \cap S_7,$$

$$\omega_0 = (s, \quad s, \quad d, \quad s, \quad d, \quad d, \quad s) \tag{8}$$

where the subsets S_i and D_j correspond to the "s" and "d" entries in ω_0 as I've indicated in (8). To capture the intuitive notion that the fate of each victim is "independent" of the combined fates of the others, shouldn't we apply the multiple "product" rule (4) to the intersection in (8)? If so, we'll be *forced* to an elementary probability assignment

$$p(\omega_0) = P(S_1 \cap S_2 \cap D_3 \cap S_4 \cap D_5 \cap D_6 \cap S_7)$$

$$= P(S_1)P(S_3)P(D_3)P(S_4)P(D_5)P(D_6)P(S_7)$$

$$= p \cdot p \cdot (1-p) \cdot p \cdot (1-p) \cdot (1-p) \cdot p = p^4(1-p)^3. \tag{9}$$

This is just the same reasoning as I used for the case of tossing a coin and a die simultaneously (Example 1) in Sec. 20.7. In that example it led to the "product scheme" for elementary probabilities in Fig. 20-13. If we continue to apply it here to other patterns ω, we'll find ourselves *forced* to assign to each ω an elementary

$$p(\omega) = p^k(1-p)^{7-k}, \quad \text{where } k \text{ is the number of "s's" in } \omega. \tag{10}$$

I invite you to check (via the binomial expansion of Sec. 6.8) that such $p(\omega)$'s do add up to 1. (Do Problem 3 of Sec. 20.14.)

Note finally that there are exactly 7 patterns ω which have only one "*d*" entry and the rest "*s*'s"—one pattern for each possible position of the "*d*." They each have elementary probability $p^6(1-p)$. Together they constitute the subset C representing the result "exactly 6 survive." So we should have

$$P(C) = 7p^6(1-p). \tag{11}$$

If an individual has chances $p = 0.4$ for survival, then

$$P(C) = 7(0.4)^6(0.6) = 0.018 \text{ approximately} \tag{12}$$

—less than $\frac{1}{3}$ the value I got in Sec. 1.2 with $p = 0.5$.

(See Problem 8 of Sec. 20.14 for a general check that product assignments such as (10) do yield *independence* for subsets such as in (8).)

In the next section I'll apply the "probability chain" relation (2) to sets which are not independent.

20.12   RAGS TO RICHES, AND BACK

To get a crude picture of how wealth is distributed in the United States, some economists set a rather arbitrary "poverty level"— which they adjust between nonfarm and farm occupations and from year to year to take into account the changing value of the dollar. Accordingly, U.S. families fall into two categories: "*a*"—those with annual incomes above the poverty level, and "*b*"—those below. From one year to the next, various families change categories—and others remain. Think of picking a family at random and of watching it for many years. What are the relative chances for its being well off ("*a*") or poor ("*b*") at some date far in the future? Do such probabilities even make sense? And if they do, how strongly would they be influenced by information as to the category in which the family is *now*?

Here is an *idealized model* by which we might explore such questions under the crude assumption that *major social and economic conditions remain the same for a long time*. A second key assumption is that *once we know the category of a family in a given year, all further information about its previous history will be irrelevant for estimating its future fortunes*. (Such a condition might hold, more or less, for a large ethnically homogeneous slice of the population.)

Suppose we could write a list "Ω" of all possible future economic histories for the randomly chosen family, and that we could assign probabilities $P(S)$ to subsets S of Ω in a reasonable way. How might we expect the numbers $P(S)$ to reflect the basic assumptions of the model? Let's denote by "A_n" the subset of all possible histories which would place the chosen family in category "a" at the end of the nth year of observation; and by "B_n" the complementary subset which would place the family in category "b" at that time. If we somehow knew in which category the family would be at the end of the $(n-1)$st year, how would that information affect our estimates for one year later? Precisely via the four *conditional* probabilities in the following table:

After n transitions

	"a"	"b"
"a"	$P_{A_{n-1}}(A_n)$	$P_{A_{n-1}}(B_n)$
"b"	$P_{B_{n-1}}(A_n)$	$P_{B_{n-1}}(B_n)$

After $n-1$ transitions (rows)   (1)

People usually call such quantities "one-step transition probabilities." What can we expect of them in light of the basic assumptions for the model? If general conditions stay the same, then the transition probabilities should not depend on the particular pair of years $n-1$ and n. We can relabel them more simply, without "$n-1$" and "n," as in the next table:

To

	"a"	"b"
"a"	p_{aa}	p_{ab}
"b"	p_{ba}	p_{bb}

From (rows)   (2)

Note in these tables that, since $A_n \cup B_n = \Omega$, the probabilities in any row add to 1:

$$p_{aa} + p_{ab} = 1 \quad \text{and} \quad p_{ba} + p_{bb} = 1. \tag{3}$$

Now let's look at the "long run" — at $P(A_n)$ and $P(B_n)$ for *large* n. If such probabilities do tend to "long run" limiting values, they should differ only slightly from their counterparts, $P(A_{n-1})$ and $P(B_{n-1})$ of the previous year. Can we relate the two sets of numbers precisely? Yes, *because a family can arrive at the nth year only via one or the other category during the $(n-1)$st year.* So

$$P(A_n) = P(A_{n-1})P_{A_{n-1}}(A_n) + P(B_{n-1})P_{B_{n-1}}(A_n) \tag{4}$$

and

$$P(B_n) = P(A_{n-1})P_{A_{n-1}}(B_n) + P(B_{n-1})P_{B_{n-1}}(B_n) \tag{5}$$

—by the "reconstruction principle" of Fig. 20-7. I've rewritten these equations in Fig. 20-21, using the shorter notation of table 2.

FIGURE 20-21

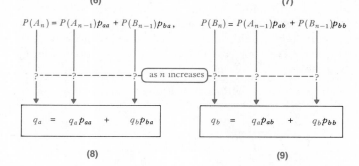

$$(6) \qquad\qquad (7)$$

$(8) \qquad\qquad\qquad (9)$

If long run limits do exist,

$$\lim_{n\to\infty} P(A_n) = \lim_{n\to\infty} P(A_{n-1}) = q_a \tag{10}$$

and

$$\lim_{n\to\infty} P(B_n) = \lim_{n\to\infty} P(B_{n-1}) = q_b, \tag{11}$$

for a family to be in category "a" or in "b," then these limits q_a and q_b must satisfy the simultaneous equations (8) and (9)—where the coefficients p_{aa}, p_{ba}, and so on, are given. Moreover,

$$q_a + q_b = \lim_{n\to\infty} P(A_n) + \lim_{n\to\infty} P(B_n)$$
$$= \lim_{n\to\infty} [P(A_n) + P(B_n)] = \lim_{n\to\infty} 1 = 1. \tag{12}$$

To solve for q_a and q_b, let's rewrite (8) and (9) as

$$(p_{aa} - 1)q_a + p_{ba}q_b = 0 \tag{13}$$

and

$$p_{ab}q_a + (p_{bb} - 1)q_b = 0. \tag{14}$$

And using the relations $p_{ab} = 1 - p_{aa}$ and $p_{ba} = 1 - p_{bb}$ from (3), we can rewrite (13) and (14) once more as

$$-p_{ab}q_a + p_{ba}q_b = 0 \tag{15}$$

and

$$p_{ab}q_a - p_{ba}q_b = 0. \tag{16}$$

Note that (16) is really the same as (15) except for a factor of -1, so it gives no added information. But if we take (15) and (12) together,

$$\left\{ \begin{aligned} -p_{ab}q_a + p_{ba}q_b &= 0 \\ q_a + q_b &= 1 \end{aligned} \right\},$$

we can eliminate q_b and q_a separately — to get

$$q_a = \frac{p_{ab}}{p_{ba} + p_{ab}} \quad \text{and} \quad q_b = \frac{p_{ab}}{p_{ba} + p_{ab}} \qquad (17)$$

— provided p_{ba} and p_{ba} are not both 0. From what do these results flow? Merely from the supposition that limits q_a and q_b do exist, and from the basic assumption that the one-step transition probabilities p_{ij} don't depend on n. *Nowhere did I state in which category a family might start at $n = 0$.* We would be *forced* to the same results (17) if we had restricted the original Ω to the subset A_0 corresponding to information that the family started out in "a," and if "$P(S)$" in fact stood for the conditional probability function $P_{A_0}(S)$. Similarly if we knew that the family started out in "b," and $P(S) = P_{B_0}(S)$.

A conclusion: *If "long run" probabilities q_a and q_b exist at all, they must be independent of the starting condition of the family.* Moreover — as (17) shows — they will be proportional to the "crossover" transition probabilities p_{ba} and p_{ab}.

Although the United States is not homogeneous, and the years 1962 and 1963 were not in a period of unchanging conditions, approximate data are available from those years by which we might construct a concrete example of table 2, namely:

		End of 1963	
		"a"	"b"
End of 1962	"a"	0.95	0.05
	"b"	0.19	0.81

(18)

The quantity 0.95 is the fraction of those families with 1962 incomes above \$3000 whose 1963 income was also above \$3000. (Less for farm families.) And 0.05 refers to the rest of the 1962 "a" families — those whose earnings slipped below \$3000 in 1963. Similarly for the second row. Will you accept these fractions as approximate one-step transition probabilities for an *individual* randomly chosen family? If so, and if 1962–1963 conditions did prevail for many years, and if long run limits q_a and q_b did exist — those limits would have to be

$$q_a = \frac{0.19}{0.19 + 0.05} = 0.79 \text{ (approx)}$$

and

$$q_b = \frac{0.05}{0.19 + 0.05} = 0.21 \text{ (approx)}. \qquad (19)$$

(The actual fractions for "nonpoor" and "poor" in 1968 were 0.82 and 0.18.)

But need limiting values q_a and q_b *necessarily* exist? The following table of transition probabilities

	To	
	"a"	"b"
From { "a"	0	1
"b"	1	0

(20)

describes an extreme case where all families change categories after each year. Thus if a family starts out rich, with $P(A_0) = 1$, the subsequent $P(A_n)$'s will alternate $0, 1, 0, 1, \ldots$ forever, and have no limit.

Would you CONJECTURE that limits q_a and q_b must exist whenever all the entries in the table are nonzero—that is, *whenever there is a positive probability for going from any category to any other category in a single step?*

To follow up these ideas—and to see how we might actually calculate transition probabilities for more than one step—let's try to visualize more clearly the set Ω of possible future outcomes for a chosen family. One way is to represent each outcome by a graph or "path," whose nth vertex height indicates the category in which the family will lie after the nth transition—as in Fig. 20-22. Then we can represent the result that the chosen family will be in category "a" just after the mth transition by the subset A_m of all paths with mth vertex at level "a"—as in Fig. 20-23. Similarly for the subset B_m.

FIGURE 20-22

FIGURE 20-23

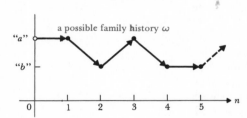

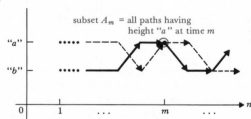

Moreover, we can represent a *specific history for the family through the first k units of time* by an *intersection* of sets, such as

$$A_0 \cap A_1 \cap B_2 \cap B_3 \cap A_4 \qquad (\text{here } k = 4).$$

(21)

This intersection is the set of all paths which follow the specific (black) route in Fig. 20-24 and then continue on arbitrarily. (If we

FIGURE 20-24

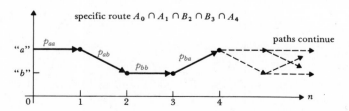

considered only histories of length 4, then the intersection (21) would consist of a single path.) What probability should we assign to an intersection such as (21)? By the "probability chain" relation of the last section, we should have

$$P(A_0 \cap A_1 \cap B_2 \cap B_3 \cap A_4)$$
$$= P(A_0)P_{A_0}(A_1)P_{A_0 \cap A_1}(B_2)P_{A_0 \cap A_1 \cap B_2}(B_3)P_{A_0 \cap A_1 \cap B_2 \cap B_3}(A_4). \quad (22)$$

Recall now the second basic assumption of the model: that once we know in which category the family will be at time $n-1$, our estimates for where it will be at time n should not be affected by any information regarding the family at times *before* $n-1$. Shouldn't we incorporate this assumption via equalities such as

$$P_{A_0 \cap A_1}(B_2) = P_{A_1}(B_2) = p_{ab},$$
$$P_{A_0 \cap A_1 \cap B_2}(B_3) = P_{B_2}(B_3) = p_{bb},$$

and

$$P_{A_0 \cap A_1 \cap B_2 \cap B_3}(A_4) = P_{B_3}(A_4) = p_{ba}. \quad (23)$$

If so, then once we choose a "starting probability" $P(A_0)$, we'll be *forced* to the assignment

$$P(A_0 \cap A_1 \cap B_2 \cap B_3 \cap A_4) = P(A_0)p_{aa}p_{ab}p_{bb}p_{ba}. \quad (24)$$

And if we want to express information that the chosen family starts in category "a," we should assign conditional probability

$$P_{A_0}(A_1 \cap B_2 \cap B_3 \cap A_4) = \frac{P(A_0 \cap B_1 \cap A_2 \cap B_3 \cap A_4)}{P(A_0)}$$
$$= p_{aa}p_{ab}p_{bb}p_{ba} \quad (25)$$

—just the *product* of the (green) one-step transition probabilities which we can associate with individual segments of the route in Fig. 20-24. What conditional probability should we then assign to a set such as A_4 itself—without restrictions as to where the family will be at intermediate times $n = 1, 2,$ and 3? I invite you to check that we're forced to the assignment

$$P_{A_0}(A_4) = \begin{cases} \text{the sum of products as in (24)} \\ \text{for all possible 4-segment routes} \\ \text{between "}a\text{" and "}a\text{."} \end{cases} \quad (26)$$

(Do Problem 12 of Sec. 20.14.) We might call the quantity in (26) a "4-step transition probability." More generally, let's DEFINE *k-step transition probabilities:*

	To "a"	"b"
From "a"	$p_{aa}^{(k)} = P_{A_n}(A_{n+k})$	$p_{ab}^{(k)} = P_{A_n}(B_{n+k})$
"b"	$p_{ba}^{(k)} = P_{B_n}(A_{n+k})$	$p_{bb}^{(k)} = P_{B_n}(B_{n+k})$

(27)

to describe a transition between some time n and a later time $n+k$. By the basic assumption that conditions don't change, these quantities should not depend on the particular time n, merely on the difference of times k. Just as in (26), we can assign concrete values to the $p_{ij}^{(k)}$'s in terms of the original p_{ij}'s via the rule

$$p_{i_0 j_0}^{(k)} = \begin{cases} \text{the sum of products of } p_{ij}\text{'s} \\ \text{corresponding to all possible } k\text{-segment} \\ \text{routes between "}i_0\text{" and "}j_0\text{"} \end{cases} \tag{28}$$

where i_0 and $j_0 = a$ or b. (Again, for a check, see Problem 12 of Sec. 20.14.) Note also that the probabilities in each row of (27) add to 1, since $A_{n+k} \cup B_{n+k} = 1$.

Is there any other way to calculate the $p_{ij}^{(k)}$'s, less tedious than the rule in (28)? And, if so, what will it imply about the long run behavior of the $p_{ij}^{(k)}$'s as the time lapse k gets larger and larger? In answer, let's return to the idea I used in (4) and (5). Namely: any path which goes through a particular level at time n must have been *either at "a" or at "b" at time $n-1$*. It must also have been *either at "a" or at "b" at time 1*. These "either ... or ..." alternatives allow a breakdown of sets of paths and of corresponding probabilities, such as I've indicated schematically in Figs. 20-25 and 20-26 (where the subscripts i and j can stand for either "a" or "b").

FIGURE 20-25

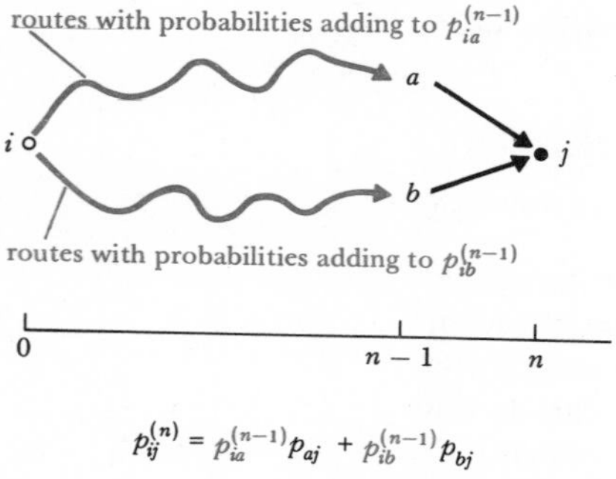

routes with probabilities adding to $p_{ia}^{(n-1)}$

routes with probabilities adding to $p_{ib}^{(n-1)}$

$$p_{ij}^{(n)} = p_{ia}^{(n-1)} p_{aj} + p_{ib}^{(n-1)} p_{bj}$$

FIGURE 20-26

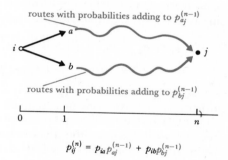

routes with probabilities adding to $p_{aj}^{(n-1)}$

routes with probabilities adding to $p_{bj}^{(n-1)}$

$$p_{ij}^{(n)} = p_{ia} p_{aj}^{(n-1)} + p_{ib} p_{bj}^{(n-1)}$$

In Fig. 20-25, the equation

$$p_{ij}^{(n)} = p_{ia}^{(n-1)} p_{aj} + p_{ib}^{(n-1)} p_{bj} \tag{29}$$

is merely a restatement of equations (4) and (5), with P replaced by conditional probabilities P_{A_0} or P_{B_0}. And in Fig. 20-26, the equation

$$p_{ij}^{(n)} = p_{ia} p_{aj}^{(n-1)} + p_{ib} p_{bj}^{(n-1)} \tag{30}$$

follows by similar arguments. I invite you to supply the details in doing Problem 13 of Sec. 20.14. Equations (29) and (30) show how we can calculate successive sets of values $p_{ij}^{(n)}$ from previously calculated values $p_{ij}^{(n-1)}$. In the simplest case, $n=2$, we'll have

$$p_{ij}^{(2)} = p_{ia} p_{aj} + p_{ib} p_{bj}, \tag{31}$$

each term on the right-hand side corresponding to a different route from "i" to "j"—either via "a" or via "b." Concretely, in terms of the 1962–1963 data in table (18), we can calculate the probability for a poor family ("b") in 1962 to become nonpoor ("a") by 1964, as

$$p_{ba}^{(2)} = p_{ba}p_{aa} + p_{bb}p_{ba}$$
$$= (0.19)(0.95) + (0.81)(0.19) = 0.33 \text{ approx.}$$

(32)

With the relations (29) and (30) to show how transition probabilities behave for long lapses of time, we can finally settle the earlier conjecture on "long-run" probabilities q_a and q_b:

Theorem (on "long-run Markov probabilities"): Suppose that all the entries in the table

p_{aa}	p_{ab}
p_{ba}	p_{bb}

are greater than 0, and that the sum in each row is 1 (so that the p_{ij}'s do qualify as "one-step transition probabilities"). And in terms of these entries, calculate "n-step transition probabilities" by either (equivalent) formula,

$$p_{ij}^{(n)} = p_{ia}^{(n-1)}p_{aj} + p_{ib}^{(n-1)}p_{bj} \quad \text{or} \quad p_{ij}^{(n)} = p_{ia}p_{aj}^{(n-1)} + p_{ib}p_{bj}^{(n-1)},$$

(33)

where $n = 2, 3, 4, \ldots$, and i and $j = $ "a" or "b." Then there exist limits

$$q_a = \lim_{n \to \infty} p_{ia}^{(n)} \quad \text{and} \quad q_b = \lim_{n \to \infty} p_{ib}^{(n)},$$

each independent of the particular "starting" subscript $i = $ "a" or "b."

Like the "law of large numbers" in Sec. 20-3, this result speaks of "long-run regularities" which seem to govern probabilities involving many trials. Only here, the chances for each trial *may* depend on the result of the trial just before it. Models with such "one-step memory" were first studied by A. A. Markov—and now bear his name.

Here is how the values $p_{ij}^{(n)}$ get *squeezed* toward limits—much like the "inside" and "outside" areas of Chap. 17:

A proof of the theorem (on "long-run Markov probabilities"): Since $p_{ia} + p_{ib} = 1$, the right-hand side of the equation

$$p_{ij}^{(n)} = (p_{ia})p_{aj}^{(n-1)} + (p_{ib})p_{bj}^{(n-1)}$$

(34)

$$\underbrace{\hspace{3cm}}_{\text{weighting coefficients}}$$

displays the quantity $p_{ij}^{(n)}$ as an *average* of the two numbers $p_{aj}^{(n-1)}$ and $p_{bj}^{(n-1)}$—lying *between* them on the coordinate line. (Recall Problem 5(a) of Sec. 11.6.) Since this interpretation holds for $i = a$ or b and $j = a$ or b, we can conclude that both $p_{aj}^{(n)}$ and $p_{bj}^{(n)}$ lie *between* the earlier pair of values $p_{aj}^{(n-1)}$ and $p_{bj}^{(n-1)}$, for $j = a$ or b. See Fig. 20-27 for an example. For fixed j, the left-hand members of all such pairs must

FIGURE 20-27

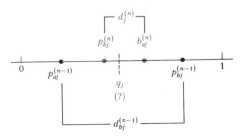

have a least upper bound; and the right-hand members, a greatest lower bound. Must these two bounds have the same value—call it q_j? And will

$$\lim_{n \to \infty} p_{aj}^{(n)} = q_j = \lim_{n \to \infty} p_{bj}^{(n)}? \tag{35}$$

Just as for the area approximations in Sec. 17.9, the answer will be "yes" if we can show that the distances

$$d_j^{(n)} = |p_{aj}^{(n)} - p_{bj}^{(n)}| \tag{36}$$

(note j in 2nd subscript)

tend to zero. To see how each $d_j^{(n)}$ relates to the preceding $d_a^{(n-1)}$ and $d_b^{(n-1)}$, let's use the alternate expression (29) for fixed j, and write

$$p_{aj}^{(n)} = p_{aa}^{(n-1)} p_{aj} + p_{ab}^{(n-1)} p_{bj}$$

and

$$p_{bi}^{(n)} = p_{ba}^{(n-1)} p_{aj} + p_{bb}^{(n-1)} p_{bj}.$$

Since $p_{ab}^{(n-1)} = 1 - p_{aa}^{(n-1)}$ and $p_{bb}^{(n-1)} = 1 - p_{ba}^{(n-1)}$, we can rewrite these equations as

$$p_{aj}^{(n)} = p_{aa}^{(n-1)}(p_{aj} - p_{bj}) + p_{bj} \tag{37}$$

and

$$p_{bj}^{(n)} = p_{ba}^{(n-1)}(p_{aj} - p_{bj}) + p_{bj}. \tag{38}$$

Now subtract (38) from (37) to get

$$[p_{aj}^{(n)} - p_{bj}^{(n)}] = [p_{aa}^{(n-1)} - p_{ba}^{(n-1)}](p_{aj} - p_{bj}). \tag{39}$$

Take absolute values in (39) to get

$$d_j^{(n)} \leq d_a^{(n-1)} |p_{aj} - p_{bj}| \qquad \text{for } j = a \text{ or } b. \tag{40}$$

Check that if all of the one-step p_{ij}'s are > 0, then both possibilities for the last factor in (40), $|p_{aa} - p_{ba}|$ and $|p_{ab} - p_{bb}|$, must be less than some positive constant $c < 1$.

Conclusion:

$$d_a^{(n)} \leq d_a^{(n-1)} c \leq d_a^{(n-2)} c^2 \leq \cdots \leq d_a^{(1)} c^{n-1} \tag{41}$$

and similarly,

$$d_b^{(n)} \leq d_a^{(n-1)} c \leq \cdots \leq d_a^{(1)} c^{n-1}. \tag{42}$$

So the $d_j^{(n)}$'s are forced to zero by the powers c^{n-1} as n increases. I invite you to work out further details for this proof in doing Problem 14 of Sec. 20.14.

20.13   MATRICES

In studying passage from "poverty" to "nonpoverty" status and back, in the last section, I considered "one-step" and "n-step" "transition probabilities."

And it seemed natural to display them in 2×2 arrays:

$$\begin{bmatrix} p_{11} & p_{12} \\ p_{21} & p_{22} \end{bmatrix} \quad \text{and} \quad \begin{bmatrix} p_{11}^{(n)} & p_{12}^{(n)} \\ p_{21}^{(n)} & p_{22}^{(n)} \end{bmatrix}. \tag{1}$$

Here I've replaced subscripts "a" (for "above poverty level") and "b" (for "below poverty level") by integers 1 and 2. What the key equation (29) of the last section did was to give a formula telling how to put together two arrays to get a new one—see Fig. 20-28.

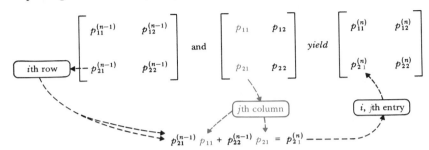

FIGURE 20-28

The (black) entries in the ith row of the first array, paired with the (green) entries in the jth column of the second array, yield the i,jth entry of the new array. And this rule holds for $i = 1$ or 2 and $j = 1$ or 2.

Long ago people noticed the same kind of formula holding in connection with arrays of coefficients of simultaneous linear equations as they change under substitution. See Fig. 20-29.

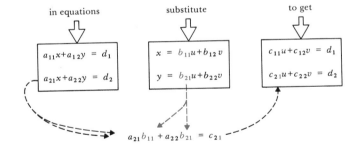

FIGURE 20-29

And so people came to regard square arrays, such as

$$A = \begin{bmatrix} a_{11} & a_{12} \\ a_{21} & a_{22} \end{bmatrix}, \quad B = \begin{bmatrix} b_{11} & b_{12} \\ b_{21} & b_{22} \end{bmatrix}, \quad \text{and} \quad C = \begin{bmatrix} c_{11} & c_{12} \\ c_{21} & c_{22} \end{bmatrix}, \tag{2}$$

as having a life of their own. And they interpreted the relationship in Fig. 20-29—which we can abbreviate symbolically by

"$A \otimes B = C$"

as setting up a new kind of "multiplication" between these new quantities. If we let

$$M = \begin{bmatrix} p_{11} & p_{12} \\ p_{21} & p_{22} \end{bmatrix} \tag{3}$$

denote the array of "one-step transition probabilities" of the last section, then in terms of the "new multiplication" we can express the array of "n-step transition probabilities" as

$$\begin{bmatrix} p_{11}^{(n)} & p_{12}^{(n)} \\ p_{21}^{(n)} & p_{22}^{(n)} \end{bmatrix} = \underbrace{M \otimes M \otimes \cdots \otimes M}_{n \text{ factors}} = \text{``}M^n\text{''}. \tag{4}$$

And the key result on "long-run" probabilities for "Markov" models (Theorem B of the last section) says that, in some sense

$$\lim_{n \to \infty} M^n = \begin{bmatrix} q_a & q_b \\ q_a & q_b \end{bmatrix}.$$

Is it possible to handle 3×3 arrays,

$$M = \begin{Bmatrix} p_{11} & p_{12} & p_{13} \\ p_{21} & p_{22} & p_{23} \\ p_{31} & p_{32} & p_{33} \end{Bmatrix} \tag{5}$$

and 4×4, and $k \times k$ arrays in a similar way—to get similar results? If so, then at one fell swoop we might handle all sorts of applications. In studying the economy, for example, we needn't divide families coarsely into merely two categories, "poor" and "nonpoor." We could assign them to smaller, more meaningful categories depending on ethnic origin, education, precise income, and so on.

Much can be done with such arrays—currently called "matrices." In Problem 9 of Sec. 4.13 I suggested that you explore the algebraic properties of 2×2 matrices in analogy with ordinary numbers. I invite you to review that material, and to explore further in doing Problems 18 and 19 of the next section.

20.14 PROBLEMS ON INDEPENDENCE, MARKOV MODELS, AND MATRICES

First, you might look again at those problems in Sec. 3.6 that involve independence for *more* than two subsets.

1. If you send three independent messages for help, with respective probabilities of 0.2, 0.4, and 0.7 for getting through, what's the probability
   (a) that none will get through?
   (b) that at least one will get through?
   (c) that at least two will get through?
2. Suppose that the probability of an accident on any one airplane flight could be estimated as some value p.
   (a) In terms of p, what's the probability that there will be *no* accidents on 100 successive independent flights?
   (b) Find the same probability as in part (a) for 101 flights.
   (c) Find the probability that *at least one* accident will occur during 101 independent flights. For $p = 0.001$, how much larger is this probability than that in part (b)?

(d) Given that 100 flights have occurred *without* accident, what's the (conditional) probability that a 101st independent flight *will* have an accident? What about the feeling of some habitual air travelers that sooner or later "one's time must come"?

3. In Example 1 of Sec. 20.11, I again discussed the case of $n = 7$ independent victims of a disease, each having probability p $(0 \leqslant p \leqslant 1)$ for surviving. And I argued that we should assign probability

$$p(\omega) = p^k(1-p)^{n-k} \tag{*}$$

to any possible outcome ω representing the survival of a particular k of the n victims. Now, for any fixed number n victims, check these claims:

(a) There are exactly

$$\binom{n}{k} = \frac{n!}{k!(n-k)!}$$

distinct ways in which exactly k of the n victims can be chosen by fate for survival, for any given $k = 0, 1, 2, \ldots, n$.
(Suggestion: See Sec. 6.8.)

(b) For a given k, the probability that "exactly k victims will survive" (not saying *which* particular k persons) must be

$$\binom{n}{k}p^k(1-p)^{n-k}. \tag{**}$$

(c) The sum of the elementary probabilities $p(\omega)$ for all possible ω's coincides with the sum of the probabilities in (**) for all $k = 0, 1, 2, \ldots, n$, and equals 1.
(Suggestion: Apply the "binomial expansion" of Sec. 6.8 to $1^n = [p + (1-p)]^n$.)

4. *Trees and paths.* Here is another way to picture the possible outcomes of an experiment involving n independent trials each having probability p for success. (In Example 1 of Sec. 20.11, I used "n-tuples" such as $\omega = (s, s, d, s, d, d, s)$.) Draw a sideways growing "tree" with successive generations of segments indicating by their directions (upward = success, downward = failure) what the results can be on successive trials. See the figure. Assign value p to each upward segment, and $1-p$ to each downward segment.

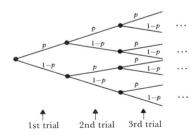

1st trial 2nd trial 3rd trial

(a) Check that each possible rightward moving path in the tree corresponds to a unique possible outcome ω for the experiment of n trials; and that the *product* of the values assigned to the individual segments of the path is exactly the elementary probability $p(\omega)$ in (*) of Problem 3.

(b) Check that the quantity in (**) of Problem 3 is just the compound probability of the collection of all paths in the tree which have exactly k upward segments.

(c) A third way to picture possible outcomes of an experiment with n trials is via paths such as I've pictured in Fig. 20-17—all starting on the left, however, at altitude zero. Each $+1$ segment corresponds to a success and each -1 segment to a failure. Check that, if there are exactly k successes and $n-k$ failures, the height of the path after n segments must be $k-(n-k)=2k-n$ (for any fixed $k=0, 1, 2, \ldots, n$). Check that the quantity in (*) of Problem 3 is just the elementary probability for any single path having exactly k "$+1$" segments; and that the quantity (**) of Problem 3 is the total probability of all paths which end up at height $2k-n$ after n segments.

5. Often people can't easily decide whether or not to go along with a certain kind of activity, so they propose to watch the results of independent trials involving the activity—saying, "I'll go along if there are at least two successes out of three trials." Then, still unsure, they may say, "Let's see if there are at least 3 successes out of 5 trials," or "4 successes out of 7 trials," and so on. Suppose that there is probability p for success on any one trial.

(a) In terms of p, compute the probabilities for 2 successes out of 3, 3 out of 5, and 4 out of 7; and compare them for $p = \frac{1}{3}, \frac{1}{2}, \frac{2}{3}$.

(b) In terms of p, find the conditional probability for getting at least 3 out of 5 successes, given reports that at least 2 out of 3 successes have already occurred. Evaluate this probability for $p = \frac{1}{3}, \frac{1}{2}, \frac{2}{3}$.

*6. Suppose that a machine produces transistors, with the probability for any one transistor to be defective equal to p.

(a) If each item is independent of the others, show that the probability for exactly k out of a batch of n transistors to be defective is

$$\binom{n}{k} p^k (1-p)^{n-k}. \tag{*}$$

(b) Calculate the values in (*) and graph them vs. k, for $n = 5$, and $p = 0.01$ and 0.1.

(c) When the machine is working normally, $p = 0.01$, say. For purposes of "quality control," an inspector draws a sample of 5 transistors from each hour's produce of the machine. He assumes that the condition of any one transistor (defective or not) is independent of that of any other. Show how to determine the largest possible "cutoff" value—an integer $N \leqslant 5$—with the following property: the inspector can, with 90% chances ("confidence") for being right, assume that the machine is working normally that hour if the number k of defectives in the sample is $\leqslant N$.

Equivalently: the probability that the inspector will order an unnecessary and expensive readjustment of the machine, because $k > N$, should be less than 10%.

(d) Suppose that $p = 0.1$ when the machine is poorly adjusted. With the cutoff test of part (c), what's the probability that poor adjustment will go undetected?

7. Think of tossing two "untrue" dice, one red and one green. Let's assign equal elementary probabilities to each of the 36 possible outcomes. Now consider these three results:

     A: "the red die shows an odd number,"
     B: "the green die shows an odd number,"
     C: "the sum of the numbers on both dice is odd."

(a) Check that any *two* of these results are independent.

(b) Check that all *three results* together are *not* independent.

(c) Intuitively, if you know that A and B have occurred, can't you conclude that C definitely has not occurred? Mathematically, check that the relationship (4) in Sec. 20.11 doesn't hold.

*8. Extend the concepts and methods in Problem 3 of Sec. 20.10 to a joint experiment, with outcomes $\omega = (a_i, b_j, c_k, \ldots)$, composed of *more than two* individual experiments—having separate lists of outcomes Ω_a, Ω_b, Ω_c, and so on. Assign elementary probabilities $p(\omega)$ via a "product rule," and show that any subsets $S_a, \tilde{S}_b, S_c, \ldots$, corresponding to outcomes in respective individual experiments $(\Omega_a, \Omega_b, \Omega_c, \ldots)$ must be independent.

9. Suppose that the 1982–1983 data for transitions of families between nonpoor ("a") and poor ("b") categories will turn out as in the following table.

End of 1983

	"a"	"b"
End of 1982 "a"	0.95	0.05
"b"	0.45	0.55

And suppose that economic and social conditions will remain stable for decades thereafter.

(a) What are the chances for a family which is "poor" on December 31, 1982, still to be "poor" on December 31, 1983? To be "nonpoor" on December 31, 1983?

(b) Suppose that a family is "poor" on December 31, 1982. Draw the 4 possible family histories for the two transitions 1982–1983 and 1983–1984 (as in Fig. 20-22), and label the path segments by transition probabilities as in Fig. 20-24. You might also combine these paths into a "tree" as in Problem 4.

(c) What are the chances that the family in part (b) will be "poor" on December 31, 1984? Compute this from the probabilities in part (a) and the conditional probabilities in the table, via the relationships (4) and (5) of Sec. 20.12 (with $n = 2$).

(d) Check that the probability in part (c) is the *sum*, for all paths leading from "*a*" to "*a*," of the *products of the one-step transition probabilities along the segments of each path*.

(e) Repeat parts (c) and (d) to find the probability that the family will be "nonpoor" on December 31, 1984.

(f) Repeat parts (c)–(e) for *three* transitions, to find the probabilities that the family will be "poor" or "nonpoor" on December 31, 1985.

(g) Find (approximately) the probabilities that the family will be "poor" or "nonpoor" after many years—say, in 2001. (Suggestion: See (12)–(17) in Sec. 20.12.)

10. Sensitive electronic devices can be influenced by random internal and external factors to go from a state ("*a*") of satisfactory functioning to a state ("*b*") of unsatisfactory functioning, or back again—the extent of the influence depending on the current state of the device ("*a*" or "*b*"). Suppose that the *day to day* transition probabilities of one such device can be described by the numbers in the table of Problem 9, and that the device is functioning well today.

(a) What are the chances that it will be functioning well the day after tomorrow?

(b) What are the chances, approximately, that it will be functioning well two months hence?

11. When other factors are constant, the public health aspect of a contagious disease may vary, from month to month, between conditions of "control" ("*a*") to conditions of "epidemic" ("*b*")—the outlook for each succeeding month depending essentially on conditions during the current month. Suppose that *month to month* transition probabilities can be described by the numbers in the table of Problem 9.

(a) What are the chances for a transition from "control" to "epidemic" conditions in 2 months? In 3 months?

(b) What are the chances for a return from "epidemic" to "control" conditions in 3 months?

(c) What are the long-range chances for an epidemic during any particular month?

*12. Extend the results of Problem 9(b) to paths representing k-step transition histories—for a general table of one-step transition probabilities $\{p_{ij}\}$ as in (2) of Sec. 20.12—to represent the overall transition probability $p_{i_0 j_0}^{(k)}$ from "state i_0" (= "*a*" or "*b*") to "state j_0" (= "*a*" or "*b*") as a sum, over all possible paths from "i_0" to "j_0," of the products of p_{ij}'s along the segments of each path.

*13. Show why the relationship (30) holds, in Sec. 20.12.

14. Help complete the proof of the theorem on "long-run Markov probabilities" in Sec. 20.12: Let u_j be the least upper bound of the left-hand members of the pairs $\{p_{aj}^{(n)}, p_{bj}^{(n)}\}$ which I pictured in Fig. 20-27, and let v_j be the greatest lower bound of the right-hand members. Using the result that $\lim_{n \to \infty} |p_{aj}^{(n)} - p_{bj}^{(n)}| = 0$,

got at the end of Sec. 20.12, show that we must have $u_j = v_j$; and moreover, that

$$\lim_{n \to \infty} p_{aj}^{(n)} = u_j = v_j = \lim_{n \to \infty} p_{bj}^{(n)}.$$

*15. Suppose that both you and an opponent each have two options for action in an encounter. Label your options #1 and #2, and his options also # 1 and # 2. Suppose that each of you must choose his option before the encounter in ignorance of what the other is choosing. Suppose also that the entry a_{ij} in the matrix

$$
\begin{array}{cc}
 & \text{His options} \\
 & \begin{array}{cc} \#1 & \#2 \end{array} \\
\text{Your options} \begin{array}{c} \#1 \\ \#2 \end{array} & \begin{bmatrix} 2 & -1 \\ 0 & 1 \end{bmatrix}
\end{array}
$$

represents the number of dollars which you must pay to your opponent if you act according to your option #i and he acts according to his option #j. If both you and your opponent act perfectly rationally, what's the greatest number of dollars you will have to pay? What's the most he can hope to get?

16. Suppose that a manufacturer considers two possible schemes for assigning prices to "economy" and "deluxe" versions of an item — as in the following table.

Price of item	Scheme 1	Scheme 2
"Economy version"	$1.20	$1.50
"Deluxe version"	$2.30	$2.10

Which scheme will yield more revenue? Suppose that a buyer will apportion $100 worth of purchases in the amounts $x for "economy" units and $(100−x) for "deluxe" units.

(a) As functions of x $(0 \leq x \leq 100)$, plot the manufacturer's total revenue $R_1(x)$ under Scheme 1 and $R_2(x)$ under Scheme 2.

(b) For which x will the two schemes yield the same total revenue?

(c) If the buyer is highly likely to favor "economy" versions which scheme is better for the manufacturer?

(d) If, on repeated occasions, the buyer is likely to choose x "at random" between $50 and $150, which scheme will yield more average revenue? (Suggestion: Compare

$$(1/100) \int_{50}^{150} R_1(x) \, dx \quad \text{with} \quad (1/100) \int_{50}^{150} R_2(x) \, dx$$

in the spirit of Secs. 18.3 and 20.2.)

(e) How do your formulas for $R_1(x)$ and $R_2(x)$ compare with the relations (4) and (5) of Sec. 20.12?

17. (a) Evaluate the four numbers c_{ij} according to the scheme in Fig. 20-29, given the values

$a_{11} = 1$	$a_{12} = 0$
$a_{21} = 2$	$a_{22} = -1$

and

$b_{11} = 3$	$b_{12} = -1$
$b_{21} = -2$	$b_{22} = \frac{1}{2}$

(b) Note that the scheme in Fig. 20-29 for computing entries c_{ij} of the "matrix product" $C = A \otimes B$ is the same as I discussed in Problem 9 of Sec. 4.13. Do, or review, parts (a)–(h) of that problem.

*18. Suppose we have a *sequence* of matrices

$$A_1 = \begin{bmatrix} a_{11}^{(1)} & a_{12}^{(1)} \\ a_{21}^{(1)} & a_{22}^{(1)} \end{bmatrix}, A_2 = \begin{bmatrix} a_{11}^{(2)} & a_{12}^{(2)} \\ a_{21}^{(2)} & a_{22}^{(2)} \end{bmatrix}, \dots, A_n = \begin{bmatrix} a_{11}^{(n)} & a_{12}^{(n)} \\ a_{21}^{(n)} & a_{22}^{(n)} \end{bmatrix}, \dots$$

—for example the n-step transition probability matrices in (4) of Sec. 20.13. Let's say that such a sequence converges to a limiting matrix

$$A = \begin{bmatrix} a_{11} & a_{12} \\ a_{21} & a_{22} \end{bmatrix} \qquad (\text{in symbols, } \lim_{n \to \infty} A_n = A)$$

if corresponding sequences of entries converge, that is, if

$$\lim_{n \to \infty} a_{ij}^{(n)} = a_{ij} \qquad \text{for each } i = 1, 2 \text{ and } j = 1, 2.$$

(a) Show that with this definition, convergence of matrices has a property similar to convergence of real numbers:

if $\lim_{n \to \infty} A_n = A$ *and* $\lim_{n \to \infty} B_n = B$, *then* $\lim_{n \to \infty} A_n \otimes B_n = A \otimes B.$

(b) Explore other similarities to convergence of real numbers.

*19. How would you extend the notion of matrix product $A \otimes B$ pictured in Fig. 20-28 to matrices involving 3 rows and columns each? Consider also the parallel question of how to get n-step transition probabilities from $(n-1)$-step transition probabilities for situations which involve passages between *three* possible "states"—for example, "a" = "low income," "b" = "middle income," and "c" = "high income." How would you extend Fig. 20-28?

20.15 SUMMARY OF CHAPTER 20

See Sec. 20.1 for a review of common requirements for assigning probabilities—and for a discussion of their origins.

Definition: a *random variable:* any function whose domain is under consideration as a set Ω of possible outcomes of some experiment. (Sec. 20.2)

Definitions: If numbers $f(1), f(2), \ldots, f(n)$ have corresponding probabilities $p_1, p_2, \ldots, p_n$, where the p_i's add to 1, then we can regard the sum

$$f(1)p_1 + f(2)p_2 + \cdots + f(n)p_n$$

as an *average* of the f_i's. If a function f is defined on an interval $[a, b]$, all of whose inputs we consider as equally likely outcomes of an experiment, then we can regard the definite integral

$$\frac{1}{b-a} \int_a^b f(x)\, dx$$

as an *average* output. (More generally, the quantity $\int_0^\infty f(x)g(x)\, dx$ can serve this purpose, where g is a "probability density" function.) (Sec. 20.2)

Remark: The average of a sum of functions is the sum of their individual averages.
(Sec. 20.2)

For an application to random "matching," see Sec. 20.2.

For a "law of large numbers" relating the probability of success for one toss to the net win per toss over many trials, see Sec. 20.3.

Definition: If probabilities P have already been assigned to subsets of a set Ω, and if $P(R) > 0$ for a given subset R, then we can regard

$$P_R(S) = \frac{P(S \cap R)}{P(R)}$$

as the *conditional probability* of a subset S given information that the actual outcome lies in R.
(Sec. 20.5)

Remark: In its own right $P_R(S)$ has all the properties of a probability function.

Relations for reconstruction of original probabilities from given original and conditional probabilities:

$$P(R \cap S) = P(R)P_R(S);$$

$$P(S) = P(R_1)P_{R_1}(S) + P(R_2)P_{R_2}(S) + \cdots + P(R_n)P_{R_n}(S),$$

when the R_i are mutually exclusive and have Ω as their union. Here $P(S)$ is displayed as an *average* of the $P_{R_i}(S)$.
(Sec. 20.6)

The "formula of Bayes" relates conditional probabilities in one direction to those in another:

$$P_S(R_i) = \frac{P(R_i)P_{R_i}(S)}{P(R_1)P_{R_1}(S) + \cdots + P(R_n)P_{R_n}(S)}.$$

(Sec. 20.6)

For an application to medical diagnosis, see Sec. 20.6.

For "conditional probabilities" entering via the forms

$$P(S) = \int_a^b P_{R_x}(S)\, dx \quad \text{and} \quad P(S) = \int_a^b P_{R_x}(S)g(x)\, dx$$

see Sec. 20.6.

To see which is better, one expensive battery or two cheap ones, see Example 5 of Sec. 20.6.

A "*probability chain*" relating many subsets (whose intersections have nonzero probabilities):

$$P(S_1 \cap S_2 \cap \cdots \cap S_n)$$

$$= P(S_1)P_{S_1}(S_2)P_{S_1 \cap S_2}(S_3) \cdots P_{S_1 \cap S_2 \cap \cdots \cap S_{n-1}}(S_n).$$

(Sec. 20.11)

Definitions: If probabilities P are assigned to subsets of Ω, call subsets A and B *independent* if $P(A \cap B) = P(A)P(B)$ (Sec. 20.8). Call a collection of subsets independent if

$$P(S_1 \cap S_2 \cap \cdots \cap S_n) = P(S_1)P(S_2) \cdot \cdots \cdot P(S_n)$$

for every choice of finitely many subsets $S_1, S_2, \ldots, S_n$ from the collection.

(Sec. 20.11)

For guidelines on how to construct a model so that given results will appear as "independent," see Secs. 20.8 and 20.11.

For the probability of ultimate victory through many trials—as given by a "difference equation"—see Sec. 20.9.

In Sec. 20.12: a "Markov" model for transitions of families between "poor" and "nonpoor" status. The model involves a sequence of results, each with conditional probability determined only by the previous result—there being no "memory" farther into the "past." "Long-run" probabilities and "n-step" probabilities can be calculated from "one-step" probabilities.

See Sec. 20.13 for an indication of the role of square arrays—"matrices"—in storing and relating information.

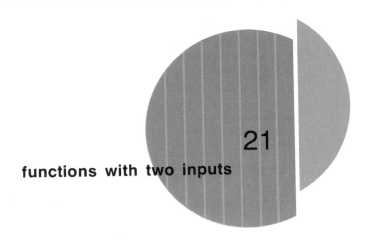

21

functions with two inputs

In this chapter I'll briefly discuss the notion of a "function with two inputs," its rates of change, and how to find its maximum and minimum outputs.

21.1 EXAMPLES AND GRAPHS

Here are just a few examples where *two* quantities *jointly* determine the value of a third.

EXAMPLE 1. The incubation time t and the average lifetime H determine the size to which a 10^6 member bacterial population will grow in t hours—namely, $S(t, H) = 10^6 e^{(1/H)t}$ (from Sec. 13.3).

EXAMPLE 2. The base radius r and the height h of a right circular cylinder determine its volume—call it $V(r, h)$: $V(r, h) = \pi r^2 h$.

EXAMPLE 3. The number of man hours x (per day) and the amount of capital equipment y (in dollars) available to a firm ideally determine its daily productive capacity (in dollars)—call it $p(x, y)$. In Problem 8 of Sec. 7.4, I explored a particularly simple form for p, namely $p(x, y) = xy$. Sometimes economists use models with the slightly more complicated form $p(x, y) = Cx^q y^r$—where C, q, and r are constants estimated from observed production records, q and r having values between 0 and 1. (Such models are supposed to approximate actual production only for ranges $a \leq x \leq b$ and $c \leq y \leq d$ where the firm has not yet reached a "point of diminishing returns.")

How can we capture mathematically the notion of two quantities x and y determining a third "output" quantity—call it "$f(x, y)$"? One way—just a special case of the general "function" notion in Chapter 2—is to assign to each possible (ordered) *pair* of values (x, y)

its unique corresponding output $f(x, y)$. See the top diagram in Fig. 21-1. Alternatively, we could picture the value $f(x, y)$ as flowing from the two "separate" inputs x and y, as in the bottom diagram of Fig. 21-1. In a sense, the two pictures are equivalent, differing only by the relative positions of the symbols "x" and "y" on the left-hand side. Let's think of either as representing a *"function f with two inputs."*

FIGURE 21-1   two pictures of a function of two variables

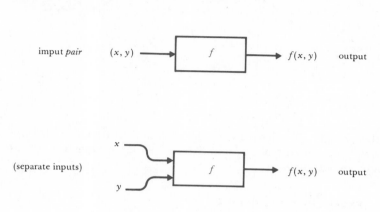

imput *pair* $(x, y) \longrightarrow$ [f] $\longrightarrow f(x, y)$ output

(separate inputs) $x \searrow$ [f] $\longrightarrow f(x, y)$ output
                      $y \nearrow$

FIGURE 21-2

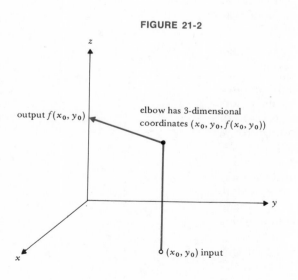

output $f(x_0, y_0)$

elbow has 3-dimensional coordinates $(x_0, y_0, f(x_0, y_0))$

(x_0, y_0) input

FIGURE 21-3

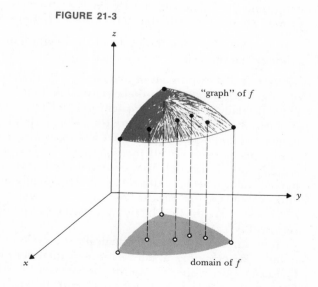

"graph" of f

domain of f

In earlier chapters I used (2-dimensional) graphs to picture the fluctuations of functions with a single input. What analogous device can we use for thinking about functions with two inputs? Why not go to three dimensions? There we can locate each input pair (x_0, y_0) as a point in a horizontal xy plane, and then locate the corresponding output $f(x_0, y_0)$ as a point on a vertical z axis. Follow the green arrow in Fig. 21-2. As in two dimensions, the *elbow point* of the arrow pictures the correspondence compactly. And if we consider all input pairs in the domain of a function f, their corresponding elbow points constitute a sort of "surface" in 3-dimensional space. See Fig. 21-3. Let's call that subset of 3-dimensional space the *graph of f*. It's the set of all (ordered) triples of the form $(x, y, f(x, y))$ corresponding to pairs (x, y) in the domain of f.

21.2 CHANGES IN INDIVIDUAL INPUTS

How do outputs $f(x, y)$ change when we go from one input pair to another? The simplest approach to an answer is first to hold one of the inputs fixed and see what happens when we change the other. Suppose we hold y fixed, say, at the value $y = y_0$. Then the resulting relationship between inputs x and outputs $f(x, y_0)$ defines a *new function of the single input x — call it, say,*

$$g_{y_0}(x) = f(x, y_0). \tag{1}$$

(In (1) I've used the subscript y_0 to point out that the very definition of g depends on the particular fixed value $y = y_0$.)

EXAMPLE 1. The production function $p(x, y) = Cx^q y^r$ in Example 3 of the last section, where $x =$ the number of man hours and $y =$ the amount of capital equipment of a firm. For a fixed amount y_0 of capital equipment, the function

$$g_{y_0}(x) = p(x, y_0) = Cx^q y_0{}^r = (Cy_0{}^r)x^q$$

merely displays the firm's production as proportional to the qth power of its labor supply x — at least for x within a suitable interval $[a, b]$.

How does the graph of a function $f(x, y)$ — sitting in 3-dimensional space — relate to the ordinary graph of $g_{y_0}(x) = f(x, y_0)$? Think of the vertical "plane" of all points in 3-dimensional space whose y coordinate is fixed at y_0 — that is, all triples of the form (x, y_0, z) where x and z are any real numbers. In Fig. 21-4 I've indicated how such a (green) plane intersects the "surface-like" graph of a function f in a (green) "*curve*" — the set of all triples of the form $(x, y_0, f(x, y_0))$ corresponding to pairs (x, y_0) in the domain of f.

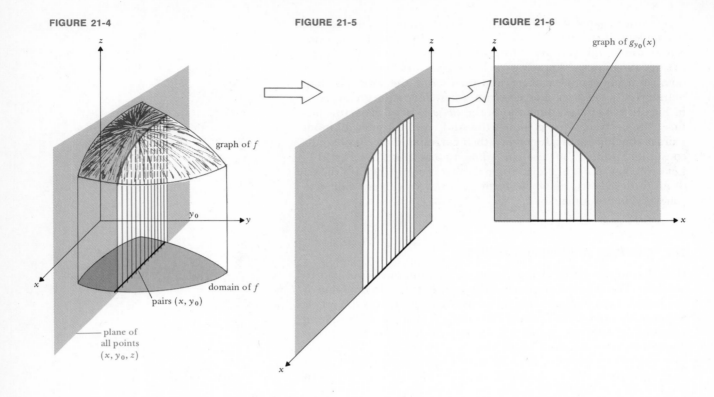

FIGURE 21-4 FIGURE 21-5 FIGURE 21-6

Isn't the green curve essentially the graph of $g_{y_0}(x)$ — especially when we extract it as in Fig. 21-5, or view it in standard position as in Fig. 21-6? There a triple $(x, y_0, f(x, y_0))$ gets compressed into a pair

$$(x, f(x, y_0)) = (x, g_{y_0}(x)).$$

Now let's hold the x input of a function $f(x, y)$ fixed at a value $x = x_0$. Then we'll get a new function of the single input y:

$$h_{x_0}(y) = f(x_0, y). \tag{2}$$

EXAMPLE 2. Again the production function of Example 1, $p(x, y) = Cx^a y^r$. For a *fixed* number x_0 of man hours, the function

$$h_{x_0}(y) = p(x_0, y) = Cx_0^a y^r = (Cx_0^a)y^r$$

displays the firm's production as proportional to the rth power of the capital y invested in equipment — at least for y in a suitable interval $[c, d]$.

Just as before, given the graph of a function $f(x, y)$ in 3-dimensional space, we can get the ordinary graph of $h_{x_0}(y) = f(x_0, y)$ by slicing the graph of f by a vertical "plane" — this time consisting of all points with coordinates (x_0, y, z), as in Fig. 21-7.

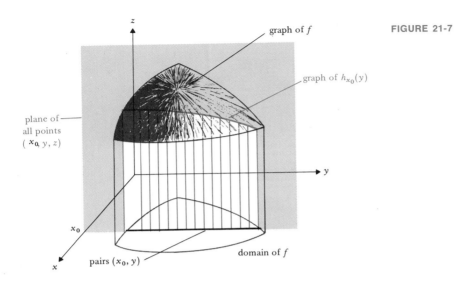

graph of f

graph of $h_{x_0}(y)$

plane of all points (x_0, y, z)

z

y

x_0

x

pairs (x_0, y)

domain of f

FIGURE 21-7

In practice, surfaces in three dimensions are often hard to draw. So what people do is *work backward:* They visualize the graph of $f(x, y)$ *via* the graphs of $g_{y_0}(x)$ and $h_{x_0}(y)$ in "representative" vertical slices. I've used this procedure in Fig. 21-8 to sketch the graphs of two functions from examples of the last section.

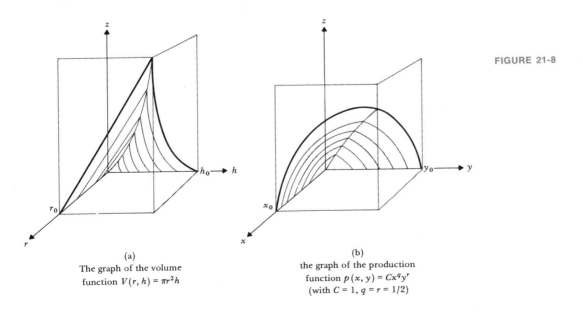

FIGURE 21-8

(a)
The graph of the volume function $V(r, h) = \pi r^2 h$

(b)
the graph of the production function $p(x, y) = Cx^q y^r$ (with $C = 1$, $q = r = 1/2$)

Another device for picturing a function $f(x, y)$ is to think of slicing its graph by (green) *horizontal* planes at various altitudes $z = z_0$, as in Fig. 21-9.

FIGURE 21-9

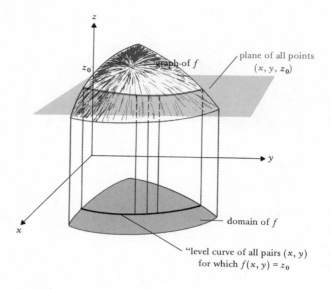

plane of all points
(x, y, z_0)

graph of f

z_0

domain of f

"level curve of all pairs (x, y)
for which $f(x, y) = z_0$

For a fixed z_0 such a slice produces a (green) curve whose (black) shadow in the xy plane is just the set—usually called a *"level curve"* —of all points (x, y) whose corresponding output $f(x, y) = z_0$. In Fig. 21-10, I've sketched several members of the families of "level curves" corresponding to the two cases in Fig. 21-8.

FIGURE 21-10

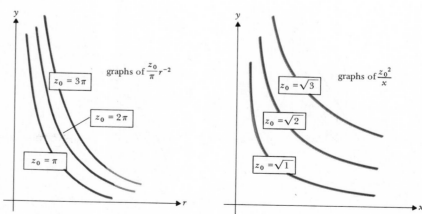

graphs of $\dfrac{z_0}{\pi} r^{-2}$

$z_0 = 3\pi$

$z_0 = 2\pi$

$z_0 = \pi$

graphs of $\dfrac{z_0^2}{x}$

$z_0 = \sqrt{3}$

$z_0 = \sqrt{2}$

$z_0 = \sqrt{1}$

if $V(r, h) = \pi r^2 h = z_0$, then $h = \dfrac{z_0}{\pi} r^{-2}$

if $p(x, y) = x^{\frac{1}{2}} y^{\frac{1}{2}} = z_0$, then $y = \dfrac{z_0^2}{x}$

You might also recall my using level curves of a production function $p(x, y) = xy$ in Problem 8 of Sec. 7.4, in order to find the combination of labor and capital which would yield the greatest product, when there was a restriction $4x + y = \$1000$.

21.3 RATES OF CHANGE

To explore changes in a function $f(x, y)$, why not apply results we know for functions with a single input to $g_{y_0}(x) = f(x, y_0)$ and $h_{x_0}(y) = f(x_0, y)$? In particular, let's calculate derivatives of g and of h—if they exist. Here is some common NOTATION for these so-called "*partial derivatives*":

for $[g_{y_0}(x)]'$ at an input $x = x_0$, write $\quad \dfrac{\partial f}{\partial x}(x_0, y_0)$ (1)

(the "partial derivative of f with respect to x at (x_0, y_0)");

for $[h_{x_0}(y)]'$ at an input $y = y_0$, write $\quad \dfrac{\partial f}{\partial y}(x_0, y_0)$ (2)

(the "partial derivative of f with respect to y at (x_0, y_0)").

This notation keeps the original f in evidence, and also—via the "denominator" symbols—indicates which input is considered as "changing." (The form $\dfrac{\partial}{\partial x}$ is a modification of Leibniz's notation $\dfrac{d}{dx}$, which I mentioned in Sec. 14.2.)

EXAMPLE 1. For the cylinder volume function $V(r, h) = \pi r^2 h$, let $G_{h_0}(r) = (\pi h_0)r^2$ and $H_{r_0}(h) = (\pi r_0^2)h$. Then

$$\frac{\partial V}{\partial r}(r_0, h_0) = [G_{h_0}(r)]'_{\text{at } r_0} = (\pi h_0)[r^2]'_{\text{at } r_0} = 2\pi r_0 h_0$$

and

$$\frac{\partial V}{\partial h}(r_0, h_0) = [H_{r_0}(h)]'_{\text{at } h_0} = (\pi r_0^2)[h]'_{\text{at } h_0} = \pi r_0^2.$$

EXAMPLE 2. For the production function $p(x, y) = Cx^q y^r$, where

$$g_{y_0}(x) = (Cy_0^r)x^q \quad \text{and} \quad h_{x_0}(y) = (Cx_0^q)y^r,$$

we'll have

$$\frac{\partial p}{\partial x}(x_0, y_0) = [(Cy_0^r)x^q]'_{\text{at } x_0} = (Cy_0^r)[x^q]'_{\text{at } x_0}$$

$$= (Cy_0^r)(qx_0^{q-1})$$ (3)

(dollars per man hour)

and

$$\frac{\partial p}{\partial y}(x_0, y_0) = \left[(Cx_0{}^q)y^r\right]'_{\text{at } y_0} = (Cx_0{}^q)\left[y^r\right]'_{\text{at } y_0}$$

$$= (Cx_0{}^q)(ry_0{}^{r-1}) \tag{4}$$

(dollars per dollar of equipment).

With C, r, q, x_0, and y_0 all positive, the derivatives (3) and (4) must be positive, too. What can we conclude about the production idealized by the function $p(x, y)$? If we increase the number of man hours from the value x_0 to a slightly larger value x_1, or if we increase the capital equipment from the value y_0 to a slightly larger value y_1, then the total production will increase too. Now this will be true for any starting pair (x_0, y_0) of labor and capital — within the domain where p is supposed valid. Why can't the firm therefore keep increasing its production by hiring more and more people (x), or buying more and more equipment (y)? In the case of labor, the answer is that labor costs money. Suppose, for concreteness, that workers at the firm earn \$3 per hour. What will happen if the firm keeps its capital equipment fixed at some value y_0, and increases its use of labor from some value x_0 man hours to $x_0 + 1$ hours? It will have to pay out \$3 more in labor, and will receive in added earnings

$$p(x_0+1, y_0) - p(x_0, y_0) = g_{y_0}(x_0+1) - g_{y_0}(x_0) \text{ dollars.} \tag{5}$$

Let's approximate this difference of outputs by the product of a derivative and a difference of inputs (as in Sec. 15.7) — namely, by

$$\left[g_{y_0}(x)\right]'_{\text{at } x_0}(x_0+1-x_0) = \left[\frac{\partial p}{\partial x}(x_0, y_0) \text{ dollars per man hour}\right]$$

$$\cdot \quad [1 \quad \text{man hour}]$$

$$= Cy_0{}^r q x_0{}^{q-1} \text{ dollars.} \tag{6}$$

If the approximate added earnings in (6) *exceed* the added cost \$3, the firm profits by its increase in labor. In the opposite case, the firm loses. Conclusion: for fixed y_0, the firm can afford to increase its labor force only to an amount x_0 such that

$$\frac{\partial p}{\partial x}(x_0, y_0) = \text{the hourly wage} \tag{7}$$

(since $(Cy_0{}^r q)x_0{}^{q-1}$ *decreases* with increasing x_0, when $q < 1$).

In Fig. 21-11, I've sliced the 3-dimensional graph of a function $f(x, y)$ *simultaneously* by the green vertical planes of Figs. 21-5 and 21-8. They intersect each other above the point (x_0, y_0). And they provide a *joint* picture of the (green) graphs of $g_{y_0}(x) = f(x, y_0)$ and $h_{x_0}(y) = f(x_0, y)$. In each vertical plane I've also drawn a (black) line segment having the slope of the (green) graph lying in that plane — as calculated above (x_0, y_0).

FIGURE 21-11

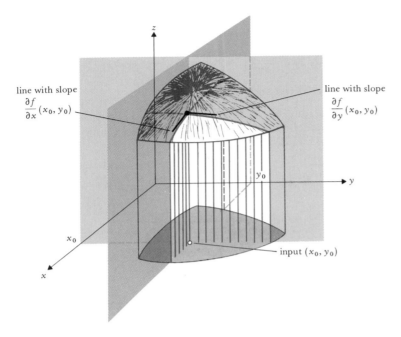

line with slope
$\dfrac{\partial f}{\partial x}(x_0, y_0)$

line with slope
$\dfrac{\partial f}{\partial y}(x_0, y_0)$

input (x_0, y_0)

So far I've discussed *separate* changes of x and y. What happens to outputs $f(x, y)$ if the inputs x and y change *simultaneously*? To make the notion more precise, let's suppose that the values x and y change with time t according to functional rules

$$x = X(t) \quad \text{and} \quad y = Y(t). \tag{8}$$

Then the $f(x, y)$ output will itself be determined by t, via the rule

$$F(t) = f(X(t), Y(t)). \tag{9}$$

For a diagram of the "composition" involved in (9), see Fig. 21-12.

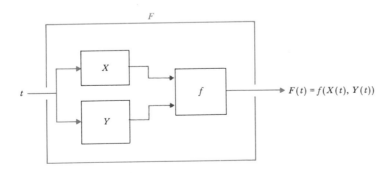

FIGURE 21-12

Would you CONJECTURE that as t changes the overall change in $F(t)$ will be simply a *sum* of changes due to $X(t)$ and $Y(t)$ separately? And can we hope to compute the overall *rate* of change $F'(t_0)$ at some input t_0 in terms of such separate rates as

$$X'(t_0), \quad Y'(t_0), \quad \frac{\partial f}{\partial x}(x_0, y_0), \quad \text{and} \quad \frac{\partial f}{\partial y}(x_0, y_0),$$

(where $x_0 = X(t_0)$ and $y_0 = Y(t_0)$)

—supposing that all these derivatives exist? To answer, I've indicated in Fig. 21-13 a scheme similar to those I used in Figs. 14-10 and 14-16 to handle $(f+g)'$ and $[g(f)]'$.

FIGURE 21-13

$$\frac{F(t)-F(t_0)}{t-t_0} = \frac{f(X(t),Y(t))-f(X(t_0),Y(t_0))}{t-t_0} = \frac{f(X(t),Y(t))-f(X(t_0),Y(t))+f(X(t_0),Y(t))-f(X(t_0),Y(t_0))}{t-t_0}$$

$$= \frac{f(X(t),Y(t))-f(X(t_0),Y(t))}{t-t_0} + \frac{f(X(t_0),Y(t))-f(X(t_0),Y(t_0))}{t-t_0}$$

$$= \left[\frac{f(X(t),Y(t))-f(X(t_0),Y(t))}{X(t)-X(t_0)}\right]\left[\frac{X(t)-X(t_0)}{t-t_0}\right] + \left[\frac{f(X(t_0),Y(t))-f(X(t_0),Y(t_0))}{Y(t)-Y(t_0)}\right]\left[\frac{Y(t)-Y(t_0)}{t-t_0}\right]$$

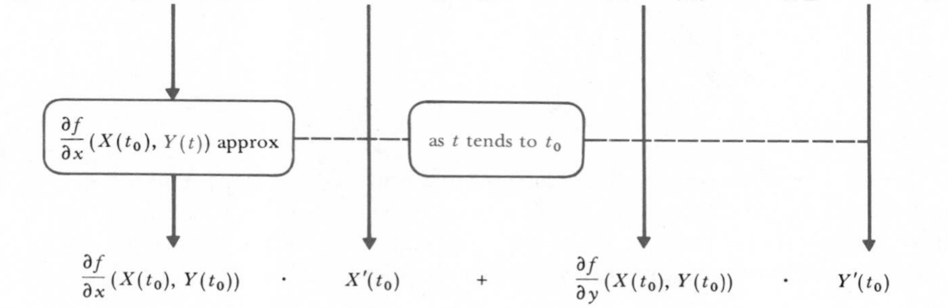

$$\frac{\partial f}{\partial x}(X(t_0),Y(t)) \text{ approx} \qquad \text{as } t \text{ tends to } t_0$$

$$\frac{\partial f}{\partial x}(X(t_0),Y(t_0)) \quad \cdot \quad X'(t_0) \quad + \quad \frac{\partial f}{\partial y}(X(t_0),Y(t_0)) \quad \cdot \quad Y'(t_0)$$

For the scheme to work, we would have to make special provision, as I did in Sec. 14.8, in case the denominator expressions $X(t)-X(t_0)$ or $Y(t)-Y(t_0)$ become 0, and we would have to know that $\frac{\partial f}{\partial x}(x,y)$ is close to $\frac{\partial f}{\partial x}(x_0,y_0)$ when (x,y) is close to (x_0,y_0). I invite you to handle such matters conveniently via the Mean Value Theorem, in doing Problem 11 of the next section. Here is a precise result:

Theorem A (on "overall change"): Suppose that $f(x,y)$ is defined on an "open, rectangular" domain

$$\mathscr{D} = \{\text{all } (x,y) \quad \text{with} \quad a < x < b \quad \text{and} \quad c < y < d)\}.$$

And suppose that we can calculate partial derivatives

$$\frac{\partial f}{\partial x}(x_0,y_0) \quad \text{and} \quad \frac{\partial f}{\partial y}(x_0,y_0) \tag{10}$$

for each pair of values (x_0,y_0) in $\mathscr{D}$. Suppose these partial derivatives are themselves *"continuous at any point (x_0,y_0)"* in $\mathscr{D}$ in the sense that

$$\lim_{n\to\infty} \frac{\partial f}{\partial x}(x_n,y_n) = \frac{\partial f}{\partial x}(x_0,y_0) \tag{11}$$

and

$$\lim_{n \to \infty} \frac{\partial f}{\partial y}(x_n, y_n) = \frac{\partial f}{\partial y}(x_0, y_0) \tag{12}$$

for any sequence $\{(x_n, y_n)\}$ of points in $\mathscr{D}$ with

$$\lim_{n \to \infty} x_n = x_0 \quad \text{and} \quad \lim_{n \to \infty} y_n = y_0. \tag{13}$$

Finally, suppose that $X(t)$ and $Y(t)$ are differentiable functions defined for $\alpha < t < \beta$, X with its range in $\langle a, b \rangle$ and Y with its range in $\langle c, d \rangle$; so that we can define $F(t) = f(X(t), Y(t))$ for $\alpha < t < \beta$. If t_0 is an input in $\langle \alpha, \beta \rangle$, and if

$$x_0 = X(t_0) \quad \text{and} \quad Y_0 = Y(t_0)$$

then

$$F'(t_0) = \left[\frac{\partial f}{\partial x}(x_0, y_0) \right] X'(t_0) + \left[\frac{\partial f}{\partial y}(x_0, y_0) \right] Y'(t_0). \tag{14}$$

This result (14)—which appears in Fig. 21-13—says that the instantaneous overall rate of change in F is indeed none other than the *sum* of the instantaneous rates of change of f via the separately changing inputs $x = X(t)$ and $y = Y(t)$. And we can calculate these separate rates via "chain rule" products.

Here's how to interpret (14) in terms of *differences* rather than derivatives: Pick an input $t_1 > t_0$. *If $t_1 - t_0$ is small enough,* then

$$\frac{F(t_1) - F(t_0)}{t_1 - t_0} \quad approximates\ F'(t_0), \tag{15a}$$

$$\frac{X(t_1) - X(t_0)}{t_1 - t_0} \quad approximates\ X'(t_0), \tag{15b}$$

and

$$\frac{Y(t_1) - Y(t_0)}{t_1 - t_0} \quad approximates\ Y'(t_0), \tag{15c}$$

by the very definition of derivatives. Substitute (15) into (14) and multiply through by $t_1 - t_0$ to get

$$F(t_1) - F(t_0)\ approximately\ equal\ to$$

$$\left[\frac{\partial f}{\partial x}(x_0, y_0) \right][X(t_1) - X(t_0)] + \left[\frac{\partial f}{\partial y}(x_0, y_0) \right][Y(t_1) - Y(t_0)]. \tag{16}$$

(How good the approximation in (16) is depends on how small $t_1 - t_0$ is.)

EXAMPLE 3. To study the effect upon the volume $V(r, h) = \pi r^2 h$ of a right circular cylinder caused by a *joint* change in the sizes of the radius r and the height h, let's think of these quantities as varying with time according to some rules $r = R(t)$ and $h = H(t)$. Then at an instant t_0, when $R(t_0) = r_0$ and $H(t_0) = h_0$, the instantaneous rate of change of volume will be

$$[V(R(t), H(t))]' = \left[\frac{\partial V}{\partial r}(r_0, h_0)\right]R'(t_0) + \left[\frac{\partial V}{\partial h}(r_0, h_0)\right]H'(t_0)$$

$$= [2\pi r_0 h_0]R'(t_0) + [\pi r_0^2]H'(t_0). \tag{17}$$

(I calculated $\dfrac{\partial V}{\partial r}$ and $\dfrac{\partial V}{\partial h}$ in Example 1.) Concretely, suppose the radius is 2 inches and the height 3 inches at an instant t_0 when both are changing at the rate of $\frac{1}{2}$ inch per minute. Then the volume at that instant must be increasing at the rate of

$$[2\pi 2 \cdot 3]\frac{1}{2} + [\pi 2^2]\frac{1}{2} = 8\pi \text{ cubic inches per minute.} \tag{18}$$

EXAMPLE 4. Suppose that a firm hires an extra man and thus increases its available daily man hours by 8 units. And suppose that on the same day it installs an additional \$200 machine. By how much will it have increased its productive capacity that day? If the firm's output can be described by a production function $p(x, y) = Cx^q y^r$ such as I considered in Example 2, then we can get an approximate answer as follows. Think of the manpower and capital investment available at time t as describable by functions $X(t)$ and $Y(t)$. Let's interpret the given data by saying that during a "short" interval $[t_0, t_1]$, these two functions increased by the amounts

$$X(t_1) - X(t_0) = 8 \text{ man hours,} \quad \text{and} \quad Y(t_1) - Y(t_0) = \$200. \tag{19}$$

Then according to (16), the productive capacity $P(t) = p(X(t), Y(t))$ should increase during $[t_0, t_1]$ by an amount

$P(t_1) - P(t_0)$ *approximately equal to*

$$\left[\frac{\partial p}{\partial x}(x_0, y_0)\right][X(t_1) - X(t_0)] + \left[\frac{\partial p}{\partial y}(x_0, y_0)\right][Y(t_1) - Y(t_0)]$$

$$= [Cq x_0^{q-1} y_0^r]8 + [Cr x_0^q y_0^{r-1}]200. \tag{20}$$

Here $x_0 = X(t_0)$, the amount of labor available just before the new man came; and $y_0 = Y(t_0)$, the amount of capital equipment just before the new machine was installed. (I calculated $\dfrac{\partial p}{\partial x}$ and $\dfrac{\partial p}{\partial y}$ in Example 2.) For concreteness, suppose that $x_0 = 100$ man hours, that $y_0 = \$10,000$, that the earlier production figure was $p(x_0, y_0) = \$1000$, and that estimates showed $q = r = \frac{1}{2}$ approximately. Then we could solve for C:

$$\$1000 = C(100)^{1/2}(10,000)^{1/2} = \$C(1000)$$

or $C = 1$. And in (20) we would have

$$P(t_1) - P(t_0) = \left[1 \cdot \frac{1}{2} \cdot (100)^{-1/2} \cdot (10,000)^{1/2}\right]8$$

$$+ \left[1 \cdot \frac{1}{2} \cdot (100)^{1/2} \cdot (10,000)^{-1/2}\right]200 = 5 \cdot 8 + \frac{1}{20}200 = \$50.$$

21.4 PROBLEMS ON PARTIAL DERIVATIVES AND GRAPHS

Problems 1–5 refer to the following list of functions f, where each f is defined for all (x, y) with $0 \leqslant x \leqslant 1$ and $0 \leqslant y \leqslant 1$.

(i) $f(x, y) = x + y$ (ii) $f(x, y) = xy$

(iii) $f(x, y) = xy^2$ (iv) $f(x, y) = e^{-x}y$

(v) $f(x, y) = \sqrt{x^2 + y^2}$

°1. For each f in the list:

(a) Write a formula and draw a graph for $g_0(x) = f(x, 0)$, for $g_1(x) = f(x, 1)$, and for $g_{3/2}(x) = f(x, 3/2)$.

(b) Write a formula and draw a graph for $h_0(y) = f(0, y)$, for $h_1(y) = f(1, y)$, and for $h_{3/2}(y) = f(3/2, y)$.

(c) Sketch "level curves," as in Fig. 21-10, corresponding to the outputs

$$f(x, y) = 1, \quad f(x, y) = 2, \quad f(x, y) = 3.$$

(d) Use parts (a), (b), and (c) to sketch the graph of $f(x, y)$ in three dimensions.

°2. For each f in the list, compute the partial derivatives

$$\frac{\partial f}{\partial x}(x_0, y_0) \quad \text{and} \quad \frac{\partial f}{\partial y}(x_0, y_0)$$

at the following input pairs:

$$(x_0, y_0) = (1, 1), \left(1, \frac{3}{2}\right), \left(\frac{3}{2}, 1\right), \quad \text{and} \quad \left(\frac{3}{2}, \frac{3}{2}\right).$$

°3. For each f in the list, approximate the differences of outputs $|f(1, 1.2) - f(1, 1)|$ and $|f(1.2, 1) - f(1, 1)|$, as in (5) and (6) of Sec. 21.3.

°4. Suppose that $X(t) = \sin t$ and $Y(t) = \cos t$ for $-\pi \leqslant t \leqslant \pi$. For each $f(x, y)$ in the list, let $F(t) = f(X(t), Y(t)) = f(\sin t, \cos t)$. Use the result on "overall change" (Theorem A) in Sec. 21.3 to evaluate $F'(t_0)$ at $t_0 = 0, \pi/2$, and π.

°5. For each $F(t)$ in Problem 4, approximate the difference $|F(0.1) - F(0)|$ in terms of $\sin 0.1$ and $\cos 0.1$, as in (16) of Sec. 21.3.

6. Suppose that a packager of salmon considers increasing the size of his cans.

(a) If they presently have radius $r = 1\frac{1}{2}$ inches and height $h = 2$ inches, which plan will increase the volume more: a slight increase in radius or a slight increase in height?

(b) What if the dimensions in part (a) are reversed?

(c) By approximately how many cubic inches will the packager increase the volume of the can in part (a) if he increases both r and h by, say, $\frac{1}{4}$ inch?

7. Suppose that the daily productive capacity (in dollars) of a firm depends on the number of man hours x available per day and on the capital investment $\$y$ via a relationship of the form $p(x, y) = x^{1/2}y^{1/2}$, say for $50 \leqslant x \leqslant 150$ and $\$5000 \leqslant y \leqslant \$1500 -$ as in Example 3 of Sec. 21.1 and Example 2 of Sec. 21.3.

(a) Sketch a graph of $g_{y_0}(x) = p(x, y_0)$ as a function of x for $y_0 = \$10,000$.

(b) Sketch a graph of $\dfrac{\partial p}{\partial x}(x, y_0)$ (the *rate* at which p increases with x) as a function of x for $y_0 = \$10,000$.

(c) Suppose that the present capital investment is $y_0 = \$10,000$ and the present daily manpower is 80 man hours. Suppose furthermore, that the firm plans to keep its capital investment the same and to start hiring more manpower at \$2.75 an hour. Until what manpower level can the firm continue such hiring before the added manhours cause a diminishing net daily profit?

(Suggestion: Recall (6) and (7) in Sec. 21.3.)

(d) Here is an alternate way of considering part (c): Let $N(x) = p(x, y_0) - 2.75x - C$ denote the net daily profit: the daily revenue minus daily labor costs which depend on x, and minus fixed daily costs C related to the capital investment. Find the input x for which $N(x)$ will be a maximum.

(e) Suppose that the present investment and manpower of the firm—and the present wages—are as in part (c), and that the firm has only a relatively small number of dollars D available to improve productivity. What fraction z ($0 \leqslant z \leqslant 1$) of D should the firm spend on more manpower and what fraction on more capital investment, in order to increase daily productivity the most?

Suggestion: According to Theorem A on "overall change" in Sec. 21.3—especially (16)—the change in productivity will be approximately

$$\frac{\partial p}{\partial x}(x_0, y_0)\left[\frac{zD}{2.75}\right] + \frac{\partial p}{\partial y}(x_0, y_0)\left[(1-z)D\right],$$

a quantity which depends *linearly* on z. Which z in $[0, 1]$ will maximize it?

(f) Regarding the calculation in part (e), what general relationship between $\dfrac{\partial p}{\partial x}(x_0, y_0)$, $\dfrac{\partial p}{\partial y}(x_0, y_0)$, and the hourly wage rate determines whether a firm should best increase labor only or investment only?

8. Suppose that $P_0 = (x_0, y_0)$ and $P_n = (x_n, y_n)$ for $n = 1, 2, 3, \ldots$, represent points in the plane. Show that the following two definitions are *equivalent*:

(i) $\lim\limits_{n \to \infty} P_n = P_0$ *means* $\{\lim\limits_{n \to \infty} x_n = x_0$ and $\lim\limits_{n \to \infty} y_n = y_0\}$

(ii) $\lim\limits_{n \to \infty} P_n = P_0$ *means* $\lim\limits_{n \to \infty} \sqrt{(x_n - x_0)^2 + (y_n - y_0)^2} = 0$

(the "distance" between P_n and P_0 tends to 0).

9. Here is a definition of limits for functions of two inputs analogous to that in Sec. 11.1 for functions of one input.

Definition: $\lim\limits_{(x,y) \to (x_0, y_0)} f(x, y) = L$ *means that* $\lim\limits_{n \to \infty} f(x_n, y_n) = L$ *for* ANY *sequence of input pairs* $P_n = (x_n, y_n)$ *with* $P_n \neq P = (x_0, y_0)$ *for all n and with* $\lim\limits_{n \to \infty} P_n = P$ *as in Problem 8.*

Which of the properties in Sec. 11.7 for limits of one input hold true for limits of two inputs?

10. Here is a definition of continuity for functions of two inputs analogous to that in Sec. 11.2 for functions of one input:

Definition: $f(x, y)$ is *continuous at* (x_0, y_0) if

$$\lim_{(x, y) \to (x_0, y_0)} f(x, y) = f(x_0, y_0),$$ as defined in Problem 9.

(a) Show that the definition is equivalent to the following requirement (analogous to the alternate definition for functions of one input, in Theorem B of Sec. 11.3):

$$\lim_{n \to \infty} (x_n, y_n) = (x_0, y_0) \ always \ implies \ \lim_{n \to \infty} f(x_n, y_n) = f(x_0, y_0).$$

(b) Which of the properties of continuity in Sec. 11.10 for functions of one input hold true for functions of two inputs?

*11. Here is a more general formulation for the results on "overall change" (Theorem A and approximation (16)) in Sec. 21.3. Consider two input pairs (x_0, y_0) and (x_1, y_1); and display the difference of corresponding outputs by the scheme of Fig. 21-13:

$$f(x_1, y_1) - f(x_0, y_0) = [f(x_1, y_1) - f(x_0, y_1)]$$
$$+ [f(x_0, y_1) - f(x_0, y_0)] \qquad (*)$$

Now, the first bracket in (*) is just the difference

$$g_{y_1}(x_1) - g_{y_1}(x_0), \qquad (**)$$

where $g_{y_1}(x) = f(x, y_1)$. We're assuming that a derivative $[g_{y_1}(x)]' = \dfrac{\partial f}{\partial x}(x, y_1)$ exists at all x's between x_0 and x_1. So let's apply the Mean Value Theorem to the difference (**) and write

$$f(x_1, y_1) - f(x_0, y_1) = g_{y_1}(x_1) - g_{y_1}(x_0)$$
$$= \left[\frac{\partial}{\partial x} f(x_c, y_1) \right] [x_1 - x_0], \qquad (***)$$

where x_c is some number *between* x_0 and x_1.

(a) Apply the same reasoning to the second bracket in (*) to get

$$f(x_0, y_1) - f(x_0, y_0) = \left[\frac{\partial f}{\partial y}(x_0, y_c) \right] [y_1 - y_0], \qquad \binom{**}{**}$$

where y_c is some number between y_0 and y_1.

(b) Put (***) and (**/**) together to get a kind of "*Mean Value result for functions of two inputs*":

$$f(x_1, y_1) - f(x_0, y_0) = \frac{\partial f}{\partial x}(x_c, y_1) [x_1 - x_0]$$
$$+ \frac{\partial f}{\partial y}(x_0, y_c) [y_1 - y_0], \qquad (\dagger)$$

where x_c lies between x_0 and x_1 and y_c lies between y_0 and y_1.

(c) Under the hypotheses of Theorem A in Sec. 21.3, why can we replace the x_c and y_c in (†) by x_0 and y_0, and say that

$$f(x_1, y_1) - f(x_0, y_0) \quad \textit{approximately equals}$$

$$\frac{\partial f}{\partial x}(x_0, y_0)\,[x_1 - x_0] + \frac{\partial f}{\partial y}(x_0, y_0)\,[y_1 - x_0] \qquad (\dagger\dagger)$$

for small differences $|x_1 - x_0|$ and $|y_1 - y_0|$?

(d) To prove the statements about derivatives in Theorem A, pick any sequence of inputs $t_n \neq t_0$ with $\lim_{n\to\infty} t_n = t_0$. Let $x_0 = X(t_0)$ and $y_0 = Y(t_0)$; and for $n = 1, 2, 3, \ldots$, let $x_n = X(t_n)$ and $y_n = Y(t_n)$. Replace the pair (x_1, y_1) in (†) by (x_n, y_n), and get corresponding numbers $x_{c,n}$ and $y_{c,n}$. Show that

$$\lim_{n\to\infty} x_{c,n} = x_0 \quad \text{and} \quad \lim_{n\to\infty} y_{c,n} = y_0. \qquad (\dagger\dagger\dagger)$$

Next, divide (†††) through by $t_n - t_0$ and let n increase. Use continuity of $\dfrac{\partial f}{\partial x}$ and $\dfrac{\partial f}{\partial y}$ to show that

$$\frac{\partial f}{\partial t}(t_0) = \frac{\partial f}{\partial x}(x_0, y_0)\,X'(t_0) + \frac{\partial f}{\partial y}(x_0, y_0)\,Y'(t_0).$$

21.5   HOW TO FIND A MAXIMUM OUTPUT f(x, y)

Suppose that $f(x, y)$ is defined for all points (x, y) in some rectangle of the xy plane, and that $f(x_0, y_0)$ is an absolute maximum for some point (x_0, y_0). Then the "surface-like" graph of f will have its greatest height above (x_0, y_0). And, in particular, any "curve" *in* the surface will have *its* greatest height when passing above (x_0, y_0).

FIGURE 21-14

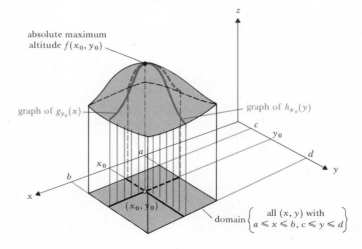

Still more particularly, we might expect the graph of $g_{y_0}(x) = f(x, y_0)$ to reach its greatest altitude at $x = x_0$, and the graph of $h_{x_0}(y) = f(x_0, y)$ to reach its greatest altitude at $y = y_0$. See Fig. 21-14 for another joint picture of such graphs. Now if the point (x_0, y_0) lies *strictly inside* the rectangle, and if $g_{y_0}(x)$ has a derivative at $x = x_0$ and $h_{x_0}(y)$ has a derivative at $y = y_0$, shouldn't we expect these derivatives to be *zero*, by the old results on maxima of functions of a single input (Sec. 12.7)? If so, then we have the

Theorem B (*"a condition for inside maxima and minima"*): If $f(x, y)$ is defined for $a \le x \le b$ and $c \le y \le d$, and if $f(x_0, y_0)$ is an absolute maximum or an absolute minimum for some input (x_0, y_0) with $a < x_0 < b$ and $c < y_0 < d$, then

$$\frac{\partial f}{\partial x}(x_0, y_0) = 0 \quad \text{and} \quad \frac{\partial f}{\partial y}(x_0, y_0) = 0 \tag{1}$$

provided these derivatives exist.

(I invite you to check out the details of this result in Problem 2(c) of Sec. 21.7.)

Just as for functions of a single variable, the requirements (1) can greatly narrow down any search for an actual maximum or minimum. Here is an example.

EXAMPLE 1. Consider the function $f(x, y) = (x^2 + 3y^2) e^{-x^2 - y_0^2}$, defined on the rectangle of all (x, y) with $|x| \le 100$ and $|y| \le 100$. At which input (x_0, y_0) might $f(x_0, y_0)$ be an absolute maximum? To search for candidates, let's calculate partial derivatives

$$\frac{\partial f}{\partial x}(x, y) = 2xe^{-x^2 - y^2} + (x^2 + 3y^2)(-2x)e^{-x^2 - y^2}$$
$$= 2xe^{-x^2 - y^2}[1 - (x^2 + 3y^2)] \tag{2}$$

and

$$\frac{\partial f}{\partial y}(x, y) = 6ye^{-x^2 - y^2} + (x^2 + 3y^2)(-2y)e^{-x^2 - y2}$$
$$= 2ye^{-x^2 - y^2}[3 - (x^2 + 3y^2)]. \tag{3}$$

These exist at all inputs in the domain. For which inputs (x_0, y_0) will $\frac{\partial f}{\partial x}(x_0, y_0) = 0$ and $\frac{\partial f}{\partial y}(x_0, y_0) = 0$ simultaneously? Check that $(x_0, y_0) = (0, 0)$ is one "solution." Are there others? Suppose $x_0 = 0$ but $y_0 \ne 0$. Then $\frac{\partial f}{\partial x}(x_0, y_0) = 0$ in (2); and in (3), $\frac{\partial f}{\partial y}(x_0, y_0) = 2y_0 e^{-y^2} \cdot$ $[3 - 3y_0^2]$, which quantity equals 0 when $y_0 = \pm 1$. So the inputs $(0, 1)$ and $(0, -1)$ are two more "solutions." Similarly, if $y_0 = 0$ but $x_0 \ne 0$, we can get two more "solutions," $(1, 0)$ and $(-1, 0)$. What if both $x_0 \ne 0$ and $y_0 \ne 0$? Then, in order to have $\frac{\partial f}{\partial x} = 0$ and $\frac{\partial f}{\partial y} = 0$ in we would have to have

$$1 - (x_0^2 + 3y_0^2) = 0 \quad \text{and} \quad 3 - (x_0^2 + 3y_0^2) = 0 \tag{4}$$

simultaneously—which is impossible, since $1 \neq 3$. Thus $\dfrac{\partial f}{\partial y}(x_0, y_0)$ $= 0$ *only* for the inputs (x_0, y_0) in the following table.

(x_0, y_0)	$(0, 0)$	$(0, 1)$	$(0, -1)$	$(1, 0)$	$(-1, 0)$
$f(x_0, y_0)$	0	$3e^{-1}$	$3e^{-1}$	e^{-1}	e^{-1}

Check, furthermore, that all inputs (x, y) on the perimeter of the domain—whether either $|x| = 100$, or $|y| = 100$, or both—must yield outputs $f(x, y) = (x^2 + 3y^2)e^{-x^2 - y^2} < 3e^{-1}$. (This is because e^u is much larger than u whenever u is large.)

Conclusion: *If f* has an absolute maximum at all, it can't occur on the perimeter; hence it must occur at an inside point; hence it must occur at one of the points listed in the table. Hence it must be $f(0, 1) = f(0, -1) = 3e^{-1}$.

(I invite you to check that an absolute maximum must exist—just as for continuous functions of a single input defined on closed intervals. Do Problem 11 in Sec. 21.7.)

In the next section I'll discuss another example of searching for a special input point *inside* a region—to get an *absolute minimum* for error incurred in "fitting" observed data by a line. But first, note how Theorem B ("a condition for inside maxima and minima") can help narrow a search down to the perimeter of a domain.

EXAMPLE 2. Suppose again, as in Example 4 of Sec. 21.3 that we can represent the daily productive capacity of a firm by $p(x, y) = x^{1/2}y^{1/2}$, where x is the number of man hours available daily and y is the investment in machinery. Suppose further that labor costs \$3 per man hour, that there are 330 working days in a year, and that the firm can afford to have no more than \$109,000 tied up in machinery and wages during a year. That is, we must have

(\$3 per hour)(x hours per day)(330 days) + \$$y$ = $990x + y$

$$\leqslant \$109{,}000. \qquad (5)$$

Subject to this condition, what pair of values (x, y) will *maximize* the productive capacity $p(x, y)$?

To answer, note that because of the inequality (5) and the fact that x and y must be nonnegative, we can restrict our consideration to points (x, y) of a triangular region "T" of the xy plane, bounded by the x axis, the y axis, and the line "L" with equation

$$990x + y = 109{,}000 \qquad (6)$$

—as shaded in Fig. 21-15. Let's think of the region T as the domain of the production function $p(x, y) = x^{1/2}y^{1/2}$. Can $p(x', y')$ be an absolute maximum for some point (x', y') *inside* T? No. Because in that case $p(x', y')$ would still be an absolute maximum if we restricted the domain of p to some rectangle inside T and containing (x', y')—as I've indicated in Fig. 21-15.

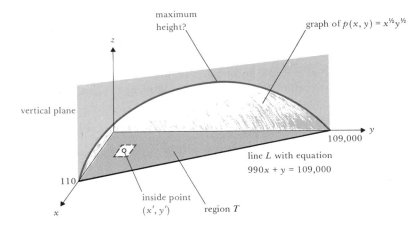

maximum height?

graph of $p(x, y) = x^{1/2}y^{1/2}$

FIGURE 21-15

vertical plane

109,000

line L with equation
$990x + y = 109,000$

inside point
(x', y')

region T

And then Theorem B ("a condition for inside maxima and minima") would require that

$$\frac{\partial p}{\partial x}(x', y') = 0 \quad \text{and} \quad \frac{\partial p}{\partial y}(x', y') = 0. \tag{7}$$

But, as I calculated in Example 2 of Sec. 21.3

$$\frac{\partial p}{\partial x}(x', y') = \frac{1}{2}(x')^{-1/2}(y')^{-1/2} > 0 \quad \text{and} \quad \frac{\partial p}{\partial y}(x', y') = \frac{1}{2}(x')^{1/2}(y')^{-1/2} > 0, \tag{8}$$

at *all* points (x', y') *inside* T. Conclusion: if an absolute maximum occurs at all, it must do so for some input point on the *perimeter* of T. Check that $p(x, y) = 0$ whenever x or $y = 0$, whereas $p(x, y) > 0$ for $x > 0$ and $y > 0$. Hence, if a maximum occurs at all, it must do so for some point on the line L. In Fig. 21-15 I've drawn a (green) vertical plane above this line. It intersects the surface-like graph of p in a (green) curve. Where does that curve reach its maximum height? To answer, note that along the line L, y is related to x via the equation

$$y = 109,000 - 990x. \tag{9}$$

Hence along the line L

$$\begin{aligned} p(x, y) = p(x, 109,000 - 990x) &= x^{1/2}(109,000 - 990x)^{1/2} \\ &= P(x), \text{ a function of the single input } x, \end{aligned} \tag{10}$$

for $0 \leqslant x \leqslant b$, where $b = 109,000/990$. To find an absolute maximum for $P(x)$ on $[0, b]$, let's find an input x_0 such that $P'(x_0) = 0$; that is, such that

$$\begin{aligned} P'(x_0) = &\frac{1}{2}x_0^{-1/2}(109,000 - 990x_0)^{1/2} \\ &+ \frac{1}{2}x_0^{1/2}(109,000 - 990x_0)^{-1/2}(-990) = 0. \end{aligned} \tag{11}$$

Multiply (11) through by $2x_0^{1/2}(109,000 - 990x_0)^{1/2}$ to get

$$(109,000 - 990x_0) + (-990)x_0 = 0 \tag{12}$$

or

$$x_0 = \frac{109,000}{2(990)} = 55 \text{ (man hours) approx.}$$

Since $P(0) = P(b) = 0$, the input x_0 does provide an absolute maximum for the function $P(x)$ on the interval $[0, b]$. Thus x_0 together with its corresponding

$$y_0 = 109,000 - 990x_0 = \$54,500 \qquad (13)$$

must provide an absolute maximum output

$$P(x_0, y_0) = x_0^{1/2} y_0^{1/2} = \$1730 \text{ dollars} \qquad (14)$$

for p on the line L and on the entire domain T — provided an absolute maximum exists at all (and one does, as I invite you to check in Problem 11 of Sec. 21.7).

21.6   HOW BEST TO "FIT" A STRAIGHT LINE THROUGH DATA POINTS

Suppose that at four successive medical checkups — separated by 6-month intervals — a patient's blood cholesterol levels read $y_1 = 210$ points, $y_2 = 190$ points, $y_3 = 250$ points, and $y_4 = 230$ points. I've plotted these data in black in Fig. 21-16. How can we predict what the patient's cholesterol level might be at his next 6-month checkup (at time $t_5 = 5/2$)?

FIGURE 21-16

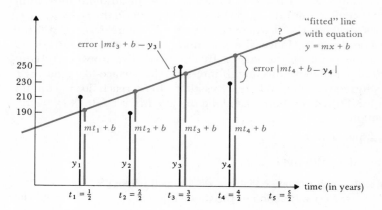

The method most people use to make such forecasts is to "fit" a line, with equation $y = mx + b$, to the given data and to "predict" the future level at time t_5 as the altitude $mt_5 + b$. (See the green line in Fig. 21-16.) This amounts to working with a model wherein the cholesterol level is assumed to be a linear function of time, $f(t) = mt + b$. In practice the main problem then is to choose values for m and b wisely. What criterion should one follow in making such a choice? A leading point of view is that one should choose m and b so as to make for as *little error as possible* between the *already observed* values y_i and the altitudes $mt_i + b$ along the line at corresponding times t_i. For each t_i, the error (in absolute value) is $|(mt_i+b)-y_i|$. How can we lump all these separate errors into one *total* error—which we might then try to minimize by choosing m and b wisely? One way would be simply to consider the sum

$$(mt_1+b-y_1)+(mt_2+b-y_2)+(mt_3+b-y_3)+(mt_4+b-y_4). \tag{1}$$

But the separate terms in such a sum might almost cancel each other out and conceal big errors at individual times t_i. A second way would be to add absolute values:

$$|mt_1+b-y_1|+|mt_2+b-y_2|+|mt_3+b-y_3|+|mt_4+b-y_4|. \tag{2}$$

The only thing wrong with such a version of "total error" is that absolute values are sometimes hard to work with. (Recall from Fig. 11-22 that a function such as $|x|$ has no derivative at $x=0$.) To avoid the difficulties of both (1) and (2) people usually choose the so-called "root mean square error"

$$\sqrt{[(mt_1+b)-y_1]^2+[(mt_2+b)-y_2]^2+[(mt_3+b)-y_3]^2+[(mt_4+b)-y_4]^2}. \tag{3}$$

You might also recall from Sec. 4.2 that we can interpret the quantity in (3) as the *distance* between two "points," P and Q, in 4-dimensional space—one whose coordinates are the observed values, $P=(y_1,y_2,y_3,y_4)$, and one whose coordinates are the "fitted" values $Q=(mt_1+b,mt_2+b,mt_3+b,mt_4+b)$.

The problem of minimizing the quantity (3) is the same as the problem of minimizing its *square*, whose dependence on m and b I'll denote as a function of two inputs

$$f(m,b)=[(mt_1+b)-y_1]^2+[(mt_2+b)-y_2]^2+[(mt_3+b)-y_3]^2 \\ +[(mt_4+b)-y_4]^2. \tag{4}$$

(For convenience, we might think of f as defined on a large rectangle in an mb plane, say, with $|m|\le 100$ and $|b|\le 300$.) If we multiply out the [ ] quantities on the right-hand side of (4) and collect terms, we can rewrite f in the form,

$$f(m,b)=m^2(t_1{}^2+t_2{}^2+t_3{}^2+t_4{}^2)+4b^2+2mb(t_1+t_2+t_3+t_4) \\ -2m(t_1y_1+t_2y_2+t_3y_3+t_4y_4)-2b(y_1+y_2+y_3+y_4) \\ +(y_1{}^2+y_2{}^2+y_3{}^2+y_4{}^2). \tag{5}$$

How can we find a pair of values (m_0,b_0) which will reduce the squared error $f(m,b)$ to an absolute minimum? Let's use the theorem of this section ("a condition for maxima and minima") as a guide, and calculate partial derivatives

$$\frac{\partial f}{\partial m}(m,b)=2m(t_1{}^2+t_2{}^2+t_3{}^2+t_4{}^2)+2b(t_1+t_2+t_3+t_4) \\ -2(t_1y_1+t_2y_2+t_3y_3+t_4y_4) \tag{6}$$

and

$$\frac{\partial f}{\partial b}(m,b)=8b+2m(t_1+t_2+t_3+t_4)-2(y_1+y_2+y_3+y_4). \tag{7}$$

Next, let's set the quantities (6) and (7) equal to zero, to get the simultaneous equations

$$Sm + Tb = U \atop Tm + 4b = V \Bigg\}, \tag{8}$$

where

$$S = t_1{}^2 + t_2{}^2 + t_3{}^2 + t_4{}^2 = \frac{1^2 + 2^2 + 3^2 + 4^2}{4} = \frac{15}{2},$$

$$T = t_1 + t_2 + t_3 + t_4 = \frac{1 + 2 + 3 + 4}{2} = 5,$$

$$U = t_1 y_1 + t_2 y_2 + t_3 y_3 + t_4 y_4 = \frac{210 + 2 \cdot 190 + 3 \cdot 250 + 4 \cdot 230}{2} = 1130,$$

and

$$V = y_1 + y_2 + y_3 + y_4 = 210 + 190 + 250 + 230 = 880.$$

The equations have a unique simultaneous solution

$$m_0 = \frac{4U - TV}{4S - T^2} = \frac{120}{5} = 25, \qquad b_0 = \frac{SV - TU}{4S - T^2} = \frac{940}{5} = 188 \tag{9}$$

since $4S - T^2 = 5 \neq 0$.

If the "squared error" function $f(m, b)$ does reach an absolute minimum at some point (m, b) inside the rectangle where $|m| \leqslant 100$ and $|b| \leqslant 300$, it must be at $(m_0, b_0) = (25, 188)$. Why not then predict the patient's next cholesterol reading as

$$m_0 t_5 + b_0 = 25\left(\frac{5}{2}\right) + 188 = 250.5 \text{ points (?)} \tag{10}$$

I invite you to check, in Problems 11 and 10 of the next section, that an absolute minimum for $f(m, b)$ must exist, and that it can't occur when $|m| \geqslant 100$ or $|b| \geqslant 300$. So the pair $(25, 188)$ does provide the least possible error.

21.7 PROBLEMS ON FINDING MAXIMA AND MINIMA

°1. Find the absolute maximum and the absolute minimum of each of the following functions: (Don't forget to compare interior outputs with those on the perimeter of the domain.)

    (a) $f(x, y) = x - x^2 y + y^2$ for $0 \leqslant x \leqslant 2$ and $0 \leqslant y \leqslant 2$

    (b) $f(x, y) = e^{xy} - x$ for $-2 \leqslant x \leqslant 2$ and $0 \leqslant y \leqslant 2$

    (c) $f(x, y) = \dfrac{y}{1 + x^2}$ for $0 \leqslant x \leqslant 1$ and $-1 \leqslant y \leqslant 1$

    (d) $f(x, y) = \sqrt{x^2 + y^2}$ for $0 \leqslant x \leqslant 1$ and $0 \leqslant y \leqslant 1$

    (e) $f(x, y) = x^3 - x^2 y + y^2$ for $-2 \leqslant x \leqslant 2$ and $-2 \leqslant y \leqslant 2$

    (f) $f(x, y) = y^3 - 3x^2 y + xy$ for $-10 \leqslant x \leqslant 10$ and $-10 \leqslant y \leqslant 10$

2. Suppose that $f(x, y)$ is a function defined on some domain $\mathcal{D}$ of input pairs (x, y). By analogy with the definitions in Sec. 12.6 for functions of one input, call an output $f(x_0, y_0)$ a *relative maximum*

if there is some rectangle R, containing (x_0, y_0) in its interior, such that $f(x, y) \leq f(x_0, y_0)$ for all inputs (x, y) in R. (R should be of the form {all (x, y) with $a_1 \leq x \leq b_1$ and $c_1 \leq y \leq d_1$}, with $a_1 < x_0 < b_1$ and $c_1 < y_0 < d_1$.) Define a *relative minimum* similarly. (Note: $f(x_0, y_0)$ is an *absolute maximum* if $f(x, y) \leq f(x_0, y_0)$ for *all* input pairs (x, y) in $\mathcal{D}$. Similarly for an absolute minimum.)

(a) If $f(x_0, y_0)$ is a relative maximum of $f(x, y)$, why must $g_{y_0}(x_0) = f(x_0, y_0)$ also be a relative maximum for the function of one input $g_{y_0}(x) = f(x, y_0)$; and why must $h_{x_0}(y_0) = f(x_0, y_0)$ also be a relative maximum for the function $h_{x_0}(y) = f(x_0, y)$?

(b) Answer part (a) for relative minima.

(c) How does the "condition for inside maxima and minima" (Theorem B) in Sec. 21.5 follow from the corresponding result for functions of one input, Theorem E (on "derivatives at maxima and minima") in Sec. 12.7?

3. Need $f(x_0, y_0)$ necessarily be a relative maximum or minimum (as defined in Problem 2) if

$$\frac{\partial f}{\partial x}(x_0, y_0) = 0 \quad \text{and} \quad \frac{\partial f}{\partial y}(x_0, y_0) = 0?$$

(Suggestion: Consider $f(x, y) = x^3 y^3$ for example.)

°4. Find all the relative maxima and minima of the functions in Problem 1.

5. Suppose that you wanted to construct a closed box out of cardboard, to hold 1 cubic foot of material. What dimensions should you plan for the faces of the box so as to use the *least* amount of cardboard? (See the figure.)

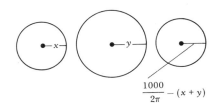

(Suggestions: You need volume $xyz = 1$, and should minimize the total surface area

$$2xy + 2yz + 2xz. \tag{*}$$

Substitute $z = 1/xy$ into (*) to get a function $f(x, y)$ defined for all $x > 0$ and all $y > 0$. Find candidates $f(x_0, y_0)$ for an absolute minimum and compare them with other outputs.)

6. How should you apportion 1000 yards of fencing to the perimeters of three circular regions so as to enclose the *maximum* total area? Which arrangement would yield the *minimum* total area? (See the figure; and recall the corrals and silos of Example 1 in Chap. 1.)

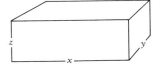

$$\frac{1000}{2\pi} - (x + y)$$

7. Here are (seasonally adjusted) percentages of unemployment in the U.S. labor force at various times during 1970:

Month	Jan.	May	June	Sept.
%	3.8	5.0	4.7	5.5

Use the method of Sec. 21.6 to predict from the given data what the percentage of unemployment might be in January, 1971.

8. Here are composite retail price figures for food in the U.S. during several years (relative to a value of 100 in 1957–1959):

Year	1966	1967	1968	1969
$	114.2	115.2	119.3	122.0

What value would you predict for 1971?

9. Here are approximate radii of a growing bacterial colony at different times:

Time	noon	4 p.m.	8 p.m.
Radius r in millimeters	1	2.2	7.8

What radius would you predict for 12 midnight?
   (a) Does it make sense to fit the data with a straight line — in view of the population growth models in previous chapters?
   (b) If the size of the population can indeed be approximated well by an exponential function $S(t) = Ne^{(1/H)t}$ as in Sec. 6.5, and if the area of the colony is proportional to its size, then might we not expect the radius of the colony to vary with time according to some rule such as $R(t) = Ce^{(1/2H)t}$, where C is a constant of proportionality?
   (c) Note that

$$f(t) = \log_e R(t) = \log_e C + \frac{1}{2H}t$$

depends on t *linearly*. In view of (b), why not convert the radii r_i in the table to the form $s_i = \log_e r_i$, and then use the method of Sec. 21.7 to predict a value for s at midnight? Then let $r = e^s$. (Consult a table of logs to get a concrete answer.)

10. Check that the function $f(m, b)$ in (5) of Sec. 21.6 can have no outputs when $|m| \geqslant 100$ or $|b| \geqslant 300$ which are greater than the output $f(m_0, b_0)$ corresponding to the values $m_0 = 25$ and $b_0 = 188$ in (9) of Sec. 21.6.

*11. (a) Suppose that a sequence of points $P_n = (x_n, y_n)$ for $n = 1, 2, 3, \ldots$ is confined to a given rectangle $R = \{$all (x, y) with $a \leqslant x \leqslant b$ and $c \leqslant y \leqslant d\}$. (That is, $a \leqslant x_n \leqslant b$ and $c \leqslant y_n \leqslant d$ for all n.) Show that there must be some point $P_0 = (x_0, y_0)$ of the rectangle such that $\lim_{n \to \infty} P_n = P_0$ (as defined in Problem 8 of Sec. 21.4.)

   Suggestion: Via Theorem B on "convergent subsequences" in Sec. 10.4, some subsequence $\{x_{n_k}\}$ of the x_n's must converge to some number x_0 in $[a, b]$. Apply the same theorem to the corresponding subsequence $\{y_{n_k}\}$.

(b) Use the result of part (a) and the method of Figs. 12-14 through 12-16 (in Sec. 12.5) to show that if a function $f(x, y)$ is *continuous* on a rectangle R (containing its perimeter) then it must be *bounded* on R. That is,

$$|f(x, y)| \leq b \qquad \text{for all } (x, y) \text{ in } R,$$

for some $b \geq 0$. (Recall the definitions of "continuity" for $f(x, y)$ in Problem 10 of Sec. 21.4.)

(c) Use the results of parts (a) and (b) and the method of Figs. 12-17 through 12-19 (in Sec. 12.5) to show that *if a function $f(x, y)$ is continuous on a rectangle R (containing its perimeter), then it must have an absolute maximum and an absolute minimum on R.*

12. If a rectangle R doesn't contain its perimeter as in Problem 11, need the claims (a)–(c) of that problem still hold?

21.8   SUMMARY OF CHAPTER 21

Definition. A function of two (real numbered) inputs is a rule which assigns a unique real number $f(x, y)$ to each pair (x, y) of real numbers in some domain.

See Sec. 21.1 for an interpretation of this definition and for a picture of a *graph* of $f(x, y)$ in three dimensions.

See Sec. 21.2 for a discussion of the two functions of a single input, $g_{y_0}(x) = f(x, y_0)$ and $h_{x_0}(y) = f(x_0, y)$, which we can get by holding y fixed at y_0 or x fixed at x_0—and for pictures of corresponding graphs.

Definition and notation. The partial derivatives of $f(x, y)$ at (x_0, y_0) are

$$\frac{\partial f}{\partial x}(x_0, y_0) = \text{the ordinary derivative } [g_{y_0}(x)]' \text{ at } x = x_0$$

and

$$\frac{\partial f}{\partial y}(x_0, y_0) = \text{the ordinary derivative } [h_{x_0}(y)]' \text{ at } y = y_0,$$

provided these exist.
(Sec. 21.3)

Theorem (on "overall change"): Suppose that $f(x, y)$ is defined on an "open rectangular" domain

$$\mathscr{D} = \{\text{all } (x, y) \text{ with } a < x < b \text{ and } c < y < d\}.$$

And suppose that we can calculate partial derivatives $\dfrac{\partial f}{\partial x}(x_0, y_0)$ and $\dfrac{\partial f}{\partial y}(x_0, y_0)$ for each pair (x_0, y_0) in $\mathscr{D}$. Suppose these partial derivatives are themselves "continuous" at any point (x_0, y_0) in $\mathscr{D}$ in the sense that

$$\lim_{n \to \infty} \frac{\partial f}{\partial x}(x_n, y_n) = \frac{\partial f}{\partial x}(x_0, y_0) \quad \text{and} \quad \lim_{n \to \infty} \frac{\partial f}{\partial y}(x_n, y_n) = \frac{\partial f}{\partial y}(x_0, y_0)$$

for any sequence of points $\{(x_n, y_n)\}$ in $\mathscr{D}$ with $\lim_{n \to \infty} x_n = x_0$ and $\lim_{n \to \infty} y_n = y_0$. Finally, suppose that $X(t)$ and $Y(t)$ are differentiable functions defined for $\alpha < t < \beta$, X with its range in $\langle a, b \rangle$ and Y with its range in $\langle c, d \rangle$; so that we can define $F(t) = f(X(t), Y(t))$ for $\alpha < t < \beta$. If t_0 is an input in $\langle \alpha, \beta \rangle$, and $x_0 = X(t_0)$ and $y_0 = Y(t_0)$, then

$$F'(t_0) = \left[\frac{\partial f}{\partial x}(x_0, y_0) \right] X'(t_0) + \left[\frac{\partial f}{\partial y}(x_0, y_0) \right] Y'(t_0).$$

See Sec. 21.3 for this result and for a corresponding version in terms of approximation of differences. See Problem 11 of Sec. 21.4 for a more general "mean value" result.

Theorem ("a condition for inside maxima and minima"): If $f(x, y)$ is defined for $a \leqslant x \leqslant b$ and $c \leqslant y \leqslant d$, and if $f(x_0, y_0)$ is an absolute maximum or an absolute minimum for some input (x_0, y_0) with $a < x_0 < b$ and $c < y_0 < d$, then

$$\frac{\partial f}{\partial x}(x_0, y_0) = 0 \quad \text{and} \quad \frac{\partial f}{\partial y}(x_0, y_0) = 0,$$

provided these derivatives exist.
(Sec. 21.5)

For conditions which guarantee that an absolute maximum and minimum must exist, see Problem 11 of Sec. 21.7.

For an application on how to find the "best" line to "fit" given data, see Sec. 21.5.

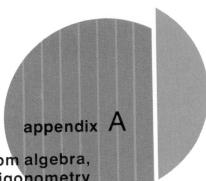

appendix A

a review of concepts from algebra,
geometry, and trigonometry

A.1 SOME BASIC CONCEPTS OF ALGEBRA

Unless otherwise specified, letters a, b, c, and x, y, z refer to real numbers, and letters i, j, k, m, and n refer to positive integers.

Some rules for addition, multiplication, and inequalities:

$a + 0 = a$

$a + b = b + a$

$(a + b) + c = a + (b + c)$

$a \cdot 1 = a$

$a \cdot 0 = 0$

$ab = ba$

$(ab)c = a(bc)$

$a(b + c) = ab + ac$

If $ab = 0$, then either $a = 0$ or $b = 0$, or both.

If $a \neq b$, then either $a < b$ or $a > b$.

If $a < b$ and $b < c$, then $a < c$.

If $a < b$, then $a + c < b + c$.

If $a < b$ and $c > 0$, then $ac < bc$.

If $a < b$ and $c < 0$, then $ac > bc$.

If $ab > 0$, then either

$a > 0$ *and* $b > 0$

or

$a < 0$ *and* $b < 0$.

If $ab < 0$, then either

$a < 0$ *and* $b > 0$

or

$a > 0$ *and* $b < 0$.

Notation: $a \leq b$ means *either* $a = b$ *or* $a < b$

$a < b < c$ means $a < b$ *and* $b < c$

$a \leq b \leq c$ means $a \leq b$ *and* $b \leq c$

Definitions of exponents:

$$a^n = a \cdot a \cdot a \cdots a \quad (n \text{ factors})$$

If $a \neq 0$, $a^{-1} = \dfrac{1}{a}$ and $a^0 = 1$.

Some rules for exponents:

$$a^m a^n = a^{m+n}$$
$$a^{-m} a^{-n} = a^{-(m+n)}$$
$$a^m a^{-n} = a^{m-n}$$
$$(a^m)^n = a^{mn}$$
$$(ab)^n = a^n b^n$$

If $b \neq 0$, then $\left(\dfrac{a}{b}\right)^n = \dfrac{a^n}{b^n}$.

(*Convention:* ab^n means $a(b^n)$, not $(ab)^n$.)

Definition of roots:

$a^{1/n}$ (or $\sqrt[n]{a}$) denotes a number b (if one exists) such that $b^n = a$. (There can exist no such real number b if $a < 0$ and n is even.)

Some rules for roots:

$$(ab)^{1/n} = a^{1/n} b^{1/n}$$

If $b \neq 0$, then $\left(\dfrac{a}{b}\right)^{1/n} = \dfrac{a^{1/n}}{b^{1/n}}$.

By definition, $a^{m/n} = (a^m)^{1/n}$.

$$a^{-m/n} = \frac{1}{a^{m/n}} \quad (\text{if } a \neq 0)$$

$$(ab)^{m/n} = a^{m/n} b^{m/n}$$
$$a^{i/j} a^{m/n} = a^{i/j + m/n} = a^{(in + jm)/jn}$$

Some rules for factoring:

$$x^2 + 2xy + y^2 = (x+y)^2$$
$$x^2 - 2xy + y^2 = (x-y)^2$$
$$x^2 + (a+b)x + ab = (x+a)(x+b)$$
$$x^2 - y^2 = (x-y)(x+y)$$
$$x^3 - y^3 = (x-y)(x^2 + xy + y^2)$$
$$x^n - y^n = (x-y)(x^{n-1} + x^{n-2}y + x^{n-3}y^2 + \cdots + xy^{n-2} + y^{n-1}).$$

The method of "completing the square": If $a \neq 0$, then

$$ax^2 + bx = a\left[x^2 + \left(\frac{b}{a}\right)x\right]$$
$$= a\left[x^2 + 2\left(\frac{b}{2a}\right)x + \left(\frac{b}{2a}\right)^2 - \left(\frac{b}{2a}\right)^2\right]$$
$$= a\left[x^2 + 2\left(\frac{b}{2a}\right)x + \left(\frac{b}{2a}\right)^2\right] - \frac{b^2}{4a}$$
$$= a\left(x + \frac{b}{2a}\right)^2 - \frac{b^2}{4a}.$$

Definition of the "absolute value $|a|$" of a number a:

$$|a| = \begin{cases} a & \text{if } a \geqslant 0 \\ -a & \text{if } a < 0 \end{cases}$$

Some rules for absolute values:

$$|ab| = |a| \cdot |b|$$
$$|a+b| \leqslant |a| + |b|$$

The "quadratic formula": If $a \neq 0$ and $b^2 - 4ac \geqslant 0$, then

$$ax^2 + bx + c = a(x - r_1)(x - r_2),$$

where

$$r_1 = -\frac{b}{2a} + \frac{1}{2a}\sqrt{b^2 - 4ac} \quad \text{and} \quad r_2 = -\frac{b}{2a} - \frac{1}{2a}\sqrt{b^2 - 4ac}.$$

A.2 EQUATIONS

Definition of an "equation": a statement that two mathematical quantities are the same.

The quantities may be expressed in terms of specific constants a, b, $c, \ldots$, and also unspecified numbers x, y, $z, \ldots$ —called "variables."

Definition of a "solution" of an equation involving one variable x: any specific number x_0 which when substituted for x makes the equation a *true* statement.

There may be more than one such "solution." The collection of all solutions of an equation is its "*solution set.*"

EXAMPLE. The "solution set" of the equation $x^2 = 4$ consists of the numbers 2 and -2.

An operation such as multiplying both sides of an equation by the same nonzero constant c, or adding c to both sides of an equation, produces another equation which is *equivalent* to the given equation in the sense that it has the *same solution set*.

EXAMPLE. The equation

$$2x^2 + 4x - 6 = 0 \tag{1}$$

is equivalent to

$$x^2 + 2x - 3 = 0,$$

and to

$$x^2 + 2x + 1 = 4,$$

and to

$$(x + 1)^2 = 4. \tag{2}$$

To satisfy equation (2) we must have either

$$x + 1 = 2, \text{ that is, } x = 1;$$

or
$$x + 1 = -2, \text{ that is } x = -3.$$

The solution set common to both equations (1) and (2) consists of the two numbers 1 and -3.

Definition of a "simultaneous solution" of two equations involving two "variables" x and y: any *pair* of specific numbers x_0 and y_0 which when substituted for x and y respectively cause both equations to be true statements. The collection of all such pairs constitutes the *"simultaneous solution set"* of the two equations.

Definition of a "linear equation": one of the form
$$ax + by + \cdots = d$$
wherein variables appear (if at all) in separate terms and only with exponent 1.

The usual method for treating a system of two simultaneous equations is to manipulate them algebraically so as to replace them by a simpler system of equations which is *equivalent* to the original one in the sense that it has the same simultaneous solution set. Usually one tries to "eliminate" one of the variables from the old equations.

How to find the simultaneous solution set of a system of 2 linear equations in 2 variables:

$$ax + by = e \qquad \qquad (3.1)$$
$$cx + dy = f \qquad \qquad (3.2)$$

when $ad - bc \neq 0$. Multiply the first equation through by d and the second through by b to get an equivalent system

$$adx + bdy = ed \qquad \qquad (4.1)$$
$$bcx + bdy = bf \qquad \qquad (4.2)$$

Then "eliminate y" by subtracting the second equation from the first to get

$$(ad - bc)x = ed - bf. \qquad \qquad (5)$$

Together with, say, (3.2), (5) yields a new simultaneous system equivalent to the original (3); namely,

$$x = \frac{ed - bf}{ad - bc} \qquad \qquad (6.1)$$
$$cx + dy = f \qquad \qquad (6.2)$$

The equation (6.1) yields a unique x_0 value for a simultaneous solution; and substitution of that value into (6.2) will yield a unique corresponding y_0 value.

EXAMPLE.

$$x + 2y = 4$$
$$3x - y = 5$$

Multiply the first equation through by -1 and the second by 2, to get

$$\left.\begin{array}{l} -x-2y=-4 \\ 6x-2y=10 \end{array}\right\};$$

and subtract to get

$$\left.\begin{array}{l} 7x+0y=14 \\ 3x-y=5 \end{array}\right\},$$

or

$$\left.\begin{array}{l} x=2 \\ y=3x-5 \end{array}\right\},$$

whose unique solution is $(x_0=2, y_0=1)$.

If $ad-bc=0$ in (3), one of the equations must be a multiple of the other. In this case, there will either be no simultaneous solutions or else the simultaneous solution set will consist of *infinitely* many pairs (x, y).

EXAMPLE. The system

$$\left.\begin{array}{l} x+3y=1 \\ 2x+6y=1 \end{array}\right\}$$

has no solution. (If (x_0, y_0) were a solution, then we would have

$$1 = 2x_0 + 6y_0 = 2(x_0 + 3y_0) = 2\cdot 1 = 2.)$$

EXAMPLE. The system

$$x+3y=1$$

$$2x+6y=2$$

has as simultaneous solutions all pairs of the form $(x, (1-x)/3)$ where x is any real number.

Define "*simultaneous solution sets*" similarly when there are more than two "variables." Treat a system of, say, three linear equations in three variables x, y, and z by trying to eliminate variables one at a time as in (3)–(6). Thus given the system

$$a_1x+b_1y+c_1z=e_1 \tag{7.1}$$

$$a_2x+b_2y+c_2z=e_2 \tag{7.2}$$

$$a_3x+b_3y+c_3z=e_3 \tag{7.3}$$

first try to eliminate z from (6.1) and (6.2). Then try to eliminate z from (6.2) and (6.3). Having done so you should have *two* simultaneous equations in x and y. Find solutions for these (if there are any) and then solve for z via (7.1) or (7.2) or (7.3).

EXAMPLE.

$$x + 3y + z = 1 \tag{8.1}$$

$$2x + y - z = 0 \tag{8.2}$$

$$x - y + 2z = 2 \tag{8.3}$$

Add (8.1) and (8.2) to get

$$3x + 4y = 1. \tag{9}$$

From (8.2) and (8.3) get

$$5x + y = 2. \tag{10}$$

Solve (9) and (10) simultaneously to get

$$x_0 = \frac{7}{17}, \quad y_0 = -\frac{1}{17}. \tag{11}$$

Substitute (11) into (8.2) to get $z_0 = 13/17$.

A.3 INEQUALITIES

Definition of a "solution" of an inequality involving a variable x: any specific number x_0 which when substituted for x makes the given inequality a true statement. The collection of all solutions of a given inequality is its "*solution set.*"

If several inequalities are given involving x, their "*simultaneous solution set*" is the collection of all specific numbers x_0 with the following property: when x_0 is substituted for x simultaneously into the given inequalities, all of them will be true statements.

EXAMPLE. The simultaneous solution set of the inequalities

$$x - 6 \leqslant 0 \quad \text{and} \quad x - 1 \geqslant 0$$

consists of all numbers x_0 between 1 and 6 inclusive: all x_0 with $1 \leqslant x_0 \leqslant 6$.

There may be *no* simultaneous solutions.

EXAMPLE. No real number x_0 can satisfy both of the inequalities

$$x \geqslant 6 \quad \text{and} \quad x \leqslant 1$$

simultaneously.

According to the rules for inequalities in A.1, the following operations upon a given inequality will produce a new inequality which is *equivalent* to the given one in the sense that it has the *same solution set*:

  (i) adding the same constant to both sides of the inequality,
 (ii) multiplying both sides by the same positive constant,
(iii) multiplying both sides by the same negative constant and reversing the inequality.

EXAMPLE. The inequality

$$\frac{5x-7}{2} < 2x+1$$

is equivalent to

$$5x-7 < 4x+2,$$

and to

$$5x < 4x+9,$$

and to

$$x < 9.$$

The last version most easily exposes the solution set common to all of the inequalities: all real numbers $x_0 < 9$.

EXAMPLE. The inequality

$$\frac{2x-7}{x-1} \leq 1. \tag{1}$$

Note that the number 1 can't be a solution since it would render the left-hand side of (1) meaningless. Suppose that x_0 now represents some particular solution. There are two cases, as in the following table.

Case (i)	Case (ii)
$x_0 > 1,$ (2)	$x_0 < 1,$ (2′)
that is,	that is,
$x_0 - 1 > 0.$ (3)	$x_0 - 1 < 0.$ (3′)
Multiply (1) by the *positive* number $x_0 - 1$ to get	Multiply (1) by the *negative* number $x_0 - 1$ to get
$2x_0 - 7 \leq x_0 - 1,$ (4)	$2x_0 - 7 \geq x_0 - 1,$ (4′)
or	or
$x_0 \leq 6.$ (5)	$x_0 \geq 6.$ (5′)
Inequalities (5) and (2) together read	Inequality (5′) contradicts (2′), so case (ii) is impossible.
$1 < x_0 \leq 6.$ (6)	

Thus the only possible solutions for (1) are the x_0's in (6). To check that all such x_0's *are* indeed solutions of (1), let's work backward: (6) implies (5), which implies (4). Also (6) implies that $x_0 - 1 > 0$ (via (2) and (3)). Multiply (4) by the *positive* number $1/(x_0 - 1)$ to get (1).

Inequalities involving absolute values: The "solution set" of the inequality

$$|x-a| \leqslant b \tag{7}$$

(where $b \geqslant 0$) *consists of all numbers between* $a-b$ *and* $a+b$: that is, of all x_0 with

$$a-b \leqslant x_0 \leqslant a+b. \tag{8}$$

Here are the reasons. Suppose that x_0 now represents some particular solution of (7). There are two possible cases, as in the following table.

Case (i)		Case (ii)	
$x_0 \geqslant a,$	(9)	$x_0 < a,$	(9')
that is,		that is,	
$x_0 - a \geqslant 0.$	(10)	$x_0 - a < 0.$	(10')
In this case, (7) means		In this case, (7) means	
$x_0 - a \leqslant b,$	(11)	$-(x_0 - a) \leqslant b,$	(11')
or		or	
$x_0 \leqslant a+b.$	(12)	$x_0 \geqslant a-b.$	(12')
Now (9) also implies that		Now (9') also implies that	
$x_0 \geqslant a-b.$	(13)	$x_0 \leqslant a+b.$	(13')
Inequalities (13) and (12) together read		Inequalities (13') and (12') together read	
$a-b \leqslant x_0 \leqslant a+b.$	(8)	$a-b \leqslant x_0 \leqslant a+b.$	(8)

Thus the only possible solutions for (7) are the x_0's in (8). To check that all such x_0's are indeed solutions of (7), look again at the separate cases (i) and (ii). In (i), (12) and (9) imply (11) and (10), and these imply (7). Similarly for case (ii).

EXAMPLE. If $|x+2| \leqslant 6$, that is, if $|x-(-2)| < 6$, then

$$-2-6 \leqslant x \leqslant -2+6.$$

Conversely, if x satisfies the inequalities in (14) simultaneously, then

$$|x+2| \leqslant 6. \tag{14}$$

The "solution set" of the inequality

$$|x-a| > b \tag{15}$$

consists of all members x_0 for which

$$\text{either}\quad x_0 < a - b \quad\text{or}\quad x_0 > a + b \tag{16}$$

(that is, all numbers x_0 which don't satisfy (8).)

EXAMPLE. If $|3x+1| > 9$, then equivalently $|x + \frac{1}{3}| > 3$, or $|x - (-\frac{1}{3})| > 3$; and

$$\text{either}\quad x < -\frac{1}{3} - 3 \quad\text{or}\quad x > -\frac{1}{3} + 3. \tag{17}$$

Conversely, if x satisfies either inequality in (17), then $|3x+1| > 9$.

A.4 SOME RESULTS FROM GEOMETRY

Definition of "similar triangles". Corresponding sides are proportional and corresponding angles are equal. See Fig. A-1.

FIGURE A-1

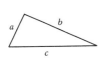 

$$\frac{a'}{a} = \frac{b'}{b} = \frac{c'}{c}$$

Two triangles formed with parallel bases, as in Fig. A-2, are similar.

FIGURE A-2

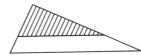

Two right triangles with corresponding sides perpendicular, as in Fig. A-3, must have equal angles and be similar.

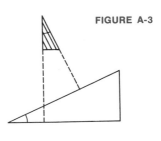

FIGURE A-3

Some formulas for length, area, and volume. The circumference of a circle of radius r and diameter d has length $2\pi r = \pi d$.

The area of a rectangle with base length b and height h is bh.

The area of a parallelogram with base length b and height h is bh. See Fig. A-4.

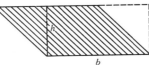

FIGURE A-4

The area of a triangle with base length b and height h is $\frac{1}{2}bh$. See Fig. A-5.

FIGURE A-5

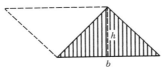

The area of a trapezoid with base lengths b_1 and b_2 and height h is $\frac{1}{2}(b_1 + b_2)h$. See Fig. A-6.

FIGURE A-6

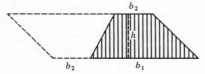

The area of a circle of radius r is πr^2.

The surface area of a right-circular cylinder of base radius r and height h is $2\pi rh$. See Fig. A-7.

FIGURE A-7

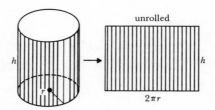

The surface area of a right-circular cone of base radius r and "slant height" l is πrl. See Fig. A-8.

FIGURE A-8

The "Pythagorean Theorem". For a right triangle, as in Fig. A-9, the areas of squares along the sides must add: $c^2 = a^2 + b^2$.

FIGURE A-9

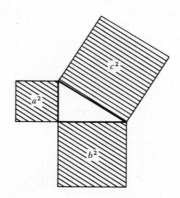

The volume of a vertical prism with base area A and height h is Ah. See Fig. A-10.

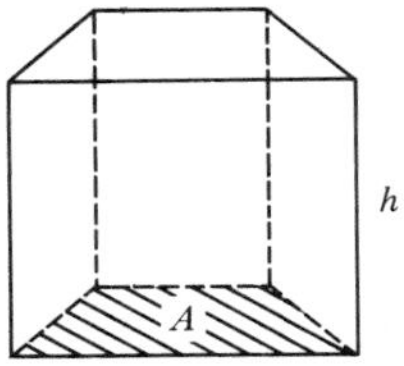

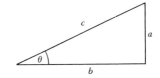

FIGURE A-10

The volume of a right-circular cylinder with base radius r and height h is $\pi r^2 h$.

The volume of a sphere of radius r is $\frac{4}{3} \pi r^3$.

A.5 SOME BASIC CONCEPTS OF TRIGONOMETRY

Definitions of trigonometric quantities in terms of a right triangle (Fig. A-11).

FIGURE A-11

$$\sin \theta = \frac{a}{c} \qquad \text{cosecant } \theta = \frac{c}{a} = \frac{1}{\sin \theta} \quad (\text{if } a \neq 0)$$

$$\cos \theta = \frac{b}{c} \qquad \text{secant } \theta = \frac{c}{b} = \frac{1}{\cos \theta} \quad (\text{if } b \neq 0)$$

$$\tan \theta = \frac{a}{b} \quad (\text{if } b \neq 0) \qquad \text{cotan } \theta = \frac{b}{a} = \frac{1}{\tan \theta} \quad (\text{if } a \neq 0)$$

$$= \frac{\sin \theta}{\cos \theta}$$

The *"law of sines"*: with angles and corresponding sides labeled as in Fig. A-12, we must have

FIGURE A-12

$$\frac{\sin \alpha}{a} = \frac{\sin \beta}{b} = \frac{\sin \gamma}{c}.$$

The *"law of cosines"*: for an angle θ, and sides labeled as in Fig. A-13 — with c opposite to θ — we must have

FIGURE A-13

$$c^2 = a^2 + b^2 - 2ab \cos \theta.$$

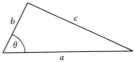

Measurement of "angle" in terms of arclength: "radians."

The angle θ corresponds to, and is "measured" by, the ratio

$$\frac{\text{length of arc}}{\text{length of radius}} = \frac{t}{r} \text{ "radian" units.}$$

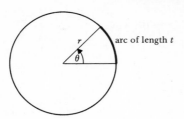

arc of length t

The angle, and corresponding arc, are often considered as wound more than once around the circle—either counterclockwise (positively) or clockwise (negatively). Here are samples of corresponding measurements (Fig. A-14):

In degrees	In radians
720°	4π
360°	2π
180°	π
90°	$\dfrac{\pi}{2}$
30°	$\dfrac{\pi}{6}$
0°	0
$-30°$	$-\dfrac{\pi}{6}$
$-180°$	$-\pi$
$-720°$	-4π

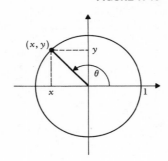

Definitions of trigonometric quantities in terms of cartesian coordinates, for angles θ of any size (Fig. A-15):

$$\sin \theta = \frac{y}{1} \qquad\qquad \text{cosecant } \theta = \frac{1}{y} \quad (\text{if } y \neq 0)$$

$$\cos \theta = \frac{x}{1} \qquad\qquad \text{secant } \theta = \frac{1}{x} \quad (\text{if } x \neq 0)$$

$$\tan \theta = \frac{y}{x} \quad (\text{if } x \neq 0) \qquad \text{cotan } \theta = \frac{x}{y} \quad (\text{if } y \neq 0)$$

Values of the trigonometric quantities for several angles

Angle in degrees	Angle in radians	Sine	Cosine	Tangent
0	0	0	1	0
30°	$\pi/6$	$\frac{1}{2}$	$\frac{1}{2}\sqrt{3}$	$\frac{1}{3}\sqrt{3}$
45°	$\pi/4$	$\frac{1}{2}\sqrt{2}$	$\frac{1}{2}\sqrt{2}$	1
60°	$\pi/3$	$\frac{1}{2}\sqrt{3}$	$\frac{1}{2}$	$\sqrt{3}$
90°	$\pi/2$	1	0	undefined
135°	$\frac{3}{4}\pi$	$\frac{1}{2}\sqrt{2}$	$-\frac{1}{2}\sqrt{2}$	-1
180°	π	0	-1	0
$-30°$	$-\pi/6$	$-\frac{1}{2}$	$\frac{1}{2}\sqrt{3}$	$-\frac{1}{3}\sqrt{3}$
$-45°$	$-\pi/4$	$-\frac{1}{2}\sqrt{2}$	$\frac{1}{2}\sqrt{2}$	-1
$-90°$	$-\pi/2$	-1	0	undefined

(For relationships between corresponding angles in different quadrants, see the list of identities at the end of this section.)

Figure A-16 shows a sample geometric argument for the identity

$$\sin (\theta + \phi) = \sin \theta \cos \phi + \cos \theta \sin \phi.$$

In the figure both angles and their sum are $< \pi/2$. The shaded triangles are similar.

Here is a *list of identities holding for angles θ and ϕ of all sizes.*

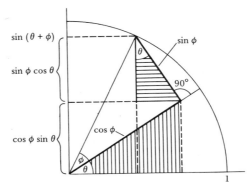

$$\cos^2 \theta + \sin^2 \theta = 1$$
$$1 + \tan^2 \theta = \sec^2 \theta$$
$$\cot^2 \theta + 1 = \csc^2 \theta$$
$$\cos (-\theta) = \cos \theta$$
$$\sin (-\theta) = -\sin \theta$$
$$\cos (\pi - \theta) = -\cos \theta$$
$$\sin (\pi - \theta) = \sin \theta$$

$$\cos \left(\frac{\pi}{2} - \theta\right) = \sin \theta$$

$$\sin \left(\frac{\pi}{2} - \theta\right) = \cos \theta$$

$$\cos (\theta + \phi) = \cos \theta \cos \phi - \sin \theta \sin \phi$$
$$\cos (\theta - \phi) = \cos \theta \cos \phi + \sin \theta \sin \phi$$
$$\sin (\theta + \phi) = \sin \theta \cos \phi + \cos \theta \sin \phi$$
$$\sin (\theta - \phi) = \sin \theta \cos \phi - \cos \theta \sin \phi$$
$$\sin (2\theta) = 2 \sin \theta \cos \theta$$
$$\cos (2\theta) = \cos^2 \theta - \sin^2 \theta$$
$$= 2 \cos^2 \theta - 1$$
$$= 1 - 2 \sin^2 \theta$$

$$\cos^2 \theta = \frac{1}{2} [1 + \cos (2\theta)]$$

$$\sin^2 \theta = \frac{1}{2} [1 - \cos (2\theta)]$$

$$\sin \theta + \sin \phi = 2 \sin \left(\frac{\theta + \phi}{2}\right) \cos \left(\frac{\theta - \phi}{2}\right)$$

$$\sin \theta - \sin \phi = 2 \cos \left(\frac{\theta + \phi}{2}\right) \sin \left(\frac{\theta - \phi}{2}\right)$$

$$\cos \theta + \cos \phi = 2 \cos \left(\frac{\theta + \phi}{2}\right) \cos \left(\frac{\theta - \phi}{2}\right)$$

$$\cos \theta - \cos \phi = -2 \sin \left(\frac{\theta + \phi}{2}\right) \sin \left(\frac{\theta - \phi}{2}\right).$$

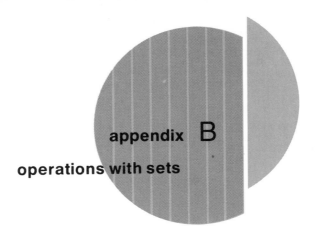

appendix B
operations with sets

B.1 BASIC DEFINITIONS AND RELATIONSHIPS

Definition. A *set* is a collection of objects. The objects are often called the *elements* of the set.

Notation: $S = \{(\text{some description of the objects})\}$.

EXAMPLES

The set consisting of the first three positive integers	$= \{1,\ 2,\ 3\}$
The set consisting of all positive integers	$= \{1, 2, 3, \ldots, n, \ldots\}$
The set consisting of all even positive integers	$= \{2, 4, 6, \ldots, 2n, \ldots\}$
The set consisting of all real numbers between 0 and 1 inclusive	$= \{\text{all } x \text{ with } 0 \leq x \leq 1\}$
The set consisting of all distinct ordered pairs of the symbols H and T	$= \{HH, HT, TH, TT\}$

Definition. A *subset B* of a given set A is a set of objects each of which is an element of A. Notation: $B \subset A$.

EXAMPLE. $A = \{1, 2, 3\}, B = \{1, 2\}$.

EXAMPLE. See the encircled sets in Fig. B-1.

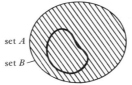

set A set B $B \subset A$ **FIGURE B-1**

711

Definition. The *union* of two sets A and B is the set consisting of all objects that are *either* in A or in B *or in both*. Notation: $A \cup B$ (the order of writing is immaterial).

EXAMPLE. $A = \{1, 2\}$, $B = \{2, 3\}$. $A \cup B = \{1, 2, 3\}$.   Note   that 2 is in both A and B.

EXAMPLE. See the encircled sets in Fig. B-2.

FIGURE B-2

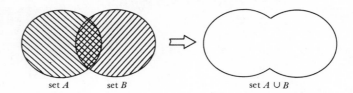

set A set B set $A \cup B$

Definition. The *intersection* of two sets A and B is the set consisting of all objects that are both in A *and* in B. Notation: $A \cap B$ (the order of writing is immaterial).

EXAMPLE. $A = \{1, 2\}, B = \{2, 3\}. A \cap B = \{2\}.$

EXAMPLE. See the enclosed sets in Fig. B-3.

FIGURE B-3

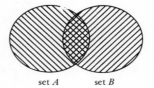

set A set B set $A \cap B$

The last two definitions can be extended for a finite collection of sets. Thus the *union* $A_1 \cup A_2 \cup \cdots \cup A_n$ consists of all objects which have the property of being in A_1 *or* in A_2 *or* $\cdots$ *or* in A_n or in several together. The *intersection* $A_1 \cap A_2 \cap \cdots \cap A_n$ consists of all objects which have the property of being in A_1 *and* in A_2 *and* $\cdots$ *and* in A_n.

EXAMPLE. See the encircled sets in Fig. B-4.

FIGURE B-4

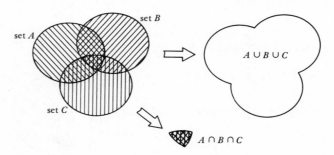

Notation: $A \cap B = \emptyset$ means A and B have no element in common. The symbol $\emptyset$ is sometimes thought of as referring to an "empty set." Similarly $A_1 \cap A_2 \cap \cdots \cap A_n = \emptyset$ means that there is no element common to all the A_i.

EXAMPLE. See Fig. B-5.

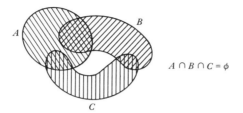

$A \cap B \cap C = \phi$

FIGURE B-5

Definition. If $A \subset S$, then the *complement of A in S* is the set of all elements of S that are *not* in A. Notation: $S - A$. If the set S is fixed in some discussion and there is no ambiguity, then write A' for $S - A$.

EXAMPLE. $S = \{1, 2, 3\}, A = \{1, 3\}, S - A = \{2\}$.

EXAMPLE. See Fig. B-6.

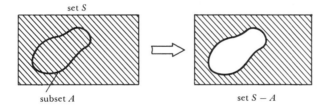

set S

subset A

set $S - A$

FIGURE B-6

As in algebra, parentheses show the order in which set operations are to be taken: for example, $A \cap (B \cup C)$ means *first* form $B \cup C$, then intersect with A.

EXAMPLE. $A = \{1, 2, 3\}$, $B = \{1, 4\}$, $C = \{2, 4\}$; $B \cup C = \{1, 2, 4\}$, and $A \cap (B \cup C) = \{1, 2\}$.

Identities which hold for any sets $A, B, C, \ldots$:

  (i) If $A \subset B$ and $B \subset C$, then $A \subset C$.
 (ii) $(A \cup B) \cup C = A \cup (B \cup C)$.
(iii) $(A \cap B) \cap C = A \cap (B \cap C)$.
 (iv) $A \cap (B \cup C) = (A \cap B) \cup (A \cap C)$.

EXAMPLE. See Fig. B-7.

FIGURE B-7

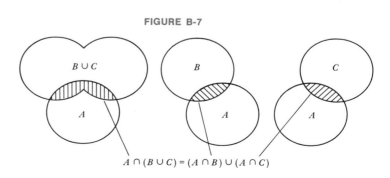

$A \cap (B \cup C) = (A \cap B) \cup (A \cap C)$

(v) If $A \subset B$ then $B' \subset A'$.

EXAMPLE. See Fig. B-8.

FIGURE B-8

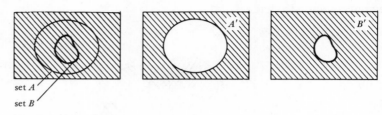

set A
set B

(vi) $(A \cup B)' = (A') \cap (B')$.

EXAMPLE. See Fig. B-9.

FIGURE B-9

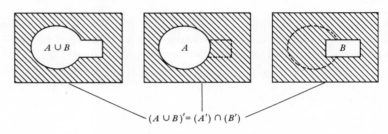

$(A \cup B)' = (A') \cap (B')$

(vii) $(A \cap B)' = (A') \cup (B')$.

EXAMPLE. See Fig. B-10.

FIGURE B-10

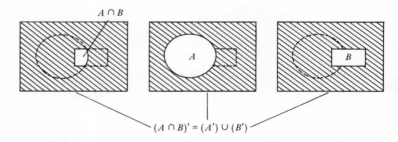

$(A \cap B)' = (A') \cup (B')$

B.2 CONNECTIONS BETWEEN SUBSETS AND STATEMENTS

Often it is convenient to list the set of outcomes of an experiment. For example the set $\Omega = \{1, 2, 3, 4, 5, 6\}$ describes all possible outcomes for the number which will appear on the top face of a die when it it is tossed. *Subsets* of Ω then correspond to *statements* we can make about the result of the experiment. For example, the subset

$A = \{2, 4, 6\}$ corresponds to the statement, "the number is even."

The complement

$A' = \{1, 3, 5\}$ corresponds to the statement, "the number is *not* even."

The subset

$B = \{4, 5, 6\}$ corresponds to the statement, "the number is at least 4."

The union

$A \cup B = \{2, 4, 5, 6\}$ corresponds to the statement, "the number is even *or* at least 4, *or both*."

The subset

$A \cap B = \{4, 6\}$ corresponds to the statement, "the number is even *and* at least 4."

In all cases the following correspondence holds between logical operations and language connectives:

complement $(')$ $\leftrightarrow$ *not* . . .

union $(\cup)$ $\leftrightarrow$ . . . *or* . . . *(or both)*

and

intersection $(\cap)$ $\leftrightarrow$ . . . *and* . . . .

answers to selected problems

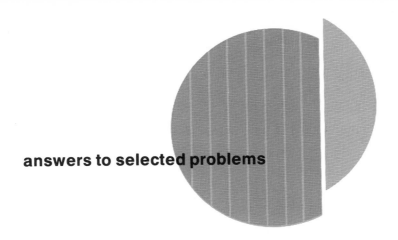

answers to selected problems

CHAPTER 2

Section 2.2

1. d, e, g, functions; c, f not functions.

3. (b) $g(0) = -1$; (c) $g(-1) = -\frac{1}{2}$; (d) $g(10) = \frac{1}{9}$; (f) $\dfrac{a+b-2}{(a-1)(b-1)}$; (g) $-\dfrac{1}{a}$; (h) $\dfrac{1}{a}$; (i) $\dfrac{a}{1-a}$.

5. (b) A function with
    domain $x \geqslant 0$,
    range $0 \leqslant f(x) \leqslant 2$ and $f(x) < -2$,
    and rule
    $$f(x) = \begin{cases} x \text{ for } 0 \leqslant x \leqslant 2 \\ -x \text{ for } x > 2 \end{cases}$$

   (c) Not a function since $f(2)$ is not unique. (d) Not a function since each input has two outputs.
   (e) A function with   (f) A function with
       domain all reals,   domain $-3 \leqslant x \leqslant 3$
       range $f(x) \geqslant 0$,   range $-27 \leqslant x \leqslant 27$ and
       rule $f(x) = |x|$.   rule $f(x) = x^3$.

7. $A(x) = 100x - 2x^2$, $0 \leqslant x \leqslant 50$.

9. $V(r) = 50r$.

11. $40{,}000$; $2^{10} \cdot 10{,}000$; $2^n \cdot 10{,}000$.

13. b, e, have both properties; c, f, g have property (ii); d has property (i); h has neither property.

15. (b) $y = 1$; (c) $-3 \leqslant y \leqslant -1$; (d) $2, 1, 0$; (e) Rationals of the form $y = (1/n)$, where n is a positive
        integer; $0 < y \leqslant 1$; (f) $2, 3, 3\frac{1}{3}, 3\frac{1}{2}, 4$; (g) All positive numbers. (h) All positive numbers.
    (i) $y = 0$; (j) $0 < y \leqslant 1$.

17. (b) 1(e), 1(g); (d) No, $f(\frac{3}{2}) = f(\frac{1}{2}) = 2\frac{1}{4}$. (e) Yes, 5(b), 5(f).

19. (b) All irrational x and all rational x such that $|x| \geqslant 1$; (c) $f(g(x)) - g(x) = 0$ for all x;
    (d) $-1 \leqslant x \leqslant 1$; (e) $0, 1, -1$.

Section 2.4

1. (b) max 1 and min 1 for all real x; (c) max 4 at $x = 2$, min 0 at $x = 0$; (d) max 0 and min 0 for all real
       x; (e) No max, no min; (f) No max, no min; (g) max 1 at $x = -1$ and at $1 \leqslant x \leqslant 2$, no min;
    (i) max 16 at $x = -4$, min 0 at $x = 0$; (j) No max; min 0 at $x = 0$; (k) max 1 for $x > 0$, min -1 for
       $x < 0$; (m) max 1 at $x = 0$, no min; (n) max 1 at $x = 2$, min 0 at $x = 1$; (o) No max, min 0 at $x = 1$.

5. Square, $\frac{1}{2}$ ft by $\frac{1}{2}$ ft.

7. (a) $xr = -2000r^2 + 1000r$; (b) $r = \frac{1}{4}$.

9. $r = 10$ ft, $h = \dfrac{16}{\pi}$ ft.

CHAPTER 3

Section 3.4

1. (ii) $B = \{HH, TH\}$, (iii) (b) $A \cap B = \{H,H\}$; (d) $\{HT, TT\}$; (f) $\{HT, TH, TT\}$; (g) $\{HT, TH\}$.

3. $P(A) = \frac{1}{2}, P(B) = \frac{2}{3}; P(A \cap B) = \frac{1}{3}, P(A \cup B) = \frac{5}{6}$.

5. $\Omega = \{HHH, HHT, HTH, THH, TTH, THT, HTT, TTT\}$; P (of each event) $= \frac{1}{8}$.

7. (c) $P(A_0) = \frac{1}{8}, P(A_1) = P(A_2) = \frac{3}{8}, P(A_3) = \frac{1}{8}$; (d) \$1.50.

9. P (two aces in version I) $= \frac{1}{5}$; P (two aces in version II) $= \frac{1}{3}$.

11. $P(E) = \frac{1}{8}$; P (all correct) $= \frac{1}{4}$.

13. P (odd) $= \frac{9}{21}$, P (even) $= \frac{12}{21}$.

15. $\frac{1}{2}$ short.

17. (a) P (bb) $= \frac{1}{2}$, (b) P (blue eyes) $= 1$, (c) P (blue eyes) $= 0$, (d) P (blue eyes) $= \frac{1}{4}$.

Section 3.6

1. (ii) $\frac{1}{2}$, (iii) $\frac{1}{2}$, (iv) Yes.

3. (i) $P(A) = \frac{1}{2}, P(A') = \frac{1}{2}, P(C) = \frac{1}{2}, P(A' \cap C) = \frac{1}{4}, P(A \cap C) = \frac{1}{4}$; independent
   (ii) $P(A \cup B) = \frac{3}{4}, P((A \cup B) \cap C) = \frac{3}{8}$; independent
   (iii) $P(A \cap B \cap C) = \frac{1}{8}$.

5. S' and T independent.

7. (a) $\frac{1}{32}$, (b) $\frac{3}{16}$.

9. $\frac{3}{98}$.

11. (a) 0.144, (b) 0.856, (c) 0.388.

13. $x < \frac{1}{3}$.

15. P (both brown eyed) $= \frac{1}{4}$, P (both blue eyed) $= \frac{1}{4}$, P (one blue, one brown) $= \frac{1}{2}$.

CHAPTER 4

Section 4.3

1. (b) $|x| = 2$

(c) $[-1, 3]$

(d) $\langle 2, 4 \rangle$

(e) all $x, x \neq 0$

(f) $[2, 4]$, (g) $x > 3$ or $x < -1$, (h) $[-4, 2]$, (i) $x = 3$, (j) $|x| = 2$.

3. (b) $|x| < 2$, (c) $|x+4| < 1$, (d) $|x+1| \leqslant 2$, (e) $|x| > 2$, (f) $|x-2| > 2$, (g) $|x+\frac{1}{2}| \leqslant \frac{1}{2}$,
   (h) $\left|x - \dfrac{d+c}{2}\right| \leqslant \dfrac{d-c}{2}$.

9. $Q = \left(\dfrac{x_1+x_2}{2}, \dfrac{y_1+y_2}{2}\right)$.

11. (a) On (b) Outside (c) Inside.

13. (b) $(-2,1), 4$; (c) $(0,1), 3$.

Section 4.6

3. (c) $y = 3x - 2$, (d) $y = -\frac{2}{3}x + \frac{7}{3}$, (e) $x = -5$, (f) $y = 6$, (g) $y = 2x - 1$, (h) $y = -4x - 7$,
   (i) $y = 2x$, (j) $y = -\frac{1}{2}x$.

7. $4y = 3x - 19$.

9. $x^2 + 4 = 4y$.

11. (a) $y = \left(\dfrac{c}{a+b}\right)x$, (b) $y = \left(\dfrac{c}{b-a}\right)(x-a)$, (c) $y = \dfrac{c}{2}$; $x = \dfrac{a+b}{2}$.

Section 4.8

7. (d) Nonwhite adult: males steepest decline. Nonwhite teenagers: least decline.

11. (a) $f(1)$ not unique, (b) If $-1 \leqslant x \leqslant 1, f(x)$ not unique, (c) $f(x_0)$ not unique.

13. (a) y-axis (b) Origin (c) Neither
    (d) (b) Even (c) Neither (d) Odd (e) Even
    (f) $-x$ not in domain   (g) Odd.

15. f symmetric about $x = \dfrac{-b}{2a}$; g symmetric about $x = \dfrac{b}{2a}$.

Section 4.10

1. $\frac{13}{4}$ 3. $\frac{1}{3}$.   7. $\frac{56}{81}$

9. $\dfrac{n^2}{100}; \dfrac{11}{100}$.

11. $\frac{19}{75}$.

CHAPTER 5

Section 5.5

3. (b) $h+f$, (c) $f-2g$, (d) $h+g$, (e) $-h-4f$, (f) $-h+g$.

7. (a) c times slope of f; (b) Sum of slopes; (c) Product of slopes.

9. (a) $f(x)g(x) = \frac{1}{2}(2x+1), 0 \leqslant x \leqslant 1; -g(x) = -(2x+1), 0 \leqslant x \leqslant 1; (g+f)(x) = 2x + \frac{3}{2}, 0 \leqslant x \leqslant 1$;
   $g(x)h(x) = -\frac{2}{3}x^2 + \frac{5}{3}x + 1, 0 \leqslant x \leqslant 1$. (b) $f(g(x)) = \frac{1}{2}, 0 \leqslant x \leqslant 1; g(f(x)) = 2, 0 \leqslant x \leqslant 3$.
   (c) $g(h(x)) = -\frac{2}{3}x + 3, 0 \leqslant x \leqslant 3; h(g(x)) = -\frac{2}{3}x + \frac{2}{3}, 0 \leqslant x \leqslant 1$.

11. (b) $x^4 - 2x^3 + 2x^2 - x + 1$, (c) $\dfrac{3}{4}, \dfrac{13}{16}, \dfrac{217}{256}, \dfrac{57073}{65536}$, (e) 1, (f) $\dfrac{3}{2}, \dfrac{7}{4}, \dfrac{37}{16}, \dfrac{1033}{256}, \dfrac{868,177}{65,536}$.

13. (b) max and min reversed. (c) Same zeros.

15. (a) Even, even, even. (b) Odd, even, odd. (c) Neither, odd, even. (d) Neither, odd, even.

Section 5.7

3. $g(y) = \dfrac{y-b}{m}$, $m \neq 0$; exists for $m \neq 0$; yes; $\dfrac{1}{m}, \dfrac{-b}{m}$.

5. $r = \sqrt{A/\pi}$, $A > 0$; $r = \sqrt{10/\pi}$.

7. Yes, $f(x) = \begin{cases} -x, & -1 < x < 0 \\ x, & 2 < x < 3 \end{cases}$.

CHAPTER 6

Section 6.9

1. (b) $\frac{33}{2}$, (c) 165, (d) 120, (e) 5, (f) 1, (g) 10.

3. (a) $-1760a^3b^9$, (b) $\dbinom{50}{20} x^{30}y^{20}$, (c) $-1716x^6y^7$.

5. (a) $(1+1)^n = \dbinom{n}{0} + \dbinom{n}{1} + \cdots + \dbinom{n}{n-1} + \dbinom{n}{n}$, (b) 2^n.

11. (b) 60; (c) 12; (d) 48; (e) 73.

13. (a) 1225; (b) 600; (c) 625.

15. (a) 9!; (b) 2880.

17. (a) 6840; (b) $\frac{1}{20}$; (c) $\frac{3}{20}$.

19. (a) $\frac{1}{55}$; (b) $\frac{2}{11}$; (c) No.

21. Yes.

CHAPTER 7

Section 7.4

1. (b) 0; (c) 2; (d) $1 - \dfrac{1}{x^2}$; (e) $3x^2$; (f) $3x^2 - 3$; (g) $-2x + 1$.

3. $x_0 = \dfrac{-b}{2a}$.

7. (a) $T(x) = -170x^2 + 710{,}000x + 682{,}500{,}000$, (b) \$2088.

Section 7.7

1. (a) $v(t) = -32t + 8$, $a(t) = -32$, (b) 1001 at $t = \frac{1}{4}$.

3. $t = 62.5$ at 15,625.

5. $\frac{7}{3}$.

CHAPTER 8

Section 8.3

1. (c) Obtain the sequence $\left\{\dfrac{100}{n}\right\}$ by multiplying each term of the null sequence $\left\{\dfrac{1}{n}\right\}$ by 100.

(d) The sequence $\left\{\dfrac{1}{2n-1}\right\}$ is a subsequence of $\left\{\dfrac{1}{n}\right\}$. (e) Multiply each term of the null sequence $\left\{\dfrac{1}{n}\right\}$ by $\dfrac{5}{2}$ to obtain the sequence $\left\{\dfrac{5}{2n}\right\}$. (f) Observe that $|a_n| = \dfrac{1}{n}$. Hence $\{|a_n|\}$ is a null sequence, so $\{a_n\}$ is null also. (g) Observe that $a_n = \left(\dfrac{1}{n}\right)^{1/2}$. Since $\left\{\dfrac{1}{n}\right\}$ is null, so is $\{a_n\}$. (h) This sequence differs from the null sequence $\left\{\frac{1}{n}\right\}$ in only finitely many places. (i) Interlace the null sequences $\left\{\frac{1}{2n}\right\}$ and $\{0\}$ to obtain $\{a_n\}$. (j) The sequence $\left\{\left(\frac{1}{n^2}\right)\left(\frac{1}{n+2}\right)\right\}$ is the term-by-term product of the null sequences $\left\{\frac{1}{n^2}\right\}$ and $\left\{\frac{1}{n+2}\right\}$. (k) Observe that $\left|\frac{n^2}{n^3+1}\right| < \frac{n^2}{n^3} = \frac{1}{n}$, so $\left\{\frac{n^2}{n^3+1}\right\}$ is a null sequence. (l) Observe that $|a_n| = \frac{\sqrt{n}}{n+1} < \frac{\sqrt{n}}{n} = \left(\frac{1}{n}\right)^{1/2}$. Since $\left\{\left(\frac{1}{n}\right)^{1/2}\right\}$ is null, so is $\{|a_n|\}$, and hence, so is $\{a_n\}$. (m) This is the term-by-term sum of the null sequences $\left\{\frac{1}{n}\right\}$ and $\left\{\frac{1}{n+1}\right\}$.

(n) This is the term-by-term sum of $\left\{\frac{2}{n}\right\}$ and $\left\{\frac{3}{5n}\right\}$. (o) This sequence is the term-by-term product of the null sequences $\left\{\frac{1}{n}\right\}$ and $\left\{\frac{1}{n+1}\right\}$. Alternatively, it is the term-by-term sum of $\left\{\frac{1}{n}\right\}$ and $\left\{-\frac{1}{n+1}\right\}$.

(p) $\{a_n\}$ is the term-by-term sum of $\left\{\frac{1}{4}\right\}$ and $\left\{-\frac{1}{n^2}\right\}$. (q) $\{a_n\}$ is the term-by-term sum of $\left\{\frac{1}{n^3}\right\}$ and $\left\{-\frac{2}{n}\right\}$. (r) Observe that the sequence $\left\{2-\frac{1}{n}\right\}$ is bounded by 2. Thus a_n is the product of a null sequence and a bounded sequence. (s) Note that $\left\{(-1)^n\left(\frac{n}{n+1}\right)\right\}$ is a bounded sequence. Thus, $\{a_n\}$ is the product of a bounded sequence and a null sequence. (t) Obtain $\{a_n\}$ by raising each term of the null sequence $\left\{\frac{1}{n}\right\}$ to the fixed power $\frac{3}{2}$. (u) Observe that $|a_n| = \frac{1}{n^3+1}$. Since $\{|a_n|\}$ is a null sequence, so is $\{a_n\}$. (v) Property (k).

3. (c) $|a_n| = 1$. Thus, $\{|a_n|\}$ is not a null sequence, so neither is $\{a_n\}$. (d) The sequence is not bounded.
(e) The subsequence $1, 9, 25, \ldots$ is not bounded, hence not null.
(f) $|a_n| = n$. $\{|a_n|\}$ is therefore not null, so neither is $\{a_n\}$. (g) The subsequence $\{\frac{1}{2}, \frac{1}{2}, \ldots\}$ is not null.
(h) The subsequence $\left\{1-\frac{2}{n}\right\}$ is not null. See discussion.

CHAPTER 8

Section 8.6

1. (c) $N(\frac{1}{10}) = 1001; N(\frac{1}{100}) = 10{,}001$, (d) $N(\frac{1}{10}) = 6; N(\frac{1}{100}) = 52$, (e) $N(\frac{1}{10}) = 26; N(\frac{1}{100}) = 251$,

(f) $N(\frac{1}{10}) = 11; N(\frac{1}{100}) = 101$, (g) $N(\frac{1}{10}) = 101; N(\frac{1}{100}) = 10001$, (h) $N(\frac{1}{10}) = 11; N(\frac{1}{100}) = 101$,

(i) $N(\frac{1}{10}) = 4; N(\frac{1}{100}) = 7$, (k) $N(\frac{1}{10}) = 11; N(\frac{1}{100}) = 101$, (l) $N(\frac{1}{10}) = 101; N(\frac{1}{100}) = 10001$,

(m) $N(\frac{1}{10}) = 21; N(\frac{1}{100}) = 201$, (n) $N(\frac{1}{10}) = 41; N(\frac{1}{100}) = 401$, (o) $N(\frac{1}{10}) = 4; N(\frac{1}{100}) = 11$,

(p) $N(\frac{1}{10}) = 21; N(\frac{1}{100}) = 201$, (q) $N(\frac{1}{10}) = 41; N(\frac{1}{100}) = 401$, (r) $N(\frac{1}{10}) = 21; N(\frac{1}{100}) = 201$,

(s) $N(\frac{1}{10}) = 5; N(\frac{1}{100}) = 15$, (t) $N(\frac{1}{10}) = 5; N(\frac{1}{100}) = 25$, (u) $N(\frac{1}{10}) = 4; N(\frac{1}{100}) = 11$

(v) $N(\frac{1}{10}) = 11; N(\frac{1}{100}) = 101$.

Section 8.9

1. (c) $\epsilon_0 = \frac{1}{2}, n_k = 2k$, (d) $\epsilon_0 = \frac{1}{2}, n_k = k$, (e) $\epsilon_0 = \frac{1}{2}, n_k = 2k-1$, (f) $\epsilon_0 = \frac{1}{2}, n_k = k$, (g) $\epsilon_0 = \frac{1}{4}, n_k = 2k-1$,
(h) $\epsilon_0 = \frac{1}{2}, n_k = 2(k+1)$.

CHAPTER 9

Section 9.3

1. (b) $\dfrac{n-1}{n+1} - 1 = \dfrac{-2}{n+1}$ is null. (c) $\dfrac{3n}{n} - 3 = 0$ is null. (d) $\dfrac{3n+1}{n} - 3 = \dfrac{1}{n}$ is null. (e) $\dfrac{2n^2+1}{n^3} = \dfrac{2}{n} + \dfrac{1}{n^3}$

is null. (f) $a_n = \dfrac{1}{1\cdot 2} + \dfrac{1}{2\cdot 3} + \cdots + \dfrac{1}{n(n+1)} = (1-\tfrac{1}{2}) + (\tfrac{1}{2}-\tfrac{1}{3}) + \cdots + \left(\dfrac{1}{n} - \dfrac{1}{n+1}\right) = 1 - \dfrac{1}{n+1}$.

Thus $a_n - 1 = \dfrac{1}{n+1}$ is a null sequence. (g) *Hint:* $\dfrac{2}{n(n+2)} = \dfrac{1}{n} - \dfrac{1}{(n+1)}$.

(h) $\left(\dfrac{n+1}{n}\right)\left(2 - \dfrac{1}{n}\right) - 2 = \dfrac{1}{n} + \dfrac{1}{n^2}$ is null. (i) $\left(\dfrac{3n}{n+2}\right)\left(\dfrac{5n+4}{n+1}\right) - 15 = \left(\dfrac{33n+30}{n+2}\right)\left(\dfrac{1}{n+1}\right)$ is null.

(j) *Hint:* $1 + 2 + \cdots + n = \dfrac{n(n+1)}{2}$.

3. (b) Unbounded; no limit, (c) $\lim\limits_{n\to\infty} a_n = 1$, (d) $\lim\limits_{n\to\infty} a_n = 1$, (e) Unbounded; no limit, (f) No limit:
see Example 3, Sec. 9.2, (g) $\lim\limits_{n\to\infty} a_n = \tfrac{1}{3}$.

5. The perimeter lengths should appear to converge.

7. No. Each term of the sequence $a_n = 2$, so $\lim\limits_{n\to\infty} a_n = 2$. But only $\sqrt{2}$ running feet of carpet are needed to cover the ramp.

Section 9.6

1. (c) $\dfrac{n-1}{n+1} = \dfrac{n}{n+1} - \dfrac{1}{n+1} = \dfrac{1}{1 + \dfrac{1}{n}} - \dfrac{1}{n+1}$. Use Properties I and L.

(d) $\dfrac{2n^2+1}{n^3} = \dfrac{2}{n} + \dfrac{1}{n^3}$. Use property I.

(e) $\dfrac{1}{1\cdot 2} + \dfrac{1}{2\cdot 3} + \cdots + \dfrac{1}{n(n+1)} = 1 - \dfrac{1}{n+1}$. Use properties G and I.

(f) $\dfrac{2n+5}{n+2} = \dfrac{2n}{n+2} + \dfrac{5}{n+2} = 2\left(\dfrac{1}{1 + \dfrac{2}{n}}\right) + \dfrac{5}{n+2}$. Use properties H, I, and L.

(g) Show that $\lim\limits_{n\to\infty}\left(3 + \dfrac{1}{n}\right) = 3$ by using properties G and I. Then use Problem (f) above and property J.

(h) Use property I to show $\lim\limits_{n\to\infty}\left(7 - \dfrac{1}{n^2}\right) = 7$.

Use properties G and I to show $\lim\limits_{n\to\infty}\left(-3 + \dfrac{1}{n}\right) = -3$. Then use property L.

(i) $\lim\limits_{n\to\infty}\left(\dfrac{1}{n} + \dfrac{1}{n^2}\right) = 0$ by property I. $\lim\limits_{n\to\infty}\left(2 - \dfrac{1}{n^2}\right) = 2$ by properties I and G. Use property L.

(j) $\dfrac{3n}{n+2} = \left(\dfrac{3n}{n}\right)\left(\dfrac{1}{1 + \dfrac{2}{n}}\right) = 3\left(\dfrac{1}{1 + \dfrac{2}{n}}\right)$, so $\lim\limits_{n\to\infty}\dfrac{3n}{n+2} = 3$. Then use property M.

(k) $\lim\limits_{n\to\infty}\left(1 + \dfrac{1}{n}\right) = 1$. Use property M.

3. (a) Use property I (J for the part on multiplication) twice. (b) $a_n^2 = (a_n)(a_n)$. Use property J. (*Note:* This also follows directly from property M.) (c) Use (b) above, and induction. (*Note:* This also follows immediately from property M.) (d) Use property O twice. (e) Use property B.

5. *Hint:*

$$\frac{\sqrt[3]{r_n} - \sqrt[3]{q_n}}{r_n - q_n} = \frac{1}{r_n^{2/3} + r_n^{1/3}q_n^{1/3} + q_n^{2/3}}$$

Proceed as in Problem 4.

7. (a)–(d): $\lim\limits_{n\to\infty} \dfrac{f(r_n) - f(q_n)}{r_n - q_n} = 7$ in all cases. (e) The "slope" of f at $x_0 = 2$ exists, and is equal to the sum of the "slopes" at $x_0 = 2$ of the functions $3x^2, -5x, 4$.

9. (a)–(d): $(3x^2 - 5x + 4)'_{\text{at}-1} = -11$.

Section 9.8

3. If $\{c_n\}$ is formed by interlacing $\{a_n\}$ and $\{b_n\}$, then $\{c_n - A\}$ is just $\{a_n - A\}$ and $\{b_n - A\}$ interlaced.

5. *Hint:* Suppose $B < A$. Choose $\epsilon = \dfrac{A-B}{2}$ and use the definition of convergence to zero on the sequence $\{a_n - A\}$ to show that $\{b_n - B\}$ cannot converge to zero.

7. *Hint:* Use the fact that $\{a_n - A\}$ is not null, and Problem 2 of Sec. 8.9.

9. *Hints:*

(a) $|a_n^{1/q} - A^{1/q}| = \dfrac{|a_n - A|}{a_n^{1/q} + a_n^{(q-2)/q}A^{1/q} + \cdots + A^{(q-2)/q}}$ (b) $a_n^{1/q} + a_n^{(q-2)/q}A^{1/q} + \cdots + A^{(q-1)/q} > A^{(q-1)/q}$

(c) Proceed as in Problem 8.

Section 9.11

1. A sequence $\{a_n\}$ is called "divergent negatively" if, given any real number b, there is some integer $N(b)$ such that $a_n < b$ for all $n \geq N(b)$.

3. (a) Does not converge. (b) Converges. (c) Does not converge. (d) Converges. (e) Converges. (f) Converges. (g) Converges. (h) Converges. (i) Converges. (j) Converges. (k) Does not converge.

5. $\{a_n b_n\}$ may be bounded: Let

$$a_n = \begin{cases} 0 & \text{if } n \text{ is even} \\ n & \text{if } n \text{ is odd} \end{cases}$$

and

$$b_n = \begin{cases} n & \text{if } n \text{ is even} \\ \dfrac{1}{n^2} & \text{if } n \text{ is odd.} \end{cases}$$

Then

$$a_n b_n = \begin{cases} 0 & \text{if } n \text{ is even} \\ \dfrac{1}{n} & \text{if } n \text{ is odd} \end{cases}$$

is bounded. And, in fact,

$$\lim_{n\to\infty} (a_n b_n) = 0.$$

CHAPTER 10

Section 10.5

1. (a) No least upper bound; greatest lower bound $= 1$; no common bound.

(c) (i)

(ii)

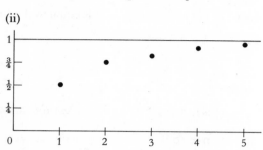

(iii) Least upper bound $= 1$. (iv) Greatest lower bound $= \frac{1}{2}$. (v) Common bound $= 1$. (d) Least upper bound $= \frac{5}{8}$; greatest lower bound $= 0$; common bound $= \frac{5}{8}$. (e) Least upper bound $= -1$; no greatest lower bound; no common bound. (f) No least upper bound; no greatest lower bound; no common bound. (g) Least upper bound $= 2$; greatest lower bound $= -2$; common bound $= 2$.

(h) Least upper bound $= \frac{2}{3}$; greatest lower bound $= -\frac{1}{2}$; common bound $= \frac{1}{2}$. (i) Least upper bound $= 5$; greatest lower bound $= 3$; common bound $= 5$. (j) Least upper bound $= 1$; greatest lower bound $= -\frac{1}{4}$; common bound $= 1$. (k) Least upper bound $= 100$; greatest lower bound $= 1$; common bound $= 100$. (l) Least upper bound $= 2$; greatest lower bound $= \frac{2}{3}$; common bound $= 2$.

(m) Least upper bound $= 0$; no greatest lower bound; no common bound.

5. Suppose d and d' are two least upper bounds for a given sequence. Then $d < d'$, since d is a least upper bound, and $d' < d$ for similar reasons. But $d < d'$ and $d' < d$ is absurd.
A similar argument holds for greatest lower bound.

7. A number d is an upper bound of a set S if for each $x \in S, x \leqslant d$. d is the least upper bound of S if given any other upper bound, d', then $d \leqslant d'$.
Similar definitions hold for lower bound and greatest lower bound.

$\{x \text{ with } 0 < x \leqslant 1\}$ has least upper bound $= 1$, and greatest lower bound $= 0$.

$\{\text{all } x < 0\}$ has least upper bound $= 0$, and no greatest lower bound.

9. *Hint:* Use the same method as in the proof of Theorem B of Sec. 10.3 to show that A must be a lower bound, and then that A must be the greatest lower bound.

11. Follow suggestions given in problem.

13. Follow suggestions given in problem.

Section 10.7

1. (b) $S = 1/9$; (c) $S = 3/11$; (d) $S = 8/33$; (e) $S = 15/111$; (f) $S = 1234/9999$; (g) $S = 31746/111,111$.

3. (a) Yes; (b) yes.

5. The sum of the series is defined to be the limit of the sequence of partial sums. A sequence can have only one limit.

7. *Hint:* Let $S_n = s_1 + s_2 + \cdots + s_n$ and $T_n = t_1 + t_2 + \cdots + t_n$. Show that for each n, $S_n \leqslant T_n$, and use the definition of limit of sequence.

9. *Hint:* A typical even term of the sequence of partial sums is

$$S_{2n} = (|s_1| - |s_2|) + (|s_3| - |s_4|) + \cdots + (|s_{2n-1}| - |s_{2n}|).$$

Show that each term in parentheses is ≥ 0. A typical odd term in the sequence of partial sums is

$$S_{2n+1} = |s_1| - (|s_2| - |s_3|) - (|s_4| - |s_5|) - \cdots - (|s_{2n}| - |s_{2n+1}|).$$

Again, each term in parentheses is ≥ 0.

11. (a) Yes. Compare this problem with problem 10(c). (b) $[\frac{1}{4}, \frac{1}{2}] \cup [\frac{3}{4}, 1]$ has length $L = \frac{1}{2}$. The probability of getting a head on the second toss is $\frac{1}{2}$. (c) $[\frac{1}{2}, \frac{3}{4}]$ has length $\frac{1}{4}$. The probability of a head on the first toss and a tail on the second is $\frac{1}{4}$.

General conclusion: The probability of any particular set of outcomes for the experiment is precisely the length of that subset of $[0,1]$ which corresponds to that set of outcomes.

CHAPTER 11

Section 11.3

1. (a) 0, (b) 3, (c) 3, (d) 3, (e) Does not exist. (f) 0, (g) 3, (h) -3, (i) 0, (j) 1, does not exist. (k) 8, 0, (l) $2, \frac{1}{2}, 1$, (m) Does not exist. (n) 1.

3. Yes. No.

5. (a) No. (b) Yes, g continuous at 0.

7. f continuous at 0.

9. (a) $\frac{1}{6}, \frac{1}{30}$, (b) $\frac{1}{4}, \frac{1}{20}; \frac{1}{6}, \frac{1}{30}$, (c) Impossible, $A = 1$.

Section 11.6

3. (a) $f(x) = x$, (b) $f(x) = \begin{cases} -1, x < 0 \\ 1, x \geq 0 \end{cases}$ (c) $f(x) = [x]$, (d) $f(x) = \begin{cases} x, x \neq 1,2 \\ 0, x = 1 \\ 3, x = 2 \end{cases}$.

(e) $f(x) = \begin{cases} 0, x \neq 1, 2, 3, \ldots \\ -1, x = 1, 2, 3, \ldots \end{cases}$. (f) $f(x) = x^2 + 2$, (g) $y = |x|$, (h) $f(x) = 1, x \leq 1$. (For $x \geq 1$, see Sec. 11.3, Problem 5.)

Section 11.9

1. (a) 0, (b) No, (c) $-\frac{1}{2}$, (d) 2, (e) No, (f) No, (g) No, (h) 0, (i) No, (j) $\frac{1}{6}$, (k) 1.

CHAPTER 12

Section 12.4

1.

	glb	lub
(a)	1	None
(b)	2	None
(c)	0	1
(d)	0	1
(e)	-2	2
(f)	$-\frac{1}{2}$	$\frac{1}{5}$
(g)	0	1
(h)	0	1
(i)	$-\sqrt{2}$	$\sqrt{2}$

3.

	lub	in S
(a)	1	No
(b)	2	Yes
(c)	1	Yes
(d)	1	Yes

5.

		lub	glb
(a)		1	-1
(b)		1	-1
(c)		1	0
(d)		1	0
(e)		1	0
(f)		2	0
(g)	i)	None	-1
	ii)	None	0
	iii)	-1	$-\frac{1}{2}$
(h)	i)	1	$-\frac{1}{2}$
	ii)	1	0
(i)		1	0
(j)		1	0

Section 12.8

1.

		max	min
(a)	i)	1	-1
	ii)	None	-1
	iii)	None	None
(b)	i)	1	0
	ii)	1	0
(c)	i)	1	0
	ii)	1	None
	iii)	1	0
(d)		2	0
(e)	i)	None	-1
	ii)	None	None
	iii)	None	None
(f)		None	-1
(g)	i)	1	$\frac{1}{2}$
	ii)	1	None
(h)	i)	1	0
	ii)	None	0
	iii)	None	0
(i)		2	0
(j)		1	-1
(k)		$\frac{5}{2}$	0.

3. Domain not closed interval for (a) ii, iii), (c) ii), (e) all), (f), (g) ii), (h) ii, iii).

5. (b) 0; (g) 0; (i) 0; (j) 1.

7. (b) $2x-2$; min 1; max 4 (c) $-2x+4$; min 2; max 0,4 (d) $3x^2+2$; min -1; max 2 (e) $4x^3+6x^2$;

   min $-\frac{3}{2}$; max 3 (f) $4x^3-6x^2+8x$; min 0; max -4 (g) $1-\dfrac{1}{x^2}$; min 1; max 2.

9. $p'(x) = 2 - \dfrac{2A}{x^2}, x_0 = \sqrt{A}.$

11. $-1 + \sqrt{2}$ mi from S_1.

Section 12.10

1. (a) $\frac{1}{10}, \frac{1}{100}$, (b) Impossible. (c) $\frac{1}{20}, \frac{1}{200}$, (d) $\frac{1}{200}, \frac{1}{2000}$, (e) Impossible. (f) $\frac{1}{20}, \frac{1}{200}$, (g) $\frac{1}{40}, \frac{1}{400}$,
   (h) Impossible. (i) Impossible.

CHAPTER 13

Section 13.5

5. $200\, e^{16}$.

7. (a) $M_{\text{loss}}(t) = KM(t_0)(t-t_0)$, (b) $M'(t) = KM(t), K$ constant.

Section 13.7

1. (a) $3 = \log_2 8$, (b) $2 = \log_3 9$, (c) $-4 = \log_{10}(0.0001)$, (d) $y = \log_x z$, (e) $3^3 = 27$, (f) $4^{-2} = \frac{1}{16}$,
   (g) $e^0 = 1$, (h) $x^y = z$.

3. (a) x, (b) $\dfrac{1}{x^2}$, (c) $\dfrac{1}{x}$, (d) $\dfrac{1}{x}$, (e) x^2, (f) $x + x^2 + 1$, (g) $\log_e x - 3x^2$.

5. (d), (l), (m), (n), (p) neither strictly increasing nor strictly decreasing.

7. No.

11. (a), (c), (d), yes; (b), no.

13. $T = 3 \log_e 2, T = -3 \log_e 2$.

Section 13.9

1. (a) Yes, yes, $x = 0,1$. (b) Yes, yes, $x = 0,1$. (c) No, yes, $x = 2 - \sqrt{3}$. (d) Yes, no. (e) Yes, no.
   (f) Yes, no.

3. (a) $f'(x) = \frac{4}{3}x, f'(1) = \frac{4}{3}$; (b) $q = 1$.

CHAPTER 14

Section 14.3

1. (b) $x + 2, x \neq 1$; (c) $x + 1, x \neq 1$; (d) $1, x \neq 5$; (e) $1, x \neq x_0$; (f) $\frac{-1}{x^3}, x \neq 1$.

3. (a) 2.

7. 1800–1850.

9. (b).

11. (a) $3x^2$, (b) $2x + 1$, (c) $\frac{1}{x^2}; x \neq 0$, (d) $\frac{-2}{x^3}; x \neq 0$, (e) $\frac{1}{(x+1)^2}; x \neq -1$, (f) $\frac{1}{\sqrt{2x}}; x \neq 0$,

   (g) $1 - \frac{1}{x^2}; x \neq 0$.

Section 14.6

1. (a) $4x^3 - 15x^2 + 12x - 11$, (b) $35x^4 - 35x^6$, (c) $x^3 + x^2 + x + 1$, (d) $x^2(5x^2 - 3)$, (e) $x^2 - x - 6$,
   (f) $6x^2 - 19x - 7$, (g) $\frac{2}{x^3}; x \neq 0$, (h) $\frac{-4x}{(x^2-1)^2}$, (i) $\frac{ad - bc}{(cx+d)^2}$,

   (j) $2\left(x - \frac{1}{x^3}\right)$, (k) $\begin{cases} 6x - 9x^2, x < 1 \\ -3 \quad , x > 1 \end{cases}$ does not exist, $x = 1$; (l) $\begin{cases} 2x + \dfrac{1}{9}, x > 0 \\ \dfrac{1}{(x+3)^2}, -1 < x < 0 \end{cases}$ does not exist, $x = 0$;

   (m) $x^2(5x^2 - 3) + \frac{2}{x^3}, x \neq 0$, (n) $\frac{2}{x^3} + \frac{-4x}{(x^2-1)^2}, x \neq 0, \pm 1$.

Section 14.9

1. (a) $h(x) = -6x + 13; h'(x) = -6$, (b) $h(x) = (3x^2 + 1)^3; h'(x) = 18x(3x^2 + 1)^2$, (c) $h(x) = \frac{2x+1}{2(2x^2 + 2x + 1)}$;

   $h'(x) = \frac{-2x(2x+1)}{(2x^2 + 2x + 1)^2}$, (d) $h(x) = \left(\frac{3x-2}{2x-6}\right)^2; h'(x) = \frac{-7(3x-2)}{2(x-3)^2}$.

5. 60π.

7. 2.3 ft/sec.

9. (b) $t_{max} = 3.12$ sec; $h_{max} = 156.8$ ft, (c) $d'(t) = \frac{(100t - 16t^2)(100 - 32t)}{\sqrt{2500 + (100t - 16t^2)^2}}$.

Section 14.12

3. (a) None, (b) None, (c) min, $x = 0$, (d) min, $x = \pm 1$, (e) None, (f) max, $x = \frac{1}{e}$, (g) max, $x = e$,
   (h) None, (i) min, $x = 0$, (j) max, $x = 0$.

5. $2^{15/8}$.

7. (b) $\frac{1}{2}$, (c) -1, (d) $-\frac{5}{9}$, (e) 1, (f) 0.

9. (c) $\frac{3}{5}(x+2)^{-2/5}$.

CHAPTER 15

Section 15.6

1. (a) $-1+\sqrt{6}$, (b) 1, (c) $\dfrac{-1\pm\sqrt{7}}{3}$, (d) 1, (e) $\dfrac{2+\sqrt{\frac{90}{13}}}{3}$, (f) $\pm\sqrt{\frac{1}{2}}$, (g) $0, \frac{1}{2}, 1$, (h) 1,

    (i) $\log_e(e-1)$, (j) $e^{1-(\log 3/3)} < x_0 < e$.

3. f not continuous at 0.

9. (b) Convex $[-4, 4]$, (c) Convex $[0, 4]$; concave $[-4, 0]$, (d) Convex throughout, (e) $[-100, \frac{1}{2}]$ concave; $[\frac{1}{2}, 100]$ convex, (g) $[-100, 0]$ concave; $[0, 100]$ convex, (h) $[-100, 0], [2, 100]$ convex; $[0, 2]$ concave, (i) Convex throughout, (j) Convex throughout, (k) Convex throughout,

    (l) Concave throughout, (m) Concave throughout,

    (n) $\left[-100, \sqrt{\dfrac{5-\sqrt{17}}{2}}\right], \left[\sqrt{\dfrac{5+\sqrt{17}}{2}}, 100\right]$ convex; $\left[\sqrt{\dfrac{5-\sqrt{17}}{2}}, \sqrt{\dfrac{5+\sqrt{17}}{2}}\right]$ concave.

13. (b) max at $x=\frac{1}{3}$, concave. (c) min at $x=-1$, convex. (d) Discontinuous at $x=0$, decreasing for $x < 0$, increasing for $x > 0$, convex for $x^4 > \frac{3}{2}$, concave for $x^4 < \frac{3}{2}$. (e) Increasing for $x > -1$, decreasing for $x < -1$. (f) Decreasing for $-1-\sqrt{2} < x, < -1+\sqrt{2}$; discontinuous at $x=-1$.

    (g) Concave on $x < 0$, convex for $x > 0$. (h) Decreasing for $x > 4$, increasing for $x < 4$, discontinuous at $x=-2$. (i) Decreasing for all $x \neq 1$, convex for $x > 1$, concave for $x < 1$. (j) Decreasing and convex for $x < -2$, constant for $-2 \leq x < 1$, convex and increasing for $x > 1$. (k) Decreasing and convex for $x \leq 0$, increasing and convex for $0 < x \leq 1$, decreasing and convex for $1 < x \leq 2$, constant for $x \geq 2$, discontinuous at $x=-1, 1, 2$. (l) Increasing and concave for $x < 1$, decreasing and concave for $1 < x < 2$, decreasing and convex for $x > 2$. (m) Decreasing for $x < \frac{1}{5}\log\frac{3}{2}$, increasing for $x > \frac{1}{5}\log\frac{3}{2}$, convex everywhere. (n) Increasing for $x > 1$, decreasing for $x < 0$, and decreasing for $0 < x < 1$, convex everywhere. (o) Increasing for $x > 1$, decreasing for $0 < x < 1$, convex for $x < e$.

CHAPTER 15

Section 15.8

1. (a) 1.995; error $\leq \frac{1}{32}(0.02)^2 = 0.0128$, (b) 3.074; error $\leq \frac{2}{3^7}(0.2)^2 \approx 0.00004$, (c) 1.03; error $\leq \frac{4}{25}$

    $(0.15)^2 = 0.0036$, (d) 1.03; error $\leq \frac{12}{(0.99)^5}(0.0001) \approx 0.0012$, (e) 1.064; error $\leq \frac{3}{4.7}(0.9)^2 \approx 0.05$,

    (f) 1.9875; error $\leq \frac{3}{16(128)}(0.6)^2 \approx 0.0005$, (g) 0.1103; error ≤ 0.000008,

    (h) 2.0072; error $\leq \frac{0.45}{4608} \approx 0.00009$.

3. 6.033.

5. (a) $a=\dfrac{f''(x_0)}{2}$; $b=f'(x_0)-x_0 f''(x_0)$; $c=f(x_0)-x_0 f'(x_0)+\dfrac{x_0{}^2}{2}f''(x_0)$, (b) $2+\frac{1}{4}(0.12)-\frac{3}{32}(0.12)^2 = 2.0286$.

7. $r_1 = 2, r_2 = 2.016$.

Section 15.11

1. (b) $\dfrac{-1}{x^2}$, (c) $\dfrac{-1}{2x^2}+2\sqrt{x}$, (d) $\dfrac{x^3}{3}-\dfrac{1}{x}-x$, (e) $-\dfrac{1}{x}-x$, (f) $\dfrac{-2}{x^4}$, (g) $2\sqrt{x+4}$, (h) $\dfrac{x^3}{6}+\dfrac{2}{x}$, (i) $\dfrac{(x^2+1)^4}{4}$,

   (j) $\frac{2}{3}\sqrt{x^2+8}$, (k) $(x+3)(x^2+1)$, (l) $(x^3+1)^2$, (m) $\dfrac{-1}{x+2}$, (n) $\sqrt{x^2+1}$, (o) $\dfrac{3x^2+2}{x^2+1}$, (p) $\frac{8}{3}\sqrt{x^3+8}$,

   (q) $\dfrac{-(e^x+1)^2}{2}$, (r) $\frac{1}{4}(\log_e x)^8$, (s) $-\dfrac{1}{x-1}$, (t) $\frac{2}{3}\sqrt{a^4+x^4}$, (u) $-\dfrac{1}{x-1}-\dfrac{1}{3(x-1)^3}$, (v) $\frac{2}{3}\sqrt{x^3+3x}$,

   (w) $2\sqrt{x^2+3x}$, (x) $\dfrac{a^2x^2}{2}+\dfrac{2ab}{5}x^5+\dfrac{bx^8}{8}$, (y) $\dfrac{2}{b}\sqrt{a+bx^n}$, (z) $\frac{3}{2}e^{x^2}$.

3. (a) $e^x(x^2-2x+2)$, (b) $\frac{4}{25}(e^{5x})(5x-1)$, (c) $-e^{-x}[3(x+1)+1]$, (d) $x^2e^{2x}-\dfrac{6e^{2x}}{4}[2x-1]+\frac{3}{2}e^{2x}$,

   (e) $\dfrac{x^2}{2}\log_e x-\dfrac{x^2}{4}$, (f) $x\log_e x-x$, (g) $\dfrac{(x+1)^2}{2}\log_e(x+1)-\dfrac{(x+1)^2}{4}-[(x+1)\log_e(x+1)-(x+1)^2]$,

   (h) $\dfrac{x^4}{4}\log_e x-\dfrac{x^4}{16}$, (i) $a\left[\dfrac{x^2}{2}\log_e x-\dfrac{x^2}{4}\right]+b[x\log_e x-x]$, (j) $\dfrac{(x+1)^3}{3}\log_e(x+1)-\dfrac{(x+1)^3}{9}$

   $-(x+1)^2\log_e(x+1)+\dfrac{(x+1)^2}{2}+(x+1)\log_e(x+1)-(x+1)$, (l) $e^x[x^2-2x+2]$.

   (m) $x^n e^x - n\int x^{n-1}e^x\,dx$.

5. $F(x)=\begin{cases}\dfrac{x^2}{2}, & 0\leqslant x\leqslant 1\\[2mm]-\dfrac{x^2}{2}, & -1\leqslant x\leqslant 0\end{cases}$

7. f increasing on $\langle-\infty, 100\rangle$, decreasing elsewhere.

9. $f(t)=ab^2e^{-bt}+[f'(t_1)+abe^{-t_1}]t+f'(t)-ab^2e^{-t_1}-t_1[f'(t_1)+abe^{-t_1}]$.

CHAPTER 16

Section 16.3

1. (a) $f(1)=5e^{-3}, f(5)=5e^{-15}, f(10)=5e^{-30}$, (b) $30e^{0.002}, 30e^{0.01}, 30e^{0.02}$, (c) $10^6e^{0.75}, 10^6e^{3.75}, 10^6e^{7.5}$.

3. (a) $t=\left(\dfrac{\log_e\frac{3}{4}}{\log_e\frac{1}{2}}\right)5750\approx 2357.5$, (b) $t=\left(\dfrac{\log_e\frac{1}{4}}{\log_e\frac{1}{2}}\right)5750\approx 10{,}500.0$.

5. (a) $f'(t)=0.01f(t)$, (b) $100\log_e 2$ is the time, (c) $66.6\log_e 2$.

7. Ratio is $\frac{1}{3}$ idealists.

9. (a) $P_n=A^nP_0+\left(\dfrac{1-A^n}{1-A}\right)B$.

Section 16.8

1. (b) $\dfrac{\pi}{6}, \dfrac{\pi}{6}\pm\dfrac{\pi}{2}, \dfrac{\pi}{6}\pm\pi, \dfrac{\pi}{6}\pm 2\pi, \dfrac{\pi}{6}\pm 4\pi, \dfrac{\pi}{4}, \dfrac{\pi}{4}\pm\dfrac{\pi}{2}, \dfrac{\pi}{4}\pm\pi, \dfrac{\pi}{4}\pm 2\pi, \dfrac{\pi}{4}\pm 4\pi$.

3. (b) $\tan v=\dfrac{A}{B}$; (c) $\sqrt{A^2+B^2}\cos(u-v)$.

5. $\sqrt{A^2+B^2}\cos\left[\omega t-\arctan\dfrac{A}{B}\right]$.

7. ω times.

9. (b) $3 \sec^2 3t$, (c) $-\csc^2 \dfrac{v}{2}$, (d) $\sec x \tan x$, (e) $\sin x \cos x$, (f) $\dfrac{1}{\sqrt{\cos 2t}}$, (g) $\sec^2 3u$,

(h) $\cos x - x \sin x$, (i) $\dfrac{u \cos u - \sin u}{u^2}$, (j) $-\sin 2x \sin x + 2 \cos x \cos 2x$, (k) $a \cot ax$,

(l) $e^{ax}(b \cos bx + a \sin bx)$, (m) $\dfrac{\sec^2 (x/2)}{\tan (x/2)}$, (n) $-2 \sin x \cos x$, (o) $x^{\sin x}\left(\dfrac{\sin x}{x} + \cos x \log x\right)$,

(p) $\dfrac{\arccos x + \arcsin x}{(\sqrt{1-x^2})(\arccos^2 x)}$.

17. $t = \pi/200$ sec.

Section 16.11

1. (a) $5 \sin^4 x \cos x$, (b) $\dfrac{-2 \sin x \cos x}{[\sin^2 x + 1]^2}$, (c) $\dfrac{-x}{\sqrt{1-x^2}}$, (d) $6x \cos (3x^2 + 2)$, (e) $\dfrac{x \sin (\sqrt{1-x^2})}{\sqrt{1-x^2}}$,

(f) $x(2 \cos x^3 \cos x^2 - 3x \sin x^3 \sin x^2)$, (g) $\tan x$, (h) $10x \sec^2 (5x^2)$, (i) $\dfrac{-2}{(x-1)^2} \sec^2 \left(\dfrac{x+1}{x-1}\right)$,

(j) $\sec x \tan x$, (k) $-3 \csc x \cot x$, (l) $\dfrac{3}{\sqrt{1-(3x+2)^2}}$, (m) $\dfrac{1}{\sqrt{1-x^2}}$, (n) $\dfrac{-2}{(x-1)^2}\left[\dfrac{1}{1+\left(\dfrac{x+1}{x-1}\right)^2}\right]$,

(o) $\dfrac{2e^{\arcsin 2x}}{\sqrt{1-4x^2}}$, (p) $\dfrac{1}{\sqrt{1-x^2}} \dfrac{\arccos x + \arcsin x}{(\arccos x)^2}$, (q) $\dfrac{-x}{\sqrt{1-x^2}}$.

3. (b) $\dfrac{x^2}{2} \arctan x - \log_e \sqrt{1+x^2}$, (c) $x \arcsin x - \sqrt{1-x^2}$, (d) $x \tan x - \log (\cos x)$.

CHAPTER 17

Section 17.4

5. (a) 1, (b) $\frac{1}{2}$, (c) $\frac{1}{4}$, (d) $\frac{1}{3}$, (c) $\frac{1}{4}$, (f) $\dfrac{1}{n}$; (b), (c), (e), (f) arise from adding points to (a).

(c), (e), (f) arise from adding points to (b). (e), (f) arise from adding points to (c). (e), (f) arise from adding points to (d). (f) arises from adding points to (e).

7. (a) $S_{\sigma_n} = 2 - \dfrac{1}{n^3}[\frac{1}{6}(n-1)(n)(2n-1)]$, (b) $\lim_{n\to\infty} S_{\sigma_n} = 2 - \frac{1}{3}$, (c) $\lim_{n\to\infty} S_{\sigma_n} = 2 - \frac{1}{3}$.

9. (a) $S_{\sigma_n} = \dfrac{1}{n^4} \dfrac{(n-1)^2(n^2)}{4}$, $\lim_{n\to\infty} S_{\sigma_n} = \frac{1}{4}$, (b) $S_{\sigma_n} = \dfrac{1}{n^4} \dfrac{n^2(n+1)^2}{4}$, $\lim_{n\to\infty} S_{\sigma_n} = \frac{1}{4}$.

11. (a) 100, 100, 172, 100; (b) 1000, 1000, 1720, 1000.

13. (b) $S_{\sigma_n} = 1 - \dfrac{1}{8n^3}\left[\dfrac{n(n+1)(2n+1)}{6}\right]$; $\lim_{n\to\infty} S_{\sigma_n} = 1 - \frac{1}{24} = \frac{23}{24}$,

(c) $S_{\sigma_n} = \frac{7}{8} - \dfrac{1}{4n^3}\left[\dfrac{n(n+1)}{2}\right] - \dfrac{1}{8n^3}\left[\dfrac{n(n+1)(2n+1)}{6}\right]$, $\lim_{n\to\infty} S_{\sigma_n} = \frac{17}{24}$.

15. $S_{\sigma_n} = 3\left[2 - \dfrac{1}{n^3}\left[\dfrac{n(n+1)(2n+1)}{6}\right]\right]$, $\lim_{n\to\infty} S_{\sigma_n} = 3(2 - \frac{1}{3}) = 4$.

Section 17.8

1. (a) $e^{-1}-e^{-2}$; (b) e^2-e^{-2}; (c) $\frac{3}{4}$; (d) $2\sqrt{6}-2\sqrt{2}$; (e) $2-\frac{2}{3}\sqrt{7}$; (f) $\frac{1}{2}e^4+3e^2-\frac{1}{2}e^{-4}-3e^{-2}$;
   (g) $\frac{80}{81}$; (h) 2; (i) $\frac{1}{2}e^4+e-\frac{3}{2}$; (j) e^2+e-2; (k) $4\frac{3}{4}$.

3. (b) 2, (c) $A = \begin{cases} \text{positive in } [-3,-2] \text{ and } [1,3], \\ \text{negative in } [-2,1] \end{cases}$
   (d) $A = 1+\frac{1}{2}e^2-e-e^{-1}+\frac{1}{2}e^{-2}$, (e) $A = 1$.

5. Yes.

7. (a) Yes. (b) Yes. (c) No.

9. $\left(\sqrt[3]{\frac{3}{80}}\right)\left(\frac{3}{20}\right)(2^{5/3}-1)$.

11. $P = \dfrac{\pi}{6}\left[4\sqrt{1-(\frac{1}{32})^2}-4\sqrt{1-(\frac{1}{16})^2}+\frac{1}{8}\left(\frac{\pi}{3}-\arcsin\frac{1}{16}\right)\right]$.

13. (b) Area $= 1$. (c) $A(M) = 1-\dfrac{1}{M}$; limit $= 1$.

15. (a) $\log_e 2$. (b) $\frac{2}{3}$. (c) 3. (d) 7.

17. (b) $\dfrac{A}{3}(x_i^3-x_{i-1}^3)+\dfrac{B}{2}(x_i^2-x_{i-1}^2)+C(x_i-x_{i-1})$.

CHAPTER 18

Section 18.2

1. (b) 665, (c) $\dfrac{211}{1944}$, (d) $e-1$, (e) $\frac{1}{2}(e^2-1)$, (f) $\log_e 2$, (g) $\frac{1}{8}(9^4-1)$, (h) $\frac{13}{3}$, (i) $\frac{1}{18}$,
   (j) $\frac{1}{3}[\log_e 10-\log_e 7] = 0.11889$, (k) $\frac{1}{3}(e^3-1)$, (l) $2\sqrt{7}-2$, (m) $\sqrt{2}-1$.

3. $V = \frac{1}{3}\pi r^2 h$.

5. $V = \frac{4}{3}\pi r^3$.

7. (a) $\dfrac{64\pi}{45}$, (b) $\pi(1-e^{-2})$, (c) $\pi\left[\dfrac{1}{2}+\dfrac{\pi}{4}\right]$, (d) $\pi\sqrt{2}$.

11. 78.5×10^4 ft/lb.

13. (a) 4 times as much. (b) Same amount.

15. 8×10^5.

17. $L(b) = \int_0^b\sqrt{1+(3x^2)^2}\,dx$; $W = \int_0^1 x^3\sqrt{1+(3x^2)^2}\,dx$.

19. (a) Yes, (b) No, (c) No.

21. (c) $2,459,125$, (d) Multiply by $1/\sin 45° = 2/\sqrt{2}$.

23. $A_{\text{trap}} = 260$ sq. ft; $A_{\text{par}} = 1,333,333$; parabolic can withstand more.

25. (a) $H'(x) = -f(x)$, (b) $k'(t) = -f'(t)g[f(t)]$, (c) $k'(t) = -2t\sin t^2$.

27. (a) $W = \displaystyle\int_0^t \dfrac{200(4000)^2}{[f(t)]^2}f'(t)\,dt$, (b) $\dfrac{dW}{dt}\bigg|_{t=t_1} = \dfrac{200(4000)^2}{(5000)^2}\cdot4 = 512$.

29. (a) $2V$ min, (b) $h(t) = \sqrt{(t/\pi)+81}$.

33. (c) $\frac{8}{3}+e^3-e^2$.

Section 18.8

1. (a) $\dfrac{b+a}{2}$, (b) $\dfrac{b^{n+1}-a^{n+1}}{(n+1)(b-a)}$, (c) 0, (d) $\dfrac{e^b-e^a}{b-a}$.

3. 3,360,000.   5. $P(19) = e^{-57/13}$.

7. (a) $r^2/100$, (b) $r/50$, (c) $6\frac{2}{3}$, (d) $\frac{2}{3}$ hr.   13. 9.

Section 18.10

1. (b) $2\sqrt{2}-2$, (c) $\frac{10}{3}(\sqrt{2}-1)$, (d) $\dfrac{-1}{1+\log_e 2}+1 \approx 0.41$, (e) $\arctan(\log_e 2)$, (f) $\dfrac{2-\sqrt{2}}{2+\sqrt{2}}$,

   (g) $\dfrac{\pi}{4}-\arctan\dfrac{\sqrt{2}}{2}$, (h) $\dfrac{e-1}{2(e+1)}$, (i) $\arctan e - \dfrac{\pi}{4}$, (j) $\dfrac{\pi}{12}+\log_e 2$, (k) $1-2\log_e 2$,

   (l) $\dfrac{\log_e 10}{2}-\dfrac{\log_e 14}{2}+\dfrac{2}{\sqrt{31}}\arctan\left(\dfrac{1+(\sqrt{3}/2)}{(\sqrt{31}/2)}\right)-\dfrac{2}{\sqrt{31}}\arctan\left(\dfrac{\sqrt{3}}{\sqrt{31}}\right)$,

   (m) $\frac{1}{3}(\log_e 14 - \log_e 5) - \frac{1}{3}\sqrt{\frac{3}{5}}\arctan\dfrac{2}{\sqrt{5/3}}+\frac{1}{3}\sqrt{\frac{3}{5}}\arctan\sqrt{\frac{3}{5}}$.

3. (d) $\dfrac{1}{8}\left[\dfrac{1}{1-(2/\sqrt{5})}-\log_e\left(1-\dfrac{2}{\sqrt{5}}\right)-\dfrac{1}{1+(2/\sqrt{5})}+\log_e\left(1+\dfrac{2}{\sqrt{5}}\right)\right]$.

CHAPTER 19

Section 19.2

1. (a) $3[1-(\frac{1}{2})^{2/3}]$, (b) $[\tan 4]^{1/2}-[\tan 2]^{1/2}$, (c) $\sqrt{2}/4$, (d) $\frac{1}{2}\arctan\frac{1}{4}$, (e) $-\frac{1}{35}[(\sqrt{2})^7-1]$,

   (f) $\dfrac{3}{2}\left[\dfrac{\pi}{6}\right]^{1/2}$, (g) $\dfrac{(\log_e 3)^4}{4}$, (h) $\frac{1}{2}\arcsin\frac{1}{2}$, (i) $\dfrac{3}{4}\left[\dfrac{\pi}{4}\right]$, (j) $\frac{1}{24}$.

Section 19.4

1. $A = \frac{1}{7}, B = -\frac{1}{7}$.

3. (a) $8.5 + 14\log_e 2$, (b) $1 + \log_e\dfrac{4}{\sqrt{15}}$, (c) $\dfrac{48}{245}[\log_e 2]-\dfrac{2}{21}$, (d) $\log_e\left[\dfrac{54}{10^{3/2}}\right]+2\arctan\frac{1}{3}$, (e) $\frac{2}{5}$,

   (f) $\dfrac{1}{2}-\dfrac{2}{\sqrt{3}}\left[\arctan\dfrac{7}{\sqrt{3}}-\arctan\dfrac{5}{\sqrt{3}}\right]$.

Section 19.7

1. (a) $\frac{1}{2}\left[\arctan\sqrt{2}-\dfrac{\pi}{4}\right]$, (b) $2[2\sqrt{2}-2.5-2\log_e(1+\sqrt{2})]$, (c) $-\frac{1}{2}[\frac{1}{2}-2\log_e 3] = \log_e 3 - \frac{1}{4}$,

   (d) $\frac{1}{2}\log_e 3$, (e) $-2\left\{\sqrt{\frac{3}{2}}-\sqrt{\frac{1}{2}}-\sqrt{2}\left[\log_e\left(\dfrac{\sqrt{2}+\sqrt{\frac{3}{2}}}{\sqrt{\frac{1}{2}}}\right)-\log_e\left(\dfrac{\sqrt{2}+\sqrt{\frac{1}{2}}}{\sqrt{\frac{3}{2}}}\right)\right]\right\}$.

   (f) $\sqrt[6]{2}-\dfrac{\sqrt{2}}{6}-\dfrac{5}{6}+\log_e\left[\dfrac{2}{1+\sqrt[6]{2}}\right]$, (g) $\dfrac{116}{45}$, (h) $-\dfrac{4}{3}\left[\sqrt{11}-\sqrt{8}+\log_e\left(\dfrac{1+\sqrt{8}}{1+\sqrt{11}}\right)\right]+(-28.25)$.

Section 19.9

1. (a) $\frac{2}{3}$, (b) $4(\log_e 2)^3-\frac{3}{4}(\log_e 2)^2+\frac{3}{8}(\log_e 2)-\frac{3}{128}(2^3-1)$, (c) $\dfrac{(\log_e 2)^4}{4}$,

(d) $\frac{1}{2}[(x^n e^x - x^n e^{-x})]_{-1}^1 - n \int_{-1}^1 x^{n-1} e^x \, dx + n \int_{-1}^1 x^{n-1} e^{-x} \, dx.$ By symmetry, if n is odd, each expression $=$ 0. If n is even, first expression is 0.

Section 19.11

1. (b) $\frac{1}{60}$.

3. (a) 0, (b) 0, $m \neq 1$, (c) $\dfrac{(-1)^{m+1}-1}{m+1}$, (d) 6/55, (e) 0, (f) $\frac{3}{2}\sqrt{2}-2$, (g) $-\frac{1}{4}-\log_e \dfrac{\sqrt{2}}{2}$, (h) $\frac{1}{2}$,

   (i) $\frac{1}{3}\log_e (1+\tan 1)$, (j) $\tan 1 - 1$, (k) $\sqrt{2}/5$, (l) $\frac{1}{2}$, (m) $\frac{1}{2}$, (n) $\dfrac{(\sec 1)^4 - 1}{4} - \dfrac{(\tan 1)^2}{2} - \log_e \cos(1)$.

Section 19.13

1. (a) $\frac{1}{2}\left[\sqrt{3}+\dfrac{2\pi}{3}\right]$, (b) $\log_e (1+\sqrt{2})$, (c) 0, (d) $\dfrac{\pi}{2}-1$, (e) $\dfrac{\pi}{2}$, (f) $\dfrac{2}{9}-\dfrac{2}{3\sqrt{3}}$, (g) $\dfrac{5\pi}{2}$, (h) $\sqrt{27}-\pi$,

   (i) $\sqrt{18}-\sqrt{13}+2\log_e\left[\dfrac{2+\sqrt{13}}{3+\sqrt{18}}\right]$, (j) $\dfrac{1}{4}\left[\dfrac{\pi}{2}+\arctan\dfrac{1}{2}\right]$.

3. (a) $\frac{1}{2}\left[4\sqrt{15}-2\sqrt{3}+\log_e\left(\dfrac{2+\sqrt{3}}{4+\sqrt{15}}\right)\right]$, (b) $\dfrac{1}{\sqrt{2}}$, (c) $\frac{1}{2}[\sqrt{2}+\log_e(1+\sqrt{2})]$, (d) $\dfrac{\pi}{4}$.

Section 19.14

1. (a) $\dfrac{8}{27}[10^{3/2}-1]$, (b) $\log_e (2+\sqrt{3})$, (c) $\sqrt{8}+\log_e\left[\dfrac{2+\sqrt{8}}{\sqrt{8}-2}\right]$,

   (d) $1+\sqrt{2}+\sqrt{e^2+1}+\log_e\left[\dfrac{1+\sqrt{2}}{1+\sqrt{e^2+1}}\right]$.

Section 19.16

1. (a) $n=6, n=10$; (b) $n=12$.

3. For fixed x, choose m so that

$$\frac{|x|^{m+1}}{0.005} \leqslant m!$$

5. Choose m so that

$$\frac{2^m m!}{1\cdot 3 \cdots (2m-1)} \geqslant 240.$$

CHAPTER 20

Section 20.4

1. (a) $x = 2\sin\theta\cos\theta; y = 2\sin^2\theta$, (b) $|OP| = 2\sin\theta$, (c) 0.

3. (d) $\dfrac{8}{100}$.

5. (a) $P(A_0) = P(A_4) = \frac{1}{16}$, $P(B_j) = \frac{3}{8}$ (b) $h_{\text{arg}} = \frac{5}{2}$, $P(A_0) = P(A_5) = \frac{1}{32}$

   $P(A_1) = P(A_3) = \frac{4}{16}$ $P(A_1) = P(A_4) = \frac{5}{32}$

   $P(A_2) = \frac{6}{16}$ $F_{\text{arg}} = \frac{1}{2}$, $P(A_2) = P(A_3) = \frac{10}{32}$

   (c) No.

9. (b) $P \leqslant 0.04$.

Section 20.7

1. (a) $\frac{9}{20}$, (b) $\frac{2}{5}$.

3. (a) $\frac{1}{2}$, (b) $\frac{1}{4}$, (c) $\dfrac{\pi}{9}$.

5. (a) $\dfrac{3017}{10875}$, (b) $\dfrac{491}{727}$, (c) $\dfrac{2536}{7137}$.

7. No.

11. (a) $P(M) = 0.53, P_M(X) = 0.65, P_F(X) = 0.35$, (b) 0.51.

13. (a) Equally likely.

Section 20.10

1. $P(H, 1) = P(H, 2) = P(H, 4) = P(H, 5) = P(H, 6) = \frac{2}{21}$
   $P(T, 1) = P(T, 2) = P(T, 4) = P(T, 5) = P(T, 6) = \frac{1}{21}$
   $P(H, 3) = \frac{4}{21}, P(T, 3) = \frac{2}{21}$

5. (c) $\frac{4}{25}$.

7. (a) $\frac{2}{3}$, (b) $\frac{2}{3}$, (c) $\dfrac{1}{1 + (\frac{3}{4})^{100}}$.

Section 20.14

1. (a) 0.144.

5. (b) $P(3) = p^3(1) + 3p^2(1-p)[2p(1-p) + p^2]$; $p = \frac{1}{3}, \frac{13}{81}$; $p = \frac{1}{2}, \frac{13}{32}$; $p = \frac{2}{3}, \frac{76}{81}$.

9. (a) 0.55, 0.45, (c) 0.3050.

CHAPTER 21

Section 21.4

1. (a)

	$g_0(x)$	$g_1(x)$	$g_{3/2}(x)$
(i)	0	x	$x + \frac{3}{2}$
(ii)	0	x	$\frac{3}{2}x$
(iii)	0	x	$\frac{9}{4}x$
(iv)	0	e^{-x}	$\frac{3}{2}e^{-x}$
(v)	$|x|$	$\sqrt{x^2+1}$	$\sqrt{x^2+\frac{9}{4}}$

(b)

	$h_0(y)$	$h_1(y)$	$h_{3/2}(y)$
(i)	y	$1 + y$	$\frac{3}{2} + y$
(ii)	0	y	$\frac{3}{2}y$
(iii)	0	y^2	$\frac{3}{2}y^2$
(iv)	y	$e^{-1}y$	$e^{-3/2}y$
(v)	$|y|$	$\sqrt{1+y^2}$	$\sqrt{y^2+\frac{9}{4}}$

3.

	$|f(1, 1.2) - f(1,1)| \approx$	$|f(1.2, 1) - f(1,1)| \approx$
(i)	0.2	0.2
(ii)	0.2	0.2
(iii)	0.2	0.4
(iv)	$0.2e^{-1}$	$0.2e^{-1}$
(v)	$0.2/\sqrt{2}$	$0.2/\sqrt{2}$

5. $|F(0.1)-F(0)| \approx$

   (i) $\sin(0.1)+\cos(0.1)-1$
   (ii) $\sin^2(0.1)+(\cos(0.1))(\cos(0.1)-1)$
   (iii) $\cos^2(0.1)\sin(0.1)+[2\sin(0.1)\cos(0.1)][\cos(0.1)-1]$
   (iv) $[-e^{-\sin(0.1)}\cos(0.1)\sin(0.1)]+[e^{-\sin(0.1)}][\cos(0.1)-1]$
   (v) $\sin^2(0.1)+\cos(0.1)[\cos(0.1)+1]$

7. (c)–(d) $\left(\dfrac{50}{2.75}\right)^2,$

   $p(x, 10{,}000)-2.75x = 100\sqrt{x}-2.75x,$
   $N'(x) = 50x^{-1/2}-2.75.$

Section 21.7

1. (a) max at $(\frac{1}{4}, 2) = 4\frac{1}{8}$; min at $(2, 2) = -2$, (b) max at $(2, 2) = e^4-2$; min at $(2, 0) = -1$, (c) max at $(1, 1) = 1$; min at $(0, -1) = -1$, (d) max at $(1, 1) = \sqrt{2}$; min at $(0, 0) = 0$, (e) max at $(2, -2) = 20$; min at $(-2, -2) = -12$, (f) max at $(-10, 10) = 2100$; min at $(-10, 10) = -2100$.

3. No.

5. $x = y = z = 1, f(x,y) = 2xy+\dfrac{2}{x}+\dfrac{2}{y}.$

7. $\dfrac{8315}{1310}$

9. $r = 19.3.$

index

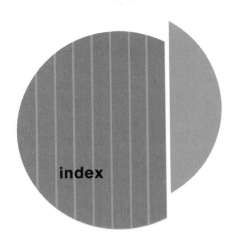

index